INTRODUCTION

The National Library of Medicine (NLM) designed the *List of Serials Indexed for Online Users* (LSI) to provide bibliographic information for serials from which articles are indexed with the MeSH® vocabulary and cited in MEDLINE®, the backbone of NLM's PubMed® database. The symbol "s)" is used before titles that are routinely monitored, but indexed selectively; only articles relating to the fields of biomedicine and life sciences are indexed from these journals. Some serials cited in MEDLINE are not included in this publication because they are not monitored on an on-going basis and have yielded only a few citations over many years.

The symbol "*" identifies titles indexed in *Abridged Index Medicus*, which ceased hardcopy publication with the December 1997 issue, but is still available online in NLM's PubMed® database as a search subset limit called "Core clinical journals."

The 2008 edition contains 13,014 serial titles, including 5,246 titles currently indexed for MEDLINE as of January 2008, cited alphabetically by abbreviated title followed by full title.

FILING ORDER

Entries are sorted letter by letter. Numbers sort before letters. Special characters are ignored in sorting, except for the "&", which sorts before numbers.

ABBREVIATIONS OF TITLES

The title abbreviations appearing in the *List of Serials Indexed for Online Users* are constructed using the *List of Title Word Abbreviations* (LTWA). The LTWA is maintained by the ISSN (International Standard Serial Number) International Centre. For more information about the Centre and its LTWA, please consult the ISSN Web site at http://www.issn.org.

As of March 2007 (i.e., for titles first in the 2008 LSI), NLM began accepting the abbreviations assigned by the International Standard Serial Number (ISSN) Centre and modify the punctuation and capitalization to conform to NLM standards. The ISSN key title abbreviation is stripped of all punctuation except for parentheses around a title qualifier.

DATES OF PUBLICATION

The dates of publication appear on the line below the title. These data contain the date of the first issue for titles currently published and the first and last dates for titles that have ceased publication or have been superseded or continued by another title. Unknown years are indicated with a "?". The dates given are publication dates, and do not necessarily represent NLM's holdings or issues indexed.

INTERNATIONAL STANDARD SERIAL NUMBER

The International Standard Serial Number (ISSN) is a serial identifier consisting of a unique seven-digit number and an eighth check digit. The ISSN uniquely identifies a serial title, regardless of language, and is therefore useful in international information exchange and in machine storage of serials data. The ISSN is assigned to a serial title by the appropriate national center of the ISSN Network, which is coordinated by the ISSN International Centre in Paris. The National Serials Data Program (NSDP) of the Library of Congress is the United States Center of the ISSN Network. The ISSN is irrevocably linked to the key title of the serial. If the title of a continuing serial changes, a new ISSN must be assigned to the new title. If a title is published in both print and electronic format, there should be a separate ISSN for each format. In the *List of Serials Indexed for Online Users*, the ISSN is printed on the third line of the entry, and the format corresponding to each ISSN is designated by a parenthetical (P) for "print" or (E) for "electronic" following the number. More information about the ISSN is available at http://www.issn.org.

PERMANENT PAPER NOTICE

Entries for indexed serials known to be printed on acid-free paper contain the designation 'Acid-free'. The Acid-free notice appears to the left of the NLM unique identifier.

To report other indexed serials printed on acid-free paper, contact: Head, Preservation and Collection Management Section, National Library of Medicine, 8600 Rockville Pike, Bethesda, MD 20894. For additional information about Acid-Free Paper for Biomedical Literature, see http://www.nlm.nih.gov/pubs/factsheets/acidfree.html

The latest edition of American National Standard ANSI/NISO Z39.48, "Permanence of Paper for Publications and Documents in Libraries and Archives" can be found at http://www.niso.org/.

NLM UNIQUE IDENTIFIER

The NLM unique identifier consists of either a number with up to nine digits or an eight-digit number followed by an alphabetic character. It is used by medical libraries in reporting serial holdings data to DOCLINE Serial Holdings (formerly called SERHOLD ®), NLM's database of machine-readable holdings statements for serial titles held by U.S., Canadian, and Mexican biomedical libraries. The unique identifier appears on the right-hand side of the last line of each entry. In PubMed this number is labeled as "JID" in the MEDLINE display format and as "NLM ID" in the Entrez Journals database (http://www.ncbi.nlm.nih.gov/entrez/query.fcgi?db=J ournals).

When requesting serial interlibrary loans from the National Library of Medicine outside of DOCLINE® (NLM's automated interlibrary loan request routing and referral system), please include the NLM call number (or On Order or In Process notation) and the NLM unique identifier. Holdings information indicating what issues of a title NLM owns and the NLM call number can be found in NLM's online catalog, LocatorPlus, at http://locatorplus.gov. Indexing coverage and detailed bibliographic records can be found at LocatorPlus and the NLM Catalog, an Entrez database, at http://www.nlmcatalog.nlm.nih.gov.

Information about journal selection for indexing at NLM can be found at http://www.nlm.nih.gov/pubs/factsheets/jsel.html. Questions can also be directed to NLM's Customer Service Desk at custserv@nlm.nih.gov (1-888-3563656).

1

1199 News
1199 news. National Union of Hospital and
Health Care Employees. District 1199
0012-6535
Continues: 1199 drug & hospital news.
19uu   9875136

2

20 Century Br Hist
20 century British history
0955-2359
1990   9015384

A

A M A Arch Ind Hyg Occup Med
A. M. A. archives of industrial hygiene and
occupational medicine
Continues Archives of industrial hygiene and
occupational medicine. Continued by A. M. A.
archives of industrial health.
1950-1954   14470080R

AACN Adv Crit Care
AACN advanced critical care
1559-7768   1559-7776
Continues: AACN clinical issues.
2006   101269322

AACN Clin Issues
AACN clinical issues
1079-0713
Continues: AACN clinical issues in critical
care nursing. Continued by: AACN advanced
critical care.
1995-2006   9508191

AACN Clin Issues Crit Care Nurs
AACN clinical issues in critical care nursing
1046-7467
Continued by: AACN clinical issues.
1990-1994   9009969

AADE Ed J
AADE editors' journal
0160-6999
Formed by the union of The Bulletin -
American Association of Dental Editors,
and Transactions - American Association of
Dental Editors.
1974-1983   7708172

AANA J
AANA journal
0094-6354
Continues Journal of the American
Association of Nurse Anesthetists.
1974   0431420

AANNT J
AANNT journal / the American Association
of Nephrology Nurses and Technicians
0744-1479
Continues: Journal of the American
Association of Nephrology Nurses &
Technicians. Continued by: ANNA journal.
1981-1984   8207766

AAOHN J
AAOHN journal: official journal of the
American Association of Occupational
Health Nurses
0891-0162
Continues: Occupational health nursing.
1986   8608669

AAPPO J
AAPPO journal: the journal of the
American Association of Preferred Provider
Organizations
1054-5913
Continued by: Health care innovations.
1991-1994   9206330

AAPS J
The AAPS journal
                                       1550-7416
Continues: AAPS PharmSci.
2004   101223209

AAPS PharmSci
AAPS pharmSci
                                       1522-1059
Continued by: AAPS journal.
1999-2004   100897065

AAPS PharmSciTech
AAPS PharmSciTech
                                       1530-9932
2000   100960111

AARN News Lett
AARN news letter
0001-0197
Continued by: Alberta RN.
1945-1998   1251052

AAUP Bull
AAUP bulletin: quarterly publication of
the American Association of University
Professors
0001-026X
Continues: Bulletin of the American
Association of University Professors.
American Association of University
Professors. Continued by: Academe
(Washington, D.C.: 1979).
1956-1978   9878133

AB Bookm Wkly
AB bookman's weekly: for the specialist
book world
0001-0340
Continues: Antiquarian bookman.
1967-1999   9877112

Abbottempo
Abbottempo
0567-4824
Formed by the union of What's new,
Abbotterapia, and Abbotherapie.
1963-1967   14480040R

Abdom Imaging
Abdominal imaging
0942-8925   1432-0509
Merger of: Gastrointestinal radiology; and:
Urologic radiology.
1993   9303672

Abh Gesch Med Naturwiss
Abhandlungen zur Geschichte der Medizin
und der Naturwissenschaften
0174-870X
1934   14480310R

ABNF J
The ABNF journal: official journal of the
Association of Black Nursing Faculty in
Higher Education, Inc
1046-7041
1990   9112807

Abstr Int Congr Trop Med Malar
Abstracts. International Congress on
Tropical Medicine and Malaria (4th: 1948:
Washington, D. C.)
1948   24320650R

Acad Emerg Med
Academic emergency medicine: official
journal of the Society for Academic
Emergency Medicine
1069-6563   1553-2712
1994   9418450

Acad Manage J
Academy of Management journal. Academy
of Management
0001-4273
Continues: Journal of the Academy of
Management. Superseded in part by:
Academy of Management review.
1963   7703609

Acad Manage Rev
Academy of management review. Academy
of Management
0363-7425
Supersedes in part: Academy of management
journal.
1976   9877758

Acad Med
Academic medicine: journal of the
Association of American Medical Colleges
1040-2446   1938-808X
Continues: Journal of medical education.
1989   8904605

Acad Nurse
The Academic nurse: the journal of the
Columbia University School of Nursing
1062-0249
Continues: SNC.
1987   9114562

Acad Peru Cir
Academia Peruana de Cirugía
0001-3854
Continues the Boletín of the Academia
Peruana de Cirugía, Lima.
1950-1980   14490460R

Acad Psychiatry
Academic psychiatry: the journal of the
American Association of Directors of
Psychiatric Residency Training and the
Association for Academic Psychiatry
1042-9670
Continues: Journal of psychiatric education.
1989   8917200

Acad Radiol
Academic radiology
1076-6332   1878-4046
1994   9440159

Acad Rev Calif Acad Periodontol
Academy review of the California Academy
of Periodontology, United States Section,
ARPA Internationale
0008-0810
Merged with Parodontologie (Zurich,
Switzerland: 1954) to form Parodontologie
and academy review.
1953-1966   7503275

Acarologia
Acarologia
0044-586X
1959   14510400R

Acc Chem Res
Accounts of chemical research
0001-4842   1520-4898
1968   0157313

Accad Medica
Accademia medica
Continues the Bollettino of the Accademia
medica di Genova.
1930-19uu   14510510R

Accao Med
Acção médica
0870-0311
1936   14520180R

Access Manag J
Access management journal
1551-9023
Continues: NAHAM access management journal.
2003   101203872

Accid Anal Prev
Accident; analysis and prevention
0001-4575   1879-2057
1969   1254476

Accid Emerg Nurs
Accident and emergency nursing
0965-2302
Continued by: International emergency nursing.
1993-2007   9305090

Account Res
Accountability in research
0898-9621   1545-5815
1989   9100813

ACP J Club
ACP journal club
1056-8751   1539-8560
Absorbed some articles and abstracts also published in: Evidence-based medicine, 2000- Issued as a supplement to: Annals of internal medicine, 1991-1994; became an independent publication in 1995; absorbed by Annals of internal medicine, 2008.
1991   9104824

Acquis Med Recent
Acquisitions médicales récentes
0075-4463
1946-1981   0373054

ACRH Rep
ACRH [reports]. U.S. Atomic Energy Commission
1954-19uu   0137764

Across Board (NY)
Across the board
0147-1554
Absorbed: Focus. Continues: Conference Board record.
1976   9877747

ACS Chem Biol
ACS chemical biology
1554-8929   1554-8937
2006   101282906

ACS Nano
ACS nano
1936-0851   1936-086X
2007   101313589

Act Hepato
Acta hepatologica
Continued by Acta hepato-splenologica.
1953-1958   14530110R

Act Nerv Super (Praha)
Activitas nervosa superior
0001-7604
Continued by: Homeostasis in health and disease.
1959-1990   0400662

Acta Acad Med Wuhan
Acta Academiae Medicinae Wuhan = Wu-han i hsüeh yüan hsüeh pao
0253-3316
Continues: Wu-han i hsüeh yüan hsüeh pao. Continued by: Journal of Tongji Medical University.
1981-1985   8300028

Acta Allergol
Acta allergologica
0001-5148
Continued by Allergy.
1948-1977   0370567

Acta Allergol Suppl (Copenh)
Acta allergologica. Supplementum
0065-096X
1950-1977   0421021

Acta Anaesthesiol
Acta anaesthesiologica
0001-5156
Continued by Acta anaesthesiologica italica.
1950-1971   0340732

Acta Anaesthesiol Belg
Acta anaesthesiologica Belgica
0001-5164
1950   0421022

Acta Anaesthesiol Scand
Acta anaesthesiologica Scandinavica
0001-5172   1399-6576
1957   0370270

Acta Anaesthesiol Scand Suppl
Acta anaesthesiologica Scandinavica. Supplementum
0515-2720
1959   0370271

Acta Anaesthesiol Sin
Acta anaesthesiologica Sinica
0529-5769
Continues: Ma zui xue za zhi. Continued by: Acta anaesthesiologica Taiwanica.
1994-2003   9432542

Acta Anaesthesiol Taiwan
Acta anaesthesiologica Taiwanica: official journal of the Taiwan Society of Anesthesiologists
1875-4597   1875-452X
Continues: Acta anaesthesiologica Sinica.
2004   101214918

Acta Anat (Basel)
Acta anatomica
0001-5180
Continues: Bio-morphosis. Continued by: Cells tissues organs.
1945-1998   0370272

Acta Anat Suppl (Basel)
Acta anatomica. Supplementum
0365-0332
1944-1980   0370273

Acta Anthropogenet
Acta anthropogenetica
0258-0357
1976-1985   7801158

Acta Argent Fisiol Fisiopatol
Acta argentina de fisiología y fisiopatología
1950-1954   14520280R

Acta Astronaut
Acta astronautica
0094-5765
Supersedes: Astronautica acta.
1974   9890631

Acta Belg Arte Med Pharm Mil
Acta Belgica de arte medicinali et pharmaceutica militari
Continues Annales belges de médecine militaire. Continued by: Acta Belgica.
1955-1981   0063222

Acta Belg Med Phys
Acta Belgica. Medica physica: organe officiel de la Société royale belge de médecine physique et de réhabilitation
0771-5684
Continues: Journal belge de médecine physique et de réhabilitation. Continued by: European journal of physical medicine & rehabilitation.
1983-1990   8307581

Acta Biochim Biophys Acad Sci Hung
Acta biochimica et biophysica; Academiae Scientiarum Hungaricae
Continued by: Acta biochimica et biophysica Hungarica.
1966-1985   0067725

Acta Biochim Biophys Hung
Acta biochimica et biophysica Hungarica
0237-6261
Continues: Acta biochimica et biophysica. Continued by: Neurobiology (Budapest, Hungary).
1986-1992   8701158

Acta Biochim Biophys Sin (Shanghai)
Acta biochimica et biophysica Sinica
1672-9145   1745-7270
Continues: Sheng wu hua xue yu sheng wu wu li xue bao.
2004   101206716

Acta Biochim Pol
Acta biochimica Polonica
0001-527X
1954   14520300R

Acta Bioeng Biomech
Acta of bioengineering and biomechanics / Wrocław University of Technology
1509-409X
1999   101194794

Acta Biol Acad Sci Hung
Acta biologica Academiae Scientiarum Hungaricae
0001-5288
Continues: Hungarica acta biologica. Continued by: Acta biologica Hungarica.
1950-1982   0370274

Acta Biol Exp (Warsz)
Acta biologiae experimentalis
0365-0820
Continued by Acta neurobiologiae experimentalis.
1928-1969   1246764

Acta Biol Hung
Acta biologica Hungarica
0236-5383
Continues: Acta biologica.
1983   8404358

Acta Biol Med (Gdansk)
Acta biologica et medica
0065-1087
Continued by: Acta biologica.
1957-1974   0370275

Acta Biol Med Ger
Acta biologica et medica Germanica
0001-5318
Continued by Biomedica acta.
1958-1982   0370276

Acta Biomater
Acta biomaterialia
1742-7061   1878-7568
2005   101233144

Acta Biomed
Acta bio-medica: Atenei Parmensis
0392-4203
Continues: Acta bio-medica de L'Ateneo parmense.
2002   101295064

Acta Biomed Ateneo Parmense
Acta bio-medica de L'Ateneo parmense:
organo della Società di medicina e scienze
naturali di Parma
0392-4203
Continues: L'Ateneo parmense. Acta bio-
medica. Continued by: Acta bio-medica.
1981-2001   8106323

Acta Biotheor
Acta biotheoretica
0001-5342   1572-8358
1935   0421520

Acta Brevia Neerl Physiol Pharmacol Microbiol E A
Acta brevia Neerlandica de physiologia,
pharmacologia, microbiologia e.a
0365-0766
Merged with: Archives néerlandaises de
physiologie de l'homme et des animaux. to
form: Acta physiologica et pharmacologica
Neerlandica.
1931-1950   14520330R

Acta Cancerol (Lima)
Acta cancerológica
1013-5545   1810-8296
1960   0370300

Acta Cardiol
Acta cardiologica
0001-5385
Continues: Bulletin de la Société belge de
cardiologie.
1946   0370570

Acta Cardiol Suppl
Acta cardiologica. Supplementum
0373-7934
1946   0376316

Acta Chem Scand
Acta chemica Scandinavica
0001-5393
1947-1973   0421263

Acta Chem Scand
Acta chemica Scandinavica (Copenhagen,
Denmark: 1989)
0904-213X
Formed by the union of: Acta chemica
Scandinavica. Series A. Physical and
inorganic chemistry. and: Acta chemica
Scandinavica. Series B. Organic chemistry
and biochemistry. Absorbed in part by:
Journal of the Chemical Society. Perkin
transactions I; Journal of the Chemical
Society. Perkin transactions II: and: Journal
of the Chemical Society. Dalton transactions.
1989-1999   9012772

Acta Chem Scand A
Acta chemica Scandinavica. Series A:
Physical and inorganic chemistry
0302-4377
Continues in part Acta chemica
Scandinavica. Merged with: Acta chemica
Scandinavica. Series B. Organic chemistry
and biochemistry. to form: Acta chemica
Scandinavica (Copenhagen, Denmark: 1989).
1974-1988   0421761

Acta Chem Scand B
Acta chemica Scandinavica. Series B:
Organic chemistry and biochemistry
0302-4369
Continues in part Acta chemica Scandinavica.
Merged with: Acta chemica Scandinavica.
Series A. physical and inorganic chemistry.
to form: Acta chemica Scandinavica
(Copenhagen. Denmark: 1989).
1974-1988   0421265

Acta Chir Acad Sci Hung
Acta chirurgica Academiae Scientiarum
Hungaricae
0001-5431
Continued by Acta chirurgica Hungarica.
1960-1982   2984283R

Acta Chir Belg
Acta chirurgica Belgica
0001-5458
Continues: Journal de chirurgie et annales de
la Société belge de chirurgie.
1946   0370571

Acta Chir Hung
Acta chirurgica Hungarica
0231-4614
Continues: Acta chirurgica Academiae
Scientiarum Hungaricae. Absorbed by:
Magyar sebészet. 2000
1983-1999   8309977

Acta Chir Ital
Acta chirurgica Italica
0001-5466
Continues Acta chirurgica Patavina.
1954   0370303

Acta Chir Iugosl
Acta chirurgica Iugoslavica
0354-950X
Supersedes: Acta chirurgica.
1954   0372631

Acta Chir Orthop Traumatol Cech
Acta chirurgiae orthopaedicae et
traumatologiae Cechoslovaca
0001-5415
Continues Sborník pro chirurgii pohybového
ústrojí.
1950   0407123

Acta Chir Patav
Acta chirurgica Patavina
Continued by Acta chirurgica Italica.
1944-1953   14530010R

Acta Chir Plast
Acta chirurgiae plasticae
0001-5423
1959   0370301

Acta Chir Scand
Acta chirurgica Scandinavica
0001-5482
Continues in part Nordiskt mediciniskt arkiv.
Continued by: European journal of surgery.
1920-1990   7906530

Acta Chir Scand Suppl
Acta chirurgica Scandinavica.
Supplementum
0301-1860
Continued by: European journal of surgery.
Supplement.
1922-1991   0370305

Acta Cient Venez
Acta científica venezolana
0001-5504
1950   0070154

Acta Cir Bras
Acta cirúrgica brasileira / Sociedade
Brasileira para Desenvolvimento Pesquisa
em Cirurgia
0102-8650   1678-2674
1986   9103983

Acta Clin Belg
Acta clinica Belgica
0001-5512
Supersedes Bulletin de la Société clinique des
hôpitaux de Bruxelles.
1946   0370306

Acta Clin Belg Suppl
Acta clinica Belgica. Supplementum
0567-7386
1965   0043523

Acta Clin Croat
Acta clinica Croatica
0353-9466   1333-9451
Continues: Anali Kliničke bolnice "Dr M.
Stojanovic".
1991   9425483

Acta Clin Odontol
Acta clínica odontológica: organo de
difusion academica de Sociedad Antioqueña
de Endodoncistas ... [et al.]
0120-9906
Continues: Revista nacional de endodoncia.
1980-1984   8503035

Acta Crystallogr
Acta crystallographica
0365-110X
1948-1967   0211526

Acta Crystallogr A
Acta crystallographica. Section A, Crystal
physics, diffraction, theoretical and general
crystallography
0567-7394
Continues in part: Acta crystallographica.
Continued by: Acta crystallographics. Section
A. Foundations of crystallography.
1968-1982   0211627

Acta Crystallogr A
Acta crystallographica. Section A,
Foundations of crystallography
0108-7673   1600-5724
Continues: Acta crystallographica. Section A.
Crystal physics, diffraction, theoretical and
general crystallography.
1983   8305825

Acta Crystallogr B
Acta crystallographica. Section B, Structural
science
0108-7681   1600-5740
Continues: Acta crystallographica. Section
B. Structural crystallography and crystal
chemistry.
1983   8403252

Acta Crystallogr B
Acta crystallographica. Section B:
Structural crystallography and crystal
chemistry
0567-7408
Continues in part Acta crystallographica.
Continued by Acta crystallographica. Section
B. Structural science.
1968-1982   0211630

Acta Crystallogr C
Acta crystallographica. Section C, Crystal
structure communications
0108-2701   1600-5759
Continues: Crystal structure communications.
Electronic papers section continued by: Acta
crystallographica. Section E. Structure reports
online.
1983   8305826

Acta Crystallogr D Biol Crystallogr
Acta crystallographica. Section D, Biological
crystallography
0907-4449   1399-0047
1993   9305878

Acta Crystallogr Sect F Struct Biol Cryst Commun
Acta crystallographica. Section F, Structural
biology and crystallization communications
1744-3091
2005   101226117

Acta Cytol
Acta cytologica
0001-5547
  Absorbed: Transactions [of the] annual
  meeting. Inter-society Cytology Council.
  1957   0370307

Acta Derm Venereol
Acta dermato-venereologica
0001-5555
1920   0370310

Acta Derm Venereol Suppl (Stockh)
Acta dermato-venereologica. Supplementum
0365-8341
1929   0370311

Acta Dermatol Kyoto Engl Ed
Acta dermatologica-Kyoto. English edition
0376-0189
  Absorbed by: Acta dermatologica-Kyoto.
  1967-1972   0266344

Acta Dermatovenerol Alp Panonica Adriat
Acta dermatovenerologica Alpina, Panonica,
et Adriatica
1318-4458   1581-2979
  Continues: Acta dermatovenerologica
  Iugoslavica.
  1992   9422563

Acta Dermatovenerol Croat
Acta dermatovenerologica Croatica: ADC /
Hrvatsko dermatolosko drustvo
1330-027X
1993   9433781

Acta Diabetol
Acta diabetologica
0940-5429   1432-5233
  Continues: Acta diabetologica latina.
  1991   9200299

Acta Diabetol Lat
Acta diabetologica latina
0001-5563
  Continued by: Acta diabetologica.
  1964-1991   0123567

Acta Embryol Exp (Palermo)
Acta embryologiae experimentalis
0065-1184
  Continues: Acta embryologiae et
  morphologiae experimentalis. Continued
  by: Acta embryologiae et morphologiae
  experimentalis. New series.
  1969-1979   0236000

Acta Embryol Morphol Exp
Acta embryologiae et morphologiae
experimentalis
0567-7416
  Continued by: Acta embryologiae
  experimentalis..
  1957-1968   0235532

Acta Embryol Morphol Exp
Acta embryologiae et morphologiae
experimentalis ("Halocynthia" Association")
0391-9706
  Continues: Acta embryologiae experimentalis.
  Continued by: Animal biology.
  1980-1991   8108943

Acta Endocrinol (Copenh)
Acta endocrinologica
0001-5598
  Absorbed: Acta endocrinologica.
  Supplementum. Continued by: European
  journal of endocrinology.
  1948-1993   0370312

Acta Endocrinol Iber
Acta endocrinologica Iberica
1951-1952   14530070R

Acta Endocrinol Suppl (Copenh)
Acta endocrinologica. Supplementum
0300-9750
  Absorbed by: Acta endocrinologica.
  1948-1988   0370313

Acta Eur Fertil
Acta Europaea fertilitatis
0587-2421
1969-1995   1300660

Acta Gastroenterol Belg
Acta gastro-enterologica Belgica
0001-5644
  Continues: Journal belge de gastro-
  entérologie.
  1946   0414075

Acta Gastroenterol Latinoam
Acta gastroenterologica Latinoamericana
0300-9033
1969   0261505

Acta Genet Med Gemellol (Roma)
Acta geneticae medicae et gemellologiae
0001-5660
1952-1998   0370314

Acta Genet Stat Med
Acta genetica et statistica medica
0567-7440
  Continued by: Human heredity.
  1948-1968   0200600

Acta Gerontol (Milano)
Acta gerontologica
0001-5741
1951-1999   7501996

Acta Ginecol (Madr)
Acta ginecológica
0001-5776
1950   0370317

Acta Gynaecol Obstet Hisp Lusit
Acta gynaecologica et obstetrica Hispano-
Lusitana
0001-5784
  Continues in part Acta endocrinologica et
  gynaecologica Hispano-Lusitana. Continued
  by Acta obstétrica y ginecológica hispano-
  lusitana.
  1951-1966   0147664

Acta Haematol
Acta haematologica
0001-5792   1421-9662
1948   0141053

Acta Haematol Pol
Acta haematologica Polonica
0001-5814
1970   0262610

Acta Hepatogastroenterol (Stuttg)
Acta hepato-gastroenterologica
0300-970X
  Continues Acta hepato-splenologica.
  Continued by Hepato-gastroenterology.
  1972-1979   0340734

Acta Hepatosplenol
Acta hepato-splenologica
0001-5822
  Continues Acta hepatologica. Continued by
  Acta hepato-gastroenterologica.
  1959-1971   0340735

Acta Hist Leopoldina
Acta historica Leopoldina
0001-5857
196u   0060677

Acta Hist Med Vallisoletana Monogr
Acta histórico-médica vallisoletana.
Monografías
0210-9360
1973   7907017

Acta Hist Sci Nat Med
Acta historica scientiarum naturalium et
medicinalium
0065-1311
1942   0416660

Acta Histochem
Acta histochemica
0065-1281   1618-0372
1954   0370320

Acta Histochem Suppl
Acta histochemica. Supplementband
0567-7556
1958-1992   0061372

Acta Hosp
Acta hospitalia
0044-6009
1961   0401031

Acta Iber Radiol Cancerol
Acta ibérica radiológica-cancerológica
0001-589X
  Continues Radiológica-cancerólogica.
  1952-1980   0370321

Acta Isot (Padova)
Acta isotopica
0001-5911
1961-1971   0421025

Acta Leiden
Acta Leidensia
0065-1362
1926-1992   0413650

Acta Leprol
Acta leprologica
0001-5938
1960   0037353

Acta Med Acad Sci Hung
Acta medica Academiae Scientiarum
Hungaricae
0001-5989
  Supersedes Hungarica acta medica.
  Continued by Acta medica Hungarica.
  1950-1982   0370323

Acta Med Austriaca
Acta medica Austriaca
0303-8173   1563-2571
  Supersedes: Wiener Zeitschrift für innere
  Medizin und ihre Grenzgebiete. Absorbed by:
  Wiener klinische Wochenschrift.
  1974-2004   7501997

Acta Med Austriaca Suppl
Acta medica Austriaca. Supplement
0303-8181
1974   7502262

Acta Med Biol (Niigata)
Acta medica et biologica
0567-7734
1953   0243663

Acta Med Croatica
Acta medica Croatica: časopis Hrvatske
akademije medicinskih znanosti
1330-0164
  Continues: Acta medica iugoslavica.
  1991   9208249

Acta Med Hidalguense
Acta médica hidalguense
1948-1962   14540010R

Acta Med Hisp
Acta médica hispánica
1943-1950   14540020R

Acta Med Hung
Acta medica Hungarica
0236-5286
     Continues: Acta medica Academiae
     Scientiarum Hungaricae.
1983-1994   8400269

Acta Med Indones
Acta medica Indonesiana
0125-9326
1968   7901042

Acta Med Iran
Acta medica Iranica
0044-6025   1735-9694
1956   14540050R

Acta Med Ital Mal Infett Parassit
Acta medica Italica di malattie infettive e
parassitarie
     Continued by Acta medica Italica di medicina
     tropicale e subtropicale e di gastroenterologia.
1946-1960   14540070R

Acta Med Ital Med Trop Subtrop Gastroenterol
Acta medica Italica di medicina tropicale e
subtropicale e di gastroenterologia
0001-6039
     Continues Acta medica Italica di malattie
     infettive e parassitarie.
1961-1965   14540080R

Acta Med Iugosl
Acta medica Iugoslavica
0375-8338
     Continued by: Acta medica Croatica.
1947-1991   0370324

Acta Med Leg Soc (Liege)
Acta medicinae legalis et socialis
0065-1397
     Continued by: Acta medicinae legalis.
1948-199u   7611894

Acta Med Nagasaki
Acta medica Nagasakiensia
0001-6055
     Continues the European language section of
     Nagasaki Igakkai zasshi.
1939   0372633

Acta Med Okayama
Acta medica Okayama
0386-300X
     Continues Acta medicinae Okayama.
1973   0417611

Acta Med Okayama
Acta medicinae Okayama
0001-6152
     Continues Arbeiten aus der Medizinischen
     Universität zu Okayama. Continued by Acta
     medica Okayama.
1952-1972   0417612

Acta Med Orient
Acta medica Orientalia
     Continued by Israel medical journal.
1942-1958   14540100R

Acta Med Patav
Acta medica Patavina
0001-6063
1940-1976   0376306

Acta Med Patavina Suppl
Acta medica Patavina. Supplemento
1955-1967   14540110R

Acta Med Philipp
Acta medica Philippina
0001-6071
1939   0312677

Acta Med Pol
Acta medica Polona
0001-608X
1960-1990   0370326

Acta Med Port
Acta médica portuguesa
0870-399X   1646-0758
1979   7906803

Acta Med Scand
Acta medica Scandinavica
0001-6101
     Continues in part: Nordiskt medicinskt arkiv.
     Avd. 2. Arkiv foer inre medicin. Continued
     by: Journal of internal medicine.
1919-1988   0370330

Acta Med Scand Suppl
Acta medica Scandinavica. Supplementum
0365-463X
     Continued by: Journal of internal medicine.
     Supplement.
1921-1988   0370331

Acta Med Turc
Acta medica Turcica
0567-7750
1948-1972   0413651

Acta Med Vet (Napoli)
Acta medica veterinaria
0001-6136
1955-1996   0000212

Acta Med Vietnam
Acta medica Vietnamica
0001-6144
     Supersedes L'Extrême-Orient médical.
1957-1973   0116720

Acta Medica (Hradec Kralove)
Acta medica (Hradec Králové) / Universitas
Carolina, Facultas Medica Hradec Králové
1211-4286
     Continues: Sborník vědeckých prací Lékařské
     fakulty Karlovy University v Hradci Králové.
1996   9705947

Acta Medica (Hradec Kralove) Suppl
Acta medica (Hradec Králové).
Supplementum Universitas Carolina,
Facultas Medica Hradec Králové
1211-247X
     Continues: Sborník vědeckých prací Lékarské
     fakulty Karlovy univerzity v Hradci Králové.
     Supplementum.
199u   9815916

Acta Medica Cordoba
Acta medica
0515-2917
1956-1981   14530160R

Acta Microbiol Acad Sci Hung
Acta microbiologica Academiae Scientiarum
Hungaricae
0001-6187
     Continued by Acta microbiologica Hungarica.
1954-1982   0370333

Acta Microbiol Bulg
Acta microbiologica Bulgarica
0204-8809
     Formed by the union of Prilozhna
     mikrobiologiia and of Acta microbiologica,
     virologica et immunologica.
1978-1993   7901426

Acta Microbiol Hung
Acta microbiologica Hungarica
0231-4622
     Continues: Acta microbiologica Academiae
     Scientiarum Hungaricae. Continued by: Acta
     microbiologica et immunologica Hungarica.
1983-1993   8400270

Acta Microbiol Immunol Hung
Acta microbiologica et immunologica
Hungarica
1217-8950
     Continues: Acta microbiologica Hungarica.
1994   9434021

Acta Microbiol Pol
Acta microbiologica Polonica
0137-1320
     Formed by the union of: Acta microbiologica
     Polonica. Series A. Microbiologia generalis,
     and: Acta microbiologica Polonica. Series B,
     Microbiologia applicata. Continued by: Polish
     journal of microbiology.
1976-2003   7610362

Acta Microbiol Pol A
Acta microbiologica Polonica. Series A:
Microbiologia generalis
0567-7815
     Supersedes in part Acta microbiologica
     Polonica; microbiologia generalis,
     agrobiologica et technica. Merged with
     Acta microbiologica Polonica. Series B:
     Microbiologia applicata to form Acta
     microbiologica Polonica.
1969-1975   7610360

Acta Microbiol Pol B
Acta microbiologica Polonica. Series B:
Microbiologia applicata
0567-7823
     Supersedes in part Acta microbiologica
     Polonica; microbiologia generalis,
     agrobiologica et technica. Merged with
     Acta microbiologica Polonica. Series
     A: Microbiologia generalis to form Acta
     microbiologica Polonica.
1969-1975   7610361

Acta Microbiol Virol Immunol (Sofiia)
Acta microbiologica, virologica et
immunologica
0324-0452
     Supersedes Izvestiia na Mikrobiologicheskiia
     institut. Merged with Prilozhna
     mikrobiologiia to form Acta microbiologica
     Bulgarica.
1975-1977   7600027

Acta Morphol Acad Sci Hung
Acta morphologica Academiae Scientiarum
Hungaricae
0001-6217
     Continued by Acta morphologica Hungarica.
1951-1982   0370334

Acta Morphol Acad Sci Hung Suppl
Acta morphologica Academiae Scientiarum
Hungaricae. Supplementum
1954-1973   0375331

Acta Morphol Hung
Acta morphologica Hungarica
0236-5391
     Continues: Acta morphologica Academiae
     Scientiarum Hungaricae.
1983-1992   8307964

Acta Morphol Neerl Scand
Acta morphologica Neerlando-Scandinavica
0001-6225
     Supersedes Acta Neerlandica morphologiae
     normalis et pathologicae, issued 1937-49.
     Continued by: European journal of morphology.
1956-1989   0370335

Acta Myol
Acta myologica: myopathies and
cardiomyopathies: official journal of the
Mediterranean Society of Myology / edited
by the Gaetano Conte Academy for the
study of striated muscle diseases
1128-2460
     Continues: Acta cardiomiologica.
1997   9811169

Acta Neerl Morphol Norm Pathol
Acta Neerlandica morphologiae normalis et
pathologicae
0365-4907
Continued by: Acta morphologica Neerlando-
Scandinavica.
1938-1949   **14540160R**

Acta Neurobiol Exp (Wars)
Acta neurobiologiae experimentalis
0065-1400
Continues Acta biologiae experimentalis.
1970   **1246675**

Acta Neurochir (Wien)
Acta neurochirurgica
0001-6268   0942-0940
1950   **0151000**

Acta Neurochir Suppl
Acta neurochirurgica. Supplement
0065-1419
Continues: Acta neurochirurgica.
Supplementum.
1994   **100962752**

Acta Neurochir Suppl (Wien)
Acta neurochirurgica. Supplementum
0065-1419
Continued by: Acta neurochirurgica.
Supplement.
1950-1994   **0140560**

Acta Neurol (Napoli)
Acta neurologica
0001-6276
1946-1994   **0421100**

Acta Neurol Belg
Acta neurologica Belgica
0300-9009
Continues in part Acta neurologica et
psychiatrica Belgica.
1970   **0247035**

Acta Neurol Latinoam
Acta neurológica latinoamericana
0001-6306
1955-1987   **9421556**

Acta Neurol Psychiatr Belg
Acta neurologica et psychiatrica Belgica
0001-6284
Continues Journal belge de neurologie et de
psychiatrie. Continued by Acta neurologica
Belgica and Acta psychiatrica Belgica.
1948-1969   **0247036**

Acta Neurol Scand
Acta neurologica Scandinavica
0001-6314   1600-0404
Continues in part Acta psychiatrica et
neurologica Scandinavica.
1961   **0370336**

Acta Neurol Scand Suppl
Acta neurologica Scandinavica.
Supplementum
0065-1427   1600-5449
Supersedes in part Acta psychiatrica et
neurologica Scandinavica, Supplementum.
1962   **0370337**

Acta Neurol Taiwan
Acta neurologica Taiwanica
1028-768X
Continues: Acta neurologica Sinica.
1996   **9815355**

Acta Neurol [Quad] (Napoli)
Acta neurologica. Quaderni
0515-2976
1950-1994   **7506814**

Acta Neuropathol
Acta neuropathologica
0001-6322   1432-0533
1961   **0412041**

Acta Neuropathol Suppl
Acta neuropathologica. Supplementum
0065-1435
1962-1983   **0370342**

Acta Neuroveg (Wien)
Acta neurovegetativa
0375-9245
Continued by the Journal of neuro-visceral
relations.
1950-1967   **0162324**

Acta Neuroveg Suppl
Acta neurovegetativa. Supplementum
1952-1962   **1303605**

Acta Obstet Ginecol Hisp Lusit
Acta obstétrica y ginecológica hispano-lusitana
0210-9832
Continues Acta gynaecologica et obstetrica
Hispano-Lusitana.
1968-1984   **0147634**

Acta Obstet Ginecol Hisp Lusit Suppl
Acta obstetrica y ginecologica hispano-
lusitana. Suplemento
0300-8940
1969-1973   **0221541**

Acta Obstet Gynaecol Jpn
Acta obstetrica et gynaecologica Japonica
0001-6330
Continues Journal of the Japanese Obstetrical
and Gynecological Society. Absorbed by:
Nippon Sanka Fujinka Gakkai zasshi.
1969-1976   **0202673**

Acta Obstet Gynecol Scand
Acta obstetricia et gynecologica
Scandinavica
0001-6349   1600-0412
Continues: Acta gynecologica Scandinavica.
1926   **0370343**

Acta Obstet Gynecol Scand Suppl
Acta obstetricia et gynecologica
Scandinavica. Supplement
0300-8835
1926-1998   **0337655**

Acta Odontol Latinoam
Acta odontológica latinoamericana: AOL
0326-4815
1984   **8610218**

Acta Odontol Pediatr
Acta de odontología pediátrica
0252-1032
1980-1987   **8112880**

Acta Odontol Scand
Acta odontologica Scandinavica
0001-6357   1502-3850
1939   **0370344**

Acta Odontol Scand Suppl
Acta odontologica Scandinavica.
Supplementum
0365-530X
1939-1976   **0370345**

Acta Odontol Venez
Acta odontológica venezolana
0001-6365
1963   **14540210R**

Acta Oncol
Acta oncologica (Stockholm, Sweden)
0284-186X   1651-226X
Continues: Acta radiologica. Oncology.
Continued in part by: Reviews in oncology.
1987   **8709065**

Acta Oncol (Madr)
Acta oncológica
0001-6381
1962-1976   **0370346**

Acta Ophthalmol
Acta ophthalmologica
1755-375X   1755-3768
Continues: Acta ophthalmologica
Scandinavica.
2008   **101468102**

Acta Ophthalmol (Copenh)
Acta ophthalmologica
0001-639X
Continued by: Acta ophthalmologica
Scandinavica.
1923-1994   **0370347**

Acta Ophthalmol Scand
Acta ophthalmologica Scandinavica
1395-3907   1600-0420
Continues: Acta ophthalmologica. Continued
by: Acta ophthalmologica.
1995-2007   **9507578**

Acta Ophthalmol Scand Suppl
Acta ophthalmologica Scandinavica.
Supplement
1395-3931
Continues: Acta ophthalmologica.
Supplement. Continued by: Acta
ophthalmologica. Supplement.
1995-2007   **9516974**

Acta Ophthalmol Suppl
Acta ophthalmologica. Supplement
Continues: Acta ophthalmologica.
Supplementum. Continued by: Acta
ophthalmologica Scandinavica. Supplement.
1985-1994   **9216417**

Acta Ophthalmol Suppl
Acta ophthalmologica. Supplementum
0065-1451
Continued by: Acta ophthalmologica.
Supplement.
1932-1984   **0370350**

Acta Ophthalmol Suppl (Oxf)
Acta ophthalmologica. Supplement
1755-3776
Continues: Acta ophthalmologica
Scandinavica. Supplement.
2008   **101485969**

Acta Orthop
Acta orthopaedica
1745-3674   1745-3682
Continues: Acta orthopaedica Scandinavica.
2005   **101231512**

Acta Orthop Belg
Acta orthopaedica Belgica
0001-6462
Continues: Bulletin of the Société belge
d'orthopédie et de chirurgie de l'appareil
moteur.
1946   **2985165R**

Acta Orthop Scand
Acta orthopaedica Scandinavica
0001-6470
Continued by: Acta orthopaedica.
1930-2004   **0370352**

Acta Orthop Scand Suppl
Acta orthopaedica Scandinavica.
Supplementum
0300-8827
Continued by: Acta orthopaedica.
Supplementum.
1934-2004   **0370353**

Acta Orthop Suppl
Acta orthopaedica. Supplementum
1745-3690   1745-3704
Continues: Acta orthopaedica Scandinavica.
Supplementum.
2005   101244827

Acta Orthop Traumatol Turc
Acta orthopaedica et traumatologica turcica
1017-995X
1962   9424806

Acta Ortop Mex
Acta ortopédica mexicana
Continues: Revista mexicana de ortopedia y
traumatología (1995).
2002   101190312

Acta Otolaryngol
Acta oto-laryngologica
0001-6489   1651-2251
Supersedes: Nordisk tidskrift för oto-rhino-
laryngologi.
1918   0370354

Acta Otolaryngol Suppl
Acta oto-laryngologica. Supplementum
0365-5237
1920   0370355

Acta Otorhinolaryngol Belg
Acta oto-rhino-laryngologica Belgica
0001-6497
Continues: Bulletin of the Société belge
d'otologie, de laryngologie et de rhinologie.
Continued by: B-ENT.
1947-2004   0373057

Acta Otorhinolaryngol Ital
Acta otorhinolaryngologica Italica:
organo ufficiale della Società italiana di
otorinolaringologia e chirurgia cervico-
facciale
0392-100X   1827-675X
Continues: Annali di laringologia, otologia,
rinologia, e faringologia.
1981   8213019

Acta Otorinolaryngol Iber Am
Acta oto-rino-laringológica ibero-americana
0001-6500
Continued by: Anales otorrinolaringológicos
ibero-americanos.
1950-1973   7610363

Acta Otorrinolaringol Esp
Acta otorrinolaringológica española
0001-6519
1949   14540260R

Acta Paediatr
Acta paediatrica (Oslo, Norway: 1992)
0803-5253   1651-2227
Continues: Acta paediatrica Scandinavica.
1992   9205968

Acta Paediatr Acad Sci Hung
Acta paediatrica Academiae Scientiarum
Hungaricae
0001-6527
Continued by ACta paediatrica Hungarica.
1960-1982   0372634

Acta Paediatr Belg
Acta paediatrica Belgica
0001-6535
Supersedes: Société belge de pédiatrie.
Bulletin. Absorbed by: European journal of
pediatrics.
1946-1981   0372635

Acta Paediatr Hung
Acta paediatrica Hungarica
0001-6527
Continues: Acta paediatrica Academiae
Scientiarum Hungaricae.
1983-1994   8307729

Acta Paediatr Jpn
Acta paediatrica Japonica; Overseas edition
0374-5600
Continues: Paediatria Japonica. Continued by:
Pediatrics international.
1963-1998   0370357

Acta Paediatr Lat
Acta paediatrica Latina
0365-5504
1948-1995   0370360

Acta Paediatr Scand
Acta paediatrica Scandinavica
0001-656X
Continues Acta paediatrica. Continued by:
Acta paediatrica (Oslo, Norway: 1992).
1965-1991   0000211

Acta Paediatr Scand Suppl
Acta paediatrica Scandinavica. Supplement
0300-8843
Continues Acta paediatrica. Supplementum.
Continued by: Acta paediatrica (Oslo,
Norway: 1992). Supplement.
1965-1991   0173166

Acta Paediatr Suppl
Acta paediatrica (Oslo, Norway: 1992).
Supplement
0803-5326
Supplement to: Acta paediatrica (Oslo,
Norway: 1992). Continues: Acta paediatrica
Scandinavica. Supplement.
1992   9315043

Acta Paediatr Suppl
Acta paediatrica. Supplementum
Continued by Acta paediatrica Scandinavica.
Supplementum.
1924-1964   14540280R

Acta Paediatr Taiwan
Acta paediatrica Taiwanica = Taiwan er ke
yi xue hui za zhi
1608-8115
Continues: Zhonghua Minguo xiao er ke yi
xue hui za zhi. Continued by: Pediatrics and
neonatology.
1999-2008   100958202

Acta Paedopsychiatr
Acta paedopsychiatrica
0001-6586
Continues Zeitschrift für Kinderpsychiatrie.
1953-1994   0400661

Acta Pathol Jpn
Acta pathologica japonica
0001-6632
Continued by: Pathology international.
1951-1993   0372637

Acta Pathol Microbiol Immunol Scand Suppl
Acta pathologica, microbiologica, et
immunologica Scandinavica. Supplement
0108-0172
Continues: Acta pathologica et
microbiologica Scandinavica. Supplement.
Continued by: APMIS. Supplementum.
1982-1987   8211441

Acta Pathol Microbiol Immunol Scand [A]
Acta pathologica, microbiologica, et
immunologica Scandinavica. Section A,
Pathology
0108-0164
Continues: Acta pathologica et
microbiologica Scandinavica. Section A,
Pathology. Merged with: Acta pathologica,
microbiologica, et immunologica
Scandinavica. Section B. Microbiology,
and: Acta pathologica, microbiologica, et
immunologica Scandinavica. Section C,
Immunology, to form: APMIS.
1982-1987   8206622

Acta Pathol Microbiol Immunol Scand [B]
Acta pathologica, microbiologica, et
immunologica Scandinavica. Section B,
Microbiology
0108-0180
Continues: Acta pathologica et
microbiologica Scandinavica. Section
B, Microbiology. Merged with: Acta
pathologica, microbiologica, et immunologica
Scandinavica. Section A, Pathology, and: Acta
pathologica, microbiologica, et immunologica
Scandinavica. Section C, Immunology, to
form: APMIS.
1982-1987   8206623

Acta Pathol Microbiol Immunol Scand [C]
Acta pathologica, microbiologica, et
immunologica Scandinavica. Section C,
Immunology
0108-0202
Continues: Acta pathologica et
microbiologica Scandinavica. Section
C, Immunology. Merged with: Acta
pathologica, microbiologica, et immunologica
Scandinavica. Section A, Pathology, and: Acta
pathologica, microbiologica, et immunologica
Scandinavica. Section B, Microbiology, to
form: APMIS.
1982-1987   8206624

Acta Pathol Microbiol Scand
Acta pathologica et microbiologica
Scandinavica
0365-5555
1924-1969   7508471

Acta Pathol Microbiol Scand Suppl
Acta pathologica et microbiologica
Scandinavica. Supplement
Continues: Acta pathologica et microbiologica
Scandinavica. Supplementum. Continued
by: Acta pathologica, microbiologica, et
immunologica Scandinavica. Supplement.
1970-1981   8211440

Acta Pathol Microbiol Scand Suppl
Acta pathologica et microbiologica
Scandinavica. Supplementum
0065-1486
Continued by Acta pathologica et
microbiologica Scandinavica. Supplement.
1926-1969   14610060R

Acta Pathol Microbiol Scand [A]
Acta pathologica et microbiologica
Scandinavica. Section A, Pathology
0365-4184
Continues in part Acta pathologica et
microbiologica Scandinavica. Continued
by Acta pathologica, microbiologica, et
immunologica Scandinavica. Section A,
Pathology.
1970-1981   7508468

Acta Pathol Microbiol Scand [B]
Acta pathologica et microbiologica
Scandinavica. Section B, Microbiology
0105-0656
Continues in part Acta pathologica et
microbiologica Scandinavica. Section B:
Microbiology and immunology. Continued
by Acta pathologica, microbiologica, et
immunologica Scandinavica. Section B,
Microbiology.
1975-1981   7508472

**Acta Pathol Microbiol Scand [B] Microbiol
Immunol**
Acta pathologica et microbiologica
Scandinavica. Section B: Microbiology and
immunology
0365-5571
Continues in part Acta pathologica et
microbiologica Scandinavica.
1970-1974   7508470

Acta Pathol Microbiol Scand [C]
Acta pathologica et microbiologica
Scandinavica. Section C, Immunology
0304-1328
Continues in part Acta pathologica et
microbiologica Scandinavia. Section B:
Microbiology and immunology. Continued
by Acta pathologica, microbiologica, et
immunologica Scandinavica. Section C,
Immunology.
1975-1981   7508469

Acta Pediatr Esp
Acta pediátrica española
0001-6640
Continues Acta pediátrica.
1946   0405466

Acta Pharm
Acta pharmaceutica (Zagreb, Croatia)
1330-0075
Continues: Acta pharmaceutica Jugoslavica.
1992   9303678

Acta Pharm Hung
Acta pharmaceutica Hungarica
0001-6659
Continues Gyógyszerésztudományi értesítö,
issued 1925-48.
1953   0414322

Acta Pharm Int
Acta pharmaceutica internationalia
1950-1953   14610080R

Acta Pharm Nord
Acta pharmaceutica Nordica
1100-1801
Formed by the union of: Acta pharmaceutica
Suecica, and: Farmaci (Scientific ed.), and:
Norvegica pharmaceutica acta. Absorbed by:
European journal of pharmaceutical sciences.
1989-1992   8915967

Acta Pharm Suec
Acta pharmaceutica Suecica
0001-6675
Merged with: Farmaci (Scientific ed.) and:
Norvegica pharmaceutica acta, to form: Acta
pharmaceutica Nordica.
1964-1988   0000216

Acta Pharmacol Sin
Acta pharmacologica Sinica
1671-4083   1745-7254
Continues: Zhongguo yao li xue bao.
2000   100956087

Acta Pharmacol Toxicol (Copenh)
Acta pharmacologica et toxicologica
0001-6683
Continued by: Pharmaology & toxicology.
1945-1986   0370572

Acta Physiol (Oxf)
Acta physiologica (Oxford, England)
1748-1708   1748-1716
Continues: Acta physiologica Scandinavica.
2006   101262545

Acta Physiol Acad Sci Hung
Acta physiologica Academiae Scientiarum
Hungaricae
0001-6756
Supersedes Hungarica acta physiologica.
Continued by Acta physiologica Hungarica.
1950-1982   0371156

Acta Physiol Hung
Acta physiologica Hungarica
0231-424X
Continues: Acta physiologica Academiae
Scientiarum Hungaricae.
1983   8309201

Acta Physiol Lat Am
Acta physiologica latino americana
0001-6764
Continued by Acta physiologica et
pharmacologica latinoamericana.
1950-1983   0060610

Acta Physiol Pharmacol Bulg
Acta physiologica et pharmacologica
Bulgarica
0323-9950
Supersedes Izvestiia na Instituta po
fiziologiia.
1974   7512568

Acta Physiol Pharmacol Latinoam
Acta physiologica et pharmacologica
latinoamericana: organo de la Asociación
Latinoamericana de Ciencias Fisiológicas
y de la Asociación Latinoamericana de
Farmacología
0326-6656
Continues: Acta physiologica latino
americana. Continued by: Acta physiologica,
pharmacologica, et therapeutica
latinoamericana.
1984-1990   8409686

Acta Physiol Pharmacol Neerl
Acta physiologica et pharmacologica
Neerlandica
0001-6748
Formed by the union of: Archives
néerlandaises de physiologie de l'homme et
des animaux, and: Acta brevia Neerlandica de
physiologia, pharmacologia, microbiologia
e.a. Absorbed by: European journal of
pharmacology.
1950-1969   14610130R

Acta Physiol Pharmacol Ther Latinoam
Acta physiologica, pharmacologica et
therapeutica latinoamericana: órgano
de la Asociación Latinoamericana de
Ciencias Fisiológicas y [de] la Asociación
Latinoamericana de Farmacología
0327-6309
Continues: Acta physiologica et
pharmacologica latinoamericana.
1991-1999   9200300

Acta Physiol Pol
Acta physiologica Polonica
0044-6033
Continued by: Journal of physiology and
pharmacology.
1950-1990   2985166R

Acta Physiol Scand
Acta physiologica Scandinavica
0001-6772   1365-201X
Supersedes: Skandinavisches Archiv für
Physiologie. Continued by: Acta physiologica
(Oxford, England).
1940-2005   0370362

Acta Physiol Scand Suppl
Acta physiologica Scandinavica.
Supplementum
0302-2994
1940-2002   0376307

Acta Physiother Rheumatol Belg
Acta physiotherapica et rheumatologica
Belgica
Supersedes Annales de médecine physique
et de physio-biologie et de rhumatisme.
Continued by the Journal belge de médecine
physique et de rhumatologie.
1946-1955   17810470R

Acta Pol Pharm
Acta poloniae pharmaceutica
0001-6837
1937   2985167R

Acta Psiquiatr Psicol Am Lat
Acta psiquiátrica y psicológica de América
latina
0001-6896
Continues Acta psiquiátrica y psicológica
argentina.
1964   0373060

Acta Psychiatr Belg
Acta psychiatrica Belgica
0300-8967
Continues in part Acta neurologica et
psychiatrica Belgica.
1970   0247037

Acta Psychiatr Neurol
Acta psychiatrica et neurologica
0365-558X
Continued by: Acta psychiatrica et
neurologica Scandinavica.
1926-1950   14610150R

Acta Psychiatr Neurol Scand Suppl
Acta psychiatrica et neurologica
Scandinavica. Supplementum
0365-5067
Continues: Acta psychiatrica et neurologica.
Supplementum. Split into: Acta neurologica
Scandinavica. Supplementum, and: Acta
psychiatrica Scandinavica. Supplementum.
1951-1961   14610180R

Acta Psychiatr Neurol Suppl
Acta psychiatrica et neurologica.
Supplementum
Continued by: Acta psychiatrica et
neurologica Scandinavica. Supplementum.
1932-1951   14610170R

Acta Psychiatr Scand
Acta psychiatrica Scandinavica
0001-690X   1600-0447
Continues in part Acta psychiatrica et
neurologica Scandinavica.
1961   0370364

Acta Psychiatr Scand Suppl
Acta psychiatrica Scandinavica.
Supplementum
0065-1591   1600-5473
Continues in part Acta psychiatrica et
neurologica Scandinavica, Supplementum.
1961   0370365

Acta Psychol (Amst)
Acta psychologica
0001-6918   1873-6297
1935   0370366

Acta Psychother Psychosom
Acta psychotherapeutica et psychosomatica
0365-5822
Continues: Acta psychotherapeutica,
psychosomatica et orthopaedagogica.
Continued by: Psychotherapy and
psychosomatics.
1953-1964   0000220

Acta Psychother Psychosom Orthopaedagog
Acta psychotherapeutica, psychosomatica et
orthopaedagogica
0365-5679
Continued by: Acta psychotherapeutica et
psychosomatica. 1960
1953-1959   101259884

Acta Radiol
Acta radiologica (Stockholm, Sweden: 1987)
0284-1851   1600-0455
Continues: Acta radiologica: diagnosis.
1987   8706123

Acta Radiol Cancerol
Acta radiologica et cancerologica.
Bohemoslovencia
Continued by Ceskoslovenská roentgenologie.
1938-1954   14610230R

Acta Radiol Diagn (Stockh)
Acta radiologica: diagnosis
0567-8056
Continues in part: Acta radiologica.
Continued by: Acta radiologica (Stockholm,
Sweden: 1987).
1963-1986   0370367

Acta Radiol Oncol
Acta radiologica. Oncology
0349-652X
Continues: Acta radiologica. Oncology,
radiation therapy, physics and biology.
Continued by: Acta oncologica (Stockholm,
Sweden).
1984-1986   8209606

Acta Radiol Oncol Radiat Phys Biol
Acta radiologica: oncology, radiation,
physics, biology
0348-5196
Continues: Acta radiologica: therapy, physics,
biology. Continued by: Acta radiologica:
oncology, radiation therapy, physics and
biology.
1978-1979   7805897

Acta Radiol Oncol Radiat Ther Phys Biol
Acta radiologica. Oncology, radiation
therapy, physics and biology
Continues: Acta radiologica: oncology.
radiation, physics, biology. Continued by:
Acta radiologica. Oncology.
1980-1983   101470759

Acta Radiol Suppl
Acta radiologica. Supplementum
0365-5954
Continued by: Acta radiologica.
Supplement.
1921-2003   0370370

Acta Radiol Suppl (Stockholm)
Acta radiologica. Supplement
Continues: Acta radiologica.
Supplementum.
2004   101470699

Acta Radiol Ther Phys Biol
Acta radiologica: therapy, physics,
biology
0567-8064
Continues: Acta radiologica. Continued
by: Acta radiologica: oncology, radiation,
physics, biology.
1963-1977   0000201

Acta Reumatol Port
Acta reumatológica portuguesa
0303-464X
1973   0431702

Acta Rheumatol Scand
Acta rheumatologica Scandinavica
0001-6934
Continued by: Scandinavian journal of
rheumatology..
1955-1971   0321403

Acta Rheumatol Scand Suppl
Acta rheumatologica Scandinavica.
Supplementum
0065-163X
1958-1971   0400312

Acta Rhumatol
Acta rhumatologica
0250-4642
Continues: Acta rhumatologica Belgica.
Continued by: Clinical rheumatology.
1979-1981   7908064

Acta Rhumatol Belg
Acta rhumatologica Belgica
0378-9497
Supersedes Annales de médecine physique.
Revue française du rhumatisme, and, in
part, Journal belge de rhumatologie et de
médecine physique. Belgisch tijdschrift
voor reumatologie en fysische geneeskunde.
Continued by Acta rhumatologica.
1977-1978   7903226

Acta Sch Med Univ Kioto
Acta Scholae Medicinalis Universitatis in
Kioto
0001-6950
Continues Acta Scholae Medicinalis
Universitatis Imperialis in Kioto, issued
1916/17-1946.
1949-1970   7611898

Acta Sci Sin
Acta scientia Sinica = Chung-kuo k'o hsüeh
0365-7183
Continued by: Scientia Sinica.
1952-1954   8209607

Acta Soc Med Ups
Acta Societatis Medicorum Upsaliensis
0001-6985
Continues: Upsala läkereförenings
förhandlingar. Continued by: Upsala journal
of medical sciences.
1950-1971   0332127

Acta Soc Med Ups Suppl
Acta Societatis Medicorum Upsaliensis.
Supplementum
Continued by: Supplement to the Upsala
journal of medical sciences.
1953-1971   0332130

Acta Sociomed Scand
Acta socio-medica Scandinavica
0044-6041
Continued by: Scandinavian journal of social
medicine..
1969-1972   2985168R

Acta Sociomed Scand Suppl
Acta socio-medica Scandinavica.
Supplement
0301-7664
Continued by: Scandinavian journal of social
medicine. Supplementum.
1969-1972   0414076

Acta Stomatol Belg
Acta stomatologica Belgica
0001-7000
Continues Revue belge de stomatologie.
1960-1997   0421026

Acta Stomatol Croat
Acta stomatologica Croatica
0001-7019
1966   0253456

Acta Stomatol Int
Acta stomatologica internationalia:
revue scientifique et bulletin officiel de
l'Association stomatologique internationale
0255-4410
1980-1987   8807267

Acta Suom Laak Duodecim
Acta. Toimituksia. ser. A. Suomalainen
lääkäriseura Duodecim
Continued by Annales medicinae
experimentalis et biologiae Fenniae.
1929-1947   21030300R

Acta Theriol (Warsz)
Acta theriologica
0001-7051
1955   0314001

Acta Trop
Acta tropica
0001-706X   1873-6254
1944   0370374

Acta Trop Suppl
Acta tropica. Supplementum
0365-1541
1945-1987   7611896

Acta Tuberc Belg
Acta tuberculosea Belgica
Continues Revue belge de la tuberculose.
Continued by Acta tuberculosea et
pneumologica Belgica.
1948-1958   14610280R

Acta Tuberc Jpn
Acta tuberculosea Japonica
0567-8161
Merged with: Kyōto Daigaku Kekkaku
Kenkyūjo kiyō, to form: Kyōto Daigaku
Kekkaku Kyōbu Shikkan Kenkyūjo kiyō.
1951-1966   0157725

Acta Tuberc Pneumol Belg
Acta tuberculosea et pneumologica Belgica
0001-7078
Continues Acta tuberculosea Belgica. Merged
with Scandinavian journal of respiratory
diseases to form European journal of
respiratory diseases.
1959-1979   0370376

Acta Tuberc Pneumol Scand
Acta tuberculosea et pneumologica
Scandinavica
0365-7531
Continues Acta tuberculosea Scandinavica.
Continued by the Scandinavian Journal of
respiratory diseases.
1962-1965   0064362

Acta Tuberc Pneumol Scand Suppl
Acta tuberculosea et pneumologica
Scandinavica. Supplementum
Continues: Supplementum of the Acta
tuberculosea Scandinavica. Continued by:
Supplementum of the Scandinavian journal of
respiratory diseases.
1962-1965   0064754

Acta Tuberc Scand
Acta tuberculosea Scandinavica
Continued by Acta tuberculosea et
pneumologica Scandinavica.
1925-1961   14610290R

Acta Tuberc Scand Suppl
Acta tuberculosea Scandinavica.
Supplementum
Continued by the Supplementum of the Acta
tuberculosea et pneumologica Scandinavica.
1934-1961   14610300R

Acta Unio Int Contra Cancrum
Acta - Unio Internationalis Contra Cancrum
0365-3056
1936-1964   7502506

Acta Univ Carol Med Monogr
Acta Universitatis Carolinae. Medica.
Monographia
0567-8250
1960   0177667

Acta Univ Carol [Med] (Praha)
Acta Universitatis Carolinae. Medica
0001-7116
Absorbed Universitas Carolinae. Medica, in
1958.
1954   2985169R

Acta Univ Palacki Olomuc Fac Med
Acta Universitatis Palackianae Olomucensis
Facultatis Medicae
0301-2514
Continues: Acta Universitatis Palackianae
Olomucensis. Numbering continued by:
Biomedical papers of the Medical Faculty
of the University Palacký, Olomouc,
Czechoslovakia, formerly issued as a
subseries.
1960-2000   0363112

Acta Urol
Acta urologica
1947-1949   14620010R

Acta Urol Belg
Acta urologica Belgica
0001-7183
Continues Journal belge d'urologie.
1955-2000   0377045

Acta Vet (Beogr)
Acta veterinaria
0567-8315
1951   14620020R

Acta Vet Acad Sci Hung
Acta veterinaria Academiae Scientiarum
Hungaricae
0001-7205
Supersedes Acta veterinaria Hungarica.
Continued by Acta veterinaria Hungarica.
1951-1982   0370377

Acta Vet Hung
Acta veterinaria Hungarica
0236-6290
Continues: Acta veterinaria Academiae
Scientiarum Hungaricae.
1983   8406376

Acta Vet Scand
Acta veterinaria Scandinavica
0044-605X   1751-0147
1959   0370400

Acta Vet Scand Suppl
Acta veterinaria Scandinavica.
Supplementum
0065-1699
Absorbed by: Acta veterinaria Scandinavica.
1966-2004   0061331

Acta Virol
Acta virologica
0001-723X   1336-2305
1957   0370401

Acta Vitaminol
Acta vitaminologica
Continued by: Acta vitaminologica et
enzymologica.
1947-1966   0134541

Acta Vitaminol Enzymol
Acta vitaminologica et enzymologica
0300-8924
Continues: Acta vitaminologica.
1967-1985   0135063

Acta Zool Pathol Antverp
Acta zoologica et pathologica Antverpiensia
0001-7280
Continues the Bulletins of the Société royale
de zoologie d'Anvers.
1966-1992   0100314

Actas CIBA
Actas Ciba
1669-4112
1934-1953   14620060R

Actas Dermatol Dermatopatol
Actas de dermatología & dermatopatología
2001   101138323

Actas Dermosifiliogr
Actas dermo-sifiliográficas
0001-7310   1578-2190
1909   0373062

Actas Esp Psiquiatr
Actas españolas de psiquiatría
1139-9287
Continues: Actas luso-españolas de
neurología, psiquiatría y ciencias afines.
1999   100886502

Actas Luso Esp Neurol Psiquiatr
Actas luso-españolas de neurología y
psiquiatría
0001-7329
Continues: Actas españolas de neurología
y psiquiatría. Continued by: Actas luso-
españolas de neurología, psiquiatría y
ciencias afines.
1947-1971   0355646

Actas Luso Esp Neurol Psiquiatr Cienc Afines
Actas luso-españolas de neurología,
psiquiatría y ciencias afines
0300-5062
Continues: Actas luso-españolas de
neurología y psiquiatría. Continued by: Actas
españolas de psiquiatría.
1972-1998   0355573

Actas Reun Cient Cuerfo Fac Inst Policlin
Actas de las reuniones científicas del cuerpo
facultativo del Instituto Policlínico
194u-1993   0410423

Actas Urol Esp
Actas urologicas españolas
0210-4806   1699-7980
1977   7704993

Actual Anatpathol
Actualités anatomo-pathologiques
1958-19uu   14620310R

Actual Biol
Actualités biologiques
1954-1956   14620330R

Actual Cardiol Angeiol Int (Paris)
Actualités cardiologiques et angéiologiques
internationales
0365-1045
Continued by Annales de cardiologie et
d'angéiologie.
1948-1967   0143027

Actual Endocrinol (Paris)
Actualités endocrinologiques
0065-1826
1960-1973   0370405

Actual Hepatogastroenterol (Paris)
Actualités hépato-gastro-entérologiques
0240-8007
Continues Actualités hépato-gastro-
entérologiques de l'Hôtel-Dieu. Continued
by Annales de gastroentérologie et
d'hépatologie.
1968-1969   0264367

Actual Medica
Actualidad médica
0365-7965
1911-1979   14620190R

Actual Neurophysiol (Paris)
Actualités neurophysiologiques
0567-882X
1959-1974   7513548

Actual Odonto Estomatol Esp
Actualidad odontoestomatologica española /
Ilustre Consejo General de Colegios de
Odontólogos y Estomatólogos de España
1136-4386
Continues: Revista de actualidad
odontoestomatológica española. Continued
by: R.O.E..
1995-1995   9614683

Actual Odontostomatol (Paris)
Actualités odonto-stomatologiques
0001-7817
1947   0370406

Actual Pediatr (Granada)
Actualidad pediátrica; revista de
bibliografía internacional
0001-7671
1952-1974   2985171R

Actual Pharm
Actualités pharmaceutiques
0515-3700
Supersedes Officine & techniques.
1961   0043545

Actual Pharmacol (Paris)
Actualités pharmacologiques
0567-8854
1949-1988   0370407

Actual Physiol Pathol (Paris)
Actualités de physiologie pathologique
0567-8714
1966-1973   7611901

Acupunct Electrother Res
Acupuncture & electro-therapeutics
research
0360-1293
1975   7610364

Acupunct Med
Acupuncture in medicine: journal of the
British Medical Acupuncture Society
0964-5284
Absorbed: Svensk tidskrift for medicinsk
akupunktur. 2004
1983   9304117

Acute Card Care
Acute cardiac care
1748-2941   1748-295X
Continues: International journal of
cardiovascular interventions.
2006   101276603

Acute Care
Acute care
0254-0819
Continues: Biotelemetry and patient
monitoring.
1984-1989   8412026

AD Nurse
AD nurse
0887-2198
Continued by: Advancing clinical care.
1986-1989   8704179

ADA Forecast
ADA forecast
0001-0847
Supersedes Diabetic news. Continued by
Diabetes forecast.
1948-1974   7506508

ADA News
ADA news
0001-0855
Continued by: American Dental Association
news.
1970-1986   0253044

Adapt Phys Activ Q
Adapted physical activity quarterly: APAQ
0736-5829   1543-2777
1984   **8701671**

Addict Behav
Addictive behaviors
0306-4603   1873-6327
1975   **7603486**

Addict Biol
Addiction biology
1355-6215   1369-1600
1996   **9604935**

Addict Dis
Addictive diseases
0094-0267
Continued by Chemical dependencies.
1974-1979   **0425064**

Addict Sci Clin Pract
Addiction science & clinical practice
1940-0632   1940-0640
Continues: Science & practice perspectives.
2007   **101316917**

Addiction
Addiction (Abingdon, England)
0965-2140   1360-0443
Continues: British journal of addiction.
1993   **9304118**

Additamenta Folia Med Neerl
Folia medica Neerlandica. Additamenta
1962-1964   **0067036**

Adicciones
Adicciones
0214-4840
1989   **9605506**

ADM
ADM (Asociación Dental Mexicana: 1986)
0001-0944
Continues: Revista ADM. Continued by:
Revista ADM (Asociación Dental Mexicana:
1988).
1986-1987   **8712346**

ADM
ADM; revista de la Asociación Dental
Mexicana
0001-0944
Continued by Revista ADM.
1943-1979   **0370411**

Adm Manage
Administrative management
0001-8376
Continues: Office management and American
business. Merged with: Word processing &
information systems, ISSN 0279-7992, to
form: Office administration and automation,
ISSN 0745-4325.
1961-1982   **9875709**

Adm Ment Health
Administration in mental health
0090-1180
Continued by: Administration and policy in
metal health.
1972-1988   **0361564**

Adm Policy Ment Health
Administration and policy in mental health
0894-587X   1573-3289
Absorbed: Mental health services research.
2006- Continues: Administration in mental
health.
1988   **8914574**

Adm Radiol
Administrative radiology: AR
0738-6974
Continued by: Administrative radiology journal.
198u-199u   **8712333**

Adm Radiol J
Administrative radiology journal: AR
Continues: Administrative radiology.
1995-2001   **9702245**

Adm Sci Q
Administrative science quarterly
0001-8392
1956   **0240207**

Adm Soc Work
Administration in social work
0364-3107   1544-4376
1977   **7800009**

Admit Manage J
The Admitting management journal
Continues: Journal for hospital admitting
management. Continued by: NAHAM
management journal.
1988-1990   **8812074**

Adolesc Med
Adolescent medicine (Philadelphia, Pa.)
1041-3499
Continued by: Adolescent medicine clinics.
1990-2003   **9006270**

Adolesc Med Clin
Adolescent medicine clinics
1547-3368
Continues: Adolescent medicine
(Philadelphia. Pa.). Continued by: Adolescent
medicine - state of the art reviews.
2004-2006   **101196463**

Adolesc Med State Art Rev
Adolescent medicine: state of the art reviews
1934-4287
Continues: Adolescent medicine clinics.
2007   **101314248**

Adolesc Psychiatry
Adolescent psychiatry
0065-2008
1971   **1302147**

Adolescence
Adolescence
0001-8449
1966   **0123667**

Adult Educ
Adult education
0001-8481
Formed by the union of: Adult education
bulletin; and: Adult education journal.
Continued by: Adult education quarterly
(American Association for Adult and
Continuing Education).
1950-1983   **9877760**

Adv Alcohol Subst Abuse
Advances in alcohol & substance abuse
0270-3106
Continues: Drug abuse & alcoholism review.
Continued by: Journal of addictive diseases.
1981-1990   **8107172**

Adv Anat Embryol Cell Biol
Advances in anatomy, embryology, and cell
biology
0301-5556
Continues Ergebnisse der Anatomie und
Entwicklungsgeschichte.
1973   **0407712**

Adv Anat Pathol
Advances in anatomic pathology
1072-4109   1533-4031
1994   **9435676**

Adv Appl Microbiol
Advances in applied microbiology
0065-2164
1959   **0370413**

Adv Behav Biol
Advances in behavioral biology
0099-6246
Supersedes Advances in mental science.
1971   **1304163**

Adv Biochem Eng Biotechnol
Advances in biochemical engineering/
biotechnology
0724-6145   1616-8542
Continues: Advances in biochemical
engineering.
1983   **8307733**

Adv Biochem Psychopharmacol
Advances in biochemical
psychopharmacology
0065-2229
1969-1995   **0211233**

Adv Biol Med Phys
Advances in biological and medical physics
0065-2245
1948-1980   **0370414**

Adv Biol Skin
Advances in biology of skin
0065-2253
Absorbed by: Journal of investigative
dermatology.
1960-1972   **0426664**

Adv Biomed Eng Med Phys
Advances in biomedical engineering and
medical physics
0065-2261
1968-1971   **7611904**

Adv Biophys
Advances in biophysics
0065-227X
1970   **0262476**

Adv Biosci
Advances in the biosciences
0065-3446
1967-1994   **0225721**

Adv Biotechnol Processes
Advances in biotechnological processes
0736-2293
1983-1990   **8305187**

Adv Cancer Res
Advances in cancer research
0065-230X
1953   **0370416**

Adv Carbohydr Chem
Advances in carbohydrate chemistry
Continued by Advances in carbohydrate
chemistry and biochemistry.
1945-1968   **0240536**

Adv Carbohydr Chem Biochem
Advances in carbohydrate chemistry and
biochemistry
0065-2318
Continues Advances in carbohydrate
chemistry.
1969   **0240537**

Adv Card Surg
Advances in cardiac surgery
0889-5074
1990-2001   **9007186**

Adv Cardiol
Advances in cardiology
0065-2326   1662-2839
Continues Fortschritte der Kardiologie.
1970   **0270063**

Adv Cardiopulm Dis
Advances in cardiopulmonary diseases
0065-2334
1963-1969   **14630130R**

Adv Cell Biol
Advances in cell biology
0065-2369
1970-1971   0235424

Adv Chemother
Advances in chemotherapy
0567-9877
United with: Advances in pharmacology,
to form: Advances in pharmacology and
chemotherapy.
1964-1968   0236562

Adv Child Dev Behav
Advances in child development and behavior
0065-2407
1963   0370417

Adv Chromatogr
Advances in chromatography
0065-2415
1965   0121020

Adv Chronic Kidney Dis
Advances in chronic kidney disease
1548-5595   1548-5609
Continues: Advances in renal replacement
therapy.
2004   101209214

Adv Clin Care
Advancing clinical care: official journal of
NOAADN
1042-9565
Continues: AD nurse.
1989-1991   8912856

Adv Clin Chem
Advances in clinical chemistry
0065-2423
1958   2985173R

Adv Clin Path
Advances in clinical pathology: the official
journal of Adriatic Society of Pathology
1125-5552
1997   9709997

Adv Clin Pharmacol
Advances in clinical pharmacology
0303-2671
Continues Advances of clinical pharmacology.
Supplement to the International journal
of clinical pharmacology, therapy, and
toxicology.
1974-1978   0430232

Adv Clin Rehabil
Advances in clinical rehabilitation
0892-8878
Continues: Annual review of rehabilitation.
1987-1990   8809051

Adv Colloid Interface Sci
Advances in colloid and interface science
0001-8686   1873-3727
1967   8706645

Adv Comp Physiol Biochem
Advances in comparative physiology and
biochemistry
0065-244X
1962-1982   0370422

Adv Contracept
Advances in contraception: the official
journal of the Society for the Advancement
of Contraception
0267-4874
1985-1999   8607435

Adv Cyclic Nucleotide Protein Phosphorylation Res
Advances in cyclic nucleotide and protein
phosphorylation research
0747-7767
Continues: Advances in cyclic nucleotide
research. Continued by: Advances in second
messenger and phosphorprotein research.
1984-1986   8404639

Adv Cyclic Nucleotide Res
Advances in cyclic nucleotide research
0084-5930
Continued by: Advances in cyclic nucleotide
and protein phosphorylation research.
1972-1983   0341362

Adv Cytopharmacol
Advances in cytopharmacology
0084-5949
1971-1979   1301733

Adv Data
Advance data
0147-3956
Continued by: National health statistics
reports.
1976-2008   7703830

Adv Dent Res
Advances in dental research
0895-9374   1544-0737
1987-uuuu   8802131

Adv Dermatol
Advances in dermatology
0882-0880
Continues: Current issues in dermatology.
1986   8606032

Adv Drug Deliv Rev
Advanced drug delivery reviews
0169-409X   1872-8294
1987   8710523

Adv Drug Res
Advances in drug research
0065-2490
1964   0040021

Adv Endocrinol Metab
Advances in endocrinology and metabolism
1049-6734
1990-1996   9102501

Adv Enzyme Regul
Advances in enzyme regulation
0065-2571   1873-2437
1963   0044263

Adv Enzymol Relat Areas Mol Biol
Advances in enzymology and related areas
of molecular biology
0065-258X
Continues Advances in enzymology and
related subjects of biochemistry.
1967   0337243

Adv Enzymol Relat Subj Biochem
Advances in enzymology and related
subjects of biochemistry
0096-5316
Continued by Advances in enzymology and
related area of molecular biology.
1941-1966   0337244

Adv Exp Med Biol
Advances in experimental medicine and
biology
0065-2598
1967   0121103

Adv Fluorine Res
Advances in fluorine research and dental
caries prevention
0567-994X
1962-1966   14630160R

Adv Food Nutr Res
Advances in food and nutrition research
1043-4526
Continues: Advances in food research.
1989   9001271

Adv Food Res
Advances in food research
0065-2628
Continued by: Advances in food and nutrition
research.
1948-1988   0370423

Adv Food Res Suppl
Advances in food research. Supplement
0065-2636
1969-1980   0221542

Adv Genet
Advances in genetics
0065-2660
Absorbed: Molecular genetic medicine, in
1995.
1947   0370421

Adv Gerontol
Advances in gerontology = Uspekhi
gerontologii / Rossiĭskaiâ akademiiâ nauk,
Gerontologicheskoe obshchestvo
1561-9125
19uu   100971443

Adv Gerontol Res
Advances in gerontological research
0065-2709
1964-1972   0436264

Adv Health Econ Health Serv Res
Advances in health economics and health
services research
0731-2199
Continues: Research in health economics.
1981   8206631

Adv Health Econ Health Serv Res Suppl
Advances in health economics and health
services research. Supplement
1054-1888
1990-199u   9013413

Adv Health Sci Educ Theory Pract
Advances in health sciences education:
theory and practice
1382-4996   1573-1677
1996   9612021

Adv Heterocycl Chem
Advances in heterocyclic chemistry
0065-2725
1963   0370424

Adv Hum Genet
Advances in human genetics
0065-275X
1970   1256347

Adv Immun Cancer Ther
Advances in immunity and cancer therapy
0178-2134
1985-1986   8601071

Adv Immunol
Advances in immunology
0065-2776
1961   0370425

Adv Inorg Biochem
Advances in inorganic biochemistry
0190-0218
1979-1996   7909203

Adv Intern Med
Advances in internal medicine
0065-2822
1942-2001   0370427

Adv Lipid Res
Advances in lipid research
0065-2849
1963-1993   0000262

Adv Mar Biol
Advances in marine biology
0065-2881
1963   0370431

Adv Med Sci
Advances in medical sciences
1896-1126
Continues: Roczniki Akademii Medycznej w
Białymstoku (1995).
2006   101276222

Adv Metab Disord
Advances in metabolic disorders
0065-2903
Continued by: Advances in metabolism.
1964-1988   0370430

Adv Microb Physiol
Advances in microbial physiology
0065-2911
1967   0117147

Adv Mind Body Med
Advances in mind-body medicine
1470-3556
Continues: Advances (New York, N.Y.).
1998   9813115

Adv Morphog
Advances in morphogenesis
0065-2962
1961-1973   7611906

Adv Myocardiol
Advances in myocardiology
0270-4056
Supersedes Recent advances in studies on
cardiac structure and metabolism.
1980-1985   8000285

Adv Neonatal Care
Advances in neonatal care: official journal of
the National Association of Neonatal Nurses
1536-0903   1536-0911
2001   101125644

Adv Nephrol Necker Hosp
Advances in nephrology from the Necker
Hospital
0084-5957
1971-2001   0311622

Adv Neuroimmunol
Advances in neuroimmunology
0960-5428
1991-1996   9108376

Adv Neurol
Advances in neurology
0091-3952
1973   0367524

Adv Nurse Pract
Advance for nurse practitioners
1096-6293
1993   9892010

Adv Nutr Res
Advances in nutritional research
0149-9483
1977   7802764

Adv Ophthalmic Plast Reconstr Surg
Advances in ophthalmic plastic and
reconstructive surgery
0276-3508
1982-1992   8213022

Adv Ophthalmol
Advances in ophthalmology = Fortschritte der
Augenheilkunde = Progrès en ophtalmologie
0065-3004
Continues: Fortschritte der Augenheilkunde.
Merged with: Bibliotheca ophthalmologica,
and: Modern problems in ophthalmology, to
form: Developments in ophthalmology.
1969-1981   0263212

Adv Oral Biol
Advances in oral biology
0065-3020
1964-1970   0000261

Adv Otorhinolaryngol
Advances in oto-rhino-laryngology
0065-3071   1662-2847
1969   0242534

Adv Parasitol
Advances in parasitology
0065-308X
1963   0370435

Adv Pathobiol
Advances in pathobiology
0099-1147
1975-1980   7511090

Adv Pediatr
Advances in pediatrics
0065-3101
1942   0370436

Adv Pediatr Infect Dis
Advances in pediatric infectious diseases
0884-9404
1986-1999   8803391

Adv Perit Dial
Advances in peritoneal dialysis. Conference
on Peritoneal Dialysis
1197-8554
1985   9104803

Adv Pest Control Res
Advances in pest control research
0568-0107
1957-1968   14640020R

Adv Pharm Sci
Advances in pharmaceutical sciences
0065-3136
1964   0040024

Adv Pharmacol
Advances in pharmacology
0568-0123
United with: Advances in chemotherapy,
to form: Advances in pharmacology and
chemotherapy.
1962-1968   0236563

Adv Pharmacol
Advances in pharmacology (San Diego,
Calif.)
1054-3589
Continues: Advances in pharmacology and
chemotherapy.
1990   9015397

Adv Pharmacol Chemother
Advances in pharmacology and
chemotherapy
0065-3144
Formed by the union of Advances in
pharmacology and Advances in chemotherapy
and continues vol. numbering of the former.
Continued by: Advances in pharmacology
(San Diego, Calif.).
1969-1984   0237113

Adv Physiol Educ
Advances in physiology education
1043-4046   1522-1229
1989   100913944

Adv Pract Nurs Q
Advanced practice nursing quarterly
1080-4293
1995-1998   9515177

Adv Pract Nurse
Advanced practice nurse: APN
1076-7231
1994-1996   9442478

Adv Prostaglandin Thromboxane Leukot Res
Advances in prostaglandin, thromboxane,
and leukotriene research
0732-8141
Continues: Advances in prostaglandin and
thromboxane research.
1982-1995   8211444

Adv Prostaglandin Thromboxane Res
Advances in prostaglandin and thromboxane
research
0361-5952
Continued by Advances in prostaglandin,
thromboxane, and leukotriene research series.
1976-1980   7610366

Adv Protein Chem
Advances in protein chemistry
0065-3233
1944   0116732

Adv Psychobiol
Advances in psychobiology
0065-3241
1972-1976   0337407

Adv Psychosom Med
Advances in psychosomatic medicine
0065-3268   1662-2855
Continues Fortschritte der psychosomatischen
Medizin.
1967   0101303

Adv Ren Replace Ther
Advances in renal replacement therapy
1073-4449
Continued by: Advances in chronic kidney
diseases.
1994-2004   9433799

Adv Reprod Physiol
Advances in reproductive physiology
0065-3322
1966-1973   7513188

Adv Sci
Advancement of science
0001-866X
Supersedes Report of the annual meeting of
the British Association for the Advancement
of Science.
1939-1971   0370412

Adv Second Messenger Phosphoprotein Res
Advances in second messenger and
phosphoprotein research
1040-7952
Continues: Advances in cyclic nucleotide and
protein phosphorylation research.
1988-1999   8807408

Adv Sex Horm Res
Advances in sex hormone research
0098-0137
1975-1980   7504908

Adv Shock Res
Advances in shock research
0195-878X
1979-1983   7908298

Adv Skin Wound Care
Advances in skin & wound care
1527-7941   1538-8654
Continues: Advances in wound care.
2000   100911021

Adv Sociodent Res
Advances in socio-dental research
0092-9816
1973-1975   0410245

Adv Space Biol Med
Advances in space biology and medicine
1569-2574
1991   9316462

Adv Space Res
Advances in space research: the official
journal of the Committee on Space Research
(COSPAR)
0273-1177
    Formed by the union of: Advances in space
    exploration; Life sciences and space research;
    and, Space research. Absorbed: COSPAR
    information bulletin with 1999.
1981   9878935

Adv Steroid Biochem Pharmacol
Advances in steroid biochemistry and
pharmacology
0065-339X
1970-1979   1251746

Adv Surg
Advances in surgery
0065-3411
1965   0045335

Adv Tech Stand Neurosurg
Advances and technical standards in
neurosurgery
0095-4829
1974   7501064

Adv Ther
Advances in therapy
0741-238X   1865-8652
1984   8611864

Adv Tracer Methodol
Advances in tracer methodology
0065-3497
1963-1968   14640050R

Adv Tuberc Res
Advances in tuberculosis research.
Fortschritte der Tuberkuloseforschung.
Progrès de l'exploration de la tuberculose
0065-3500
    Continues the same title formerly issued as
    part of Bibliotheca tuberculosea.
1972-1985   0347575

Adv Vet Sci
Advances in veterinary science
0096-7653
    Continued by Advances in veterinary science
    and comparative medicine.
1953-1968   0216704

Adv Vet Sci Comp Med
Advances in veterinary science and
comparative medicine
0065-3519
    Continues: Advances in veterinary science.
    Continued by: Advances in veterinary
    medicine.
1969-1995   0216540

Adv Virus Res
Advances in virus research
0065-3527
1953   0370441

Adv Wound Care
Advances in wound care: the journal for
prevention and healing
1076-2191
    Continues: Decubitus. Continued by:
    Advances in skin & wound care.
1994-1999   9432971

Adverse Drug React Acute Poisoning Rev
Adverse drug reactions and acute poisoning
reviews
0260-647X
    Continued by: Adverse drug reactions and
    toxicological reviews.
1982-1990   8217118

Adverse Drug React Toxicol Rev
Adverse drug reactions and toxicological
reviews
0964-198X
    Continues: Adverse drug reactions and
    acute poisoning reviews. Continued by:
    Toxicological reviews.
1991-2002   9109474

Advert Age
Advertising age
0001-8899
    Absorbed: Advertising agency (Bristol,
    Conn.: 1958). Sept. 1958
1930   9877308

Aeromed Acta
Aeromedica acta
0568-0549
1952-1979   14640080R

Aeromed Rev
Aeromedical reviews
0065-3683
1957-1984   0373063

Aerosp Am
Aerospace America
0740-722X
    Continues: Astronautics & aeronautics.
1984   100971388

Aerosp Med
Aerospace medicine
0001-9402
    Continues: Journal of aviation medicine.
    Continued by: Aviation, space, and
    environmental medicine.
1959-1974   7501696

Aesthet Surg J
Aesthetic surgery journal / the American
Society for Aesthetic Plastic surgery
1090-820X   1527-330X
    Continues: Aesthetic surgery quarterly.
1997   9707469

Aesthetic Plast Surg
Aesthetic plastic surgery
0364-216X   1432-5241
1976   7701756

Afghan Med J
Afghan medical journal
1956-1963   14650160R

AFL CIO Am Fed
The AFL-CIO American federationist. AFL-
CIO
0149-2489
    Continues: American federationist.
1976   9877748

AFOSR TN United States Air Force Off Sci Res
AFOSR TN. United States. Air Force. Office
of Scientific Research
1950-uuuu   22410530R

AFOSR TR United States Air Force Off Sci Res
AFOSR TR. United States. Air Force. Office
of Scientific Research
1950-uuuu   22410510R

Afr Dent J
African dental journal: official publication of
the Federation of African Dental Associations
= Journal dentaire africain / FADA
0794-7348
1987-1996   8813229

Afr Fr Chir
Afrique française chirurgicale
1943-1965   0370447

Afr Health Sci
African health sciences
1680-6905   1729-0503
2001   101149451

Afr J Health Sci
African journal of health sciences
1022-9272
1994   9439497

Afr J Med Med Sci
African journal of medicine and medical
sciences
0309-3913
    Continues The African journal of medical
    sciences.
1976   7801013

Afr J Med Sci
The African journal of medical sciences
0002-0028
    Continued by African journal of medicine and
    medical sciences.
1970-1973   7611908

Afr J Psychiatry
The African journal of psychiatry. Le
Journal africain de psychiatrie
0331-0175
1975-1981   7802295

Afr J Reprod Health
African journal of reproductive health
1118-4841
1997   9712263

Age Ageing
Age and ageing
0002-0729   1468-2834
1972   0375655

Aged Care Serv Rev
Aged care & services review
0161-1151
1978-1981   7808411

Ageing Res Rev
Ageing research reviews
1568-1637   1872-9649
    Continues in part: Mechanisms of ageing and
    development.
2002   101128963

Agents Actions
Agents and actions
0065-4299
    Continued by: Inflammation research.
1969-1994   0213341

Agents Actions Suppl
Agents and actions. Supplements
0379-0363
1977-1998   7801014

Aggiorn Clinico Ter
Aggiornamenti clinicoterapeutici
0002-0907
1960-1974   0376310

Aggiorn Fisiol
Aggiornamenti di fisiologia
0568-2215
1950-1960   14650240R

Aggiorn Sulle Mal Infez
Aggiornamenti sulle malattie da infezione
    Continued by Aggiornamenti su malattie
    infettive ed immunologia.
1955-1968   1260261

Aggiorn Ter Oftalmol
Aggiornamenti di terapia oftalmologica
0002-0915
1949 — 0370450

Aggress Behav
Aggressive behavior
0096-140X — 1098-2337
1974 — 7502265

Aging
Aging
0002-0966
1951-1996 — 0050677

Aging (Milano)
Aging (Milan, Italy)
0394-9532
Continued by: Aging, clinical and
experimental research.
1989-2001 — 9102503

Aging Cell
Aging cell
1474-9718 — 1474-9726
2002 — 101130839

Aging Clin Exp Res
Aging clinical and experimental research
1594-0667
Continues: Aging (Milan, Italy).
2002 — 101132995

Aging Leis Living
Aging & leisure living
0194-455X
Supersedes Concern in care of the aging.
1978-1981 — 7910857

Aging Male
The aging male: the official journal of the
International Society for the Study of the
Aging Male
1368-5538 — 1473-0790
1998 — 9808210

Aging Ment Health
Aging & mental health
1360-7863 — 1364-6915
1997 — 9705773

Aging Trends
Aging trends (Hyattsville, Md.)
1932-1643 — 1932-1651
2001 — 101128131

Agnes Karll Schwest Krankenpfleger
Die Agnes Karll-Schwester, der
Krankenpfleger
Continued by: Krankenpflege (Frankfurt am
Main, Germany).
1947-1971 — 0321470

Agressologie
Agressologie: revue internationale de physio-
biologie et de pharmacologie appliquées aux
effets de l'agression
0002-1148
1960-1994 — 0121575

Agri
Ağrı: Ağrı (Algoloji) Derneği'nin Yayın
organıdır = The journal of the Turkish
Society of Algology
1300-0012
1989 — 9426197

Agric Biol Chem
Agricultural and biological chemistry
0002-1369
Continues the Bulletin of the Agricultural
Chemical Society of Japan. Continued by:
Bioscience, biotechnology, and biochemistry.
1961-1991 — 0370452

AHA Hosp Technol Ser
AHA hospital technology series
0735-4681
Continued by: Hospital technology series.
1981-1983 — 9880754

AHIP Cover
AHIP Coverage
1551-8442
Continues: Healthplan (Washington, D.C.).
2004 — 101223105

AHME J
AHME journal
0090-7782
Continues AHME newsletter, issued Jan.
1969-May? 1970. Continued by Journal -
Association for Hospital Medical Education.
1970-1976 — 0362122

Ahot Beyisrael
ha-Ahot be-Yisrael
0048-1165
1948 — 2985175R

AHP J
AHP journal / Association for Healthcare
Philanthropy
1551-840X
Continues: Journal (Association for
Healthcare Philanthropy (U.S.)).
2001 — 101138795

Ai Zheng
Ai zheng = Aizheng = Chinese journal of
cancer
1000-467X
1982 — 9424852

AIA J
AIA journal. American Institute of
Architects
0001-1479
Continues: Journal of the American Institute
of Architects (1944). Continued by:
Architecture (Washington, D.C.).
1957-1983 — 9875078

Aichi Gakuin Daigaku Shigakkai Shi
Aichi Gakuin Daigaku Shigakkai shi
0044-6912
1964 — 7501066

Aichi Gakuin Dent Sci
Aichi-Gakuin dental science
0916-2062
1988 — 9206301

AIDS
AIDS (London, England)
0269-9370 — 1473-5571
1987 — 8710219

AIDS Action Policy Brief
AIDS Action policy brief
1932-2291 — 1932-2704
uuuu — 101129445

AIDS Action Update
AIDS action update / AIDS Action
Foundation
Continued by: AIDS action quarterly.
1987-1996 — 9014916

AIDS Alert
AIDS alert
0887-0292
Continues: Common sense about AIDS.
1986 — 8608900

AIDS Behav
AIDS and behavior
1090-7165 — 1573-3254
1997 — 9712133

AIDS Care
AIDS care
0954-0121 — 1360-0451
1989 — 8915313

AIDS Clin Care
AIDS clinical care
1043-1543
1989 — 9000367

AIDS Clin Rev
AIDS clinical review
1045-2877
1989 — 8914235

AIDS Educ Prev
AIDS education and prevention: official
publication of the International Society for
AIDS Education
0899-9546 — 1943-2755
1989 — 9002873

AIDS Inst Newsl
AIDS Institute newsletter. New York (State).
AIDS Institute
Merged with: Disease control bulletin, to
form Epidemiology notes.
1984-1985 — 8812089

AIDS Lit Law Rev
AIDS literature & law review
1083-8589
Continues: AIDS literature & news review.
1995-2001 — 9508188

AIDS Patient Care
AIDS patient care
0893-5068
Continued by: AIDS patient care and STDs.
1987-1995 — 8710781

AIDS Patient Care STDS
AIDS patient care and STDs
1087-2914 — 1557-7449
Absorbed: Pediatric AIDS and HIV infection.
June 1997 Continues: AIDS patient care.
1996 — 9607225

AIDS Policy Law
AIDS policy & law
0887-1493
1986 — 8703425

AIDS Public Policy J
AIDS & public policy journal
0887-3852
1986 — 8708548

AIDS Read
The AIDS reader
1053-0894
1991 — 9206753

AIDS Res
AIDS research
0737-6006
Continued by: AIDS research and human
retroviruses..
1983-1986 — 8310361

AIDS Res Hum Retroviruses
AIDS research and human retroviruses
0889-2229 — 1931-8405
Continues: AIDS research.
1987 — 8709376

AIDS Rev
AIDS reviews
1139-6121 — 1698-6997
1999 — 101134876

AIDS Treat News
AIDS treatment news
1052-4207
1987 — 8809835

AIHA J (Fairfax, Va)
AIHA journal: a journal for the science of occupational and environmental health and safety
1542-8117   1542-8125
Continues: AIHAJ. Merged with: Applied occupational and environmental hygiene, to form: Journal of occupational and environmental hygiene.
2002-2003   101146781

AIHAJ
AIHAJ: a journal for the science of occupational and environmental health and safety
1529-8663
Continues: American Industrial Hygiene Association journal. Continued by: AIHA journal.
2000-2001   100939625

Air Med J
Air medical journal
1067-991X   1532-6497
Absorbed: AirMed. 2001 Continues: Journal of air medical transport.
1993   9312325

Air Med News Lett
Air medical news-letter. Great Britain. Medical Dept. of the Navy
1945-19uu   17210240R

Air Waste
Air & waste: journal of the Air & Waste Management Association
1073-161X
Continues: Journal of the Air & Waste Management Association. Continued by: Journal of the Air & Waste Management Association (1995).
1993-1994   9433394

Air Water Pollut
Air and water pollution
0568-3408
Continues: International journal of air and water pollution. Split into: Atmospheric environment, and: Water research.
1961-1966   0101051

AJNR Am J Neuroradiol
AJNR. American journal of neuroradiology
0195-6108   1936-959X
1980   8003708

AJR Am J Roentgenol
AJR. American journal of roentgenology
0361-803X   1546-3141
Continues: American journal of roentgenology, radium therapy and nuclear medicine.
1976   7708173

AJS
AJS; American journal of sociology
0002-9602   1537-5390
Continues the American journal of sociology.
1964   0234014

Akad Iatr
Akademaike iatrike
1937-1970   0370453

Aktuel Probl Phoniatr Logop
Aktuelle Probleme der Phoniatrie und Logopädie. Current problems in phoniatrics and logopedics. Problèmes actuels de phoniatrie et de logopédie
0070-2072
1960-1965   7611910

Aktuelle Gerontol
Aktuelle Gerontologie
0300-5704
Continues Actuelle Gerontologie. Absorbed by: Zeitschrift für Gerontologie.
1974-1983   0421403

Aktuelle Otorhinolaryngol
Aktuelle Oto-Rhino-Laryngologie
0065-5570
Continues: Zwanglose Abhandlungen aus dem Gebiet der Hals-Nasen-Ohren-Heilkunde.
1969-1988   0177222

Aktuelle Probl Chir
Aktuelle Probleme in der Chirurgie
0065-5589
1966-1977   0267464

Aktuelle Probl Chir Orthop
Aktuelle Probleme in Chirurgie und Orthopädie
0378-8504
Supersedes Aktuelle Probleme in der Chirurgie. Continued by: Aktuelle Probleme aus Chirurgie und Orthopädie, which is unnumbered.
1977-uuuu   7705398

Aktuelle Radiol
Aktuelle Radiologie
0939-267X
Continues: Röntgen-Blätter. Absorbed by: RöFo.
1991-1998   9102962

Aktuelle Traumatol
Aktuelle Traumatologie
0044-6173
Continues: Actuelle Traumatologie. Absorbed by: Zeitschrift fur orthopadie und unfallchirurgie.
1974-2007   0421405

Aktuelle Urol
Aktuelle Urologie
0001-7868   1438-8820
Continues Actuelle Urologie.
1974   0421406

Akush Ginekol (Mosk)
Akusherstvo i ginekologiia
0002-3906
Formed by the union of Zhurnal akusherstva i zhenskikh bolezneĭ and Ginekologiia i akusherstvo.
1936   0370456

Akush Ginekol (Sofiia)
Akusherstvo i ginekologiiâ
0324-0959
1962   0370455

Al Mihan Al Tibbiyah
al-Mihan al-tibbiyah
0021-0927
Continued by al-Majallah al-tibbiyah al-'Iraqiyah.
1953-1966   0342064

Ala Dent Rev
Alabama dental review
0516-3927
1953-1963   0242776

Ala J Med Sci
The Alabama journal of medical sciences
0002-4252
1964-1988   0376521

Ala Med
Alabama medicine: journal of the Medical Association of the State of Alabama
0738-4947
Continues: Journal of the Medical Association of the State of Alabama. Continued by: MASA review.
1983-1996   8310343

Ala Nurse
The Alabama nurse
0002-4317
Supersedes Alabama State Nurses' Association. Bulletin.
1947   14720150R

ALAFO
ALAFO; revista de la Asociación Latinoamericana de Facultades de Odontología
0258-7459
Continued by: Revista ALAFO.
1966-1982   0203272

Alaska Med
Alaska medicine
0002-4538
1959   0370457

Alaska Nurse
The Alaska nurse
0002-4546
1951   0042336

Albany Law Rev
Albany law review
0002-4678
Beginning with 1996, absorbed: State constitutional commentaries and notes, as an annual special issue with title: State constitutional commentary.
1948   9892402

Alberta Med Bull
Alberta medical bulletin
0002-4848
1935-1976   0415505

Albrecht Von Graefes Arch Klin Exp Ophthalmol
Albrecht von Graefes Archiv für klinische und experimentelle Ophthalmology. Albrecht von Graefe's archive for clinical and experimental ophthalmology
0065-6100
Continues: Albrecht von Graefe's Archiv für Ophthalmologie. Continued by: Graefe's archive for clinical and experimental ophthalmology.
1965-1981   0044637

Albrecht Von Graefes Arch Ophthalmol
Albrecht von Graefe's Archiv für Ophthalmologie
0376-0200
Continues: Archiv für Ophthalmologie. Absorbed: Archiv für Augenheilkunde. Continued by: Albrecht von Graefes Archiv für klinische und experimentelle Ophthalmologie.
1871-1965   0061573

Alcohol
Alcohol (Fayetteville, N.Y.)
0741-8329   1873-6823
Absorbed: Alcohol and drug research.
1984   8502311

Alcohol Alcohol
Alcohol and alcoholism (Oxford, Oxfordshire)
0735-0414   1464-3502
Continues: British journal on alcohol and alcoholism.
1983   8310684

Alcohol Alcohol Suppl
Alcohol and alcoholism (Oxford, Oxfordshire). Supplement
1358-6173
1987   8804836

Alcohol Clin Exp Res
Alcoholism, clinical and experimental research
0145-6008   1530-0277
1977   7707242

Alcohol Drug Res
Alcohol and drug research
0883-1386
Continues: Substance and alcohol actions/misuse.
1986-1987   8601074

Alcohol Health Res World
Alcohol health and research world
0090-838X
Continued by: Alcohol research & health.
1973-1998   0365245

Alcohol Res Health
Alcohol research & health: the journal of the National Institute on Alcohol Abuse and Alcoholism
1535-7414
Continues: Alcohol health and research world.
1999   100900708

Alergia
Alergia
0002-5151
Formed by the union of Revista mexicana de alergología and Alergia (Buenos Aires) Continued by: Revista alergia México.
1953-1986   0140326

Alex Dent J
Alexandria dental journal: ADJ
1976   9426498

Alexander Blain Hosp Bull
Alexander Blain Hospital bulletin
0097-1820
1942-1954   14720440R

Alger Medicale
Algérie médicale
Continues Journal de médecine et de chirurgie de l'Afrique de nord.
1927-1962   14720550R

Aliment Pharmacol Ther
Alimentary pharmacology & therapeutics
0269-2813   1365-2036
1987   8707234

Aliment Vie
L' Alimentation et la vie
0065-6267
Continues Bulletin de la Société scientifique d'hygiène alimentaire et d'alimentation rationnelle de l'homme.
1949-1983   0064233

Alkaloids Chem Biol
The Alkaloids. Chemistry and biology
1099-4831
Continues: Alkaloids. Chemistry and pharmacology.
1998   9812842

Allerg Asthma (Leipz)
Allergie und Asthma
0375-8443
Continued by Allergie und Immunologie.
1955-1970   0313664

Allerg Asthmaforsch
Allergie- und Asthmaforschung
0516-7132
1957-1969   0370461

Allerg Immunol (Leipz)
Allergie und Immunologie
0323-4398
Continues Allergie und Asthma. Absorbed by: Allergologie.
1971-1991   0314702

Allerg Immunol (Paris)
Allergie et immunologie
0397-9148
Continued by: European annals of allergy and clinical immunology.
1969-2002   0245775

Allerg Pointe Claire
Allergie (Pointe-Claire, Québec)
0841-9027
1988   101083690

Allergol Immunopathol (Madr)
Allergologia et immunopathologia
0301-0546   1578-1267
1973   0370073

Allergol Int
Allergology international: official journal of the Japanese Society of Allergology
1323-8930   1440-1592
1996   9616296

Allergy
Allergy
0105-4538   1398-9995
Continues Acta allergologica.
1978   7804028

Allergy Asthma Proc
Allergy and asthma proceedings: the official journal of regional and state allergy societies
1088-5412
Continues: Allergy proceedings.
1996   9603640

Allergy Proc
Allergy proceedings: the official journal of regional and state allergy societies
1046-9354
Continues: New England and regional allergy proceedings. Continued by: Allergy and asthma proceedings.
1988-1995   8902396

Allg Homoopath Ztg
Allgemeine homöopathische Zeitung für wissenschaftliche und praktische Homöopathie
0002-5887
Continued by: Allgemeine homöopathische Zeitung.
1832-1994   0370462

Allied Health Behav Sci
Allied health and behavioral sciences
0190-0331
1978-1981   7806480

Alma Mater (Baltimore)
The Alma mater
0065-6445
1959   14730200R

Alpha Omega Fr
Alpha Omega France
0222-0458
Supersedes: Alpha Omega.
1978   9885200

Alpha Omegan
The Alpha omegan
0002-6417
1916   14730480R

Alsk Health Profile
Alaska health profile
19uu   9715340

Alta RN
Alberta RN / Alberta Association of Registered Nurses
1481-9988
Continues: AARN newsletter.
1998   100883278

Altern Entwickl Aging Dev
Altern und Entwicklung. Aging and development
0084-6252
1971-1972   1307126

Altern Lab Anim
Alternatives to laboratory animals: ATLA
0261-1929
Continues: ATLA abstracts.
1981   8110074

Altern Med Rev
Alternative medicine review: a journal of clinical therapeutic
1089-5159
1996   9705340

Altern Ther Health Med
Alternative therapies in health and medicine
1078-6791
1995   9502013

ALTEX
ALTEX: Alternativen zu Tierexperimenten
0946-7785
Continues: Alternativen zu Tierexperimenten.
1994   100953980

Alumnae Mag
The Alumnae magazine
0002-6700
Continues The Johns Hopkins nurses alumnae magazine. Continued by The Alumni magazine.
1956-1971   7706527

Alumnae Mag Columbia Univ Presbyt Hosp Sch Nurs Alumnae Assoc
Alumnae magazine (Columbia University-Presbyterian Hospital School of Nursing Alumnae Association)
0069-634X
Continued by: Alumni magazine (Columbia University-Presbyterian Hospital School of Nursing Alumni Association)
1906-1984   0042365

Alumni Bull Sch Dent Indiana Univ
Alumni bulletin - School of Dentistry, Indiana University
0073-7119
1938   7604908

Alumni Bull Univ Mich Sch Dent
Alumni bulletin. University of Michigan. School of Dentistry
0887-4387
Continued by: Alumni news. University of Michigan. School of Dentistry.
1937-1970   21430160R

Alumni Bull West Reserv Univ Sch Med
Alumni bulletin. Western Reserve University. School of Medicine
Continues The clinical bulletin of the School of Medicine of Western University and its associated hospitals. Continued by Case Western Reserve medical alumni bulletin.
1947-1967   0154405

Alumni Mag
The Alumni magazine
0149-2608
Continues: Alumnae magazine. Continued by: Johns Hopkins Nurses' alumni magazine.
1972-1987   7705977

Alumni Mag Columbia Univ Presbyt Hosp Sch Nurs Alumni Assoc
Alumni magazine (Columbia University-Presbyterian Hospital School of Nursing Alumni Association)
0898-4093
Continues: Alumnae magazine (Columbia University-Presbyterian Hospital School of Nursing Alumnae Association).
1985   8504267

Alzheimer Dis Assoc Disord
Alzheimer disease and associated disorders
0893-0341   1546-4156
1987   8704771

Alzheimers Dement
Alzheimer's & dementia: the journal of the Alzheimer's Association
1552-5260   1552-5279
2005   101231978

Am Ann Deaf
American annals of the deaf
0002-726X
Continues American annals of the deaf and dumb.
1886   0414670

Am Arch
The American archivist
0360-9081
1938   14740240R

Am Arch Rehabil Ther
American archives of rehabilitation therapy
0002-7324
1953-1987   0370464

Am Assoc Ind Nurses J
American Association of Industrial Nurses journal
0098-6097
Continued by Occupational health nursing.
1953-1968   7501070

Am Behav Sci
The American behavioral scientist
0002-7642
1960   0055030

Am Biotechnol Lab
American biotechnology laboratory
0749-3223
1983   8804377

Am Clin
America clínica
Continues Médicas; revista interamericana de selecciones de medicina, cirugía y especialidades.
1942-1964   0370463

Am Clin Lab
American clinical laboratory
1041-3235
Continues: American clinical products review.
1988-2002   8903666

Am Coll Physicians Obs
American College of Physicians observer
0279-9529
Continues: Forum on medicine. Continued by: ACP observer.
1981-1991   8102266

Am Correct Ther J
American corrective therapy journal
0002-8088
Continues Journal of the Association for Physical and Mental Rehabilitation. Continued by: Clinical kinesiology.
1967-1987   0135256

Am Demogr
American demographics
0163-4089
Absorbed: Marketing tools. Aug. 1998 Absorbed by: Advertising age.
1979-2004   9878837

Am Drug
American druggist
0190-5287
Continues: American druggist and pharmaceutical record. Absorbed: Aromatics. Continued by: American druggist merchandising.
1923-1972   7809986

Am Econ Rev
The American economic review
0002-8282
1911   14810500R

Am Educ
American education
0002-8304
1965-1985   7703832

Am Fam Physician
American family physician
0002-838X   1532-0650
Continues American family physician/GP.
1970   1272646

Am Fam Physician GP
American family physician/GP
0572-3612
Formed by the union of the American family physician and GP. Reverted to the former title with the Dec. 1970 issue.
1970-1970   1273362

Am Heart Hosp J
The American heart hospital journal
1541-9215   1751-7168
2003   101156064

Am Heart J
American heart journal
0002-8703   1097-6744
1925   0370465

Am Herit Invent Technol
American heritage of invention & technology
8756-7296
1985   8801250

Am Hist Rev
The American historical review
0002-8762
Superseded in part by: Recently published articles, ISSN 0145-5311, formerly issued as part of the American historical review.
1895   01210290R

Am Imago
The American imago; a psychoanalytic journal for the arts and sciences
0065-860X   1085-7931
1939   0370466

Am Ind Hyg Assoc J
American Industrial Hygiene Association journal
0002-8894
Continues: American Industrial Hygiene Association quarterly. Continued by: AIHAJ.
1958-1999   0371160

Am Ind Hyg Assoc Q
American Industrial Hygiene Association quarterly
0096-820X
Continues: Industrial hygiene. Continued by: American Industrial Hygiene Association journal.
1946-1957   14811020R

Am Indian Alsk Native Ment Health Res
American Indian and Alaska native mental health research (Online)
                                     1533-7731
1999   100970957

Am Indian Alsk Native Ment Health Res
American Indian and Alaska native mental health research: journal of the National Center
0893-5394
Continues: White Cloud journal of American Indian mental health.
1987-1999   8909511

Am Indian Alsk Native Ment Health Res Monogr Ser
American Indian and Alaska native mental health research (Monographic series)
1046-7750
1988-1994   9314637

Am J Acupunct
American journal of acupuncture
0091-3960
1973-1999   0367526

Am J Addict
The American journal on addictions / American Academy of Psychiatrists in Alcoholism and Addictions
1055-0496   1521-0391
1992   9208821

Am J Alzheimers Dis Other Demen
American journal of Alzheimer's disease and other dementias
1533-3175   1938-2731
Continues: American journal of Alzheimer's disease.
2000   101082834

Am J Anat
The American journal of anatomy
0002-9106
Continued by: Developmental dynamics.
1901-1991   0376312

Am J Anesthesiol
The American journal of anesthesiology
1078-4500
Continues: Anesthesiology review.
1995-2001   9504685

Am J Art Ther
American journal of art therapy
0007-4764
Continues Bulletin of art therapy.
1969-2002   0237447

Am J Audiol
American journal of audiology
1059-0889
1991   9114917

Am J Bioeth
The American journal of bioethics: AJOB
1526-5161   1536-0075
2001   100898738

Am J Bot
American journal of botany
0002-9122   1537-2197
1914   0370467

Am J Card Imaging
American journal of cardiac imaging
0887-7971
1987-1996   8706659

Am J Cardiol
The American journal of cardiology
0002-9149   1879-1913
Absorbed: Bulletin of the American College of Cardiology. Supersedes: Transactions of the American College of Cardiology.
1958   0207277

Am J Cardiovasc Drugs
American journal of cardiovascular drugs: drugs, devices, and other interventions
1175-3277
2001   100967755

Am J Cardiovasc Pathol
The American journal of cardiovascular pathology
0887-8005
1987-1995   8702438

Am J Chin Med
The American journal of Chinese medicine
0192-415X
Continues Comparative medicine East and West.
1979   7901431

Am J Chin Med (Gard City N Y)
The American journal of Chinese medicine
0090-2942
Continued by Comparative medicine East and West.
1973-1977   0354717

Am J Clin Dermatol
American journal of clinical dermatology
1175-0561
2000   100895290

Am J Clin Hypn
The American journal of clinical hypnosis
0002-9157
1958   0100626

Am J Clin Nutr
The American journal of clinical nutrition
0002-9165
    Continues: Journal of clinical nutrition.
1954   0376027

Am J Clin Oncol
American journal of clinical oncology
0277-3732   1537-453X
    Continues: Cancer clinical trials.
1982   8207754

Am J Clin Pathol
American journal of clinical pathology
0002-9173   1943-7722
1931   0370470

Am J Community Psychol
American journal of community psychology
0091-0562   1573-2770
1973   0364535

Am J Contact Dermat
American journal of contact dermatitis:
official journal of the American Contact
Dermatitis Society
1046-199X   1532-8163
    Continued by: Dermatitis.
1990-2003   9100472

Am J Crit Care
American journal of critical care: an
official publication, American Association of
Critical-Care Nurses
1062-3264
1992   9211547

Am J Dent
American journal of dentistry
0894-8275
1988   8806701

Am J Dermatopathol
The American Journal of dermatopathology
0193-1091   1533-0311
1979   7911005

Am J Dig Dis
The American journal of digestive diseases
0002-9211
    Continues: American journal of digestive
    diseases and nutrition. Continued by:
    Digestive diseases and sciences.
1938-1978   0404011

Am J Dis Child
American journal of diseases of children
(1911)
0096-8994
    Continued by: A.M.A. American journal of
    diseases of children.
1911-1950   9814246

Am J Dis Child
American journal of diseases of children
(1960)
0002-922X
    Continues: A.M.A. journal of diseases of
    children. Continued by: Archives of pediatrics
    & adolescent medicine.
1960-1993   0370471

Am J Disaster Med
American journal of disaster medicine
1932-149X
2006   101291100

Am J Drug Alcohol Abuse
The American journal of drug and alcohol
abuse
0095-2990   1097-9891
1974   7502510

Am J Econ Sociol
American journal of economics and
sociology
0002-9246
1941   14820160R

Am J EEG Technol
The American journal of EEG technology
0002-9238
    Continued by: American journal of
    electroneurodiagnostic technology.
1961-1995   0370504

Am J Electroneurodiagnostic Technol
American journal of electroneurodiagnostic
technology
1086-508X
    Continues: American journal of EEG
    technology.
1996   9607038

Am J Emerg Med
The American journal of emergency
medicine
0735-6757   1532-8171
1983   8309942

Am J Epidemiol
American journal of epidemiology
0002-9262   1476-6256
    Continues American journal of hygiene.
1965   7910653

Am J Forensic Med Pathol
The American journal of forensic medicine
and pathology: official publication of the
National Association of Medical Examiners
0195-7910   1533-404X
1980   8108948

Am J Gastroenterol
The American journal of gastroenterology
0002-9270   1572-0241
    Continues Review of gastroenterology.
1954   0421030

Am J Geriatr Cardiol
The American journal of geriatric
cardiology
1076-7460   1751-715X
199u   9215283

Am J Geriatr Pharmacother
The American journal of geriatric
pharmacotherapy
1543-5946
2003   101190325

Am J Geriatr Psychiatry
The American journal of geriatric
psychiatry: official journal of the American
Association for Geriatric Psychiatry
1064-7481   1545-7214
1993   9309609

Am J Health Behav
American journal of health behavior
1087-3244
    Continues: Health values.
1996   9602338

Am J Health Plann
American journal of health planning
0363-7719
1976-1978   7701759

Am J Health Promot
American journal of health promotion:
AJHP
0890-1171
1986   8701680

Am J Health Syst Pharm
American journal of health-system
pharmacy: AJHP: official journal of
the American Society of Health-System
Pharmacists
1079-2082   1535-2900
    Continues: American journal of hospital
    pharmacy.
1995   9503023

Am J Hematol
American journal of hematology
0361-8609   1096-8652
1976   7610369

Am J Hosp Care
The American journal of hospice care
0749-1565
    Continued by: American journal of hospice &
    palliative care.
1984-1990   8502312

Am J Hosp Palliat Care
The American journal of hospice &
palliative care
1049-9091   1938-2715
    Absorbed: Journal of terminal oncology. 2004
    Continues: American journal of hospice care.
1990   9008229

Am J Hosp Pharm
American journal of hospital pharmacy
0002-9289
    Continues: Bulletin of the American Society
    of Hospital Pharmacists. Absorbed: Clinical
    pharmacy. Continued by: American journal of
    health-system pharmacy.
1958-1994   0370474

Am J Hum Biol
American journal of human biology: the
official journal of the Human Biology
Council
1042-0533   1520-6300
1989   8915029

Am J Hum Genet
American journal of human genetics
0002-9297   1537-6605
1949   0370475

Am J Hypertens
American journal of hypertension: journal
of the American Society of Hypertension
0895-7061   1879-1905
    Continues: Journal of clinical hypertension.
1988   8803676

Am J Ind Med
American journal of industrial medicine
0271-3586   1097-0274
1980   8101110

Am J Infect Control
American journal of infection control
0196-6553   1527-3296
1980   8004854

Am J Kidney Dis
American journal of kidney diseases: the
official journal of the National Kidney
Foundation
0272-6386   1523-6838
1981   8110075

Am J Knee Surg
The American journal of knee surgery
0899-7403
    Continued by: Journal of knee surgery.
1988-2001   8804841

Am J Law Med
American journal of law & medicine
0098-8588
1975   7509572

Am J Manag Care
The American journal of managed care
1088-0224 1936-2692
1995 9613960

Am J Med
The American journal of medicine
0002-9343 1555-7162
1946 0267200

Am J Med Electron
The American journal of medical electronics
0096-5286
Continued by Medical research engineering.
1961-1966 0061651

Am J Med Genet
American journal of medical genetics
0148-7299 1096-8628
Split into: American journal of medical genetics. Part A; American journal of medical genetics. Part B, Neuropsychiatric genetics; and, American journal of medical genetics. Part C, Seminars in medical genetics.
1977-2002 7708900

Am J Med Genet A
American journal of medical genetics. Part A
1552-4825 1552-4833
Continues in part: American journal of medical genetics.
2003 101235741

Am J Med Genet B Neuropsychiatr Genet
American journal of medical genetics. Part B, Neuropsychiatric genetics: the official publication of the International Society of Psychiatric Genetics
1552-4841 1552-485X
Continues in part: American journal of medical genetics.
2003 101235742

Am J Med Genet C Semin Med Genet
American journal of medical genetics. Part C, Seminars in medical genetics
1552-4868 1552-4876
Continues in part: American journal of medical genetics.
2003 101235745

Am J Med Genet Suppl
American journal of medical genetics. Supplement
1040-3787
1986-1990 8706133

Am J Med Qual
American journal of medical quality: the official journal of the American College of Medical Quality
1062-8606 1555-824X
Continues: Quality assurance and utilization review.
1992 9300756

Am J Med Sci
The American journal of the medical sciences
0002-9629 1538-2990
Continues: Philadelphia journal of the medical and physical sciences. Absorbed: Philadelphia monthly journal of medicine and surgery, Mar. 1828, and: American medical recorder (1928), July 1829.
1827 0370506

Am J Med Technol
The American journal of medical technology
0002-9335
Continues the Bulletin of the American Society of Clinical Laboratory Technicians. Merged with: Journal of the American Medical Technologists, to form: Journal of medical technology.
1936-1983 0370505

Am J Ment Defic
American journal of mental deficiency
0002-9351
Supersedes: Proceedings and addresses of the annual session of the American Association on Mental Deficiency. American Association on Mental Deficiency. Continued by: American journal of mental retardation.
1940-1987 0372647

Am J Nephrol
American journal of nephrology
0250-8095 1421-9670
1981 8109361

Am J Nurs
The American journal of nursing
0002-936X 1538-7488
1900 0372646

Am J Obstet Gynecol
American journal of obstetrics and gynecology
0002-9378 1097-6868
Continues: American journal of obstetrics and diseases of women and children.
1920 0370476

Am J Occup Ther
The American journal of occupational therapy.: official publication of the American Occupational Therapy Association
0272-9490
1947 7705978

Am J Ophthalmol
American journal of ophthalmology
0002-9394 1879-1891
Absorbed the following journals in 1918: Annals of ophthalmology, the Ophthalmic record, Ophthalmology, the Ophthalmic yearbook, Ophthalmic literature, and Anales de oftamología.
1884 0370500

Am J Optom Arch Am Acad Optom
American journal of optometry and archives of American Academy of Optometry
0002-9408
Continues: American journal of optometry. Absorbed: Report of the transactions of the ... Annual Meeting of the American Academy of Optometry. American Academy of Optometry. Meeting. 1940 Continued by: American journal of optometry and physiological optics.
1941-1973 0420462

Am J Optom Physiol Opt
American journal of optometry and physiological optics
0093-7002
Continues American journal of optometry and archives of American Academy of Optometry. Continued by: Optometry and vision science.
1974-1988 0417614

Am J Orthod
American journal of orthodontics
0002-9416
Continues the Orthodontics section of the American journal of orthodontics and oral surgery, and assumes the vol. numbering of the journal. Continued by: American journal of orthodontics and dentofacial orthopedics.
1948-1986 0370501

Am J Orthod Dentofacial Orthop
American journal of orthodontics and dentofacial orthopedics: official publication of the American Association of Orthodontists, its constituent societies, and the American Board of Orthodontics
0889-5406 1097-6752
Continues: American journal of orthodontics.
1986 8610224

Am J Orthop
The American journal of orthopedics
0065-9002
Continues: Orthopedics. Continued by: American journal of orthopedic surgery.
1960-1967 0134543

Am J Orthop
American journal of orthopedics (Belle Mead, N.J.)
1078-4519 1934-3418
Continues: Orthopaedic review.
1995 9502918

Am J Orthop Surg
The American journal of orthopedic surgery
0065-9002
Continues: American journal of orthopedics.
1968-1970 7611912

Am J Orthopsychiatry
The American journal of orthopsychiatry
0002-9432
1930 0400640

Am J Otol
The American journal of otology
0192-9763
Continued by: Otology & neurotology.
1979-2000 7909513

Am J Otolaryngol
American journal of otolaryngology
0196-0709 1532-818X
1979 8000029

Am J Pathol
The American journal of pathology
0002-9440 1525-2191
Supersedes: Journal of medical research.
1925 0370502

Am J Pediatr Hematol Oncol
The American journal of pediatric hematology/oncology
0192-8562
Continued by: Journal of pediatric hematology/oncology.
1979-1994 7908071

Am J Perinatol
American journal of perinatology
0735-1631 1098-8785
1983 8405212

Am J Pharm Educ
American journal of pharmaceutical education
0002-9459 1553-6467
Supersedes the Proceedings of the annual meeting of the American Association of Colleges of Pharmacy.
1937 0372650

Am J Pharm Sci Support Public Health
American journal of pharmacy and the sciences supporting public health
0002-9467
Continues: American journal of pharmacy.
1937-1978 0416354

Am J Pharmacogenomics
American journal of pharmacogenomics: genomics-related research in drug development and clinical practice
1175-2203
Merged with: Molecular diagnosis, to form: Molecular diagnosis & therapy.
2001-2005 100967746

Am J Phys Anthropol
American journal of physical anthropology
0002-9483 1096-8644
1918 0400654

Am J Phys Med
American journal of physical medicine
0002-9491
Continues: Occupational therapy and rehabilitation. Continued by: American journal of physical medicine & rehabilitation.
1952-1987   0370503

Am J Phys Med Rehabil
American journal of physical medicine & rehabilitation / Association of Academic Physiatrists
0894-9115   1537-7385
Continues: American journal of physical medicine.
1988   8803677

Am J Physiol
The American journal of physiology
0002-9513
1898   0370511

Am J Physiol Cell Physiol
American journal of physiology. Cell physiology
0363-6143   1522-1563
1977   100901225

Am J Physiol Endocrinol Metab
American journal of physiology. Endocrinology and metabolism
0193-1849   1522-1555
Continues in part: American journal of physiology. Endocrinology, metabolism and gastrointestinal physiology.
1980   100901226

Am J Physiol Gastrointest Liver Physiol
American journal of physiology. Gastrointestinal and liver physiology
0193-1857   1522-1547
Continues in part: American journal of physiology. Endocrinology, metabolism and gastrointestinal physiology.
1980   100901227

Am J Physiol Heart Circ Physiol
American journal of physiology. Heart and circulatory physiology
0363-6135   1522-1539
1977   100901228

Am J Physiol Imaging
American journal of physiologic imaging
0885-8276
1986-1992   8610225

Am J Physiol Lung Cell Mol Physiol
American journal of physiology. Lung cellular and molecular physiology
1040-0605   1522-1504
1989   100901229

Am J Physiol Regul Integr Comp Physiol
American journal of physiology. Regulatory, integrative and comparative physiology
0363-6119   1522-1490
1977   100901230

Am J Physiol Renal Physiol
American journal of physiology. Renal physiology
0363-6127   1522-1466
Continues: American journal of physiology. Renal, fluid and electrolyte physiology.
1997   100901990

Am J Pract Nurs
American journal of practical nursing
0569-6054
Formed by the union of Practical nursing digest and National Federation of Licensed Practical Nurses. Newsletter [new ser.] Superseded by Bedside nurse.
1965-1967   0001470

Am J Prev Med
American journal of preventive medicine
0749-3797   1873-2607
1985   8704773

Am J Primatol
American journal of primatology
0275-2565   1098-2345
1981   8108949

Am J Proctol
American journal of proctology
0002-9521
Continued by American journal of proctology, gastroenterology & colon & rectal surgery.
1950-1977   0370472

Am J Proctol Gastroenterol Colon Rectal Surg
American journal of proctology, gastroenterology & colon & rectal surgery
0162-6566
Continues American journal of proctology. Continued by: Gastroenterology & endoscopy news.
1978-1985   7910860

Am J Psychiatry
The American journal of psychiatry
0002-953X   1535-7228
Continues: American journal of insanity.
1921   0370512

Am J Psychoanal
American journal of psychoanalysis
0002-9548
1941   0372630

Am J Psychol
The American journal of psychology
0002-9556
1887   0370513

Am J Psychother
American journal of psychotherapy
0002-9564
Absorbed: Journal of psychotherapy practice and research. 2002
1947   0110672

Am J Public Health
American journal of public health
0090-0036   1541-0048
Continues in part: American journal of public health and the nation's health.
1971   1254074

Am J Public Health Nations Health
American journal of public health and the nation's health
0002-9572
The American Public Health Association yearbook for 1933-42 issued as supplement to the journal; for 1948-53 as pt. 2 of the May issue. Formed by the merger of the Nation's health and the American journal of public health, and assumed the vol. numbering of the latter. In 1971, separated again into the same two journals.
1928-1970   • 1254075

Am J Reprod Immunol
American journal of reproductive immunology (New York, N.Y.: 1989)
1046-7408   1600-0897
Absorbed: Early pregnancy (Online). 2004
Continues: American journal of reproductive immunology and microbiology.
1989   8912860

Am J Reprod Immunol
American journal of reproductive immunology: AJRI: official journal of the American Society for the Immunology of Reproduction and the International Coordination Committee for Immunology of Reproduction
0271-7352
Continued by: American journal of reproductive immunology and microbiology.
1980-1984   8111069

Am J Reprod Immunol Microbiol
American journal of reproductive immunology and microbiology: AJRIM
8755-8920
Continues: American journal of reproductive immunology. Continued by: American journal of reproductive immunology (New York, N.Y.: 1989).
1985-1988   8501543

Am J Respir Cell Mol Biol
American journal of respiratory cell and molecular biology
1044-1549   1535-4989
1989   8917225

Am J Respir Crit Care Med
American journal of respiratory and critical care medicine
1073-449X   1535-4970
Continues: American review of respiratory disease.
1994   9421642

Am J Respir Med
American journal of respiratory medicine: drugs, devices, and other interventions
1175-6365
Continued by: Treatments in respiratory medicine.
2002-2003   101132974

Am J Rhinol
American journal of rhinology
1050-6586
Continued by: American journal of rhinology & allergy.
1987   8807268

Am J Roentgenol Radium Ther
The American journal of roentgenology and radium therapy
0092-5632
Continues: American journal of roentgenology. Continued by: American journal of roentgenology, radium therapy, and nuclear medicine.
1923-1951   0404014

Am J Roentgenol Radium Ther Nucl Med
The American journal of roentgenology, radium therapy, and nuclear medicine
0002-9580
Continues: American journal of roentgenology and radium therapy. Continued by: AJR. American journal of roentgenology.
1952-1975   7605534

Am J Sociol
The American journal of sociology
0002-9602
Continued by AJS; American journal of sociology.
1895-1964   0233711

Am J Speech Lang Pathol
American journal of speech-language pathology / American Speech-Language-Hearing Association
1058-0360
1991   9114726

Am J Sports Med
The American journal of sports medicine
0363-5465   1552-3365
Continues The Journal of sports medicine.
1976   7609541

Am J Surg
American journal of surgery
0002-9610
Continues: American surgery and gynecology.
1905   0370473

Am J Surg Pathol
The American journal of surgical pathology
0147-5185   1532-0979
1977   7707904

Am J Syph Gonorrhea Vener Dis
American journal of syphilis, gonorrhea, and venereal diseases
0096-6738
1917-1954   14830110R

Am J Ther
American journal of therapeutics
1075-2765   1536-3686
1994   9441347

Am J Transplant
American journal of transplantation: official journal of the American Society of Transplantation and the American Society of Transplant Surgeons
1600-6135   1600-6143
2001   100968638

Am J Trop Med Hyg
The American journal of tropical medicine and hygiene
0002-9637   1476-1645
Formed by the union of the American journal of tropical medicine and the Journal of the National Malaria Society.
1952   0370507

Am J Vet Res
American journal of veterinary research
0002-9645
1940   0375011

Am Laund Dig
American laundry digest
0002-9718
Merged with: Laundry news; to form: American laundry news.
19uu-1996   9877761

Am Libr
American libraries
0002-9769
Supersedes ALA bulletin.
1970   0230462

Am Lung Assoc Bull
American Lung Association bulletin
0092-5659
Continues the Bulletin of the National Tuberculosis and Respiratory Disease Association.
1973-1983   0404016

Am Med News
American medical news
0001-1843
Continues the AMA news.
1969   0226412

Am Nat
The American naturalist
0003-0147   1537-5323
1867   2984688R

Am Nurse
The American nurse
0098-1486
Continues ANA in action.
1972   7506499

Am Orthopt J
The American orthoptic journal
0065-955X
Absorbed by: Ophthalmology.
1951   0370520

Am OSE Rev
American OSE review
1942-1951   14840110R

Am Pharm
American pharmacy
0160-3450
Continues Journal of the American Pharmaceutical Association. published 1961-1977. Continued by: Journal of the American Pharmaceutical Association (Washington, D.C.: 1996).
1978-1995   7801164

Am Pract Dig Treat
American practitioner and digest of treatment
Formed by the union of the American practitioner and the Digest of treatment. Continued by American practitioner.
1950-1961   14840350R

Am Prof Pharm
American professional pharmacist
0096-0349
Supersedes Practical druggist and spatula. Continued by: Pharmacy times.
1935-1969   0216453

Am Psychol
The American psychologist
0003-066X
1946   0370521

Am Rehabil
American rehabilitation
0362-4048
1975   7610370

AM Rep
AM [reports]. United States. Office of Aviation Medicine
1964-1969   0075052

Am Rev Respir Dis
The American review of respiratory disease
0003-0805
Continues: American review of tuberculosis and pulmonary diseases. Continued by: American journal of respiratory and critical care medicine.
1959-1993   0370523

Am Rev Sov Med
American review of Soviet medicine
1943-1948   14840620R

Am Rev Tuberc
American review of tuberculosis
0096-0381
Continued by the American review of tuberculosis and pulmonary diseases.
1917-1954   14840640R

Am Sci
American scientist
0003-0996
Continues: Sigma Xi quarterly. Society of the Sigma Xi.
1942   0370514

Am Sociol Rev
American sociological review
0003-1224
1936   0370515

Am Surg
The American surgeon
0003-1348
Continues the Southern surgeon.
1951   0370522

Am Univ Law Rev
The American University law review
0003-1453
Continues: American University intramural law review.
1957   9891709

Am Zool
American zoologist
0003-1569
Continued by: Integrative and comparative biology.
1961-2001   0370516

AMA Am J Dis Child
A.M.A. American journal of diseases of children
0096-8994
Continues: American journal of diseases of children (1911). Continued by: A.M.A. journal of diseases of children.
1950-1955   14470010R

AMA Arch Derm
A. M. A. archives of dermatology
0096-5359
Continues A. M. A. archives of dermatology and syphilology. Continued by Archives of dermatology.
1955-1960   14470050R

AMA Arch Derm Syphilol
A. M. A. archives of dermatology and syphilology
0096-5979
Continues Archives of dermatology and syphilology. Continued by A. M. A. archives of dermatology.
1950-1954   14470040R

AMA Arch Ind Health
A.M.A. archives of industrial health
Continues: A.M.A. archives of industrial hygiene and occupational medicine. Continued by: Archives of environmental health.
1955-1960   14470090R

AMA Arch Intern Med
A.M.A. archives of internal medicine
0888-2479
Continues: Archives of internal medicine (Chicago, Ill.: 1908). Continued by: Archives of internal medicine.
1950-1960   14470100R

AMA Arch Neurol
A. M. A. archives of neurology
0375-8540
Supersedes the section on neurology of the A. M. A. Archives of neurology and psychiatry. Continued by Archives of neurology.
1959-1960   14470110R

AMA Arch Neurol Psychiatry
A. M. A. archives of neurology and psychiatry
0096-6886
Continues Archives of neurology and psychiatry. Superseded by the A. M. A. archives of general psychiatry and the A. M. A. archives of neurology.
1950-1959   14470130R

AMA Arch Ophthalmol
A.M.A. archives of ophthalmology
0096-6339
Continues Archives of ophthalmology, published Chicago, v. 1-44, no. 3, 1929-Sept. 1950. Continued by Archives of ophthalmology, published Chicago, v. 64-July 1960- .
1950-1960   7706524

AMA Arch Otolaryngol
A.M.A. archives of otolaryngology
0096-6894
Continues Archives of otolaryngology.
Continued in 1960 by Archives of
otolaryngology (Chicago, Ill.: 1960)
1950-1960 **14470140R**

AMA Arch Pathol
A. M. A. archives of pathology
0096-6711
Continues Archives of pathology. Continued
by Archives of pathology.
1950-1960 **14470150R**

AMA Arch Surg
A.M.A. archives of surgery
0096-6908
Continues Archives of surgery, published
1920-1950. Continued by Archives of surgery
(Chicago, Ill.: 1969).
1950-1960 **14470160R**

Amatus Lusit
Amatus Lusitanus; revista de medicina
e cirurgia
1941-1950 **14730540R**

AMB Rev Assoc Med Bras
AMB; revista da Associação Médica Brasileira
0102-843X
Continues Revista da Associação Médica
Brasileira. Continued by: Revista da
Associação Médica Brasileira (1992).
1968-1991 **0165700**

Ambio
Ambio
0044-7447
1972 **0364220**

Ambix
Ambix
0002-6980
1937 **14730560R**

Ambul Care
Ambulatory care
0894-3672
Continues: Emergence.
1984-1988 **8704157**

Ambul Outreach
Ambulatory outreach
1094-6829
Formed by the union of: Outreach;
Legislative and regulatory monitor; and:
Professional opportunities.
1997-2000 **9711806**

Ambul Pediatr
Ambulatory pediatrics: the official journal
of the Ambulatory Pediatric Association
1530-1567 **1539-4409**
2001 **101089367**

AMD TR Rep
AMD-TR [reports]. United States. Aerospace
Medical Division
1965-1968 **0047634**

AMDI Boll
AMDI bollettino
0001-1908
1955-1979 **7513559**

AMFAR Rep
AmFAR report / American Foundation for
AIDS Research
1988-1996 **8812078**

AMHC Forum
AMHC forum
0883-0401
Continues: Association of Mental Health
Chaplains. AMHC newsletter. Continued by:
Cura animarum.
1973-1983 **8411239**

AMIA Annu Symp Proc
AMIA ... Annual Symposium proceedings /
AMIA Symposium. AMIA Symposium
1559-4076
Continues: Proceedings. AMIA Symposium.
2003 **101209213**

Amif
AMIF
Continued by: Revue médicale de l'AMIF.
1952-1984 **14470210R**

Amino Acids
Amino acids
0939-4451 **1438-2199**
1991 **9200312**

AMRL TR
AMRL-TR. Aerospace Medical Research
Laboratories (6570th)
196u-1977 **0032311**

AMRO
AMRO
Continues: Medical record and health care
information journal. Continued by: IHRIM.
1988-1994 **8909516**

Amyloid
Amyloid: the international journal of
experimental and clinical investigation: the
official journal of the International Society
of Amyloidosis
1350-6129 **1744-2818**
1994 **9433802**

Amyotroph Lateral Scler
Amyotrophic lateral sclerosis: official
publication of the World Federation of
Neurology Research Group on Motor
Neuron Diseases
1748-2968 **1471-180X**
Continues: Amyotrophic lateral sclerosis and
other motor neuron disorders.
2006 **101283386**

Amyotroph Lateral Scler Other Motor Neuron Disord
Amyotrophic lateral sclerosis and other
motor neuron disorders: official publication
of the World Federation of Neurology,
Research Group on Motor Neuron Diseases
1466-0822
Continued by: Amyotrophic lateral sclerosis.
1999-2005 **100964775**

An Azevedos
Anais Azevedos
0003-2425
1949-1975 **14920050R**

An Acad Bras Cienc
Anais da Academia Brasileira de Ciências
0001-3765 **1678-2690**
Continues the Revista of the Academia
Brasileira de Sciências.
1929 **7503280**

An Argent Oftalmol
Anales argentinos de oftalmología
1939-1947 **0001770**

AN Ark Nurse
AN. Arkansas nurse
0094-0488
1973-1974 **0423664**

An Asoc Quim Farm Uruguay
Anales. Asociación de Química y Farmacia
del Uruguay
1898-1952 **15330160R**

An Ateneo Clin Quir Montev
Anales. Ateneo de Clínica Quirúrgica,
Montevideo
1935-1960 **15410040R**

An Bras Derm Sifilogr
Anais brasileiros de dermatologia e
sifilografia
Continues Annaes brasileiros de dermatologia
e syphilographia. Continued by Anais
brasileiros de dermatologia.
193u-1960 **0116747**

An Bras Dermatol
Anais brasileiros de dermatologia
0365-0596
Continues Anais brasileiros de dermatologia
e sifilografia.
1961 **0067662**

An Bras Ginecol
Anais brasileiros de ginecologia
Continues Annaes brasileiros de gynecologia.
Continued by Jornal brasileiro de ginecologia.
1940-1969 **1263440**

An Casa Salud Valdecilla
Anales de la Casa de Salud Valdecilla
0301-3839
1930-1968 **7506830**

An Cir (Rosario)
Anales de cirugía
0066-1465
1935-1983 **0376524**

An Enferm
Anais de enfermagem
Continued by: Revista brasileira de
enfermagem.
1932-1954 **14920070R**

An Esc Nacl Saude Publica Med Trop (Lisb)
Anais da Escola Nacional de Saúde Pública
e de Medicina Tropical
0075-9767
Supersedes Anais do Instituto de Medicina
Tropical. Superseded by Anais do Instituto de
Higiene e Medicina Tropical.
1967-1972 **7500780**

An Esp Odontoestomatol
Anales españoles de odontoestomatología
0003-2557
1942-1976 **0370533**

An Esp Pediatr
Anales españoles de pediatría
0302-4342 **1577-2799**
Continued by: Anales de pediatría (Barcelona,
Spain: 2003).
1968-2002 **0420463**

An Fac Farm Porto
Anais da Faculdade de Farmácia do Porto
1939-1973 **7506826**

An Fac Med Lima
Anales. Universidad Nacional Mayor de San
Marcos. Facultad de Medicina
Supersedes a periodical with the same title,
issued 1862-1904. Continued by Anales del
Programa Académico de Medicina
1918-1968 **18330640R**

An Fac Med Montev
Anales de la Facultad de Medicina de
Montevideo
Continues: Anales de la Facultad de
Medicina, Universidad de la República,
Montevideo, Uruguay.
1978-1981 **9203129**

An Fac Med Porto Alegre
Anais da Faculdade de Medicina de Pôrto
Alegre
0365-205X
1938-1978 **0256550**

An Fac Med Recife
Anais da Faculdade de Medicina do Recife
Continued by Anais da Faculdade de
Medicina da Universidade do Recife.
1934-1944 **7806485**

An Fac Med Univ Repub Montev Urug
Anales de la Facultad de Medicina,
Universidad de la República, Montevideo,
Uruguay
0365-2297
Continued by: Anales de la Facultad de
medicina de Montevideo.
1916-1970 **7506831**

An Fac Med Univ Sao Paulo
Anais. Universidade de São Paulo.
Faculdade de Medicina
Continues the faculty's Annaes.
1940-1957 **20610370R**

An Fac Odontol
Anales de la Facultad de Odontología
0083-4785
1955 **7506832**

An Fac Odontol Univ Fed Pernambuco
Anais da Faculdade de Odontologia da
Universidade Federal de Pernambuco
0083-3908
Continues: Anais da Faculdade de
Odontologia, Universidade do Recife.
1964-1993 **7502729**

An Fac Quim Farm (Santiago)
Anales de la Facultad de Química y
Farmacia
0300-9912
Continues Tesis de químicos. Continued by
Anales de la Facultad de Ciencias Químicas.
1956-1973 **7506833**

An Farm Hosp (Madr)
Anales de farmacia hospitalaria
0517-6794
1957-1968 **14920290R**

An Hosp St Cruz San Pablo
Anales del Hospital de la Santa Cruz y San
Pablo
0301-3626
Continues: Annals of the Hospital General de
Catalunya of Barcelona. Continued by: Sant
Pau.
1951-1977 **7502514**

An Hosp Varsovia
Anales. Toulouse. Hospital Varsovia
0755-9704
1940-19uu **21230340R**

An Inst Barraquer
Anales del Instituto Barraquer
0020-3645
Supersedes Estudios e informaciones
oftalmológicas.
1959 **7502515**

An Inst Hig Med Trop (Lisb)
Anais do Instituto de Higiene e Medicina
Tropical
0303-7762
Supersedes Anais da Escola Nacional de
Saúde Pública e de Medicina Tropical.
1973-1984 **7500781**

An Inst Invest Odontol (Maracaibo)
Anales - Instituto de Investigaciones
Odontológicas, Universidad del Zulia
Continued by: Cuaderno del Instituto de
Investigaciones Odontológicas..
1964-1973 **7506829**

An Inst Invest Vet
Anales del Instituto de Investigaciones
Veterinarias
0365-3536
Continues Anales de la Facultad de
Veterinaria de la Universidad de Madrid y del
Instituto de Investigaciones Veterinarias.
1953-1979 **7505191**

An Inst Med Trop (Lisb)
Anais do Instituto de Medicina Tropical
0365-3307
Continued by: Anais da Escola Nacional de
Saúde Pública e de Medicina..
1943-1966 **7502512**

An Matern Sao Paulo
Anais. São Paulo, Brazil (City) Maternidade
1955-1966 **20610310R**

An Med (Lima)
Anales de medicina (Lima, Peru)
0300-0052
Continues: Anales del Programa Académico
de Medicina. Continued by: Anales de la
Facultad de Medicina (Lima, Peru: 1990).
1971-1989 **0347357**

An Med Cir
Anales de medicina y cirugía
1919-1979 **0376313**

An Med Cir
Anales de medicina: Cirugía
0517-6816
Continues in part: Anales de medicina.
Continued by: Anales de medicina.
1955-1972 **0377477**

An Med Concepc
Anales médicos de Concepción
1944-1963 **14930260R**

An Med Espec
Anales de medicina: Especialidades
0517-6832
Continues in part and is continued by Anales
de medicina.
1955-1972 **0400163**

An Med Interna
Anales de medicina interna (Madrid, Spain:
1984)
0212-7199
1984 **9112183**

An Med Med
Anales de medicina: Medicina
0517-6824
Continues in part and is continued by Anales
de medicina.
1955-1972 **0377500**

An Med Publica
Anales de medicina pública
1949-1955 **14930030R**

An Microbiol (Rio J)
Anais de microbiologia
0485-1854
1951-1982 **0413653**

An Nestle (B Aires)
Anales Nestlé
0325-545X
1942-1983 **14930270R**

An Nestle (Rio De Janeiro)
Anais Nestlé
1944-1992 **14920090R**

An Otorrinolaringol Ibero Am
Anales otorrinolaringológicos ibero-
americanos
0303-8874
Supersedes Acta oto-rino-laringológica ibero-
americana.
1974 **7605535**

An Paul Med Cir
Anais paulistas de medicina e cirurgia
0003-245X
Continues Annaes paulistas de medicina e
cirurgia.
1941 **0373070**

An Pediatr (Barc)
Anales de pediatría (Barcelona, Spain: 2003)
1695-4033
Continues: Anales españoles de pediatría.
2003 **101162596**

An Programa Acad Med (Lima)
Anales del Programa Académico de
Medicina / Universidad Nacional Mayor de
San Marcos de Lima
0300-9025
Continues: Anales of the Facultad de
Medicina (Lima, Peru: 1943). Continued by:
Anales de medicina (Lima, Peru).
1969-1970 **0264671**

An R Acad Nac Med (Madr)
Anales de la Real Academia Nacional de
Medicina
0034-0634
1879 **7505188**

An Real Acad Farm
Anales de la Real Academia de Farmacia
0034-0618 1697-4298
Continues: Anales de la Academia Nacional
de Farmacia. Continued by: Anales de la Real
Academia Nacional de Farmacia.
1940-2002 **14490140R**

An Sist Sanit Navar
Anales del sistema sanitario de Navarra
1137-6627
1997 **9710381**

An Soc Pueric B Aires
Anales de la Sociedad de Puericultura de
Buenos Aires
0326-5188
Continued by: Revista de la Sociedad de
Puericultura de Buenos Aires.
1935-1943 **20810740R**

ANA Clin Conf
ANA clinical conferences
0093-0423
Continued by Clinical conference papers.
1967-1971 **7509335**

ANA Clin Sess
ANA clinical sessions
0065-9495
1966-1974 **7511412**

ANA Publ
American Nurses Association Publications
19uu **9870008**

Anadolu Kardiyol Derg
Anadolu kardiyoloji dergisi: AKD = the
Anatolian journal of cardiology
1302-8723 1308-0032
2001 **101095069**

Anaerobe
Anaerobe
1075-9964 1095-8274
1995 **9505216**

Anaesth Intensive Care
Anaesthesia and intensive care
0310-057X
1972 **0342017**

Anaesth Resusc Intensive Ther
Anaesthesia, resuscitation, and intensive
therapy
0301-0864
1973-1976 **0371112**

Anaesthesia
Anaesthesia
0003-2409   1365-2044
1946   0370524

Anaesthesiol Intensive Ther
Anaesthesiology intensive therapy
1642-5758   1731-2531
200u   101472620

Anaesthesiol Reanim
Anaesthesiologie und Reanimation
0323-4983
Absorbed by: Anästhesiologie,
Intensivmedizin, Notfallmedizin,
Schmerztherapie.
1976-2004   7611455

Anaesthesist
Der Anaesthesist
0003-2417   1432-055X
1952   0370525

Anal Bioanal Chem
Analytical and bioanalytical chemistry
1618-2642   1618-2650
Merger of: Analusis; Química analítica
(Belaterra, Spain); and: Fresenius' journal
of analytical chemistry, continuing the
numbering of the latter.
2002   101134327

Anal Biochem
Analytical biochemistry
0003-2697   1096-0309
1960   0370535

Anal Cell Pathol
Analytical cellular pathology: the journal of
the European Society for Analytical Cellular
Pathology
0921-8912
Continued by: Cellular oncology.
1989-2003   8911016

Anal Chem
Analytical chemistry
0003-2700   1520-6882
Continues Industrial and engineering
chemistry; analytical edition.
1947   0370536

Anal Chim Acta
Analytica chimica acta
0003-2670   1873-4324
1947   0370534

Anal Quant Cytol
Analytical and quantitative cytology
0190-0471
Continued by Analytical and quantitative
cytology and histology.
1979-1984   7911206

Anal Quant Cytol Histol
Analytical and quantitative cytology and
histology / the International Academy
of Cytology [and] American Society of
Cytology
0884-6812
Continues: Analytical and quantitative
cytology.
1985   8506819

Anal Sci
Analytical sciences: the international
journal of the Japan Society for Analytical
Chemistry
0910-6340   1348-2246
1985   8511078

Anal Soc Biol Bogota
Anales. Sociedad de Biologia de Bogotá
1943-1959   20810480R

Analecta Med Hist
Analecta medico-historica
0066-1384
1966-1968   0050255

Analyst
The Analyst
0003-2654   1364-5528
1876   0372652

Analyst (Lond)
The Analyst
1834-1840   0166656

Anasth Intensivther Notfallmed
Anästhesie, Intensivtherapie,
Notfallmedizin
0174-1837
Continues Praktische Anästhesie,
Wiederbelebung und Intensivtherapie.
Continued by: Anästhesiologie,
Intensivmedizin, Notfallmedizin,
Schmerztherapie.
1980-1990   8005775

Anasthesiol Intensivmed Notfallmed
Schmerzther
Anästhesiologie, Intensivmedizin,
Notfallmedizin, Schmerztherapie: AINS
0939-2661   1439-1074
Absorbed: Anaesthesiologie und Reanimation.
Continues: Anästhesie, Intensivtherapie,
Notfallmedizin.
1991   9109478

Anasthesiol Intensivmed Prax
Anästhesiologische und intensivmedizinische
Praxis
0303-6200
Continues Anaesthesiologische Praxis.
Superseded by Intensivmedizinische Praxis.
Supplement to Chirurgische Praxis.
1972-1979   0436571

Anat Anz
Anatomischer Anzeiger
0003-2786
Continued by: Annals of anatomy.
1886-1991   0370541

Anat Chir
Anatomia e chirurgia
0517-7146
1956-1969   0370537

Anat Clin
Anatomia clinica
0343-6098
Continued by: Surgical and radiologic
anatomy.
1978-1985   7808897

Anat Embryol (Berl)
Anatomy and embryology
0340-2061   1432-0568
Continues: Zeitschrift für Anatomie und
Entwicklungsgeschichte. Continued by: Brain
structure & function.
1974-2006   7505194

Anat Histol Embryol
Anatomia, histologia, embryologia
0340-2096   1439-0264
Continues Zentralblatt für Veterinärmedizin.
Reihe C: Anatomie. Histologie.
Embryologie.
1973   7704218

Anat Pathol
Anatomic pathology (Chicago, Ill.: annual)
1056-5884
Continues: Pathology annual.
1996   9703615

Anat Rec
The Anatomical record
0003-276X   1097-0185
Vol. 1 issues with: American journal of
anatomy, v. 6-7. Split into: Anatomical
record. Part A, Discoveries in molecular,
cellular, and evolutionary biology; and:
Anatomical record. Part B, New anatomist.
1906-2002   0370540

Anat Rec (Hoboken)
Anatomical record (Hoboken, N.J.: 2007)
1932-8486   1932-8494
2007   101292775

Anat Rec A Discov Mol Cell Evol Biol
The anatomical record. Part A, Discoveries
in molecular, cellular, and evolutionary
biology
1552-4884   1552-4892
Continues in part: Anatomical record.
2003-2006   101234285

Anat Rec B New Anat
Anatomical record. Part B, New anatomist
1552-4906   1552-4914
Continues in part: Anatomical record.
2003-2006   101234289

Anat Rec Suppl
The Anatomical record. Supplement:
an offical publication of the American
Association of Anatomists
0749-3002
1983-1983   8402176

Anat Sci Educ
Anatomical sciences education
1935-9772   1935-9780
2007   101392205

Anat Sci Int
Anatomical science international / Japanese
Association of Anatomists
1447-6959   1447-073X
Continues in part: Kaibogaku zasshi.
2002   101154140

Andrologia
Andrologia
0303-4569   1439-0271
Continues Andrologie.
1974   0423506

Andrologie
Andrologie
0303-4569
Continued by Andrologia.
1969-1973   0423126

ANEC
ANEC
0044-930X
1966-1979   1304656

Anesteziol Reanimatol
Anesteziologiia i reanimatologiia
0201-7563
Continues Eksperimental'naia khirurgiia i
anesteziologiia.
1977   7705399

Anesth Anal
Anesthésie et analgésie
0301-4452
Continued by Anesthésie, analgésie,
réanimation.
1935-1956   0404020

Anesth Analg
Anesthesia and analgesia
0003-2999   1526-7598
Continues: Current researches in anesthesia
& analgesia.
1957   1310650

Anesth Analg (Paris)
Anesthésie, analgésie, réanimation
0003-3014
Continues Anesthésie et analgésie. Merged with Annales de L'anesthésiologie française, to form Annales françaises d'anesthésie et de réanimation.
1957-1981   0404017

Anesth Pain Control Dent
Anesthesia & pain control in dentistry
1055-7601
1992-1993   9207842

Anesth Prog
Anesthesia progress
0003-3006
Continues the Journal of the American Dental Society of Anesthesiology.
1966   0043533

Anesthesiol Clin
Anesthesiology clinics
1932-2275
Continues: Anesthesiology clinics of North America.
2006   101273663

Anesthesiol Clin North America
Anesthesiology clinics of North America
0889-8537   1558-4259
Continues in part: Clinics in anaesthesiology. Continued by: Anesthesiology clinics.
1987-2005   8810131

Anesthesiol Rev
Anesthesiology review
0093-4437
Continued by: American journal of anesthesiology.
1974-1994   0414774

Anesthesiology
Anesthesiology
0003-3022   1528-1175
1940   1300217

Angeiol Ann Soc Fr Angeiol Histopathol
Angéiologie et annales de la Société française d'angéiologie et d'histopathologie
Continues: Annales of the Société française d'angéiologie et d'histopathologie. Continued by: Angéiologie.
1951-1959   0060642

Angeiologie
Angéiologie
0003-3049
Continues Angéiologie et annales de la Société française d'angéiologie et d'histopathologie.
1959   0060612

Angew Chem Int Ed Engl
Angewandte Chemie (International ed. in English)
1433-7851   1521-3773
1962   0370543

Angew Chem Weinheim Bergstr Ger
Angewandte Chemie (Weinheim an der Bergstrasse, Germany)
0044-8249
Continues: Angewandte Chemie. A. Wissenschaftlicher Teil. Beginning with May 1988 (except June, Aug. 1988), has supplemental section: Advanced materials, which as of Jan. 1989 is also separately published under the same title in Deerfield Beach, Fla. Beginning with issue for Mar. 31, 1995, every second issue includes separately paged publication: Chemistry (Weinheim an der Bergstrasse, Germany), ISSN 0947-6539; issued separately, 1997- Issued also in an English language version: Angewandte Chemie (International ed. in English), ISSN 0570-0833, 1962-
1949   100955692

Angew Parasitol
Angewandte Parasitologie
0003-3162
Continued by: Applied parasitology.
1960-1992   0370544

Angiogenesis
Angiogenesis
0969-6970   1573-7209
1997   9814575

Angiol Sosud Khir
Angiologiiâ i sosudistaiâ khirurgiiâ = Angiology and vascular surgery
1027-6661
1995   9604504

Angiologia
Angiología
0003-3170
1949   0370545

Angiologica
Angiologica
0003-3189
Continued by Blood vessels.
1964-1973   0427125

Angiology
Angiology
0003-3197   1940-1574
Absorbed Vascular diseases, Jan. 1969.
1950   0203706

Angle Orthod
The Angle orthodontist
0003-3219
1931   0370550

Anglo Ger Med Rev
Anglo-German medical review. Deutsch-englische medizinische Rundschau
0003-3332
1960-1972   7611915

Anim Behav
Animal behaviour
0003-3472
Continues the British journal of animal behaviour.
1958   0376746

Anim Biotechnol
Animal biotechnology
1049-5398   1532-2378
1990   9011409

Anim Blood Groups Biochem Genet
Animal blood groups and biochemical genetics
0003-3480
Continued by: Animal genetics.
1970-1985   0263344

Anim Blood Groups Biochem Genet Suppl
Animal blood groups and biochemical genetics. Supplement
0300-5518
1972-1985   0356270

Anim Cogn
Animal cognition
1435-9448   1435-9456
1998   9814573

Anim Def
The Animals' defender
Continues the Zoophilist and animals' defender. Merged with Anti-vivisection news to form Animals' defender and anti-vivisection news.
1915-1956   14940150R

Anim Genet
Animal genetics
0268-9146   1365-2052
Continues: Animal blood groups and biochemical genetics.
1986   8605704

Anim Health Res Rev
Animal health research reviews / Conference of Research Workers in Animal Diseases
1466-2523
2000   101083072

Anim Learn Behav
Animal learning & behavior
0090-4996
Supersedes in part: Psychonomic science. Continued by: Learning & behavior.
1973-2002   0357415

Anim Reprod Sci
Animal reproduction science
0378-4320   1873-2232
1978   7807205

Ankara Univ Hekim Fak Derg
Ankara Üniversitesi Diş Hekimliği Fakültesi dergisi = The Journal of the Dental Faculty of Ankara University
1016-8710
1974   9004485

ANL Rep
ANL
0192-3188
1946-198u   21830310R

Ann Acad Med Singapore
Annals of the Academy of Medicine, Singapore
0304-4602
1972   7503289

Ann Acad Med Stetin
Annales Academiae Medicae Stetinensis
1427-440X
Continues Rocznik Pomorskiej Akademii Medyczej im. Gen. Karola świerczewskiego w Szczecinie.
1963   7506854

Ann Acad Med Stetin Supl
Annales Academiae Medicae Stetinensis. Suplement
1427-4930
196u   7506853

Ann Acad Sci Fenn A
Annales Academiae Scientiarum Fennicae. Ser. A.5, Medica
0066-1996
Continues Suomalaisen Tiedeakatemian toimituksia. Sar. A.5, Medica-anthropologica.
1961-1986   7604095

Ann Acad Sci Fenn [Biol]
Suomalainen Tiedeakatemia toimituksia. Sar. A.4: Biologica
0066-1988
Continues in part: Suomalainen Tiedeakatemia toimituksia. Sar. A.
1941-19uu   0413756

Ann Afr Med
Annals of African medicine
1596-3519
200u   101231417

Ann Agric Environ Med
Annals of agricultural and environmental medicine: AAEM
1232-1966
1994   9500166

Ann Allergy
Annals of allergy
0003-4738
Continued by: Annals of allergy, asthma & immunology.
1943-1994   0372346

Ann Allergy Asthma Immunol
Annals of allergy, asthma & immunology: official publication of the American College of Allergy, Asthma, & Immunology
1081-1206   1534-4436
Continues: Annals of allergy.
1995   9503580

Ann Am Acad Pol Soc Sci
The Annals of the American Academy of Political and Social Science
0002-7162
1890   7505202

Ann Anat
Annals of anatomy = Anatomischer Anzeiger: official organ of the Anatomische Gesellschaft
0940-9602   1618-0402
Continues: Anatomischer Anzeiger.
1992   100963897

Ann Anat Pathol (Paris)
Annales d'anatomie pathologique
0003-3871
Continues: Annales d'anatomie pathologique et d'anatomie normale me'dico-chirurgicale. Continued by: Annales de pathologie.
1956-1980   0370553

Ann Anesthesiol Fr
Annales de l'anesthésiologie française
0003-4061
Separated from: Agressologie. Merged with: Anesthésie. analgésie. réanimation. to form: Annales françaises d'anesthésie et de réaimation.
1963-1981   0372332

Ann Appl Biol
The Annals of applied biology
0003-4746
1914   0064717

Ann Aust Coll Dent Surg
Annals of the Australian College of Dental Surgeons
0004-8895
Continued by: Annals of the Royal Australian College of Dental Surgeons.
1967-1971   7513553

Ann Behav Med
Annals of behavioral medicine: a publication of the Society of Behavioral Medicine
0883-6612   1532-4796
Absorbed in 1992: Behavioral medicine abstracts.
1985   8510246

Ann Belg Med Mil
Annales belges de médecine militaire. Belgisch tijdschrift voor militaire geneeskunde
Continued by Acta Belgica de arte medicinali et pharmaceutica militari.
1848-1954   14940340R

Ann Biochem Exp Med
Annals of biochemistry and experimental medicine
1941-1963   0002045

Ann Biol Anim Biochim Biophys
Annales de biologie animale, biochimie, biophysique
0003-388X
Continued by Reproduction. nutrition. développement.
1961-1979   0040752

Ann Biol Clin (Paris)
Annales de biologie clinique
0003-3898
1943   2984690R

Ann Biomed Eng
Annals of biomedical engineering
0090-6964   1521-6047
Absorbed: Journal of bioengineering. 1979
1972   0361512

Ann Bot (Lond)
Annals of botany
0305-7364   1095-8290
1887   0372347

Ann Card Anaesth
Annals of cardiac anaesthesia
0971-9784
1998   9815987

Ann Cardiol Angeiol (Paris)
Annales de cardiologie et d'angéiologie
0003-3928   1768-3181
Continues: Actualités cardiologiques et angéiologiques internationales.
1968   0142167

Ann Chim
Annali di chimica
0003-4592
Continues Annali di chimica applicata. Continued by: ChemSusChem.
1950-2007   7610375

Ann Chimie Sci Materiaux
Annales de chimie--science des matériaux
0151-9107
Continues: Annales de chimie.
1978   9875491

Ann Chir
Annales de chirurgie
0003-3944
Absorbed: Annales de chirurgie thoracique et cardio-vasculaire. Lyon chirurgical. Chirurgie. Absorbed by: Journal de chirurgie.
1947-2006   0140722

Ann Chir Gynaecol
Annales chirurgiae et gynaecologiae
0355-9521
Continues Annales chirurgiae et gynaecologiae fenniae. Continued by: Scandinavian journal of surgery.
1976-2001   7609767

Ann Chir Gynaecol Fenn
Annales chirurgiae et gynaecologiae Fenniae
0003-3855
Continues Suomalainen Lääkäriseura Duodecim. Acta. Toimituksia. ser. B. Continued by Annales chirurgiae et gynaecologiae.
1946-1975   7609198

Ann Chir Gynaecol Fenn Suppl
Annales chirurgiae et gynaecologiae Fenniae. Supplementum
0066-2038
Continued by Annales chirurgiae et gynaecologiae. Supplementum.
1946-1975   7702958

Ann Chir Gynaecol Suppl
Annales chirurgiae et gynaecologiae. Supplementum
0355-9874
Continues Annales chirurgiae et gynaecologiae Fenniae. Supplementum.
1976   7702959

Ann Chir Infant
Annales de chirurgie infantile
0003-3952
Continued by Chirurgie pédiatrique.
1960-1977   0376315

Ann Chir Main
Annales de chirurgie de la main: organe officiel des sociétés de chirurgie de la main
0753-9053
Continued by: Annales de chirurgie de la main et du membre supérieur.
1982-1989   8411230

Ann Chir Main Memb Super
Annales de chirurgie de la main et du membre supérieur: organe officiel des sociétés de chirurgie de la main = Annals of hand and upper limb surgery
1153-2424
Continues: Annales de chirurgie de la main. Continued by: Chirurgie de la main.
1990-1999   9011039

Ann Chir Plast
Annales de chirurgie plastique
0003-3960
Continued by Annales de chirurgie plastique et esthétique.
1956-1982   2983317R

Ann Chir Plast Esthet
Annales de chirurgie plastique et esthétique
0294-1260   1768-319X
Continues: Annales de chirurgie plastique.
1983   8305839

Ann Chir Thorac Cardiovasc
Annales de chirurgie thoracique et cardio-vasculaire
0066-2054
Continued by issues of Annales de chirurgie with theme title. Chirurgie thoracique et cardio-vasculaire.
1962-1978   0140655

Ann Clin Biochem
Annals of clinical biochemistry
0004-5632
Continues Proceedings of the Association of Clinical Biochemists.
1969   0324055

Ann Clin Lab Sci
Annals of clinical and laboratory science
0091-7370   1550-8080
Continues Annals of clinical laboratory science.
1973   0410247

Ann Clin Lab Sci
Annals of clinical laboratory science
0095-8905
Continued by Annals of clinical and laboratory science.
1971-1973   0410250

Ann Clin Microbiol Antimicrob
Annals of clinical microbiology and antimicrobials
1476-0711
19uu   101152152

Ann Clin Psychiatry
Annals of clinical psychiatry: official journal of the American Academy of Clinical Psychiatrists
1040-1237   1547-3325
1989   8911021

Ann Clin Res
Annals of clinical research
0003-4762
Formed by the merger of Annales medicinae internae Fenniae and Annales paediatriae Fenniae. Merged with: Medical biology, to form: Annals of medicine.
1969-1988   0220042

Ann Dent
Annals of dentistry
0003-4770
Continues: Journal of the New York Academy of Dentistry. Continued by: Annals of the New York Academy of Dentistry.
1936-2003   0372350

Ann Dermatol Syphiligr (Paris)
Annales de dermatologie et de syphiligraphie
0003-3979
Merged with Bulletin de la Sociétété française de dermatologie et de syphiligraphie to form Annales de dermatologie et de vénéréologie.
1868-1976   0370561

Ann Dermatol Venereol
Annales de dermatologie et de vénéréologie
0151-9638
Formed by the union of: Annales de dermatologie et de syphiligraphie, and: Bulletin de la Société française de dermatologie et de syphiligraphie.
1977   7702013

Ann Diagn Pathol
Annals of diagnostic pathology
1092-9134   1532-8198
1997   9800503

Ann Droit Int Med
Annales de droit international médical
0517-8517
1957   14940460R

Ann Dyslexia
Annals of dyslexia
0736-9387   1934-7243
Continues: Bulletin of the Orton Society.
1982   8406611

Ann Emerg Med
Annals of emergency medicine
0196-0644   1097-6760
Continues: JACEP.
1980   8002646

Ann Endocrinol (Paris)
Annales d'endocrinologie
0003-4266
1939   0116744

Ann Entomol Soc Am
Annals of the Entomological Society of America
0013-8746
1908   7503290

Ann Epidemiol
Annals of epidemiology
1047-2797   1873-2585
1990   9100013

Ann Fac Med Chir Univ Studi Perugia
Annali della Facoltà di medicina e chirurgia della Università degli studi di Perugia
0365-2270
1885-1996   7506856

Ann Falsif Fraud
Annales des falsifications et des fraudes
0365-2157
Continues: Annales des falsifications. Continued by: Annales des falsifications et de l'expertise chimique.
1917-1959   8009688

Ann Fam Med
Annals of family medicine
1544-1709   1544-1717
2003   101167762

Ann Fr Anesth Reanim
Annales françaises d'anesthèsie et de rèanimation
0750-7658   1769-6623
Formed by the union of: Annales de l'anesthésiologie française; and Anesthésie, analgésie, réanimation.
1982   8213275

Ann Gastroenterol Hepatol (Paris)
Annales de gastroentérologie et d'hépatologie
0066-2070
Continues Actualités hépato-gastro-entérologiques.
1970-1998   0263111

Ann Genet
Annales de génétique
0003-3995
Continued by: European journal of medical genetics.
1958-2004   0370562

Ann Genet Sel Anim
Annales de génétique et de sélection animale
0003-4002
Continued by: Génétique, sélection, évolution.
1969-1982   0257341

Ann Health Law
Annals of health law / Loyola University Chicago, School of Law, Institute for Health Law
1075-2994
1992   9306639

Ann Hematol
Annals of hematology
0939-5555   1432-0584
Absorbed: Hematology and cell therapy. Continues: Blut.
1991   9107334

Ann Hepatol
Annals of hepatology: official journal of the Mexican Association of Hepatology
1665-2681
2002   101155885

Ann Histochim
Annales d'histochimie
0003-4355
Continued by: Cellular and molecular biology, including cyto-enzymology.
1956-1976   0370554

Ann Homeopath Fr
Les Annales homéopathiques françaises
0003-4444
Continued by: Homéopathie.
1958-1983   2984691R

Ann Hum Biol
Annals of human biology
0301-4460   1464-5033
1974   0404024

Ann Hum Genet
Annals of human genetics
0003-4800   1469-1809
Continues Annals of eugenics.
1954   0416661

Ann Hyg
Annals of hygiene
0743-3298
1884-1897   0001130

Ann Hyg Med Colon
Annales d'hygiène et de médecine coloniales
1898-1914   0001760

Ann Hyg Publique Ind Soc (1923)
Annales d'hygiène publique, industrielle et sociale
0365-2882
Continues in part: Annales d'hygiène publique et de médecine légale. Merged with: Diététique et collectivités (1953), to form: Diététique et collectivités… et les Annales d'hygiène publique, industrielle et sociale.
1923-1951   15010120R

Ann ICRP
Annals of the ICRP
0146-6453   1872-969X
1977   7708044

Ann Ig
Annali di igiene: medicina preventiva e di comunità
1120-9135
Continues: Nuovi annali d'igiene e microbiologia.
1989   9002865

Ann Ig (Roma)
Annali d'igiene
Continues Annali d'igiene sperimentale. Absorbed by: Nuovi annali d'igiene e microbiologia in 1952.
1916-1951   15020140R

Ann Immunol (Paris)
Annales d'immunologie
0300-4910
Formed by the union of Annales de l'Institut Pasteur, in part, and of Revue d'immunologie. Continued by Annales de l'Institut Pasteur. Immunologie.
1973-1984   0353045

Ann Immunol Hung
Annales immunologiae Hungaricae
0570-1708
1958-1986   0373074

Ann Inst Pasteur (Paris)
Annales de l'Institut Pasteur
0020-2444
Continued in part by Annales de microbiologie.
1887-1972   7512320

Ann Inst Pasteur Immunol
Annales de l'Institut Pasteur. Immunologie
0769-2625
Continues: Annales d'immunologie. Continued by: Annales de l'Institut Pasteur. Immunology.
1985-1986   8503043

Ann Inst Pasteur Immunol
Annales de l'Institut Pasteur. Immunology
0769-2625
Continues: Annales de l'Institut Pasteur. Immunologie. Continued by: Research in immunology.
1986-1988   8701983

Ann Inst Pasteur Lille
Annales de l'Institut Pasteur de Lille
0073-8573
1948-1971   7502518

Ann Inst Pasteur Microbiol
Annales de l'Institut Pasteur. Microbiologie
0769-2609
Continues: Annales de microbiologie. Continued by: Annales de l'Institut Pasteur. Microbiology.
1985-1986   8503044

Ann Inst Pasteur Microbiol
Annales de l'Institut Pasteur. Microbiology
0769-2609
Continues: Annales de l'Institut Pasteur.
Microbiologie. Continued by: Research in
microbiology.
1986-1988　　　　　8701984

Ann Inst Pasteur Virol
Annales de l'Institut Pasteur. Virology
0769-2617
Continues: Annales de l'Institut Pasteur.
Virologie. Continued by: Research in
virology.
1986-1988　　　　　8702442

Ann Intern Med
Annals of internal medicine
0003-4819　　　　　1539-3704
Supersedes: Annals of clinical medicine.
1927　　　　　0372351

Ann Isnardi Auxol Norm Patol
Annali Isnardi di auxologia normale e
patologica
1954-1963　　　　　15020150R

Ann Ist Carlo Forlanini
Annali dell'Istituto "Carlo Forlanini"
0021-2431
Continued by: Annali dell'Istituto "Carlo
Forlamini" (1981).
1937-1969　　　　　7502519

Ann Ist Super Sanita
Annali dell'Istituto superiore di sanità
0021-2571
Supersedes: Rendiconti dell'Istituto superiore
di sanità.
1965　　　　　7502520

Ann Ital Chir
Annali italiani di chirurgia
0003-469X
1922　　　　　0372343

Ann Ital Dermatol Sifilogr
Annali italiani di dermatologia e sifilografia
Continued by: Annali italiani di dermatologia
clinica e sperimentale.
1945-1960　　　　　15020160R

Ann Ital Med Int
Annali italiani di medicina interna: organo
ufficiale della Società italiana di medicina
interna
0393-9340
Continued by: Internal and emergency
medicine.
1986-2005　　　　　8806705

Ann Ital Pediatr
Annali italiani di pediatria
1948-1975　　　　　0372345

Ann Laringol Otol Rinol Faringol
Annali di laringologia, otologia, rinologia,
faringologia
0066-2267
Continued by: Acta otorhinolaryngologica
Italica.
1900-1980　　　　　0400641

Ann Med
Annals of medicine
0785-3890　　　　　1365-2060
Formed by the union of: Annals of clinical
research. and: Medical biology.
1989　　　　　8906388

Ann Med (Milano)
Annali medici
0517-8681
1957-1972　　　　　0373076

Ann Med Exp Biol Fenn
Annales medicinae experimentalis et
biologiae Fenniae
0003-4479
Continues the Acta. Ser. A, of the Societas
Medicorum Fennica Duodecim. Continued by
Medical biology.
1947-1973　　　　　0420465

Ann Med Intern Fenn
Annales medicinae internae Fenniae
0365-4362
Continues in part: Acta Societatis Medicorum
Fennicae Duodecim. ser. B. Merged with
Annales paediatriae Fenniae to form Annals
of clinical research.
1946-1968　　　　　0221122

Ann Med Intern Fenn Suppl
Annales medicinae internae Fenniae.
Supplementum
0365-4427
Merged with the Supplementum of Annales
paediatriae Fenniae to form the Supplement
of Annals of clinical research.
1947-1967　　　　　0254714

Ann Med Interne (Paris)
Annales de médecine interne
0003-410X
Continues: Bulletins et mémoires de la
Société médicale des hôpitaux de Paris.
Absorbed by: Presse médicale.
1969-2003　　　　　0171744

Ann Med Leg Criminol Police Sci Toxicol
Annales de médecine légale, criminologie,
police scientifique et toxicologie
1921-1967　　　　　15010050R

Ann Med Nancy
Annales médicales de Nancy
0003-4460
Supersedes Revue médicale de Nancy.
Continued by Annales médicales de Nancy et
de l'Est.
1962-1978　　　　　0372333

Ann Med Nav (Roma)
Annali di medicina navale
0392-9418
1895-1992　　　　　0373072

Ann Med Nav Trop
Annali di medicina navale e tropicale
Continues: Annali di medicina navale e
coloniale. Continued by: Annali di medicina
navale.
1951-1960　　　　　15020060R

Ann Med Psychol (Paris)
Annales médico-psychologiques
0003-4487
Absorbed: Annales de psychiatrie. 2002
1843　　　　　2984692R

Ann Med Sect Pol Acad Sci
Annals of the Medical Section of the Polish
Academy of Sciences
0048-4733
1966-1976　　　　　7505203

Ann Med Soc
Les Annales de médecine sociale
Continued by: Annales de médecine
praticienne et sociale.
1944-1953　　　　　15010060R

Ann Med Sondalo
Annali medici di Sondalo
0402-4710
1956-1973　　　　　0377216

Ann Med Univ Bialyst Pol
Annals of the Medical University, Białystok,
Poland = Roczniki Akademii Medycznej w
Białymstoku
Continues: Roczniki Akademii Medycznej
w Białymstoku. Continued by: Roczniki
Akademii Medycznej w Białymstoku (1995).
1992-1993　　　　　9439578

Ann Med Vet
Annales de médecine vétérinaire
0003-4118
1852-2003　　　　　0373073

Ann Microbiol (Paris)
Annales de microbiologie
0300-5410
Continues in part Annales de l'Institut
Pasteur. Continued by Annales de l'Institut
Pasteur. Microbiologie.
1973-1984　　　　　0354704

Ann Microbiol Enzimol
Annali di microbiologia ed enzimologia
0003-4649
Continues: Annali di microbiologia.
Continued by: Annals of microbiology.
1957-1999　　　　　0406005

Ann N Y Acad Sci
Annals of the New York Academy of
Sciences
0077-8923　　　　　1749-6632
Supersedes: Annals of the Lyceum of Natural
History of New York.
1877　　　　　7506858

Ann Nestle [Eng]
Annales Nestlé [English ed.]
0517-8606
195u　　　　　15010200R

Ann Nestle [Fr]
Annales Nestlé. [Ed. française]
0250-9644
1949　　　　　2984694R

Ann Nestle [Ger]
Annales Nestlé. [Deutsche Aufl.]
0250-9652
1953　　　　　0372336

Ann Neurol
Annals of neurology
0364-5134　　　　　1531-8249
1977　　　　　7707449

Ann Neuropsichiatr Psicoanal
Annali di neuropsichiatria e psicoanalisi
Supersedes Rivista di psicopatologia,
neuropsichiatria e psicoanalisi and Annali di
nevrologia.
1954-1979　　　　　0401033

Ann Noninvasive Electrocardiol
Annals of noninvasive electrocardiology:
the official journal of the International
Society for Holter and Noninvasive
Electrocardiology, Inc
1082-720X　　　　　1542-474X
1996　　　　　9607443

Ann Nucl Med
Annals of nuclear medicine
0914-7187　　　　　1864-6433
1987　　　　　8913398

Ann Nutr Aliment
Annales de la nutrition et de l'alimentation
0003-4037
Merged with: Nutrition and metabolism. to
form: Annals of nutrition & metabolism.
1947-1980　　　　　0372653

Ann Nutr Metab
Annals of nutrition & metabolism
0250-6807   1421-9697
  Continues: Nutrition and metabolism.
1981   8105511

Ann Occup Hyg
The Annals of occupational hygiene
0003-4878   1475-3162
1958   0203526

Ann Ocul (Paris)
Annales d'oculistique
0003-4371
  Merged with Archives d'ophtalmologie to
  form Journal français d'ophtalmologie.
1838-1977   0370555

Ann Odontostomatol (Lyon)
Annales odonto-stomatologiques
0066-2194
1944-1978   0401032

Ann Oncol
Annals of oncology: official journal of the
European Society for Medical Oncology /
ESMO
0923-7534   1569-8041
1990   9007735

Ann Ophthalmol
Annals of ophthalmology
0003-4886
  Merged with: Glaucoma, to form: Annals of
  ophthalmology-glaucoma.
1969-1994   0210137

Ann Ophthalmol (Skokie)
Annals of ophthalmology (Skokie, Ill.)
1530-4086   1558-9951
  Continues: Annals of ophthalmology-
  glaucoma.
1999   100893534

Ann Osp Maria Vittoria Torino
Annali dell'Ospedale Maria Vittoria di
Torino
0390-5454
  Continues Giornale di batteriologia, virologia
  ed immunologia ed annali dell'Ospedale
  Maria Vittoria de Torino. Parte 2: Sezione
  clinica.
1974-1991   7511607

Ann Ostet Ginecol Med Perinat
Annali di ostetricia, ginecologia, medicina
perinatale
0300-0087
  Continues Annali di ostetricia e ginecologia.
1972-1998   0347360

Ann Otol Rhinol Laryngol
The Annals of otology, rhinology, and
laryngology
0003-4894
  Absorbed: Index of oto-laryngology.
  Continues in part: Annals of ophthalmology
  and otology.
1897   0407300

Ann Otol Rhinol Laryngol Suppl
The Annals of otology, rhinology &
laryngology. Supplement
0096-8056
1971   1256156

Ann Otolaryngol
Les Annales d'oto-laryngologie
0003-438X
  Formed by the merger of the Annales des
  maladies de l'oreille, du larynx, du nez et
  du pharynx and Archives internationales de
  laryngologie, otologie, rhinologie et broncho-
  oesophagoscopie. Continued by: Annales
  d'oto-laryngologie et de chirurgie de la face.
1931-1962   15010150R

Ann Otolaryngol Chir Cervicofac
Annales d'oto-laryngologie et de chirurgie
cervico faciale: bulletin de la Société d'oto-
laryngologie des hôpitaux de Paris
0003-438X
  Continues: Annales d'oto-laryngologie
  et de chirurgie de la face. Absorbed:
  Journal français d'oto-rhino-laryngologie;
  audiophonologie, chirurgie maxillo-faciale.
  2004 Cahiers d'O.R.L. de chirurgie cervico-
  faciale et d'audiophonologie.
1963   9431026

Ann Ottalmol Clin Ocul
Annali di ottalmologia e clinica oculistica
0003-4665
1917-2001   9309994

Ann Paediatr
Annales paediatrici. International review of
pediatrics
0365-4966
  Continues: Jahrbuch für Kinderheilkunde.
  Continued by: Pediatric research.
1938-1966   2984695R

Ann Paediatr Fenn
Annales paediatriae Fenniae
0570-1732
  Merged with Annales medicinae internae
  Fenniae to form Annals of clinical research.
1954-1968   0221123

Ann Parasitol Hum Comp
Annales de parasitologie humaine et
comparée
0003-4150
  Continued by: Parasite (Paris, France).
1923-1993   0376525

Ann Pathol
Annales de pathologie
0242-6498
  Absorbed: Clinical and experimental
  pathology. Continues: Annales d'anatomie
  pathologique.
1981   8106337

Ann Pediatr (Paris)
Annales de pédiatrie
0066-2097
1954-1999   2984696R

Ann Periodontol
Annals of periodontology / the American
Academy of Periodontology
1553-0841
1996-2003   9702874

Ann Pharm Fr
Annales pharmaceutiques françaises
0003-4509
  Formed by the merger of Journal de
  pharmacie et de chimie, and Bulletin des
  sciences pharmacologiques.
1943   2985176R

Ann Pharmacother
The Annals of pharmacotherapy
1060-0280   1542-6270
  Continues: DICP.
1992   9203131

Ann Phys
Annalen der Physik
0003-3804
  Supersedes Neues Journal der Physik.
1799   14940290R

Ann Phys Med
Annals of physical medicine
0365-5547
  Continued by Rheumatology and physical
  medicine.
1952-1970   0256644

Ann Physiol Anthropol
The Annals of physiological anthropology =
Seiri Jinruigaku Kenkyūkai kaishi
0287-8429
  Continued by: Applied human science.
1983-1994   8506625

Ann Plast Surg
Annals of plastic surgery
0148-7043   1536-3708
1978   7805336

Ann R Australas Coll Dent Surg
Annals of the Royal Australasian College of
Dental Surgeons
0158-1570
  Continues Annals of the Royal Australian
  College of Dental Surgeons.
1977   8006208

Ann R Coll Surg Engl
Annals of the Royal College of Surgeons of
England
0035-8843   1478-7083
1947   7506860

Ann Radiol (Paris)
Annales de radiologie
0003-4185
1958-1997   0372331

Ann Radiol Diagn (Bologna)
Annali di radiologia diagnostica
0003-4673
  Continues Annali di radiologia e fisica
  medica. Continued by: Diagnostica per
  immagini.
1939-1977   0372654

Ann Readapt Med Phys
Annales de réadaptation et de médecine
physique: revue scientifique de la Société
française de rééducation fonctionnelle de
réadaptation et de médecine physique
0168-6054   1768-3203
  Continues: Annales de médecine physique.
1982   8701687

Ann Rech Vet
Annales de recherches vétérinaires. Annals
of veterinary research
0003-4193
  Supersedes Recherches vétérinaires.
  Continued by: Veterinary research.
1970-1992   1267230

Ann Rheum Dis
Annals of the rheumatic diseases
0003-4967   1468-2060
  Continues: Rheumatic diseases.
1939   0372355

Ann Sanita Pubblica
Annali della sanità pubblica
0021-3071
  Continues: Notiziario dell'amministrazione
  sanitaria.
1948   0071152

Ann Saudi Med
Annals of Saudi medicine
0256-4947
  Continues: King Faisal Specialist Hospital
  medical journal.
1985   8507355

Ann Sci
Annals of science
0003-3790
1936   0372361

Ann Sci Univ Besancon Med
Annales scientifiques de l'Université de
Besançon. Médecine
0523-0667
1957-1975   7505200

Ann Sclavo
Annali Sclavo; rivista di microbiologia e di immunologia
0003-472X
1959-1982 2985177R

Ann Sclavo Collana Monogr
Annali Sclavo. Collana monografica
0003-472X
Continues: Annali Sclavo.
1984-1986 8701688

Ann Soc Angeiol Histopathologie
Annales. Société française d'angéiologie et d'histopathologie
Continued by Angéiologie et annales de la Société française d'angéiologie et d'histopathologie.
1948-1950 14940110R

Ann Soc Belg Med Trop
Annales de la Société belge de médecine tropicale
0772-4128
Continues Annales des Sociétés belges de médecine tropicale. de parasitologie. et de mycologie (varies slightly). Merged with: Journal of tropical medicine and hygiene; Tropical and geographical medicine; and: Tropical medicine and parasitology: to form: Tropical medicine & international health.
1972-1995 7511864

Ann Soc Belg Med Trop (1920)
Annales de la Société belge de médecine tropicale
0365-6527
Continued by: Annales des sociétés belges de médecine tropicale. de parasitologie et de mycologie.
1920-1963 7506848

Ann Soc Belges Med Trop Parasitol Mycol
Annales des sociétés belges de médecine tropicale, de parasitologie, et de mycologie
0037-9638
Continues. and is continued by. the Annales de la Société belge de médecine tropicale.
1964-1971 0343144

Ann Soc R Sci Med Nat Brux
Annales de la Société royale des sciences médicales et naturelles de Bruxelles
0772-3997
Supersedes the society's Annales et bulletin. issued 1912-39.
1948-1967 7506850

Ann Stomatol (Roma)
Annali di stomatologia
0003-4681
Formed by the union of: Annali di stomatologia e dell'Istituto Superiore di Odontoiatria "G. Eastman." ISSN 0375-8516, and: Clinica odontoiatrica. ISSN 0366-6794.
1959 0404022

Ann Surg
Annals of surgery
0003-4932 1528-1140
1885 0372354

Ann Surg Oncol
Annals of surgical oncology
1068-9265 1534-4681
1994 9420840

Ann Thorac Cardiovasc Surg
Annals of thoracic and cardiovascular surgery: official journal of the Association of Thoracic and Cardiovascular Surgeons of Asia
1341-1098
1995 9703158

Ann Thorac Surg
The Annals of thoracic surgery
0003-4975 1552-6259
1965 15030100R

Ann Transplant
Annals of transplantation: quarterly of the Polish Transplantation Society
1425-9524
1996 9802544

Ann Trop Med Parasitol
Annals of tropical medicine and parasitology
0003-4983
1907 2985178R

Ann Trop Paediatr
Annals of tropical paediatrics
0272-4936 1465-3281
1981 8210625

Ann Tuberc
Annals of tuberculosis
1950-1960 15030110R

Ann Univ Mariae Curie Sklodowska [Med]
Annales Universitatis Mariae Curie-Skłodowska. Sectio D: Medicina
0066-2240
1946 0414101

Ann Univ Sarav [Med]
Annales Universitatis Saraviensis. Medizin
0003-4533
Continued by: Annales Universitatis Saraviensis medicinae.
1953-1976 0414102

Ann Urol (Paris)
Annales d'urologie
0003-4401
1969 0212342

Ann Vasc Surg
Annals of vascular surgery
0890-5096 1615-5947
1986 8703941

Ann West Med Surg
Annals of western medicine and surgery
1947-1952 15030120R

ANNA J
ANNA journal / American Nephrology Nurses' Association
8750-0779
Continues: AANNT journal. Continued by: Nephrology nursing journal.
1984-1999 8411466

Annals N Y Acad Dent
The annals of the New York Academy of Dentistry
1931-6585
Continues: Annals of dentistry.
2004 101252990

Annee Biol
L'Année biologique
0003-5017
1895-2001 0372330

Annee Endocrinol
L'Année endocrinologique
0365-1940
1949-1973 7606934

Annee Psychol
L'Année psychologique
0003-5033
1894 0372363

Annee Ther
L'Année thérapeutique
1920-1963 0123166

Annee Ther Clin Ophtalmol
L'Année thérapeutique et clinique en ophtalmologie
0301-4495
Continues L'Année thérapeutique en ophtalmologie.
1956-1990 0405351

Annu Conf Res Med Educ
Annual Conference on Research in Medical Education. Conference on Research in Medical Education
0190-7255
Formed by the union of: Program. annual Conference on Research in Medical Education and Complete papers - Annual Conference on Research in Medical Education. Continued by Conference on Research in Medical Education. Proceedings of the … Annual Conference on Research in Medical Education.
1971-1982 7801910

Annu Meet Am Inst Oral Biol
Annual meeting - American Institute of Oral Biology
0098-6119
1944-1993 7501078

Annu Proc Assoc Adv Automot Med
Annual proceedings / Association for the Advancement of Automotive Medicine. Association for the Advancement of Automotive Medicine
1540-0360
Continues: Proceedings. Association for the Advancement of Automotive Medicine. Conference.
1994 101152228

Annu Rep Div Biol Med Res Argonne Natl Lab
Annual report - Division of Biological and Medical Research, Argonne National Laboratory. Argonne National Laboratory. Division of Biological and Medical Research
Continues Argonne National Laboratory. Division of Biological and Medical Research. Biological and medical research division semiannual report.
1964-1980 7701761

Annu Rep Gorgas Meml Lab Rep Audit
Annual report of the Gorgas Memorial Laboratory and report of audit. Gorgas Memorial Laboratory
0190-6992
Supersedes Gorgas Memorial Laboratory, Panama. Annual report of the Gorgas Memorial Institute. Continued by Gorgas Memorial Laboratory. Annual report of the work and operations of the Gorgas Memorial Laboratory.
1934-1960 7800301

Annu Rep La Dep Public Welf
Annual report. Louisiana. Dept. of Public Welfare
194u-1965 0117661

Annu Rep R Soc Promot Health
Annual report of the Council. Royal Society of Health (Great Britain)
Continues the Annual report of the Council of the Royal Sanitary Institute, London.
1955-1981 20440830R

Annu Rep Res Inst Environ Med Nagoya Univ
Annual report of the Research Institute of Environmental Medicine, Nagoya University
0469-4759
Continued by Environmental medicine.
1949-1980 0412665

Annu Rep United States Natl Mus
Annual report. United States National Museum
1884-1964 0243633

Annu Rev Biochem
Annual review of biochemistry
0066-4154
1932
1545-4509
2985150R

Annu Rev Biomed Eng
Annual review of biomedical engineering
1523-9829
1999
1545-4274
100883581

Annu Rev Biophys
Annual review of biophysics
1936-122X
Continues: Annual review of biophysics and
biomolecular structure.
2008
101469708

Annu Rev Biophys Bioeng
Annual review of biophysics and
bioengineering
0084-6589
Continued by: Annual review of biophysics
and biophysical chemistry.
1972-1984
0332636

Annu Rev Biophys Biomol Struct
Annual review of biophysics and
biomolecular structure
1056-8700
Continues: Annual review of biophysics and
biophysical chemistry. Continued by: Annual
review of biophysics.
1992-2007
1545-4266
9211097

Annu Rev Biophys Biophys Chem
Annual review of biophysics and biophysical
chemistry
0883-9182
Continues: Annual review of biophysics and
bioengineering. Continued by: Annual review
of biophysics and biomolecular structure.
1985-1991
8505748

Annu Rev Cell Biol
Annual review of cell biology
0743-4634
Continued by: Annual review of cell and
developmental biology.
1985-1994
8602195

Annu Rev Cell Dev Biol
Annual review of cell and developmental
biology
1081-0706
Continues: Annual review of cell biology.
1995
9600627

Annu Rev Clin Psychol
Annual review of clinical psychology
1548-5951
2005
1548-5951
101235325

Annu Rev Entomol
Annual review of entomology
0066-4170
1956
0372367

Annu Rev Genet
Annual review of genetics
0066-4197
1967
0117605

Annu Rev Genomics Hum Genet
Annual review of genomics and human
genetics
1527-8204
2000
1545-293X
100911346

Annu Rev Gerontol Geriatr
Annual review of gerontology & geriatrics
0198-8794
1980
8100572

Annu Rev Immunol
Annual review of immunology
0732-0582
1983
8309206

Annu Rev Med
Annual review of medicine
0066-4219
1950
1545-326X
2985151R

Annu Rev Microbiol
Annual review of microbiology
0066-4227
1947
1545-3251
0372370

Annu Rev Neurosci
Annual review of neuroscience
0147-006X
1978
7804039

Annu Rev Nucl Sci
Annual review of nuclear science
0066-4243
Continued by Annual review of nuclear and
particle science.
1952-1977
7905958

Annu Rev Nurs Res
Annual review of nursing research
0739-6686
1983
8406387

Annu Rev Nutr
Annual review of nutrition
0199-9885
1981
8209988

Annu Rev Pathol
Annual review of pathology
1553-4006
2006
1553-4014
101275111

Annu Rev Pharmacol
Annual review of pharmacology
0066-4251
Continued by Annual review of pharmacology
and toxicology.
1961-1975
7607089

Annu Rev Pharmacol Toxicol
Annual review of pharmacology and
toxicology
0362-1642
Continues Annual review of pharmacology.
1976
7607088

Annu Rev Phys Chem
Annual review of physical chemistry
0066-426X
1950
15040080R

Annu Rev Physiol
Annual review of physiology
0066-4278
1939
1545-1585
0370600

Annu Rev Phytopathol
Annual review of phytopathology
0066-4286
1963
0372373

Annu Rev Plant Biol
Annual review of plant biology
1543-5008
Continues: Annual review of plant physiology
and plant molecular biology.
2002
1545-2123
101140127

Annu Rev Psychol
Annual review of psychology
0066-4308
1950
0372374

Annu Rev Public Health
Annual review of public health
0163-7525
1980
8006431

Annu Rev Rehabil
Annual review of rehabilitation
0197-2251
Continued by: Advances in clinical
rehabilitation.
1980-1986
8101117

Annu Rev Sex Res
Annual review of sex research
1053-2528
1990
9200315

Annu Stat Assist Previd Soc
Annuario statistico dell'assistenza e della
previdenza sociale. Istituto centrale di
statistica (Italy)
0075-1790
Continued by: Annuario statistico della
previdenza e dell'assistenza sociale.
1952-1975
23210510R

Annu Stat Suppl Soc Secur Bull
Annual statistical supplement, ... to the
Social security bulletin
1553-0949
Continues: Social security bulletin. Annual
statistical supplement.
1992
1553-0663
9604640

Annu Symp Nurs Fac Pract
Annual Symposium on Nursing Faculty
Practice
1983-uuuu
100960803

Anot Pediatr
Anotaciones pediátricas
0402-5555
1954-1975
2985152R

ANPHI Pap
ANPHI papers
0065-0676
1966
0102537

ANS Adv Nurs Sci
ANS. Advances in nursing science
0161-9268
1978
1550-5014
7809992

Anthropol Anz
Anthropologischer Anzeiger; Bericht über
die biologisch-anthropologische Literatur
0003-5548
Absorbed: Zeitschrift für Morphologie und
Anthropologie. 2002
1924
0372377

Anthropologie
L'Anthropologie
0003-5521
Formed by the union of Matériaux pour
l'histoire naturelle et primitive de l'homme,
Revue d'anthropologie, and Revue
d'ethnographie.
1890
2985154R

Antibiot Annu
Antibiotics annual
0570-3131
Continued by Antimicrobial agents annual.
1953-1960
15110220R

Antibiot Chemother
Antibiotica et chemotherapia. Fortschritte.
Advances. Progrès
Continued by Antibiotics and chemotherapy.
1954-1970
1304167

Antibiot Chemother
Antibiotics and chemotherapy
0066-4758
Continues Antibiotica et chemotherapia.
1971
1662-2863
1305576

Antibiot Khimioter
Antibiotiki i khimioterapiiâ = Antibiotics and chemoterapy [sic] / Ministerstvo meditsinskoĭ i mikrobiologicheskoĭ promyshlennosti SSSR
0235-2990
Continues: Antibiotiki i meditsinskaia biotekhnologiia.
1988　　　　8803688

Antibiot Med Biotekhnol
Antibiotiki i meditsinskaia biotekhnologiia = Antibiotics and medical biotechnology / Ministerstvo meditsinskoĭ promyshlennosti SSSR
0233-7525
Continues: Antibiotiki. Continued by: Antibiotiki i khimioterapiia.
1985-1987　　　　8502784

Antibiotic Med Clin Ther
Antibiotic medicine & clinical therapy
0570-3107
Continues: Antibiotic medicine. Absorbed by: Antibiotics & chemotherapy.
1956-1961　　　　15110190R

Antibiotica
Antibiotica
0003-5629
1963-1975　　　　0400642

Antibiotiki
Antibiotiki
0003-5637
Continued by Antibiotiki i meditsinskaia biotekhnologiia.
1956-1984　　　　0375020

Antibiotiki (Mosc)
Antibiotiki
1948-19uu　　　　15110270R

Anticancer Agents Med Chem
Anti-cancer agents in medicinal chemistry
1871-5206　　　　1875-5992
Continues: Current medicinal chemistry. Anti-cancer agents.
2006　　　　101265649

Anticancer Drug Des
Anti-cancer drug design
0266-9536
Absorbed by: Oncology research. 2002
1985-2001　　　　8603523

Anticancer Drugs
Anti-cancer drugs
0959-4973　　　　1473-5741
1990　　　　9100823

Anticancer Res
Anticancer research
0250-7005
1981　　　　8102988

Antimicrob Agents Chemother
Antimicrobial agents and chemotherapy
0066-4804　　　　1098-6596
Continues: Antimicrobial agents and chemotherapy, issued annually 1961-1970.
1972　　　　0315061

Antimicrob Agents Chemother (Bethesda)
Antimicrobial agents and chemotherapy
Continues: Antimicrobial agents annual. Superseded by: Antimicrobial agents and chemotherapy.
1961-1970　　　　0116415

Antioquia Med
Antioquia médica
0044-8389
Formed by the union of the Anales of the Academia de Medicina de Medellín and the Boletín clínico of the Universidad de Antioquia, Facultad de Medicina, Medellín.
1950-1984　　　　0413655

Antioxid Redox Signal
Antioxidants & redox signaling
1523-0864　　　　1557-7716
1999　　　　100888899

Antisense Nucleic Acid Drug Dev
Antisense & nucleic acid drug development
1087-2906
Continues: Antisense research and development. Continued by: Oligonucleotides.
1996-2003　　　　9606142

Antisense Res Dev
Antisense research and development
1050-5261
Continued by: Antisense & nucleic acid drug development.
1991-1995　　　　9110698

Antivir Chem Chemother
Antiviral chemistry & chemotherapy
0956-3202
1990　　　　9009212

Antivir Ther
Antiviral therapy
1359-6535
1996　　　　9815705

Antiviral Res
Antiviral research
0166-3542　　　　1872-9096
1981　　　　8109699

Antonie Van Leeuwenhoek
Antonie van Leeuwenhoek
0003-6072　　　　1572-9699
Supersedes Nederlandsch tijdschrift voor hygiëne, microbiologie en serologie.
1934　　　　0372625

Anu Bras Odontol
Anuario Brasileiro De Odontologia
1972-1974　　　　9877853

Anxiety
Anxiety
1070-9797
Merged with: Depression (New York, N.Y.), to form: Depression and anxiety.
1994-1996　　　　9432921

Anxiety Stress Coping
Anxiety, stress, and coping
1061-5806　　　　1477-2205
Continues: Anxiety research.
1992　　　　9212242

ANZ J Surg
ANZ journal of surgery
1445-1433　　　　1445-2197
Continues: Australian and New Zealand journal of surgery.
2001　　　　101086634

AOHA
AOHA: a publication of the American Osteopathic Hospital Association
1058-6385
Continues: AOHA today. Continued by: AOHA progress.
1991-1992　　　　9112809

AOHA Today
AOHA today
1044-1980
Continues: Osteopathic hospital leadership. Continued by: AOHA.
1989-1991　　　　8911799

AORN J
AORN journal
0001-2092
Supersedes OR nursing.
1963　　　　0372403

Apar Respir Tuberc
Aparato respiratorio y tuberculosis
0365-5709
Merged with the Boletín of the Hospital-Sanatorio "El Peral," Santiago, to form Enfermedades del tórax y tuberculosis
1935-1957　　　　15120020R

Apex
Apex
0003-6439
Continues: U. C. H. dental journal.
1970-1980　　　　0260637

APIC
APIC
0161-8717
Continues APIC newsletter. Continued by APIC journal.
1977-1977　　　　7804271

APMIS
APMIS: acta pathologica, microbiologica, et immunologica Scandinavica
0903-4641　　　　1600-0463
Formed by the union of: Acta pathologica, microbiologica, et immunologica Scandinavica. Section A, Pathology, and: Acta pathologica, microbiologica, et immunologica Scandinavica. Section B, Microbiology, and: Acta pathologica, microbiologica, et immunologica Scandinavica. Section C, Immunology.
1988　　　　8803400

APMIS Suppl
APMIS. Supplementum
0903-465X
Continues: Acta pathologica, microbiologica, et immunologica Scandinavica. Supplement. Supplement to: APMIS.
1988　　　　8812090

Apollonia (Malmo)
Apollonia
0518-1372
1952-19uu　　　　9875593

Apollonia (Sydney)
Apollonia
0066-5339
1950　　　　15120050R

Apoptosis
Apoptosis: an international journal on programmed cell death
1360-8185　　　　1573-675X
1996　　　　9712129

Apoth Kunst
Apotheker und Kunst
0341-0110
1955-1979　　　　7908311

Appetite
Appetite
0195-6663　　　　1095-8304
1980　　　　8006808

Appl Anthropol
Applied anthropology
0093-2914
1941-1948　　　　0412666

Appl Biochem Biotechnol
Applied biochemistry and biotechnology
0273-2289　　　　1559-0291
Continues: Journal of solid-phase biochemistry. Continued in part by: Molecular biotechnology.
1981　　　　8208561

Appl Bioinformatics
Applied bioinformatics
1175-5636
2002　　　　101150311

Appl Cardiol
Applied cardiology
8750-0426
Continues: CVP. Continued by: Cardiology management.
1984-1986   8411017

Appl Cardiopulm Pathophysiol
Applied cardiopulmonary pathophysiology: ACP
0920-5268
1987-2000   8801258

Appl Environ Microbiol
Applied and environmental microbiology
0099-2240   1098-5336
Continues Applied microbiology.
1976   7605801

Appl Ergon
Applied ergonomics
0003-6870   1872-9126
1969   0261412

Appl Health Econ Health Policy
Applied health economics and health policy
1175-5652
2002   101150314

Appl Human Sci
Applied human science: journal of physiological anthropology
1341-3473
Continues: Annals of physiological anthropology. Continued by: Journal of physiological anthropology and applied human science.
1995-1999   9506216

Appl Immunohistochem Mol Morphol
Applied immunohistochemistry & molecular morphology: AIMM / official publication of the Society for Applied Immunohistochemistry
1541-2016   1533-4058
Formed by the union of: Applied immunohistochemistry, and: Cell vision, and continues the numbering of the former.
1999   100888796

Appl Microbiol
Applied microbiology
0003-6919
Continued by Applied and environmental microbiology.
1953-1975   7605802

Appl Microbiol Biotechnol
Applied microbiology and biotechnology
0175-7598   1432-0614
Continues: European journal of applied microbiology and biotechnology.
1984   8406612

Appl Neurophysiol
Applied neurophysiology
0302-2773
Continues Confinia neurologica. Continued by: Stereotactic and functional neurosurgery.
1975-1988   7600656

Appl Neuropsychol
Applied neuropsychology
0908-4282   1532-4826
1994   9507620

Appl Nurs Res
Applied nursing research: ANR
0897-1897   1532-8201
1988   8901557

Appl Occup Environ Hyg
Applied occupational and environmental hygiene
1047-322X   1521-0898
Continues: Applied industrial hygiene. Merged with: AIHA journal, to form: Journal of occupational and environmental hygiene.
1990-2003   9103256

Appl Opt
Applied optics
0003-6935   1539-4522
1962   0247660

Appl Parasitol
Applied parasitology
0943-0938
Continues: Angewandte Parasitologie.
1993-1996   9308726

Appl Pathol
Applied pathology
0252-1172
1983-1989   8308921

Appl Physiol Nutr Metab
Applied physiology, nutrition, and metabolism = Physiologie appliquée, nutrition et métabolisme
1715-5312   1715-5320
Continues: Canadian journal of applied physiology.
2006   101264333

Appl Psychophysiol Biofeedback
Applied psychophysiology and biofeedback
1090-0586   1573-3270
Continues: Biofeedback and self-regulation.
1997   9712383

Appl Radiat Isot
Applied radiation and isotopes: including data, instrumentation and methods for use in agriculture, industry and medicine
0969-8043   1872-9800
Absorbed: Nuclear geophysics. Continues: International journal of radiation applications and instrumentation. Part A, Applied radiation and isotopes.
1993   9306253

Appl Radiol
Applied radiology
0160-9963
Continues Applied radiology and nuclear medicine.
1976   7708167

Appl Res Ment Retard
Applied research in mental retardation
0270-3092
Merged with: Analysis and intervention in developmental disabilities, to form: Research in developmental disabilities.
1980-1986   8101119

Appl Spectrosc
Applied spectroscopy
0003-7028
Continues: Bulletin of the Society for Applied Spectroscopy.
1951   0372406

Appl Theor Electrophor
Applied and theoretical electrophoresis: the official journal of the International Electrophoresis Society
0954-6642
1988-1996   8915308

Appl Ther
Applied therapeutics
0570-4944
1960-1970   1310652

Aptechn Delo
Aptechnoe delo
Continued by Farmatsiia.
1952-1966   0136645

Aquat Toxicol
Aquatic toxicology (Amsterdam, Netherlands)
0166-445X   1879-1514
1981   8500246

Arb Gesch Med Giessen
Arbeiten zur Geschichte der Medizin in Giessen
0174-268X
1979   8005330

Arb Paul Ehrlich Inst Bundesamt Sera Impfstoffe Frankf A M
Arbeiten aus dem Paul-Ehrlich-Institut (Bundesamt für Sera und Impfstoffe) zu Frankfurt a.M
0936-8671
Continues: Arbeiten aus dem Paul-Ehrlich-Institut, dem Georg-Speyer-Haus und dem Ferdinand-Blum-Institut zu Frankfurt a.M.
1988   8912864

Arb Paul Ehrlich Inst Georg Speyer Haus Ferdinand Blum Inst Frankf A M
Arbeiten aus dem Paul-Ehrlich-Institut, dem Georg-Speyer-Haus und dem Ferdinand-Blum-Institut zu Frankfurt a.M
0066-5665
Continues Arbeiten aus dem Paul Ehrlich-Institut und dem Georg Speyer-Hause zu Frankfurt a.M. Continued by: Arbeiten aus dem Paul-Ehrlich-Institut (Bundesamt für Sera und Impfstoffe) zu Frankfurt a.M.
1950-1988   7505218

Arbeitsphysiologie
Arbeitsphysiologie; internationale Zeitschrift für angewandte Physiologie
Continued by Internationale Zeitschrift für angewandte Physiologie einschliesslich Arbeitsphysiologie.
1928-1954   15120390R

Arch Anat Cytol Pathol
Archives d'anatomie et de cytologie pathologiques
0395-501X
Continues: Archives d'anatomie pathologique. Continued by: Clinical and experimental pathology.
1976-1998   7609770

Arch Anat Histol Embryol
Archives d'anatomie, d'histologie et d'embryologie normales et expérimentales
0249-5554
Continues: Archives d'anatomie, d'histologie et d'embryologie.
1956-1994   0372423

Arch Anat Microsc Morphol Exp
Archives d'anatomie microscopique et de morphologie expérimentale
0003-9594
Continues: Archives d'anatomie microscopique, issued 1897-1939/40. Continued by: Biological structures and morphogenesis.
1947-1987   0406007

Arch Anat Pathol (Paris)
Archives d'anatomie pathologique
0003-9608
Continued by Archives d'anatomie et de cytologie pathologiques.
1953-1975   7609771

Arch Androl
Archives of andrology
0148-5016   1521-0375
Absorbed: Advances in reproduction.
Continued by: Systems biology in
reproductive medicine.
1978-2007   7806755

Arch Anim Nutr
Archives of animal nutrition
1745-039X   1477-2817
Continues: Archiv für Tierernährung.
2004   101222433

Arch Antropol Crim Psichiatr Med Leg
Archivio di antropologia criminale,
psichiatria e medicina legale
0390-573X
Continues: Archivio di psichiatria.
neuropatologia. antropologia criminale e
medicina legale. Continued by: Minerva
medicolegale.
1909-1949   15220040R

Arch Argent Dermatol
Archivos argentinos de dermatología
0066-6750
1951   0372456

Arch Argent Kinesiol Kinesiter Kinefilax
Archivos argentinos de kinesiología;
kinesiterapia y kinefilaxia
0326-5595
1948-1950   15220320R

Arch Argent Pediatr
Archivos argentinos de pediatría
0325-0075   1668-3501
Supersedes Archivos latino-americanos de
pediatría.
1930   0372460

Arch Argent Repub Secr Salud Publica
Archivos. Argentine Republic. Secretaría de
Salud Pública
1946-19uu   22920480R

Arch Argent Tisiol
Archivos argentinos de tisiología
0301-8342
Continues Archivos de tisiología.
1938-1956   0411754

Arch Argent Tisiol Neumonol
Archivos argentinos de tisiología y
neumonología
0004-0509
Continues Archivos argentinos de tisiología.
1956-1980   0417511

Arch Asoc Evit Ceguera Mex
Archivos. Asociación para Evitar la Ceguera
en México
0004-489X
Merged with Anales de la Sociedad Mexicana
de Oftalmología: to form: Revista mexicana
de oftalmología.
1942-1986   0372473

Arch Belg
Archives belges = Belgisch archief
Continues: Archives belges de médecine
sociale. hygiène. médecine du travail et
médecine légale. Continued by: Archives of
public health.
1982-1989   8302753

Arch Belg Dermatol
Archives belges de dermatologie
0301-8636
Continues Archives belges de dermatologie et
de syphiligraphie.
1973-1974   0412667

Arch Belg Dermatol Syphiligr
Archives belges de dermatologie et de
syphiligraphie
0003-956X
Continued by Archives belges de
dermatologie.
1938-1972   0412670

Arch Belg Med Soc
Archives belges de médecine sociale,
hygiène, médecine du travail et médecine
légale. Belgisch archief van sociale
geneeskunde, hygiëne, arbeidsgeneeskunde
en gerechtelijke geneeskunde
0003-9578
Continues the Archives de médecine sociale
et d'hygiène et revue de pathologie et de
physiologie du travail. issued 1938-40.
Absorbed the Revue de droit pénal et de
criminologie et archives internationales de
médecine légale in May 1946. Continued by
Archives belges.
1946-1981   0372420

Arch Biochem
Archives of biochemistry
Continued by Archives of biochemistry and
biophysics.
1942-1951   15210080R

Arch Biochem Biophys
Archives of biochemistry and biophysics
0003-9861   1096-0384
Absorbed: Molecular cell biology research
communications. Nov. 2001 Continues:
Archives of biochemistry.
1951   0372430

Arch Biol (Liege)
Archives de biologie
0003-9624
Continued by: Archives of biology.
1880-1985   0400643

Arch Biol Andina
Archivos de biología andina
0250-5037
Continues Archivos del Instituto de Biología
Andina.
1977-1979   8004626

Arch Biol Med Exp (Santiago)
Archivos de biología y medicina
experimentales
0004-0533
Continued in 1992. with Vol. 25. no. 1. by:
Biological research.
1964-1992   0321546

Arch Bras Med
Archivos brasileiros de medicina
1911-1951   15230060R

Arch Bronconeumol
Archivos de bronconeumología
0300-2896
1964   0354720

Arch Cardiol Mex
Archivos de cardiología de México
1405-9940
Continues: Archivos del Instituto de
Cardiología de México.
2001   101126728

Arch Cardiovasc Dis
Archives of cardiovascular diseases
1875-2136
Continues: Archives des maladies du coeur et
des vaisseaux.
2008   101465655

Arch Chir Neerl
Archivum chirurgicum Neerlandicum
0004-0657
Continued by The Netherlands journal of
surgery.
1949-1979   8004861

Arch Chir Torac Cardiovasc
Archivio di chirurgia toracica e
cardiovascolare
0391-7029
Continues Archivio di chirurgia del torace.
1966-2002   0135774

Arch Clin Neuropsychol
Archives of clinical neuropsychology: the
official journal of the National Academy of
Neuropsychologists
0887-6177   1873-5843
1986   9004255

Arch Col Med El Salv
Archivos del Colegio Médico de El Salvador
0010-0641
1947-1976   7503299

Arch Cuba
Archivos. Cuba. Instituto Nacional de
Hidrología y Climatología Médicas
1946-1951   16430580R

Arch Cuba Cancerol
Archivos cubanos de cancerología
Absorbed by: Boletín of the Liga contra el
Cáncer.
1942-1959   15230090R

Arch De Vecchi Anat Patol
Archivio "de Vecchi" per l'anatomia
patologica e la medicina clinica
0004-0061
1938-1983   0372455

Arch Derm Syphilol
Archives of dermatology and syphilology
0096-6029
Supersedes the Journal of cutaneous diseases
including syphilis. Continued by the A. M. A.
archives of dermatology and syphilology.
1920-1950   14470030R

Arch Dermatol
Archives of dermatology
0003-987X   1538-3652
Continues: A. M. A. archives of dermatology.
1960   0372433

Arch Dermatol Forsch
Archiv für dermatologische Forschung
0003-9187
Continues Archiv für klinische und
experimentelle Dermatologie. Continued by
Archives for dermatological research.
1971-1975   7512588

Arch Dermatol Res
Archives for dermatological research. Archiv
für dermatologische Forschung
0340-3696
Continues Archiv für dermatologische
Forschung. Continued by Archives of
dermatological research.
1975-1977   7512589

Arch Dermatol Res
Archives of dermatological research
0340-3696   1432-069X
Continues Archives for dermatological
research. Archiv für dermatologische
Forschung.
1978   8000462

Arch Dermatol Syph
Archiv für Dermatologie und Syphilis
0365-6020
Continues: Vierteljahresschrift für
Dermatologie und Syphilis. Continued by:
Archiv für klinische und experimentelle
Dermatologie.
1889-1955   15130110R

Arch Dis Child
Archives of disease in childhood
0003-9888   1468-2044
Absorbed: British journal of children's
diseases. Some issues, 1988?-1993, have
supplement called: Archives of disease
in childhood. Fetal and neonatal edition,
issued separately, 1994- . Complemented by:
Archives of disease in childhood. Education
and practice edition, 2004-
1926   0372434

Arch Dis Child Educ Pract Ed
Archives of disease in childhood. Education
and practice edition
1743-0585   1743-0593
2004   101220684

Arch Dis Child Fetal Neonatal Ed
Archives of disease in childhood. Fetal and
neonatal edition
1359-2998   1468-2052
Issues for July 1988?-1993 were issued as
supplements to some issues of Archives of
disease in childhood, repeating its numbering
and paged continuously with that publication.
Beginning with v. 70 in 1994, issue number
and pagination are independent.
1988   9501297

Arch Emerg Med
Archives of emergency medicine
0264-4924
Continued by: Journal of accident &
emergency medicine.
1984-1993   8500828

Arch Enferm Coraz Vasos
Archivos de enfermedades del corazón y
vasos
Absorbed the Archiva cardio-rheumatologica
hispanica in Jan. 1956.
1944-1967   2984703R

Arch Environ Contam Toxicol
Archives of environmental contamination
and toxicology
0090-4341   1432-0703
1973   0357245

Arch Environ Health
Archives of environmental health
0003-9896
Supersedes: A. M. A. archives of industrial
health. Continued by: Archives of
environmental & occupational health.
1960-2004   0212627

Arch Environ Occup Health
Archives of environmental & occupational
health
1933-8244
Continues: Archives of environmental health.
2005   101282564

Arch Esp Morfol
Archivo español de morfología
0004-0436
Continued by: Archivo español de morfología
(Valencia, Spain: 1996).
1941-1967   15220270R

Arch Esp Urol
Archivos españoles de urología
0004-0614   1576-8260
1944   0064757

Arch Exp Veterinarmed
Archiv für experimentelle Veterinärmedizin
0003-9055
Continues Experimentelle Veterinärmedizin.
1952-1991   0372410

Arch Facial Plast Surg
Archives of facial plastic surgery: official
publication for the American Academy of
Facial Plastic and Reconstructive Surgery,
Inc. and the International Federation of
Facial Plastic Surgery Societies
1521-2491   1538-3660
1999   100883500

Arch Fam Med
Archives of family medicine
1063-3987
1992-2000   9300357

Arch Farmacol Sper Sci Affin
Archivio di farmacologia sperimentale e
scienze affini
1902-1955   15220090R

Arch Farmacol Toxicol
Archivos de farmacología y toxicología
0304-8616
Supersedes Archivos del Instituto de
Farmacología Experimental (Medicina).
1975-1986   7601472

Arch Fisiol
Archivio di fisiologia
0004-0096
1903-1979   0372447

Arch Fr Mal App Dig
Archives françaises des maladies de
l'appareil digestif
0003-9772
Continues Archives des maladies de l'appareil
digestif et des maladies de la nutrition.
Merged with Biologie et gastro-entérologie to
form Gastroentérologie clinique et biologique.
1966-1976   0044500

Arch Fr Pediatr
Archives françaises de pédiatrie
0003-9764
Formed by the merger of Archives de
médecine des enfants, Bulletins of the Société
de pédiatrie de Paris, and Revue française de
pédiatrie. Merged with: Pédiatrie, to form:
Archives de pédiatrie.
1942-1993   0372421

Arch Fund Roux Ocefa
Archivos de la Fundación Roux-Ocefa
0016-271X
Supersedes Archivos de histología normal y
patológica.
1967-1977   7502529

Arch Gen Psychiatry
Archives of general psychiatry
0003-990X   1538-3636
Continues: A.M.A. archives of general
psychiatry.
1960   0372435

Arch Genet (Zur)
Archiv für Genetik
0300-984X
Continues the Archiv of the Julius
Klaus-Stiftung für Vererbungsforschung,
Sozialanthropologie und Rassenhygiene.
1972-1979   0333473

Arch Gerontol Geriatr
Archives of gerontology and geriatrics
0167-4943   1872-6976
Absorbed: Archives of gerontology and
geriatrics. Supplement.
1982   8214379

Arch Gerontol Geriatr Suppl
Archives of gerontology and geriatrics.
Supplement
0924-7947
Absorbed by: Archives of gerontology and
geriatrics.
1989-2004   8911786

Arch Gesamte Psychol
Archiv für die gesamte Psychologie
0724-7842
Continues: Philosophische Studien (Leipzig,
Germany. Continued by: Archiv für
Psychologie.
1903-1969   1305110

Arch Gesamte Virusforsch
Archiv für die gesamte Virusforschung
0003-9012
Continued by Archives of virology.
1939-1974   7506868

Arch Geschwulstforsch
Archiv für Geschwulstforschung
0003-911X
1949-1991   0372411

Arch Gewerbepathol Gewerbehyg
Archiv für Gewerbepathologie und
Gewerbehygiene
Continued by Internationales Archiv für
Gewerbepathologie und Gewerbehygiene.
1930-1961   17640440R

Arch Gynakol
Archiv für Gynäkologie
0003-9128
Supersedes Monatsschrift für Geburtskunde
und Frauenkrankheiten. Continued by
Archives of gynecology.
1870-1978   0372655

Arch Gynecol
Archives of gynecology
0170-9925
Continues Archiv für Gynäkologie. Continued
by: Archives of gynecology and obstetrics.
1978-1987   7901051

Arch Gynecol Obstet
Archives of gynecology and obstetrics
0932-0067   1432-0711
Continues: Archives of gynecology.
1987   8710213

Arch Hist Filoz Med
Archiwum historii i filozofii medycyny /
Polskii Towarzystwo Historii Medycyny i
Farmacji
0860-1844
Continues: Archiwum historii medycyny.
1985   8609303

Arch Hist Med (Warsz)
Archiwum historii medycyny
0004-0762
Continues Archiwum historji i filozofji
medycyny, oraz historji nauk przyrodniczych,
issued 1924-48. Continued by: Archiwum
historii i filozofii medycyny.
1957-1985   0123544

Arch Histol Cytol
Archives of histology and cytology
0914-9465   1349-1717
Continues: Archivum histologicum
Japonicum.
1988   8806082

Arch Histol Jpn
Archivum histologicum Japonicum. Nippon
soshikigaku kiroku
0004-0681
Continued by: Archives of histology and
cytology.
1950-1987   0146564

Arch Histol Norm Patol
Archivos de histología normal y patológica
0518-3677
1942-1965   0104067

Arch Hosp (Paris)
Archives hospitalières
Continues the Bulletin of Hôpital Saint-Michel. Paris. Continued by Nouvelles archives hospitalières.
1933-1964   0373101

Arch Hosp Univ
Archivos. Havana. Universidad. Hospital Universitario "General Calixto García"
1949-1961   17240430R

Arch Hyg Bakteriol
Archiv für Hygiene und Bakteriologie
0003-9144
Continued by: Zentralblatt für Bakteriologie. Parasitenkunde. Infektionskrankheiten und Hygiene. 1. Abt. Originale. Reihe B: Hygiene - Präventive Medizin.
1883-1971   0331541

Arch Iatr Epistem
Archeion iatrikōn epistēmōn
1945-1965   15120480R

Arch Immunol Ther Exp (Warsz)
Archivum immunologiae et therapiae experimentalis
0004-069X   1661-4917
Continues: Archiwum immunologii i terapii doświadczalnej.
1962   0114365

Arch Ind Hyg Occup Med
Archives of industrial hygiene and occupational medicine
Supersedes Journal of industrial hygiene and toxicology and Occupational medicine. Continued by A. M. A. archives of industrial hygiene and occupational medicine.
1950-1950   14470070R

Arch Inn Med
Archiv für innere Medizin
1949-1951   15130230R

Arch Insect Biochem Physiol
Archives of insect biochemistry and physiology
0739-4462   1520-6327
1983   8501752

Arch Inst Biol Andina
Archivos del Instituto de Biología Andina
0020-3750
Continued by: Archives de biologiá andina.
1965-1973   7505226

Arch Inst Cardiol Mex
Archivos del Instituto de Cardiología de México
0020-3785
Continues the Archivos latino americanos de cardiología y hematología. Continued by: Archivos de cardiología de México.
1944-2000   0400463

Arch Inst Farmacol Exp (Madr)
Archivos del Instituto de Farmacología Experimental (Medicina)
0024-9629
Continued by: Archivos de farmacología y toxicología..
1949-1971   0412062

Arch Inst Pasteur Alger
Archives de l'Institut Pasteur d'Algérie Institut Pasteur d'Algérie
0020-2460
Continues in part: Archives des Instituts Pasteur de l'Afrique du Nord.
1923   0373031

Arch Inst Pasteur Hell
Archives de l'Institut Pasteur hellénique
0004-6620
1923-1983   7502528

Arch Inst Pasteur Madagascar
Archives de l'Institut Pasteur de Madagascar
0020-2495
Continues the Archives de l'Institut Pasteur de Tananarive.
1954   7502526

Arch Inst Pasteur Maroc
Archives. Institut Pasteur du Maroc
0301-8652
1932-1962   0413113

Arch Inst Pasteur Martinique
Archives de l'Institut Pasteur de la Martinique
1948-1976   7509325

Arch Inst Pasteur Tunis
Archives de l'Institut Pasteur de Tunis
0020-2509
Continues in part: Archives des Instituts Pasteur de l'Afrique du Nord.
1923   7502527

Arch Int Hist Sci (Paris)
Archives internationales d'histoire des sciences
0003-9810
Supersedes: Archeion.
1947   0372422

Arch Int Neurol
Archives internationales de neurologie, des maladies héréditaires, de médecine mentale et psychosomatique
Continues Archives de neurologie.
1910-1953   0002344

Arch Int Pharmacodyn Ther
Archives internationales de pharmacodynamie et de thérapie
0301-4533
Continues: Archives internationales de pharmacodynamie. Absorbed by: Fundamental & clinical pharmacology.
1899-1996   0405353

Arch Int Physiol
Archives internationales de physiologie
0301-4541
Supersedes the Travaux du Laboratoire de Léon Fredericq of the Institut de physiologie. Université de Liège. Continued by Archives internationales de physiologie et de biochimie. Continued by: Archives internationales de physiologie et de biochimie.
1904-1954   0405354

Arch Int Physiol Biochim
Archives internationales de physiologie et de biochimie
0003-9799
Continues Archives internationales de physiologie. Continued by: Archives internationales de physiologie, de biochimie et biophysique.
1955-1990   0405355

Arch Int Physiol Biochim Biophys
Archives internationales de physiologie, de biochimie et de biophysique
0778-3124
Continues: Archives internationales de physiologie et de biochimie. Continued by: Archives of physiology and biochemistry.
1991-1994   9111069

Arch Interam Rheumatol
Archives of interamerican rheumatology: A.I.R
1956-1965   0253226

Arch Intern Med
Archives of internal medicine
0003-9926   1538-3679
Continues: A.M.A. archives of internal medicine.
1960   0372440

Arch Intern Med (Chic)
Archives of internal medicine (Chicago, Ill.: 1908)
0730-188X
Continued by: A.M.A. archives of internal medicine.
1908-1950   9716392

Arch Internazionale Studi Neurol
Archivio internazionale di studi neurologici
1950-1952   15220170R

Arch Invest Med (Mex)
Archivos de investigación médica
0066-6769
Continued by: Archives of medical research.
1970-1991   0262036

Arch Iran Med
Archives of Iranian medicine
1029-2977
1998   100889644

Arch Ital Anat Embriol
Archivio italiano di anatomia e di embriologia. Italian journal of anatomy and embryology
0004-0223
Continued by: Italian journal of anatomy and embryology.
1902-1991   2985162R

Arch Ital Anat Istol Patol
Archivio italiano di anatomia e istologia patologica
0004-0231
1930-1974   0372443

Arch Ital Biol
Archives italiennes de biologie
0003-9829
1882   0372441

Arch Ital Chir
Archivio italiano di chirurgia
0004-024X
1919-1976   0372444

Arch Ital Dermatol Sifilogr Venereol
Archivio italiano di dermatologia, sifilografia, e venereologia
Continued by Archivio italiano di dermatologia, venereologia, e sessuologia.
1925-1957   15220190R

Arch Ital Dermatol Venereol Sessuol
Archivio italiano di dermatologia, venereologia, e sessuologia
0300-8991
Continues Archivio italiano di dermatologia, sifilografia, e venereologia.
1959-1975   0372445

Arch Ital Laringol
Archivii italiani di laringologia
0365-3234
1881-1970   0401163

Arch Ital Mal Appar Dig
Archivio italiano delle malattie dell'apparato digerente
0004-0215
1931-1978   2985163R

Arch Ital Otol Rinol Laringol
Archivio italiano di otologia, rinologia e
laringologia
0004-0258
Continued by Archivio italiano di otologia,
rinologia, laringologia e patologia cervico-
facciale.
1893-1967 0205024

Arch Ital Otol Rinol Laringol Patol Cervicofacc
Archivio italiano di otologia, rinologia,
laringologia, e patologia cervico-facciale
0301-3685
Continues Archivio italiano di otologia,
rinologia, e laringologia. Superseded by
Nuovo archivio italiano di otologia, rinologia,
e laringologia.
1967-1971 0377771

**Arch Ital Otol Rinol Laringol Patol Cervicofacc
Suppl**
Archivio italiano di otologia, rinologia,
laringologia e patologia cervico-facciale.
Supplemento
0373-7594
Continues Archivio italiano di otologia,
rinologia e laringologia. Supplemento.
1967-1970 0205027

Arch Ital Otol Rinol Laringol Suppl
Archivio italiano di otologia, rinologia e
laringologia. Supplemento
Continued by Archivio italiano di otologia,
rinologia, laringologia e patologia cervico-
facciale. Supplemento.
1949-1966 0205025

Arch Ital Patol Clin Tumori
Archivio italiano di patologia e clinica dei
tumori
0004-0266
1957-1973 0205312

Arch Ital Pediatr Pueric
Archivio italiano di pediatria e puericoltura
0004-0274
1932-1969 0372446

Arch Ital Sci Farmacol
Archivio italiano di scienze farmacologiche
1932-1965 15220230R

Arch Ital Sci Med Trop Parassitol
Archivio italiano di scienze mediche tropicali
e di parassitologia
0004-0282
Continues Archivio italiano di scienze
mediche coloniali e di parassitologia.
1950-1973 7611922

Arch Ital Urol
Archivio italiano di urologia
0365-351X
Continued by Archivio italiano di urologia e
nefrologia.
1924-1967 0162115

Arch Ital Urol Androl
Archivio italiano di urologia, andrologia:
organo ufficiale [di] Società italiana
di ecografia urologica e nefrologica /
Associazione ricerche in urologia
1124-3562
Continues: Archivio italiano di urologia,
nefrologia, andrologia.
1993 9308247

Arch Ital Urol Nefrol
Archivio italiano di urologia e nefrologia
0004-0290
Continues Archivio italiano di urologia.
1967-1986 0162114

Arch Ital Urol Nefrol Androl
Archivio italiano di urologia,
nefrologia, andrologia: organo ufficiale
dell'Associazione per la ricerca in urologia =
Urological, nephrological, and andrological
sciences
1120-8538
Continues: Archivio italiano di urologia e
nefrologia. Continued by: Archivio italiano di
urologia, andrologia.
1987-1992 8809080

**Arch Julius Klaus Stift Vererbungsforsch
Sozialanthropol Rassenhyg**
Archiv der Julius Klaus-Stiftung für
Vererbungsforschung, Sozialanthropologie
und Rassenhygiene
0003-8881
1925-1969 7502525

Arch Kinderheilkd
Archiv für Kinderheilkunde
0003-9179
Supersedes Central-Zeitung für
Kinderheilkunde. Continued by Klinische
Pädiatrie.
1880-1971 0326076

Arch Kinderheilkd Suppl
Archiv für Kinderheilkunde. Beihefte
0066-6378
Continued by Bücherei des Pädiaters.
1931-1971 0346014

Arch Klin Exp Dermatol
Archiv für klinische und experimentelle
Dermatologie
0300-8614
Continues Archiv für Dermatologie
und Syphilis. Continued by Archiv für
dermatologische Forschung.
1955-1971 1256765

Arch Klin Exp Ohren Nasen Kehlkopfheilkd
Archiv für klinische und experimentelle
Ohren- Nasen- und Kehlkopfheilkunde
0003-9195
Continues Archiv für Ohren-, Nasen- und
Kehlkopfheilkunde, Vereinigt mit Zeitschrift
für Hals-, Nasen- und Ohrenheilkunde.
Continued by Archives of oto-rhino-
laryngology.
1966-1973 0414103

Arch Klin Med
Archiv für klinische Medizin
0365-3773
Formed by the union of Zeitschrift für
klinische Medizin and Deutsches Archiv
für klinische Medizin and assumed the
vol. numbering of the latter. Continued by:
European journal of clinical investigation.
1966-1969 0246646

Arch Kreislaufforsch
Archiv für Kreislaufforschung
0003-9217
Supplement to Zeitschrift für
Kreislaufforschung. Continued by Basic
research in cardiology with issues for 1972
retaining this as added title.
1937-1972 0360076

Arch Kriminol
Archiv für Kriminologie
0003-9225
Continues Archiv für Kriminal-Anthropologie
und Kriminalistik.
1916 0002256

Arch Latinoam Nutr
Archivos latinoamericanos de nutrición
0004-0622
Continues Archivos venezolanos de nutrición.
1966 0067507

Arch Lebensmittelhyg
Archiv für lebensmittelhygiene
0003-925X
Continues Lebensmitteltierarzt.
1955 7505221

Arch Mal Appar Dig Mal Nutr
Archives des maladies de l'appareil digestif
et des maladies de la nutrition
0365-4117
Continued by Archives françaises des
maladies de l'appareil digestif.
1907-1965 0061476

Arch Mal Coeur Vaiss
Archives des maladies du coeur et des
vaisseaux
0003-9683
Continues Archives des maladies du coeur,
des vaisseaux, et du sang. Continued by:
Archives of cardiovascular diseases.
1937-2007 0406011

Arch Mal Prof
Archives des maladies professionnelles de
médecine du travail et de sécurité sociale
0003-9691
Continues: Archives des maladies
professionnelles. Continued by: Archives des
maladies professionnelles et de médecine du
travail.
1946-1992 2985157R

Arch Maragliano Patol Clin
Archivio "E. Maragliano" di patologia e
clinica
0004-0193
Continues: Annali dell'Istituto Maragliano.
1946-1980 2985161R

Arch Maragliano Patolog Clin Collana Monogr
Collana di monografie. Archivio "E.
Maragliano" di patologia e clinica
1949-196u 15220150R

Arch Med Cuba
Archivos médicos de Cuba
Continues Archivos médicos de San Lorenzo.
1952-1957 15240100R

Arch Med Exp
Archivos de medicina experimental; trabajos
del Instituto Nacional de Ciencias Médicas
0004-0568
1942-1963 15230250R

Arch Med Gen Trop
Archives de médecine générale et tropicale
0365-4656
Continues Archives de médecine générale
et coloniale. Continued by Archives
méditerranéennes de médecine.
1950-1965 0051452

Arch Med Infant
Archivos de medicina infantil
Absorbed by: Revista cubana de pediatría.
1932-1960 15230260R

Arch Med Intern
Archivos de medicina interna (Montevideo,
Uruguay)
0250-3816
1979 9203134

Arch Med Interna
Archivio di medicina interna
0004-010X
1949 0421741

Arch Med Mutual
Archivio di medicina mutualistica
1956-1978 2985164R

Arch Med Panamenos
Archivos médicos panameños
Formed by the union of the Boletín of the Asociación Médica Nacional de la República de Panamá and the Archivos of the Hospital Santo Tomás. Panamá. Superseded by Revista médica de Panamá.
1952-1969   **0245567**

Arch Med Res
Archives of medical research
0188-4409   1873-5487
Continues: Archivos de investigación médica.
1992   **9312706**

Arch Med Sadowej Kryminol
Archiwum medycyny sądowej i kryminologii
0324-8267
Continues Archivum medycyny sądowej, psychiatrii sądowej i kryminalistyki.
1968   **1260766**

Arch Med Soc
Archives de médecine sociale
1945-1951   **15140120R**

Arch Medicos Mex
Archivos médicos mexicanos
1943-1962   **0372461**

Arch Mediterr Med
Archives méditerranéennes de médecine
0003-9845
Continues Archives de médecine générale et tropicale. Absorbed by: Corse méditerranée médicale.
1966-1969   **0414104**

Arch Mex Venereol Dermatol
Archivos mexicanos de venereología y dermatología
0365-4702
1936-19uu   **15240160R**

Arch Microbiol
Archives of microbiology
0302-8933   1432-072X
Continues: Archiv für Mikrobiologie.
1974   **0410427**

Arch Middx Hosp
Archives. Middlesex Hospital
1903-1955   **18340010R**

Arch Mikrobiol
Archiv für Mikrobiologie
0003-9276
Continued by: Archives of microbiology.
1930-1973   **0411220**

Arch Monaldi
Archivio Monaldi per la tisiologia e le malattie dell'apparato respiratorio
0004-0185
Continues Archivio di tisiologia e delle malattie del'apparato respiratorio.
1970-1986   **1263173**

Arch Monaldi Mal Torace
Archivio Monaldi per le malattie del torace
1120-0391
Continues: Archivio Monaldi per la tisiologia e le malattie dell'apparato respiratorio. Continued by: Monaldi archives for chest disease.
1987-1992   **8902999**

Arch Neerl Physiol Homme Anim
Archives néerlandaises de physiologie de l'homme et des animaux
0365-4958
Merged with: Acta Brevia Neerlandica de physiologia, pharmacologia, microbiologia e. a., to form: Acta physiologica et pharmacologica neerlandica.
1916-1947   **15210030R**

Arch Neurobiol (Madr)
Archivos de neurobiologiá
0004-0576
Continued by: Archivos de psiquiatría (Madrid. Spain).
1920-1999   **2984704R**

Arch Neurocir
Archivos de neurocirugía
Supersedes Archivos argentinos de neurología. Superseded by Anales de neurocirugía.
1944-1954   **15230300R**

Arch Neurol
Archives of neurology
0003-9942   1538-3687
Continues: A. M. A. archives of neurology.
1960   **0372436**

Arch Neurol Psychiatry
Archives of neurology and psychiatry
0096-6754
Continued by: A. M. A. archives of neurology and psychiatry.
1919-1950   **14470120R**

Arch Odonto Estomatol
Archivos de odonto estomatologia
0213-4144
1985   **8703422**

Arch Oftalmol B Aires
Archivos de oftalmología de Buenos Aires
0066-6777
1925   **0372462**

Arch Ohren Nasen Kehlkopfheilkd
Archiv für Ohren-, Nasen- und Kehlkopfheilkunde, vereinigt mit Zeitschrift für Hals-, Nasen- und Ohrenheilkunde
0365-5245
Continues Archiv für Ohrenheilkunde. Absorbed Zeitschrift für Hals-, Nasen- und Ohrenheilkunde in 1947. Continued by Archiv für klinische und experimentelle Ohren-. Nasen- und Kehlkopfheilkund.
1915-1965   **0063661**

Arch Ophtalmol (Paris)
Archives d'ophtalmologie
0399-4236
Continues Archives d'ophtalmologie et revue générale d'ophtalmologie. Merged with Annales d'oculistique to form Journal français d'ophtalmologie.
1976-1977   **7701763**

Arch Ophtalmol Rev Gen Ophtalmol
Archives d'ophtalmologie et revue générale d'ophtalmologie
0003-973X
Formed by the union of Archives d'ophtalmologie and Revue générale d'ophtalmologie. Continued by Archives d'ophtalmologie.
1937-1975   **7611921**

Arch Ophthal
Archives of ophthalmology
0093-0326
Supersedes Archives of ophthalmology, published New York. v. 8-57, 1879-1928. Continued by A.M.A. archives of ophthalmology.
1929-1950   **7706533**

Arch Ophthalmol
Archives of ophthalmology
0003-9950   1538-3601
Continues: A.M.A. archives of ophthalmology.
1960   **7706534**

Arch Oral Biol
Archives of oral biology
0003-9969   1879-1506
1959   **0116711**

Arch Orthop Trauma Surg
Archives of orthopaedic and trauma surgery
0936-8051   1434-3916
Continues: Archives of orthopaedic and traumatic surgery.
1989   **9011043**

Arch Orthop Trauma Surg
Archives of orthopaedic and traumatic surgery. Archiv für orthopädische und Unfall-Chirurgie
0344-8444
Continues Archiv für orthopädische und Unfall-Chirurgie. Continued by: Archives of orthopaedic and trauma surgery.
1978-1988   **7803037**

Arch Orthop Unfallchir
Archiv für orthopädische und Unfall-Chirurgie
0003-9330
Continues Archiv für Orthopädie, Mechanotherapie und Unfallchirurgie. Continued by Archives of orthopaedic and traumatic surgery. Archiv für orthopädische und Unfall-Chirurgie.
1918-1977   **0002266**

Arch Ortop
Archivio di ortopedia
0004-0118
Continued by Archivio di ortopedia e reumatologia.
1884-1973   **7508491**

Arch Ostet Ginecol
Archivio di ostetricia e ginecologia
0004-0126
1894-1986   **0404251**

Arch Otolaryngol
Archives of otolaryngology
0276-0673
Continued in 1950 by: A.M.A. archives of otolaryngology.
1925-1950   **9716259**

Arch Otolaryngol
Archives of otolaryngology (Chicago, Ill.: 1960)
0003-9977
Continues: A.M.A. archives of otolaryngology. Continued by: Archives of otolaryngology--head & neck surgery.
1960-1985   **0376526**

Arch Otolaryngol Head Neck Surg
Archives of otolaryngology--head & neck surgery
0886-4470   1538-361X
Continues: Archives of otolaryngology (Chicago, Ill.: 1960).
1986   **8603209**

Arch Otorhinolaryngol
Archives of oto-rhino-laryngology
0302-9530
Continues Archiv für klinische und experimentelle Ohren- Nasen- und Kehlkopfheilkunde. Continued by: European archives of oto-rhino-laryngology.
1973-1989   **0414105**

Arch Otorhinolaryngol Suppl
Archives of oto-rhino-laryngology. Supplement = Archiv für Ohren-, Nasen- und Kehlkopfheilkunde. Supplement
0724-7907
Continued by: European archives of oto-rhino-laryngology. Supplement. Supplement to: Archives of oto-rhino-laryngology.
1983-1991   **8308479**

Arch Ottamol
Archivio di ottalmologia
0004-0134
Merged with Rassegna italiana d'ottalmologia
to form Archivio e rassegna italiana di
ottalmologia.
1893-1965   0347200

Arch Panama City
Archivos. Panama (City) Hospital Santo
Tomás
Merged with the Boletín of the Asociacion
Médica Nacional de la República de Panamá
to form Archivos médicos panameños.
1946-1949   **19520070R**

Arch Pathol
Archives of pathology
0363-0153
Continues: A. M. A. archives of pathology.
Continued by: Archives of pathology &
laboratory medicine.
1960-1975   7605251

Arch Pathol (Chic)
Archives of pathology
0361-7017
Continues Archives of pathology and
laboratory medicine. Continued by A. M. A.
archives of pathology.
1928-1950   7605250

Arch Pathol Lab Med
Archives of pathology & laboratory
medicine
0003-9985   **1543-2165**
Continues: Archives of pathology.
1976   7607091

Arch Patol Clin Med
Archivio di patologia e clinica medica
0004-0142
1921-1971   0372450

Arch Pediatr
Archives de pédiatrie: organe officiel de la
Sociéte française de pédiatrie
0929-693X
Formed by the merger of: Pédiatrie, and:
Archives françaises de pédiatrie.
1994   9421356

Arch Pediatr
Archives of pediatrics
0096-6630
Merged with American practitioner and
Quarterly review of pediatrics to form
Clinical pediatrics. Absorbed the International
medical magazine in Feb. 1904.
1884-1962   **15210180R**

Arch Pediatr (Barc)
Archivos de pediatría
0402-9054
1950-2001   0373106

Arch Pediatr Adolesc Med
Archives of pediatrics & adolescent medicine
1072-4710   **1538-3628**
Continues: American journal of diseases of
children (1960).
1994   9422751

Arch Pediatr Urug
Archivos de pediatría del Uruguay
0004-0584
Supersedes the Boletín of the Sociedad de
Pediatría de Montevideo.
1930   0372463

Arch Peru Patol Clin
Archivos peruanos de patología y clínica
0365-5652
1947-1973   0422306

Arch Pharm
Archiv der Pharmazie
Continues in part: Annalen der Pharmacie.
Merged with the Berichte of the Deutsche
Pharmazeutische Gesellschaft to form Archiv
der Pharmazie und Berichte der Deutschen
Pharmazeutischen Gesellschaft.
1835-1923   **15130020R**

Arch Pharm (Weinheim)
Archiv der Pharmazie
0365-6233
Continues in part Archiv der Pharmazie und
Berichte der Deutschen Pharmazeutischen
Gesellschaft.
1972   0330167

Arch Pharm Ber Dtsch Pharm Ges
Archiv der Pharmazie und Berichte der
Deutschen Pharmazeutischen Gesellschaft
0376-0367
Continued in part by Archiv der Pharmazie.
1924-1971   0340675

Arch Pharm Res
Archives of pharmacal research
0253-6269
1978   8000036

Arch Phys Med
Archives of physical medicine
0096-6622
Continues Archives of physical therapy.
Continued by Archives of physical medicine
and rehabilitation.
1945-1952   **15210200R**

Arch Phys Med Rehabil
Archives of physical medicine and
rehabilitation
0003-9993   **1532-821X**
Continues: Archives of physical medicine.
1953   **2985158R**

Arch Phys Ther (Leipz)
Archiv für physikalische Therapie
0376-1630
Continued by: Zeitschrift für Physiotherapie.
1949-1970   9810655

Arch Physiol Biochem
Archives of physiology and biochemistry
1381-3455   **1744-4160**
Continues: Archives internationales de
physiologie, de biochimie et de biophysique.
1995   9510153

Arch Psicol Neurol Psichiatr
Archivio di psicologia, neurologia e
psichiatria
0004-0150
Continues: Archivio de psicologia,
neurologia, psichiatria e psicoterapia.
1946-1998   **2984697R**

Arch Psychiatr Nervenkr
Archiv für Psychiatrie und
Nervenkrankheiten
Merged with Zeitschrift für die gesamte
Neurologie und Psychiatrie in 1947
to form Archiv für Psychiatrie und
Nervenkrankheiten, vereinigt mit Zeitschrift
für die gesamte Neurologie und Psychiatrie.
1868-1944   **15130310R**

Arch Psychiatr Nervenkr
Archiv für Psychiatrie und
Nervenkrankheiten
0003-9373
Continues Archiv für Psychiatrie und
Nervenkrankheiten, vereinigt mit Zeitschrift
für die gesamte Neurologie und Psychiatrie.
Continued by European archives of psychiatry
and neurological sciences.
1970-1983   1270313

Arch Psychiatr Nervenkr Z Gesamte Neurol Psychiatr
Archiv für Psychiatrie und
Nervenkrankheiten, vereinigt mit Zeitschrift
für die gesamte Neurologie und Psychiatrie
0003-9373
Continued by Archiv für Psychiatrie und
Nervenkrankheiten.
1947-1970   1270314

Arch Psychiatr Nurs
Archives of psychiatric nursing
0883-9417   **1532-8228**
1987   8708534

Arch Psychol (Frankf)
Archiv für Psychologie
0066-6475
Continues Archiv für die gesamte
Psychologie.
1970-1990   1305270

Arch Putti Chir Organi Mov
Archivio "Putti" di chirurgia degli organi di
movimento
0066-670X
1951-199u   0372453

Arch Radiol
Archivio di radiologia
1925-1956   **15220130R**

Arch Rhumatol
Archives de rhumatologie
1936-1947   0002331

Arch Roum Pathol Exp Microbiol
Archives roumaines de pathologie
expérimentales et de microbiologie
0004-0037
Continued by: Romanian archives of
microbiology and immunology.
1928-1990   0421056

Arch Sci Biol (Bologna)
Archivio di scienze biologiche
0004-0169
1919-1978   0400644

Arch Sci Med (Torino)
Archivio per le scienze mediche
0004-0312
Absorbed by: Gazzetta medica italiana, 1984.
1876-1983   0372451

Arch Sci Physiol (Paris)
Archives des sciences physiologiques
0003-9713
1947-1974   7600478

Arch Sex Behav
Archives of sexual behavior
0004-0002   **1573-2800**
1971   1273516

Arch Soc Cir Chile
Archivos de la Sociedad de Cirujanos de
Chile
Continued by Revista chilena de chirgía.
1949-1975   7505225

Arch Soc Esp Oftalmol
Archivos de la Sociedad Española de
Oftalmología
0365-6691
Continues: Archivos de la Sociedad
Oftalmológica Hispano-Americana.
1971   1304603

Arch Soc Estud Clin Habana
Archivos. Sociedad de Estudios Clínicos de
la Habana
1881-1960   **20810620R**

Arch Stomatol
Archives de stomatologie
Continues the Archives wallonnes de stomatologie. Absorbed Annales belges de stomatologie. issued 1912-39.
1947-1958   15140170R

Arch Stomatol (Napoli)
Archivio stomatologico
0004-0320
Continues: Atti della dini a odontologica e della Società napoletana di stomatologia.
1960   0372454

Arch Suicide Res
Archives of suicide research: official journal of the International Academy for Suicide Research
1381-1118   1543-6136
1995   9504451

Arch Surg
Archives of surgery
0272-5533
Continued by: A.M.A. archives of surgery.
1920-1950   2985160R

Arch Surg
Archives of surgery (Chicago, Ill.: 1960)
0004-0010   1538-3644
Continues: A.M.A. archives of surgery.
1960   9716528

Arch Tierernahr
Archiv für Tierernährung
0003-942X   1477-2817
Continued by: Archives of animal nutrition.
1950-2003   0217641

Arch Tisiol
Archivio di tisiologia
Continued by Archivio di tisiologia e delle malattie dell'apparato respiratorio.
1946-1954   15220140R

Arch Tisiol Mal Appar Respir
Archivio di tisiologia e delle malattie dell'apparato respiratorio
0365-7426
Continues Archivio di tisiologia. Continued by Archivio Monaldi per la tisiologia e le malattie dell'apparato respiratorio.
1955-1969   1263557

Arch Toxicol
Archives of toxicology
0340-5761   1432-0738
Continues Archiv für Toxikologie.
1974   0417615

Arch Toxicol Suppl
Archives of toxicology. Supplement. = Archiv für Toxikologie. Supplement
0171-9750
1978-1998   7802567

Arch Toxikol
Archiv für Toxikologie
0003-9446
Continues Sammlung von Vergiftungsfällen. Continued by Archives of toxicology.
1954-1974   0434110

Arch Urug Med Cir Espec
Archivos uruguayos de medicina, cirugía y especialidades
1932-1966   15240210R

Arch Venez Med Trop Parasitol Med
Archivos venezolanos de medicina tropical y parasitología médica
0301-5130
Continues Archivos venezolanos de patología tropical y parasitología médica. issued 1948-54.
1959-1973   0405361

Arch Vet Ital
Archivio veterinario italiano
0004-0479
1950-1997   0040527

Arch Vet Pol
Archivum veterinarium Polonicum / Polish Academy of Sciences, Committee of Veterinary Sciences
1230-5359
Continues: Polskie archiwum weterynaryjne. Continued by: Polish journal of veterinary sciences.
1992-1996   9313674

Arch Virol
Archives of virology
0304-8608   1432-8798
Continues Archiv für die gesamte Virusforschung.
1975   7506870

Arch Virol Suppl
Archives of virology. Supplementum
0939-1983
1991   9214275

Arch Womens Ment Health
Archives of women's mental health
1434-1816   1435-1102
1998   9815663

Archaea
Archaea (Vancouver, B.C.)
1472-3646   1472-3654
2002   101142614

Archit Rec
Architectural record
0003-858X
Absorbed: Western architect and engineer. Jan. 1962 American architect and architecture. Mar. 1938
1891   9877762

Architecture
Architecture (Washington, D.C.)
0746-0554
Continues: AIA journal. American Institute of Architects. Absorbed: Progressive architecture. Jan. 1996 Architectural technology. Oct. 1986
1983   9880305

Archivio Chir Torace
Archivio di chirurgia del torace
Continued by Archivio di chirurgia toracica e cardiovascolare.
1947-1965   0135734

Archivos Soc Oftalmol Hisp Am
Archivos de la Sociedad Oftalmológica Hispano-Americana
0365-7051
Continues: Archivos de oftalmología Hispano Americanos. Continued by: Archivos de la Sociedad Española de Oftalmología.
1942-1970   7506872

Arcisp S Anna Ferrara
L' Arcispedale S. Anna di Ferrara
0004-0819
1948-1976   0373110

Arctic Med Res
Arctic medical research
0782-226X
Continues: Nordic Council for Arctic Medical Research report. Continued by: International journal of circumpolar health.
1984-1996   8602204

Arerugi
Arerugī = [Allergy]
0021-4884
1952   0241212

Argos
Argos (Utrecht, Netherlands)
0923-3970
1989   9708906

Arh Farm (Belgr)
Arhiv za farmaciju
0004-1963
1951   0373077

Arh Hig Rada
Arhiv za higijenu rada
Continued by Arhiv za higijenu rada i toksikologiju.
1950-1955   15240400R

Arh Hig Rada Toksikol
Arhiv za higijenu rada i toksikologiju
0004-1254
Continues: Arhiv za higijenu rada.
1956   0373100

Ariz Dent J
The Arizona dental journal
0004-1459
1955-1978   0372657

Ariz Med
Arizona medicine
0004-1556
Continues: Southwestern medicine. Absorbed by: Western journal of medicine.
1944-1985   0372465

Ariz Nurse
The Arizona nurse
0004-1599
1947   15240450R

Ark Dent
Arkansas dentistry
1056-4764
Continues: Arkansas dental journal.
1991   9104816

Ark Dent J
The Arkansas dental journal
0004-1769
Continued by: Arkansas dentistry.
1930-1990   15310090R

Ark Light Newsl
The Ark-light newsletter
0004-1696
1945-1973   0102754

Arkh Anat Gistol Embriol
Arkhiv anatomii, gistologii i émbriologii
0004-1947
Continues Russkiĭ arkhiv anatomii. gistologii i embriologii. Continued by: Morfologiia (Saint Petersburg. Russia).
1931-1991   0370603

Arkh Patol
Arkhiv patologii
0004-1955
Continues Arkhiv patologicheskoĭ anatomiĭ i patologicheskoĭ fiziologii.
1946   0370604

ARN J
ARN journal: the official journal of the Association of Rehabilitation Nurses
0362-3505
Continued by: Rehabilitation nursing.
1975-1980   7609209

Arq Bras Cardiol
Arquivos brasileiros de cardiologia
0066-782X   1678-4170
1948   0421031

Arq Bras Endocrinol Metabol
Arquivos brasileiros de endocrinologia e
metabologia
0004-2730   1677-9487
Continues: Arquivos brasileiros de
endocrinologia.
1955   0403437

Arq Bras Med
Arquivos brasileiros de medicina
0365-0723
Formed by the union of Archivos brasileiros
de medicina and Arquivos de clínica and
assumed the vol. numbering of the former.
Continued in part by: Arquivos brasileiros de
pediatria.
1952   15310420R

Arq Bras Med Nav
Arquivos brasileiros de medicina naval
0365-074X
1940   15310430R

Arq Bras Oftalmol
Arquivos brasileiros de oftalmologia
0004-2749   1678-2925
Continues: Revista de Oftalmologia de Sao
Paulo.
1938   0400645

Arq Cent Estud Curso Odontol
Arquivos do Centro de Estudos do curso de
odontologia
0102-5902
Continues Arquivos do Centro de Estudos
da Faculdade de Odontologia da U. F. M. G.
Continued by: Arquivos em odontologia.
1974-1996   7506874

Arq Cent Estud Fac Odontol UFMG (Belo Horiz)
Arquivos do Centro de Estudos da
Faculdade de Odontologia da U. F. M. G
0004-2838
Continues Arquivos do Centro de Estudos,
Faculdade de Odontologia da U. M. G.
Continued by: Arquivos do Centro de Estudos
do Curso de Odontologia.
1964-1973   7506873

Arq Cir Clin Exp
Arquivos de cirurgia clinica e experimental
0066-7846
1937-1969   0413656

Arq Clin (Rio De J)
Arquivos de clínica
1945-1951   15310570R

Arq Fac Hig Saude Publica Univ Sao Paulo
Arquivos da Faculdade de Higiene e Saúde
Pública da Universidade de São Paulo
0365-2203
Continued by: Revista de saúde pública..
1947-1966   7505230

Arq Gastroenterol
Arquivos de gastroenterologia
0004-2803   1678-4219
1964   15310600R

Arq Hig Saude Publica
Arquivos de higiene e saúde pública
0004-2811
1936-1969   7512592

Arq Inst Biol (Sao Paulo)
Arquivos do Instituto Biológico
0020-3653
Continues Archivos do Instituto Biologico.
1938   7505232

Arq Inst Bras Invest Tubers
Arquivos. Instituto Brasileiro para
Investigação da Tuberculose
Continued by Arquivos brasileiros de
tuberculose e doenças do torax.
1937-1964   0112531

Arq Inst Farm
Arquivos. Coimbra. Universidade. Instituto
de Farmacologia e Terapêutica Experimental
0412-8877
1931-1994   16310070R

Arq Med Cirur Pernamb
Arquivos de medicina e cirurgia de
Pernambuco
1949-19uu   15310630R

Arq Min Leprol
Arquivos mineiros de leprologia
1941-1963   0376321

Arq Neuropsiquiatr
Arquivos de neuro-psiquiatria
0004-282X   1678-4227
1943   0125444

Arq Oncol
Arquivos de oncología
0365-6268
1956-1979   0372470

Arq Patol
Arquivo de patologia
0004-2714
1925-1975   0376530

Arq Pediatr
Arquivos de pediatria ...
1928-1963   15310660R

Arq Port Bioquim
Arquivos portugueses de bioquímica
1957-1964   15320040R

Arq Port Oftalmol
Arquivos portugueses de oftalmologia
0377-922X
1949-1981   7611923

Arq Rio Gd Sul Braz State
Arquivos. Rio Grande do Sul, Brazil (State)
Departamento Estadual de Saúde
1940-uuuu   22921080R

Arquivo
Arquivo; Orgao Da Sociedade Brasileira De
Implantologia Bucal
197u   9875597

Ars Curandi Odontol
Ars curandi em odontologia
0100-2147
1974-1981   7907865

Ars Med
Ars medici
0004-2897
1911   0372471

Ars Med Rev Int Med Prat
Ars medici; revue internationale pour le
médecin praticien
Merged with Nouveautés médicales to form
Ars medici; nouveautés médicales pour le
médecin praticien.
1946-1964   0063132

Ars Med [2]
Ars medica. 2. Abt. Griechisch-lateinische
Medizin
0571-1355
1968-1981   0156341

Ars Med [3]
Ars medica. 3. Abt. Arabische Medizin
1971-1972   0312606

Arsb Goteb Tandlak Sallsk
Årsbok. Göteborgs tandläkare-sällskap
0072-4831
1918-1988   17140250R

Arsb Odontol Samf Finl
Årsbok. Odontologiska samfundet i Finland
0078-3358
1937   19320330R

Arsskr Sydven Medicinhist Sallsskapet
Aarsskrift - Sydsvenska medicinhistoriska
sällskapet
Continued by Sydsvenska medicinhistoriska
sällskapets årsskrift.
1964-1970   0100346

Arterioscler Thromb
Arteriosclerosis and thrombosis: a journal
of vascular biology / American Heart
Association
1049-8834
Continues: Arteriosclerosis (Dallas, Tex.).
Continued by: Arteriosclerosis, thrombosis,
and vascular biology.
1991-1994   9101388

Arterioscler Thromb Vasc Biol
Arteriosclerosis, thrombosis, and vascular
biology
1079-5642   1524-4636
Continues: Arteriosclerosis and thrombosis.
1995   9505803

Arteriosclerosis
Arteriosclerosis (Dallas, Tex.)
0276-5047
Continued by: Arteriosclerosis and
thrombosis.
1981-1990   8401388

Arthritis Care Res
Arthritis care and research: the official
journal of the Arthritis Health Professions
Association
0893-7524
Continued in 2001 as a section of: Arthritis
and rheumatism. Odd numbered v. from v.
45- contain the section.
1988-2000   8809082

Arthritis Res
Arthritis research
1465-9905   1465-9913
Continued by: Arthritis research & therapy.
1999-2002   100913255

Arthritis Res Ther
Arthritis research & therapy
1478-6354   1478-6362
Continues: Arthritis research.
2003   101154438

Arthritis Rheum
Arthritis and rheumatism
0004-3591   1529-0131
Absorbed: Arthritis care and research.
1958   0370605

Arthropod Struct Dev
Arthropod structure & development
1467-8039   1873-5495
Continues: International journal of insect
morphology & embryology.
2000   100972232

Arthroscopy
Arthroscopy: the journal of arthroscopic
& related surgery: official publication
of the Arthroscopy Association of North
America and the International Arthroscopy
Association
0749-8063   1526-3231
1985   8506498

Articulator (Columb)
The Articulator
0272-9067
1971-1982   8009441

Articulator (Syd)
The Articulator
1973-19uu   15320210R

Artif Cells Blood Substit Immobil Biotechnol
Artificial cells, blood substitutes, and
immobilization biotechnology
1073-1199   1532-4184
Continues: Biomaterials, artificial cells, and
immobilization biotechnology.
1994   9431307

Artif Intell Med
Artificial intelligence in medicine
0933-3657   1873-2860
1989   8915031

Artif Life
Artificial life
1064-5462   1530-9185
1994   9433814

Artif Limbs
Artificial limbs
0004-3729
1954-1972   0370606

Artif Organs
Artificial organs
0160-564X   1525-1594
1977   7802778

Arukoru Kenkyuto Yakubutsu Ison
Arukōru kenkyū to yakubutsu izon =
Japanese journal of alcohol studies & drug
dependence
0389-4118
Continues: Arukōru kenkyū. Continued by:
Nihon Arukōru, Yakubutsu Igakkai zasshi.
1981-1995   8213278

Arzneimittelforschung
Arzneimittel-Forschung
0004-4172
1951   0372660

Arztebl Rheinl Pfalz
Aerzteblatt Rheinland-Pfalz
0001-9488
Continues the Mitteilungsblatt der
Aerzteschaft Rheinland-Pfalz.
1961   0376663

Arztl Dienst
Der Ärztliche Dienst
Continues Der Sanitätsdienst bei der
Deutschen Reichsbahn. Issued Aug.
1949-Dez. 1953 as a supplement to Die
Bundesbahn under title: Der Ärztliche Dienst
bei der Deutschen Bundesbahn.
1949-1976   14640230R

Arztl Forsch
Ärztliche Forschung
0001-9496
1947   7611907

Arztl Fortbild
Die Ärztliche Fortbildung
0001-950X
Continues Regensburger ärztliche
Fortbildung.
1953-1971   0402620

Arztl Jugendkd
Ärztliche Jugendkunde
0001-9518
Continues Gesundheit und Erziehung.
1959-1991   0370444

Arztl Monatshefte Berufl Fortbild
Ärztliche Monatshefte für berufliche
Fortbildung. Cahiers mensuels de médecine
0365-639X
1945-1953   14640270R

Arztl Prax
Aerztliche Praxis
0001-9534
1949   0370446

Arztl Sammelbl
Ärztliche Sammelblätter
0344-631X
Merged with Der Landarzt to form Zeitschrift
für Allgemeinmedizin.
1908-1963   7704214

Arztl Wochensch
Ärztliche Wochenschrift
0365-6403
Supersedes: Internist.
1946-1960   14640350R

ASA Newsl
ASA newsletter
0270-5877
Continues Newsletter of the American
Society of Anesthesiologists.
1965   0140166

ASAIO J
ASAIO journal (American Society for
Artificial Internal Organs: 1992)
1058-2916   1538-943X
Absorbed: Abstracts, annual meeting.
American Society for Artificial Internal
Organs. Continues: ASAIO transactions.
1992   9204109

ASAIO Trans
ASAIO transactions / American Society for
Artificial Internal Organs
0889-7190
Formed by the union of: Transactions -
American Society for Artificial Internal
Organs. and: ASAIO journal. Continued
by: ASAIO journal (American Society for
Artificial Internal Organs: 1992).
1986-1991   8611947

ASDA News
ASDA news (American Student Dental
Association: 1981)
0277-3627
Continues: New dentist.
1981   9879740

ASDC J Dent Child
ASDC journal of dentistry for children
Continues: Journal of dentistry for children.
Continued by: Journal of dentistry for
children (Chicago, Ill.).
1968-2002   0146172

Asepsis
Asepsis
1062-0281
197u-1997   9008247

ASGSB Bull
ASGSB bulletin: publication of the
American Society for Gravitational and
Space Biology
0898-4697
Continued by: Gravitational and space
biology bulletin.
1988-1995   9890632

ASHA
ASHA
0001-2475
Absorbed by: ASHA leader.
1959-1999   0370563

ASHA Monogr
ASHA monographs
0066-071X
Continues Monograph supplement of the
Journal of speech and hearing disorders.
1965-1993   14470400R

ASHA Suppl
ASHA. Supplement
1072-8929
1990-1999   9214642

Asia Oceania J Obstet Gynaecol
Asia-Oceania journal of obstetrics and
gynaecology / AOFOG
0389-2328
Continues: Journal of the Asian Federation of
Obstetrics and Gynaecology. Continued by:
Journal of obstetrics and gynaecology (Tokyo,
Japan).
1980-1994   8102781

Asia Pac J Clin Nutr
Asia Pacific journal of clinical nutrition
0964-7058   1440-6047
Absorbed: Proceedings of the Nutrition
Society of Australia. Nutrition Society of
Australia. Conference. 2001
1992   9440304

Asia Pac J Public Health
Asia-Pacific journal of public health / Asia-
Pacific Academic Consortium for Public
Health
1010-5395   1941-2479
1987   8708538

Asian Am Pac Isl J Health
Asian American and Pacific Islander journal
of health
1072-0367
1993-200u   9417466

Asian Cardiovasc Thorac Ann
Asian cardiovascular & thoracic annals
0218-4923   1816-5370
1993   9503417

Asian J Aesthet Dent
Asian journal of aesthetic dentistry / the
Asian Academy of Aesthetic Dentistry
0218-3781
1993   9318734

Asian J Androl
Asian journal of andrology
1008-682X   1745-7262
1999   100942132

Asian J Infect Dis
Asian journal of infectious diseases
0129-4024
1977-1979   7802571

Asian J Surg
Asian journal of surgery / Asian Surgical
Association
1015-9584
Continues: Southeast Asian journal of
surgery.
1988   8900600

Asian Pac J Allergy Immunol
Asian Pacific journal of allergy and
immunology / launched by the Allergy and
Immunology Society of Thailand
0125-877X
1983   8402034

Asian Pac J Cancer Prev
Asian Pacific journal of cancer prevention:
APJCP
1513-7368
2000   101130625

Ask Sihhiye Derg
Askerî sihhiye dergisi
Continues Askerî sihhiye mecmuasi.
1949-19uu   15320490R

Asklepii
Asklepii: bolgaro-sovetskii ezhegodnik istorii
i teorii meditsiny
0324-1300
1970   0315615

ASNA Rep
ASNA reporter
19uu   9880184

Aspen Emphysema Conf
Aspen Emphysema Conference
19uu-1972   100960810

Aspens Advis Nurse Exec
Aspen's advisor for nurse executives
0883-9743
Continued by: Patient care management.
1985-2000   8607450

Assay Drug Dev Technol
Assay and drug development technologies
1540-658X   1557-8127
2002   101151468

Assertive Nurse
Assertive Nurse
Continued by: Holistic Assertive Nurse.
1978-1980   9878686

Assessment
Assessment
1073-1911   1552-3489
1994   9431219

Assist Inferm Ric
Assistenza infermieristica e ricerca: AIR
1592-5986
Continues: Rivista dell'infermiere.
1999   100901776

Assist Soc
L'Assistenza sociale
0392-1026
1947-2003   15330670R

Assist Technol
Assistive technology: the official journal of
RESNA
1040-0435
1989   8917250

Assoc Manage
Association management
0004-5578
Continues: Journal (American Society of
Association Executives). Absorbed: ASAE
news. American Society of Association
Executives. Here's how. Leadership issue
superseded by: Leadership.
1963   9877763

Assoc Soc Manager
Association & society manager
0004-5292
1969-1988   9877810

Asthet Med (Berl)
Ästhetische Medizin
0400-6755
Continues Medizinische Kosmetik. Continued
by Cosmotologica.
1960-1969   0253745

Astragale
Astragale
1958-19uu   15340610R

Astrameddelande
Astrameddelande
19uu-19uu   15340640R

Astrobiology
Astrobiology
1531-1074   1557-8070
2001   101088083

At Energy Biophys Biol Med
Atomic energy in biophysics, biology and
medicine
0276-9824
Absorbed by: U. S. Atomic Energy
Commission. Nuclear science abstracts.
1948-1948   15410190R

At Energy Rev
Atomic energy review
0004-7112
1963-1980   0376323

Aten Primaria
Atencion primaria / Sociedad Española de
Medicina de Familia y Comunitaria
0212-6567   1578-1275
1983   9111075

Ateneo Parmense Acta Biomed
L'Ateneo parmense. Acta bio-medica:
organo della Società di medicina e scienze
naturali di Parma
Continues: L'Ateneo parmense. Sezione I,
Acta bio-medica. Continued by: Acta bio-
medica de L'Ateneo parmense.
1973-1980   8106465

Ateneo Parmense [1]
L'Ateneo parmense. Sezione I: Acta bio-
medica
0390-7953
Continues in part L'Ateneo parmense.
Continued by L'Ateneo parmense. Acta bio-
medica.
1965-1972   0064375

Athena
Athena; rassegna mensile di biologia, clinica
e terapia
1932-1958   0370611

Atheroscler Suppl
Atherosclerosis. Supplements
1567-5688   1878-5050
2000   100973461

Atherosclerosis
Atherosclerosis
0021-9150   1879-1484
Continues: Journal of atherosclerosis
research.
1970   0242543

Atlas Oral Maxillofac Surg Clin North Am
Atlas of the oral and maxillofacial surgery
clinics of North America
1061-3315   1558-4275
1993   9312707

Atlas Radiol Clin Presse Med
Atlas de radiologie clinique de la Presse
médicale
0067-0278
1953-1969   0200733

Atmos Environ
Atmospheric environment
0004-6981
Supersedes: Air and water pollution.
Supersedes: Air and water pollution.
Split into: Atmospheric environment.
Part A, General topics; and: Atmospheric
environment. Part B, Urban atmosphere.
1967-1989   0100776

Atomes
Atomes
1946-1970   0254724

Atompraxis
Atompraxis
0571-8198
1955-1970   15410280R

Attach Hum Dev
Attachment & human development
1461-6734   1469-2988
1999   100901315

Atti Accad Fisiocrit Siena
Atti della R. Accademia dei fisiocritici in
Siena
Continues the Atti of the Accademia delle
scienze detta de' fisiocritici, issued 1760-
1841. Split into the Atti of the academy's
Sezione medico-fisica and its Sezione agraria.
1862-1930   7508347

Atti Accad Fisiocrit Siena [Med Fis]
Atti della Accademia dei fisiocritici in Siena.
Sezione medico-fisica
0065-0722
Continues in part: Atti della R. Accademia
dei fisiocritici in Siena. Includes 1933-53 the
Studi della Facoltà medica senese. Merged
with the Atti of the academy's Sezione agraria
to form: Atti dell'Accademia delle scienze
de Siena detta de' fisiocritici.
1931-1968   7506880

Atti Accad Med Lomb
Atti della Accademia medica lombarda
0001-4427
Continues the Atti of the Società lombarda
di scienze mediche e biologiche, Milan
(Founded 1946).
1960-1990   7503302

Atti Clin Otorinolaringoitr Univ Palermo
Atti. Università di Palermo. Clinica oto-rino-
laringoiatrica
1946-1974   19510530R

Atti Congr Naz Soc Ital Med Leg
Atti del congresso nazionale. Società italiana
di medicina legale e delle assicurazioni
1898   24920370R

Atti Mem Accad Stor Arte Sanit
Atti e memorie della Accademia di storia
dell'arte sanitaria
0365-4109
Continues Bollettino dell'Istituto storico
italiano dell'arte sanitaria. Supplement to
Rassegna di clinica, terapia e scienze affini.
1935-1966   7503303

Atti Soc Ital Cardiol
Atti della Società italiana di cardiologia
0081-069X
Continues: Atti. Gruppo cardiologico italiano.
1949-1980   7506884

Attual Dent
Attualità dentale
Continued by: Attualità dentale (Milan, Italy:
1994).
1985-1993   8708541

Attual Diet
L'Attualità dietetica
0403-9440
1956-1967   15410370R

Attual Ematol
Attualita in ematologia
1955-19uu   15410380R

Attual Med
L'Attualita medica
Supersedes Igea. Issued as supplement to
Annali d'igiene, 1936-45? and anno 1-4 are
bound with v. 46-49 of that periodical.
1936-1967   15410390R

Attual Ostet Ginecol
Attualità di ostetricia e ginecologia
0004-7317
1955-1985   0117270

AUAA J
AUAA journal: official journal of the American Urological Association Allied
0882-9594
Continued by: Urologic nursing.
1980-1988   8402038

Audiol Neurootol
Audiology & neuro-otology
1420-3030   1421-9700
1996   9606930

Audiology
Audiology: official organ of the International Society of Audiology
0020-6091
Continues: International audiology.
Merged with: British journal of audiology.
and: Scandinavian audiology, to form:
International journal of audiology.
1971-2001   1273752

Augment Altern Commun
Augmentative and alternative communication (Baltimore, Md.: 1985)
0743-4618   1477-3848
1985   8504574

Auris Nasus Larynx
Auris, nasus, larynx
0385-8146   1879-1476
1973   7708170

Aust Clin Rev
Australian clinical review / Australian Medical Association [and] the Australian Council on Hospital Standards
0726-3139
Continued by: Journal of quality in clinical practice.
1981-1993   8300517

Aust Coll Midwives Inc J
Australian College of Midwives Incorporated journal
1031-170X
Continued by: Australian journal of midwifery.
1988-2000   8903009

Aust Crit Care
Australian critical care: official journal of the Confederation of Australian Critical Care Nurses
1036-7314
Continues: Confederation of Australian Critical Care Nurses journal.
1992   9207852

Aust Dent J
Australian dental journal
0045-0421
Formed by the union of: Australian journal of dentistry; Dental journal of Australia; and: Queensland dental journal.
1956   0370612

Aust Dent Pract
Australian dental practice
1320-2340
Continues: Dental reporter. Continued by: Australasian dental practice.
1990-1997   9204105

Aust Endod J
Australian endodontic journal: the journal of the Australian Society of Endodontology Inc
1329-1947
Continues: Australian endodontic newsletter.
1998   100888004

Aust Fam Physician
Australian family physician
0300-8495
Absorbed: Annals of general practice.
1972   0326701

Aust Health Rev
Australian health review: a publication of the Australian Hospital Association
0156-5788   1449-8944
1978   8214381

Aust Hosp
The Australian hospital
1933-1949   15420270R

Aust Hosp
Australian hospital
0314-0024
Supersedes National hospital and health care.
Continued by: Health professional.
1976-1990   7704769

Aust J Adv Nurs
The Australian journal of advanced nursing: a quarterly publication of the Royal Australian Nursing Federation
0813-0531
1983   8409358

Aust J Biol Sci
Australian journal of biological sciences
0004-9417
Continues: Australian journal of scientific research. Ser. B: Biological sciences.
Absorbed in part by: Australian journal of plant physiology. Continued in part by: Reproduction, fertility, and development.
1953-1988   0370613

Aust J Biotechnol
Australian journal of biotechnology
0819-3355
Merged with: ABA bulletin: to form: Australasian biotechnology.
1987-1991   8811037

Aust J Dent
The Australian journal of dentistry
1897-1955   15420280R

Aust J Exp Biol Med Sci
The Australian journal of experimental biology and medical science
0004-945X
Continued by: Immunology and cell biology.
1924-1986   0416662

Aust J Holist Nurs
The Australian journal of holistic nursing
1322-8803
1994   100886426

Aust J Midwifery
Australian journal of midwifery: professional journal of the Australian College of Midwives Incorporated
1445-4386
Continues: Australian College of Midwives Incorporated journal. Continued by: Women and birth.
2001-2005   101096027

Aust J Ophthalmol
Australian journal of ophthalmology
0310-1177
Supersedes Transactions of the Australian College of Ophthalmologists. Merged with Transactions of the Ophthalmological Society of New Zealand, to form Australian and New Zealand journal of ophthalmologists.
1973-1984   0365543

Aust J Optom
The Australian journal of optometry
0045-0642
Continues the Australasian journal of optometry. Continued by: Clinical & experimental optometry.
1959-1985   15420110R

Aust J Physiother
The Australian journal of physiotherapy
0004-9514
1954   0370615

Aust J Public Health
Australian journal of public health
1035-7319
Continues: Community health studies.
Continued by: Australian and New Zealand journal of public health.
1991-1995   9105166

Aust J Rural Health
The Australian journal of rural health
1038-5282   1440-1584
1992   9305903

Aust J Sci
The Australian journal of science
0365-3668
Continues: Search (Sydney).
1938-1970   0263662

Aust J Sci Med Sport
Australian journal of science and medicine in sport
0813-6289
Formed by the union of: Australian journal of sports medicine and exercise sciences; and: Australian journal of sport sciences. Continued by: Journal of science and medicine in sport.
1984-1997   9012781

Aust J Sci Res (B)
Australian journal of scientific research. Ser. B: Biological sciences
Continued by: Australian journal of biological sciences.
1948-1952   15420300R

Aust J Zool
Australian journal of zoology
0004-959X
1953   0001061

Aust Med Rec J
Australian medical record journal / Medical Record Association of Australia
0817-3907
Continues: Australian medical record.
Continued by: Health information management.
1983-1993   8807862

Aust N Z Gen Pract
The Australian and New Zealand general practitioner
0045-0227
Formed by the union of General practitioner of Australia and New Zealand and Medical topics. Superseded by GP. The Australian & New Zealand general practitioner.
1953-1970   7805150

Aust N Z J Med
Australian and New Zealand journal of medicine
0004-8291
Continues: Australasian annals of medicine.
Continued by: Internal medicine journal.
1971-2000   1264322

Aust N Z J Ment Health Nurs
The Australian and New Zealand journal of mental health nursing
1324-3780   1440-0979
Continues: Australian journal of mental health nursing. Continued by: International journal of mental health nursing.
1994-2001   9442872

Aust N Z J Obstet Gynaecol
The Australian & New Zealand journal of
obstetrics & gynaecology
0004-8666   1479-828X
1961   0001027

Aust N Z J Obstet Gynaecol Suppl
The Australian & New Zealand journal of
obstetrics & gynaecology. Supplement
0004-8666
1967-19uu   0252122

Aust N Z J Ophthalmol
Australian and New Zealand journal of
ophthalmology
0814-9763   1440-1606
  Merger of: Australian journal of
  ophthalmology; and Transactions of the
  Ophthalmological Society of New Zealand.
  Continued by: Clinical & experimental
  ophthalmology.
1985-1999   8505423

Aust N Z J Psychiatry
The Australian and New Zealand journal of
psychiatry
0004-8674   1440-1614
1967   0111052

Aust N Z J Public Health
Australian and New Zealand journal of
public health
1326-0200
  Continues: Australian journal of public
  health.
1996   9611095

Aust N Z J Surg
The Australian and New Zealand journal of
surgery
0004-8682
  Supersedes the Journal of the College of
  Surgeons of Australasia. Continued by: ANZ
  journal of surgery.
1931-2000   0373115

Aust Nurs J
Australian nursing journal (July 1993)
1320-3185
  Continues: Australian nursing journal (June
  1993).
1993   9317904

Aust Nurs J
Australian nursing journal (June 1993)
  Continues: Australian nurses journal.
  Continued by: Australian nursing journal
  (July 1993).
1993-1993   9317903

Aust Nurses J
The Australian nurses' journal
0045-0758
  Continued by: Australian nursing journal
  (June 1993).
1971-1993   0370074

Aust Occup Ther J
Australian occupational therapy journal
0045-0766   1440-1630
  Continues the Bulletin of the Australian
  Association of Occupational Therapists.
1963   15420200R

Aust Orthod J
Australian orthodontic journal
0587-3908
1967   1260462

Aust Paediatr J
Australian paediatric journal
0004-993X
  Continued by: Journal of paediatrics and
  child health.
1965-1989   15420340R

Aust Prosthodont J
Australian prosthodontic journal /
Australian Prosthodontic Society
0819-0887
  Continues: Australian Prosthodontic Society
  bulletin.
1987-1995   8803700

Aust Prosthodont Soc Bull
Australian Prosthodontic Society bulletin
0816-4460
  Continues: Australian Society of
  Prosthodontists bulletin. Continued by:
  Australian prosthodontic journal.
1984-1986   8609734

Aust Soc Prosthodontists Bull
Australian Society Of Prosthodontists
Bulletin
0816-8261
  Continued by: Australian Prosthodontic
  Society Bulletin.
1971-1983   9880197

Aust Vet J
Australian veterinary journal
0005-0423
  Continues the Journal of the Australian
  Veterinary Association.
1927   0370616

Australas Ann Med
Australasian annals of medicine
0571-9283
  Continues: Proceedings. Royal Australasian
  College of Physicians. Continued by:
  Australian and New Zealand journal of
  medicine.
1952-1970   1264321

Australas Biotechnol
Australasian biotechnology
1036-7128
  Formed by the union of: ABA bulletin, and:
  Australian journal of biotechnology.
1991   9113681

Australas J Ageing
Australasian journal on ageing
1440-6381   1741-6612
  Continues: Australian journal on ageing.
1998   9808874

Australas J Dermatol
The Australasian journal of dermatology
0004-8380   1440-0960
  Continues Australian journal of dermatology.
1967   0135232

Australas J Optom
The Australasian journal of optometry
  Absorbed: Optometrist of N.S.W..
  Commonwealth optometrist. Continued by:
  Australian journal of optometry.
1930-1959   15420100R

Australas J Pharm
The Australasian journal of pharmacy
0004-8399
  Supersedes the Australasian chemist and
  druggist. Absorbed Chemist and druggist
  and pharmacist of Australasia in Sept.
  1934. Continued by: Australian journal of
  pharmacy.
1886-1971   0322433

Australas Nurses J
The Australasian nurses journal
0301-018X
  Supersedes S. A. nurses journal.
1971-1983   0367666

Australas Nurses J
The Australasian nurses' journal
0301-018X
  Continued by the Australian nurses' journal.
1902-1951   15420320R

Australas Phys Eng Sci Med
Australasian physical & engineering sciences
in medicine / supported by the Australasian
College of Physical Scientists in Medicine
and the Australasian Association of Physical
Sciences in Medicine
0158-9938
  Continues: Australasian physical sciences in
  medicine.
1980   8208130

Australas Psychiatry
Australasian psychiatry: bulletin of Royal
Australian and New Zealand College of
Psychiatrists
1039-8562   1440-1665
1991   9613603

Australas Radiol
Australasian radiology
0004-8461   1440-1673
  Continues: Journal of the College of
  Radiologists of Australasia. College of
  Radiologists of Australasia. Continued by:
  Journal of medical imaging and radiation
  oncology.
1966-2007   0047441

Autism
Autism: the international journal of research
and practice
1362-3613
1997   9713494

Autoimmun Rev
Autoimmunity reviews
1568-9972   1873-0183
2002   101128967

Autoimmunity
Autoimmunity
0891-6934   1607-842X
1988   8900070

Auton Autacoid Pharmacol
Autonomic & autacoid pharmacology
1474-8665   1474-8673
  Continues: Journal of autonomic
  pharmacology.
2002   101157306

Auton Neurosci
Autonomic neuroscience: basic & clinical
1566-0702   1872-7484
  Continues: Journal of the autonomic nervous
  system.
2000   100909359

Autophagy
Autophagy
1554-8627   1554-8635
2005   101265188

Auxiliaire
L'Auxiliaire
0703-9484
  Continues: La Revue des infirmières et
  infirmiers auxiliaires du Québec. Continued
  by: L'Infirmière auxiliaire.
1977-1982   7802177

Av Odontoestomatol
Avances en odontoestomatologia
0213-1285
1985   8612453

Av Periodoncia
Avances en periodoncia
1130-1457
  Continued by: Avances en periodoncia e
  implantología oral.
1989-1993   9114922

Avenir Med
L'Avenir médical
0761-1218
  Continues: Cahiers de l'avenir médical.
1947-1959   15430170R

Aviakosm Ekolog Med
Aviakosmicheskaia i ekologicheskaia
meditsina = Aerospace and environmental
medicine
0233-528X
Continues: Kosmicheskaia biologiia i
aviakosmicheskaia meditsina.
1992   9305904

Avian Dis
Avian diseases
0005-2086
1957   0370617

Avian Pathol
Avian pathology: journal of the W.V.P.A
0307-9457   1465-3338
1972   8210638

Aviat Space Environ Med
Aviation, space, and environmental medicine
0095-6562
Continues Aerospace medicine.
1975   7501714

AWHONN Lifelines
AWHONN lifelines / Association of Women's
Health, Obstetric and Neonatal Nurses
1091-5923   1552-6356
Continued by: Nursing for women's health.
1997-2007   9708553

AWHONN Voice
AWHONN voice / Association of Women's
Health, Obstetric, and Neonatal Nurses
(AWHONN)
1066-2944
Continues: NAACOG newsletter.
1993-1996   9306666

**AWHONNS Clin Issues Perinat Womens Health
Nurs**
AWHONN's clinical issues in perinatal and
women's health nursing
1066-3614
Continues: NAACOG's clinical issues
in perinatal and women's health nursing.
Absorbed by: Journal of obstetric,
gynecologic, and neonatal nursing.
1993-1993   9311009

Axone
Axone (Dartmouth, N.S.)
0834-7824
Continued by: Canadian journal of
neuroscience nursing =.
1979-2007   8804393

Azerbaidzhanskii Meditsinskii Zhurnal
Azerbaĭdzhanskiĭ meditŝinskiĭ zhurnal =
Aserbaidschanische medizinische Zeitschrift
0005-2523
Continues: Bakinskiĭ meditŝinskiĭ zhurnal.
Continued by: Azәrbaycan tibb jurnalı.
1928-199u   0372664

B

B C Med J
British Columbia medical journal
0007-0556
Continued by: BC medical journal.
1959-2000   0376326

B-ENT
B-ENT
1781-782X
Continues: Acta oto-rhino-laryngologica
belgica.
2005   101247842

Babiski Vestn
Babiški vestnik
193u-1969   15430490R

Backgr Pap
Background paper (United States. Physician
Payment Review Commission)
Merged with: Report to Congress (United
States. Physician Payment Review
Commission: Series), to form: Physician
Payment Review Commission (Series).
1989-1989   9417780

Bacteriol Rev
Bacteriological reviews
0005-3678
Continued by Microbiological reviews.
1937-1977   0370620

Bacteriol Virusol Parazitol Epidemiol
Bacteriologia, virusologia, parazitologia,
epidemiologia (Bucharest, Romania: 1990)
1220-3696
Continues: Revista de igienă. bacteriologie,
virusologie, parazitologie, epidemiologie.
pneumoftiziologie. Bacteriologia, virusologia,
parazitologia, epidemiologia.
1990   9204448

Bacteriol Virusol Parazitol Epidemiol (Bucur)
Bacteriologia, virusologia, parazitologia,
epidemiologia
0301-7338
Continues Microbiologia, parazitologia,
epidemiologia. Continued by Revista
de igienă. bacteriologie, virusologie,
parazitologie. epidemiologie.
pneumoftiziologie. Seria: Bacteriologie,
virusologie. parazitologie. epidemiologie.
1974-1974   7501477

Baillieres Best Pract Res Clin Endocrinol Metab
Baillière's best practice & research. Clinical
endocrinology & metabolism
Continues: Baillière's clinical endocrinology
and metabolism. Continued by: Best practice
& research. Clinical endocrinology &
metabolism.
1999-2000   100957144

Baillieres Best Pract Res Clin Gastroenterol
Baillière's best practice & research. Clinical
gastroenterology
Continues: Baillière's clinical
gastroenterology. Continued by: Best practice
& research. Clinical gastroenterology.
1999-2000   100894206

Baillieres Best Pract Res Clin Haematol
Baillière's best practice & research. Clinical
haematology
Continues: Baillière's clinical haematology.
Continued by: Best practice & research.
Clinical haematology.
1999-2000   100900679

Baillieres Best Pract Res Clin Obstet Gynaecol
Baillière's best practice & research. Clinical
obstetrics & gynaecology
Continues: Baillière's clinical obstetrics and
gynaecology. Continued by: Best practice &
research. Clinical obstetrics & gynaecology.
1999-2000   100890322

Baillieres Best Pract Res Clin Rheumatol
Baillière's best practice & research. Clinical
rheumatology
Continues: Baillière's clinical rheumatology.
Continued by: Best practice & research.
Clinical rheumatology.
1999-2000   100883496

Baillieres Clin Endocrinol Metab
Baillière's clinical endocrinology and
metabolism
0950-351X
Continues in part: Clinics in endocrinology
and metabolism. Continued by: Baillière's
best practice & research. Clinical
endocrinology & metabolism.
1987-1998   8704785

Baillieres Clin Gastroenterol
Baillière's clinical gastroenterology
0950-3528
Continues in part: Clinics in gastroenterology.
Continued by: Baillière's best practice &
research. Clinical gastroenterology.
1987-1998   8704786

Baillieres Clin Haematol
Baillière's clinical haematology
0950-3536
Continues in part: Clinics in haematology.
Continued by: Baillière's best practice &
research. Clinical haematology.
1987-1998   8800474

Baillieres Clin Neurol
Baillière's clinical neurology
0961-0421
1992-1997   9214291

Baillieres Clin Obstet Gynaecol
Baillière's clinical obstetrics and
gynaecology
0950-3552
Continues in part: Clinics in obstetrics and
gynaecology. Continued by: Baillière's best
practice & research. Clinical obstetrics &
gynaecology.
1987-1998   8710782

Baillieres Clin Rheumatol
Baillière's clinical rheumatology
0950-3579
Continues in part: Clinics in rheumatic
diseases. Continued by: Baillière's best
practice & research. Clinical rheumatology.
1987-1998   8805770

Balance
Balance (Alexandria, Va.)
1094-6195
Merger of: Journal of long term care
administration; and: Long-term care
administrator; and: College notes.
1997-2001   9716690

Baltim Health News
Baltimore health news
0045-1363
1924-1975   22620200R

Band
Das Band; Monatsblatt für Kranke und
Gesunde
1935   15440060R

Bangladesh Med Res Counc Bull
Bangladesh Medical Research Council
bulletin
0377-9238
1975   7607686

Barbados Nurs J
Barbados nursing journal
1967-1968   0251043

Barrons
Barron's national business and financial
weekly
0005-6073
Continues: Barron's. Continued by: Barron's
(Chicopee, Mass.).
1942-1994   9877850

Basal Facts
Basal facts
0147-9679
Supersedes The Journal of the American
Academy for Functional Prosthodontics.
1976-1987   7705821

Basal Facts
Basal facts (Chicago, Ill.: 1974)
Continued by: Basal facts.
19uu-1975   100909953

Basic Appl Histochem
  Basic and applied histochemistry
  0391-7258
    Continues Rivista di istochimica, normale e
    patologica. Continued by: European journal
    of basic and applied histochemistry.
  1979-1990   7910664

Basic Clin Pharmacol Toxicol
  Basic & clinical pharmacology & toxicology
  1742-7835   1742-7843
    Continues: Pharmacology & toxicology.
  2004   101208422

Basic Life Sci
  Basic life sciences
  0090-5542
  1973-1999   0360077

Basic Res Cardiol
  Basic research in cardiology
  0300-8428   1435-1803
    Continues Archiv für Kreislaufforschung and
    retains this as added title.
  1973   0360342

Bassini
  "Il Bassini"
  1956-1972   15440380R

Baxter Health Policy Rev
  The Baxter health policy review
  1992-1996   9616732

Bayer Aztebl
  **Bayerisches Ärzteblatt: amtliches Organ der
  Bayerischen Landesärztekammer und ihrer
  Bezirksvereine**
  0005-7126
  1946   0372665

Baylor Dent J
  The Baylor dental journal
  0005-7258
  1939   0375023

Baylor Nurs Educ
  Baylor nursing educator
  0270-7799
  1979-1980   8005335

Bedside Nurse
  Bedside nurse
  0005-7665
    Supersedes American journal of practical
    nursing. Continued by Nursing care.
  1968-1973   0366113

Begg J Orthod Theory Treat
  **Begg journal of orthodontic theory and
  treatment**
  0067-4869
  1962-1969   15440530R

Beginnings
  **Beginnings (American Holistic Nurses'
  Association)**
  1071-2984
  1981   9303087

Behav Biol
  Behavioral biology
  0091-6773
    Continues: Communications in behavioral
    biology. Part A: Original articles. Continued
    by: Behavioral and neural biology.
  1972-1978   0326100

Behav Brain Res
  Behavioural brain research
  0166-4328   1872-7549
  1980   8004872

Behav Brain Sci
  The Behavioral and brain sciences
  0140-525X   1469-1825
  1978   7808666

Behav Genet
  Behavior genetics
  0001-8244   1573-3297
  1970   0251711

Behav Healthc
  Behavioral healthcare
  1931-7093
    Formed by the union of: Behavioral health
    management, and: Behavioral healthcare
    tomorrow.
  2006   101269325

Behav Healthc Tomorrow
  Behavioral healthcare tomorrow
  1063-8490
    Merged with: Behavioral health management,
    to form: Behavioral healthcare.
  1992-2005   9308264

Behav Med
  Behavioral medicine (Washington, D.C.)
  0896-4289
    Continues: Journal of human stress.
  1988   8804264

Behav Modif
  Behavior modification
  0145-4455   1552-4167
  1977   7803043

Behav Neural Biol
  Behavioral and neural biology
  0163-1047
    Continues: Behavioral biology. Continued by:
    Neurobiology of learning and memory.
  1979-1994   7905471

Behav Neurol
  Behavioural neurology
  0953-4180
  1988   8914585

Behav Neuropsychiatry
  Behavioral neuropsychiatry
  0005-7932
  1969-1977   0247440

Behav Neurosci
  Behavioral neuroscience
  0735-7044
    Continues in part: Journal of comparative and
    physiological psychology.
  1983   8302411

Behav Pharmacol
  Behavioural pharmacology
  0955-8810   1473-5849
  1989   9013016

Behav Processes
  Behavioural processes
  0376-6357   1872-8308
  1976   7703854

Behav Res Methods
  Behavior research methods
  1554-351X   1554-3528
    Continues: Behavior research methods,
    instruments, & computers.
  2005   101244316

Behav Res Methods Instrum Comput
  **Behavior research methods, instruments, &
  computers: a journal of the Psychonomic
  Society, Inc**
  0743-3808
    Continues: Behavior research methods and
    instrumentation. Continued by: Behavior
    research methods.
  1984-2004   8413015

Behav Res Ther
  Behaviour research and therapy
  0005-7967   1873-622X
  1963   0372477

Behav Sci
  Behavioral science
  0005-7940
    Merged with: System research, to form:
    System research and behavioral science.
  1956-1996   2984722R

Behav Sci Law
  Behavioral sciences & the law
  0735-3936   1099-0798
  1983   8404861

Behav Sleep Med
  Behavioral sleep medicine
  1540-2002   1540-2010
  2003   101149327

Behav Ther
  Behavior therapy
  0005-7894   1878-1888
    Absorbed: Newsletter. Association for
    Advancement of Behavior Therapy.
  1970   1251640

Behaviour
  Behaviour
  0005-7959
  1947   15440560R

Behring Inst Mitt
  Behring Institute Mitteilungen
  0301-0457
    Continues Behringwerk-Mitteilungen.
  1972-1997   0367532

Beijing Da Xue Xue Bao
  **Beijing da xue xue bao. Yi xue ban = Journal
  of Peking University. Health sciences**
  1671-167X
    Continues: Beijing yi ke da xue xue bao.
  2001   101125284

Beitr Gerichtl Med
  Beiträge zur gerichtlichen Medizin
  0067-5016
  1911-1992   0400646

Beitr Gesch Pharm Ihrer Nachbargeb
  **Beiträge zur Geschichte der Pharmazie und
  ihrer Nachbargebiete**
  1955   0958008R

Beitr Hyg Epidemiol
  Beiträge zur Hygiene und Epidemiologie
  0067-5083
  1943-1981   0372500

Beitr Infusionsther
  **Beiträge zur Infusionstherapie =
  Contributions to infusion therapy**
  1011-6974
    Continues: Beiträge zu Infusionstherapie
    und klinische Ernährung. Continued
    by: Beiträge zur Infusionstherapie und
    Transfuzionsmedizin.
  1988-1993   8812367

Beitr Infusionsther Transfusionsmed
  **Beiträge zur Infusionstherapie und
  Transfusionsmedizin = Contributions to
  infusion therapy and transfusion medicine**
  1023-2028
    Continues: Beiträge zur Infusionstherapie.
  1994-1996   9442459

Beitr Infusionther Klin Ernahr
  **Beiträge zu Infusionstherapie und klinische
  Ernährung**
  0378-8679
    Continued by: Beiträge zur Infusionstherapie.
  1978-1988   7905962

Beitr Klin Chir
  Beiträge zur klinischen Chirurgie
    Continued by Bruns' Beiträge zur klinischen
    Chirurgie.
  1883-1916   15510240R

Beitr Klin Erforsch Tuberk Lungenkr
Beiträge zur Klinik und Erforschung der
Tuberkulose und der Lungenkrankheiten
0300-9696
Continues Beiträge zur Klinik der
Tuberkulose und spezifischen Tuberkulose-
Forschung. Continued by Pneumonologie.
1965-1970 1247056

Beitr Klin Neurol Psychiatr
Beiträge zur klinischen Neurologie und
Psychiatrie
0138-5097
Continues: Sammlung zwangloser
Abhandlungen aus dem Gebiete der
Psychiatrie und Neurologie.
1981-1990 8309595

Beitr Krebsforsch
Beiträge zur Krebsforschung
0067-5113
1953-1975 0372501

Beitr Neurochir
Beiträge zur Neurochirurgie
0067-5156
1959-1970 0372502

Beitr Orthop Traumatol
Beiträge zur Orthopädie und Traumatologie
0005-8149
Continues Beiträge aus dem gesamten
Arbeitsbereich der Orthopädie und
chirurgisch-medizinischen Technik.
1960-1990 0372503

Beitr Pathol
Beiträge zur Pathologie
0005-8165
Continues Beiträge zur pathologischen
Anatomie und zur allgemeinen Pathologie.
Continued by Pathology, research and pactice.
1970-1977 0264676

Beitr Pathol Anat
Beiträge zur pathologischen Anatomie und
zur allgemeinen Pathologie
0366-2446
Continued by Beiträge zur Pathologie.
1886-1969 0264677

Beitr Rheumatol
Beiträge zur Rheumatologie
0067-5199
1958-1984 0372504

Beitr Sexualforsch
Beiträge zur Sexualforschung
0067-5210
1952 0064523

Beitr Silikoseforsch
Beiträge zur Silikose-Forschung
0376-0243
Continued by Beiträge zur Silikose-
Forschung (Pneumokoniose)
1949-1969 0256173

Beitr Silikoseforsch Pneumokoniose
Beiträge zur Silikose-Forschung
(Pneumokoniose)
0067-5229
Continues Beiträge zur Silikose-Forschung.
1970-1976 0255314

Beitr Trop Landwirtsch Veterinarmed
Beiträge zur tropischen Landwirtschaft und
Veterinärmedizin
0301-567X
Continues Beiträge zur tropischen
und subtropischen Landwirtschaft und
Tropenveterinärmedizin.
1973-1992 0410253

Belg Tijdschr Geneesk
Belgisch tijdschrift voor geneeskunde
0366-368X
Continued by: Tijdschrift voor Geneeskunde.
1945-1965 15510370R

Benders Health Care Law Mon
Bender's health care law monthly
1091-5982
Continues: Health care law newsletter.
Continued by: Health care law monthly.
1995-1998 9603909

Benefits Q
Benefits quarterly
8756-1263
1985 9112812

Ber Bonn Univ Poliklin Mund Zahn Kieferkr
Berichte Aus Der Bonner Universitatsklinik
Und Poliklinik Fur Mund-, Zahn- Und
Kieferkrankheiten
19uu 9875604

Ber Naturforsch Ges Freibg Br
Berichte. Naturforschende Gesellschaft zu
Freiburg i. B
Continues: Berichte über die Verhandlungen.
1885 0020267

Ber Wiss
Berichte zur Wissenschaftsgeschichte
0170-6233
1978 7909914

Ber Zusammenkunft Dtsch Ophthalmol Ges
Bericht über die Zusammenkunft. Deutsche
Ophthalmologische Gesellschaft
0070-427X
Continues the Bericht über die Versammlung
of the Ophthalmologische Gesellschaft.
Continued by Fortschritte der Ophthalmolgie.
1920-1980 7505238

Berita Jururawat
Berita jururawat
0067-5814
Continued by the Nursing journal of
Singapore.
1968-1971 0412063

Berl Med
Berliner Medizin
Continues Berliner Gesundheitsblatt.
1956-1968 0233261

Berl Munch Tierarztl Wochenschr
Berliner und Münchener tierärztliche
Wochenschrift
0005-9366
Formed by the merger of Berliner tierärztliche
Wochenschrift and Münchener tierärztliche
Wochenschrift.
1938 0003163

Berl Tierarztl Wochenschr
Berliner tierärztliche Wochenschrift
Continues: Rundschau auf dem Gebiete der
Thiermedicin und vergleichenden Pathologie.
Merged with Münchener tierärztliche
Wochenschrift to form Berliner und
Münchener tierärztliche Wochenschrift.
1888-1938 15520260R

Berufsdermatosen
Berufs-Dermatosen
0005-9498
Continues Dermatologische Gutachten.
Continued by Dermatosen in Beruf und
Umwelt. Occupational and environmental
dermatoses.
1953-1977 0372506

Berufsdermatosen (Monogr)
Berufsdermatosen. Monographien
1955-1964 0372507

Best Pract Benchmarking Healthc
Best practices and benchmarking in
healthcare: a practical journal for clinical
and management application
1085-0635
1996-1997 9605850

Best Pract Res Clin Anaesthesiol
Best practice & research. Clinical
anaesthesiology
1753-3740 1532-169X
Continues Baillière's best practice &
research. Clinical anaesthesiology.
2001 101121446

Best Pract Res Clin Endocrinol Metab
Best practice & research. Clinical
endocrinology & metabolism
1521-690X 1532-1908
Continues: Baillière's best practice &
research. Clinical endocrinology &
metabolism.
2001 101120682

Best Pract Res Clin Gastroenterol
Best practice & research. Clinical
gastroenterology
1521-6918 1532-1916
Continues: Baillière's best practice &
research. Clinical gastroenterology.
2001 101120605

Best Pract Res Clin Haematol
Best practice & research. Clinical
haematology
1521-6926 1532-1924
Continues: Baillière's best practice &
research. Clinical haematology.
2001 101120659

Best Pract Res Clin Obstet Gynaecol
Best practice & research. Clinical obstetrics
& gynaecology
1521-6934 1532-1932
Continues: Baillière's best practice &
research. Clinical obstetrics & gynaecology.
2001 101121582

Best Pract Res Clin Rheumatol
Best practice & research. Clinical
rheumatology
1521-6942 1532-1770
Continues: Baillière's best practice &
research. Clinical rheumatology.
2001 101121149

Bests Rev Life Health Insur Ed
Best's review. Life-health insurance edition
0005-9706
Formed by the union of: Best's insurance
news (Life ed.). and: Flitcraft courant.
Merged with: Best's review (Property/
casualty insurance ed.). to form: Best's review
(Oldwick, N.J.: 2000).
1969-1999 1263174

BETA
BETA bulletin of experimental treatments
for AIDS: a publication of the San Francisco
AIDS foundation
1058-708X
1990 9113964

Bibl Anat
Bibliotheca anatomica
0067-7833
1961-1988 0372510

Bibl Cardiol
Bibliotheca cardiologica
0067-7906
1939-1989 0372511

Bibl Gastroenterol
Bibliotheca gastroenterologica
0067-7949
1960-1970 7511109

Bibl Gynaecol
Bibliotheca gynaecologica
0301-3197
Continues Abhandlungen aus der
Geburtshülfe und Gynäkologie und ihren
Grenzgebieten. Supplement to Gynaecologia.
1948-1970   **1257334**

Bibl Haematol
Bibliotheca haematologica
0067-7957
Supplement to Acta haematologica and, 1960-
to Vox sanguinis. Continued by: Current
studies in hematology and blood transfusion.
1955-1985   **0372513**

Bibl Hig Instituta NR Srb
Biblioteka Higijenskog instituta NR Srbije
Continued by Biblioteka Zavoda za
zdravstvenu zaštitu NR Srbije
1952-1960   **0064720**

Bibl Laeger
Bibliotek for laeger
0006-1786
Absorbed: Medicinsk Forum.
1821   **15530210R**

Bibl Microbiol
Bibliotheca microbiologica
0067-8058
1960-1972   **0401637**

Bibl Nutr Dieta
Bibliotheca nutritio et dieta
0067-8198
Continued by: Forum of nutrition.
1960-2001   **0413657**

Bibl Ophthalmol
Bibliotheca ophthalmologica: supplementa
ad ophthalmologica
0067-8090
Continues: Abhandlungen aus der
Augenheilkunde und ihren Grenzgebieten.
Supplement to: Ophthalmologica, 1939-1965.
Merged with: Advances in ophthalmology,
and: Modern problems in ophthalmology, to
form: Developments in ophthalmology.
1939-1977   **0400647**

Bibl Paediatr
Bibliotheca paediatrica
0301-357X
Continues: Abhandlungen aus der
kinderheilkunde und ihren Grenzgebieten.
Continued by: Monographs in pediatrics.
1945-1968   **1264603**

Bibl Psychiatr
Bibliotheca psychiatrica
0067-8147
Continues: Bibliotheca psychiatrica et
neurologica. Continued by: Key issues in
mental health.
1970-2005   **0255452**

Bibl Psychiatr Neurol
Bibliotheca psychiatrica et neurologica
0366-256X
Continues: Abhandlungen aus der Neurologie,
Psychiatrie, Psychologie und ihren
Grenzgebieten. vol. 88, 1948 Continued by:
Bibliotheca psychiatrica.
1948-1969   **0256714**

Bibl Radiol
Bibliotheca radiologica
0067-8155
1959-1975   **0372515**

Bibl Tuberc
Bibliotheca tuberculosea
0300-1121
Continued by Bibliotheca tuberculosea et
medicinae thoracalis (v. 25 in this sequence
also has the later title) Issued 1948-55 as a
supplement to Schweizerische Zeitschrift für
Tuberkulose; 1956-61, to Schweizerische
Zeitschrift für Tuberkulose und Pneumologie;
1963-64, as an addition to Medicina
thoracalis.
1948-1970   **0347361**

Bibliogr Hisp
Bibliografía hispánica
0212-5129
Supersedes Bibliografía general española e
hispano-americano.
1942-1957   **58510580R**

Biblioteksbladet
Biblioteksbladet
0006-1867
1916   **57630560R**

Biken J
Biken journal
0006-2324
1958-1987   **0373117**

Bildgebung
Bildgebung = Imaging
1012-5655
Continues: Diagnostic imaging in clinical
medicine.
1988-1996   **8904648**

Bilt Hematol Transfuz
Bilten za hematologiju i transfuziju
0350-2023
Supersedes Bilten transfuzije. Continued by:
Bilten za hematologiju i transfuziologiju.
1973-1990   **7601504**

Bilt Mednar Fed Zob Teh
Bilten Mednarodne Federacije Zobotehnikov
= Bulletin Of The International Federation
Of Dental Technicians. Bulletin De La
Federation Internationale Prothesistes
Dentaires. Bulletin Der Internationalen
Foderation Der Zahntechniker
1966   **9883867**

Bilt Udruz Ortodonata Jugosl
Bilten Udruženja ortodonata Jugoslavije =
Bulletin of Orthodontic Society of Yugoslavia
0350-1043
1968-200u   **9005846**

Bing Du Xue Bao
Bing du xue bao = Chinese journal of
virology / [bian ji, Bing du xue bao bian ji
wei yuan hui]
1000-8721
1985   **8803009**

Binocul Vis Strabismus Q
Binocular vision & strabismus quarterly
1088-6281
Continues: Binocular vision & eye muscle
surgery quarterly.
1996   **9607281**

Biocell
Biocell: official journal of the Sociedades
Latinoamericanas de Microscopía
Electronica ... et. al
0327-9545
Continues: Microscopía electrónica y biología
celular.
1994   **9438655**

Biochem Biophys Res Commun
Biochemical and biophysical research
communications
0006-291X   1090-2104
Continued in part by: Molecular cell biology
research communications. Apr. 1999
1959   **0372516**

Biochem Cell Biol
Biochemistry and cell biology = Biochimie et
biologie cellulaire
0829-8211   1208-6002
Continues: Canadian journal of biochemistry
and cell biology.
1986   **8606068**

Biochem Clin
Biochemical clinics
0523-624X
1963-1964   **7611939**

Biochem Exp Biol
Biochemistry and experimental biology
0366-0060
Continues Biochimica e biologia
sperimentale.
1971-1980   **0416171**

Biochem Genet
Biochemical genetics
0006-2928   1573-4927
1967   **0126611**

Biochem Int
Biochemistry international
0158-5231
Continued by: Biochemistry and molecular
biology international.
1980-1992   **8100311**

Biochem J
The Biochemical journal
0264-6021   1470-8728
1906   **2984726R**

Biochem Med
Biochemical medicine
0006-2944
Continued by: Biochemical medicine and
metabolic biology.
1967-1985   **0151424**

Biochem Med Metab Biol
Biochemical medicine and metabolic biology
0885-4505
Continues: Biochemical medicine. Continued
by: Biochemical and molecular medicine.
1986-1994   **8605718**

Biochem Mol Biol Int
Biochemistry and molecular biology
international
1039-9712
Continues: Biochemistry international.
Continued by: IUBMB life.
1993-1999   **9306673**

Biochem Mol Med
Biochemical and molecular medicine
1077-3150
Continues: Biochemical medicine and
metabolic biology. Continued by: Molecular
genetics and metabolism.
1995-1997   **9508702**

Biochem Pharmacol
Biochemical pharmacology
0006-2952
1958   **0101032**

Biochem Soc Symp
Biochemical Society symposium
0067-8694   1744-1439
1948   **7506896**

Biochem Soc Trans
Biochemical Society transactions
0300-5127 1470-8752
1973 7506897

Biochem Z
Biochemische Zeitschrift
0366-0753
Absorbed: Beiträge zur chemischen
Physiologie und Pathologie. Continued by:
European journal of biochemistry.
1906-1966 15540070R

Biochemistry
Biochemistry
0006-2960 1520-4995
1962 0370623

Biochemistry (Mosc)
Biochemistry. Biokhimiiâ
0006-2979 1608-3040
1956 0376536

Biochim Biophys Acta
Biochimica et biophysica acta
0006-3002
1947 0217513

Biochimie
Biochimie
0300-9084 1638-6183
Continues the Bulletin of the Société de
chimie biologique.
1971 1264604

Bioconjug Chem
Bioconjugate chemistry
1043-1802 1520-4812
1990 9010319

Biocontrol Sci
Biocontrol science
1342-4815
1996 9712121

Biodegradation
Biodegradation
0923-9820
1990 9100834

BioDrugs
BioDrugs: clinical immunotherapeutics,
biopharmaceuticals and gene therapy
1173-8804
Continues: Clinical immunotherapeutics.
1997 9705305

Biodynamica
Biodynamica
0006-3010
1934-1973 0372520

Bioelectrochem Bioenerg
Bioelectrochemistry and bioenergetics
(Lausanne, Switzerland)
0302-4598
Separated from: Journal of electroanalytical
chemistry (Lausanne. Switzerland).
Continued by: Bioelectrochemistry
(Amsterdam. Netherlands).
1992-1999 9888877

Bioelectrochemistry
Bioelectrochemistry (Amsterdam,
Netherlands)
1567-5394 1878-562X
Continues: Bioelectrochemistry and
bioenergetics (Lausanne. Switzerland: 1992).
2000 100953583

Bioelectromagnetics
Bioelectromagnetics
0197-8462 1521-186X
1980 8008281

Bioessays
BioEssays: news and reviews in molecular,
cellular and developmental biology
0265-9247 1521-1878
1984 8510851

Bioethics
Bioethics
0269-9702 1467-8519
1987 8704792

Bioethics Q
Bioethics quarterly
0163-9803
Continues Bioethics Northwest. Continued by
Journal of bioethics.
1980-1981 8008852

Biofactors
BioFactors (Oxford, England)
0951-6433
1988 8807441

Biofeedback Self Regul
Biofeedback and self-regulation
0363-3586
Continued by: Applied psychophysiology and
biofeedback.
1976-1996 7605548

Biofizika
Biofizika
0006-3029
1956 0372666

Biofouling
Biofouling
0892-7014 1029-2454
1988 9200331

Biogerontology
Biogerontology
1389-5729
2000 100930043

Bioinformatics
Bioinformatics (Oxford, England)
1367-4803 1460-2059
Continues: Computer applications in the
biosciences.
1998 9808944

Bioinorg Chem
Bioinorganic chemistry
0006-3061
Continued by: Journal of inorganic
biochemistry..
1971-1978 1305411

Bioinspir Biomim
Bioinspiration & biomimetics
1748-3182 1748-3190
2006 101292902

Biokhimiia
Biokhimiiâ (Moscow, Russia)
0320-9725
1936 0372667

Biol
O Biologico
0366-0567
1935 15610210R

Biol Blood Marrow Transplant
Biology of blood and marrow
transplantation: journal of the
American Society for Blood and Marrow
Transplantation
1083-8791 1523-6536
1995 9600628

Biol Bull
The Biological bulletin
0006-3185
Continues: Zoölogical bulletin.
1899 2984727R

Biol Bull Acad Sci USSR
Biology bulletin of the Academy of Sciences
of the USSR
0098-2164
Continued by: Izvestiia Rossiĭskoĭ Akademii
Nauk. Seriia biologicheskaia. English. Biology
bulletin of the Russian Academy of Sciences.
1974-1991 7513560

Biol Cell
Biology of the cell / under the auspices of the
European Cell Biology Organization
0248-4900 1768-322X
Continues: Biologie cellulaire.
1981 8108529

Biol Chem
Biological chemistry
1431-6730
Continues: Biological chemistry Hoppe-Seyler.
1996 9700112

Biol Chem Hoppe Seyler
Biological chemistry Hoppe-Seyler
0177-3593
Continues: Hoppe-Seyler's Zeitschrift für
physiologische Chemie. Continued by:
Biological chemistry.
1985-1996 8503054

Biol Cybern
Biological cybernetics
0340-1200 1432-0770
Continues Kybernetik.
1975 7502533

Biol Direct
Biology direct
1745-6150
2006 101258412

Biol Gastroenterol (Paris)
Biologie et gastro-entérologie
0006-3258
Merged with Archives françaises des
maladies de l'appareil digestif to form
Gastroentérologie clinique et biologique.
Supplement to: Archives françaises des
maladies de l'appareil digestif.
1968-1976 0146364

Biol Hum Aff
Biology and human affairs: a British Social
Hygiene Council publication
0006-3355
Continues: Biology (British Social Hygiene
Council). Continued by: Social biology and
human affairs.
1943-1979 8213039

Biol Lat
Biologica Latina
0006-3150
Supersedes Annali di biologia normale e
patologica.
1948-1969 0372521

Biol Lett
Biology letters
1744-9561 1744-957X
Separated from: Proceedings. BIological
science.
2005 101247722

Biol Listy
Biologické listy
0366-0486
1913-2001 0234431

Biol Mass Spectrom
Biological mass spectrometry
1052-9306
Continues: Biomedical & environmental mass
spectrometry. Merged with: OMS, Organic
mass spectrometry, to form: Journal of mass
spectrometry.
1991-1994 9102982

Biol Med
Biologie et médecine
1947-1952   **15610220R**

Biol Med (Paris)
Biologie médicale
0006-3266
Supersedes another periodical with the same title.
1971-1975   **0347257**

Biol Med (Paris)
Biologie médicale
0006-3266
Continued by: Biologie médicale.
1903-1971   **0356566**

Biol Met
Biology of metals
0933-5854
Continued by: Biometals.
1988-1991   **8915662**

Biol Neonat
Biologia neonatorum. Neo-natal studies
0523-6525
Continues Etudes néo-natales. Issued under the auspices of the Centre international de l'enfance. Continued by Biology of the neonate.
1959-1969   **0067712**

Biol Neonate
Biology of the neonate
0006-3126   **1421-9727**
Continues: Biologia neonatorum. Absorbed: Developmental pharmacology and therapeutics. 1994- Continued by: Neonatology.
1970-2006   **0247551**

Biol Pharm Bull
Biological & pharmaceutical bulletin
0918-6158   **1347-5215**
Continues: Journal of pharmacobio-dynamics.
1993   **9311984**

Biol Psychiatry
Biological psychiatry
0006-3223   **1873-2402**
Supersedes: Recent advances in biological psychiatry.
1969   **0213264**

Biol Psychol
Biological psychology
0301-0511   **1873-6246**
1973   **0375566**

Biol Reprod
Biology of reproduction
0006-3363   **1529-7268**
1969   **0207224**

Biol Res
Biological research
0716-9760   **0717-6287**
Continues: Archivos de biología y medicina experimentales.
1992   **9308271**

Biol Res Nurs
Biological research for nursing
1099-8004
1999   **9815758**

Biol Res Pregnancy Perinatol
Biological research in pregnancy and perinatology
0724-438X
Continues: International journal of biological research in pregnancy.
1983-1987   **8302758**

Biol Rev Camb Philos Soc
Biological reviews of the Cambridge Philosophical Society
1464-7931   **1469-185X**
Continues: Biological reviews and biological proceedings of the Cambridge Philosophical Society.
1935   **0414576**

Biol Rev City Coll
The Biological review of the City College
1938-1958   **0101241**

Biol Sci Space
Biological sciences in space = Uchū seibutsu kagaku
0914-9201   **1349-967X**
1987   **100972048**

Biol Signals
Biological signals
1016-0922
Continued by: Biological signals and receptors.
1992-1997   **9210083**

Biol Signals Recept
Biological signals and receptors
1422-4933
Continues: Biological signals. Continued by: Neuro-Signals.
1998-2001   **9808792**

Biol Struct Morphog
Biological structures and morphogenesis
0989-8972
Continues: Archives d'anatomie microscopique et de morphologie expérimentale.
1988-1992   **8807439**

Biol Trace Elem Res
Biological trace element research
0163-4984   **1559-0720**
1979   **7911509**

Biologia (Bratisl)
Biologia
0006-3088
Continues the Biologický sborník.
1953   **0370624**

Biologica (Santiago)
Biologica (Santiago, Chile)
0300-9866
1944-1967   **0376537**

Biologicals
Biologicals: journal of the International Association of Biological Standardization
1045-1056   **1095-8320**
Continues: Journal of biological standardization.
1990   **9004494**

Biologist (London)
Biologist (London, England)
0006-3347
Continues: Institute of Biology journal.
1969   **9108399**

Biom J
Biometrical journal. Biometrische Zeitschrift
0323-3847   **1521-4036**
Continues: Biometrische Zeitschrift.
1977   **7708048**

Biom Z
Biometrische Zeitschrift
0006-3452
Continued by Biometrical journal.
1959-1976   **0372670**

Biomacromolecules
Biomacromolecules
1525-7797   **1526-4602**
2000   **100892849**

Biomarkers
Biomarkers: biochemical indicators of exposure, response, and susceptibility to chemicals
1354-750X   **1366-5804**
1996   **9606000**

Biomater Artif Cells Artif Organs
Biomaterials, artificial cells, and artificial organs
0890-5533
Continues: Biomaterials, medical devices, and artificial organs. Continued by: Biomaterials, artificial cells, and immobilization biotechnology.
1987-1991   **8802605**

Biomater Artif Cells Immobilization Biotechnol
Biomaterials, artificial cells, and immobilization biotechnology: official journal of the International Society for Artificial Cells and Immobilization Biotechnology
1055-7172
Continued by: Artificial cells, blood substitutes, and immobilization biotechnology.
1991-1993   **9111988**

Biomater Med Devices Artif Organs
Biomaterials, medical devices, and artificial organs
0090-5488
Continued by: Biometerials, artificial cells, and artificial organs.
1973-1986   **0356630**

Biomaterials
Biomaterials
0142-9612   **1878-5905**
1980   **8100316**

Biomech Model Mechanobiol
Biomechanics and modeling in mechanobiology
1617-7959   **1617-7940**
2002   **101135325**

Biomed Biochim Acta
Biomedica biochimica acta
0232-766X
Continues: Acta biologica et medica Germanica.
1983-1991   **8304435**

Biomed Chromatogr
Biomedical chromatography: BMC
0269-3879   **1099-0801**
1986   **8610241**

Biomed Commun
Biomedical communications
0092-8607
1973-1984   **0353474**

Biomed Eng
Biomedical engineering
0006-2898
Continued by: Journal of medical engineering & technology..
1965-1976   **0076362**

Biomed Eng (NY)
Biomedical engineering
0006-3398   **1573-8256**
1967   **0140672**

Biomed Eng Online
Biomedical engineering online
    1475-925X
2002   **101147518**

Biomed Environ Mass Spectrom
Biomedical & environmental mass
spectrometry
0887-6134
Continues: Biomedical mass spectrometry.
Continued by: Biological mass spectrometry.
1986-1990   8603224

Biomed Environ Sci
Biomedical and environmental sciences: BES
0895-3988
1988   8909524

Biomed Instrum
Bio-Medical instrumentation
1964-1964   0003354

Biomed Instrum Technol
Biomedical instrumentation & technology /
Association for the Advancement of Medical
Instrumentation
0899-8205
Formed by the merger of: Medical
instrumentation, and: Biomedical technology
today.
1989   8905560

Biomed Khim
Biomeditŝinskaiâ khimiiâ
Continues: Voprosy meditŝinskoĭ khimii.
2003   101196966

Biomed Mass Spectrom
Biomedical mass spectrometry
0306-042X
Continued by: Biomedical & environmental
mass spectrometry.
1974-1985   0430246

Biomed Mater
Biomedical materials (Bristol, England)
1748-6041   1748-605X
2006   101285195

Biomed Mater Eng
Bio-medical materials and engineering
0959-2989
1991   9104021

Biomed Microdevices
Biomedical microdevices
1387-2176   1572-8781
1998   100887374

**Biomed Pap Med Fac Univ Palacky Olomouc
Czech Repub**
Biomedical papers of the Medical Faculty
of the University Palacký, Olomouc,
Czechoslovakia
1213-8118
Vols. 53-144, published 1985-2000, issued as
a subseries of Acta Universitatis Palackianae
Olomucensis Facultatis Medicae. Issued
independently, continuing the numbering of
the earlier main series, beginning with v. 145,
no. 1 (Sept. 2001).
1985   101140142

Biomed Pept Proteins Nucleic Acids
Biomedical peptides, proteins & nucleic
acids: structure, synthesis & biological
activity
1353-8616
1994-1997   9506699

Biomed Pharmacother
Biomedicine & pharmacotherapy =
Biomédecine & pharmacothérapie
0753-3322   1950-6007
Continues: Biomedicine.
1982   8213295

Biomed Purv
Bio-medical purview
1961-1963   15610300R

Biomed Res
Biomedical research (Tokyo, Japan)
0388-6107   1880-313x
1980   8100317

Biomed Sci
Biomedical science
0955-9701
1990-1991   9010320

Biomed Sci Instrum
Biomedical sciences instrumentation
0067-8856   1938-1158
1963   0140524

Biomed Sci Technol
Biomedical science and technology
1051-2020
1991-1992   9104836

Biomed Tech (Berl)
Biomedizinische Technik. Biomedical
engineering
0013-5585
Continues: Elektromedizin.
1971   1262533

Biomedica
Biomédica: revista del Instituto Nacional de
Salud
0120-4157
1981   8205605

Biomedicine
Biomedicine / [publiée pour l'A.A.I.C.I.G.]
0300-0893
Continues: Revue européenne d'études
cliniques et biologiques. Continued by:
Biomedicine & pharmacotherapy.
1973-1981   0361342

Biomembranes
Biomembranes
0067-8864
1971-1984   2984282R

Biometals
Biometals: an international journal on the
role of metal ions in biology, biochemistry,
and medicine
0966-0844   1572-8773
Continues: Biology of metals.
1992   9208478

Biometrics
Biometrics
0006-341X   1541-0420
1945   0370625

Biometrika
Biometrika
0006-3444
1901   0413661

Biomol Eng
Biomolecular engineering
1389-0344
Continues: Genetic analysis. Continued by:
New biotechnology.
1999-2007   100928062

Bioorg Chem
Bioorganic chemistry
0045-2068   1090-2120
1971   1303703

Bioorg Khim
Bioorganicheskaia khimiia
0132-3423
1975   7804941

Bioorg Med Chem
Bioorganic & medicinal chemistry
0968-0896   1464-3391
1993   9413298

Bioorg Med Chem Lett
Bioorganic & medicinal chemistry letters
0960-894X   1464-3405
1991   9107377

Biopharm Drug Dispos
Biopharmaceutics & drug disposition
0142-2782   1099-081X
1979   7911226

Biophys Chem
Biophysical chemistry
0301-4622   1873-4200
1973   0403171

Biophys J
Biophysical journal
0006-3495   1542-0086
1960   0370626

Biophys Struct Mech
Biophysics of structure and mechanism
0340-1057
Continued by European biophysics journal.
1974-1984   7502020

Biophysics (Oxf)
Biophysics
0006-3509
1957   0376540

Biophysik
Biophysik
0006-3517
Continued by Radiation and environmental
biophysics.
1963-1973   0413060

Biopolym Symp
Biopolymers symposia
1964-1964   23630410R

Biopolymers
Biopolymers
0006-3525   1097-0282
Absorbed: Biospectroscopy. 2000
1963   0372525

Bioprocess Biosyst Eng
Bioprocess and biosystems engineering
1615-7591   1615-7605
Continues: Bioprocess engineering (Berlin,
Germany).
2001   101088505

Bioprocess Technol
Bioprocess technology
0888-7470
Continued by: Biotechnology and
bioprocessing series.
1986-1999   8601086

Bioresour Technol
Bioresource technology
0960-8524   1873-2976
Formed by the union of: Biomass (Barking,
London, England); and: Biological wastes;
and continues the vol. numbering of the latter.
1991   9889523

Biorheology
Biorheology
0006-355X
1962   0372526

Biorheology Suppl
Biorheology. Supplement: the official journal
of the International Society of Biorheology
0891-978X
1984-1984   8503530

Bios
Bios
0366-2284
1930   15620020R

Biosci Biotechnol Biochem
Bioscience, biotechnology, and biochemistry
0916-8451   1347-6947
Continues: Agricultural and biological
chemistry.
1992   9205717

Biosci Rep
Bioscience reports
0144-8463
1981   8102797

Bioscience
Bioscience
0006-3568
Continues the A. I. B. S. bulletin. Absorbed
AIBS newsletter, Jan. 1970.
1964   0231737

Biosecur Bioterror
Biosecurity and bioterrorism: biodefense
strategy, practice, and science
1538-7135   1557-850X
2003   101156085

Biosens Bioelectron
Biosensors & bioelectronics
0956-5663   1873-4235
Continues: Biosensors.
1990   9001289

Biosensors
Biosensors
0265-928X
Continued by: Biosensors & bioelectronics.
1985-1989   8601088

Bioseparation
Bioseparation
0923-179X
1990-2001   9011423

Biospectroscopy
Biospectroscopy
1075-4261
Absorbed by: Biopolymers.
1995-1999   9605413

Biostatistics
Biostatistics (Oxford, England)
1465-4644   1468-4357
2000   100897327

Biosystems
Bio Systems
0303-2647   1872-8324
Continues Currents in modern biology.
1974   0430773

Biotech Histochem
Biotechnic & histochemistry: official
publication of the Biological Stain
Commission
1052-0295   1473-7760
Continues: Stain technology.
1991   9107378

Biotechniques
BioTechniques
0736-6205   1940-9818
1983   8306785

Biotechnol Adv
Biotechnology advances
0734-9750   1873-1899
1983   8403708

Biotechnol Annu Rev
Biotechnology annual review
1387-2656
1995   9616443

Biotechnol Appl Biochem
Biotechnology and applied biochemistry
0885-4513   1470-8744
Continues: Journal of applied biochemistry.
1986   8609465

Biotechnol Bioeng
Biotechnology and bioengineering
0006-3592   1097-0290
Continues: Journal of biochemical and
microbiological technology and engineering.
1962   7502021

Biotechnol Bioeng Symp
Biotechnology and bioengineering
symposium
0572-6565
1967-1986   1302775

Biotechnol Focus
Biotechnology focus
0935-1043
1988-1992   9200334

Biotechnol Genet Eng Rev
Biotechnology & genetic engineering reviews
0264-8725
1984   8510274

Biotechnol J
Biotechnology journal
1860-6768   1860-7314
2006   101265833

Biotechnol Lett
Biotechnology letters
0141-5492   1573-6776
Absorbed: Biotechnology techniques. 2000
1979   8008051

Biotechnol Prog
Biotechnology progress
8756-7938   1520-6033
1985   8506292

Biotechnol Ther
Biotechnology therapeutics
0898-2848
1989-1995   8918082

Biotechnology
Biotechnology (Reading, Mass.)
0740-7378
1982-1995   8300602

Biotechnology (N Y)
Bio/technology (Nature Publishing
Company)
0733-222X
Continued by: Nature biotechnology.
1983-1996   8309273

Biotelem Patient Monit
Biotelemetry and patient monitoring
0378-309X
Continues Biotelemetry. Continued by Acute
care.
1978-1982   7805924

Biotelemetry
Biotelemetry
0301-5912
Continued by Biotelemetry and patient
monitoring.
1974-1977   0430774

Biotherapy
Biotherapy (Dordrecht, Netherlands)
0921-299X
1988-1998   8903031

Bipolar Disord
Bipolar disorders
1398-5647   1399-5618
1999   100883596

Birth
Birth (Berkeley, Calif.)
0730-7659   1523-536X
Continues: Birth and the family journal.
1982   8302042

Birth Defects Orig Artic Ser
Birth defects original article series
0547-6844
1965-1996   0003403

Birth Defects Res A Clin Mol Teratol
Birth defects research. Part A, Clinical and
molecular teratology
1542-0752   1542-0760
Continues: Teratology.
2003   101155107

Birth Defects Res B Dev Reprod Toxicol
Birth defects research. Part B,
Developmental and reproductive toxicology
1542-9733   1542-9741
Continues: Teratogenesis, carcinogenesis, and
mutagenesis.
2003   101155115

Birth Defects Res C Embryo Today
Birth defects research. Part C, Embryo
today: reviews
1542-975X   1542-9768
2003   101167665

Birth Gaz
The Birth gazette
0890-3255
Continues: Practicing midwife.
1986-2000   9306676

Biul Inst Med Morsk Gdansk
Biuletyn Instytutu Medycyny Morskiej w
Gdańsku
0020-4463
Continues Biuletyn Państwowego Instytutu
Medycyny Morskiej i Tropikalnej w Gdańsku.
Biulleten' Gosudarstvennogo Instituta
morskoĭ i tropicheskoĭ meditsiny v Gdan'ske.
Bulletin of the State Institute of Marine
and Tropical Medicine inGdańsk, Poland.
Continued by Bulletin of the Institute of
Maritime and Tropical Medicine in Gdynia.
1957-1974   7603013

Biul Inst Rosl Lecz Inst Przem Zielar Pozn Pol
Biuletyn Instytutu Roślin Leczniczych.
Instytut Przemysłu Zielarskiego (Poznań,
Poland)
Continues Biuletyn of the Państwowy
Instytut Naukowy Leczniczych Surowców
Roślinnych. Continued by Herba Polonica.
1965-19uu   0242245

Biul Panstw Inst Med Morsk Trop J W Gdansku
Biuletyn Państwowego Instytutu Medycyny
Morskiej i Tropikalnej w Gdańsku.
Biulleten' Gosudarstvennogo Instituta
morskoĭ i tropicheskoĭ meditsiny v
Gdan'ske. Bulletin of the State Institute of
Marine and Tropical Medicine in Gdańsk,
Poland
0208-5089
Continues Bulletin of the Institute of Marine
and Tropical Medicine, Medical Academy
in Gdańsk, Poland. Continued by Biuletyn
Instytutu Medycyny Morskiej w Gdańsku.
1950-1956   7802786

Biull Eksp Biol Med
Biulleten' eksperimental'noĭ biologii i
meditsiny
0365-9615
1936   0370627

**Biull Vsesoiuznogo Kardiol Nauchn Tsentra AMN
SSSR**
Biulleten' Vsesoiuznogo kardiologicheskogo
nauchnogo tsentra AMN SSSR
0201-7369
1978-1989   8003723

Biulleten Russ SFSR Minist Zdravookhraneniia Uchenyi Meditsinskii sov
Biulleten'. Russian S.F.S.R. Ministerstvo Zdravookhraneniia. Uchenyĭ meditsinskiĭ sovet
1960-1972   0025435

BJOG
BJOG: an international journal of obstetrics and gynaecology
1470-0328   1471-0528
Continues: British journal of obstetrics and gynaecology.
2000   100935741

BJR Suppl
BJR supplement / BIR
0961-2653
Continues: British journal of radiology. Supplement. Supplement to: British journal of radiology.
1989   9011426

BJU Int
BJU international
1464-4096   1464-410X
Some issues consist of: European urology update series, formerly issued separately.
1999   100886721

Bl Zahnheilkd
Blätter für Zahnheilkunde. Bulletin dentaire
0084-7917
1940-1972   0373120

Blood
Blood
0006-4971   1528-0020
1946   7603509

Blood Cells
Blood cells
0340-4684
Continued by: Blood cells, molecules & diseases.
1975-1994   7513567

Blood Cells Mol Dis
Blood cells, molecules & diseases
1079-9796   1096-0961
Continues: Blood cells.
1995   9509932

Blood Coagul Fibrinolysis
Blood coagulation & fibrinolysis: an international journal in haemostasis and thrombosis
0957-5235   1473-5733
1990   9102551

Blood Press
Blood pressure
0803-7051   1651-1999
1992   9301454

Blood Press Monit
Blood pressure monitoring
1359-5237   1473-5725
1996   9606438

Blood Press Suppl
Blood pressure. Supplement
0803-8023
1992   9300787

Blood Purif
Blood purification
0253-5068   1421-9735
1983   8402040

Blood Rev
Blood reviews
0268-960X   1532-1681
1987   8708558

Blood Transfus
Blood transfusion = Trasfusione del sangue
1723-2007
Continues: Trasfusione del sangue.
2003   101237479

Blood Vessels
Blood vessels
0303-6847
Continues Angiologica. Continued by: Journal of vascular research.
1974-1991   0427130

Blue Cross Assoc Res Ser
Blue Cross Association research series
0095-6740
Continues Blue Cross reports; research series.
1974-1975   7501729

Blut
Blut
0006-5242
Absorbed Folia haematologica, München, in 1965. Continued by: Annals of hematology.
1955-1990   0173401

Blutalkohol
Blutalkohol
0006-5250
1961   0372531

BMB Rep
BMB reports
1976-6696   1976-670X
Continues: Journal of biochemistry and molecular biology.
2008   101465334

BMC Biochem
BMC biochemistry
    1471-2091
2000   101084098

BMC Bioinformatics
BMC bioinformatics
    1471-2105
2000   100965194

BMC Biol
BMC biology
    1741-7007
2003   101190720

BMC Biotechnol
BMC biotechnology
    1472-6750
2001   101088663

BMC Cancer
BMC cancer
    1471-2407
2001   100967800

BMC Cardiovasc Disord
BMC cardiovascular disorders
    1471-2261
2001   100968539

BMC Cell Biol
BMC cell biology
    1471-2121
2000   100966972

BMC Clin Pharmacol
BMC clinical pharmacology
    1472-6904
2001   101088667

BMC Complement Altern Med
BMC complementary and alternative medicine
    1472-6882
2001   101088661

BMC Dermatol
BMC dermatology
    1471-5945
2001   100968541

BMC Dev Biol
BMC developmental biology
    1471-213X
2001   100966973

BMC Ecol
BMC ecology
    1472-6785
2001   101088674

BMC Emerg Med
BMC emergency medicine
    1471-227X
2001   100968543

BMC Evol Biol
BMC evolutionary biology
    1471-2148
2001   100966975

BMC Fam Pract
BMC family practice
    1471-2296
2000   100967792

BMC Gastroenterol
BMC gastroenterology
    1471-230X
2001   100968547

BMC Genet
BMC genetics
    1471-2156
2000   100966978

BMC Genomics
BMC genomics
    1471-2164
2000   100965258

BMC Geriatr
BMC geriatrics
    1471-2318
2001   100968548

BMC Health Serv Res
BMC health services research
    1472-6963
2001   101088677

BMC Immunol
BMC immunology
    1471-2172
2000   100966980

BMC Infect Dis
BMC infectious diseases
    1471-2334
2001   100968551

BMC Med
BMC medicine
    1741-7015
2003   101190723

BMC Med Educ
BMC medical education
    1472-6920
2001   101088679

BMC Med Ethics
BMC medical ethics
    1472-6939
2000   101088680

BMC Med Genet
BMC medical genetics
    1471-2350
2000   100968552

BMC Med Imaging
BMC medical imaging
1471-2342
2001 100968553

BMC Med Inform Decis Mak
BMC medical informatics and decision
making
1472-6947
2001 101088682

BMC Med Res Methodol
BMC medical research methodology
1471-2288
2001 100968545

BMC Microbiol
BMC microbiology
1471-2180
2001 100966981

BMC Mol Biol
BMC molecular biology
1471-2199
2000 100966983

BMC Musculoskelet Disord
BMC musculoskeletal disorders
1471-2474
2000 100968565

BMC Nephrol
BMC nephrology
1471-2369
2000 100967793

BMC Neurol
BMC neurology
1471-2377
2001 100968555

BMC Neurosci
BMC neuroscience
1471-2202
2000 100966986

BMC Ophthalmol
BMC ophthalmology
1471-2415
2001 100967802

BMC Pediatr
BMC pediatrics
1471-2431
2001 100967804

BMC Pharmacol
BMC pharmacology
1471-2210
2001 100967806

BMC Physiol
BMC physiology
1472-6793
2001 101088687

BMC Plant Biol
BMC plant biology
1471-2229
2001 100967807

BMC Pregnancy Childbirth
BMC pregnancy and childbirth
1471-2393
2001 100967799

BMC Psychiatry
BMC psychiatry
1471-244X
2001 100968559

BMC Public Health
BMC public health
1471-2458
2001 100968562

BMC Pulm Med
BMC pulmonary medicine
1471-2466
2001 100968563

BMC Struct Biol
BMC structural biology
1472-6807
2001 101088689

BMC Surg
BMC surgery
1471-2482
2001 100968567

BMC Syst Biol
BMC systems biology
1752-0509
2007 101301827

BMC Urol
BMC urology
1471-2490
2001 100968571

BMC Vet Res
BMC veterinary research
1746-6148
2005 101249759

BMC Womens Health
BMC women's health
1472-6874
2001 101088690

BMJ
BMJ (Clinical research ed.)
0959-8138 1468-5833
Continues: British medical journal (Clinical
research ed.).
1988 8900488

BMJ (Int Ed)
BMJ (International edition)
0959-8146
1988 101090866

BMJ Clin Evid
BMJ clinical evidence
1752-8526
Continues: Clinical evidence.
2006 101294314

BMQ
BMQ; the Boston medical quarterly
0524-1162
1950-1966 0120774

BNWL Rep
BNWL [reports]. U.S. Atomic Energy
Commission
1965-1977 0036320

Body Image
Body image
1740-1445 1873-6807
2004 101222431

Body Posit
The Body positive
1048-4396
198u-2006 9887196

Boei Eisei
[Bōei eisei] Japanese Defense Forces medical
journal
0006-5528
Continues Hoan eisei.
1959-1997 17410030R

Bol Acad Nac Med
Boletim da Academia Nacional de Medicina
0001-3838
Continued by: Anais da Academia Nacional
de Medicina. SR0075997
1889-199u 7504608

Bol Acad Peru Cir
Boletín. Academia Peruana de Cirugía
Supersedes Rivista de Cirugía. Continued by
Academia Peruana de Cirugía.
1947-1950 14490470R

Bol Agrup Medica Estud La Paz
Boletín ... Agrupación Médica de Estudios,
La Paz
1945-19uu 14650300R

Bol Asoc Argent Odontol Ninos
Boletín de la Asociación Argentina de
Odontología para Niños
0518-9160
1959 7505278

Bol Asoc Med P R
Boletín de la Asociación Médica de Puerto Rico
0004-4849
1903 7505267

Bol Asoc Med Santiago Caballer
Boletín. Asociación Médica de Santiago de
los Caballeros
1943-195u 15330340R

Bol Asoc Medica Nac Repub Panama
Boletín. Asociación Médica Nacional de la
República Panamá
Merged with the Archivos of the Hospital
Santo Tomás of Panama to form Archivos
médicos panameños.
1938-1951 15330420R

Bol Asoc Venez Enferm Prof
Boletín. Asociación Venezolana de
Enfermeras Profesionales
1966-1966 0063742

Bol B Aires Univ Nac Inst Clin Quir
Boletín. Buenos Aires. Universidad Nacional.
Instituto de Clínica Quirúrgica
1925-1950 15750790R

Bol Cent Estud Hosp Serv Estado
Boletim do Centro de Estudos, Hospital dos
Servidores do Estado
Continued by: Revista medica do HSE.
1949-1970 7505254

Bol Chil Parasitol
Boletín chileno de parasitología
0365-9402 0717-6325
Continues: Boletín de informaciones
parasitarias chilenas. Merged with:
Parasitología al día; to form: Parasitología
latinoamericana.
1954-2001 2984728R

Bol Circ Argent Odontol
Boletín - Círculo Argentino de Odontología
0069-4207
Continues the Boletín of the Círculo
Odontológico del Oeste, Buenos Aires.
1962-1969 7505270

Bol Clin
Boletín clínico
Merged with the Anales of the Academia
de Medicina de Medellín to form Antioquia
médica.
1932-1950 15630200R

Bol Clin Estat
Boletim clínico e de estatística. Lisbon.
Hospital Colonial
Continued by: hospital under its later name:
Lisbon. Hospital do Ultramar.
1948-1950 18330790R

Bol Clin Hosp Civis Lisb
Boletim clínico dos Hospitais Civis de Lisboa
0374-6070
Continues: Boletim clínico e de estatística
dos Hospitais Civis de Lisboa.
1946-198u 9427243

Bol Col Med Camaguey Cuba
Boletín. Colegio Médico de Camagüey, Cuba
1938-1959   **16310350R**

Bol Col Prof Enferm P R
Boletin - Colegio de Profesionales de la
Enfermería de Puerto Rico
0145-6245
Supersedes Puerto Rico y su enfermera.
1975-1994   **7700173**

Bol Cons Nac Tuberc Cuba
Boletín. Consejo Nacional de Tuberculosis
(Cuba)
Continues the council's Boletín de
información.
194u-19uu   **16430500R**

Bol Cuba Cuerpo Polic Nac
Boletín … Cuba. Cuerpo de la Policía
Nacional. Sección de Sanidad
1945-1951   **16430540R**

Bol Cult Inf Cons Gen Col Med Esp
Boletin cultural e informativo - Consejo
General de Colegios Medicos de España
0376-6209
1946-1970   **7607103**

Bol Dent Oper
Boletim de dentística operatória
0365-9550
1969-1974   **9430141**

Bol Dent Urug
Boletin dental uruguayo
1934-1965   **15640220R**

Bol Dir Gen Odontol (Santa Fe)
Boletín. Santa Fé, Argentine Republic
(Province) Dirección General de
Odontología
1960-19uu   **22920690R**

Bol Div Nac Dermatol Sanit
Boletim da Divisão Nacional de
Dermatologia Sanitária
0100-297X
Continues Boletim da Divisão Nacional de
Lepra.
1975-1978   **7610401**

Bol Educ Fis (Santiago)
Boletin de educación física
0716-3436
Continues: Educación física. Continued by:
Revista chilena de educación física.
1935-1950   **15630230R**

Bol Epidemiol (Mex City Mex)
Boletín epidemiológico (Mexico City,
Mexico)
1944-uuuu   **9422437**

Bol Equipe Odontol Sanit
Boletim Da Equipe De Odontologia
Sanitaria
1960-19uu   **9877837**

Bol Estud Med Biol
Boletín de estudios médicos y biológicos
0067-9666
Continues the Boletín of the Instituto de
Estudios Médicos y Biológicos. Universidad
Nacional Autónoma de México.
1967   **0136501**

Bol Fac Farm Odontol Ribeirao Preto
Boletim da Faculdade de Farmácia e
Odontologia de Ribeirão Prêto
0080-2913
Continued by: Revista da Faculdade de
Farmácia e Odontologia de Ribeirão Prêto.
1964-1970   **7509341**

Bol Fac Odontol Piracicaba
Boletim - Faculdade de Odontologia de
Piracicaba
Continues Boletim - Faculdade de Farmácia e
Odontologia de Piracicaba.
1967-1976   **7506906**

Bol Hig Ment
Boletim de higiene mental
1944-1963   **0231740**

**Bol Hosp Mil Cuba Ejercito Hosp Mil Dr Carlos
J Finlay**
Boletín del Hospital Militar. Cuba. Ejército.
Hospital Militar Dr. Carlos J. Finlay
1948-1957   **16430550R**

Bol Hosp Oftalmol
Boletín. Mexico (City) Hospital
Oftalmológico de Nuestra Señora de la Luz
0018-5760
1940-2000   **18650380R**

Bol Hosp Vina Mar
Boletín del Hospital Viña del Mar:
publicación de la Fundación Científica
"Lucas Sierra"
0367-6455
Continues: Boletín trimestral (Hospital de
Viña del Mar).
1976   **9203176**

Bol Inf Asoc Med Argent
Boletin Informativo - Asociación Médica
Argentina
1666-2687
1994   **9888996**

Bol Inf Col Odontol Estomatol (Barc)
Boletin de información - Ilustre Colegio
Oficial de Odontólogos y Estomatólogos 2. a
Región (Cataluña)
1957-1976   **7604122**

Bol Inf Dent (Madr)
Boletín de información dental
0006-6311
Continues Información dental. issued
by the Consejo General de Colegios de
Odontólogos. Continued by Revista de
actualidad estomatológica española.
1954-1983   **17610060R**

Bol Inf Hisp Am Hist Med
Boletín informativo hispanoamericano de
historia de la medicina
0523-9168
1964-1979   **0110466**

Bol Inf Parasit Chil
Boletin de informaciones parasitarias
chilenas
Continues Boletín de información técnica of
the Departamento de Parasitología. Dirección
General de Sanidad. Continued by Boletín
chileno de parasitología.
1949-1953   **15630340R**

Bol Inst Estud Med Biol Univ Nac Auton Mex
Boletin del Instituto de Estudios Médicos y
Biológicos, Universidad Nacional Autónoma
de México
0366-1695
Continues Boletín del Laboratorio de
Estudios Médicos y Biológicos, Universidad
Nacional Autónoma de México. Continued by
Boletín de estudios médicos y biológicos.
1945-1966   **7506943**

Bol Inst Int Am Prot Infanc
Boletín del Instituto Internacional
Americano de Protección a la Infancia.
Interamerican Children's Institute
0366-1849
Continued by: Boletín del Instituto
Interamericano del Niño.
1927-1957   **14820030R**

Bol Inst Psicopedag Nac
Boletín. Lima. Instituto Psicopedagógico
Nacional
1942-1962   **18330560R**

Bol Inst Pueric
Boletim do Instituto de Puericultura
Continued by the Boletim of the Instituto de
Puericultura e Pediatria Martagão Gesteira.
1938-1964   **0262147**

Bol Inst Pueric Martagao Gesteira
Boletim do Instituto de Puericultura e
Pediatria Martagão Gesteira
0080-3170
Continues the Boletim do Instituto de
Puericultura.
1965-1974   **0262272**

Bol Inst Super Hig Doutor Ricardo Jorge
Boletim do Instituto Superior de Higiene
Doutor Ricardo Jorge
Continued by: Boletim dos serviços de saúde
pública.
1946-1953   **101233389**

Bol Liga Contra Cancer Havana
Boletín de la Liga Contra el Cáncer. Liga
Contra el Cáncer (Cuba)
Absorbed: Archivos cubanos de cancerología.
Continues in part: Boletín de la Liga Contra
el Cáncer.
1930-1960   **18330120R**

Bol Mat Dent
Boletim de materiais dentários
0045-2378
1969-1971   **1265350**

Bol Med
Boletín médico
1948-1956   **15640300R**

Bol Med Hosp Infant Mex
Boletín médico del Hospital Infantil de
México
0539-6115
1944   **0414106**

Bol Mens Estad Demogr Sanit Penins Islas Adyac
Boletín mensual de estadística demográfico-
sanitaria de la península é islas adyacentes
/ Ministerio de la Gobernación del Reino,
Dirección General de Beneficencia y Sanidad
1697-6304
Continued by: Boletín demográfico sanitario.
1879-188u   **101244636**

Bol Odontol (B Aires)
Boletín odontológico
Supersedes Boletín dental argentino.
1966-1970   **0121300**

Bol Odontol (Bogota)
Boletín de odontología
1935-1972   **15640070R**

Bol Odontol Mex
Boletín odontológico mexicano
1920-19uu   **15640450R**

Bol Of Sanit Panam (Engl)
Boletín de la Oficina Sanitaria
Panamericana. English ed
0257-0092
1966-1973   **0411226**

Bol Oficina Sanit Panam
Boletín de la Oficina Sanitaria
Panamericana. Pan American Sanitary
Bureau
0030-0632
Continues: Boletín panamericano de sanidad.
Merged with: Bulletin of the Pan American
Health Organization. to form: Revista
panamericana de salud pública.
1923-1996   **0414762**

Bol Patol Med
Boletín. Madrid. Hospital Provincial.
Instituto de Patología Médica
0366-2144
Continued by: Boletin de Patologia Medica.
1946-1961   **18410490R**

Bol Protes
Boletín de prótesis
Continues Ecos de prótesis.
1966-1969   **0121301**

Bol Sanat Sao Lucas
Boletim. São Paulo, Brazil (City) Sanatorio
São Lucas
1939-1959   **20610320R**

Bol Sanid Mil
Boletin de sanidad militar
Continued by Revista de sanidad militar.
1948-1954   **15640150R**

Bol Sao Paulo Braz State Reparticao Aguas Esgotos
Boletim. São Paulo, Brazil (State)
Repartição de Aguas e Esgotos
Continued by: Revista of the Departamento
de Aguas e Esgotos of São Paulo.
1936-1952   **20610410R**

Bol Serv Odontol Sanit (Porto Alegre)
Boletim Do Servico De Odontologia
Sanitaria Da Secretaria Da Saude Do Rio
Grande Do Sul
19uu   **9875598**

Bol Soc Catalana Pediatr
Boletín de la Sociedad Catalana de Pediatría
0304-498X
Issued 1959-1962? as a supplement to Anales
de medicina. Continues Pediatría.
1959-1977   **7506930**

Bol Soc Chil Obstet Ginecol
Boletin. Sociedad Chilena de Obstetricia y
Ginecología
Continued by the Revista chilena de
obstetricia y ginecología.
1935-1960   **20140280R**

Bol Soc Cir Rosario
Boletines de la Sociedad de Cirugía de
Rosario
0037-8526
1934-1979   **7506919**

Bol Soc Cir Urug
Boletín. Sociedad de Cirugía del Uruguay
Continues the Boletín of the Sociedad de
Cirugía de Montevideo. Continued by the
Revista de cirugía del Uruguay.
1942-1964   **0143406**

Bol Soc Cubana Dermatol Sifilogr
Boletín. Sociedad Cubana de Dermatología
y Sifilografía
1929-1961   **20810450R**

Bol Soc Dent Guatem
Boletín de la Sociedad Dental de Guatemala
0081-0614
1968-1969   **7506932**

Bol Soc Estomatol Argent
Boletin De La Sociedad Estomatologica
Argentina
19uu   **9875599**

Bol Soc Med Cir Camp
Boletim. Sociedade de Medicina e Cirurgia
de Campinas
Absorbed by: Revista paulista de medicina.
1940-1949   **20820470R**

Bol Soc Med Mendoza
Boletín. Sociedad Médica de Mendoza
0326-9264
1943-1950   **20820120R**

Bol Soc Quim Peru
Boletín de la Sociedad Química del Péru
0037-8623
1934   **7506935**

Bol Soc Valencia Pediatr
Boletín de la Sociedad Valenciana de
Pediatría
0489-3824
1959-1969   **7506937**

Bol Tr Soc Argent Cir
Boletines y trabajos - Sociedad Argentina de
Cirujanos
1940-1977   **7506922**

Bol Trab Acad Argent Cir
Boletines y trabajos / Academia Argentina
de Cirugía. Academia Argentina de Cirugía
Continues: Boletines y trabajos (1911).
Sociedad de Cirugía de Buenos Aires.
Continued by: Boletines y trabajos (1953).
Sociedad de Cirugía de Buenos Aires.
1939-1953   **101219034**

Bol Trab Soc Cir B Aires
Boletines y trabajos - Sociedad de Cirugía
de Buenos Aires
0370-8896
Continues: Boletines y trabajos (1939).
Academia Argentina de Cirugía. Continued
by: Boletines y trabajos - Academia Argentina
de Cirugía.
1953-1969   **7505263**

Bol Trimest Hosp Vina del Mar
Boletín trimestral - Hospital de Vi&nhat;a
del Mar
1945-1975   **7505294**

Bol Veracruz Mexico
Boletín. Veracruz, Mexico (City) Sanatorio
"Dr. Nicandro L. Melo"
Continues the Boletín of the Sanatorio "Dr.
Rafael Lavista."
1944-1952   **21440570R**

Boll Chim Farm
Bollettino chimico farmaceutico
0006-6648
Continues: Bollettino farmaceutico.
1892   **0372534**

Boll Inf Consoc Naz (Rome)
Boleettino d'informazioni della
Consociazione nazionale infermiere
professionali e assistenti sanitarie visitatrici
Continued by Professioni infermieristiche.
1948-1969   **7505245**

Boll Ist Sieroter Milan
Bollettino dell'Istituto sieroterapico milanese
0021-2547
1917-1992   **17720040R**

Boll Mal Orecch Gola Naso
Bollettino delle malattie dell'orecchio, della
gola, del naso
0392-7024
Continues: Bollettino delle malattie
dell'orecchio, della gola, del naso, di tracheo-
bronco-esofagoscopia e di fonetica. Merged
with: Minerva otorinolaringologica; Nuovo
archivio italiano di otologia, rinologia e
laringologia; and: L'Oto-rino-laringologia
italiana, to form: Otorinolaringologia.
1950-1980   **8204413**

Boll Mem Soc Piemont Chir
Bollettino e memorie della Società
piemontese di chirurgia
0366-1970
1931   **7506972**

Boll Mem Soc Tosco Umbra Chir
Bollettino e memorie della Società tosco-
umbra di chirurgia
1940-1982   **7506973**

Boll Metallogr
Bollettino metallografico. Metallurgical
bulletin
0006-6826
1947-1972   **15710160R**

Boll Ocul
Bollettino d'oculistica
0006-677X
Continued by Bollettino di oculistica.
1922-1971   **0372535**

Boll Schermogr
Bollettino schermografico
0366-1776
1948-1963   **15710180R**

Boll Sez Reg Soc Ital Dermatol Sifilogr
Bollettino delle sezioni regionali / Società
italiana di dermatologia e sifilografia
1125-2375
1931-1937   **9430401**

Boll Soc Ital Biol Sper
Bollettino della Società italiana di biologia
sperimentale
0037-8771
1925-2001   **7506962**

Boll Soc Ital Cardiol
Bollettino della Società italiana di
cardiologia
0037-878X
Continued by Cardiologia (Rome, Italy).
1956-1981   **7506963**

Boll Soc Med Chir Bresciana
Bollettino della Società medico chirurgica
bresciana
1927-1973   **7506969**

Boll Soc Med Chir Cremona
Bollettino - Società medico chirurgica
Cremona
0037-8852
Continued by Bollettino della Società medico
chirurgica a degli ospedali provincia di
Cremona.
1947-1974   **7505295**

Boll Soc Med Chir Pisa
Bollettino - Società medico-chirurgica di
Pisa
1933-1970   **7506957**

Bologna Medica
Bologna medica
Continues Rivista medica di Bologna.
1957-19uu   **20430150R**

Bone
Bone
8756-3282   1873-2763
Continues: Metabolic bone disease & related
research.
1985   **8504048**

Bone Marrow Transplant
Bone marrow transplantation
0268-3369   1476-5365
1986   **8702459**

Bone Miner
Bone and mineral
0169-6009
1986-1994   **8610542**

Book Suppl J Child Psychol Psychiatr
Book supplement to the Journal of child
psychology and psychiatry
0164-1735
1978-1988　　　　　　　7806054

Bord Chir
Bordeaux chirurgical
0006-7660
1930-1973　　　　　　　1260056

Bord Med
Bordeaux médical
0021-7867
Supersedes Journal de médecine de Bordeaux
et du Sud-Ouest.
1968-1987　　　　　　　0134233

Bordens Rev Nutr Res
Borden's review of nutrition research
0006-7679
Continued by: Review of nutrition research.
1940-1968　　　　　　　7513569

Bosn J Basic Med Sci
Bosnian journal of basic medical sciences /
Udruženje basičnih mediciniskih znanosti =
Association of Basic Medical Sciences
1512-8601
1998　　　　　　　101200947

Bp Stat Zsebkv
Budapest statisztikai zsebkönyve
0438-2242
1950　　　　　　　7502744

Bp Szekesfov Kozeu
Budapest székesfőváros közegészségügye
1946-19uu　　　　　　　15750190R

Br Chem Dig
The British chemical digest
0366-2705
Continued by: Engineering and chemical
digest.
1946-1949　　　　　　　15730240R

Br Chirop J
The British chiropody journal
Continued by the British journal of chiropody.
1933-1965　　　　　　　0071432

Br Dent J
British dental journal
0007-0610　　　　　　　1476-5373
Absorbed Mouth mirror and Dental gazette
in 1950, and Dental magazine in Oct. 1970.
Issue for July 10, 1993 has supplement: BDA
occasional paper.
1903　　　　　　　7513219

Br Dent Nurs J
British dental nurses' journal (Fleetwood,
England: 1994)
1356-3807
Continues: British dental surgery assistant.
1994　　　　　　　9602061

Br Dent Surg Assist
The British dental surgery assistant
0007-0629
Continues: British dental nurses journal.
Continued by: British dental nurses' journal
(Fleetwood, England: 1994).
1957-1994　　　　　　　0373122

Br Food J Hyg Rev
The British food journal and hygienic review
Continues: British food journal. Continued
by: British food journal (Croydon, England).
1918-1963　　　　　　　2984729R

Br Heart J
British heart journal
0007-0769
Continued by: Heart (British Cardiac Society).
1939-1995　　　　　　　0370634

Br Homeopath J
The British homoeopathic journal
0007-0785
Formed by the merger of: British
homoeopathic review, and:Journal of the
British Homoeopathic Society. Continued by:
Homeopathy.
1911-2001　　　　　　　15730430R

Br J Addict
British journal of addiction
0952-0481
Continues: British journal of addiction to
alcohol and other drugs. Continued by:
Addiction (Abingdon, England).
1980-1992　　　　　　　8804404

Br J Addict Alcohol Other Drugs
The British journal of addiction to alcohol
and other drugs
0007-0890
Continues British journal of inebriety.
Continued by: British journal of addiction.
1947-1979　　　　　　　0372671

Br J Anaesth
British journal of anaesthesia
0007-0912　　　　　　　1471-6771
1923　　　　　　　0372541

Br J Audiol
British journal of audiology
0300-5364
Continues: Sound. Merged with: Audiology,
and: Scandinavian audiology, to form:
International journal of audiology.
1973-2001　　　　　　　0357321

Br J Audiol Suppl
British journal of audiology. Supplement
0143-764X
1977-1980　　　　　　　7801697

Br J Biomed Sci
British journal of biomedical science
0967-4845
Absorbed: Journal of biomedical sciences.
Continues: Medical laboratory sciences.
1993　　　　　　　9309208

Br J Cancer
British journal of cancer
0007-0920　　　　　　　1532-1827
1947　　　　　　　0370635

Br J Cancer Suppl
The British journal of cancer. Supplement
0306-9443
1973-1996　　　　　　　7506975

Br J Clin Pharmacol
British journal of clinical pharmacology
0306-5251　　　　　　　1365-2125
1974　　　　　　　7503323

Br J Clin Pract
The British journal of clinical practice
0007-0947
Continues Medicine illustrated.
1956-1997　　　　　　　0372546

Br J Clin Pract Suppl
British journal of clinical practice.
Supplement
0262-8767
Continued by: International journal of clinical
practice. Supplement.
197u-1997　　　　　　　8007786

Br J Clin Psychol
The British journal of clinical psychology /
the British Psychological Society
0144-6657
Continues in part: British journal of social
and clinical psychology. Continued in part by:
British journal of health psychology.
1981　　　　　　　8105533

Br J Community Nurs
British journal of community nursing
1462-4753
Continues: British journal of community
health nursing.
199u　　　　　　　9815827

Br J Dermatol
The British journal of dermatology
0007-0963　　　　　　　1365-2133
Continues: British journal of dermatology and
syphilis.
1951　　　　　　　0004041

Br J Dermatol Syph
The British journal of dermatology and
syphilis
0366-2845
Continues: British journal of dermatology,
published 1888-1916; continued by: British
journal of dermatology, published 1951- .
1917-1950　　　　　　　9716393

Br J Dis Chest
British journal of diseases of the chest
0007-0971
Continues the British journal of tuberculosis
and diseases of the chest. Continued by:
Respiratory medicine.
1959-1988　　　　　　　7511123

Br J Disord Commun
The British journal of disorders of
communication
0007-098X
Supersedes Speech pathology and therapy.
Continued by: European journal of disorders
of communication.
1966-1991　　　　　　　0052704

Br J Educ Psychol
The British journal of educational
psychology
0007-0998
Supersedes Forum of education.
1931　　　　　　　0370636

Br J Exp Pathol
British journal of experimental pathology
0007-1021
Continued by: Journal of experimental
pathology (Oxford, England).
1920-1989　　　　　　　0372543

Br J Fam Plann
The British journal of family planning
0144-8625
Continues: Journal of family planning
doctors. Continued by: Journal of family
planning and reproductive health care.
197u-2000　　　　　　　8000474

Br J Gen Pract
The British journal of general practice:
the journal of the Royal College of General
Practitioners
0960-1643　　　　　　　1478-5242
Continues: Journal of the Royal College of
General Practitioners.
1990　　　　　　　9005323

Br J Haematol
British journal of haematology
0007-1048　　　　　　　1365-2141
1955　　　　　　　0372544

Br J Health Psychol
British journal of health psychology
1359-107X
Issued as a section of: British journal of
clinical psychology, 1992-1995.
1996　　　　　　　9605409

Br J Hist Sci
British journal for the history of science
0007-0874　　　　　　　1474-001X
1962　　　　　　　0144554

Br J Hosp Med
British journal of hospital medicine
0007-1064
Supersedes: Hospital medicine. Continued by: Hospital medicine (London, England: 1998).
1968-1997 **0171545**

Br J Hosp Med (Lond)
British journal of hospital medicine (London, England: 2005)
1750-8460
Continues: Hospital medicine (London, England: 1998).
2005 **101257109**

Br J Ind Med
British journal of industrial medicine
0007-1072
Continued by: Occupational and environmental medicine.
1944-1993 **0370637**

Br J Math Stat Psychol
The British journal of mathematical and statistical psychology
0007-1102
Continues: British journal of statistical psychology.
1965 **0004047**

Br J Med Educ
British journal of medical education
0007-1110
Continued by Medical education.
1966-1975 **7610405**

Br J Med Hypn
British journal of medical hypnotism: official organ of the British Society of Medical Hypnotists
1949-1966 **9421498**

Br J Med Psychol
The British journal of medical psychology
0007-1129
Continues the Medical section of the British journal of psychology. Continued by: Psychology and psychotherapy.
1923-2001 **0370640**

Br J Neurosurg
British journal of neurosurgery
0268-8697 **1360-046X**
1987 **8800054**

Br J Nurs
The British journal of nursing
Continues the Nursing record and hospital world.
1902-1956 **15730570R**

Br J Nurs
British journal of nursing (Mark Allen Publishing)
0966-0461
Continues: Nursing.
1992 **9212059**

Br J Nutr
The British journal of nutrition
0007-1145
1947 **0372547**

Br J Obstet Gynaecol
British journal of obstetrics and gynaecology
0306-5456
Continues: Journal of obstetrics and gynaecology of the British Commonwealth. Continued by: BJOG.
1975-1999 **7503752**

Br J Ophthalmol
The British journal of ophthalmology
0007-1161 **1468-2079**
Formed by the merger of the Ophthalmic review, the Ophthalmoscope, and the Royal London Ophthalmic Hospital reports.
1917 **0421041**

Br J Oral Maxillofac Surg
The British journal of oral & maxillofacial surgery
0266-4356
Continues: The British journal of oral surgery.
1984 **8405235**

Br J Oral Surg
The British journal of oral surgery
0007-117X
Continued by The British journal of oral & Maxillofacial surgery.
1963-1983 **0400651**

Br J Orthod
British journal of orthodontics
0301-228X
Formed by the union of: Orthodontist, and: Transactions of the British Society for the Study of Orthodontics. Continued by: Journal of orthodontics.
1973-1999 **0376035**

Br J Perioper Nurs
British journal of perioperative nursing: the journal of the National Association of Theatre Nurses
1467-1026
Continues: British journal of theatre nursing. Continued by: Journal of perioperative practice.
2000-2005 **100935999**

Br J Pharmacol
British journal of pharmacology
0007-1188 **1476-5381**
Continues: British journal of pharmacology and chemotherapy.
1968 **7502536**

Br J Phys Med
The British journal of physical medicine, including its application to industry
Continues the British journal of actinotherapy and physiotherapy.
1931-1957 **15740010R**

Br J Physiol Opt
The British journal of physiological optics
0007-1218
Continues the Dioptric review and the British journal of physiological optics, new series. Continued by Ophthalmic & physiological optics.
1950-1980 **0377224**

Br J Plast Surg
British journal of plastic surgery
0007-1226
Continued by: Journal of plastic, reconstructive & aesthetic surgery.
1948-2005 **2984714R**

Br J Prev Soc Med
British journal of preventive & social medicine
0007-1242
Continues: British journal of social medicine. Continued by: Journal of epidemiology and community health.
1953-1977 **0372672**

Br J Psychiatr Soc Work
British journal of psychiatric social work
1947-1970 **1265621**

Br J Psychiatry
The British journal of psychiatry: the journal of mental science
0007-1250 **1472-1465**
Continues the Journal of mental science.
1963 **0342367**

Br J Psychiatry Suppl
The British journal of psychiatry. Supplement
0960-5371
1988 **9001294**

Br J Psychol
British journal of psychology (London, England: 1953)
0007-1269
Continues: British journal of psychology. General section.
1953 **0373124**

Br J Psychol Gen Sect
The British journal of psychology. General section
0373-2460
Continues in part: British journal of psychology (London, England: 1904). Continued by: British journal of psychology (London, England: 1953).
1920-1952 **101245095**

Br J Radiol
The British journal of radiology
0007-1285 **1748-880X**
Has supplement: British journal of radiology. Supplement, 1947-1988; BJR supplement, 1989- Formed by the union of the British journal of radiology (B. I. R. section) and the British journal of radiology (Röntgen Society section).
1928 **0373125**

Br J Radiol Suppl
British journal of radiology. Supplement
0306-8854
Continued by: BJR supplement.
1947-1988 **0400650**

Br J Rheumatol
British journal of rheumatology
0263-7103
Continues: Rheumatology and rehabilitation. Continued by: Rheumatology (Oxford, England).
1983-1998 **8302415**

Br J Sex Med
British journal of sexual medicine
0301-5572
1973-1998 **0411230**

Br J Soc Clin Psychol
The British journal of social and clinical psychology
0007-1293
Split into The British journal of social psychology; and The British journal of clinical psychology.
1962-1980 **0372552**

Br J Soc Psychol
The British journal of social psychology / the British Psychological Society
0144-6665
Continues in part: the British journal of social and clinical psychology.
1981 **8105534**

Br J Sociol
The British journal of sociology
0007-1315 **1468-4446**
1950 **0373126**

Br J Sports Med
British journal of sports medicine
0306-3674 **1473-0480**
Continues: Bulletin - British Association of Sport and Medicine.
1969 **0432520**

Br J Surg
The British journal of surgery
0007-1323 **1365-2168**
Absorbed: European journal of surgery. 2003
1913 **0372553**

Br J Theatre Nurs
The British journal of theatre nursing:
NATNews: the official journal of the
National Association of Theatre Nurses
1353-0224
Continues: NATNews. Continued by: British
journal of perioperative nursing.
1991-1999　　　　　　　　**9204117**

Br J Tuberc Dis Chest
The British journal of tuberculosis and
diseases of the chest
Continues the British journal of tuberculosis.
Continued by the British journal of diseases
of the chest.
1943-1958　　　　　　　**15740080R**

Br J Urol
British journal of urology
0007-1331
Continued by: BJU international.
1929-1998　　　　　　　**15740090R**

Br J Vener Dis
The British journal of venereal diseases
0007-134X
Continued by: Genitourinary medicine.
1925-1984　　　　　　　　**0421042**

Br Med Bull
British medical bulletin
0007-1420　　　　　　　　1471-8391
1943　　　　　　　　　　　0376542

Br Med J
British medical journal
0007-1447
Continues: Association medical journal.
Split into: British medical journal (Clinical
research edition). and: British medical journal
(Practice observed edition).
1857-1980　　　　　　　　0372673

Br Med J (Clin Res Ed)
British medical journal (Clinical research
ed.)
0267-0623
Continues in part: British medical journal.
Continued by: BMJ (Clinical research ed.).
1981-1988　　　　　　　　8302911

Br Orthopt J
The British orthoptic journal
0068-2314
Continued by: British and Irish Orthoptic
journal.
1939-2003　　　　　　　　0370644

Br Poult Sci
British poultry science
0007-1668　　　　　　　　1466-1799
1960　　　　　　　　　　15740290R

Br Sci News
British science news
Supersedes MSN; monthly science news.
1947-1950　　　　　　　15740330R

Br Vet J
The British veterinary journal
0007-1935
Continues: Veterinary journal. Continued by:
Veterinary journal (London. England: 1997).
1949-1996　　　　　　　　0372554

Brachytherapy
Brachytherapy
1538-4721
2002　　　　　　　　　101137600

Brain
Brain: a journal of neurology
0006-8950　　　　　　　　1460-2156
1878　　　　　　　　　　0372537

Brain Behav Evol
Brain, behavior and evolution
0006-8977　　　　　　　　1421-9743
1968　　　　　　　　　　0151620

Brain Behav Immun
Brain, behavior, and immunity
0889-1591　　　　　　　　1090-2139
1987　　　　　　　　　　8800478

Brain Cell Biol
Brain cell biology
1559-7105　　　　　　　　1559-7113
Continues: Journal of neurocytology.
2006　　　　　　　　　101272887

Brain Cogn
Brain and cognition
0278-2626　　　　　　　　1090-2147
1982　　　　　　　　　　8218014

Brain Dev
Brain & development
0387-7604　　　　　　　　1872-7131
1979　　　　　　　　　　7909235

Brain Inj
Brain injury: [BI]
0269-9052　　　　　　　　1362-301X
1987　　　　　　　　　　8710358

Brain Lang
Brain and language
0093-934X　　　　　　　　1090-2155
1974　　　　　　　　　　7506220

Brain Nerve
Brain and nerve = Shinkei kenkyū no shinpo
1881-6096
Merger of: Nō to shinkei, and: Shinkei
kenkyū no shimpo.
2007　　　　　　　　　101299709

Brain Pathol
Brain pathology (Zurich, Switzerland)
1015-6305　　　　　　　　1750-3639
1990　　　　　　　　　　9216781

Brain Res
Brain research
0006-8993　　　　　　　　1872-6240
Absorbed: Brain research. Brain research
protocols. 2006 Brain research. Cognitive
brain research. 2006 Brain research.
Developmental brain research. 2006 Brain
research. Molecular brain research. 2006
Continued in part by: Brain research.
Cognitive brain research.
1966　　　　　　　　　　0045503

Brain Res Brain Res Protoc
Brain research. Brain research protocols
1385-299X
Absorbed in 2006 by: Brain research.
1997-2005　　　　　　　　9716650

Brain Res Brain Res Rev
Brain research. Brain research reviews
Continues: Brain research reviews. issued
1979-88 as a subseries of: Brain research.
Continued by: Brain research reviews.
1989-2005　　　　　　　　8908638

Brain Res Bull
Brain research bulletin
0361-9230　　　　　　　　1873-2747
1976　　　　　　　　　　7605818

Brain Res Cogn Brain Res
Brain research. Cognitive brain research
0926-6410
Continues in part: Brain research. Absorbed
in 2006 by: Brain research.
1992-2005　　　　　　　　9214304

Brain Res Dev Brain Res
Brain research. Developmental brain
research
0165-3806
Continues: Developmental brain research
issued 1981-Oct. 1988 as a subseries of:
Brain research. Absorbed in 2006 by: Brain
research.
1988-2005　　　　　　　　8908639

Brain Res Gene Expr Patterns
Brain research. Gene expression patterns
1567-133X
Continues in part: Brain research. Continued
by: Gene expression patterns.
2001-2002　　　　　　　101125870

Brain Res Mol Brain Res
Brain research. Molecular brain research
0169-328X
Absorbed in 2006 by: Brain research.
Continues: Moleclular brain research. issued
1986-88 as a subseries of: Brain research.
1989-2005　　　　　　　　8908640

Brain Res Rev
Brain research reviews
0165-0173
Continues: Brain research. Brain research
reviews.
2006　　　　　　　　　101300366

Brain Struct Funct
Brain structure & function
1863-2653　　　　　　　　1863-2661
Continues: Anatomy and embryology.
2007　　　　　　　　　101282001

Brain Topogr
Brain topography
0896-0267　　　　　　　　1573-6792
1988　　　　　　　　　　8903034

Brain Tumor Pathol
Brain tumor pathology
1433-7398
Continues: Nōshuyō byōri.
1997　　　　　　　　　　9716507

Bras Med
Brasil-médico
0006-9205
1887-1971　　　　　　　　0243300

Bras Med Cir
Brasil médico-cirúrgico
Continues Brasil cirúrgico.
1941-1949　　　　　　　15720370R

Bratisl Lek Listy
Bratislavské lekárske listy
0006-9248
1921　　　　　　　　　　0065324

Braz Dent J
Brazilian dental journal
0103-6440　　　　　　　　1806-4760
1990　　　　　　　　　　9214652

Braz J Biol
Brazilian journal of biology = Revista
brasleira de biologia
1519-6984　　　　　　　　1678-4375
Continues: Revista Brasileira de biologia.
2000　　　　　　　　　101129542

Braz J Infect Dis
The Brazilian journal of infectious diseases:
an official publication of the Brazilian
Society of Infectious Diseases
1413-8670　　　　　　　　1678-4391
1997　　　　　　　　　　9812937

Braz J Med Biol Res
Brazilian journal of medical and biological research = Revista brasileira de pesquisas médicas e biológicas / Sociedade Brasileira de Biofísica ... [et al.]
0100-879X   1414-431X
Continues: Revista brasileira de pesquisas médicas e biológicas.
1981   8112917

Braz J Otorhinolaryngol
Brazilian journal of otorhinolaryngology
1808-8694   1808-8686
2000   101207337

Braz Oral Res
Brazilian oral research
1806-8324   1807-3107
Continues: Pesquisa odontológica brasileira.
2004   101307187

Breast
Breast (Edinburgh, Scotland)
0960-9776   1532-3080
1992   9213011

Breast Cancer
Breast cancer (Tokyo, Japan)
1340-6868   1880-4233
1994   100888201

Breast Cancer Res
Breast cancer research: BCR
1465-5411   1465-542X
1999   100927353

Breast Cancer Res Treat
Breast cancer research and treatment
0167-6806   1573-7217
1981   8111104

Breast Dis
Breast disease
0888-6008   1558-1551
1987   8801277

Breast J
The breast journal
1075-122X   1524-4741
1995   9505539

Breastfeed Med
Breastfeeding medicine: the official journal of the Academy of Breastfeeding Medicine
1556-8253   1556-8342
2006   101260777

Breastfeed Rev
Breastfeeding review: professional publication of the Nursing Mothers' Association of Australia
0729-2759
1982   9616903

Brevia (Rome)
"Brevia"
1948-19uu   15730080R

Brief Bioinform
Briefings in bioinformatics
1467-5463   1477-4054
2000   100912837

Brief Funct Genomic Proteomic
Briefings in functional genomics & proteomics
1473-9550   1477-4062
2002   101150306

Bristol Dig
The Bristol digest
1945-1953   15730140R

Bristol Med Chir J
Bristol medico-chirurgical journal (1963)
0308-6356
Continues: Medical journal of the South-West. Continued by: West of England medical journal.
1963-1989   0400663

Bristol Med Chir J (1883)
Bristol medico-chirurgical journal (1883)
0007-019X
Continued by: Medical journal of the South-West.
1883-1952   101281337

Broadway
The Broadway
0007-2133
Supersedes The Broad way; or, Westminster Hospital gazette, issued Feb. 1899-July 1909.
1923   0144400

Bronches
Les Bronches
0007-2222
Continued by Broncho-pneumologie.
1951-1975   7700862

Bronchopneumologie
Broncho-pneumologie
0395-3904
Continues Les Bronches.
1976-1980   7613317

Brookhaven Symp Biol
Brookhaven symposia in biology
0068-2799
Continues the Proceedings of the Biology Conference, Brookhaven National Laboratory.
1952-1990   2984279R

Brookings Bull
Brookings bulletin (Washington, D.C.: 1962)
0007-229X
Continued by: Brookings review.
1962-1982   9876873

Brookings Rev
The Brookings review
0745-1253
Continues: Brookings bulletin (Washington, D.C.: 1962).
1982   9879923

Brooklyn Hosp J
The Brooklyn Hospital journal
1939-1954   15740450R

Bruns Beitr Klin Chir
Bruns' Beiträge für klinische Chirurgie
0007-2680
Continues: Bruns' Beiträge zur klinischen Chirurgie, ISSN 0007-2680, published 1916-71. Absorbed by: Langenbecks Archiv für Chirurgie.
1971-1974   7611943

Bruns Beitr Klin Chir
Bruns' Beiträge zur klinischen Chirurgie
0007-2680
Continues Beiträge zur klinischen Chirurgie. Continued by Bruns' Beiträge für klinische Chirurgie.
1916-1971   7611944

Brux Med
Bruxelles médical
0068-3027
Supersedes Journal médical de Bruxelles, issued 1896-1914. Absorbed by: Revue médicale de Bruxelles.
1921-1979   0372561

BSCS Pam
BSCS pamphlets
1963-1965   15430430R

BTTA Rev
B.T.T.A. review
0300-9602
1971-1974   1273753

Buch Augenarzt
Bücherei des Augenarztes
0068-3361
1938-1996   0372556

Build Oper Manage
Building operating management
0007-3490
Continues: Building maintenance and modernization.
1970   9877755

Build Syst Des
Building systems design
0002-2284
Continues: Air conditioning, heating, and ventilating. Continued by: Energy engineering.
1969-1979   9877812

Bul Stiint Sect Stiint Medicale Acad Republicii Pop Romane
Buletin ştiinţific. Secţiunea de ştiinţe medicale. Academia Republicii Populare Române
1948-1957   14490480R

Bul Univ Shtet Tiranes Ser Shk Mjekesore
Buletin i Universitetit Shtetëror të Tiranës. Seria Shkencat mjekësore
0302-900X
Continued by: Buletin i Universitetit të Tiranës "Enver Hoxha". Seria Shkencat mjekësore.
1961-1975   7505300

Bulg Klin
Bŭlgarska klinika
1928-1940   0212020

Bull Acad Chir Dent (Paris)
Bulletin de l'Académie de chirurgie dentaire
0339-9710
Continues Bulletin de l'Académie dentaire. Continued by: Bulletin de l'Académie nationale de chirurgie dentaire (1983).
1974-1982   7705554

Bull Acad Dent (Paris)
Bulletin de l'Académie dentaire
0339-9729
Continues Bulletin de l'Académie nationale de chirurgie dentaire. Continued by Bulletin de l'Académie de chirurgie dentaire.
1963-1973   7503381

Bull Acad Dent Handicap
Bulletin of Academy of Dentistry for the Handicapped
0567-6657
Continued by: Newsletter of the Academy of Dentistry for the Handicapped (1966).
1963-1965   7503460

Bull Acad Gen Dent
The Bulletin of the Academy of General Dentistry
0098-3810
Continued by the Journal of the Academy of General Dentistry.
1960-1969   7503419

Bull Acad Med Clevel
Bulletin - Academy of Medicine of Cleveland
0001-4281
Continued by: Cleveland physician.
1920-1967   7503473

Bull Acad Med N J
Bulletin - Academy of Medicine of New Jersey
0001-429X
1955-1970   7503324

Bull Acad Med Tor
Bulletin of the Academy of Medicine,
Toronto
0001-4311
1927-1990   7503420

Bull Acad Natl Chir Dent
Bulletin de l'Académie nationale de
chirurgie dentaire (1983)
0339-9710
Continues: Bulletin de l'Académie de
chirurgie dentaire.
1983   8913643

Bull Acad Natl Med
Bulletin de l'Académie nationale de
médecine
0001-4079
Continues: Bulletin de l'Academie de
médecine.
1947   7503383

Bull Acad Pol Sci Biol
Bulletin de l'Académie polonaise des
sciences. Série des sciences biologiques
Continues: Bulletin de l'Académie polonaise
des sciences. Classe 2e. Continued by:
Bulletin of the Polish Academy of Sciences.
Biology.
1957-1982   7505346

Bull Acad R Med Belg
Bulletin de l'Académie royale de médecine
de Belgique
0001-4168
Merged with Mémoires de l'Académie royale
de médecine de Belgique to form Bulletin et
mémoires de l'Académie royal de médecine
de Belgique.
1841-1974   7608461

Bull Acad Serbe Sci Arts
Bulletin. Srpska akademija nauka i
umetnosti, Belgrad. Odeljenje medicinskih
nauka
0584-9829
Continues the Bulletin of the Odeljenje
medicinskih nauka of the Srpska akademija
nauka. Belgrad.
1961-1995   59530360R

Bull Acad Vet Fr
Bulletin de l'Académie vétérinaire de France
0001-4192
Continues the Bulletin of the Société centrale
de médecine vétérinaire.
1928   7503384

Bull Actual Med
Bulletin des actualités médicales
1948-1951   15820010R

Bull Acuff Clin Knoxv Tenn
Bulletin. Acuff Clinic, Knoxville, Tenn
1949-1952   14620440R

Bull Adelphi Hosp Brooklyn
Bulletin. Adelphi Hospital (Brooklyn, New
York, N.Y.)
1942-1965   15740420R

Bull Akron City Hosp
The Bulletin of Akron City Hospital
0516-3285
1952-1966   7503461

Bull Akron Dent Soc
Bulletin of the Akron Dental Society
0002-3701
193u-1981   7503422

Bull Alameda Cty Dent Soc
Bulletin - Alameda County Dental Society
0098-3764
Continues the Bulletin of the Alameda
County District Dental society.
1957-19uu   7503327

Bull Alger Carcinol
Bulletin algérien de carcinologie
1948-1958   15810070R

Bull Am Acad Psychiatry Law
The Bulletin of the American Academy of
Psychiatry and the Law
0091-634X
Supersedes the academy's Newsletter.
Continued by: Journal of the American
Academy of Psychiatry and the Law.
1972-1996   7503424

Bull Am Assoc Dent Ed
The Bulletin - American Association of
Dental Editors
0569-2555
Continues: News letter (American Association
of Dental Editors). Merged with Transactions -
American Association of Dental Editors to
form AADE editors' journal.
1963-1973   7609222

Bull Am Assoc Hist Nurs
Bulletin (American Association for the
History of Nursing)
0898-6622
1982   8711207

Bull Am Assoc Hosp Dent
Bulletin - American Association of Hospital
Dentists
Continues Bulletin - American Association of
Hospital Dental Chiefs.
1969   7505302

Bull Am Assoc Med Soc Workers
Bulletin. American Association of Medical
Social Workers
Continues the Bulletin of the American
Association of Hospital Social Workers.
Superseded by the Association's Newsletter.
1934-1949   14740590R

Bull Am Coll Nurse Midwifery
Bulletin of the American College of Nurse-
Midwifery
0098-3721
Continued by Bulletin of the American
College of Nurse-Midwives.
1955-1969   7503426

Bull Am Coll Nurse Midwives
Bulletin of the American College of Nurse-
Midwives
0002-8002
Continues the Bulletin of the American
College of Nurse-Midwifery. Continued by
the Journal of nurse-midwifery.
1969-1972   7503427

Bull Am Coll Physicians
The Bulletin of the American College of
Physicians
0002-8010
Continued by: Forum on medicine.
1960-1978   7503428

Bull Am Coll Surg
Bulletin of the American College of Surgeons
0002-8045
1916   7507024

Bull Am Pharm Assoc
Bulletin. American Pharmaceutical
Association. Committee on National
Formulary
0097-0506
Continued by: Drug standards.
1938-1951   14840210R

Bull Am Protestant Hosp Assoc
Bulletin - American Protestant Hospital
Association
0003-0635
Continued by: Care giver.
1936-1983   7505304

Bull Am Soc Hosp Pharm
Bulletin. American Society of Hospital
Pharmacists
Continued by: American journal of hospital
pharmacy.
1943-1957   14820210R

Bull Am Soc Inf Sci
Bulletin of the American Society for
Information Science / ASIS
0095-4403
Continues: ASIS newsletter. Continued
by: Bulletin of the American Society for
Information Science and Technology.
Continued in part in Apr. 1981 by: American
Society for Information Science. ASIS news.
1974-2000   9875688

Bull Anesth Hist
Bulletin of anesthesia history
1522-8649
Continues: Anesthesia History Association
newsletter.
1995   100891616

Bull Anim Health Prod Afr
Bulletin of animal health and production
in Africa. Bulletin des santé et production
animales en Afrique
0378-9721
Continues Bulletin of epizootic diseases of
Africa. Bulletin des épizooties en Afrique.
1975   7900540

Bull Assoc Am Physicians Surg
Bulletin of the Association of American
Physicians and Surgeons / Association of
American Physicians and Surgeons, Inc
Continues: News (OCoLC)50377571.
Association of American Physicians and
Surgeons.
1945-19uu   9429836

Bull Assoc Anat (Nancy)
Bulletin de l'Association des anatomistes
0376-6160
Continues: Comptes rendus de l'Association
des anatomistes. Continued by: Morphologie.
1973-1997   7503386

Bull Assoc Diplomes Microbiol Fac Pharm Nancy
Bulletin de l'Association des diplômés de
microbiologie de la Faculté de pharmacie de
Nancy
0004-5373
1931-1974   7603017

Bull Assoc Fr Etud Cancer
Bulletin de l'Association française pour
l'étude du cancer
0004-5497
Continued by Bulletin du cancer.
1908-1965   7503389

Bull Assoc Med Haiti
Bulletin. Association médicale haïtienne
1948-19uu   15340060R

Bull Atl Cape May Cty Dent Soc
Bulletin / Atlantic-Cape May County Dental
Society
1964   9884052

Bull Bergen Cty Dent Soc
The Bulletin of the Bergen County Dental
Society
0067-5776
Continued by the Journal of the Bergen
County Dental Society.
1934-1973   7503432

Bull Biol Fr Belg
Bulletin biologique de la France et de la
Belgique
0007-4187
Continues the Bulletin scientifique de la
France et de la Belgique.
1917-1979   0421527

Bull Bronx Cty Dent Soc
Bulletin. Bronx County Dental Society
1946   15740380R

Bull Brooklyn
Bulletin. Brooklyn. Jewish Hospital
1959-1961   15740470R

Bull Calcutta Sch Trop Med
Bulletin of the Calcutta School of Tropical
Medicine
0068-5372
1953-1988   7503435

Bull Calif State Nurses Assoc
Bulletin. California State Nurses' Association
Continues Pacific Coast journal of nursing.
Continued by the CSNA bulletin.
1944-1959   16020270R

Bull Can Hist Med
Bulletin canadien d'histoire de la médecine
= Canadian bulletin of medical history
0823-2105
Continues: Newsletter (Canadian Society
for the History of Medicine). Continued by:
Canadian bulletin of medical history.
1984-1986   8703431

Bull Cancer
Bulletin du cancer
0007-4551   1769-6917
Continues: Bulletin of the Association
française pour l'étude du cancer. Absorbed
in Apr. 2004: Electronic journal of oncology.
Continued in part by: Bulletin du cancer.
Radiothérapie.
1966   0072416

Bull Cancer Inst Okayama Univ Med Sch
Bulletin. Okayama Daigaku. Igakubu.
Gangen Kenkyū Shisetsu
0474-0238
1961-1962   19330530R

Bull Cancer Radiother
Bulletin du cancer. Radiothérapie: journal
de la Société française du cancer: organe
de la société française de radiothérapie
oncologique
0924-4212
Continues in part: Bulletin du cancer.
Continued by: Cancer radiothérapie.
1990-1996   9005324

Bull Cercle Benelux Hist Pharm
Bulletin - Cercle Benelux d'histoire de la
pharmacie
0528-600X
1951   7505306

Bull Cerp
Bulletin du C. E. R. P
Continues the Bulletin of the Centre d'études
et recherches psychotechniques.
1960-1975   0163727

Bull Charlotte Meml Hosp
Bulletin. Charlotte, N. C. Charlotte
Memorial Hospital
1944-1946   16120405R

Bull Chem Soc Jpn
Bulletin of the Chemical Society of Japan
0009-2673
1926   7505371

Bull Chest Dis Res Inst Kyoto Univ
Bulletin of the Chest Disease Research
Institute, Kyoto University
0009-3378
Formed by the union of Acta tuberculosea
Japonica and Kyoto Daigaku Kekkaku
Kenkyusho kiyo.
1968-1991   7505372

Bull Chic Heart Assoc
Bulletin. Chicago Heart Association
Continued by C. H. A. bulletin.
1923-1960   15930110R

Bull Chic Med Soc
Bulletin. Chicago Medical Society
Continued by Chicago medicine.
1902-1960   16130530R

Bull Cincinnati Dent Soc
Bulletin - Cincinnati Dental Society
0190-0439
Continues The Cincinnati Dental Society
bulletin. Continued by: Cincinnati Dental
Society bulletin (1979).
1975-1978   7806775

Bull Cincinnati Dent Soc
The Bulletin of the Cincinnati Dental Society
0069-4096
Continued by The Cincinnati Dental Society
bulletin.
1930-1974   7502027

Bull Cleve Dent Soc
The Bulletin of the Cleveland Dental Society
0009-8795
1914-1988   7503437

Bull Clin Neurosci
Bulletin of clinical neurosciences
0736-3583
Continues: Bulletin of the Los Angeles
neurological societies.
1983-1991   8411675

Bull Contra Costa Dent Soc
Bulletin Of The Contra Costa Dental Society
Continues: Contra Costa Dental Bulletin.
Continued by: Journal / Contra Costa Dental
Society.
1967-1967   9884678

Bull Dade Cty Med Assoc Inc
Bulletin - Dade County Medical Association
0893-4053
Continued by Miami medicine.
1932-1971   7509346

Bull Dayton Dent Soc
Bulletin. Dayton (Ohio) Dental Society
Continued by: Dayton Dental Society
bulletin.
1950-1969   16510460R

Bull Dent Guid Counc Cereb Palsy
Bulletin of the Dental Guidance Council for
Cerebral Palsy
0011-8591
Continued by Journal of the Dental Guidance
Council on the Handicapped.
1961-1974   7703860

Bull Dep Health Commonw Ky
Bulletin of the Department of Health,
Commonwealth of Kentucky. Kentucky.
Dept. of Health
Continues Bulletin of the State Board
of Health. Continued by Bulletin of the
Kentucky State Department of Health.
1934-1951   0373035

Bull Eighth Dist Dent Soc
Bulletin of the 8th District Dental Society
0190-0277
1940   7806517

Bull Eleventh Dist Dent Soc
Bulletin of the Eleventh District Dental
Society
0013-6166
1962-1980   7507027

Bull Endem Dis (Baghdad)
Bulletin of endemic diseases
0007-4845
1954-1989   0401037

Bull Entomol Res
Bulletin of entomological research
0007-4853   1475-2670
1910   2984715R

Bull Environ Contam Toxicol
Bulletin of environmental contamination
and toxicology
0007-4861   1432-0800
1966   0046021

Bull Epizoot Dis Afr
Bulletin of epizootic diseases of Africa.
Bulletin des épizooties en Afrique
0007-487X
Continued by Bulletin of animal health and
production in Africa. Bulletin de santé et
production animales en Afrique.
1953-1974   0004333

Bull Essex Cty Dent Soc
The Bulletin - Essex County Dental Society
0014-0929
1933   7608460

Bull Eur Physiopathol Respir
Bulletin européen de physiopathologie
respiratoire
0395-3890
Continues Bulletin de physio-pathologie
respiratoire. Merged with: European journal
of respiratory diseases, to form: European
respiratory journal in Jan. 1988.
1976-1987   7605263

Bull Exp Biol Med
Bulletin of experimental biology and
medicine
0007-4888
1956   0372557

Bull Fed Soc Gynecol Obstet Lang Fr
Bulletin de la Fédération des sociétés de
gynécologie et dóbstétrique de langue
française
0046-3515
Continues the Bulletin of the Association
des gynécologues et obstétriciens de
langue française. Issued as supplement to
Gynécologie et obstétrique. Continued by
the Journal de gynécologie, obstétrique et
biologie de la reproduction.
1951-1971   7503396

Bull Fifth Dist Dent Soc (Fresno)
The Bulletin of the Fifth District Dental
Society
0071-9544
195u-19uu   7507028

Bull Fifth Dist Dent Soc State N Y
Bulletin Of The Fifth District Dental Society
Of The State Of New York
1953   9878283

Bull Gastrointest Endosc
Bulletin of gastrointestinal endoscopy
1051-7472
Continues: Bulletin of gastroscopy
and esophagoscopy. Continued by:
Gastrointestinal endoscopy.
1961-1965   0004334

Bull Geisinger
Bulletin - Geisinger Medical Center
0016-5913
Continues: Bulletin of the George F.
Geisinger Memorial Hospital and Foss Clinic.
Continued by: Geisinger bulletin.
1961-1992   7503352

Bull Genesee Cty Med Soc
Bulletin - Genesee County Medical Society
0098-4426
1925 7503353

Bull Georgetown Univ Med Cent
Bulletin. Georgetown University. Medical Center
Continued by the Georgetown medical bulletin.
1947-1959 17120080R

Bull Group Eur Rech Sci Stomatol Odontol
Bulletin de Groupement européen pour la recher che scientifique en stomatologie & odontologie
0303-7479
Continues Bulletin du Groupement international pour la recherche scientifique en stomatologie. Continued by Bulletin du Groupement international pour la recherche scientifique en stomatologie & odontologie.
1974-1975 0431176

Bull Group Int Rech Sci Stomatol
Bulletin du Groupement international pour la recherche scientifique en stomatologie
0533-3288
Continued by Bulletin du Groupement européen pour la recherche scientifique en stomatologie & odontologie.
1958-1973 0431177

Bull Group Int Rech Sci Stomatol Odontol
Bulletin du Groupement international pour la recherche scientifique en stomatologie & odontologie
0250-4693
Continues Bulletin du Groupement européen pour la recherche scientifique en stomatologie & odontologie.
1976 7801698

Bull Hist Dent
Bulletin of the history of dentistry
0007-5132
Continued by: Journal of the history of dentistry.
1953-1995 15840040R

Bull Hist Med
Bulletin of the history of medicine
0007-5140 1086-3176
Continues the Bulletin of the Institute of the History of Medicine. Johns Hopkins University.
1939 0141233

Bull Hist Med Suppl
Supplements to the Bulletin of the history of medicine
1943-1951 7905480

Bull Histol Appl Tech Microsc
Bulletin d'histologie appliquée et de technique microscopique
0366-4589
Merged with Microscopie to form Bulletin de microscopie appliquée.
1924-1950 15820060R

Bull Hosp Joint Dis
Bulletin of the Hospital for Joint Diseases
0018-5647
Continued by Bulletin of the Hospital for Joint Diseases Orthopaedic Institute.
1940-1979 7505376

Bull Hosp Jt Dis
Bulletin (Hospital for Joint Diseases (New York, N.Y.))
0018-5647
Continued by: Bulletin of the NYU Hospital for joint diseases.
1992-2006 9215948

Bull Hosp Jt Dis Orthop Inst
Bulletin of the Hospital for Joint Diseases Orthopaedic Institute
0883-9344
Continues: Bulletin of the Hospital for Joint Diseases. Continued by: Bulletin (Hospital for Joint Diseases (New York, N.Y.)).
1981-1991 8207779

Bull Hosp Spec Surg
Bulletin. Hospital for Special Surgery
1958-1962 19031080R

Bull Hudson Cty Dent Soc
Bulletin. Hudson County Dental Society, Jersey City
0018-7011
1931-19uu 17440150R

Bull Hyg
Bulletin d'hygiène. Health bulletin. Montréal (Québec). Dept. of Health
Continues: Monthly bulletin. Montréal (Québec). Dept. of Hygiene and Statistics.
1916-1971 18820590R

Bull Hyg (Lond)
Bulletin of hygiene
0366-4236
Supersedes Sanitation supplements of the Tropical diseases bulletin. Continued by Abstracts on hygiene.
1926-1967 0142257

Bull Ill Dent Hyg Assoc
The bulletin of the Illinois Dental Hygienist's Association. Illinois Dental Hygienists' Association
196u-uuuu 9884600

Bull Indian Inst Hist Med Hyderabad
Bulletin of the Indian Institute of History of Medicine (Hyderabad)
0304-9558
Continues: Bulletin of the Institute of History of Medicine (Hyderabad).
1974 7510174

Bull Indiana State Dep Health
Bulletin (Indiana. State Dept. of Health)
Continues: Indiana State Board of Health bulletin.
199u-uuuu 9426559

Bull Infirm Cathol Can
Bulletin des infirmières catholiques du Canada
0007-4470
Continues Bulletin des gardes-malades catholiques.
1944-1976 1276072

Bull Inst Marit Trop Med Gdynia
Bulletin of the Institute of Maritime and Tropical Medicine in Gdynia
0324-8542
Continues Biuletyn Instytutu Medycyny Morskiej w Gdańsku. Continued by: International maritime health.
1975-1998 7603275

Bull Inst Med Res Kuala Lumpur
Bulletin - Institute for Medical Research, Kuala Lumpur
0127-273X
Supersedes the institute's Medical bulletin.
1924-1986 7506980

Bull Inst Med Res Univ Madr
Bulletin of the Institute for Medical Research, University of Madrid
0020-3955
1948-1966 7505378

Bull Inst Natl Hyg
Bulletin. Institut national d'hygiène (France)
0366-0443
Continued by: Bulletin de l'Institut national de la santé et de la recherche médicale.
1946-1964 23130530R

Bull Inst Natl Sante Rech Med
Bulletin de l'Institut national de la santé et de la recherche médicale
0553-2469
Continues Bulletin de l'Institut national d'hygiène.
1964-1971 0022726

Bull Int Acad Pol Sci Let Cl Med
Bulletin international de l'Académie polonaise des sciences et des lettres. Classe de médecine
1930-1952 9429841

Bull Int Serv Sante Armees Terre Mer Air
Bulletin international des services de santé des armées de terre, de mer et de l'air
Continued by the Revue internationale des services de santé des armées de terre, de mer, et de l'air.
1928-1957 15820130R

Bull Int Union Tuberc
Bulletin of the International Union against Tuberculosis
0074-9249
Continued by: Bulletin of the International Union against Tuberculosis and lung Disease.
1924-1986 7505385

Bull Int Union Tuberc Lung Dis
Bulletin of the International Union against Tuberculosis and Lung Disease
1011-789X
Continues: Bulletin of the International Union against Tuberculosis. Merged with: Tubercle, to form: Tubercle and lung disease.
1986-1991 8709829

Bull Jackson Park Branch Chic Med Soc
Bulletin - Jackson Park Branch, Chicago Medical Society
0098-4396
192u-1960 7503357

Bull Jersey City Margaret Hague Mat Hosp
Bulletin. Jersey City. Margaret Hague Maternity Hospital
0096-6118
1948-1957 17740430R

Bull Kanagawa Dent Coll
The Bulletin of the Kanagawa Dental College: BKDC / KDS
0385-1443
1973 8511124

Bull King Cty Med Soc
Bulletin - King County Medical Society
0023-1592
1922 7505312

Bull Kresge Eye Inst
Bulletin. Kresge Eye Institute
0096-5219
1949-1960 18210310R

Bull Linn Cty Iowa
Bulletin. Linn County (Iowa) Medical Society
1932-1951 18330750R

Bull Los Angel Cty Med Assoc
Bulletin - Los Angeles County Medical Association
0364-684X
Continued by Los Angeles County Medical Association bulletin.
1904-1971 7605261

Bull Los Angel Neuro Soc
Bulletin of the Los Angeles Neurological Society
1040-5925
Continued by the Bulletin of the Los Angeles neurological societies.
1936-1965   7505388

Bull Los Angel Surg Soc
Bulletin. Los Angeles Surgical Society
1948-1949   18340490R

Bull Los Angeles Dent Soc
Bulletin of the Los Angeles Dental Society
0076-0951
Supersedes another publication with the same title.
1962-19uu   7509358

Bull Los Angeles Neurol Soc
Bulletin of the Los Angeles neurological societies
0024-659X
Continues the Bulletin of the Los Angeles Neurological Society. Continued by Bulletin of clinical neurosciences.
1966-1982   0064572

Bull Louis A Weiss Mem Hosp
The Bulletin of Louis A. Weiss Memorial Hospital
0456-5932
1957-1968   7503462

Bull Mahoning Cty Med Soc
Bulletin. Mahoning County Medical Society
1931   18420160R

Bull Mass Nurses Assoc
Bulletin of the Massachusetts Nurses Association
0025-4843
Continued by The Massachusetts nurse.
1932-1976   7803470

Bull Math Biol
Bulletin of mathematical biology
0092-8240   1522-9602
Continues: Bulletin of mathematical biophysics.
1973   0401404

Bull Math Biophys
The Bulletin of mathematical biophysics
0007-4985
Issued Mar.-Dec. 1939 as supplement to Psychometrika. Continued by Bulletin of mathematical biology.
1939-1972   0402113

Bull McGuire Clin St Lukes Hosp Richmond St Lukes Hosp McGuire Clin
Bulletin, McGuire Clinic and St. Luke's Hospital. Richmond. St. Luke's Hospital. McGuire Clinic
1929-1950   20410230R

Bull Med
Bulletin médical
1887-1959   15830020R

Bull Med Ethics
Bulletin of medical ethics
0962-9564
Continues: Bulletin (Institute of Medical Ethics (Great Britain)).
1989   9103287

Bull Med Libr Assoc
Bulletin of the Medical Library Association
0025-7338
Continues: Aesculapian (Brooklyn, New York, N.Y.). Continued by: Journal of the Medical Library Association.
1911-2001   0421037

Bull Med Rev Med Fr Guide Prat
Bulletin médical. Revue médicale française. Guide du praticien
Continued by: Cahiers R. M. F.: bulletin médical-guide du praticien-revue médicale française.
1960-1962   15830120R

Bull Med Soc Cty Kings Kings Cty N Y
Bulletin. Medical Society of the County of Kings (Kings County, N.Y.)
Continues: Bulletin of the Medical Society of the County of Kings. Continued by: KCMS bulletin.
1924-1979   18530560R

Bull Med Soc Cty Monroe
Bulletin. Medical Society of the County of Monroe
Supersedes another periodical with the same title.
1943-1977   18530580R

Bull Med Univ Aurore
Bulletin médical. Shanghai. Université l'Aurore
0255-7029
1928-1949   20730040R

Bull Mem Acad R Med Belg
Bulletin et mémoires de l'Académie royale de médecine de Belgique
0377-8231
Continues in part: Mémoires de l'Académie royale de médecine de Belgique. Continues in part: Bulletin de l'Académie royale médecine de Belgique.
1975   7608462

Bull Mem Chir Marseille
Bulletins et mémoires. Société de chirurgie de Marseille
2021-426X
1927-1947   20821280R

Bull Mem Fac Mixte Med Pharm Dakar
Bulletins et mémoires de la Faculté mixte de médecine et de pharmacie de Dakar
Continues Bulletins et mémoires de l'Ecole préparatoire de médecine et de pharmacie, Dakar. Continued by Bulletins et mémoires de la Faculté de médecine et de pharmacie de Dakar.
1960-1970   7505420

Bull Mem Soc Chir Paris
Bulletin et mémoires de la Société des chirurgiens de Paris
0037-9220
1926-1973   7507020

Bull Mem Soc Fr Ophtalmol
Bulletins et mémoires de la Société française d'ophtalmologie
0081-1092
Continued by: Ophtalmologie.
1883-1985   7503471

Bull Mem Soc Med Hop Paris
Bulletins et mémoires de la Société médicale des hôpitaux de Paris
0366-1334
Continued by Annales de médecine interne.
1849-1968   7503472

Bull Mem Soc Med Paris (1907)
Bulletin et mémoires. Société de médecine de Paris
0995-9726
Continued by: Revue d'enseignement post-universitaire de la Société de médecine de Paris.
1907-1969   20830050R

Bull Mem Soc Med Passy Ht.-Savoie
Bulletin et mémoires de la Société médicale de Passy (Haute-Savoie)
0150-3588
1932-1971   7503417

Bull Menninger Clin
Bulletin of the Menninger Clinic
0025-9284
1936   7507032

Bull Mens Soc Med Mil Fr
Bulletin mensuel - Société de médecine militaire française
0996-1852
Continues Bulletin bi-mensuel - Société de médecine militaire française issued 1907-14. Superseded by Publication mensuelle de la Société médico-chirurgicale des hôpitaux et formations sanitaires des armées.
1915-1968   7507021

Bull Meriden Conn Hosp
Bulletin. Meriden, Conn. Hospital
1947-1958   18650160R

Bull Mich Dent Hyg Assoc
The Bulletin of the Michigan Dental Hygienists' Association
Continues The Bulletin of the Michigan State Dental Hygienist's Association. Superseded by The Bulletin of the Michigan Dental Hygienists' Association.
1968-1971   7505393

Bull Mich Dent Hyg Assoc
The Bulletin of the Michigan Dental Hygienists' Association
0746-5564
Supersedes The Bulletin of the Michigan Dental Hygienists' Association.
1971   1303036

Bull Mich State Dent Hyg Assoc
The Bulletin of the Michigan State Dental Hygienists' Association
0539-8967
Continued by The Bulletin of the Michigan Dental Hygienists' Association.
1955-1968   7505394

Bull Micr Appl
Bulletin de microscopie appliquée
Formed by the union of Microscopie and Bulletin d'histoire appliquée.
1951-1963   0137461

Bull Midtown Dent Soc
Bulletin / Midtown Dental Society
Continues: Bulletin / New York County Dental Society.
1944   9884675

Bull Millard Fillmore Hosp Buffalo
Bulletin. Buffalo. Millard Fillmore Hospital
1953-1967   15750980R

Bull Monmouth Ocean Cty Dent Soc
Bulletin / Monmouth-Ocean County Dental Society
Continues: Bulletin. Monmouth County (N.J.). Dental Society.
1964-1976   9810652

Bull Montg Bucks Dent Soc
Bulletin. Montgomery-Bucks Dental Society
0027-0156
1957-19uu   18820360R

Bull Moore White Med Found Los Angel
Bulletin. Moore-White Medical Foundation, Los Angeles
Continues Los Angeles. Moore-White Clinic. Bulletin.
1950-1956   18340480R

Bull N C Dent Soc
Bulletin. North Carolina Dental Society
Continued by the society's Journal.
1918-1951   **19210610R**

Bull N J Coll Med Dent
Bulletin Of The New Jersey College Of
Medicine And Dentistry
1965-19uu   **9883885**

Bull N J Soc Dent Child
Bulletin - New Jersey Society of Dentistry
for Children
0548-5819
1953   **7505331**

Bull N Y Acad Med
Bulletin of the New York Academy of
Medicine
0028-7091
Continues: Transactions of the New York
Academy of Medicine. New York Academy
of Medicine. Continued by: Journal of urban
health.
1925-1997   **7505398**

Bull N Y State Dent Soc Anesthesiol
Bulletin Of The New York State Dental
Society Of Anesthesiology
0028-758X
1957-1969   **9883655**

Bull N Y State Soc Dent Child
Bulletin of the New York State Society of
Dentistry for Children
0028-7741
1950   **7505400**

Bull N Z Soc Periodontol
Bulletin - N. Z. Society of Periodontology
Continued by Journal of the New Zealand
Society of Periodontology.
1956-1977   **7505323**

Bull Narc
Bulletin on narcotics
0007-523X
1949   **2984719R**

Bull Natl Clgh Poison Control Cent
Bulletin (National Clearinghouse for Poison
Control Centers (U.S.))
0049-5484
1957-1982   **7505324**

Bull Natl Inst Health
Bulletin. National Institutes of Health (U.S.)
Continues: Bulletin. National Institute of
Health (U.S.)
1949-1951   **9427282**

Bull Natl Med Dent Assoc Natl Advocates Soc
Bulletin (National Medical and Dental
Association (U.S))
0027-9676
Continues Medical & dental (National
Medical and Dental Association of America).
Continued by Annual Bulletin (National
Medical and Dental Association (U.S.)).
1967-1973   **7505325**

Bull Natl Soc Med Res
Bulletin of the National Society for Medical
Research
0028-0186
1946-1984   **7505395**

Bull Natl Tuberc Assoc
Bulletin - National Tuberculosis Association
0893-1119
Continues: Bulletin of the National
Association for the Study and Prevention
of Tuberculosis. Continued by: Bulletin of
the National Tuberculosis and Respiratory
Disease Association.
1918-1968   **7505328**

Bull Natl Tuberc Respir Dis Assoc
Bulletin - National Tuberculosis and
Respiratory Disease Association
0028-0313
Continues: Bulletin - National Tuberculosis
Association. Continued by: American Lung
Association bulletin.
1968-1973   **7505327**

Bull New Engl Med Cent
Bulletin. New England Medical Center
Merged with the Tufts medical journal to
form the Bulletin of the Tufts-New England
Medical Center.
1939-1954   **0134742**

Bull Newark Dent Club
Bulletin of the Newark Dental Club
1927   **7505401**

Bull Ninth Dist Dent Soc
Bulletin. Ninth District Dental Society of the
State of New York
0070-3710
1916-2002   **19120480R**

Bull North Dist Dent Soc
Bulletin - Northern District Dental Society
1948-1969   **7505334**

Bull North Shore Branch Chic Med Soc
Bulletin - North Shore Branch, Chicago
Medical Society
0098-4388
1930-1965   **7503360**

Bull NYU Hosp Jt Dis
Bulletin of the NYU hospital for joint
diseases
1936-9719   **1936-9727**
Continues: Bulletin of the hospital for joint
diseases.
2006   **101300541**

Bull Off Chambre Synd Med Seine
Bulletin officiel. Chambre syndicale des
médecins de la Seine
0300-5445
1949-1963   **0353367**

Bull Off Int Epizoot
Bulletin - Office international des épizooties
0300-9823
Split into separate English. French. and
Spanish editions.
1927-2002   **7503361**

Bull Okla State Dent Assoc
Bulletin. Oklahoma State Dental Association
Continued by the association's Journal.
1911-1951   **19330820R**

Bull Ophthalmol Soc Egypt
Bulletin of the Ophthalmological Society of
Egypt
0078-5342
1902   **7507035**

Bull Orange Cty Med Assoc
The bulletin of the Orange County Medical
Association
0272-9059
Absorbed by: Southern California physician.
1928-2000   **8009457**

Bull Ordre Med
Bulletin de l'Ordre des médecins
0030-4565
1941   **7507009**

Bull Osaka Med Coll
Bulletin of the Osaka Medical College
0916-2844
Continues: Bulletin of the Osaka Medical
School.
1988   **8917028**

Bull Osaka Med Sch
Bulletin of the Osaka Medical School
0030-6142
Continued by: Bulletin of the Osaka Medical
College.
1954-1987   **0406665**

Bull Osaka Med Sch Suppl
Bulletin of the Osaka Medical School.
Supplement
0078-6667
1956-1984   **0405502**

Bull Pac Coast Soc Orthod
Bulletin - Pacific Coast Society of
Orthodontists
0030-8617
Continued by: PCSO bulletin.
1922-1978   **7503362**

Bull Pan Am Health Organ
Bulletin of the Pan American Health
Organization
0085-4638
Continues the English ed. of Boletín de la
Oficina Sanitaria Panamericana. Merged with:
Boletín de la Oficina Sanitaria Panamericana,
to become: Revista panamericana de salud
pública.
1973-1996   **7505403**

Bull Parenter Drug Assoc
Bulletin of the Parenteral Drug Association
0048-2986
Continued by Journal of the Parenteral Drug
Association.
1946-1977   **7505404**

Bull Passaic Cty Dent Soc
Bulletin of the Passaic County Dental
Society
0079-0125
1940-1978   **7507037**

Bull Pharm Res Inst
Bulletin of Pharmaceutical Research
Institute
0473-4696
1950-1973   **7502538**

Bull Phila Assoc Psychoanal
Bulletin of the Philadelphia Association for
Psychoanalysis
0480-2780
1951-1973   **0427302**

Bull Phila Cty Dent Soc
The Bulletin of the Philadelphia County
Dental Society
0031-7268
Continued by: Journal of the Philadelphia
County Dental Society.
1936-1983   **7505406**

Bull Phila Pa Hosp Ayer Clin Lab
Bulletin. Philadelphia. Pennsylvania
Hospital. Ayer Clinical Laboratory
0099-7463
1903-1993   **19620140R**

Bull Physiopathol Respir (Nancy)
Bulletin de physio-pathologie respiratoire
0007-439X
Continued by Bulletin européen de
physiopathologie respiratoire.
1965-1975   **7611945**

Bull Plainfield Dent Soc
Bulletin Of The Plainfield Dental Society
1969-1971   **9883481**

Bull Pottawatomie Cty Okla
Bulletin. Pottawatomie County (Okla.)
Medical Society
193u-1964   **19720390R**

Bull Prosthet Res
Bulletin of prosthetics research
0007-506X
Continued by the Journal of rehabilitation
R&D.
1964-1982   0370646

Bull Res Counc Isr Sect E Exp Med
Bulletin of the Research Council of Israel.
Section E: Experimental medicine
Continues in part Bulletin of the Research
Council of Israel. Continued by Israel journal
of experimental medicine.
1956-1963   7509361

Bull Rheum Dis
Bulletin on the rheumatic diseases
0007-5248
1950-2004   0127416

Bull Rosl N Y St. Francis Sanat Card Child
Bulletin. Roslyn, N. Y. St. Francis
Sanatorium for Cardiac Children
Continued by the Bulletin of the hospital
under its later name: St. Francis Hospital and
Sanatorium for Cardiac Children.
1944-1953   20440150R

Bull S Diego Cty Med Soc
Bulletin - San Diego County Medical Society
Continued by San Diego physician.
1915-1968   7506993

Bull San Diego Cty Dent Soc
Bulletin - San Diego County Dental Society
0036-4010
Continued by: News (San Diego County
Dental Society).
1931-1973   7506992

Bull San Franc Cty Med Soc
Bulletin - San Francisco County Medical
Society
Continued by Bulletin of the San Francisco
Medical Society.
1928-1950   7505338

Bull San Mateo Cty Dent Soc
Bulletin - San Mateo County Dental Society
0080-598X
19uu   7503368

Bull Sangamon Cty Med Soc
Bulletin - Sangamon County Medical Society
1936-1973   7506994

Bull Sanit
Bulletin sanitaire
1901-1950   15920020R

Bull Sch Med
Bulletin Of The School Of Medicine
19uu   9875097

Bull Sch Med Univ Md
Bulletin of the School of Medicine
(Baltimore, Md.)
1048-9614
Continues: Bulletin of the University of
Maryland School of Medicine and College
of Physicians and Surgeons. Continued
by: Bulletin (University of Maryland at
Baltimore. Medical Alumni Association).
1921-1978   7506995

Bull Schweiz Akad Med Wiss
Bulletin der Schweizerischen Akademie der
Medizinischen Wissenschaften
0036-7494
Absorbed: Jahresbericht - Schewizerishe
Akademie der Medizinischen Wissenschaften,
in 1983. Continued by: Jahresbericht
(Schweizerische Akademie der Medizinischen
Wissenschaften: 1988).
1944-1988   7503414

Bull Sci Med (Bologna)
Bullettino delle scienze mediche
0007-5787
1829-1990   0372676

Bull Second Dist Dent Soc
Bulletin - Second District Dental Society
0037-055X
1915   7503372

Bull Soc Amis Sci (Med) (Poznan)
Bulletin de la Société des amis des sciences
et des lettres de Poznań. Séria C: Médecine
0551-7516
Continued by: Annals of immunology.
1949-196u   7507011

Bull Soc Belge Ophtalmol
Bulletin de la Société belge d'ophtalmologie
0081-0746
1896   7505353

Bull Soc Chim Biol (Paris)
Bulletin de la Société de chimie biologique
0037-9042
Continued by Biochimie.
1914-1970   7503398

Bull Soc Chim Fr
Bulletin de la Société chimique de France
0037-8968
Continues Bulletin de la Société chimique
de Paris. Merged with the inorganic parts
of: Bulletin des soci'et'es chimiques belges;
Chemische Berichte/Recueil; and: Gazzetta
chimica Italiana, to form: European journal
of inorganic chemistry. Merged with Liebigs
Annalen/Recueil, and with the organic parts
of: Bulletin des soci'et'es chimiques belges;
Chemische Berichte/Recueil; and: Gazzetta
chimica Italiana; to form: European journal of
organic chemistry.
1907-1997   7505355

Bull Soc Chir Paris
Bulletin. Société de chirurgie de Paris
Merged with Mémoires de la Société de
chirurgie de Paris to form Bulletins et
mémoires de la Société de chirurgie de Paris.
1848-1874   20821290R

Bull Soc Fr Dermatol Syphiligr
Bulletin de la Société française de
dermatologie et de syphiligraphie
Merged with Annales de dermatologie
et de syphiligraphie to form Annales de
dermatologie et de vénéréologie.
1890-1976   7503407

Bull Soc Int Chir
Bulletin de la Société internationale de
chirurgie
0037-945X
Superseded by World journal of surgery.
Continues Journal international de chirurgie.
1955-1975   7505358

Bull Soc Ital Med Ig Trop Sez Eritrea
Bollettino. Societa italiana di medicina e
igiene tropicale. Sezione Eritrea
1942-1950   20820820R

Bull Soc Med Afr Noire Lang Fr
Bulletin de la Société médicale d'Afrique
noire de langue française
0049-1101
Continues the Bulletin médical de l'A. O. F.
Continued by Dakar médical.
1959-1978   7503409

Bull Soc Med Hyg Alger
Bulletin. Société des médecins hygiénistes
d'Algérie
1954-196u   20830150R

Bull Soc Med Pau
Bulletin de la Société médicale de Pau
1260-4038
Continued by Bulletin de la Société médicale
de Pau et du Béarn.
1901-1965   7505361

Bull Soc Ophtalmol Fr
Bulletin des sociétés d'ophtalmologie de
France
0081-1270
1949   0372675

**Bull Soc Ophtalmol Paris Soc Ophtalmol Est
Lyon Ouest**
Bulletin de la Société d'ophtalmologie
de Paris et des sociétés d'ophtalmologie
de l'Est, de Lyon et de l'Ouest. Société
d'ophtalmologie de Paris
1888-1948   0027133

Bull Soc Pathol Exot
Bulletin de la Société de pathologie exotique
(1990)
0037-9085
Continues: Bulletin de la Société de
pathologie exotique et de ses filiales.
1990   9212564

Bull Soc Pathol Exot Filiales
Bulletin de la Société de pathologie exotique
et de ses filiales
0037-9085
Continued by: Bulletin de la Société de
pathologie exotique (1990).
1908-1989   7503399

Bull Soc Pharm Bord
Bulletin de la Société de pharmacie de
Bordeaux
0037-9093
Continues Bulletin des travaux de la Société
de pharmacie de Bordeaux.
1951   7507010

Bull Soc R Belge Gynecol Obstet
Bulletin de la Société royale belge de
gynécologie et d'obstétrique
0037-9522
Continues: Bulletin de la Société belge de
gynécologie et d'obstétrique.
1946-1969   7503410

Bull Soc Sci Med Grand Duche Luxemb
Bulletin de la Société des sciences médicales
du Grand-Duché de Luxembourg
0037-9247
1864   7503402

Bull St Louis Dent Soc
Bulletin - St. Louis Dental Society
0360-3458
Continued by The Greater St. Louis Dental
Society bulletin.
1930-1960   7513571

Bull St Louis Med Society
Bulletin. St. Louis Medical Society
Continued by St. Louis medicine.
1907-1958   20520610R

Bull St Louis Park Med Cen
Bulletin (St. Louis Park Medical Center)
Continued by Bulletin (St. Louis Park
Medical Center Research Foundation).
1956-1976   18730050R

Bull Suffolk Cty Dent Soc
Bulletin of the Suffolk County Dental
Society
0039-4688
1956   9884599

Bull Suffolk Cty Med Soc Suffolk Acad Med
Bulletin - Suffolk County Medical Society
0733-2114
Continues News letter of the Suffolk County
Medical Society.
1966   7505340

Bull Switz
Bulletin. Switzerland. Eidgenössisches
Gesundheitsamt
0257-8190
1917-1982   0422127

Bull Tenn Nurses Assoc
Bulletin - Tennessee Nurses Association
0040-3342
Continued by: Tennessee nurse.
1936-1990   7507004

Bull Tenth Dist Dent Soc (Rockville Centre)
Bulletin of the Tenth District Dental Society
of the State of New York
1080-8345
Continued by: Bulletin. Nassau County
Dental Society.
1949-1981   9875600

Bull Tex Nurses Assoc
Bulletin - Texas Nurses Association
0040-4500
Continues Texas nurses' bulletin. Continued
by Texas nursing.
1957-1973   0436151

Bull Tokyo Dent Coll
The Bulletin of Tokyo Dental College
0040-8891
Supersedes the Ronbun shu of Byorigaku
Kyoshitsu. Tokyo Shika Daigaku.
1960   7505414

Bull Tokyo Med Dent Univ
The Bulletin of Tokyo Medical and Dental
University
0040-8921
Continued by: Journal of medical and dental
sciences.
1954-1996   0405503

Bull Toledo Dent Soc
The Bulletin of the Toledo Dental Society
0040-9073
1936-1987   7507045

Bull Tor East Med Assoc
Bulletin of the Toronto East Medical
Association
1936-1968   7507046

Bull Train
Bulletin on training, trends, techniques,
topics
0272-8486
1976   9877737

Bull Tri Cty Dent Soc
The bulletin of the Tri-County Dental
Society
19uu   9875644

Bull Tufts N Engl Med Cent
Bulletin. Tufts-New England Medical Center
Formed by the merger of the Bulletin of the
New England Medical Center and the Tufts
medical journal. Continued by Tufts folia
medica.
1955-1960   0134743

Bull Tulane Univ Med Fac
The Bulletin of the Tulane Medical Faculty
0041-400X
1941-1968   15910040R

Bull U S Army Med Dep
Bulletin. United States. Army Medical Dept
Supersedes the Army medical bulletin.
Absorbed the Dental bulletin and the
Veterinary bulletin.
1943-1949   0032166

Bull Union Cty Dent Soc
Bulletin. Union County (N. J.) Dental
Society
1920   21410130R

Bull Univ Miami Sch Med Jackson Meml Hosp
The bulletin [of] the University of Miami
School of Medicine and Jackson Memorial
Hospital. University of Miami. School of
Medicine
0097-0174
Continues the Bulletin of the Jackson
Memorial Hospital and the School of
Medicine of the University of Miami.
1955-1966   18710020R

Bull Univ Minn Hosp Minn Med Found
Bulletin of the University of Minnesota
Hospitals and Minnesota Medical
Foundation. Minnesota. University.
Hospitals
Continued by the University of Minnesota
medical bulletin.
1929-1955   18730300R

Bull Utica Acad Med
Bulletin - Utica Academy of Medicine
Continued by: Bulletin. Central New York
Academy of Medicine.
1936-1964   7505341

Bull Va State Dent Assoc
The Bulletin of the Virginia State Dental
Association
Continued by Virginia dental journal.
1921-1964   7507050

Bull Val Dent Soc
Bulletin of the Valley Dental Society
0504-9822
Continues Bulletin of the Valley District
Dental Society.
1961-1966   7507048

Bull Vanc Med Assoc
Bulletin. Vancouver Medical Association
1924-1958   0032450

Bull Vener Dis
Bulletin of venereal diseases
1937-1952   15910050R

Bull Vener Dis Control
Bulletin of venereal disease control. Ontario.
Dept. of Health
1944-1954   19410130R

Bull World Health Org Suppl
Bulletin of the World Health Organization.
Supplement
0510-8659
1948-1953   8103493

Bull World Health Organ
Bulletin of the World Health Organization
0042-9686
Supersedes Bulletin of the League of Nations
Health Organization and Bulletin mensuel
de l'Office international d'hygiene publique.
Starting in 1999, incorporates: World health
forum, and: World health statistics quarterly.
1947   7507052

Bull World Med Assoc
Bulletin. World Medical Association
1948-1953   21630630R

Bull Yamaguchi Med Sch
The Bulletin of the Yamaguchi Medical
School
0513-1812
1953   0170721

Bulletin NY Med Coll
Bulletin. New York Medical College
1938-1956   19031300R

BuMed News Lett Aviat Suppl
BuMed news letter. Aviation supplement
1943-1948   22420410R

**Bundesgesundheitsblatt Gesundheitsforschung
Gesundheitsschutz**
Bundesgesundheitsblatt,
Gesundheitsforschung, Gesundheitsschutz
1436-9990   1437-1588
Merger of: Bundesgesundheitsblatt, and:
Infektionsepidemiologische Forschung, and
continues the numbering of the former.
1999   101181368

Bur
The Bur
0007-6007
1896-1993   15920110R

Burma Med J
Burma medical journal
0007-6295
Continued by: Myanmar medical journal.
1953-1989   0373132

Burns
Burns: journal of the International Society
for Burn Injuries
0305-4179   1879-1409
Continues: Burns, including thermal injury.
1989   8913178

Burns Incl Therm Inj
Burns, including thermal injury
0305-4179
Continued by: Burns.
1974-1988   7512054

Bus Health
Business and health
0739-9413
1983-2002   8409368

Bus Horiz
Business horizons
0007-6813
Two preliminary issues of this title were
published as supplements to Indiana business
review in 1956 and June 1957.
1958   9878134

Bus Insur
Business insurance
0007-6864
1967   9877801

Bus Week
Business week
0007-7135
Absorbed: Annalist. Oct. 1940 Supersedes:
Magazine of business.
1929   9876909

Butll Soc Amics Hist Cienc Farm Catalana
Butlletí de la Societat d'Amics de la Història
i de la Ciència Farmacèutica Catalana:
BSAHCFC
1133-990X
Continued by: Revista de la Societat Catalana
d'Història de la Farmàcia.
1992-2005   9425224

BZB Bayer Zahnarztebl
BZB. Bayerisches Zahnärzteblatt
0005-3473
1962-1998   0242772

C

C R Acad Sci Hebd Seances Acad Sci D
Comptes rendus hebdomadaires des
séances de l'Académie des sciences. Série D:
Sciences naturelles
0567-655X
Continues in part Comptes rendus
hebdomadaires des séances de l'Académie
des sciences. Continued by Comptes rendus
des séances de l'Académie des sciences. Série
D, Sciences naturelles.
1966-1978   7501107

C R Acad Sci III
Comptes rendus de l'Académie des sciences.
Série III, Sciences de la vie
0764-4469
Continues: Comptes rendus des séances de
l'Académie des sciences. Série III. Sciences
de la vie. Continued by: Comptes rendus
biologies.
1984-2001   8503078

C R Assoc Anat
Comptes rendus de l'Association des
anatomistes
0066-8915
Issued 1899, 1901-13 as supplement to
Bibliographie anatomique; 1926-38, as one
issue a year of the association's Bulletin;
1939-72, as the sole? issue of the Bulletin de
l'Association des anatomistes. Continued by
the Bulletin de l'Association des anatomistes.
1899-1972   7503492

C R Biol
Comptes rendus biologies
1631-0691   1768-3238
Continues: Comptes rendus de l'Académie
des sciences. Série III, Sciences de la vie.
2002   101140040

C R Hebd Seances Acad Sci
Comptes rendus hebdomadaires des séances
de l'Académie des sciences
0001-4036
The proceedings for the period prior to
1835 are contained in "Procès-verbaux
des séances de l'Académie tenues depuis
la fondation de l'Institut jusqu'au mois
d'août 1835." Split into: Comptes rendus
hebdomadaires des séances de l'Académie
des sciences. A, Sciences mathématiques, B,
Sciences physiques (1966); Comptes rendus
hebdomadaires des séances de l'Académie
des sciences. Série C, Sciences chimiques;
and: Comptes rendus hebdomadaires des
séances de l'Académie des sciences. Série D,
Sciences naturelles.
1835-1965   7501108

C R Seances Acad Sci D
Comptes rendus des séances de l'Académie
des sciences. Série D, Sciences naturelles
0567-655X
Continues: Comptes rendus hebdomadaires
des séances de l'Académie des sciences.
Série D, Sciences naturelles. Continued by:
Comptes rendus des séances de l'Académie
des sciences. Série III, Sciences de la vie.
1979-1980   8108552

C R Seances Acad Sci III
Comptes rendus des séances de l'Académie
des sciences. Série III, Sciences de la vie
0249-6313
Continues: Comptes rendus des séances de
l'Académie des sciences. Série D, Sciences
naturelles. Continued by: Comptes rendus de
l'Académie des sciences. Série III, Sciences
de la vie.
1981-1983   8108553

C R Seances Soc Biol Fil
Comptes rendus des séances de la Société de
biologie et de ses filiales
0037-9026
Continued by: Journal de la Société de
biologie.
1849-1998   7505439

C R Trav Lab Carlsberg
Comptes-rendus des travaux du Laboratoire
Carlsberg
0075-7497
Formed by the union of Comptes rendus
des travaux du Laboratoire Carlsberg. Série
chimique and Comptes rendus des travaux du
laboratoire Carlsberg. Série physiologique.
Continued by Carlsberg research
communications.
1958-1976   0421140

C R Trav Lab Carlsberg [Chim]
Comptes rendus des travaux du Laboratoire
Carlsberg. Série chimique
Continues in part Comptes rendus des travaux
du Laboratoire Carlsberg. Merged with
Comptes rendus des travaux du Laboratoire
Carlsberg. Série physiologique to form
Comptes rendus des travaux du Laboratoire
Carlsberg.
1935-1958   7706003

CA Cancer J Clin
CA: a cancer journal for clinicians
0007-9235   1542-4863
1950   0370647

Cad Saude Publica
Cadernos de saúde pública / Ministério da
Saúde, Fundação Oswaldo Cruz, Escola
Nacional de Saúde Pública
0102-311X   1678-4464
1985   8901573

Cad Ter Labor
Caderno de terapêutica Labor
1950-1965   16010010R

Caducee
Le Caducée
1944-19uu   16010080R

Caduceus
Caduceus (Springfield, Ill.)
0882-6447
1985-1997   8705827

Caementum
Caementum
1944-1974   9875601

Cah Homeopath Ther Comp
Cahiers d'homéopathie et de thérapeutique
comparée
1141-0396
1945-1961   16010370R

Cah Anesthesiol
Cahiers d'anesthésiologie
0007-9685
1953   0370650

Cah Coll Med Hop Paris
Les Cahiers du Collège de médecine des
hôpitaux de Paris
0375-877X
Continued by Les Cahiers de médecine.
1960-1969   7503474

Cah Med
Les Cahiers de médecine
0010-0978
Continues Les Cahiers du Collège de
médecine des hôpitaux de Paris.
1970-1974   0242654

Cah Med Inter Prof
Cahiers de médecine inter professionnelle
0007-9936
1961   0314571

Cah Med Union Fr
Cahiers médicaux de l'union française;
revue médico-chirurgicale de la France
d'outre-mer
1946-1950   16010420R

Cah Med Vet
Les Cahiers de médecine vétérinaire
0007-9944
1928-1980   0372701

Cah Nurs
Les cahiers du nursing
0008-0179
Continues: Les Cahiers du nursing canadien.
Continued by: Revue des infirmières et
infirmiers auxiliaires du Québec.
1963-1973   0417622

Cah Odontostomatol Touraine
Cahiers d'odonto-stomatologie
1968-1979   1276416

Cah Prothese
Les Cahiers de prothèse
0397-1643
1973   7613319

Cah Psychiatr
Cahiers de psychiatrie
1947-1967   16010330R

Cah Rmf Bull Med Guide Pract Rev
Cahiers R. M. F.: bulletin médical-guide du
praticien-revue médicale française
Continues Bulletin médical. Revue médicale
française. Guide du praticien. Continued by
Guide du praticien.
1962-1964   0004457

Cah Sociol Demogr Med
Cahiers de sociologie et de démographie
médicales
0007-9995
1961   0004455

CAL
CAL [magazine] Certified Akers
Laboratories
0007-778X
1938-1987   15930010R

Calcif Tissue Int
Calcified tissue international
0171-967X   1432-0827
Continues Calcified tissue research.
1979   7905481

Calcif Tissue Res
Calcified tissue research
0008-0594
Continued by Calcified tissue international.
1967-1978   0114414

Calcutta Med Rev
Calcutta medical review
1938-1962   16010590R

Calif Clin
The California clinician
Continues Clinical osteopathy.
1958-1964   16020110R

Calif Hosp
California hospitals
0896-2766
1986-1995   9015215

Calif Manage Rev
California management review
0008-1256
1958   9877019

Calif Med
California medicine
0008-1264
Continues California and western medicine.
Continued by the Western journal of
medicine.
1946-1973   0410260

Calif Nurse
California nurse
0008-1310
Continues: CNA bulletin. Continued by:
Registered nurse.
1969-2006   0246655

Calif Public Health Rep
California public health report. California.
Dept. of Public Health
Continues the department's Biennial report.
1943-1952   22510290R

Caliper
The Caliper
0045-4001
Continued by: Accès total.
1946-1999   16020500R

Camb Q Healthc Ethics
Cambridge quarterly of healthcare ethics:
CQ: the international journal of healthcare
ethics committees
0963-1801   1469-2147
1992   9208482

Can Anaesth Soc J
Canadian Anaesthetists' Society journal
0008-2856
Formed by the union of the Proceedings and
News letter of the society. Continued by:
Canadian journal of anaesthesia.
1954-1986   0371163

Can Assoc Radiol J
Canadian Association of Radiologists
journal = Journal l'Association canadienne
des radiologistes
0846-5371
Continues: Journal of the Canadian
Association of Radiologists.
1986   8812910

Can Bull Cardiovasc Nurs
Canadian bulletin of cardiovascular nursing
0831-4462
Continues: Bulletin (Canadian Heart
Foundation. Canadian Council of
Cardiovascular Nurses). Continued by:
Canadian journal of cardiovascular nursing.
1983-1988   8812097

Can Bull Med Hist
Canadian bulletin of medical history =
Bulletin canadien d'histoire de la médecine
0823-2105
Continues: Bulletin canadien d'histoire de la
médecine..
1987   101130981

Can Commun Dis Rep
Canada communicable disease report =
Relevé des maladies transmissibles au
Canada
1188-4169   1481-8531
Continues: Canada diseases weekly report.
1992   9303729

Can Commun Dis Rep Wkly
Canada communicable disease report
weekly
2008   101466094

Can Crit Care Nurs J
Canadian critical care nursing journal
0826-6778
1984-1992   8607463

Can Dent Hyg
The Canadian dental hygienist
0008-3380
Continued by: Probe (Ottawa, Ont.).
1966-1986   0332642

Can Dis Wkly Rep
Canada diseases weekly report = Rapport
hebdomadaire des maladies au Canada
0382-232X
Formed by the union of: Epidemiological
bulletin. and: Bulletin épidémiologique.
Continued by: Canada communicable disease
report.
1975-1991   8903726

Can Doct
Canadian doctor
0008-3429
1935-1991   0373137

Can Fam Physician
Canadian family physician Médecin de
famille canadien
0008-350X   1715-5258
Continues: Journal. College of General
Practice of Canada.
1967   0120300

Can Forces Dent Serv Bull
Canadian Forces Dental Services Bulletin
0715-6774
Continues: Canadian Forces Dental Services
Quarterly.
1980-1983   9878928

Can Forces Dent Serv Q
Canadian Forces Dental Services quarterly
0045-4850
Continues the Royal Canadian Dental Corps
quarterly.
1970-1978   1245652

Can Health Welf
Canada's health & welfare
1945-1971   16020760R

Can HIV AIDS Policy Law Newsl
Canadian HIV-AIDS policy & law
newsletter / Canadian HIV-AIDS Legal
Network = Réseau juridique canadien VIH-
SIDA
1195-5252
Continued by: Canadian HIV-AIDS policy &
law review.
1994-2000   9889371

Can HIV AIDS Policy Law Rev
Canadian HIV/AIDS policy & law review /
Canadian HIV/AIDS Legal Network
1496-399X
Continues: Canadian HIV/AIDS policy & law
newsletter. Continued by: HIV/AIDS policy
& law review.
2000-2004   101125215

Can Hosp
Canadian hospital
0008-3798
Continued by Dimensions in health service.
1924-1973   0417624

Can J Aging
Canadian journal on aging = La revue
canadienne du vieillissement
0714-9808   1710-1107
1982   8708560

Can J Anaesth
Canadian journal of anaesthesia = Journal
canadien d'anesthésie
0832-610X   1496-8975
Continues: Canadian Anaesthetists' Society
journal.
1987   8701709

Can J Appl Physiol
Canadian journal of applied physiology =
Revue canadienne de physiologie appliquée
1066-7814   1543-2718
Continues: Canadian journal of sport
sciences. Continued by: Applied physiology,
nutrition. and metabolism.
1993-2005   9306274

Can J Appl Sport Sci
Canadian journal of applied sport sciences.
Journal canadien des sciences appliquées
au sport
0700-3978
Continued by: Canadian journal of sport
sciences.
1976-1986   7801184

Can J Biochem
Canadian journal of biochemistry
0008-4018
Continues in part the Canadian journal of
biochemistry and physiology. Continued by
Canadian journal of biochemistry and cell
biology.
1964-1982   0421034

Can J Biochem Cell Biol
Canadian journal of biochemistry and cell
biology = Revue canadienne de biochimie et
biologie cellulaire
0714-7511
Continued by: Biochemistry and cell biology.
Continues: Canadian journal of biochemistry.
1983-1985   8302763

Can J Biochem Physiol
Canadian journal of biochemistry and
physiology
Continues Canadian journal of medical
sciences. Continued by Canadian journal
of biochemistry and Canadian journal of
physiology and pharmacology.
1954-1963   16030030R

Can J Cardiol
The Canadian journal of cardiology
0828-282X   1916-7075
1985   8510280

Can J Cardiovasc Nurs
Canadian journal of cardiovascular nursing
= Journal canadien en soins infirmiers
cardio-vasculaires
0843-6096
Continues: Canadian bulletin of
cardiovascular nursing.
1989   8913645

Can J Clin Pharmacol
The Canadian journal of clinical
pharmacology = Journal canadien de
pharmacologie clinique
1198-581X   1710-6222
1994   9804162

Can J Commun Ment Health
Canadian journal of community mental
health = Revue canadienne de santé mentale
communautaire
0713-3936
1982   8406631

Can J Community Dent
The Canadian journal of community
dentistry = La Revue canadienne de la
dentisterie communautaire
1986-2000   8806537

Can J Comp Med
Canadian journal of comparative medicine.
Revue canadienne de médecine comparée
0008-4050
Continues: Canadian journal of comparative
medicine and veterinary science. Continued
by: Canadian journal of veterinary research..
1968-1985   0151747

Can J Comp Med Vet Sci
Canadian journal of comparative medicine and veterinary science
0316-5957
Continues: Canadian journal of comparative medicine. Continued by: Canadian journal of comparative medicine.
1940-1968   0151757

Can J Diet Pract Res
Canadian journal of dietetic practice and research: a publication of Dietitians of Canada = Revue canadienne de la pratique et de la recherche en diététique: une publication des Diététistes du Canada
1486-3847
Continues: Journal of the Canadian Dietetic Association.
1998   9811151

Can J Exp Psychol
Canadian journal of experimental psychology = Revue canadienne de psychologie expérimentale
1196-1961
Continues: Canadian journal of psychology.
1993   9315513

Can J Gastroenterol
Canadian journal of gastroenterology = Journal canadien de gastroenterologie
0835-7900
1987   8807867

Can J Genet Cytol
Canadian journal of genetics and cytology. Journal canadien de génétique et de cytologie
0008-4093
Continued by: Genome.
1959-1986   0372706

Can J Hosp Pharm
The Canadian journal of hospital pharmacy
0008-4123
Continues the Hospital pharmacist.
1969   0215645

Can J Infect Control
The Canadian journal of infection control: the official journal of the Community & Hospital Infection Control Association-Canada = Revue canadienne de prévention des infections / Association pour la prévention des infections a l'hôpital et dans la communaute-Canada ; CHICA-CANADA
1183-5702
Continues: Infection control Canada.
1991   9114581

Can J Med Radiat Technol
The Canadian journal of medical radiation technology / CAMRT
0820-5930
Continues: Canadian journal of radiography, radiotherapy, nuclear medicine. Continued by: Journal of medical imaging and radiation sciences.
1987-2007   8710791

Can J Med Sci
Canadian journal of medical sciences
0316-4403
Continues Canadian journal of research. Section E: Medical sciences. Continued by the Canadian journal of biochemistry and physiology.
1951-1953   16030020R

Can J Med Technol
Canadian journal of medical technology
0008-4158
Absorbed in part: News bulletin. Canadian Society of Laboratory Technologists. Continued by: Canadian journal of medical laboratory science. English. Superseded in part by: News bulletin. Canadian Society of Laboratory Technologists.
1938-1995   0373141

Can J Microbiol
Canadian journal of microbiology
0008-4166   1480-3275
1954   0372707

Can J Neurol Sci
The Canadian journal of neurological sciences. Le journal canadien des sciences neurologiques
0317-1671
1974   0415227

Can J Neurosci Nurs
Canadian journal of neuroscience nursing
1913-7176
Continues: Axone (Dartmouth, N.S.).
2007   101321312

Can J Nurs Adm
Canadian journal of nursing administration
0838-2948
Continued by: Canadian journal of nursing leadership.
1988-1998   9100845

Can J Nurs Leadersh
Canadian journal of nursing leadership
1481-9643
Continues: Canadian journal of nursing administration. Continued by: Nursing leadership (Toronto, Ont.).
1999-2002   100888575

Can J Nurs Res
The Canadian journal of nursing research = Revue canadienne de recherche en sciences infirmières
0844-5621
Continues: Nursing papers.
1988   8910581

Can J Occup Ther
Canadian journal of occupational therapy. Revue canadienne d'ergothérapie
0008-4174
Continues: Canadian journal of occupational therapy and physiotherapy.
1939   0406021

Can J Oncol
The Canadian journal of oncology
1183-2509
1991-1997   9305916

Can J Ophthalmol
Canadian journal of ophthalmology. Journal canadien d'ophtalmologie
0008-4182
1966   0045312

Can J Otolaryngol
Canadian journal of otolaryngology. Journal canadien d'otolaryngologie
0045-5083
Supersedes: Proceedings of the Canadian Otolaryngological Society annual meeting. Canadian Otolaryngological Society. Continued by: Journal of otolaryngology.
1972-1975   7610409

Can J Otolaryngol Suppl
Canadian journal of otolaryngology. Journal canadien d'otolaryngologie. Supplement
0707-7289
Continued by The Journal of otolaryngology. Supplement.
1974-1975   7708917

Can J Physiol Pharmacol
Canadian journal of physiology and pharmacology
0008-4212   1205-7541
Continues in part: Canadian journal of biochemistry and physiology.
1964   0372712

Can J Psychiatr Nurs
The Canadian journal of psychiatric nursing
0008-4247
Continues: Psych nurse.
1966-1990   0074422

Can J Psychiatry
Canadian journal of psychiatry. Revue canadienne de psychiatrie
0706-7437   1497-0015
Continues: Canadian Psychiatric Association journal. Canadian Psychiatric Association.
1979   7904187

Can J Psychol
Canadian journal of psychology
0008-4255
Continues: Canadian Psychological Association. Bulletin of the Canadian Psychological Association. Continued by: Canadian journal of experimental psychology.
1947-1992   0372713

Can J Public Health
Canadian journal of public health. Revue canadienne de santé publique
0008-4263
Continues the Canadian public health journal.
1943   0372714

Can J Radiogr Radiother Nucl Med
The Canadian journal of radiography, radiotherapy, nuclear medicine
0319-4434
Continues The Canadian journal of radiography, radiotherapy, nucleography. Continued by: Canadian journal of medical radiation technology.
1974-1986   7607694

Can J Res
Canadian journal of research
1929-1950   16030060R

Can J Res E Med Sci
Canadian journal of research. Section E, Medical sciences
0366-743X
Continues in part: Canadian journal of research. Continued by: Canadian journal of medical sciences.
1944-1950   101240158

Can J Rural Med
Canadian journal of rural medicine: the official journal of the Society of Rural Physicians of Canada = Journal canadien de la médecine rurale: le journal officiel de la Société de médecine rurale du Canada
1203-7796   1488-237x
1996   9708550

Can J Sport Sci
Canadian journal of sport sciences = Journal canadien des sciences du sport
0833-1235
Continued by: Canadian journal of applied physiology. Continues: Canadian journal of applied sport sciences.
1987-1992   8707670

Can J Surg
Canadian journal of surgery. Journal canadien de chirurgie
0008-428X   1488-2310
1957   0372715

Can J Urol
The Canadian journal of urology
1195-9479
1994   9515842

Can J Vet Res
Canadian journal of veterinary research
= Revue canadienne de recherche vétérinaire
0830-9000
Continues: Canadian journal of comparative
medicine.
1986   8607793

Can J Zool
Canadian journal of zoology
0008-4301   1480-3283
Continues: Canadian journal of research.
Section D. Zoological sciences.
1951   0372716

Can Med Assoc J
Canadian Medical Association journal
0008-4409
Formed by the merger of the Montreal
medical journal and the Maritime medical
news. Continued by: CMAJ.
1911-1985   0414110

Can Ment Health
Canada's mental health
0008-2791
1953-1996   0070157

Can Nurse
The Canadian nurse
0008-4581
Continues: Canadian nurse and hospital
review. Absorbed: Infirmière canadienne.
1986 Continued in part by: Infirmière
canadienne (2000).
1924   0405504

Can Oncol Nurs J
Canadian oncology nursing journal = Revue
canadienne de nursing oncologique
1181-912X
1991   9300792

Can Oper Room Nurs J
Canadian operating room nursing journal
0712-6778
1983   8406632

Can Pharm J
Canadian pharmaceutical journal
0317-199X
Continued by: CPJ. Scientific section
superseded by Canadian journal of
pharmaceutical sciences with May 1966
issue.
1868-1984   101266775

Can Psychiatr Assoc J
Canadian Psychiatric Association journal
0008-4824
Supersedes Canadian Psychiatric Association.
Bulletin. Continued by Canadian journal of
psychiatry. Revue canadienne de psychiatrie.
1956-1978   0414266

Can Public Adm
Canadian public administration.
Administration publique du Canada
0008-4840
1958   9875219

Can Res Suppl
Cancer research. Supplement
0576-6656
1953-1956   0373144

Can Respir J
Canadian respiratory journal: journal of the
Canadian Thoracic Society
1198-2241
1994   9433332

Can Rev Sociol
Canadian review of sociology = Revue
canadienne de sociologie
1755-6171   1755-618X
Continues: Canadian review of sociology and
anthropology.
2008   101320224

Can Rev Sociol Anthropol
The Canadian review of sociology and
anthropology. La Revue canadienne de
sociologie et d'anthropologie
0008-4948
Continued by: Canadian review of sociology.
1964-2007   0323130

Can Serv Med J
Canadian services medical journal
Continues Treatment services bulletin of
the Dept. of Veterans Affairs. Continued by
Medical services journal. Canada.
1954-1957   16020700R

Can Vet J
The Canadian veterinary journal. La revue
vétérinaire canadienne
0008-5286
1960   0004653

CANA
CANA
0196-2752
Continued by: CANA. Inc..
1947-1991   7909277

Cancer
Cancer
0008-543X   1097-0142
1948   0374236

Cancer Biochem Biophys
Cancer biochemistry biophysics
0305-7232
1974-1999   7506524

Cancer Biol Ther
Cancer biology & therapy
1538-4047   1555-8576
2002   101137842

Cancer Biomark
Cancer biomarkers: section A of Disease
markers
1574-0153
2005   101256509

Cancer Biother
Cancer biotherapy
1062-8401
Continues: Selected cancer therapeutics.
Merged with: Antibody, immunoconjugates,
and radiopharmaceuticals. to form: Cancer
biotherapy & radiopharceuticals.
1993-1995   9314021

Cancer Biother Radiopharm
Cancer biotherapy & radiopharmaceuticals
1084-9785   1557-8852
Formed by the union of: Cancer biotherapy,
and: Antibody, immunoconjugates, and
radiopharmaceuticals. and continues the
numbering of the former.
1996   9605408

Cancer Causes Control
Cancer causes & control: CCC
0957-5243   1573-7225
1990   9100846

Cancer Cell
Cancer cell
1535-6108
2002   101130617

Cancer Cells
Cancer cells (Cold Spring Harbor, N.Y.:
1989)
1042-2196
Continues: Cancer cells.
1989-1991   9000382

Cancer Chemother Biol Response Modif
Cancer chemotherapy and biological
response modifiers
0921-4410
Continues: Cancer chemotherapy.
1987   8812385

Cancer Chemother Pharmacol
Cancer chemotherapy and pharmacology
0344-5704   1432-0843
1978   7806519

Cancer Chemother Rep
Cancer chemotherapy reports. Part 1
0069-0112
Supersedes Current research in cancer
chemotherapy. Merged with Cancer
chemotherpay reports. Parts 2 and 3 to form
Cancer treatment reports.
1959-1975   7607105

Cancer Chemother Rep 2
Cancer chemotherapy reports. Part 2
0069-0120
Supersedes Cancer chemotherapy screening
data. Merged with Cancer chemotherapy
reports. Parts 1 and 3 to form Cancer
treatment reports.
1968-1975   7607106

Cancer Chemother Rep 3
Cancer chemotherapy reports. Part 3
0069-0139
Merged with Cancer chemotherapy reports.
Parts 1 and 2 to form Cancer treatment
reports.
1968-1975   7609154

Cancer Clin Trials
Cancer clinical trials
0190-1206
Continued by: American journal of clinical
oncology.
1978-1981   7905482

Cancer Commun
Cancer communications
0955-3541
Continued by: Oncology research.
1989-1991   8916730

Cancer Control
Cancer control: journal of the Moffitt
Cancer Center
1073-2748   1526-2359
1994   9438457

Cancer Detect Prev
Cancer detection and prevention
0361-090X   1525-1500
1976   7704778

Cancer Detect Prev Suppl
Cancer detection and prevention.
Supplement: official publication of the
International Society for Preventive
Oncology, Inc
1043-6995
1987-1987   8808253

Cancer Drug Deliv
Cancer drug delivery
0732-9482
Continued by: Selective cancer therapeutics.
1983-1988   8409965

Cancer Epidemiol Biomarkers Prev
Cancer epidemiology, biomarkers &
prevention: a publication of the American
Association for Cancer Research,
cosponsored by the American Society of
Preventive Oncology
1055-9965   1538-7755
1991   9200608

Cancer Gene Ther
Cancer gene therapy
0929-1903   1476-5500
1994   9432230

Cancer Genet Cytogenet
Cancer genetics and cytogenetics
0165-4608   1873-4456
1979   7909240

Cancer Genomics Proteomics
Cancer genomics & proteomics
1109-6535   1790-6295
2004   101188791

Cancer Imaging
Cancer imaging: the official publication of
the International Cancer Imaging Society
1740-5025   1470-7330
2000   101172931

Cancer Immun
Cancer immunity: a journal of the Academy
of Cancer Immunology
    1424-9634
2001   101119871

Cancer Immunol Immunother
Cancer immunology, immunotherapy: CII
0340-7004   1432-0851
  Continues: Cancer immunology and
  immunotherapy.
1982   8605732

Cancer Invest
Cancer investigation
0735-7907   1532-4192
1983   8307154

Cancer J
Cancer journal (Sudbury, Mass.)
1528-9117   1540-336X
  Continues: Cancer journal from Scientific
  American.
2000   100931981

Cancer J Sci Am
The cancer journal from Scientific American
1081-4442
  Continued by: Cancer journal (Sudbury,
  Mass.).
1995-2000   9513568

Cancer Lett
Cancer letters
0304-3835   1872-7980
1975   7600053

Cancer Metastasis Rev
Cancer metastasis reviews
0167-7659   1573-7233
1982   8605731

Cancer News
Cancer news
0008-5464
  Supersedes Field army news of the American
  Cancer Society.
1947-1994   16030310R

Cancer Nurs
Cancer nursing
0162-220X   1538-9804
1978   7805358

Cancer Pract
Cancer practice
1065-4704   1523-5394
1993-2002   9312355

Cancer Prev
Cancer prevention (Philadelphia, Pa.)
1055-5897
1989-1993   9306275

Cancer Prev Control
Cancer prevention & control: CPC =
Prévention & contrôle en cancérologie: PCC
1206-548X
1997-1999   9709994

Cancer Prev Res (Phila Pa)
Cancer prevention research (Philadelphia,
Pa.)
1940-6207   1940-6215
2008   101479409

Cancer Prog
Cancer progress
1960-1963   16030320R

Cancer Radiother
Cancer radiothérapie: journal de la Société
française de radiothérapie oncologique
1278-3218
  Continues: Bulletin du cancer. Radiothérapie.
1997   9711272

Cancer Res
Cancer research
0008-5472   1538-7445
  Continues: American journal of cancer.
1941   2984705R

Cancer Sci
Cancer science
1347-9032   1349-7006
  Continues: Japanese journal of cancer
  research.
2003   101168776

Cancer Surv
Cancer surveys
0261-2429
1982-1999   8218015

Cancer Treat Rep
Cancer treatment reports
0361-5960
  Formed by the union of Cancer chemotherapy
  reports, Parts 1, 2, and 3. Absorbed by:
  Journal of the National Cancer Institute.
1976-1987   7607107

Cancer Treat Res
Cancer treatment and research
0927-3042
1981   8008541

Cancer Treat Rev
Cancer treatment reviews
0305-7372   1532-1967
1974   7502030

Cancro
Il Cancro
0008-5480
1930-1974   0421125

CANNT J
CANNT journal = Journal ACITN
1498-5136
  Continues: Journal CANNT.
1996   100959352

Cap Nurs
Capital nursing
1984   9881858

CAP Today
CAP today / College of American
Pathologists
0891-1525
  Formed by the union of: Pathologist;
  Laboratory accreditation newsletter;
  Summing up; Q-tips; Perceptions (Skokie,
  Ill.); Capitol scan; and: Counterpoints
  (Skokie, Ill.).
1987   8704824

Capitation Manag Rep
Capitation management report
1083-7183
19uu   9891256

Capitation Rates Data
Capitation rates & data
1090-1574
1996   100883481

Carbohydr Lett
Carbohydrate letters
1073-5070
1994-2001   9607448

Carbohydr Res
Carbohydrate research
0008-6215   1873-426X
1965   0043535

Carcinog Compr Surv
Carcinogenesis; a comprehensive survey
0147-4006
1976-1989   7704086

Carcinogenesis
Carcinogenesis
0143-3334   1460-2180
1980   8008055

Card Electrophysiol Rev
Cardiac electrophysiology review
1385-2264
  Absorbed by: Journal of interventional
  cardiac electrophysiology.
1997-2003   9708907

Cardiol Clin
Cardiology clinics
0733-8651   1558-2264
1983   8300331

Cardiol J
Cardiology journal
    1897-5593
  Continues: Folia cardiologica (Gdańsk,
  Poland).
2007   101392712

Cardiol Manage
Cardiology management
0892-9327
  Continues: Applied cardiology.
1987-1988   8704505

Cardiol Prat
Cardiologia pratica
0008-6339
1950-1978   0400652

Cardiol Rev
Cardiology in review
1061-5377   1538-4683
1993   9304686

Cardiol Young
Cardiology in the young
1047-9511   1467-1107
1991   9200019

Cardiologia
Cardiologia
  Continued by Cardiology.
1937-1969   1265351

Cardiologia
Cardiologia (Rome, Italy)
0393-1978
Continues: Bollettino della Società italiana di cardiologia. Merged with: Giornale italiano di cardiologia. to form: Italian heart journal.
1982-1999   **8506637**

Cardiology
Cardiology
0008-6312   1421-9751
Absorbed: Heartdrug. 2006 Continues: Cardiologia.
1970   **1266406**

Cardioscience
Cardioscience
1015-5007
1990-1995   **9014943**

Cardiovasc Clin
Cardiovascular clinics
0069-0384
1969-1993   **0213744**

Cardiovasc Diabetol
Cardiovascular diabetology
     1475-2840
2002   **101147637**

Cardiovasc Drug Rev
Cardiovascular drug reviews
0897-5957
Continues: New cardiovascular drugs. Continued by: Cardiovascular therapeutics.
1988-2007   **9006912**

Cardiovasc Drugs Ther
Cardiovascular drugs and therapy / sponsored by the International Society of Cardiovascular Pharmacotherapy
0920-3206   1573-7241
1987   **8712220**

Cardiovasc Eng
Cardiovascular engineering (Dordrecht, Netherlands)
1567-8822   1573-6806
2001   **101132083**

Cardiovasc Hematol Agents Med Chem
Cardiovascular & hematological agents in medicinal chemistry
1871-5257   1875-6182
Continues: Current medicinal chemistry. Cardiovascular and hematological agents.
2006   **101266881**

Cardiovasc Hematol Disord Drug Targets
Cardiovascular & hematological disorders drug targets
1871-529X
Continues: Current drug targets. Cardiovascular & haematological disorders.
2006   **101269160**

Cardiovasc Intervent Radiol
Cardiovascular and interventional radiology
0174-1551   1432-086X
Continues Cardiovascular radiology.
1980   **8003538**

Cardiovasc J Afr
Cardiovascular journal of Africa
1995-1892
Continues: Cardiovascular journal of South Africa.
2007   **101313864**

Cardiovasc J S Afr
Cardiovascular journal of South Africa: official journal for Southern Africa Cardiac Society [and] South African Society of Cardiac Practitioners
1015-9657   1680-0745
Continues: Cardiovascular journal of Southern Africa. Continued by: Cardiovascular journal of Africa.
1999-2007   **100964061**

Cardiovasc Nurs
Cardio-vascular nursing
0008-6355
1965-1996   **0004704**

Cardiovasc Pathol
Cardiovascular pathology: the official journal of the Society for Cardiovascular Pathology
1054-8807   1879-1336
1992   **9212060**

Cardiovasc Radiat Med
Cardiovascular radiation medicine
1522-1865
Continued by: Cardiovascular revascularization medicine.
1999-2004   **100888865**

Cardiovasc Radiol
Cardiovascular radiology
0342-7196
Continued by Cardiovascular and interventional radiology.
1977-1979   **7807044**

Cardiovasc Res
Cardiovascular research
0008-6363   1755-3245
1967   **0077427**

Cardiovasc Res Cent Bull
Cardiovascular Research Center bulletin
0008-6371
1962-1983   **0415230**

Cardiovasc Revasc Med
Cardiovascular revascularization medicine: including molecular interventions
1553-8389   1878-0938
Continues: Cardiovascular radiation medicine.
2005   **101238551**

Cardiovasc Surg
Cardiovascular surgery (London, England)
0967-2109
Continued by: Vascular.
1993-2003   **9308765**

Cardiovasc Ther
Cardiovascular therapeutics
1755-5914   1755-5922
Continues: Cardiovascular drug reviews.
2008   **101319630**

Cardiovasc Toxicol
Cardiovascular toxicology
1530-7905   1559-0259
2001   **101135818**

Cardiovasc Ultrasound
Cardiovascular ultrasound
     1476-7120
2003   **101159952**

Care Giver
Care giver: journal of the College of Chaplains
1077-8586
Continues: Bulletin - American Protestant Hospital Association. American Protestant Hospital Association. Continued by: Care giver journal.
1984-1989   **9881936**

Care Manag J
Care management journals: Journal of case management ; The journal of long term home health care
1521-0987
Formed by the union of: Journal of case management, and: Journal of long term home health care.
1999   **100888264**

Caridad Cienc Arte
Caridad, ciencia y arte
0069-0546
1963-1976   **0035654**

Caries Res
Caries research
0008-6568   1421-976X
1967   **0103374**

Caring
Caring: National Association for Home Care magazine
0738-467X
1982   **8301759**

Caritas
Caritas
1934   **9880341**

Carlsberg Res Commun
Carlsberg research communications
0105-1938
Continues Comptes-rendus des travaux du Laboratoire Carlsberg.
1976-1989   **7703861**

Carnet Econ
Carnet de l'économe
Continued by: Revue de l'économe.
1934-1950   **16040260R**

Carney Hosp J
Carney Hospital journal
0576-8039
1959-1969   **7505424**

Cas Cesk Lek
Casopis českého lékárnictva
1882-1950   **16040440R**

Cas Cesk Vet
Casopis československých veterinářů
194u-19uu   **16040450R**

Cas Lek Cesk
Casopís lékařů českých
0008-7335
1862   **0004743**

Case Rep Child Meml Hosp Chic
Case reports. Chicago. Children's Memorial Hospital
1942-1961   **16130370R**

Case Stud Health Adm
Case studies in health administration
0193-9394
1978-1993   **7707775**

Catedra Clin
Cátedra y clínica
1930-19uu   **16040510R**

Cater Health
Catering & health
0267-3851
Continued by: Hygiene and nutrition in foodservice and catering.
1988-1993   **8811334**

Cathet Cardiovasc Diagn
Catheterization and cardiovascular diagnosis
0098-6569
Continued by: Catheterization and cardiovascular interventions.
1975-1998   **7508512**

Catheter Cardiovasc Interv
Catheterization and cardiovascular
interventions: official journal of the Society
for Cardiac Angiography & Interventions
1522-1946   1522-726X
Continues: Catheterization and cardiovascular
diagnosis.
1999   100884139

Cathol Hosp
Catholic hospital
0008-8099
Supersedes Catholic hospital. Hôpital
catholique. Continued by C. H. A. C. review.
1973-1979   7502750

Cathol Nurse
The Catholic nurse
0576-9485
1952-1969   0231743

Cathol Nurse (Wallsend)
The Catholic nurse
0008-8269
1933-1973   16040540R

CBE Life Sci Educ
CBE life sciences education
1931-7913
Continues: Cell biology education.
2006   101269039

CCQ
CCQ. Critical care quarterly
0160-2551
Continued by: Critical care nursing quarterly.
1978-1986   7900428

CDA J
CDA journal California Dental Association
0091-4231
Formed by the union of Composite and
of Journal - Southern California Dental
Association. Continued by: Journal of the
California Dental Association.
1973-1988   0367730

CDC Bull
CDC bulletin. Communicable Disease
Center (U.S.)
0270-3440
Absorbed by: Public health reports.
1946-1951   21910050R

CDR (Lond Engl Rev)
CDR (London, England: Review)
0144-1108
Continued by: Communicable diseases report.
CDR review.
1991-1991   9316754

CDR (Lond Engl Wkly)
CDR (London, England: Weekly)
0144-3186
Continued by: Communicable disease report.
CDR weekly.
1991-1991   9316755

CDR Wkly (Online)
CDR weekly: communicable disease report
1991   101121060

CDS Rev
CDS review
0091-1666
Continues Fortnightly review of the Chicago
Dental Society.
1973   0351400

CDT Dig
CDT digest
1970-1975   1254500

CE Focus
Ce Focus
Continued by: Nursing Careers.
1978-1980   9878456

Ceara Med
Ceará médico: orgão do Centro Médico
Cearense
0100-4840
Continues: Norte médico.
1917-1984   8104953

Cell
Cell
0092-8674   1097-4172
1974   0413066

Cell Adhes Commun
Cell adhesion and communication
1061-5385
Continued by: Cell communication &
adhesion.
1993-2000   9417027

Cell Biochem Biophys
Cell biochemistry and biophysics
1085-9195   1559-0283
Continues: Cell biophysics.
1996   9701934

Cell Biochem Funct
Cell biochemistry and function
0263-6484   1099-0844
1983   8305874

Cell Biol Educ
Cell biology education
1536-7509
Continued by: CBE life sciences education.
2002-2005   101133110

Cell Biol Int
Cell biology international
1065-6995   1095-8355
Continues: Cell biology international reports.
1993   9307129

Cell Biol Int Rep
Cell biology international reports
0309-1651
Continued by: Cell biology international.
1977-1992   7708050

Cell Biol Rev
Cell biology reviews: CBR
1131-7108
Continues: Revisiones sobre biologia celular.
1991-1991   9114929

Cell Biol Toxicol
Cell biology and toxicology
0742-2091   1573-6822
1984   8506639

Cell Biophys
Cell biophysics
0163-4992
Continued by: Cell biochemistry and
biophysics.
1979-1995   8002185

Cell Calcium
Cell calcium
0143-4160   1532-1991
1980   8006226

Cell Commun Adhes
Cell communication & adhesion
1541-9061   1543-5180
Continues: Cell adhesion & communication.
2001   101096596

Cell Cycle
Cell cycle (Georgetown, Tex.)
1538-4101   1551-4005
2002   101137841

Cell Death Differ
Cell death and differentiation
1350-9047   1476-5403
1994   9437445

Cell Differ
Cell differentiation
0045-6039
Continued by: Cell differentiation and
development.
1972-1988   0342640

Cell Differ Dev
Cell differentiation and development: the
official journal of the International Society
of Developmental Biologists
0922-3371
Continues: Cell differentiation. Continued by:
Mechanisms of development.
1988-1990   8811335

Cell Growth Differ
Cell growth & differentiation: the molecular
biology journal of the American Association
for Cancer Research
1044-9523
Continued by: Molecular cancer research.
1990-2002   9100024

Cell Host Microbe
Cell host & microbe
1931-3128   1934-6069
2007   101302316

Cell Immunol
Cellular immunology
0008-8749   1090-2163
1970   1246405

Cell Metab
Cell metabolism
1550-4131   1932-7420
2005   101233170

Cell Microbiol
Cellular microbiology
1462-5814   1462-5822
1999   100883691

Cell Mol Biol
Cellular and molecular biology
0145-5680
Continues: Cellular and molecular biology,
including cyto-enzymology. Continued by:
Cellular & molecular biology research.
1982-1992   7801029

Cell Mol Biol (Noisy-le-grand)
Cellular and molecular biology (Noisy-le-
Grand, France)
0145-5680   1165-158X
1992   9216789

Cell Mol Biol Incl Cyto Enzymol
Cellular and molecular biology, including
cyto-enzymology
0145-5680
Continues: Annales d'histochimie. Continued
by: Cellular and molecular biology.
1977-1981   101189940

Cell Mol Biol Lett
Cellular & molecular biology letters
1425-8153   1689-1392
1996   9607427

Cell Mol Biol Res
Cellular & molecular biology research
0968-8773
Continues: Cellular and molecular biology.
1993-1995   9316986

Cell Mol Immunol
Cellular & molecular immunology
1672-7681
2004   101242872

Cell Mol Life Sci
Cellular and molecular life sciences: CMLS
1420-682X   1420-9071
Continues: Experientia.
1997   9705402

Cell Mol Neurobiol
Cellular and molecular neurobiology
0272-4340 1573-6830
1981 8200709

Cell Motil
Cell motility
0271-6585
Continued by: Cell motility and the
cytoskeleton.
1980-1985 8207421

Cell Motil Cytoskeleton
Cell motility and the cytoskeleton
0886-1544 1097-0169
Continues: Cell motility.
1986 8605339

Cell Muscle Motil
Cell and muscle motility
0730-9554
1981-1985 8107192

Cell Oncol
Cellular oncology: the official journal of the
International Society for Cellular Oncology
1570-5870 1875-8606
Continues: Analytical cellular pathology.
2004 101219418

Cell Physiol Biochem
Cellular physiology and biochemistry:
international journal of experimental
cellular physiology, biochemistry, and
pharmacology
1015-8987 1421-9778
1991 9113221

Cell Prolif
Cell proliferation
0960-7722 1365-2184
Continues: Cell and tissue kinetics.
1991 9105195

Cell Regul
Cell regulation
1044-2030
Continued by: Molecular biology of the cell.
1989-1991 9005331

Cell Res
Cell research
1001-0602 1748-7838
1990 9425763

Cell Signal
Cellular signalling
0898-6568 1873-3913
1989 8904683

Cell Stem Cell
Cell stem cell
1934-5909
2007 101311472

Cell Stress Chaperones
Cell stress & chaperones
1355-8145 1466-1268
1996 9610925

Cell Struct Funct
Cell structure and function
0386-7196 1347-3700
1975 7608465

Cell Tissue Bank
Cell and tissue banking
1389-9333 1573-6814
2000 100965121

Cell Tissue Kinet
Cell and tissue kinetics
0008-8730
Continued by: Cell proliferation.
1968-1990 0174107

Cell Tissue Res
Cell and tissue research
0302-766X 1432-0878
Continues: Zeitschrift für Zellforschung und
mikroskopische Anatomie.
1974 0417625

Cell Transplant
Cell transplantation
0963-6897
1992 9208854

Cell Vis
Cell vision: the journal of analytical
morphology
1073-1180
Merged with: Applied immunohistochemistry,
to form: Applied immunohistochemistry &
molecular morhology.
1994-1998 9434447

Cells Tissues Organs
Cells, tissues, organs
1422-6405 1422-6421
Continues: Acta anatomica.
1999 100883360

Cellule
La Cellule
0008-8757
1884-1987 16110080R

Cent Afr J Med
The Central African journal of medicine
0008-9176
1955 0372566

Cent Est Med
Le Centre-est médical
1960-1966 16110290R

Cent Estud Recur Odontol Nino
Centro de Estudios de Recursos
Odontológicos para el Niño: CERON
1012-8980
1976-1983 8409968

Cent Eur J Public Health
Central European journal of public health
1210-7778
Continues: Journal of hygiene, epidemiology,
microbiology, and immunology.
1993 9417324

Cent Med
Centre médical
0008-9826
Continues Le Centre médical et
pharmaceutique.
1931-1972 8009466

Cent Nerv Syst Trauma
Central nervous system trauma: journal of
the American Paralysis Association
0737-5999
Continued by: Journal of neurotrama.
1984-1987 8501356

Centaur Alpha Kappa Kappa
The Centaur of Alpha Kappa Kappa
1903-1980 16110090R

Centaurus
Centaurus; international magazine of the
history of science and medicine
0008-8994
1950 0372565

Cephalalgia
Cephalalgia: an international journal of
headache
0333-1024 1468-2982
1981 8200710

Cereb Cortex
Cerebral cortex (New York, N.Y.: 1991)
1047-3211 1460-2199
1991 9110718

Cereb Palsy Bull
Cerebral palsy bulletin
Continued by Developmental medicine and
child neurology.
1958-1961 16110470R

Cereb Palsy J
The Cerebral palsy journal
Continues Cerebral palsy review.
1965-1968 0101157

Cereb Palsy Rev
Cerebral palsy review
Continues: Spastic review. Continued by:
Cerebral palsy journal.
1950-1965 2984709R

Cerebellum
Cerebellum (London, England)
1473-4222 1473-4230
2002 101089443

Cerebrovasc Brain Metab Rev
Cerebrovascular and brain metabolism
reviews
1040-8827
1989-1996 8910172

Cerebrovasc Dis
Cerebrovascular diseases (Basel,
Switzerland)
1015-9770 1421-9786
1991 9100851

Certif Dent Tech
Certified dental technician
1963-1967 0033473

Cervello G Nevrol
Il Cervello; giornale di nevrologia
1922-1963 16120010R

CES Odontol
CES odontología / Instituto de Ciencias de
la Salud
0120-971X
1988-1995 9209765

Cesk Dermatol
Ceskoslovenská dermatologie
0009-0514
Continues Ceská dermatologie.
1948 0067753

Cesk Epidemiol Mikrobiol Imunol
Ceskoslovenská epidemiologie,
mikrobiologie, imunologie
0009-0522
Continues in part Ceskoslovenská hygiena,
epidemiologie, mikrobiologie. Continued by:
Epidemiologie, mikrobiologie, imunologie.
1956-1993 2984708R

Cesk Farm
Ceskoslovenská farmacie
0009-0530
Continued by: Ceská a Slovenská farmacie.
1952-1993 0372720

Cesk Fysiol
Ceskoslovenská fysiologie / Ústrední ústav
biologický
1210-6313
1952 2984710R

Cesk Gastroenterol Vyz
Ceskoslovenská gastroenterologie a výživa
0009-0565
Continues: Sborník pro pathofysiologii
trávení a výživy. Continued by: Ceská a
slovenská gastroenterologie.
1955-1993 0402356

Cesk Gynekol
Ceskoslovenská gynekologie
0374-6852
Supersedes in part Rozhledy v chirurgii a gynaekologii; vols. for 1936- called also roc. 15- in continuation of that publication's numbering. Continued by: Ceská gynekologie.
1936-1993   0042671

Cesk Hyg
Ceskoslovenská hygiena
0009-0573
Supersedes in part Ceskoslovenská hygiena, epidemiologie, mikrobiologie. Continued by: Hygiena.
1956-1993   0204003

Cesk Morfol
Ceskoslovenská morfologie
Continued in English by Folia morphologica.
1953-1964   0204372

Cesk Neurol
Ceskoslovenská neurologie
0009-0581
Continues in part Neurologie a psychiatrie československá. Continued by: Ceskoslovenská neurologie a neurochirurgie.
1956-1972   0366653

Cesk Neurol Neurochir
Ceskoslovenská neurologie a neurochirurgie
0301-0597
Continues Ceskoslovenská neurologie. Continued by: česká a Slovenská neurologie a neurochirurgie.
1973-1992   0366524

Cesk Oftalmol
Ceskoslovenská oftalmologie
0009-059X
Continued by: Ceská a slovenská oftalmologie.
1933-1994   0005023

Cesk Onkol
Ceskoslovenská onkológia
Continued by Neoplasma; československá onkológia.
1954-1956   16120070R

Cesk Otolaryngol
Ceskoslovenská otolaryngologie
0009-0603
Continued by: Ceskoslovenská otorinolaryngologie a foniatrie.
1952-1991   2984711R

Cesk Patol
Ceskoslovenská patologie
1210-7875
1965   0050734

Cesk Pediatr
Ceskoslovenská pediatrie
0069-2328
Continues Pediatrické listy.
1955   0403576

Cesk Psychiatr
Ceskoslovenská psychiatrie
0069-2336
Supersedes in part: Neurologie a psychiatrie československá. Continued by: Ceská a slovenská psychiatrie.
1956-1994   0372721

Cesk Radiol
Ceskoslovenská radiologie
0069-2344
Continues Ceskoslovenská roentgenologie. Continued by: Ceská radiologie.
1964-1993   0373147

Cesk Rentgenol
Ceskoslovenská rentgenologie
Continues Acta radiologica et cancerologica Bohemoslovenica. Continued by Ceskoslovenská radiologie.
1955-1963   16120080R

Cesk Slov Oftalmol
Ceská a slovenská oftalmologie: casopis Ceské oftalmologické spolecnosti a Slovenské oftalmologické spolecnosti
1211-9059
Continues: Ceskoslovenská oftalmologie.
1995   9600515

Cesk Stomatol
Ceskoslovenská stomatologie
0009-0654
Continues: Zubní lékářstvi. Continued by: Ceská stomatologie (Prague, Czech Republic: 1994).
1936-1993   0414240

Cesk Zdrav
Ceskoslovenské zdravotnictví
0009-0689
Absorbed Ceskoslovenská nemocnice, Jan. 1955.
1953-1991   0416604

Ceska Gynekol
Ceská gynekologie / Ceská lékarská spolecnost J. Ev. Purkyne
1210-7832
Continues: Ceskoslovenská gynekologie.
1994   9423768

Ceska Slov Farm
Ceská a Slovenská farmacie: casopis Ceské farmaceutické spolecnosti a Slovenské farmaceutické spolecnosti
1210-7816
Continues: Ceskoslovenská farmacie.
1994   9433765

Ceska Slov Psychiatr
Ceská a slovenská psychiatrie / Ceská lékarská spolecnost J.E. Purkyne
1212-0383
Continues: Ceskoslovenská psychiatrie.
1995   9516290

Ceskoslov Biol
Ceskoslovenská biologie
1952-1958   0234777

Ceskoslov Nemocnice
Ceskoslovenská nemocnice
Absorbed by: Ceskoslovenské zdravotnictví in Jan. 1955.
1930-1954   16120060R

Cesra Saule
Cesra Säule
0411-6356
1954   16120160R

CEX Rep Civ Eff Exerc
CEX [reports]; civil effects exercise. U.S. Atomic Energy Commission
195u-1971   21830350R

Ceylon Dent J
Ceylon Dental Journal
1970-1976   9880291

Ceylon Med J
The Ceylon medical journal
0009-0875
Continues: Ceylon Branch. British Medical Association. Ceylon Branch.
1952   1264702

CHAC Rev
C.H.A.C. review
0226-5923
Continues: Catholic hospital.
1980-2003   8006835

Chang Gung Med J
Chang Gung medical journal
2072-0939
Continues: Changgeng yi xue za zhi.
2000   101088034

Change
Change
0009-1383
Continues Change magazine.
1972   7703631

Changgeng Yi Xue Za Zhi
Changgeng yi xue za zhi / Changgeng ji nian yi yuan = Chang Gung medical journal / Chang Gung Memorial Hospital
Continues: Changgeng yi xue. Continued by: Chang Gung medical journal.
1984-1999   9809559

Changing Times
Changing times
0009-143X
Continues: Kiplinger magazine. Continued by: Kiplinger's personal finance magazine.
1949-1991   9877765

Channels (Austin)
Channels (Austin, Tex.)
1933-6950
2007   1933-6969
    101321614

Chaos
Chaos (Woodbury, N.Y.)
1054-1500
1991   1089-7682
    100971574

Chart
Chart
0069-2778
Continues the ISNA.
1956   7502539

Chekh Fiziol
Chekhoslovatskaia fiziologiia
Continued by Physiologia Bohemoslovenica.
1952-1955   16120460R

Chekhoslovatskaia Biol
Chekhoslovatskaia biologiia
1952-1954   16120450R

Chem Asian J
Chemistry, an Asian journal
1861-4728
2006   1861-471X
    101294643

Chem Ber
Chemische Berichte
0009-2940
Continues: Berichte. Deutsche Chemische Gesellschaft, Berlin. Part B (Organic chemistry) merged with: Liebigs Annalen der Chemie, 1995-1996, to form: Liebigs Annalen. Merged with: Recueil (Koninklijke Nederlandse Chemische Vereniging), in 1997, to form: Chemische Berichte/Recueil.
1947-1996   0372723

Chem Biodivers
Chemistry & biodiversity
1612-1872
2004   1612-1880
    101197449

Chem Biol
Chemistry & biology
1074-5521
1994   1879-1301
    9500160

Chem Biol Drug Des
Chemical biology & drug design
1747-0277
Continues: Journal of peptide research.
2006   1747-0285
    101262549

Chem Biol Interact
Chemico-biological interactions
0009-2797   1872-7786
1969   0227276

Chem Br
Chemistry in Britain
0009-3106
Formed by the merger of the Proceedings of
the Chemical Society and the Journal of the
Royal Institute of Chemistry. Continued by:
Chemistry world.
1965-2003   0005130

Chem Commun (Camb)
Chemical communications (Cambridge,
England)
1359-7345   1364-548X
Continues: Journal of the Chemical Society.
Chemical communications.
1996   9610838

Chem Depend
Chemical dependencies
0276-5608
Continues: Addictive diseases.
1980-1982   8101573

Chem Drug Export Rev
The Chemist and druggist export review
0366-6085
Continued by the Export review of the British
drug and chemical industries.
1940-1951   16130070R

Chem Immunol
Chemical immunology
1015-0145
Continues: Progress in allergy. Continued by:
Chemical immunology and allergy.
1989-2002   9001090

Chem Immunol Allergy
Chemical immunology and allergy
1660-2242   1662-2898
Continues: Chemical immunology.
2003   101183835

Chem Ind
Chemistry & industry
0009-3068
1923   0373151

Chem Pharm Bull (Tokyo)
Chemical & pharmaceutical bulletin
0009-2363   1347-5223
Continues: Pharmaceutical bulletin.
1958   0377775

Chem Phys Lipids
Chemistry and physics of lipids
0009-3084   1873-2941
1966   0067206

Chem Rec
Chemical record (New York, N.Y.)
1527-8999   1528-0691
2001   101085550

Chem Res Toxicol
Chemical research in toxicology
0893-228X   1520-5010
1988   8807448

Chem Rev
Chemical reviews
0009-2665   1520-6890
1924   2985134R

Chem Senses
Chemical senses
0379-864X   1464-3553
Continues: Chemical senses and flavor.
1980   8217190

Chem Soc Rev
Chemical Society reviews
0306-0012   1460-4744
Formed by the merger of Quarterly reviews
and the Royal Institute of Chemistry's RIC
reviews.
1972   0335405

Chembiochem
Chembiochem: a European journal of
chemical biology
1439-4227   1439-7633
2000   100937360

Chemioterapia
Chemioterapia: international journal of the
Mediterranean Society of Chemotherapy
0392-906X
Continued by: Journal of chemotherapy
(Florence, Italy). Formed by the union
of: Chemioterapia antimicrobica. and:
Chemioterapia oncologica.
1982-1988   8401667

Chemistry
Chemistry (Weinheim an der Bergstrasse,
Germany)
0947-6539   1521-3765
1995   9513783

Chemistry (Easton)
Chemistry
0009-305X
Continues Chemistry leaflet. Superseded by
SciQuest.
1944-1979   7905485

ChemMedChem
ChemMedChem
1860-7179   1860-7187
Continues: Farmaco (Società chimica
italiana).
2006   101259013

Chemosphere
Chemosphere
0045-6535   1879-1298
1972   0320657

Chemotherapia (Basel)
Chemotherapia
0366-7170
Continued by Chemotherapy.
1960-1967   0144510

Chemotherapy
Chemotherapy
0009-3157   1421-9794
Continues Chemotherapia.
1968   0144731

Chemphyschem
Chemphyschem: a European journal of
chemical physics and physical chemistry
1439-4235   1439-7641
Continues: Journal de chimie physique et de
physico-chimie biologique.
2000   100954211

ChemSusChem
ChemSusChem
1864-5631   1864-564X
Continues: Annali di chimica.
2008   101319536

Chest
Chest
0012-3692   1931-3543
Continues: Diseases of the chest.
1970   0231335

Chest Surg Clin N Am
Chest surgery clinics of North America
1052-3359
Continued by: Thoracic surgery clinics.
1991-2003   9208495

Chic Med Sch Q
The Chicago Medical School quarterly
0009-3629
1940-1973   7505427

Chief Inf Off J
Chief information officer journal
0899-0182
Absorbed: Journal of network management.
Absorbed by: Journal of business strategy.
1988-1993   9884216

Child
The Child
1936-1953   16130750R

Child Abuse Negl
Child abuse & neglect
0145-2134   1873-7757
1977   7801702

Child Adolesc Psychiatr Clin N Am
Child and adolescent psychiatric clinics of
North America
1056-4993   1558-0490
1992   9313451

Child Care Health Dev
Child: care, health and development
0305-1862   1365-2214
Absorbed: Ambulatory child health. 2002
1975   7602632

Child Dev
Child development
0009-3920   1467-8624
1930   0372725

Child Health Alert
Child health alert
1064-4849
1983   9881972

Child Health Care
Children's health care: journal of the
Association for the Care of Children's Health
0273-9615   1532-6888
Continues: Journal of the Association for the
Care of Children's Health.
1980   8101257

Child Maltreat
Child maltreatment
1077-5595
1996   9602869

Child Nephrol Urol
Child nephrology and urology
1012-6694
Continues: International journal of pediatric
nephrology.
1989-1992   8910177

Child Neuropsychol
Child neuropsychology: a journal on normal
and abnormal development in childhood and
adolescence
0929-7049   1744-4136
1995   9512515

Child Psychiatry Hum Dev
Child psychiatry and human development
0009-398X   1573-3327
1970   1275332

Child Psychol Psychiatry Review
Child psychology & psychiatry review
1360-6417
Continued by: Child and adolescent mental
health.
1996-2001   9713493

Child Today
Children today
0361-4336
Continues: Children (Washington, D.C.).
1972-1997   0320227

Child Welfare
Child welfare
0009-4021
Continues: Bulletin. Child Welfare League of America.
1948   0372735

Children
Children
0009-4064
Supersedes the Child. Superseded by Children today.
1954-1971   0320036

Childs Brain
Child's brain
0302-2803
Split into: Child's nervous system; and Pediatric neuroscience.
1975-1984   7505428

Childs Nerv Syst
Child's nervous system: ChNS: official journal of the International Society for Pediatric Neurosurgery
0256-7040   1433-0350
Continues in part: Child's brain.
1985   8503227

Chilwa Kijae Hakhoe Chi
Ch'ikwa Kijae Hakhoe chi. The Journal of the Korea Research Society for Dental Materials
0302-5772
1966   0411425

Chin J Biotechnol
Chinese journal of biotechnology
1042-749X
1988-1999   9100855

Chin J Dent Res
The Chinese journal of dental research: the official journal of the Scientific Section of the Chinese Stomatological Association (CSA)
1462-6446
1998   100892845

Chin J Dig Dis
Chinese journal of digestive diseases
1443-9611   1443-9573
Continued by: Journal of digestive diseases.
2000-2006   101088612

Chin J Integr Med
Chinese journal of integrative medicine
1672-0415
Continues: Zhongguo Zhong xi yi jie he za zhi. English. Chinese journal of integrated traditional and Western medicine.
2003   101181180

Chin J Physiol
The Chinese journal of physiology
0304-4920
Continues in part: Chinese journal of physiology.
1960   7804502

Chin J Traumatol
Chinese journal of traumatology = Zhonghua chuang shang za zhi / Chinese Medical Association
1008-1275
1998   100886162

Chin Med J
Chinese medical journal
Formed by the merger of the China medical journal and the English section of the National medical journal of China, and assumed the vol. numbering of the former. Continued by: China's medicine.
1932-1966   0005256

Chin Med J (Engl)
Chinese medical journal
0366-6999
1975   7513795

Chin Med Sci J
Chinese medical sciences journal = Chung-kuo i hsüeh k'o hsüeh tsa chih / Chinese Academy of Medical Sciences
1001-9294
Continues: Proceedings of the Chinese Academy of Medical Sciences and the Peking Union Medical College.
1991   9112559

Chin Rev Trop Med
The Chinese review of tropical medicine
Supersedes Nettai igaku kenkyū.
1948-1948   16140240R

Chinas Med
China's medicine
Supersedes the Chinese medical journal.
1966-1968   0116405

Chir Dent Fr
Le Chirurgien-dentiste de France
0009-4838
Continues Le Dentiste de France.
1962   0151751

Chir Forum Exp Klin Forsch
Chirurgisches Forum für experimentelle und klinische Forschung
0303-6227
1972   0435763

Chir Ital
Chirurgia italiana
0009-4773
1947   0151753

Chir Main
Chirurgie de la main
1297-3203
Continues: Annales de chirurgie de la main et du membre supérieur.
2000   100937750

Chir Narzadow Ruchu Ortop Pol
Chirurgia narzadów ruchu i ortopedia polska
0009-479X
1928   2985137R

Chir Organi Mov
La Chirurgia degli organi di movimento
0009-4749   1973-2538
1917   0372573

Chir Patol Sper
Chirurgia e patologia sperimentale
0009-4757
Continues Patologia sperimentale e chirurgia.
1954-1988   0372731

Chir Pediatr
Chirurgie pédiatrique
0180-5738
Continues Annales de chirurgie infantile. Merged with: Zeitschrift für Kinderchirurgie, to form: European journal of pediatric surgery.
1978-1990   7804068

Chir Urol
Chirurgia urologica
0009-4811
1959-1968   0372571

Chirality
Chirality
0899-0042   1520-636X
1989   8914261

Chirop Rec
Chiropody record
Continued by Podiatry, chiropody record.
1917-1959   16140290R

Chiropodist (Lond)
Chiropodist (Society of Chiropodists)
0009-4706
Continues: Chiropodist (Incorporated Society of Chiropodists). Absorbed: British journal of chiropody. Continued by: Journal of British podiatric medicine.
1946-1990   9427242

Chiropr Hist
Chiropractic history: the archives and journal of the Association for the History of Chiropractic
0736-4377
1981   8213054

Chirurg
Der Chirurg; Zeitschrift für alle Gebiete der operativen Medizen
0009-4722   1433-0385
1928   16140410R

Chirurgia (Bucur)
Chirurgia
0009-4730
Continued by: Revista de chirurgie, oncologie, radiologie, o.r.l., oftalmologie, stomatologie. Chirurgie.
1951-1974   7501738

Chirurgia (Bucur)
Chirurgia (Bucharest, Romania: 1990)
1221-9118
Continues: Revista de chirurgie, oncologie, radiologie, o.r.l., oftalmologie, stomatologie. Chirurgie.
1990   9213031

Chirurgie
Chirurgie; mémoires de l'Académie de chirurgie
0001-4001
Continues Mémoires de l'Académie de chirurgie. Absorbed by: Annales de chirurgie.
1970-1999   0236600

Chiryo
[Chiryō] [Therapy]
0022-5207
1944   16140560R

Choices Respir Manage
Choices in respiratory management
1044-0690
Continues: Respiratory management.
1989-1992   8910181

Choix Trav Etrang
Choix de travaux étrangers
1948-1955   16140630R

Chosen Ibo
Chosen i-bo. The Korean medical journal
1947-19uu   16210020R

Choson Uihak
[Chosŏn ŭihak] [Korean medicine]
1680-8029
1954   16210070R

Chot Mai Het Kan Phayaban
Chot mai hēt kān phayābān
0125-0035
Continued by: Thai journal of nursing.
1952-1971   7605561

Christ Bioeth
Christian bioethics
1380-3603
1995   9507416

Christ Hosp Med Bull
Christ Hospital medical bulletin
1947-1952   16210080R

Christ Med Dent Soc J
Christian Medical Dental Society journal
Continues: Christian Medical Society journal.
Continued by: Today's Christian doctor.
1988-1995   9002893

Christ Nurse (Mysore)
Christian nurse
0009-5540
Continues Nursing news.
1965-19uu   0047107

Christ Nurse Int
Christian nurse international
1010-7355
1985   9882984

Chromatogr Rev
Chromatographic reviews
0009-5907
Absorbed by: Journal of chromatography.
1959-1971   0427031

Chromosoma
Chromosoma
0009-5915   1432-0886
Continues: Zeitschrift für Zellforschung und
mikroskopische Anatomie. Abteilung B,
Chromosoma.
1947   2985138R

Chromosome Res
Chromosome research: an international
journal on the molecular, supramolecular
and evolutionary aspects of chromosome
biology
0967-3849   1573-6849
1993   9313452

Chron Respir Dis
Chronic respiratory disease
1479-9723   1479-9731
2004   101197408

Chron World Health Organ
Chronicle of the World Health Organization
1010-3090
Continued by WHO chronicle.
1947-1958   23470140R

Chronic Dis Can
Chronic diseases in Canada
0228-8699
1980   8506870

Chronic Illn
Chronic illness
1742-3953   1745-9206
2005   101253019

Chronicle
The Chronicle
0030-2201
1938-1996   7505430

Chronobiol Int
Chronobiology international
0742-0528   1525-6073
1984   8501362

Chronobiologia
Chronobiologia
0390-0037
1974-1994   0434557

Chudoku Kenkyu
Chūdoku kenkyū: Chūdoku Kenkyūkai
jun kikanshi = The Japanese journal of
toxicology
0914-3777
1987   9310053

Ciba Clin Symp
Ciba clinical symposia
0362-5060
Continues: Clinical symposia (Summit, N.J.:
1948). Continued by: Clinical symposia
(Summit. N.J.: 1957).
1950-1956   101126450

Ciba Found Study Group
Ciba Foundation study group
0069-4037
1959-1971   0373160

Ciba Found Symp
Ciba Foundation symposium
0300-5208
Continued by: Novartis Foundation
symposium.
1972-1997   0356636

Ciba Symp
Ciba symposium. [English ed.]
1956-1970   15930240R

Ciba Z (Basel)
Ciba-Zeitschrift
1933-1952   1310711

Ciba-Tijdschr
Ciba-Tijdschrift
1938-1952   15930250R

CICIAMS Nouv
C.I.C.I.A.M.S. nouvelles
Merged with C.I.C.I.A.M.S. news to form
Nouvelles - Comité international catholique
des infirmiéres et assistantes médico-sociales.
News - International Committee of Catholic
Nurses and Medico-Social Workers.
1965-1974   0205132

Cien Saude Colet
Ciência & saúde coletiva
1413-8123   1678-4561
1996   9713483

Cienc Invest
Ciencia e investigación
0009-6733
1945   0372734

Cienc Med Hisp Am
Ciencias médicas hispano-americanas
1131-0707
1948-1967   0142665

CIN Plus
CIN plus
1098-7126
Absorbed by: Computers, informatics,
nursing.
1998-2002   100883848

Cinci J Med
Cincinnati journal of medicine
0009-6873
Continues Journal of medicine. Superseded
by Cincinnati medicine.
1941-1978   0405365

Cincinnati Dent Soc Bull
The Cincinnati Dental Society bulletin
0095-7909
Continues The bulletin of the Cincinnati
Dental Society. Continued by Bulletin -
Cincinnati Dental Society.
1974-1975   7502036

Cincinnati Dent Soc Bull
Cincinnati Dental Society bulletin (1979)
0894-0975
Continues: Bulletin - Cincinnati Dental
Society.
1979   8702474

Cir Bucal
Cirugia Bucal
0578-3194
1966   9879224

Cir Cir
Cirugia y cirujanos
0009-7411
1933   0372736

Cir Esp
Cirugía española
0009-739X   1578-147X
Continues: Cirugía, ginecología y urología.
1970   1254104

Cir Ginecol Urol
Cirugía, ginecología y urología
0412-5878
Supersedes Revista española de cirugía.
Continued by Cirugía española.
1950-1969   1252763

Cir Pediatr
Cirugía pediátrica: organo oficial de la
Sociedad Española de Cirugía Pediátrica
0214-1221
1988   8900492

Circ Farm
Circular farmacéutica
0009-7314
1943   16220210R

Circ J
Circulation journal: official journal of the
Japanese Circulation Society
1346-9843   1347-4820
Continues: Japanese circulation journal.
2002   101137683

Circ Odontol San Martin Tres Febr
Circulo Odontologico De San Martin Y Tres
De Febrero
1988   9884920

Circ Res
Circulation research
0009-7330   1524-4571
1953   0047103

Circ Shock
Circulatory shock
0092-6213
Continued by: Journal of inflammation.
1974-1994   0414112

Circ Shock Suppl
Circulatory shock. Supplement
0193-7545
1979-19uu   7905492

Circulation
Circulation
0009-7322   1524-4539
1950   0147763

CJEM
CJEM: Canadian journal of emergency
medical care = JCMU: journal canadien de
soins médicaux d'urgence
1481-8035
1999   100893237

CLAO J
The CLAO journal: official publication
of the Contact Lens Association of
Ophthalmologists, Inc
0733-8902
Continues: Contact and intraocular lens
medical journal. Continued by: Eye & contact
lens.
1983-2002   8302065

Cleft Palate Craniofac J
The Cleft palate-craniofacial journal: official publication of the American Cleft Palate-Craniofacial Association
1055-6656
Continues: Cleft palate journal.
1991   9102566

Cleft Palate J
The Cleft palate journal
0009-8701
Absorbed: Cranio-facial, cleft palate bibliography in Jan. 1985. Continued by: Cleft palate-craniofacial journal.
1964-1990   0372737

Cleve Clin J Med
Cleveland Clinic journal of medicine
0891-1150   1939-2869
Continues: Cleveland Clinic quarterly.
1987   8703441

Cleve Clin Q
Cleveland Clinic quarterly
0009-8787
Continues: Cleveland Clinic bulletin. Continued by: Cleveland Clinic journal of medicine.
1932-1986   0373162

Climacteric
Climacteric: the journal of the International Menopause Society
1369-7137   1473-0804
1998   9810959

Clin Adv Hematol Oncol
Clinical advances in hematology & oncology: H&O
1543-0790
2003   101167661

Clin Allergy
Clinical allergy
0009-9090
Continued by: Clinical and experimental allergy.
1971-1988   0311172

Clin Allergy Immunol
Clinical allergy and immunology
1075-7910
1994   9431211

Clin Anat
Clinical anatomy (New York, N.Y.)
0897-3806   1098-2353
1988   8809128

Clin Anesth
Clinical anesthesia
0009-9112
1963-1976   0317206

Clin Appl Thromb Hemost
Clinical and applied thrombosis/hemostasis: official journal of the International Academy of Clinical and Applied Thrombosis/Hemostasis
1076-0296
1995   9508125

Clin Auton Res
Clinical autonomic research: official journal of the Clinical Autonomic Research Society
0959-9851   1619-1560
1991   9106549

Clin Biochem
Clinical biochemistry
0009-9120   1873-2933
1967   0133660

Clin Biomech (Bristol, Avon)
Clinical biomechanics (Bristol, Avon)
0268-0033   1879-1271
1986   8611877

Clin Breast Cancer
Clinical breast cancer
1526-8209
2000   100898731

Clin Bull
Clinical bulletin
0047-6706
1971-1981   1257734

Clin Calcium
Clinical calcium
0917-5857
1991   9433326

Clin Cancer Res
Clinical cancer research: an official journal of the American Association for Cancer Research
1078-0432
1995   9502500

Clin Cardiol
Clinical cardiology
0160-9289
1978   7903272

Clin Chem
Clinical chemistry
0009-9147   1530-8561
Continues: Clinical chemist.
1955   9421549

Clin Chem Lab Med
Clinical chemistry and laboratory medicine: CCLM / FESCC
1434-6621
Continues: European journal of clinical chemistry and clinical biochemistry.
1998   9806306

Clin Chest Med
Clinics in chest medicine
0272-5231   1557-8216
1980   7907612

Clin Child Fam Psychol Rev
Clinical child and family psychology review
1096-4037   1573-2827
1998   9807947

Clin Child Psychol Psychiatry
Clinical child psychology and psychiatry
1359-1045
1996   9604507

Clin Chim Acta
Clinica chimica acta; international journal of clinical chemistry
0009-8981   1873-3492
1956   1302422

Clin Colorectal Cancer
Clinical colorectal cancer
1533-0028
2001   101120693

Clin Commun Disord
Clinics in communication disorders
1054-8505
1991-1994   9113696

Clin Contemp
Clínica contemporânea; revista de medicina e cirurgia
1645-9016
1946-1956   16230220R

Clin Cornerstone
Clinical cornerstone
1098-3597
1998   9816002

Clin Dermatol
Clinics in dermatology
0738-081X   1879-1131
1983   8406412

Clin Dev Immunol
Clinical & developmental immunology
1740-2522   1740-2530
Continues: Developmental immunology.
2003   101183692

Clin Diagn Lab Immunol
Clinical and diagnostic laboratory immunology
1071-412X   1098-6588
Continued by: Clinical and vaccine immunology.
1994-2005   9421292

Clin Diagn Ultrasound
Clinics in diagnostic ultrasound
0193-743X
1979-1995   7904770

Clin Diagn Virol
Clinical and diagnostic virology
0928-0197
Continued by: Journal of clinical virology.
1993-1998   9309653

Clin Drug Investig
Clinical drug investigation
1173-2563
Continues: Drug investigation.
1995   9504817

Clin Dysmorphol
Clinical dysmorphology
0962-8827   1473-5717
1992   9207893

Clin EEG Neurosci
Clinical EEG and neuroscience: official journal of the EEG and Clinical Neuroscience Society (ENCS)
1550-0594
Continues: Clinical EEG (electroencephalography).
2004   101213033

Clin Electroencephalogr
Clinical EEG (electroencephalography)
0009-9155
Continued by: Clinical EEG and neuroscience.
1970-2003   0236454

Clin Endocrinol (Oxf)
Clinical endocrinology
0300-0664   1365-2265
1972   0346653

Clin Endocrinol Metab
Clinics in endocrinology and metabolism
0300-595X
Split into, Baillière's clinical endocrinology and metabolism, and, Endocrinology and metabolism clinics of North America.
1972-1986   0357424

Clin Eng
Clinical engineering
0149-290X
Continues Clinical engineering news. Absorbed by: Medical instrumentation.
1976-1980   7706553

Clin Eng Inf Serv
Clinical engineering information service
0277-0393
1977-1995   8507387

Clin Eng News
Clinical engineering news
0094-7245
Continues Clinical engineering newsletter. Continued by Clinical engineering.
1974-1976   0432523

Clin Eur
Clinica europea
0009-9007
1962-1992   0151752

Clin Evid
Clinical evidence
1462-3846
Continued by: BMJ Clinical evidence.
1999-2006   100883600

Clin Excell Nurse Pract
Clinical excellence for nurse practitioners:
the international journal of NPACE
1085-2360
1997-2001   9816180

Clin Excerpts J Devoted Ther
Clinical excerpts; a journal devoted to
therapeutics
1926-1974   0345515

Clin Exp Allergy
Clinical and experimental allergy: journal of
the British Society for Allergy and Clinical
Immunology
0954-7894   1365-2222
Continues: Clinical allergy.
1989   8906443

Clin Exp Dermatol
Clinical and experimental dermatology
0307-6938   1365-2230
Supersedes Transactions of the St. John's
Hospital Dermatological Society.
1976   7606847

Clin Exp Dial Apheresis
Clinical and experimental dialysis and
apheresis
0276-5497
Continues: Journal of dialysis. Continued by:
Uremia investigation.
1981-1983   8201411

Clin Exp Hypertens
Clinical and experimental hypertension
0148-3927
Split into: Clinical and experimental
hypertension. Part A. Theory and practice;
and, Clinical and experimental hypertension.
Part B. Hypertension in pregnancy.
1978-1981   7803060

Clin Exp Hypertens
Clinical and experimental hypertension
(New York, N.Y.: 1993)
1064-1963   1525-6006
Continues: Clinical and experimental
hypertension. Part A. Theory and practice.
1993   9305929

Clin Exp Hypertens A
Clinical and experimental hypertension.
Part A, Theory and practice
0730-0077
Continues in part: Clinical and experimental
hypertension. Continued by: Clinical and
experimental hypertension (New York, N.Y.:
1993)
1982-1992   8207790

Clin Exp Hypertens B
Clinical and experimental hypertension.
Part B, Hypertension in pregnancy
0730-0085
Continues in part: Clinical and experimental
hypertension. Continued by: Hypertension in
pregnancy.
1982-1992   8207433

Clin Exp Immunol
Clinical and experimental immunology
0009-9104   1365-2249
1966   0057202

Clin Exp Med
Clinical and experimental medicine
1591-8890   1591-9528
Merger of: International journal of clinical
& laboratory research; and: Research in
experimental medicine.
2001   100973405

Clin Exp Metastasis
Clinical & experimental metastasis
0262-0898   1473-7276
1983   8409970

Clin Exp Nephrol
Clinical and experimental nephrology
1342-1751   1437-7799
1997   9709923

Clin Exp Neurol
Clinical and experimental neurology
0196-6383
Continues Proceedings of the Australian
Association of Neurologists.
1977-1994   7909724

Clin Exp Obstet Gynecol
Clinical and experimental obstetrics &
gynecology
0390-6663
1974   7802110

Clin Exp Optom
Clinical & experimental optometry: journal
of the Australian Optometrical Association
0816-4622   1444-0938
Continues: The Australian journal of
optometry.
1986   8703442

Clin Exp Pathol
Clinical and experimental pathology
1292-7953
Continues: Archives d'anatomie et de
cytologie pathologiques. Absorbed by:
Annales de pathologie.
1999-1999   100889732

Clin Exp Pharmacol Physiol
Clinical and experimental pharmacology &
physiology
0305-1870   1440-1681
Absorbed Proceedings of the Australian
Society for Medical Research with 1974
meeting.
1974   0425076

Clin Exp Pharmacol Physiol Suppl
Clinical and experimental pharmacology &
physiology. Supplement
0143-9294
1974-200u   7611484

Clin Exp Rheumatol
Clinical and experimental rheumatology
0392-856X
1983   8308521

Clin Experiment Ophthalmol
Clinical & experimental ophthalmology
1442-6404   1442-9071
Continues: Australian journal of
ophthalmology.
2000   100896531

Clin Gastroenterol
Clinics in gastroenterology
0300-5089
Split into. Baillière's clinical
gastroenterology. and, Gastroenterology
clinics of North America.
1972-1986   0365261

Clin Gastroenterol Hepatol
Clinical gastroenterology and hepatology:
the official clinical practice journal of the
American Gastroenterological Association
1542-3565   1542-7714
2003   101160775

Clin Genet
Clinical genetics
0009-9163   1399-0004
1970   0253664

Clin Genitourin Cancer
Clinical genitourinary cancer
1558-7673
Continues: Clinical prostate cancer.
2005   101260955

Clin Geriatr Med
Clinics in geriatric medicine
0749-0690
1985   8603766

Clin Gerontol
Clinical gerontologist
0731-7115
1982   8300869

Clin Ginecol
La Clinica ginecologica
0529-9608
1959-1969   2985140R

Clin Haematol
Clinics in haematology
0308-2261
Merged in part with: Clinics in oncology, to
form: Hematology/onocology clinics of North
America. Continued in part by: Baillière's
clinical haematology.
1972-1986   0331547

Clin Hemorheol Microcirc
Clinical hemorheology and microcirculation
1386-0291
Continues: Clinical hemorheology.
1997   9709206

Clin Imaging
Clinical imaging
0899-7071   1873-4499
Continues: The Journal of computed
tomography.
1989   8911831

Clin Immunol
Clinical immunology (Orlando, Fla.)
1521-6616   1521-7035
Continues: Clinical immunology and
immunopathology.
1999   100883537

Clin Immunol Immunopathol
Clinical immunology and immunopathology
0090-1229
Continued by: Clinical immunology
(Orlando, Fla.).
1972-1998   0356637

Clin Immunol Rev
Clinical immunology reviews
0277-9366
1981-1985   8202349

Clin Implant Dent Relat Res
Clinical implant dentistry and related
research
1523-0899   1708-8208
1999   100888977

Clin Infect Dis
Clinical infectious diseases: an official
publication of the Infectious Diseases Society
of America
1058-4838   1537-6591
Continues: Reviews of infectious diseases.
1992   9203213

Clin Intensive Care
Clinical intensive care: international journal of critical & coronary care medicine
0956-3075   1473-7752
1990-2006   **9101410**

Clin Interv Aging
Clinical interventions in aging
1176-9092   1178-1998
2006   **101273480**

Clin Invest Med
Clinical and investigative medicine. Médecine clinique et experimentale
0147-958X   1488-2353
1978   **7804071**

Clin Investig
The Clinical investigator
0941-0198
   Continues: Klinische Wochenschrift.
   Continued by: Journal of molecular medicine (Berlin, Germany).
1992-1994   **9207154**

Clin J
The Clinical journal
1892-1951   **16240010R**

Clin J Am Soc Nephrol
Clinical journal of the American Society of Nephrology: CJASN
1555-9041   1555-905X
2006   **101271570**

Clin J Oncol Nurs
Clinical journal of oncology nursing
1092-1095
1997   **9705336**

Clin J Pain
The Clinical journal of pain
0749-8047   1536-5409
1985   **8507389**

Clin J Sport Med
Clinical journal of sport medicine: official journal of the Canadian Academy of Sport Medicine
1050-642X   1536-3724
1991   **9103300**

Clin Lab
Clinical laboratory
1433-6510
   Continues: Klinisches Labor.
1997   **9705611**

Clin Lab (Zaragoza)
Clinica y laboratorio
0366-6751
1905-1964   **16230410R**

Clin Lab Haematol
Clinical and laboratory haematology
0141-9854   1365-2257
   Continued by: International journal of laboratory hematology.
1979-2006   **7907061**

Clin Lab Manage Rev
Clinical laboratory management review: official publication of the Clinical Laboratory Management Association / CLMA
0888-7950
   Continued by: Clinical leadership & management review.
1987-1999   **8805785**

Clin Lab Med
Clinics in laboratory medicine
0272-2712   1557-9832
1981   **8100174**

Clin Lab Sci
Clinical laboratory science: journal of the American Society for Medical Technology
0894-959X
   Continues: Journal of medical technology.
1988   **8806547**

Clin Laser Mon
Clinical laser monthly
0746-469X
   Continued by: Advanced technology in surgical care.
1983-1995   **9314884**

Clin Lat
Clinica latina
1951-19uu   **16230280R**

Clin Leadersh Manag Rev
Clinical leadership & management review: the journal of CLMA
1527-3954   1553-7072
   Continues: Clinical laboratory management review.
2000   **100900959**

Clin Linguist Phon
Clinical linguistics & phonetics
0269-9206
   Absorbed: Journal of multilingual communication disorders.
1987   **8802622**

Clin Liver Dis
Clinics in liver disease
1089-3261   1557-8224
1997   **9710002**

Clin Lung Cancer
Clinical lung cancer
1525-7304
1999   **100893225**

Clin Lymphoma
Clinical lymphoma
1526-9655
   Continued by: Clinical lymphoma & myeloma.
2000-2005   **100898741**

Clin Lymphoma Myeloma
Clinical lymphoma & myeloma
1557-9190
   Continues: Clinical lymphoma.
2005   **101256500**

Clin Mater
Clinical materials
0267-6605
   Absorbed: Critical reviews in biocompatibility. Absorbed by: Biomaterials.
1986-1994   **8707278**

Clin Med
Clinical medicine (London, England)
1470-2118
   Continues: Journal of the Royal College of Physicians of London.
2001   **101092853**

Clin Med (Northfield Il)
Clinical medicine
0412-7994
   Continues: Clinical medicine and surgery. Continued by Journal of continuing education in clinical medicine, issued as a separately paged section of Journal of continuing education in family medicine. Absorbed: Southern general practitioner in 1954; Mississippi Valley medical journal in Aug. 1960; and Antibiotics & chemotherapy in Jan. 1963
1940-1978   **7708504**

Clin Med Res
Clinical medicine & research
1539-4182   1554-6179
   Continues: Marshfield Clinic journal.
2003   **101175887**

Clin Microbiol Infect
Clinical microbiology and infection: the official publication of the European Society of Clinical Microbiology and Infectious Diseases
1198-743X   1469-0691
1995   **9516420**

Clin Microbiol Rev
Clinical microbiology reviews
0893-8512   1098-6618
1988   **8807282**

Clin Nephrol
Clinical nephrology
0301-0430
1973   **0364441**

Clin Neurol Neurosurg
Clinical neurology and neurosurgery
0303-8467   1872-6968
   Continues in part: Psychiatria, neurologia, neurochirurgia.
1974   **7502039**

Clin Neuropathol
Clinical neuropathology
0722-5091
1982   **8214420**

Clin Neuropharmacol
Clinical neuropharmacology
0362-5664   1537-162X
1976   **7607910**

Clin Neurophysiol
Clinical neurophysiology: official journal of the International Federation of Clinical Neurophysiology
1388-2457   1872-8952
   Continues: Electroencephalography and clinical neurophysiology.
1999   **100883319**

Clin Neuropsychol
The Clinical neuropsychologist
1385-4046   1744-4144
1987   **8806548**

Clin Neurosci
Clinical neuroscience (New York, N.Y.)
1065-6766
1993-1998   **9315128**

Clin Neurosurg
Clinical neurosurgery
0069-4827
1953   **2985141R**

Clin Notes Respir Dis
Clinical notes on respiratory diseases
0009-9198
1962-1983   **0400665**

Clin Nucl Med
Clinical nuclear medicine
0363-9762   1536-0229
1976   **7611109**

Clin Nuova Rass Prog Med Int
Clinica nuova; rassegna del progresso medico internazionale
   Continued by Recentia medica.
1945-1954   **16230300R**

Clin Nurs Pract Epilepsy
Clinical nursing practice in epilepsy
   Continued by: Clinical nursing practice in epilepsy (Secaucus, N.J.).
1993-199u   **9433629**

Clin Nurs Res
Clinical nursing research
1054-7738
1992   9208508

Clin Nurse Spec
Clinical nurse specialist CNS
0887-6274   1538-9782
1987   8709115

Clin Nutr
Clinical nutrition (Edinburgh, Scotland)
0261-5614   1532-1983
1982   8309603

Clin Obstet Gynaecol
Clinics in obstetrics and gynaecology
0306-3356
     Split into: Obstetrics and gynecology clinics
of North America: and: Baillière's clinical
obstetrics and gynaecology.
1974-1986   7509601

Clin Obstet Gynecol
Clinical obstetrics and gynecology
0009-9201   1532-5520
1958   0070014

Clin Occup Environ Med
Clinics in occupational and environmental
medicine
1526-0046
     Absorbed: Occupational medicine
(Philadelphia. Pa.). 2003
2001   100893239

Clin Odontoiatr Rev Mens Oper Dent Chir Orale Ortod Protesi
Clinica odontoiatrica; revista mensile
di operativa dentaria, chirurgia orale,
ortodontia e protesi
0366-6794
     Merged with: Annali di stomatologia e
dell'Istituto superiore di odontoiatria G.
Eastman. to form: Annali di stomatologia e
clinica odontoiatrica.
1946-1957   16230340R

Clin Odontol
Clinic odontologia: la revue de
l'omnipraticien
0998-3392
     Continues: Odontologia (Paris. France).
     Continued by: Clinic (Paris, France).
1989-1992   9208273

Clin Oncol
Clinical oncology
0305-7399
     Continued by European journal of surgical
oncology.
1975-1984   7511426

Clin Oncol (R Coll Radiol)
Clinical oncology (Royal College of
Radiologists (Great Britain))
0936-6555   1433-2981
1989   9002902

Clin Oral Implants Res
Clinical oral implants research
0905-7161   1600-0501
1990   9105713

Clin Oral Investig
Clinical oral investigations
1432-6981   1436-3771
1997   9707115

Clin Orthod Res
Clinical orthodontics and research
1397-5927   1600-0544
     Merged with: Journal of craniofacial
genetics and developmental biology. to form:
Orthodontics & craniofacial research.
1998-2001   9815904

Clin Orthop Relat Res
Clinical orthopaedics and related research
0009-921X   1528-1132
     Continues: Clinical orthopaedics.
1963   0075674

Clin Ortop
La Clinica ortopedica
0009-9023
1949-1976   0372601

Clin Ostet Ginecol
La Clinica ostetrica e ginecologica
0009-9031
     Continues La Clinica ostetrica. Superseded by
Patologia e clinica ostetrica e ginecologica.
1939-1972   0434562

Clin Otolaryngol
Clinical otolaryngology: official journal of
ENT-UK ; official journal of Netherlands
Society for Oto-Rhino-Laryngology &
Cervico-Facial Surgery
1749-4478   1749-4486
     Continues: Clinical otolaryngology and allied
sciences.
2005   101247023

Clin Otolaryngol Allied Sci
Clinical otolaryngology and allied sciences
0307-7772   1365-2273
     Continued by: Clinical otolaryngology.
1976-2004   7701793

Clin Otorinolaringoiatr
La Clinica otorinolaringoiatrica
0009-904X
     Continued by La Nuova clinica
otorinolaringoiatrica.
1949-1977   0372602

Clin Pediatr (Bologna)
La Clinica pediatrica
0009-9058
1919-1986   0372603

Clin Pediatr (Phila)
Clinical pediatrics
0009-9228
     Formed by the merger of American
practitioner. Archives of pediatrics. and
Quarterly review of pediatrics.
1962   0372606

Clin Perform Qual Health Care
Clinical performance and quality health care
1063-0279
     Absorbed by: British journal of clinical
governance.
1993-2000   9305935

Clin Perinatol
Clinics in perinatology
0095-5108   1557-9840
1974   7501306

Clin Pharm
Clinical pharmacy
0278-2677
     Absorbed by: American journal of hospital
pharmacy.
1982-1993   8207437

Clin Pharmacokinet
Clinical pharmacokinetics
0312-5963
1976   7606849

Clin Pharmacol Ther
Clinical pharmacology and therapeutics
0009-9236   1532-6535
1960   0372741

Clin Phys Physiol Meas
Clinical physics and physiological
measurement: an official journal of the
Hospital Physicists' Association, Deutsche
Gesellschaft für Medizinische Physik and
the European Federation of Organisations
for Medical Physics
0143-0815
     Continued by: Physiological measurement.
1980-1992   8209031

Clin Physiol
Clinical physiology (Oxford, England)
0144-5979   1365-2281
     Continued by: Clinical physiology and
functional imaging.
1981-2001   8309768

Clin Physiol Biochem
Clinical physiology and biochemistry
0252-1164
1983-1993   8305885

Clin Physiol Funct Imaging
Clinical physiology and functional imaging
1475-0961   1475-097X
     Continues: Clinical physiology (Oxford,
England).
2002   101137604

Clin Plast Surg
Clinics in plastic surgery
0094-1298   1558-0504
1974   0424767

Clin Podiatr Med Surg
Clinics in podiatric medicine and surgery
0891-8422
     Continues: Clinics in podiatry.
1986   8604974

Clin Podiatry
Clinics in podiatry
0742-0668
     Continued by: Clinics in podiatric medicine
and surgery.
1984-1985   8501789

Clin Pract Guidel Quick Ref Guide Clin
Clinical practice guideline. Quick reference
guide for clinicians
1992-1996   9214656

Clin Prev Dent
Clinical preventive dentistry
0163-9633
1979-1992   8004895

Clin Privil White Pap
Clinical privilege white paper
19uu   100892390

Clin Proc
Clinical proceedings
0366-7782
     Continues: South African journal of clinical
science.
1942-1949   16240050R

Clin Proc Child Hosp Dist Columbia
Clinical proceedings - Children's Hospital of
the District of Columbia
0009-4129
     Continued by Clinical proceedings -
Children's Hospital National Medical Center.
1944-1971   7503483

Clin Prostate Cancer
Clinical prostate cancer
1540-0352
     Continued by: Clinical genitourinary cancer.
2002-2005   101155459

Clin Psychol Psychother
Clinical psychology & psychotherapy
1063-3995   1099-0879
1993   9416196

Clin Psychol Rev
Clinical psychology review
0272-7358   1873-7811
1981   8111117

Clin Radiol
Clinical radiology
0009-9260   1365-229X
Continues the Journal of the Faculty of
Radiologists.
1960   1306016

Clin Rehabil
Clinical rehabilitation
0269-2155
1987   8802181

Clin Rep
Clinical report. University of Cape Town.
Dept. of Obstetrics
1965-1uuu   0174635

Clin Rep
Clinical reports
0401-3255
1949-1967   0425725

Clin Reprod Fertil
Clinical reproduction and fertility
0725-556X
Continued by: Reproduction, fertility, and
development.
1982-1987   8218028

Clin Res
Clinical research
0009-9279
Continues: Clinical research proceedings.
Continued by: Journal of investigative medicine.
1958-1994   7806789

Clin Res Cardiol
Clinical research in cardiology: official
journal of the German Cardiac Society
1861-0684   1861-0692
Continues: Zeitschrift für Kardiologie.
2006   101264123

Clin Resour Manag
Clinical resource management
Continues: Health care cost reengineering
report.
2000-2002   100955437

Clin Rev Allergy
Clinical reviews in allergy
0731-8235
Continued by: Clinical reviews in allergy &
immunology.
1983-1994   8308524

Clin Rev Allergy Immunol
Clinical reviews in allergy & immunology
1080-0549   1559-0267
Continues: Clinical reviews in allergy.
1995   9504368

Clin Rheum Dis
Clinics in rheumatic diseases
0307-742X
Split into: Baillière's clinical rheumatology,
and: Rheumatic diseases clinics of North
America.
1975-1986   7604943

Clin Rheumatol
Clinical rheumatology
0770-3198   1434-9949
Continues: Acta rhumatologica.
1982   8211469

Clin Sci
Clinical science
0009-9287
Supersedes Heart. Continued by Clinical
science and molecular medicine.
1933-1973   0367732

Clin Sci (Lond)
Clinical science (London, England: 1979)
0143-5221   1470-8736
Continues Clinical science and molecular
medicine.
1979   7905731

Clin Sci Mol Med
Clinical science and molecular medicine
0301-0538
Continues Clinical science. Continued by
Clinical science (London, England: 1979).
1973-1978   0367540

Clin Sci Mol Med Suppl
Clinical science and molecular medicine.
Supplement
0144-4107
1973-1978   7907311

Clin Soc J
Clinical Society journal
Continued by Agra Medical College journal.
193u-19uu   0124622

Clin Sports Med
Clinics in sports medicine
0278-5919   1556-228X
1982   8112473

Clin Symp
Clinical symposia (Summit, N.J.: 1957)
0009-9295
1957-1998   0103677

Clin Tech Small Anim Pract
Clinical techniques in small animal practice
1096-2867   1558-2272
Continues: Seminars in veterinary medicine
and surgery (small animal). Continued by:
Topics in companion animal medicine.
1998-2007   9806359

Clin Ter
La Clinica terapeutica
0009-9074   1972-6007
1951   0372604

Clin Ther
Clinical therapeutics
0149-2918
1977   7706726

Clin Tisiol
Clinica tisiológica
Supersedes Clínica tisiológica; trabajos do
Hospital Miguel Pereira.
1946-1954   16230360R

Clin Torax
Clinica del tórax
1949-1957   16230230R

Clin Toxicol
Clinical toxicology
0009-9309
Absorbed: Toxicology annual. Continued by:
Journal of toxicology. Clinical toxicology.
1968-1981   0205535

Clin Toxicol (Phila)
Clinical toxicology (Philadelphia, Pa.)
1556-3650   1556-9519
Continues: Journal of toxicology. Clinical
toxicology.
2005   101241654

Clin Transl Oncol
Clinical & translational oncology: official
publication of the Federation of Spanish
Oncology Societies and of the National
Cancer Institute of Mexico
1699-048X
Continues: Revista de oncología (Barcelona,
Spain).
2005   101247119

Clin Transpl
Clinical transplants
0890-9016
Continues: Clinical kidney transplants.
1986   8812419

Clin Transplant
Clinical transplantation
0902-0063   1399-0012
1987   8710240

Clin Trials
Clinical trials (London, England)
1740-7745   1740-7753
Continues in part: Controlled clinical trials.
2004   101197451

Clin Trials J
Clinical trials journal
0009-9325
Continued by: Clinical trials and meta-analysis.
1964-1990   0066472

Clin Trials Metaanal
Clinical trials and meta-analysis
0927-5401
Continues: Clinical trials journal.
1992-1994   9212070

Clin Vaccine Immunol
Clinical and vaccine immunology: CVI
1556-6811   1556-679X
Continues: Clinical and diagnostic laboratory
immunology.
2006   101252125

Clin Vet (Milano)
La Clinica veterinaria
0009-9082
1878-1988   0375032

Clinic (Paris)
Clinic (Paris, France)
1254-3136
Continues: Clinic odontologia.
1992   100884375

Clinica
Clinica (Bologna, Italy)
0366-6778
1935-1988   0372600

Clinics
Clinics (São Paulo, Brazil)
1807-5932   1980-5322
Continues: Revista do Hospital das Clínicas.
2005   101244734

Clinique (Paris)
Clinique (Paris, France)
0009-935X
1906-1973   9427241

Clio Med
Clio medica (Amsterdam, Netherlands)
0045-7183
1965   0057664

Cloning
Cloning
1520-4553
Continued by: Cloning and stem cells.
1999-2001   100883430

Cloning Stem Cells
Cloning and stem cells
1536-2302   1557-7457
Continues: Cloning.
2001   101125444

CMAJ
CMAJ: Canadian Medical Association journal
= journal de l'Association medicale canadienne
0820-3946   1488-2329
Continues: Canadian Medical Association
journal.
1985   9711805

CNA Bull
CNA bulletin
Continues the CSNA bulletin. Continued by
California nurse.
1961-1969   1250251

CNS Drug Rev
CNS drug reviews
1080-563X
Continued by: CNS neuroscience &
therapeutics.
1995-2007   9514898

CNS Drugs
CNS drugs
1172-7047
1994   9431220

CNS Neurol Disord Drug Targets
CNS & neurological disorders drug targets
1871-5273   1996-3181
Continues: Current drug targets. CNS and
neurological disorders.
2006   101269155

CNS Neurosci Ther
CNS neuroscience & therapeutics
1755-5930   1755-5949
Continues: CNS drug reviews.
2008   101473265

CNS Spectr
CNS spectrums
1092-8529
1996   9702877

Cochlear Implants Int
Cochlear implants international
1467-0100   1754-7628
2000   101121166

Cochrane Database Syst Rev
Cochrane database of systematic reviews
(Online)
    1469-493X
199u   100909747

Coeur Med Interne
Coeur et médecine interne
0010-0234
Continued by: La Revue de médecine interne.
1962-1980   0373165

Cogn Affect Behav Neurosci
Cognitive, affective & behavioral
neuroscience
1530-7026   1531-135X
Continues: Psychobiology (Austin. Tex.).
2001   101083946

Cogn Behav Neurol
Cognitive and behavioral neurology: official
journal of the Society for Behavioral and
Cognitive Neurology
1543-3633   1543-3641
Continues: Neuropsychiatry.
neuropsychology. and behavioral neurology.
2003   101167278

Cogn Behav Ther
Cognitive behaviour therapy
1650-6073   1651-2316
Continues: Scandinavian journal of behaviour
therapy.
2002   101143317

Cogn Neuropsychiatry
Cognitive neuropsychiatry
1354-6805   1464-0619
199u   9713497

Cogn Neuropsychol
Cognitive neuropsychology
0264-3294   1464-0627
1984   8411889

Cogn Process
Cognitive processing
1612-4782   1612-4790
2000   101177984

Cogn Psychol
Cognitive psychology
0010-0285   1095-5623
1970   0241111

Cognition
Cognition
0010-0277   1873-7838
1972   0367541

Coimbra Med
Coimbra médica
0010-0366
1881-1980   0372743

Cold Spring Harb Symp Quant Biol
Cold Spring Harbor symposia on
quantitative biology
0091-7451   1943-4456
1933   1256107

Coll Antropol
Collegium antropologicum
0350-6134
1977   8003354

Coll Relat Res
Collagen and related research
0174-173X
Continued by: Matrix (Stuttgart. Germany).
1981-1988   8102998

Coll Rev
College review (Denver, Colo.)
0742-8057
Continued by: College view.
1984-1998   8500687

Coll Works Cardiopulm Dis
Collected works on cardio-pulmonary
disease
0069-5319
1959-1982   0413664

Collana Monogr Gazz Med Sicil
Collana monografica. Gazzetta medica
siciliana
1961-1962   17040490R

Collegian
Collegian (Royal College of Nursing,
Australia)
1322-7696
1994   9612493

Colloids Surf B Biointerfaces
Colloids and surfaces. B, Biointerfaces
0927-7765   1873-4367
Continues in part: Colloids and surfaces.
1993   9315133

Colo Med
Colorado medicine
0199-7343
Continues: Rocky Mountain medical journal.
1980   8003550

Colo Nurse
Colorado nurse
0010-1680
Continued by Colorado nurse update.
19uu-1984   16320400R

Colo Nurse
Colorado nurse (1985)
8750-846X
Continues: Colorado nurse update.
1985   8502809

Colorectal Dis
Colorectal disease: the official journal of
the Association of Coloproctology of Great
Britain and Ireland
1462-8910   1463-1318
1999   100883611

Columbia Optom
The Columbia optometrist
1927-1954   16330100R

Columbus Dent Soc Bull
Bulletin. Columbus Dental Society
Continued by: Columbus bulletin.
194u-19uu   9875021

Comb Chem High Throughput Screen
Combinatorial chemistry & high throughput
screening
1386-2073   1875-5402
1998   9810948

Commitment
Commitment
0145-8698
1976-1982   7700182

Common Factor
Common factor (Stoughton, Mass.)
1992-1999   9310060

Commun Agric Appl Biol Sci
Communications in agricultural and applied
biological sciences
1379-1176
Continues: Mededelingen (Rijksuniversiteit te
Gent. Fakulteit van de Landbouwkundige en
Toegepaste Biologische Wetenschappen).
2003   101200320

Commun Behav Biol
Communications in behavioral biology. Part
A: [Original articles]
0010-3608
Continued by Behavioral biology.
1968-1971   0326114

Commun Dis Intell
Communicable diseases intelligence
0725-3141   1445-4866
1980   9108419

Commun Dis Public Health
Communicable disease and public health /
PHLS
1462-1843
Merger of: Communicable disease report.
CDR review; and: PHLS microbiology digest.
1998-2004   9808711

Commun Dis Rep CDR Rev
Communicable disease report. CDR review
1350-9349
Continues: CDR (London. England: Review).
Merged with: PHLS microbiology digest.
to form: Communicable disease and public
health.
1992-1997   9312372

Commun Dis Rep CDR Suppl
Communicable disease report. CDR
supplement
0264-1607
1991   9314041

Commun Dis Rep CDR Wkly
Communicable disease report. CDR weekly
1350-9357
Continues: CDR (London. England: Weekly).
Continued by: CDR weekly.
1992-2000   9312012

Commun Med
Communication & medicine
1612-1783   1613-3625
2004   101201068

Commun Newsl
Communique Newsletter
Supersedes: Newsletter; Wisconsin League
For Nursing. Superseded by: Communique.
1977-1981   9878931

Commun Nurs Res
Communicating nursing research
0160-1652
1968   7707277

Commun Psychopharmacol
Communications in psychopharmacology
0145-5699
1977-1980   7706729

Communique
Communiqué (Milwaukee, Wis.)
0887-4557
Continues: Newsletter (Wisconsin League for
Nursing).
1979   9879661

Community Based Public Health Policy Pract
Community-based public health policy
& practice / Partnership for the Public's
Health
2001-2004   101140094

Community Dent Health
Community dental health
0265-539X
1984   8411261

Community Dent Oral Epidemiol
Community dentistry and oral epidemiology
0301-5661   1600-0528
1973   0410263

Community Genet
Community genetics
1422-2795   1422-2833
Continued by: Public health genomics.
1998-2008   9810770

Community Health (Bristol)
Community health
0010-3837
Supersedes the Royal Institute of Public
Health and Hygiene journal. Continued by:
Community medicine.
1969-1978   0226630

Community Health Stud
Community health studies
0314-9021
Continued by: Australian journal of public
health.
1977-1990   7808693

Community Jr Coll J
Community and junior college journal
0190-3160
Continues: Junior college journal. Continued
in Aug./Sept. 1985 by: Community, technical,
and junior college journal.
1972-1985   9877754

Community Med
Community medicine
0142-2456
Continues: Community health. Continued by:
Journal of public health medicine.
1979-1989   7907617

Community Ment Health J
Community mental health journal
0010-3853   1573-2789
1965   0005735

Community Ment Health Rev
Community mental health review
0363-1605
Continued by Prevention in human services.
1976-1980   7609235

Community Nurs
Community nursing
0898-4891
1984-1986   8506876

Community Nurse
Community nurse
1351-1416
Continues: Community outlook. Absorbed
by: Professional nurse (London, England).
Sept. 2001
1995-2001   9508559

Community Outlook
Community outlook
0262-8759
Continued by: Community nurse.
1977-1995   7900730

Community Pract
Community practitioner: the journal of the
Community Practitioners' & Health Visitors'
Association
1462-2815
Continues: Health visitor.
1998   9809060

Comp Biochem Physiol
Comparative biochemistry and physiology
0010-406X
Split into: Comparative biochemistry and
physiology. A, Comparative physiology, and:
Comparative biochemistry and physiology. B,
Comparative biochemistry, and: Comparative
biochemistry and physiology. C, Comparative
pharmacology.
1960-1970   7502545

Comp Biochem Physiol A Comp Physiol
Comparative biochemistry and physiology.
A, Comparative physiology
0300-9629
Continues in part: Comparative biochemistry
and physiology. Continued by: Comparative
biochemistry and physiology. Comparative
physiology.
1971-1992   1276312

Comp Biochem Physiol A Mol Integr Physiol
Comparative biochemistry and physiology.
Part A, Molecular & integrative physiology
1095-6433   1531-4332
Continues: Comparative biochemistry and
physiology. Part A, Physiology.
1998   9806096

Comp Biochem Physiol A Physiol
Comparative biochemistry and physiology.
Part A, Physiology
1096-4940
Continues: Comparative biochemistry and
physiology. Physiology. Continued by:
Comparative biochemistry and physiology.
Part A, Molecular and integrative physiology.
1994-1997   9516062

Comp Biochem Physiol B
Comparative biochemistry and physiology.
B, Comparative biochemistry
0305-0491
Continues in part: Comparative biochemistry
and physiology, and adopts its numbering.
Continued by: Comparative biochemistry
and physiology. Biochemistry and molecular
biology.
1971-1993   2984730R

Comp Biochem Physiol B Biochem Mol Biol
Comparative biochemistry and physiology.
Part B, Biochemistry & molecular biology
1096-4959   1879-1107
Continues: Comparative biochemistry and
physiology. Biochemistry and molecular
biology.
1994   9516061

Comp Biochem Physiol Biochem Mol Biol
Comparative biochemistry and physiology.
Biochemistry and molecular biology
Continues: Comparative biochemistry and
physiology. B, Comparative biochemistry.
Continued by: Comparative biochemistry
and physiology. Part B, Biochemistry &
molecular biology.
1994-1994   9430606

Comp Biochem Physiol C
Comparative biochemistry and physiology. C,
Comparative pharmacology and toxicology
0742-8413
Continues: Comparative biochemistry and
physiology. C, Comparative pharmacology.
Continued by: Comparative biochemistry and
physiology. Pharmacology, toxicology, and
endocrinology.
1983-1993   8310013

Comp Biochem Physiol C
Comparative biochemistry and physiology.
C: Comparative pharmacology
0306-4492
Continues in part: Comparative biochemistry
and physiology. Continued by: Comparative
biochemistry and physiology. C, Comparative
pharmacology and toxicology.
1975-1982   7503763

Comp Biochem Physiol C Pharmacol Toxicol
Endocrinol
Comparative biochemistry and physiology.
Part C, Pharmacology, toxicology &
endocrinology
1367-8280
Continues: Comparative biochemistry and
physiology. Pharmacology, toxicology and
endocrinology. Continued by: Comparative
biochemistry and physiology. Toxicology &
pharmacology.
1994-1999   9516060

Comp Biochem Physiol C Toxicol Pharmacol
Comparative biochemistry and physiology.
Toxicology & pharmacology: CBP
1532-0456
Continues: Comparative biochemistry and
physiology. Part C, Pharmacology, toxicology
& endocrinology.
2000   100959500

Comp Biochem Physiol Comp Physiol
Comparative biochemistry and physiology.
Comparative physiology
Continues: Comparative biochemistry and
physiology. A, Comparative physiology.
Continued by: Comparative biochemistry and
physiology. Physiology.
1992-1994   9441449

Comp Biochem Physiol Pharmacol Toxicol
Endocrinol
Comparative biochemistry and physiology.
Pharmacology, toxicology and endocrinology
Continues: Comparative biochemistry and
physiology. C, Comparative pharmacology
and toxicology. Continued by: Comparative
biochemistry and physiology. Part C,
Pharmacology, toxicology & endocrinology.
1994-1994   9430518

Comp Biochem Physiol Physiol
Comparative biochemistry and physiology.
Physiology
Continues: Comparative biochemistry
and physiology. Comparative physiology.
Continued by: Comparative biochemistry and
physiology. Part A, Physiology.
1994-1994   9441448

Comp Gen Pharmacol
Comparative and general pharmacology
0010-4035
Continued by General pharmacology.
1970-1974   7600504

Comp Immunol Microbiol Infect Dis
Comparative immunology, microbiology and
infectious diseases
0147-9571   1878-1667
1978   7808924

Comp Med
Comparative medicine
1532-0820
Continues: Laboratory animal science.
2000   100900466

Comp Med East West
Comparative medicine East and West
0147-2917
Continues The American journal of Chinese
medicine. Continued by The American
journal of Chinese medicine.
1977-1978   7801707

Compend Contin Educ Dent
The Compendium of continuing education
in dentistry
0734-0338
Continues: Compendium on continuing
education in general dentistry. Continued by:
Compendium (Newtown, Pa.).
1980-1986   8110106

Compend Contin Educ Dent
Compendium of continuing education in
dentistry (Jamesburg, N.J.: 1995)
1548-8578
Continues: Compendium (Newtown, Pa.).
1995   9600713

Compend Contin Educ Dent Suppl
Compendium of continuing education
in dentistry. (Jamesburg, N.J.: 1995).
Supplement
Continues: Compendium (Newtown, Pa.).
Supplement.
1996-2001   101094904

Compend Contin Educ Gen Dent
The Compendium on continuing education
in general dentistry
0196-1756
Continued by: Compendium of continuing
education in dentistry.
1980-1980   8210675

Compend Contin Educ Vet
Compendium (Yardley, PA)
1940-8307   1940-8315
Continues: Compendium on continuing
education for the practicing veterinarian.
2006   101290247

Compend Suppl
Compendium (Newtown, Pa.). Supplement
Continues: Compendium of continuing
education in dentistry. Supplement. Continued
by: Compendium of continuing education
in dentistry. (Jamesburg, N.J.: 1995).
Supplement.
1987-1994   9110139

Compendium
Compendium (Newtown, Pa.)
0894-1009
Continues: Compendium of continuing
education in dentistry. Continued by:
Compendium of continuing education in
dentistry (Jamesburg, N.J.: 1995).
1986-1995   8702480

Compens Benefits Rev
Compensation and benefits review
0886-3687
Continues: Compensation review.
1985   9881799

Compens Rev
Compensation review
0010-4248
Continued by: Compensation and benefits
review.
1969-198u   9877814

Complement
Complement (Basel, Switzerland)
0253-5076
Continued by: Complement and
inflammation.
1984-1988   8409977

Complement Inflamm
Complement and inflammation
1012-8204
Continues: Complement (Basel, Switzerland).
1989-1991   8903074

Complement Ther Clin Pract
Complementary therapies in clinical
practice
1744-3881   1873-6947
Continues: Complementary therapies in
nursing & midwifery.
2005   101225531

Complement Ther Med
Complementary therapies in medicine
0965-2299   1873-6963
Continues: Complementary medical research.
1993   9308777

Complement Ther Nurs Midwifery
Complementary therapies in nursing &
midwifery
1353-6117
Continued by: Complementary therapies in
clinical practice.
1995-2004   9506953

Compr Gerontol [A]
Comprehensive gerontology. Section A,
Clinical and laboratory sciences
0902-0071
1987-1989   8710568

Compr Gerontol [B]
Comprehensive gerontology. Section B,
Behavioural, social, and applied sciences
0902-008X
1987-1989   8712368

Compr Gerontol [C]
Comprehensive gerontology. Section C,
Interdisciplinary topics
0902-0098
1987-1988   8809131

Compr Ophthalmol Update
Comprehensive ophthalmology update
1527-7313   1937-8394
2000   100910750

Compr Psychiatry
Comprehensive psychiatry
0010-440X   1532-8384
1960   0372612

Compr Ther
Comprehensive therapy
0098-8243
Supersedes: Contemporary therapy.
1975   7605837

Comput Aided Surg
Computer aided surgery: official journal
of the International Society for Computer
Aided Surgery
1092-9088   1097-0150
Continues: Journal of image guided surgery.
1997   9708375

Comput Appl Biosci
Computer applications in the biosciences:
CABIOS
0266-7061
Continued by: Bioinformatics (Oxford,
England).
1985-1997   8511758

Comput Biol Chem
Computational biology and chemistry
1476-9271   1476-928X
Continues: Computers & chemistry.
2003   101157394

Comput Biol Med
Computers in biology and medicine
0010-4825   1879-0534
1970   1250250

Comput Biomed Res
Computers and biomedical research, an
international journal
0010-4809   1090-2368
Continued by: Journal of biomedical
informatics.
1967-2000   0100331

Comput Chem
Computers & chemistry
0097-8485
Continued by: Computational biology and
chemistry.
1976-2002   7607706

Comput Healthc
Computers in healthcare
0745-1075
Continues: Computers in hospitals. Continued
by: Health management technology.
1982-1993   8303437

Comput Hosp
Computers in hospitals
0274-631X
Continued by: Computers in healthcare.
1980-1982   9879292

Comput Inform Nurs
Computers, informatics, nursing: CIN
1538-2931   1538-9774
Absorbed: Cin plus. 2003 Continues:
Computers in nursing.
2002   101141667

Comput Med Imaging Graph
Computerized medical imaging and
graphics: the official journal of the
Computerized Medical Imaging Society
0895-6111   1879-0771
Continues: Computerized radiology.
1988   8806104

Comput Methods Biomech Biomed Engin
Computer methods in biomechanics and
biomedical engineering
1025-5842   1476-8259
1997   9802899

Comput Methods Programs Biomed
Computer methods and programs in
biomedicine
0169-2607   1872-7565
Continues: Computer programs in biomedicine.
1985   8506513

Comput Nurs
Computers in nursing
0736-8593
Continued by: Computers, informatics, nursing.
1983-2002   8507717

Comput Programs Biomed
Computer programs in biomedicine
0010-468X
Continued by Computer methods and programs in biomedicine.
1970-1984   0237013

Comput Radiol
Computerized radiology: official journal of the Computerized Tomography Society
0730-4862
Continues: Computerized tomography. Continued by: Computerized medical imaging and graphics.
1982-1987   8208620

Comput Syst Bioinformatics Conf
Computational systems bioinformatics / Life Sciences Society. Computational Systems Bioinformatics Conference
1752-7791
Continues: Proceedings. IEEE Computational Systems Bioinformatics Conference
2006   101294517

Comput Tomogr
Computerized tomography
0363-8235
Continued by: Computerized radiology.
1977-1981   7703872

Computertomographie
Computertomographie
0720-0501
Continued by: Digitale Bilddiagnostik.
1981-1983   8305245

Concepts Immunopathol
Concepts in immunopathology
0255-7983
Merged with: Contributions to microbiology and immunology, to form: Contributions to microbiology.
1985-199u   8412469

Concern
Concern (Regina, Sask.)
0836-7310
Continues: Saskatchewan Registered Nurses' Association. News bulletin - Saskatchewan Registered Nurses' Association. Continued by: SRNA newsbulletin.
1987-1999   9214659

Concern Care Aging
Concern in care of the aging
0190-9754
Superseded by: Aging & leisure living.
1974-1978   7810233

Concours Med
Concours médical
0010-5309
Absorbed Connaitre; cahiers de l'humanisme médical in 1951.
1879   2984731R

Cond Reflex
Conditional reflex
0010-5392
Continued by the Pavlovian journal of biological science.
1966-1973   0412676

Conector
Conector
0325-2426
1971-1986   7610427

Conf Lyon Ophtalmol
Conférences lyonnaises d'ophtalmologie
0414-3825
1954-1994   16340250R

Conf Proc IEEE Eng Med Biol Soc
Conference proceedings: ... Annual International Conference of the IEEE Engineering in Medicine and Biology Society. IEEE Engineering in Medicine and Biology Society. Conference
1557-170X
Continues: Proceedings of the Annual International Conference of the IEEE Engineering in Medicine and Biology Society. IEEE Engineering in Medicine and Biology Society. Conference.
2004   101243413

Confed Aust Crit Care Nurses J
Confederation of Australian Critical Care Nurses journal
1033-3355
Formed by the union of: PULSE (Australian Society of Critical Care Nurses, and: CNSA journal. Continued by: Australian critical care.
1988-1991   9011101

Confin Neurol
Confinia neurologica
0010-5678
Continued by Applied neurophysiology.
1938-1975   7600680

Confin Psychiatr
Confinia psychiatrica. Borderland of psychiatry. Grenzgebiete der Psychiatrie. Les Confins de la psychiatrie
0010-5686
1958-1980   0207314

Congenit Anom (Kyoto)
Congenital anomalies
0914-3505
Continues: Senten ijō.
1987   9306292

Congenit Heart Dis
Congenital heart disease
1747-079X   1747-0803
2006   101256510

Congest Heart Fail
Congestive heart failure (Greenwich, Conn.)
1527-5299   1751-7133
Continues: Prevention and management of congestive heart failure.
1997   9714174

Congr Int Stomatol
Congrès international de stomatologie
1931-uuuu   100960817

Congr Soc Cir Chile
Congreso. Sociedad de Cirujanos de Chile
Supersedes the Relatos oficiales of the Congreso Chileno de Cirugía and the Actas of the Congreso Nacional de Cirugía. Superseded by the transactions of the Congreso Chileno de Cirugía.
1949-1952   20810580R

Conn Dent Stud J
Connecticut dental student journal / the University of Connecticut Health Center, School of Dental Medicine
0898-7394
1981   8711638

Conn Med
Connecticut medicine
0010-6178
Continues the Connecticut State medical journal.
1958   0372745

Conn Nurs News
Connecticut nursing news (Meriden, Conn.: 1980)
0278-4092
Continues: Nursing news.
1980   9878914

Conn State Med J
Connecticut state medical journal
0096-0179
Continues the Journal of the Connecticut State Medical Society. Continued by Connecticut medicine.
1940-1958   16410130R

Connect Tissue Res
Connective tissue research
0300-8207   1607-8438
1972   0365263

Conscious Cogn
Consciousness and cognition
1053-8100   1090-2376
1992   9303140

Consens Dev Conf Summ Natl Inst Health
Consensus development conference summaries / National Institutes of Health
0737-4674
Continues: National Institutes of Health consensus development conference summaries.
1980-1980   8106383

Consens Statement
Consensus statement / NIH Consensus Development Conference. National Institutes of Health Consensus Development Conference
1062-0362
Continues: National Institutes of Health consensus development conference consensus statement. Continued by: NIH consensus statement.
1990-1992   9108119

Conserv Biol
Conservation biology: the journal of the Society for Conservation Biology
0888-8892   1523-1739
1987   9882301

Consult Pharm
The Consultant pharmacist: the journal of the American Society of Consultant Pharmacists
0888-5109
1986   9013983

Consult Specif Eng
Consulting-specifying engineer
0892-5046
Formed by the union of: Consulting engineer, and: Specifying engineer.
1987   9882546

Consultant
Consultant
0010-7069
1961   7501110

Consum Health Perspect
Consumer health perspectives
0191-3921
Formed by the union of Health perspectives and Quarterly - Consumer Commission on the Accreditation of Health Services.
1978-1983   7901088

Consum Rep
Consumer reports
0010-7174
Continues Consumers union reports. Absorbed Bread and butter in Apr. 1947.
1942   0215776

Cont Lens Anterior Eye
Contact lens & anterior eye: the journal of the British Contact Lens Association
1367-0484   1476-5411
Continues: Journal of the B.C.L.A..
1997   9712714

Contact
Contact
1941-1958   0373171

Contact Dermatitis
Contact dermatitis
0105-1873   1600-0536
1975   7604950

Contact Intraocul Lens Med J
Contact and intraocular lens medical
journal
0360-1358
Supersedes Contact lens medical bulletin.
1975-1982   7509610

Contact Point
Contact point
0010-7301
1924   0417430

Contam Control
Contamination control
0010-7395
Continued by Contamination control-
biomedical environments.
1962-1972   0352463

Contam Control Biomed Environ
Contamination control-biomedical
environments
0090-2519
Continues Contamination control.
1972-1972   0352714

Contemp Adm
Contemporary administrator
0191-9873
Continued by: Contemporary administrator
for long-term care.
197u-19uu   9878791

Contemp Adm Long Term Care
Contemporary administrator for long-term
care
0745-2837
Continues: Contemporary administrator.
Continued by: Contemporary longterm care.
19uu-1984   9880785

Contemp Anesth Pract
Contemporary anesthesia practice
0191-247X
Continues: Clinical anesthesia.
1978-1987   7900421

Contemp Clin Trials
Contemporary clinical trials
1551-7144   1559-2030
Continues: Controlled clinical trials.
2005   101242342

Contemp Intern Med
Contemporary internal medicine
1042-9646
1989-1998   9007257

Contemp Issues Clin Biochem
Contemporary issues in clinical
biochemistry
0265-6701
1984-1986   8508326

Contemp Longterm Care
Contemporary longterm care
8750-9652
Continues: Contemporary administrator for
long-term care.
1985-2005   8508328

Contemp Neurol Ser
Contemporary neurology series
0069-9446
1966   0071075

Contemp Nurse
Contemporary nurse: a journal for the
Australian nursing profession
1037-6178
1992   9211867

Contemp Orthop
Contemporary orthopaedics
0194-8458
1979-1996   8219527

Contemp Pediatr
Contemporary pediatrics
8750-0507
1984   8702030

Contemp Pharm Pract
Contemporary pharmacy practice
0162-3761
1978-1982   7905177

Contemp Surg
Contemporary surgery
0045-8341
1972   0321423

Contemp Top Immunobiol
Contemporary topics in immunobiology
0093-4054
1972-1985   0314145

Contemp Top Lab Anim Sci
Contemporary topics in laboratory
animal science / American Association for
Laboratory Animal Science
1060-0558
Continues: AALAS bulletin. Continued by:
Journal of the American Association for
Laboratory Animal Science.
1992-2005   9204153

Contemp Top Mol Immunol
Contemporary topics in molecular
immunology
0090-8800
Continues Contemporary topics in
immunochemistry.
1973-1985   0363025

Contemp Urol
Contemporary urology
1042-2250
1989-2008   8912618

Contin Care
Continuing care
1057-428X
Continues: Continuing care coordinator.
1986-2004   8807456

Continuum
Continuum (Society for Social Work
Administrators in Health Care)
1082-8419
Continues: Discharge planning update.
Continued by: Continuum (Society for Social
Work Leadership in Health Care).
1995-1999   9508119

Continuum (N Y)
Continuum
0195-6043
1980   9878929

Continuum Soc Soc Work Leadersh Health Care
Continuum (Society for Social Work
Leadership in Health Care)
Continues: Continuum (Society for Social
Work Administrators in Health Care).
1998-2001   100962178

Contracept Fertil Sex
Contraception, fertilité, sexualité (1992)
1165-1083
Continues: Fertilité, contraception, sexualité
(1991). Continued by: Gynécologie,
obstétrique & fertilité.
1992-1999   9314045

Contracept Fertil Sex (Paris)
Contraception, fertilité, sexualité
0301-861X
Supersedes Fertilité, orthogénie. Continued
by: Fertilité, contraception, sexualité.
1973-1985   0411244

Contraception
Contraception
0010-7824   1879-0518
1970   0234361

Contract
Contract (New York, N.Y.: 1960)
0010-7832
Continued by: Contract design.
1960-1990   9877767

Contract Des
Contract design
1053-5632
Continues: Contract (New York, N.Y.: 1960).
1990   9892140

Contract Healthc
Contract healthcare
0891-5059
1988-1988   9883667

Contract Inter
Contract interiors
0148-012X
Continues: Interiors (Stroudsburg, Pa.).
Continued by: Interiors.
1977-1978   9877842

Contrast Media Mol Imaging
Contrast media & molecular imaging
1555-4309   1555-4317
2006   101286760

Contrib Epidemiol Biostat
Contributions to epidemiology and
biostatistics
0377-3574
1979-1995   7807252

Contrib Gynecol Obstet
Contributions to gynecology and obstetrics
0304-4246
Supersedes Fortschritte der Geburtshilfe und
Gynäkologie.
1976-2000   7702984

Contrib Med Stud
Contributions in medical studies
0886-8220
Continues: Contributions in medical history.
1986   8700062

Contrib Microbiol
Contributions to microbiology
1420-9519   1662-291X
Formed by the union of: Contributions
to microbiology and immunology; and:
Concepts in immunopathology.
1998   9815689

Contrib Microbiol Immunol
Contributions to microbiology and
immunology
0301-3081
Continues: Bibliotheca microbiologica.
Merged with: Concepts in immunopathology,
to form: Contributions to microbiology.
Merged with: Concepts in immunopathology,
to form: Contributions to microbiology.
1973-1995   0401476

Contrib Nephrol
Contributions to nephrology
0302-5144   1662-2782
1975   7513582

Contrib Primatol
Contributions to primatology
0301-4231
Supersedes Bibliotheca primatologica.
1974-1991 0420475

Contrib Sens Physiol
Contributions to sensory physiology
0069-9705
1965-1984 0006021

Control Clin Trials
Controlled clinical trials
0197-2456
Continued by: Contemporary clinical trials.
Continued in part by: Clinical trials (London, England).
1980-2004 8006242

Control Plagas
Control de plagas
1939-1950 16410510R

Convuls Ther
Convulsive therapy
0749-8055
Continued by: Journal of ECT.
1985-1997 8506311

COO Rep
COO [reports]. U.S. Atomic Energy Commission
1959-1970 21830370R

Coop Dent (B Aires)
El Cooperador dental; cooperativismo, información y ciencia odontológica
0069-9799
1933 16420030R

COPD
COPD
1541-2555 1541-2563
2004 101211769

Cor Vasa
Cor et vasa
0010-8650
1959 0372614

Cornea
Cornea
0277-3740 1536-4798
1982 8216186

Cornell Hotel Restaur Adm Q
The Cornell hotel and restaurant administration quarterly
0010-8804
1960 9877768

Cornell J Law Public Policy
Cornell journal of law and public policy
1069-0565
1992 9892180

Cornell Law Rev
Cornell law review
0010-8847
Continues: Cornell law quarterly.
1967 7703647

Cornell Med J
Cornell medical journal
1946-1951 16420420R

Cornell Vet
The Cornell veterinarian
0010-8901
1911-1994 0074245

Coron Artery Dis
Coronary artery disease
0954-6928 1473-5830
1990 9011445

Corp Comment
Corporate commentary
0749-4335
Continued by: Healthy companies.
1984-1987 8501367

Corps Med (Ettelbruck)
Le Corps médical
0376-7582
Continues Bulletin d'information du Syndicat médical du Grand-Duché de Luxembourg.
1961-1975 7600506

Corr Farm
Il Corriere dei farmacisti
0010-9207
1946-1968 16420500R

Cortex
Cortex; a journal devoted to the study of the nervous system and behavior
0010-9452
1964 0100725

Cosmetologica
Cosmetologica
0070-055X
Continues: Aesthetische Medizin. Continued by: Kosmetische Medizin.
1970-1970 0247470

Cost Containment
Cost containment
0198-9782
Merged with: Target market, to become: Health care Marketer & target market.
1979-1986 8002944

Cost Qual
Cost & quality: CQ
Continues: Cost & quality quarterly journal. Merged with the online journal: The NHCQA bulletin, to form: Real healthcare
1999-2001 101126987

Cost Qual Q J
Cost & quality quarterly journal: CQ
1079-5057
Continued by: Cost & quality.
1994-1999 9602863

CPJ
CPJ: Canadian pharmaceutical journal = RPC: la revue pharmaceutique canadienne
0828-6914
Continues: Canadian pharmaceutical journal. Continued by: Canadian pharmacists journal.
1984-2005 0372710

Cr Trav Lab Carlsberg Ser Physiol
Comptes rendus des travaux du Laboratoire Carlsberg. Série physiologique
Continues in part Comptes rendus des travaux du Laboratoire Carlsberg. Merged with Comptes rendus des travaux du Laboratoire Carlsberg. Série chimique to form Comptes rendus des travaux du Laboratoire Carlsberg.
1934-1957 0004706

Cranio
Cranio: the journal of craniomandibular practice
0886-9634
Continues: The Journal of cranio-mandibular practice.
1985 8609491

Cranio Clin Int
Cranio clinics international
1050-009X
1991-1991 9203232

CRC Crit Rev Biochem
CRC critical reviews in biochemistry
0045-6411
Continued by: Critical reviews in biochemistry and molecular biology.
1972-1988 0330403

CRC Crit Rev Bioeng
CRC critical reviews in bioengineering
0045-642X
Continued by: Critical reviews in bioengineering.
1971-1979 1307350

CRC Crit Rev Clin Lab Sci
CRC critical reviews in clinical laboratory sciences
0590-8191
Continued by: Critical reviews in clinical laboratory sciences.
1970-1980 1247734

CRC Crit Rev Clin Neurobiol
CRC critical reviews in clinical neurobiology
0742-941X
Continued by: Critical reviews in neurobiology.
1984-1987 8506657

CRC Crit Rev Clin Radiol Nucl Med
CRC critical reviews in clinical radiology and nuclear medicine
0091-6536
Continues CRC critical reviews in radiological sciences. Continued by CRC critical reviews in diagnostic imaging.
1973-1977 0372257

CRC Crit Rev Diagn Imaging
CRC critical reviews in diagnostic imaging
0147-6750
Continues CRC critical reviews in clinical radiology and nuclear medicine. Continued by: Critical reviews in diagnostic imaging.
1977-1980 7705846

CRC Crit Rev Food Sci Nutr
CRC critical reviews in food science and nutrition
0099-0248
Continues: CRC critical reviews in food technology. Continued by: Critical reviews in food science and nutrition.
1975-1979 7513255

CRC Crit Rev Immunol
CRC Critical reviews in immunology
0197-3355
Continued by: Critical reviews in immunology.
1979-1979 8106390

CRC Crit Rev Microbiol
CRC critical reviews in microbiology
0045-6454
Continued by: Critical reviews in microbiology.
1971-1979 1301620

CRC Crit Rev Radiol Sci
CRC critical reviews in radiological sciences
0007-9014
Continued by CRC critical reviews in clinical radiology and nuclear medicine.
1970-1972 0372260

CRC Crit Rev Toxicol
CRC critical reviews in toxicology
0045-6446
Continued by: Critical reviews in toxicology.
1971-1979 1305020

Creat Nurs
Creative nursing
1078-4535
Continues: Primarily nursing.
1994 9505022

Crianca Port
A Criança portuguesa
1942-1963 0401041

Crim
Criminalia
0011-1368
1933-1973　　　　　　　16430120R

Crim Behav Ment Health
Criminal behaviour and mental health:
CBMH
0957-9664　　　　　　1471-2857
1991　　　　　　　　　9309668

Crippl Child
The Crippled child
1923-1958　　　　　　16430170R

Crisis
Crisis
0227-5910
1980　　　　　　　　　8218602

Crit Care
Critical care (London, England)
1364-8535　　　　　　1466-609X
1997　　　　　　　　　9801902

Crit Care Clin
Critical care clinics
0749-0704　　　　　　1557-8232
1985　　　　　　　　　8507720

Crit Care Med
Critical care medicine
0090-3493　　　　　　1530-0293
1973　　　　　　　　　0355501

Crit Care Nurs Clin North Am
Critical care nursing clinics of North America
0899-5885
1989　　　　　　　　　8912620

Crit Care Nurs Q
Critical care nursing quarterly
0887-9303　　　　　　1550-5111
Continues: CCQ. Critical care quarterly.
1987　　　　　　　　　8704517

Crit Care Nurse
Critical care nurse
0279-5442
1980　　　　　　　　　8207799

Crit Care Resusc
Critical care and resuscitation: journal of
the Australasian Academy of Critical Care
Medicine
1441-2772
1999　　　　　　　　　100888170

Crit Care Update
Critical care update
0162-7252
1974-1983　　　　　　7802334

Crit Path AIDS Proj
Critical Path AIDS project
1085-7605
1989-uuuu　　　　　　9886098

Crit Pathw Cardiol
Critical pathways in cardiology
1535-282X　　　　　　1535-2811
2002　　　　　　　　　101165286

Crit Rev Biochem Mol Biol
Critical reviews in biochemistry and
molecular biology
1040-9238　　　　　　1549-7798
Continues: Critical reviews in biochemistry.
1989　　　　　　　　　8903774

Crit Rev Bioeng
Critical reviews in bioengineering
0731-6984
Continues: CRC critical reviews in
bioengineering. Continued by: Critical
reviews in biomedical engineering.
1980-1981　　　　　　8208626

Crit Rev Biomed Eng
Critical reviews in biomedical engineering
0278-940X
Continues: Critical reviews in bioengineering.
1981　　　　　　　　　8208627

Crit Rev Biotechnol
Critical reviews in biotechnology
0738-8551　　　　　　1549-7801
1983　　　　　　　　　8505177

Crit Rev Clin Lab Sci
Critical reviews in clinical laboratory
sciences
1040-8363　　　　　　1549-781X
Continues: CRC critical reviews in clinical
laboratory sciences.
1980　　　　　　　　　8914816

Crit Rev Comput Tomogr
Critical reviews in computed tomography
1548-7679　　　　　　1549-7844
Continues: Critical reviews in diagnostic
imaging. Absorbed by: Journal of
cardiovascular magnetic resonance.
2002-2004　　　　　　101136418

Crit Rev Diagn Imaging
Critical reviews in diagnostic imaging
1040-8371
Continues: CRC critical reviews in diagnostic
imaging. Continued by: Critical reviews in
computed tomography.
1980-2001　　　　　　8914817

Crit Rev Eukaryot Gene Expr
Critical reviews in eukaryotic gene
expression
1045-4403
1990　　　　　　　　　9007261

Crit Rev Food Sci Nutr
Critical reviews in food science and nutrition
1040-8398　　　　　　1549-7852
Continues: CRC critical reviews in food
science and nutrition.
1980　　　　　　　　　8914818

Crit Rev Immunol
Critical reviews in immunology
1040-8401
Continues: CRC critical reviews in
immunology.
1980　　　　　　　　　8914819

Crit Rev Med Inform
Critical reviews in medical informatics
0882-0503
1986-1988　　　　　　8712374

Crit Rev Microbiol
Critical reviews in microbiology
1040-841X　　　　　　1549-7828
Continues: CRC critical reviews in
microbiology.
1980　　　　　　　　　8914274

Crit Rev Neurobiol
Critical reviews in neurobiology
0892-0915
Continues: CRC critical reviews in clinical
neurobiology.
1987　　　　　　　　　8710803

Crit Rev Oncog
Critical reviews in oncogenesis
0893-9675
1989　　　　　　　　　8914610

Crit Rev Oncol Hematol
Critical reviews in oncology/hematology
1040-8428　　　　　　1879-0461
1983　　　　　　　　　8916049

Crit Rev Oral Biol Med
Critical reviews in oral biology and
medicine: an official publication of the
American Association of Oral Biologists
1045-4411　　　　　　1544-1113
Absorbed by: Journal of dental research.
1990-2004　　　　　　9009999

Crit Rev Ther Drug Carrier Syst
Critical reviews in therapeutic drug carrier
systems
0743-4863
1984　　　　　　　　　8511159

Crit Rev Toxicol
Critical reviews in toxicology
1040-8444　　　　　　1547-6898
Continues: CRC critical reviews in
toxicology.
1980　　　　　　　　　8914275

CRNA
CRNA: the clinical forum for nurse
anesthetists
1048-2687
1990-2000　　　　　　9109511

Croat Med J
Croatian medical journal
0353-9504　　　　　　1332-8166
Continues: Radovi Medicinskog fakulteta u
Zagrebu.
1992　　　　　　　　　9424324

Cron IDI
Cronache dell'IDI
1946-1969　　　　　　16430260R

Crossref Hum Resour Manage
Cross-reference on human resources
management
0190-0447
Continues: Cross-reference. Continued by
The Hospital manager.
1978-1983　　　　　　7805961

Crossreference
Cross-reference
0045-9100
Supersedes Cross-reference on careers.
Continued by: Cross-reference on human
resources management.
1971-1977　　　　　　1300264

Cruz Roja Cuba
Cruz Roja Cubana
1937-19uu　　　　　　0006250

Cryo Letters
Cryo letters
0143-2044
1979　　　　　　　　　9891832

Cryobiology
Cryobiology
0011-2240　　　　　　1090-2392
1964　　　　　　　　　0006252

Cuad Bioet
Cuadernos de bioética: revista oficial de la
Asociación Española de Bioética y Ética
Médica
1132-1989
1990　　　　　　　　　101312976

Cuad Farmacol
Cuadernos de farmacología
1948-19uu　　　　　　16430420R

Cult Divers Ment Health
Cultural diversity and mental health
1077-341X
Continued by: Cultural diversity & ethnic
minority psychology.
1995-1998　　　　　　9512524

Cult Health Sex
Culture, health & sexuality
1369-1058 1464-5351
1999 100883416

Cult Med
Cultura médica
1966-1967 0200313

Cult Med Psychiatry
Culture, medicine and psychiatry
0165-005X 1573-076X
1977 7707467

Cultur Divers Ethnic Minor Psychol
Cultural diversity & ethnic minority
psychology
1099-9809
Continues: Cultural diversity and mental
health.
1999 100956435

Cuore Circ
Cuore e circolazione
0300-8894
Continues: Malattie del cuore e dei vase.
Merged with: Folia cardiologica, and:
Malattie cardiovascolari, to form: Giornale
italiano di cardiologia.
1924-1970 1270323

Curationis
Curationis
0379-8577
Supersedes SA nursing journal. SA
verplegingstydskrif.
1978 7901092

Curr Alcohol
Currents in alcoholism
0161-8504
1976-1981 7801711

Curr Allergy Asthma Rep
Current allergy and asthma reports
1529-7322 1534-6315
Continues: Current allergy reports.
2001 101096440

Curr Allergy Rep
Current allergy reports
Continued by: Current allergy and asthma
reports.
2001-2001 101139936

Curr Alzheimer Res
Current Alzheimer research
1567-2050 1875-5828
2004 101208441

Curr Anthropol
Current anthropology
0011-3204
1960 0421035

Curr Atheroscler Rep
Current atherosclerosis reports
1523-3804 1534-6242
1999 100897685

Curr Biol
Current biology: CB
0960-9822 1879-0445
1991 9107782

Curr Cancer Drug Targets
Current cancer drug targets
1568-0096 1873-5576
2001 101094211

Curr Cardiol Rep
Current cardiology reports
1523-3782 1534-3170
1999 100888969

Curr Clin Pharmacol
Current clinical pharmacology
1574-8847
2006 101273158

Curr Clin Top Infect Dis
Current clinical topics in infectious diseases
0195-3842
1980-2002 7908990

Curr Concepts Hosp Pharm Manage
Current concepts in hospital pharmacy
management
0164-7857
1978-1989 8101581

Curr Concepts Nutr
Current concepts in nutrition
0090-0443
1972-1988 0347207

Curr Dev Psychopharmacol
Current developments in
psychopharmacology
0097-8361
1975-1981 7513831

Curr Diab Rep
Current diabetes reports
1534-4827 1539-0829
2001 101093791

Curr Diabetes Rev
Current diabetes reviews
1573-3998 1875-6417
2005 101253260

Curr Dir Autoimmun
Current directions in autoimmunity
1422-2132 1662-2936
1999 101121763

Curr Drug Deliv
Current drug delivery
1567-2018
2004 101208455

Curr Drug Discov Technol
Current drug discovery technologies
1570-1638
2004 101157212

Curr Drug Metab
Current drug metabolism
1389-2002
2000 100960533

Curr Drug Saf
Current drug safety
1574-8863
2006 101270895

Curr Drug Targets
Current drug targets
1389-4501 1873-5592
2000 100960531

Curr Drug Targets Cardiovasc Haematol Disord
Current drug targets. Cardiovascular &
haematological disorders
1568-0061
Continued by: Cardiovascular &
hematological disorders drug targets.
2001-2005 101123341

Curr Drug Targets CNS Neurol Disord
Current drug targets. CNS and neurological
disorders
1568-007X
Continued by: CNS & neurological disorders
drug targets.
2002-2005 101151150

Curr Drug Targets Immune Endocr Metabol Disord
Current drug targets. Immune, endocrine
and metabolic disorders
1568-0088
Continued by: Endocrine, metabolic &
immune disorders drug targets.
2001-2005 101121150

Curr Drug Targets Infect Disord
Current drug targets. Infectious disorders
1568-0053
Continued by: Infectious disorders drug
targets.
2001-2005 101128002

Curr Drug Targets Inflamm Allergy
Current drug targets. Inflammation and
allergy
1568-010X
Continued by: Inflammation & allergy drug
targets.
2002-2005 101160019

Curr Eye Res
Current eye research
0271-3683 1460-2202
1981 8104312

Curr Gastroenterol Rep
Current gastroenterology reports
1522-8037 1534-312X
1999 100888896

Curr Gene Ther
Current gene therapy
1566-5232
2001 101125446

Curr Genet
Current genetics
0172-8083 1432-0983
1979 8004904

Curr Heart Fail Rep
Current heart failure reports
1546-9530 1546-9549
2004 101196487

Curr Hematol Malig Rep
Current hematologic malignancy reports
1558-8211 1558-822X
2006 101262565

Curr Hematol Rep
Current hematology reports
1540-3408 1541-0714
2002-2006 101151358

Curr HIV Res
Current HIV research
1570-162X 1873-4251
2003 101156990

Curr HIV/AIDS Rep
Current HIV/AIDS reports
1548-3568 1548-3576
2004 101235661

Curr Hypertens Rep
Current hypertension reports
1522-6417 1534-3111
1999 100888982

Curr Issues Intest Microbiol
Current issues in intestinal microbiology
1466-531X
absorbed by: Current issues in molecular
biology.
2000-2007 100939156

Curr Issues Mol Biol
Current issues in molecular biology
1467-3037
Absorbed: Current issues in intestinal
microbiology.
1999 100931761

Curr Leg Thought Lawyers Dig Law Rev
Current legal thought; the lawyers' digest of
law reviews
1935-1948   58720310R

Curr Med Chem
Current medicinal chemistry
0929-8673
1994   9440157

Curr Med Chem Anticancer Agents
Current medicinal chemistry. Anti-cancer
agents
1568-0118
Continued by: Anti-cancer agents in
medicinal chemistry.
2001-2005   101123597

Curr Med Chem Cardiovasc Hematol Agents
Current medicinal chemistry.
Cardiovascular and hematological agents
1568-0169
Continued by: Cardiovascular &
hematological agents in medicinal chemistry.
2003-2005   101157213

Curr Med Drugs
Current medicine and drugs
0590-4048
Supersedes the Interim supplement to the
British encyclopedia of medical practice.
1960-1968   1260300

Curr Med Res Opin
Current medical research and opinion
0300-7995   1473-4877
1972   0351014

Curr Microbiol
Current microbiology
0343-8651   1432-0991
1978   7808448

Curr Mod Biol
Currents in modern biology
0011-4014
Continued by Bio Systems. Vol. 5. Aug.
1972-May 1974, has also later title.
1967-1974   0430261

Curr Mol Med
Current molecular medicine
1566-5240
2001   101093076

Curr Neurol Neurosci Rep
Current neurology and neuroscience reports
1528-4042   1534-6293
2000   100931790

Curr Neurovasc Res
Current neurovascular research
1567-2026   1875-5739
2004   101208439

Curr Oncol Rep
Current oncology reports
1523-3790   1534-6269
1999   100888967

Curr Opin Allergy Clin Immunol
Current opinion in allergy and clinical
immunology
1528-4050   1473-6322
2001   100936359

Curr Opin Anaesthesiol
Current opinion in anaesthesiology
0952-7907   1473-6500
1988   8813436

Curr Opin Biotechnol
Current opinion in biotechnology
0958-1669   1879-0429
1990   9100492

Curr Opin Cardiol
Current opinion in cardiology
0268-4705   1531-7080
1986   8608087

Curr Opin Cell Biol
Current opinion in cell biology
0955-0674   1879-0410
1989   8913428

Curr Opin Chem Biol
Current opinion in chemical biology
1367-5931   1879-0402
1997   9811312

Curr Opin Clin Nutr Metab Care
Current opinion in clinical nutrition and
metabolic care
1363-1950   1535-3885
1998   9804399

Curr Opin Cosmet Dent
Current opinion in cosmetic dentistry
1065-6278
Continues in part: Current opinion in
dentistry.
1993-199u   9438826

Curr Opin Crit Care
Current opinion in critical care
1070-5295   1531-7072
1995   9504454

Curr Opin Dent
Current opinion in dentistry
1046-0764
Split into: Current opinion in cosmetic
dentistry, and: Current opinion in
periodontology.
1991-1992   9106559

Curr Opin Drug Discov Devel
Current opinion in drug discovery &
development
1367-6733
1998   100887519

Curr Opin Endocrinol Diabetes Obes
Current opinion in endocrinology, diabetes,
and obesity
1752-296X   1752-2978
Continues: Current opinion in endocrinology
& diabetes.
2007   101308636

Curr Opin Gastroenterol
Current opinion in gastroenterology
0267-1379   1531-7056
1985   8506887

Curr Opin Gen Surg
Current opinion in general surgery
1065-6243
1993-1995   9314670

Curr Opin Genet Dev
Current opinion in genetics & development
0959-437X   1879-0380
1991   9111375

Curr Opin Hematol
Current opinion in hematology
1065-6251   1531-7048
1993   9430802

Curr Opin Immunol
Current opinion in immunology
0952-7915   1879-0372
1988   8900118

Curr Opin Infect Dis
Current opinion in infectious diseases
0951-7375   1535-3877
1988   8809878

Curr Opin Investig Drugs
Current opinion in investigational drugs
(London, England: 2000)
1472-4472
Merger of: Current opinion in anti-infective
investigational drugs; Current opinion in
anti-inflammatory & immunomodulatory
investigational drugs; Current opinion
in cardiovascular, pulmonary and renal
investigational drugs; Current opinion
in central & peripheral nervous systems
investigational drugs; and: Current opinion
in oncologic, endocrine & metabolic
investigational drugs.
2000   100965718

Curr Opin Lipidol
Current opinion in lipidology
0957-9672   1473-6535
1990   9010000

Curr Opin Microbiol
Current opinion in microbiology
1369-5274   1879-0364
1998   9815056

Curr Opin Mol Ther
Current opinion in molecular therapeutics
1464-8431
1999   100891485

Curr Opin Nephrol Hypertens
Current opinion in nephrology and
hypertension
1062-4821   1535-3842
1992   9303753

Curr Opin Neurobiol
Current opinion in neurobiology
0959-4388   1873-6882
1991   9111376

Curr Opin Neurol
Current opinion in neurology
1350-7540   1473-6551
Continues: Current opinion in neurology and
neurosurgery.
1993   9319162

Curr Opin Neurol Neurosurg
Current opinion in neurology and
neurosurgery
0951-7383
1988-1993   8809879

Curr Opin Obstet Gynecol
Current opinion in obstetrics & gynecology
1040-872X   1473-656X
1989   9007264

Curr Opin Oncol
Current opinion in oncology
1040-8746   1531-703X
1989   9007265

Curr Opin Ophthalmol
Current opinion in ophthalmology
1040-8738   1531-7021
1990   9011108

Curr Opin Organ Transplant
Current opinion in organ transplantation
1087-2418   1531-7013
199u   9717388

Curr Opin Otolaryngol Head Neck Surg
Current opinion in otolaryngology & head
and neck surgery
1068-9508   1531-6998
1993   9417024

Curr Opin Pediatr
Current opinion in pediatrics
1040-8703   1531-698X
1989   9000850

Curr Opin Periodontol
Current opinion in periodontology
1065-626X
Formerly a section of: Current opinion in dentistry.
1993-1997   9438825

Curr Opin Pharmacol
Current opinion in pharmacology
1471-4892
2001   100966133

Curr Opin Plant Biol
Current opinion in plant biology
1369-5266   1879-0356
1998   100883395

Curr Opin Psychiatry
Current opinion in psychiatry
0951-7367   1473-6578
1988   8809880

Curr Opin Pulm Med
Current opinion in pulmonary medicine
1070-5287   1531-6971
1995   9503765

Curr Opin Radiol
Current opinion in radiology
1040-869X
1989-1992   9000037

Curr Opin Rheumatol
Current opinion in rheumatology
1040-8711   1531-6963
1989   9000851

Curr Opin Struct Biol
Current opinion in structural biology
0959-440X
1991   9107784

Curr Opin Support Palliat Care
Current opinion in supportive and palliative care
1751-4258   1751-4266
2007   101297402

Curr Opin Urol
Current opinion in urology
0963-0643   1473-6586
1991   9200621

Curr Osteoporos Rep
Current osteoporosis reports
1544-1873   1544-2241
2003   101176492

Curr Pain Headache Rep
Current pain and headache reports
1531-3433   1534-3081
Continues: Current review of pain.
2001   100970666

Curr Pharm Biotechnol
Current pharmaceutical biotechnology
1389-2010   1873-4316
2000   100960530

Curr Pharm Des
Current pharmaceutical design
1381-6128   1873-4286
1995   9602487

Curr Popul Rep [Spec Censuses]
Current population reports. Series P-28, Special censuses
0270-6660
Continues Special censuses. Series P-SC.
1937   8004908

Curr Pract Gerontol Nurs
Current practice in gerontological nursing
1979-1979   9878284

Curr Pract Obstet Gynecol Nurs
Current practice in obstetric and gynecologic nursing
0361-9249
1976-1978   7606119

Curr Pract Orthop Surg
Current practice in orthopaedic surgery
0070-203X
1963-1979   16440080R

Curr Pract Pediatr Nurs
Current practice in pediatric nursing
0361-9257
1976-1980   7606120

Curr Probl Cancer
Current problems in cancer
0147-0272   1535-6345
1976   7702986

Curr Probl Cardiol
Current problems in cardiology
0146-2806   1535-6280
1976   7701802

Curr Probl Clin Biochem
Current problems in clinical biochemistry
0300-1725
1968-1984   0353507

Curr Probl Dermatol
Current problems in dermatology
1421-5721   1662-2944
Continues: Aktuelle Probleme der Dermatologie. Current problems in dermatology.
1968   0147371

Curr Probl Diagn Radiol
Current problems in diagnostic radiology
0363-0188   1535-6302
Continues Current problems in radiology.
1976   7607123

Curr Probl Pediatr
Current problems in pediatrics
0045-9380
Continued by: Current problems in pediatric and adolescent health care.
1970-2001   1272515

Curr Probl Pediatr Adolesc Health Care
Current problems in pediatric and adolescent health care
1538-5442   1538-3199
Continues: Current problems in pediatrics.
2001   101134613

Curr Probl Sov Med
Current problems of Soviet medicine
1958-1961   0155012

Curr Probl Surg
Current problems in surgery
0011-3840   1535-6337
1964   0372617

Curr Protein Pept Sci
Current protein & peptide science
1389-2037
2000   100960529

Curr Protoc Bioinformatics
Current protocols in bioinformatics / editoral board, Andreas D. Baxevanis ... [et al.]
1934-3396   1934-340X
2002   101157830

Curr Protoc Cell Biol
Current protocols in cell biology / editorial board, Juan S. Bonifacino ... [et al.]
1934-2500   1934-2616
2001   101287856

Curr Protoc Cytom
Current protocols in cytometry / editorial board, J. Paul Robinson, managing editor ... [et al.]
1934-9297   1934-9300
1998   100899351

Curr Protoc Hum Genet
Current protocols in human genetics / editorial board, Jonathan L. Haines ... [et al.]
1934-8266   1934-8258
2001   101287858

Curr Protoc Immunol
Current protocols in immunology / edited by John E. Coligan ... [et al.]
1934-3671   1934-368X
1992   9101651

Curr Protoc Microbiol
Current protocols in microbiology
1934-8525   1934-8533
2005   101257113

Curr Protoc Mol Biol
Current protocols in molecular biology / edited by Frederick M. Ausubel ... [et al.]
1934-3639   1934-3647
1988   8908160

Curr Protoc Neurosci
Current protocols in neuroscience / editorial board, Jacqueline N. Crawley ... [et al.]
1934-8584   1934-8576
2001   9706581

Curr Protoc Nucleic Acid Chem
Current protocols in nucleic acid chemistry / edited by Serge L. Beaucage ... [et al.]
1934-9270   1934-9289
2000   101287865

Curr Protoc Protein Sci
Current protocols in protein science / editorial board, John E. Coligan ... [et al.]
1934-3655   1934-3663
2001   101287868

Curr Protoc Stem Cell Biol
Current protocols in stem cell biology
1941-7322   1938-8969
2007   101470226

Curr Psychiatr Ther
Current psychiatric therapies
0070-2080
Supersedes: Progress in psychotherapy.
1961-1986   0142101

Curr Psychiatry Rep
Current psychiatry reports
1523-3812   1535-1645
1999   100888960

Curr Res Anesth Analg
Current researches in anesthesia & analgesia
Supersedes: Bulletin of the National Anaesthesia Research Society. Continued by: Anesthesia and analgesia; current researches.
1922-1956   14940090R

Curr Rev Pain
Current review of pain
1069-5850
Continued by: Current pain and headache reports.
1994-2000   9438797

Curr Rheumatol Rep
Current rheumatology reports
1523-3774   1534-6307
1999   100888970

Curr Sci
Current science
0011-3891
1932   0372620

Curr Sports Med Rep
Current sports medicine reports
1537-890X   1537-8918
2002   101134380

Curr Stem Cell Res Ther
Current stem cell research & therapy
1574-888X
2006   101272517

Curr Stud Hematol Blood Transfus
Current studies in hematology and blood
transfusion
0258-0330
Continues: Bibliotheca haematologica.
1986-1998   8600673

Curr Stud Nat Brain Funct
Current studies on the nature of brain
function
0574-7791
1959-1962   0402360

Curr Surg
Current surgery
0149-7944
Continues Review of surgery. Continued by:
Journal of surgical education.
1978-2006   7802123

Curr Ther Endocrinol Metab
Current therapy in endocrinology and
metabolism
0831-652X
1985-1997   8601485

Curr Ther Res Clin Exp
Current therapeutic research, clinical and
experimental
0011-393X
1959   0372621

Curr Top Cell Regul
Current topics in cellular regulation
0070-2137
1969-2000   2984740R

Curr Top Comp Pathobiol
Current topics in comparative pathobiology
0090-8584
1971-1973   0435531

Curr Top Dev Biol
Current topics in developmental biology
0070-2153
1966   0163114

Curr Top Exp Endocrinol
Current topics in experimental
endocrinology
0091-7397
1971-1983   0334341

Curr Top Eye Res
Current topics in eye research
0190-2970
1979-1984   7904214

Curr Top Hematol
Current topics in hematology
0190-1486
1978-1985   7901811

Curr Top Med Chem
Current topics in medicinal chemistry
1568-0266   1873-4294
2001   101119673

Curr Top Med Mycol
Current topics in medical mycology
0177-4204
1985-1997   8510329

Curr Top Microbiol Immunol
Current topics in microbiology and
immunology
0070-217X
Continues Ergebnisse der Mikrobiologie,
Immunitätsforschung und experimentellen
Therapie.
1967   0110513

Curr Top Mol Endocrinol
Current topics in molecular endocrinology
0094-6761
1974-1976   7500587

Curr Top Pathol
Current topics in pathology. Ergebnisse der
Pathologie
0070-2188
Continues: Ergebnisse der allgemeinen
Pathologie und pathologischen Anatomie.
1970-2001   0244762

Curr Top Radiat Res Q
Current topics in radiation research
quarterly
0011-3964
1965-1978   1276745

Curr Treat Options Oncol
Current treatment options in oncology
1527-2729   1534-6277
2000   100900946

Curr Urol Rep
Current urology reports
1527-2737   1534-6285
2000   100900943

Curr Vasc Pharmacol
Current vascular pharmacology
1570-1611
2003   101157208

Curr Womens Health Rep
Current women's health reports
1534-5874   1539-0837
2001-2003   101120027

Curso Int Oftalmol
Curso Internacional de Oftalmología. Curso
Internacional de Oftalmología
1956   24010050R

Cutan Ocul Toxicol
Cutaneous and ocular toxicology
1556-9527   1556-9535
Continues: Journal of toxicology. Cutaneous
and ocular toxicology.
2005   101266892

Cutis
Cutis; cutaneous medicine for the practitioner
0011-4162
1965   0006440

CVP
CVP
0091-4738
Continued by Applied cardiology.
1973-1984   0375425

Cyberpsychol Behav
Cyberpsychology & behavior: the impact of
the Internet, multimedia and virtual reality
on behavior and society
1094-9313   1557-8364
1998   9804397

Cyprus Med J
Cyprus medical journal
1947-1962   0372622

Cytobiologie
Cytobiologie
0070-2463
Continued by European journal of cell biology.
1969-1979   0235440

Cytobios
Cytobios
0011-4529
1969-2001   0207227

Cytogenet Cell Genet
Cytogenetics and cell genetics
0301-0171
Continued by: Cytogenetic and genome
research.
1973-2001   0367735

Cytogenet Genome Res
Cytogenetic and genome research
1424-8581   1424-859X
Continues: Cytogenetics and cell genetics.
2002   101142708

Cytogenetics
Cytogenetics
0011-4537
Continued by Cytogenetics and cell genetics.
1962-1972   0367734

Cytokine
Cytokine
1043-4666   1096-0023
1989   9005353

Cytokine Growth Factor Rev
Cytokine & growth factor reviews
1359-6101   1879-0305
Continues: Progress in growth factor research.
1996   9612306

Cytokines
Cytokines
1013-9982
1989-1993   8912908

Cytokines Cell Mol Ther
Cytokines, cellular & molecular therapy
1368-4736
Continues: Cytokines and molecular therapy.
Absorbed: in 2005 by: Cytotherapy.
1997-2002   9713367

Cytokines Mol Ther
Cytokines and molecular therapy
1355-6568
Continued by: Cytokines, cellular &
molecular therapy.
1995-1996   9509183

Cytologia (Tokyo)
Cytologia
0011-4545
1929   2984741R

Cytometry
Cytometry
0196-4763   1097-0320
Absorbed: Bioimaging. 1999 Split into:
Cytometry. Part A; and: Cytometry. Part B,
Clinical cytometry.
1980-2002   8102328

Cytometry A
Cytometry. Part A: the journal of the
International Society for Analytical Cytology
1552-4922   1552-4930
Continues in part: Cytometry.
2003   101235694

Cytometry B Clin Cytom
Cytometry. Part B, Clinical cytometry
1552-4949   1552-4957
Continues in part: Cytometry.
2003   101235690

Cytometry Suppl
Cytometry. Supplement: the journal of the
Society for Analytical Cytology
1046-7386
1987   8914279

Cytopathology
Cytopathology: official journal of the British Society for Clinical Cytology
0956-5507 1365-2303
1990 9010345

Cytotechnology
Cytotechnology
0920-9069 1573-0778
Absorbed: Methods in cell science. 2004
1987 8807027

Cytotherapy
Cytotherapy
1465-3249 1477-2566
Absorbed: Cytokines, celluar and molecular therapy. 2005
1999 100895309

Czas Stomatol
Czasopismo stomatologiczne
0011-4553
1948 2984742R

Czech Med
Czechoslovak medicine
0139-9179
Continues: Review of Czechoslovak medicine.
1978-1991 7805372

D

Daedalus
Daedalus
0011-5266
1955 0037276

Dakar Med
Dakar médical
0049-1101
Continues Bulletin de la Société médicale d'Afrique noire de langue française.
1979 7907630

Dalhousie Dent J
Dalhousie dental journal
0418-3010
1960 9881875

Dallas Med J
The Dallas medical journal
0011-586X
1901 0373173

Dalton Trans
Dalton transactions (Cambridge, England: 2003)
1477-9226 1477-9234
Continues: Dalton (Cambridge, England).
2003 101176026

Dan Med Bull
Danish medical bulletin
0907-8916 1603-9629
1954 0066040

Dan Medicinhist Arbog
Dansk medicinhistorisk årbog
0084-9588
Continues: Aarsberetning - Københavns universitets medicinsk-historiske institut og museum.
1972 0434570

Dan Tidsskr Farm
Dansk tidsskrift for farmaci
0011-6513
1926-1972 0373174

Dapim Refuiim
Dapim refuiim. Folia medica
0366-9637
1935-1969 0071461

Data Bull (Cent Stud Health Syst Change)
Data bulletin (Center for Studying Health System Change)
1997 100909932

Data Strateg Benchmarks
Data strategies & benchmarks: the monthly advisory for health care executives
1094-253X
Continued by: Performance improvement advisor.
1997-2002 9807026

DDZ
DDZ; das deutsche Zahnärzteblatt
0011-4839
Continues: Deutsche dentistische Zeitschrift.
Continued by: Das Deutsche Zahnärzteblatt.
1953-1968 2984743R

DE J Dent Eng
DE; the journal of dental engeering
0385-0129
1967 1264223

Deans List
Deans List
Continued by: Deans Notes.
1980-1983 9879285

Deans Notes
Deans Notes
Continues: Dean's list.
1984 9880408

Death Educ
Death education
0145-7624
Continued by Death studies.
1977-1984 7706740

Death Stud
Death studies
0748-1187 1091-7683
Continues: Death education.
1985 8506890

Decubitus
Decubitus
0898-1655
Continued by: Advances in wound care.
1988-1993 8901610

Del Med J
Delaware medical journal
0011-7781
Continues Delaware state medical journal.
1960 0370077

Del Nurse
Delaware nurse
1943-1972 0110777

Delt Hell Mikrobiol Hygieinol Hetair
Deltion Hellenikes Mikrobiologikes kai Hygieinologikes Hetaireias
Continued by Deltion Hellenikes Mikrobiologikes Hetaireias.
1956-1972 7507081

Delt Paidiatr Klin Panepistem Athenon
Deltion tes Paidiatrikes Klinikes tou Panepistemiou Athenon
0519-2854
1954 0420163

Deltion Iatrocheirourgike Hetaireia Athenon
Deltion. Iatrocheirourgikē Hetaireia Athēnōn
1917-1960 0374664

Dement Geriatr Cogn Disord
Dementia and geriatric cognitive disorders
1420-8008 1421-9824
Continues: Dementia (Basel, Switzerland).
1997 9705200

Dementia
Dementia (Basel, Switzerland)
1013-7424
Continued by: Dementia and geriatric cognitive disorders.
1990-1996 9010348

Demography
Demography
0070-3370
1964 0226703

Dens
Dens
0304-1476
Continues: Dental laboratorie bladet.
1971 7508531

Dens (Curitiba)
Dens
0100-2775
1971 7604963

Dens Sapiens
"Dens sapiens"
0011-8443
1940-1996 16520190R

Dent
Dent, contemporary dentistry
1015-0013
1986-1987 8800660

Dent Abstr
Dental abstracts; a selection of world dental literature
0011-8486
1956 60110120R

Dent Anaesth Sedat
Dental anaesthesia and sedation
0311-0699
1972-1984 7806536

Dent Angles
Dental Angles
0070-363X
1960-19uu 9875607

Dent Assist
The Dental assistant
0011-8508
Continued by: Dental assistant journal.
1931-1991 16520250R

Dent Assist
Dental assistant (Chicago, Ill.: 1994)
1088-3886
Continues: Dental assistant journal.
1994 9432924

Dent Assist (Waco Tx)
Dental assisting
0744-012X
Continued by: Dental office.
1981-1988 8211482

Dent Assist J
The Dental assistant journal: journal of the American Dental Assistants Association
1072-754X
Continues: Dental assistant.
1992-1993 9212282

Dent Cadmos
Dental Cadmos
0011-8524
1933 0370660

Dent Clin North Am
Dental clinics of North America
0011-8532 1558-0512
1957 0217440

Dent Concepts
Dental concepts
0011-8540
1949-1973 0413403

Dent Delin
Dental delineator
0070-3648
1934-1972
16520280R

Dent Dialogue
Dental dialogue (Bombay, India)
0970-4167
1972-1989
8604122

Dent Dienst
Dental Dienst; Fachzeitschrift für den
Dental-Markt; technisches Fachblatt für
Prothetik
0011-8559
1949-1990
16520290R

Dent Dig
Dental digest
0011-8567
Absorbed by: Quintessence international.
1895-1972
0342643

Dent Dimens
Dental dimensions
0191-2542
Continues San Fernando Valley Dental
Society bulletin.
1972
7900430

Dent Discourse
Dental Discourse
1975-1977
9877839

Dent Echo (Heidelb)
Dental echo
0011-8575
Absorbed Dental-Markt in 1938.
1926-1998
0372754

Dent Econ
Dental economics - oral hygiene
0011-8583
Continues Oral hygiene.
1968
0135416

Dent Gaz
The Dental gazette
0265-1440
Supersedes Public dental service gazette.
Absorbed by: British dental journal in 1950.
1934-1949
16520310R

Dent Health (London)
Dental health
0011-8605
1962
16520340R

Dent Hist
Dental historian: Lindsay Club newsletter
0958-6687
Continues: Occasional newsletter (Lindsay
Club).
1985
8803742

Dent Hyg (Chic)
Dental hygiene
0091-3979
Continues: Journal of the American
Hygienists' Association. Continued by:
Journal of dental hygiene.
1973-1988
0367545

Dent Hyg (San Franc)
Dental hygienist (San Francisco, Calif.)
Continues: Dental hygienists' news.
Continued by: NCSDHA dental hygienist.
194u-1970
9883653

Dent Images
Dental images
0070-3664
Continues Images; Marquette University
dental reflections.
1967-2002
0253667

Dent Implantol Update
Dental implantology update
1062-0346
1990
9114597

Dent Items Interest
Dental items of interest
0096-0195
Continues Items of interest.
1916-1953
16520420R

Dent J
Dental journal
0382-8514
Continues Journal of the Canadian Dental
Association. Continued by Journal (Canadian
Dental Association).
1974-1979
0411252

Dent J Aust
The Dental journal of Australia
Formed by the merger of the Australian
dental summary and the Dental science
journal of Australia. Superseded by the
Australian dental journal.
1929-1955
16520450R

Dent J Malays
Dental journal of Malaysia
0126-8023
Supersedes in part Dental journal of Malaysia
& Singapore.
1974-1988
7606465

Dent J Malaysia Singapore
The Dental journal of Malaysia & Singapore
0011-8648
Continues Malaysian dental journal.
Continued by Singapore dental journal.
1967-1973
7513696

Dent J Zamb
Dental journal of Zambia: official
publication of the Zambia Dental
Association
1010-7339
1986-1989
8909577

Dent Jpn (Tokyo)
Dentistry in Japan
0070-3737
Continues: Japanese dental journal.
Continued by: Japanese dental science review.
1968-2007
0226633

Dent Lab Bl
Dental laboratorie bladet
0070-3672
1950-1970
16520480R

Dent Lab Manage Today
Dental lab management today
8750-9539
Continued by: LMT.
1984-1991
8806559

Dent Lab Rev
Dental laboratory review
0011-8672
1925-1986
16520500R

Dent Labor (Munch)
Das Dental-Labor. Le Laboratoire dentaire.
The Dental laboratory
0011-8656
1953
16520470R

Dent Mag Oral Top
The Dental magazine and oral topics
0308-2245
Formed by the union of Dental magazine and
Oral topics, and continues the vol. numbering
of the former. Continued by: Dental
magazine.
1929-1968
7513257

Dent Manage
Dental management
0011-8680
1961-1991
0253341

Dent Mater
Dental materials: official publication of the
Academy of Dental Materials
0109-5641
1985
1879-0097
8508040

Dent Mater J
Dental materials journal
0287-4547
1982
1881-1361
8309299

Dent Mirror (Atlanta)
Dental Mirror
0029-3075
Continues: Bulletin - Northern District Dental
Society.
1970
9881872

Dent Mirror (Quezon City)
Dental Mirror
0011-8699
1964
9875602

Dent News
Dentist news
0770-884X
1978-1997
8804896

Dent News (Lond)
Dental news
Continued by: DP. Dental practice.
1964-1969
9883851

Dent Off
Dental office
0744-012X
Continues: Dental assisting.
1989-1995
9001328

Dent Outlook
The Dental outlook
0418-694X
Continued by: Dental outlook.
1962-1975
7613841

Dent Pract
Dental practice
0011-8710
Continues DP. Dental practice.
1976
7803067

Dent Pract (Cincinnati)
Dental practice; views, trends and news of
dentistry
1963-1967
16530060R

Dent Pract (Ewell)
DP. Dental practice
0419-8859
Absorbed Dental news. Continued by Dental
practice.
1969-1976
0265037

Dent Pract Dent Rec
The Dental practitioner and dental record
0011-8729
1950-1972
0354411

Dent Pract Manage
Dental practice management
0827-1305
1985
8604123

Dent Press
Dental press
0391-5883
Continued by Rivista italiana degli
odontotecnici.
1965-1977
7804084

Dent Prog (Chic)
Dental progress
1960-1963
16530080R

Dent Radiogr Photogr
Dental radiography and photography
0045-9941
1927-1985   0373177

Dent Rec (London)
The Dental record
Merged with Dental practitioner to form
Dental practitioner and dental record.
1881-1955   16530100R

Dent Res Grad Study
Dental research and graduate study
1917-1968   0376544

Dent Rev
Dental-revue (Solothurn, Switzerland)
0255-6928
1984-1985   8605753

Dent Rundsch
Dentistische Rundschau
Superseded by: Zahnarztliche Praxis.
1946-1950   9427886

Dent Sch Q
Dental School quarterly / the University of
Texas Health Science Center at San Antonio
0896-1247
1984-1990   8709415

Dent Stud
Dental student
0011-877X
1923-1985   0242232

Dent Surv
Dental survey
0011-8788
1929-1981   2984744R

Dent Team
Dental Team
Continued by: Dental Management.
1973-1974   9883876

Dent Teamwork
Dental teamwork
0895-318X
1987-1996   8810189

Dent Tech
The Dental technician
0011-8796
1948   0376545

Dent Ther Newsl
Dental Therapeutics Newsletter
1984-1984   9880902

Dent Today
Dentistry today
8750-2186
1980   9005357

Dent Traumatol
Dental traumatology: official publication
of International Association for Dental
Traumatology
1600-4469   1600-9657
Continues: Endodontics & dental
traumatology.
2001   101091305

Dent Update
Dental update
0305-5000
1974   7805969

Dent World
Dental world (London, England)
0965-9986
Continues: FDI news. Continued by: FDI
world.
1992-1993   9214345

Dentago
Dentago
0415-4134
1953-19uu   16520210R

Dentalhygienistnews
Dentalhygienistnews
1082-9016
1988   9816286

Dentalpractice
Dentalpractice
0199-736X
Supersedes: Dental Graduate.
1980-1982   9879018

Dentessence
Dentessence
0957-378X
1989-1990   9012823

Dentist
Dentist (Waco, Tex.)
0887-5669
1985-1990   8510873

Dentistry
Dentistry (American Student Dental
Association)
0277-3635
Continued by: Mouth (American Student
Dental Association).
1981-1999   8302067

Dentistry (Loma Linda)
Dentistry (Loma Linda, Calif.)
1057-3534
1988   9102062

Dentisuto
Dentisuto = Dentist
0387-8465
Continues: Kikan dentisuto.
1976-1993   7903695

Dentomaxillofac Radiol
Dento maxillo facial radiology
0250-832X
1972   7609576

Dentomaxillofac Radiol Suppl
Dento-maxillo-facial radiology. Supplement
0349-490X
1980-1991   8300885

Dentoral (Istanbul)
Dentoral
1969   9875603

Dentoscope
Dentoscope
0045-9968
1967-1975   0147414

Dep Health Soc Serv Q Mag
Department of Health and Social Services
quarterly magazine
Continues: HSS quarterly. Alaska. Dept. of
Health and Social Services.
1976-uuuu   9426906

Depress Anxiety
Depression and anxiety
1091-4269   1520-6394
Merger of: Anxiety; and: Depression,
assuming the vol. numbering of later title.
1997   9708816

Depression
Depression
1062-6417
Merged with: Anxiety (New York, N.Y.), to
form: Depression and anxiety.
1993-1996   9308791

Derm Beruf Umwelt
Dermatosen in Beruf und Umwelt.
Occupation and environment
0343-2432
Continues: Berufs-Dermatosen. Continued
by: Dermatologie in Beruf und Umwelt.
1978-1999   7802820

Dermatitis
Dermatitis: contact, atopic, occupational,
drug: official journal of the American
Contact Dermatitis Society, North American
Contact Dermatitis Group
1710-3568
Continues: American journal of contact
dermatitis.
2004   101207335

Dermatol Clin
Dermatologic clinics
0733-8635   1558-0520
1983   8300886

Dermatol Int
Dermatologia internationalis
0096-1108
Continues Dermatologia tropica et ecologica
geographica. Continued by the International
journal of dermatology.
1965-1969   0243670

Dermatol Monatsschr
Dermatologische Monatschrift
0011-9083
Continues Dermatologische Wochenschrift.
Continued by: Zeitschrift für Dermatologie
und deren Grenzgebiete.
1969-1993   0232053

Dermatol Nurs
Dermatology nursing / Dermatology Nurses'
Association
1060-3441
1989   9011113

Dermatol Online J
Dermatology online journal
    1087-2108
1995   9610776

Dermatol Surg
Dermatologic surgery: official publication
for American Society for Dermatologic
Surgery [et al.]
1076-0512   1524-4725
Continues: Journal of dermatologic surgery
and oncology.
1995   9504371

Dermatol Ther
Dermatologic therapy
1396-0296   1529-8019
1996   9700070

Dermatol Trop Ecol Geogr
Dermatologia tropica et ecologica
geographica
Continued by Dermatologia internationalis.
1962-1964   0112140

Dermatol Wochenschr
Dermatologische Wochenschrift
0366-8940
Continues: Monatshefte für praktische
Dermatologie. Continued by:
Dermatologische Monatschrift.
1912-1968   0232054

Dermatologica
Dermatologica
0011-9075
Continues Dermatologische Zeitschrift.
Continued by: Dermatology (Basel,
Switzerland).
1939-1991   0211607

Dermatology
Dermatology (Basel, Switzerland)
1018-8665   1421-9832
Continues: Dermatologica.
1992   9203244

Dermatovenerologia
Dermatovenerologia
19uu   9816222

Dermosifilografo (Torino)
Il Dermosifilografo
0366-886X
Continued by Minerva dermatologica.
1926-1950   16530430R

Desmos
Desmos
0011-9474
1894   16530440R

Detroit Dent Bull
Detroit dental bulletin
0011-9601
1933   16530480R

Detroit Med News
Detroit medical news
0098-471X
1933   0372756

Dev Biol
Developmental biology
0012-1606   1095-564X
1959   0372762

Dev Biol (Basel)
Developments in biologicals
1424-6074   1662-2960
Continues: Developments in biological
standardization.
2000   100940058

Dev Biol (N Y 1985)
Developmental biology (New York, N.Y.:
1985)
1985   8611888

Dev Biol Stand
Developments in biological standardization
0301-5149
Merger of: Progress in immunobiological
standardization, ISSN 0079-6344. and:
Symposia series in immunobiological
standardization, ISSN 0082-0768. and
continues the numbering of the latter.
Continued by: Developments in biologicals.
1974-1999   0427140

Dev Cell
Developmental cell
1534-5807
2001   101120028

Dev Comp Immunol
Developmental and comparative
immunology
0145-305X   1879-0089
1977   7708205

Dev Disabil Res Rev
Developmental disabilities research reviews
1940-5510   1940-5529
Continues: Mental retardation and
developmental disabilities research reviews.
2008   101319448

Dev Dyn
Developmental dynamics: an official
publication of the American Association of
Anatomists
1058-8388
Continues: American journal of anatomy.
1992   9201927

Dev Genes Evol
Development genes and evolution
0949-944X   1432-041X
Continues: Roux's archives of developmental
biology.
1996   9613264

Dev Genet
Developmental genetics
0192-253X
Continued by: Genesis (New York. N.Y.:
2000).
1979-1999   7909963

Dev Growth Differ
Development, growth & differentiation
0012-1592   1440-169X
Continues Embrologia.
1969   0356504

Dev Health Econ Public Policy
Developments in health economics and
public policy
0927-4987
1992   9209294

Dev Immunol
Developmental immunology
1044-6672
Continued by: Clinical & developmental
immunology.
1990-2002   9200624

Dev Med Child Neurol
Developmental medicine and child neurology
0012-1622   1469-8749
Continues: Cerebral palsy bulletin. Continued
in part by: Abstracts. American Academy For
Cerebral Palsy & Developmental Medicine.
Meeting. 1986-
1962   0006761

Dev Med Child Neurol Suppl
Developmental medicine and child
neurology. Supplement
0419-0238   1758-9428
Continues Supplement to Cerebral palsy
bulletin.
1962   0006762

Dev Neurobiol
Developmental neurobiology
1932-8451   1932-846X
Continues: Journal of neurobiology.
2007   101300215

Dev Neuropsychol
Developmental neuropsychology
8756-5641   1532-6942
1985   8702038

Dev Neurorehabil
Developmental neurorehabilitation
1751-8423   1751-8431
Continues: Pediatric rehabilitation.
2007   101304394

Dev Neurosci
Developmental neuroscience
0378-5866   1421-9859
1978   7809375

Dev Ophthalmol
Developments in ophthalmology
0250-3751   1662-2790
Formed by the union of: Advances
in ophthalmology. and: Bibliotheca
ophthalmologica. and: Modern problems in
ophthalmology.
1981   8010321

Dev Pharmacol Ther
Developmental pharmacology and
therapeutics
0379-8305
1980-1993   8003947

Dev Psychobiol
Developmental psychobiology
0012-1630   1098-2302
1968   0164074

Dev Psychol
Developmental psychology
0012-1649
1969   0260564

Dev Psychopathol
Development and psychopathology
0954-5794   1469-2198
1989   8910645

Dev Sci
Developmental science
1363-755X   1467-7687
1998   9814574

Dev Suppl
Development (Cambridge, England).
Supplement
1990-1994   9113706

Dev Toxicol Environ Sci
Developments in toxicology and
environmental science
0165-2214
1977-1987   7706742

Dev World Bioeth
Developing world bioethics
1471-8731   1471-8847
2001   101120122

Development
Development (Cambridge, England)
0950-1991   1477-9129
Continues: Journal of embryology and
experimental morphology.
1987   8701744

Di Yi Jun Yi Da Xue Xue Bao
Di 1 jun yi da xue xue bao = Academic
journal of the first medical college of PLA
1000-2588
Continued by: Nan fang yi ke da xue xue bao.
1981-2005   9426110

Dia Med
El Día médico
0012-1762
1928-1980   0370663

Dia Med Urug
Dia medico uruguayo
1933-1954   9428396

Diab Vasc Dis Res
Diabetes & vascular disease research:
official journal of the International Society
of Diabetes and Vascular Disease
1479-1641   1752-8984
2004   101234011

Diabet Med
Diabetic medicine: a journal of the British
Diabetic Association
0742-3071   1464-5491
1984   8500858

Diabete
Le Diabète
0012-1770
Continued by: Diabète & métabolisme.
1953-1974   2984746R

Diabete Metab
Diabète & métabolisme
0338-1684
Continued by: Diabetes & metabolism.
1975-1995   7604157

Diabetes
Diabetes
0012-1797 1939-327X
Formed by the union of: Proceedings of the American Diabetes Association, and: Diabetes abstracts.
1952 0372763

Diabetes Care
Diabetes care
0149-5992 1935-5548
1978 7805975

Diabetes Educ
The Diabetes educator
0145-7217 1554-6063
1975 7701401

Diabetes Forecast
Diabetes forecast
0095-8301
Continues ADA forecast.
1974 7504241

Diabetes Metab
Diabetes & metabolism
1262-3636
Continues: Diabète & métabolisme.
1996 9607599

Diabetes Metab Res Rev
Diabetes/metabolism research and reviews
1520-7552 1520-7560
Continues: Diabetes/metabolism reviews.
1999 100883450

Diabetes Metab Rev
Diabetes/metabolism reviews
0742-4221
Continued by: Diabetes/metabolism research and reviews.
1985-1998 8601109

Diabetes Nutr Metab
Diabetes, nutrition & metabolism
0394-3402 1720-8343
1988-2004 8813443

Diabetes Obes Metab
Diabetes, obesity & metabolism
1462-8902 1463-1326
1999 100883645

Diabetes Res
Diabetes research (Edinburgh, Scotland)
0265-5985
1984 8502339

Diabetes Res Clin Pract
Diabetes research and clinical practice
0168-8227 1872-8227
1985 8508335

Diabetes Res Clin Pract Suppl
Diabetes research and clinical practice. Supplement
1572-1671
1985-198u 8609985

Diabetes Self Manag
Diabetes self-management
0741-6253
1983 9883682

Diabetes Technol Ther
Diabetes technology & therapeutics
1520-9156
1999 100889084

Diabetologia
Diabetologia
0012-186X 1432-0428
1965 0006777

Diagn Clin Immunol
Diagnostic and clinical immunology
0895-0458
Continues: Diagnostic immunology. Absorbed by: Journal of clinical laboratory analysis.
1987-1988 8705862

Diagn Cytopathol
Diagnostic cytopathology
8755-1039 1097-0339
1985 8506895

Diagn Gynecol Obstet
Diagnostic gynecology and obstetrics
0196-9617
Continues The American journal of diagnostic gynecology and obstetrics.
1980-1982 8005367

Diagn Histopathol
Diagnostic histopathology / published in association with the Pathological Society of Great Britain and Ireland
0272-7749
Continues: Investigative & cell pathology. Absorbed by: Journal of pathology.
1981-1983 8103005

Diagn Imaging
Diagnostic imaging
0378-9837
Continues Radiologia clinica. Continued by: Diagnostic imaging in clinical medicine.
1979-1983 7908105

Diagn Imaging (San Franc)
Diagnostic imaging
0194-2514
1979 8007815

Diagn Imaging Clin Med
Diagnostic imaging in clinical medicine
0254-881X
Continues: Diagnostic imaging. Continued by: Bildgebung.
1984-1986 8400594

Diagn Immunol
Diagnostic immunology
0735-3111
Continued by: Diagnostic and clinical immunology.
1983-1986 8308082

Diagn Interv Radiol
Diagnostic and interventional radiology (Ankara, Turkey)
1305-3825 1305-3612
Continues: Tanısal ve girişimsel radyoloji.
2005 101241152

Diagn Microbiol Infect Dis
Diagnostic microbiology and infectious disease
0732-8893 1879-0070
1983 8305899

Diagn Mol Pathol
Diagnostic molecular pathology: the American journal of surgical pathology, part B
1052-9551 1533-4066
1992 9204924

Diagn Traitements
Diagnostics & traitements
1942-19uu 16620080R

Diagnosi (Napoli)
La Diagnosi; rivista mensile di medicina pratica
Continued by: Diagnosi; laboratorio e clinica.
1946-1957 0112274

Dialog Fairleigh Dickinson Univ Sch Dent
The Dialog / Fairleigh Dickinson University School of Dentistry
1969-19uu 9875957

Dialogues Clin Neurosci
Dialogues in clinical neuroscience
1294-8322
1999 101238198

Diamond
Diamond (Philadelphia, Pa.)
1991-1998 9807632

Diastema
Diastema
0419-0955
1963-1988 7801718

Dicle Univ Tip Fakul Derg
Dicle Üniversitesi Tip Fakültesi dergisi = The journal of the Faculty of Medicine, University of Dicle
Continued by: Dicle tıp dergisi.
19uu-19uu 9306723

DICP
DICP: the annals of pharmacotherapy
1042-9611
Continues: Drug intelligence & clinical pharmacy. Continued by: Annals of pharmacotherapy.
1989-1991 8904338

Differentiation
Differentiation; research in biological diversity
0301-4681 1432-0436
1973 0401650

Dig Antibiot
Digesta antibiotica
1947-1966 16620370R

Dig Dis
Digestive diseases (Basel, Switzerland)
0257-2753 1421-9875
Continues: Survey of digestive diseases.
1986 8701186

Dig Dis Sci
Digestive diseases and sciences
0163-2116 1573-2568
Continues: American journal of digestive diseases.
1979 7902782

Dig Liver Dis
Digestive and liver disease: official journal of the Italian Society of Gastroenterology and the Italian Association for the Study of the Liver
1590-8658
Continues: Italian journal of gastroenterology and hepatology.
2000 100958385

Dig Neurol Psychiatr
Digest of neurology and psychiatry
0012-2769
Continues the Abstracts and translations of the science library of the Institute of Living, Hartford.
1944 59930180R

Dig Surg
Digestive surgery
0253-4886 1421-9883
Absorbed: Surgical gastroenterology.
1984 8501808

Digestion
Digestion
0012-2823 1421-9867
Supersedes Gastroenterologia.
1968 0150472

Digitale Bilddiagn
Digitale Bilddiagnostik
0724-7591
Continues: Computertomographie.
1984-1990   8405849

Dimens Crit Care Nurs
Dimensions of critical care nursing: DCCN
0730-4625   1538-8646
1982   8211489

Dimens Health Serv
Dimensions in health service
0317-7645
Continues: Canadian hospital. Merged with:
Hospital trustee. to form: Leadership in
health services. Bound inside some issues:
surveillance.
1974-1991   0411256

Dimens Oncol Nurs
Dimensions in oncology nursing: journal of
the Division of Nursing
0885-6192
Continues: Nursing neogram.
1985-1991   8607500

Dimensions (Wash)
Dimensions/NBS
0093-0458
Continues the Technical news bulletin of the
National Bureau of Standards.
1973-1981   0411412

Dipl
The Diplomate
0096-0209
Supersedes the National Board bulletin.
Superseded in part by the National Board
examiner.
1929-1953   16620460R

Dir Boards
Directors & boards
0364-9156
1976   9877851

Director
Director (Cincinnati, Ohio)
1551-8418
Absorbed: Nurse in assisted living.
1993   9504684

Dirim
Dirim
0378-8628
1925   7706746

Dis Aquat Organ
Diseases of aquatic organisms
0177-5103
1985   8807037

Dis Chest
Diseases of the chest
0096-0217
Continued by: Chest.
1935-1969   0231342

Dis Colon Rectum
Diseases of the colon and rectum
0012-3706   1530-0358
1958   0372764

Dis Esophagus
Diseases of the esophagus: official journal of
the International Society for Diseases of the
Esophagus / I.S.D.E
1120-8694   1442-2050
Absorbed: Gullet. 1993
1988   8809160

Dis Manag
Disease management: DM
1093-507X   1557-8860
Continued by: Population health management.
1998-2008   9802539

Dis Manag Advis
Disease management advisor
1531-5681
Continues: Healthcare demand & disease
management.
2000   100961635

Dis Markers
Disease markers
0278-0240
1983   8604127

Dis Mon
Disease-a-month: DM
0011-5029   1557-8194
1954   0370657

Dis Nerv Syst
Diseases of the nervous system
0012-3714
Continued by The Journal of clinical
psychiatry.
1940-1977   0370666

Disabil Rehabil
Disability and rehabilitation
0963-8288   1464-5165
Continues: International diability studies.
1992   9207179

Disabil Rehabil Assist Technol
Disability and rehabilitation. Assistive
technology
1748-3107   1748-3115
2006   101255937

Disaster Med Public Health Prep
Disaster medicine and public health
preparedness
1935-7893   1938-744X
2007   101297401

Disasters
Disasters
0361-3666   1467-7717
1977   7702072

Disch Plann Update
Discharge planning update
0276-4652
Continued by: Continuum (Society for Social
Work Administrators in Health Care.)
1980-1995   8211490

Discov Med
Discovery medicine
1539-6509
2001   101250006

Discuss Faraday Soc
Discussions of the Faraday Society
0014-7664
Continued by: Faraday discussions of the
Chemical Society.
1947-1971   7507090

Diskussionsforum Med Ethik
Diskussionsforum medizinische Ethik
1990-1994   9216477

Dist Nurs
District nursing
0012-4044
Supersedes Queen's nurses' magazine.
Continued by the Queen's nursing journal.
1958-1973   0366533

Divulg Cult Odontol
Divulgacion cultural odontológica
0070-6752
1957-1972   0007110

Divulg Dent
Divulgación dental ...
0366-9262
1946-1950   16630020R

Divulg Med Dent
Divulgación médico-dental; boletín de
educación médico-dental y especialidades
Supersedes Divulgación dental veracruzana ...
1947-19uu   16630040R

DNA
DNA (Mary Ann Liebert, Inc.)
0198-0238
Continued by: DNA and cell biology.
1981-1989   8302432

DNA Cell Biol
DNA and cell biology
1044-5498   1557-7430
Continues: DNA (Mary Ann Liebert, Inc.).
1990   9004522

DNA Repair (Amst)
DNA repair
1568-7864
Continues: Mutation research. DNA repair.
2002   101139138

DNA Res
DNA research: an international journal for
rapid publication of reports on genes and
genomes
1340-2838   1875-6190
1994   9423827

DNA Seq
DNA sequence: the journal of DNA
sequencing and mapping
1042-5179   1029-2365
1990   9107800

Doc Geigy Acta Psychosom (Dtsch Ausg)
Documenta Geigy. Acta psychosomatica.
[Deutsche Ausg]
1958-1966   16630310R

Doc Geigy Acta Rheumatol
Documenta Geigy. Acta rheumatologica.
[English ed.]
Continues Documenta rheumatologica
[English ed.].
1959-1971   16630420R

Doc Med Geogr Trop
Documenta de medicina geographica et
tropica
Continues Documenta Neerlandica et
Indonesica de morbis tropicis. Continued by
Tropical and geographical medicine.
1952-1957   16630390R

Doc Neerl Indones Morbis Trop
Documenta Neerlandica et Indonesica de
morbis tropicis; quarterly journal of tropical
medicine and hygiene
Continued by Documenta de medicina
geographica et tropica.
1949-1951   16630400R

Doc Ophthalmol
Documenta ophthalmologica. Advances in
ophthalmology
0012-4486   1573-2622
1938   0370667

Doc Ophthalmol Proc Ser
Documenta ophthalmologica. Proceedings
series
0303-6405
1973-1998   0436163

Doc Rheumatol
Documenta rheumatologica. [Deutsche
Ausg.]
Continued by Documenta Geigy. Acta
rheumatologica. [Deutsche Ausg.]
1953-1959   16630410R

Dokl Akad Nauk
Doklady Akademii nauk / [Rossiĭskaia akademii nauk]
0869-5652
Continues: Doklady Akademii nauk SSSR.
1992   9301140

Dokl Akad Nauk SSSR
Doklady Akademii nauk SSSR
0002-3264
Supersedes in part the academy's Doklady; comptes rendus A. Continued by: Doklady Akademii nauk.
1933-1992   7505465

Dokl Biochem
Doklady biochemistry: proceedings of the Academy of Sciences of the USSR, Biochemistry section / translated from Russian
0012-4958
Translation of the articles on biochemistry from Doklady Akademii nauk SSSR, 1964-t. 322, no 3 (1992); from: Doklady Akademii nauk, t. 322, no. 4 (1992)-vol. 375, 2000. Merged with: Doklady biophysics, to form: Doklady. Biochemistry and biophysics.
1964-2000   7505458

Dokl Biochem Biophys
Doklady. Biochemistry and biophysics
1607-6729   1608-3091
English translation of the biochemistry and biophysics sections of: Doklady Akademii nauk. Merger of: Doklady biochemistry, and: Doklady biophysics.
2001   101126895

Dokl Biol Sci
Doklady biological sciences: proceedings of the Academy of Sciences of the USSR, Biological sciences sections / translated from Russian
0012-4966
Absorbed: Doklady. Botanical sciences. 2001 Continues in part Doklady biological sciences sections. Translation of articles on biology from Doklady Akademii nauk SSSR, 1964-t. 322, no. 3 (1992); from: Doklady Akademii nauk, t. 322, no. 4 (1992)-
1964   7505459

Dokl Biophys
Doklady biophysics: proceedings of the Academy of Sciences of the USSR, Biophysics section / translated from Russian
0012-4974
Continues in part: Doklady biological sciences sections. Translation of the articles on biophysics from: Doklady Akademii nauk SSSR, 1964-t. 322, no. 3 (1992); from: Doklady Akademii nauk, t. 322, no. 4 (1992)-vols. 373-375 (July-Dec. 2000). Merged with: Doklady biochemistry, to form: Doklady. Biochemistry and biophysics.
1964-2000   7505460

Dokl Bulg Acad Nauk
Doklady Bolgarskoĭ akademii nauk
1948   7509180

Domest Anim Endocrinol
Domestic animal endocrinology
0739-7240   1879-0054
1984   8505191

Domus Med
Domus medici
0214-2740
1941-1954   16630640R

Downs Syndr Res Pract
Down's syndrome, research and practice: the journal of the Sarah Duffen Centre / University of Portsmouth
0968-7912   1753-7606
1993   9508122

DP Rep
DP [reports]. U.S. Atomic Energy Commission
195u-1971   21830380R

Dr Med Penny Mag
The Doctor; a medical penny magazine
Absorbed the New doctor July 12, 1837.
1832-1837   16630130R

DRG Monit
DRG monitor
0741-6512
1983-1990   8606687

Drug Alcohol Depend
Drug and alcohol dependence
0376-8716   1879-0046
1975   7513587

Drug Alcohol Rev
Drug and alcohol review
0959-5236   1465-3362
Continues: Australian drug and alcohol review.
1990   9015440

Drug Chem Toxicol
Drug and chemical toxicology
0148-0545   1525-6014
1977   7801723

Drug Cosmet Ind
Drug and cosmetic industry
0012-6527
Absorbed in 1989: Drug and cosmetic industry catalog. Continued by: DCI.
1932-1997   0370670

Drug Deliv
Drug delivery
1071-7544   1521-0464
1993   9417471

Drug Des Deliv
Drug design and delivery
0884-2884
Continued by: Drug design and discovery.
1986-1991   8712388

Drug Des Discov
Drug design and discovery
1055-9612
Continues: Drug design and delivery.
1991-2003   9200627

Drug Dev Ind Pharm
Drug development and industrial pharmacy
0363-9045   1520-5762
Continues: Drug development communications.
1977   7802620

Drug Discov Today
Drug discovery today
1359-6446   1878-5832
1996   9604391

Drug Inf J
Drug information journal
0092-8615
Continues: Drug information bulletin.
1972   0351461

Drug Intell Clin Pharm
Drug intelligence & clinical pharmacy
0012-6578
Continues: Drug intelligence. Continued by: DICP.
1969-1988   0212457

Drug Metab Dispos
Drug metabolism and disposition: the biological fate of chemicals
0090-9556   1521-009X
1973   9421550

Drug Metab Pharmacokinet
Drug metabolism and pharmacokinetics
1347-4367   1880-0920
Continues: Yakubutsu dōtai.
2002   101164773

Drug Metab Rev
Drug metabolism reviews
0360-2532   1097-9883
1972   0322067

Drug Metabol Drug Interact
Drug metabolism and drug interactions
0792-5077
Continues: Reviews on drug metabolism and drug interactions.
1988   8904736

Drug News Perspect
Drug news & perspectives
0214-0934
1988   8809164

Drug Nutr Interact
Drug-nutrient interactions
0272-3530
1981-1988   8307198

Drug Resist Updat
Drug resistance updates: reviews and commentaries in antimicrobial and anticancer chemotherapy
1368-7646   1532-2084
1998   9815369

Drug Saf
Drug safety: an international journal of medical toxicology and drug experience
0114-5916
Continues: Medical toxicology and adverse drug experience.
1990   9002928

Drug Stand
Drug standards
Continues: Bulletin of the National Formulary Committee. Merged with: American Pharmaceutical Association. Journal of the American Pharmaceutical Association. Scientific edition, to form: Journal of pharmaceutical sciences.
1951-1960   16640280R

Drug Ther
Drug therapeutics
0163-1705
1979-1982   7908371

Drug Ther Bull
Drug and therapeutics bulletin
0012-6543
Supersedes the Medical letter, British ed.
1963   0112037

Drugs
Drugs
0012-6667
1971   7600076

Drugs Aging
Drugs & aging
1170-229X
1991   9102074

Drugs Made Ger
Drugs made in Germany
0012-6683
1958-2002   7600075

Drugs R D
Drugs in R&D
1174-5886
1999   100883647

Drugs Today (Barc)
Drugs of today (Barcelona, Spain: 1998)
1699-3993   1699-4019
    Continues: Medicamentos de actualidad.
1998   101160518

Dtsch Apoth
Der Deutsche Apotheker
0366-8622
    Continues Der Deutsche Apotheker in
    Hessen.
1953-2002   1307022

Dtsch Apoth Ztg
Deutsche Apotheker-Zeitung
0011-9857
    Absorbed: Apotheken Praxis. Vols. for 1987?-
    include: Neue Arzneimittel, previously issued
    separately. Formed by the union of Apotheker
    Zeitung and Süddeutsche Apotheker-Zeitung,
    and assumed the volume numbering of the
    latter.
1950   0372624

Dtsch Arch Klin Med
Deutsches Archiv für klinische Medizin
0366-8576
    Merged with Zeitschrift für klinische Medizin
    to form Archiv für klinische Medizin.
1865-1965   0060760

Dtsch Dent Z
Deutsche dentistische Zeitschrift
    Continued by DDZ.
1947-1952   16540120R

Dtsch Drog Ztg
Deutsche Drogistenzeitung
0012-0049
    Continues: Süddeutsche Drogisten-Zeitung.
    Continued by: DDZ. Deutsche Drogisten-
    Zeitung.
1947-1970   16540150R

Dtsch Gesundheit
Deutscher Gesundheitskalender
19uu-19uu   16610100R

Dtsch Gesundheitspolit
Deutsche Gesundheitspolitik
    Continued by Gesundheitspolitik.
1959-1959   17130050R

Dtsch Gesundheitsw
Das Deutsche Gesundheitswesen
0012-0219
    Continued by Zeitschrift für klinische
    Medizin. (Berlin, Germany: 1985).
1946-1984   0433572

Dtsch Krankenpflegez
Deutsche Krankenpflegezeitschrift
0012-074X
    Continues: Deutsche Schwesternzeitung.
    Continued by: Pflege Zeitschriift.
1971-1993   0323406

Dtsch Lebensmitt Rundsch
Deutsche Lebensmittel-Rundschau:
Zeitschrift für Lebensmittelkunde und
Lebensmittelrecht
0012-0413
1903   2984786R

Dtsch Med J
Deutsches medizinisches Journal
0012-1320
    Continues Berliner medizinische Zeitschrift.
1951-1972   0420573

Dtsch Med Rundsch
Deutsche medizinische Rundschau;
Monatsschrift mit ärztlicher Akademie
1947-1950   16540440R

Dtsch Med Wochenschr
Deutsche medizinische Wochenschrift (1946)
0012-0472   1439-4413
    Continues in part: Medizinische Zeitschrift.
1946   0006723

Dtsch Schwesternztg
Deutsche Schwesternzeitung
    Continued by Deutsche
    Krankenpflegezeitschrift.
1948-1970   0322442

Dtsch Stomatol
Deutsche Stomatologie
0012-0790
    Continued by Stomatologie der DDR.
1951-1973   0421425

Dtsch Stomatol
Deutsche Stomatologie (Berlin, Germany:
1990)
0863-4904
    Continues: Stomatologie der DDR.
1990-1991   9100497

Dtsch Tierarztl Wochenschr
Deutsche tierärztliche Wochenschrift
0012-0847
    Continues Tierärztliche Zeitschrift.
    Continued by DTW. Deutsche tierärztliche
    Wochenschrift.
1946-1970   0033620

Dtsch Tierarztl Wochenschr
DTW. Deutsche tierärztliche Wochenschrift
0341-6593
    Continues Deutsche tierärztliche
    Wochenschrift.
1971   7706565

Dtsch Z Gesamte Gerichtl Med
Deutsche Zeitschrift für die gesamte
gerichtliche Medizin
0367-0031
    Supersedes Vierteljahrschrift für gerichtliche
    Medicin und öffentliches Sanitätswesen.
    Continued by Zeitschrift für Rechtsmedizin.
1922-1970   0247674

Dtsch Z Mund Kiefer Gesichtschir
Deutsche Zeitschrift für Mund-, Kiefer- und
Gesichts-Chirurgie
0343-3137
    Merged with: Fortschritte der Kiefer- und
    Gesichts-Chirurgie; to become: Mund-,
    Kiefer- und Gesichtschirurgie.
1977-1996   8700280

Dtsch Z Nervenheilkd
Deutsche Zeitschrift für Nervenheilkunde
0367-004X
    Continued by: Zeitschrift für Neurologie.
1891-1970   0266603

Dtsch Z Verdau Stoffwechselkr
Deutsche Zeitschrift für Verdauungs- und
Stoffwechselkrankheiten
0012-1053
    Continued by: Gastroenterologisches Journal.
1938-1988   0372760

Dtsch Zahn Mund Kieferheilkd Zentralbl
Deutsche Zahn-, Mund-, und
Kieferheilkunde mit Zentralblatt
0940-855X
    Continues: Zahn-, Mund-, und
    Kieferheilkunde mit Zentralblatt. Absorbed
    by: Deutsche Zahnärztliche Zeitschrift.
1991-1992   9109513

Dtsch Zahn Mund Kieferheilkd Zentralbl Gesamte
Deutsche Zahn-, Mund-, und
Kieferheilkunde mit Zentralblatt für die
gesamte Zahn-, Mund-, und Kieferheilkunde
0012-1010
    Formed by the union of: Deutsche
    Kieferchirurgie, and: Fortschritte der
    Orthodontik, and: Vierteljahrsschrift für
    Zahnheilkunde. Continued by: Zahn-, Mund-,
    und Kieferheilkunde mit Zentralblatt.
1934-1974   0434571

Dtsch Zahnarztekal
Deutscher Zahnärztekalender
0344-2926
1937   16610160R

Dtsch Zahnarztl Z
Deutsche zahnärztliche Zeitschrift
0012-1029
1946   2984745R

Dtsch Zentralbl Krankenpfl
Deutsches Zentralblatt für Krankenpflege
0417-3678
    Continues Praxis der Psychiatrie, Neurologie
    und Grenzgebiete.
1961-1968   19730430R

Duke Law J
Duke law journal
0012-7086
    Continues: Duke bar journal.
1957   9877769

Duodecim
Duodecim; lääketieteellinen aikakauskirja
0012-7183
1885   0373207

Duodecim Suppl
Duodecim; lääketieteellinen aikakauskirja.
Supplementum
0301-8989
1939-1965   0401651

Dynamics
Dynamics (Pembroke, Ont.)
1497-3715
    Continues: Official journal of the Canadian
    Association of Critical Care Nurses.
2000   100955578

Dynamis
Dynamis (Granada, Spain)
0211-9536
1981   8610855

Dyslexia
Dyslexia (Chichester, England)
1076-9242   1099-0909
1995   9511375

Dysphagia
Dysphagia
0179-051X   1432-0460
1986   8610856

E

E N E
E N E
1941-1949   16640610R

Ear Hear
Ear and hearing
0196-0202   1538-4667
    Continues: Journal of the American Auditory
    Society.
1980   8005585

Ear Nose Throat J
Ear, nose, & throat journal
0145-5613
    Continues: Eye, ear, nose, & throat monthly.
1976   7701817

Early Hum Dev
Early human development
0378-3782 1872-6232
1977 7708381

Early Pregnancy
Early pregnancy (Online)
1537-6583
Continues a print version published
1995-97. Absorbed by: American journal of
reproductive immunology (New York, N.Y.:
1989). 2004
2000-2003 100940263

Early Pregnancy
Early pregnancy: biology and medicine:
the official journal of the Society for the
Investigation of Early Pregnancy
1354-4195
Continued in 2000 by an online version
beginning with v. 4.
1995-1997 9508879

Early Sci Med
Early science and medicine
1383-7427
1996 9610931

East Afr J Public Health
East African journal of public health
0856-8960
2004 101302040

East Afr Med J
East African medical journal
0012-835X
Continues: Kenya and East African medical
journal.
1932 0372766

East Mediterr Health J
Eastern Mediterranean health journal
= La revue de santé de la Méditerranée
orientale = al-Majallah al-ṣiḥḥīyah li-sharq
al-mutawassiṭ
1020-3397
Merger of: Eastern Mediterranean Region
epidemiological bulletin, and: Majallat
al-khidmāt al-ṣiḥḥīyah li-Iqlīm Sharq al-Baḥr
al-Mutawassiṭ.
1995 9608387

Eat Behav
Eating behaviors
1471-0153 1873-7358
2000 101090048

Eat Disord
Eating disorders
1064-0266 1532-530X
1993 9315161

Eat Weight Disord
Eating and weight disorders: EWD
1124-4909 1590-1262
1996 9707113

Ebony
Ebony
0012-9011
1945 9877770

EBRI Issue Brief
EBRI issue brief / Employee Benefit
Research Institute
0887-137X
19uu 9418660

Echo Med Cevennes
L'Echo médical des Cévennes
1900-1963 16650100R

Echo Med Nord
L'echo médical du nord
Continued by: Lille médicale.
1897-1956 16650110R

Echocardiography
Echocardiography (Mount Kisco, N.Y.)
0742-2822 1540-8175
1984 8511187

Ecohealth
EcoHealth
1612-9202 1612-9210
Merger of: Ecosystem health; and: Global
change & human health.
2004 101222144

Ecol Appl
Ecological applications: a publication of the
Ecological Society of America
1051-0761
1991 9889808

Ecol Dis
Ecology of disease
0278-4300
1982-1983 8214784

Ecol Lett
Ecology letters
1461-023X 1461-0248
1998 101121949

Ecology
Ecology
0012-9658
Continues: Plant world.
1920 0043541

Econ Hum Biol
Economics and human biology
1570-677X 1873-6130
2003 101166135

Econ Inq
Economic inquiry
0095-2583
Continues: Western economic journal.
1974 9877753

Econ Med Anim
Economie et médecine animales
0013-0524
1960-1976 0376327

Economat
L'Economat
1931-1940 16650250R

Economia Umana Rassegna Medica Internazionale
L'Economia umana; rassegna medica
internazionale
1950-1965 16650260R

Ecotoxicol Environ Saf
Ecotoxicology and environmental safety
0147-6513 1090-2414
1977 7805381

Ecotoxicology
Ecotoxicology (London, England)
0963-9292 1573-3017
199u 9885956

ED Manag
ED management: the monthly update on
emergency department management
1044-9167
1989 9425690

Edinb Dent Hosp Gaz
Edinburgh Dental Hospital gazette
0013-0907
Continues EDH gazette.
1973-1982 7506567

Edinb Med J
Edinburgh medical journal
0367-1038
Formed by the union of the Monthly journal
of medicine and the Edinburgh medical and
surgical journal.
1855-1954 0007305

EDS Mag
EDS magazine: official journal of the E.E.C.
Dental Students Committee
0937-7654
1990-1994 9206422

EDTNA ERCA J
EDTNA/ERCA journal (English ed.)
1019-083X
Continues: EDTNA journal (English ed.).
Continued by: Journal of renal care.
1985-2006 9805754

Educ Adm Q
Educational administration quarterly: EAQ
0013-161X
1965 9878136

Educ Dent (Ica)
Educación dental
0013-1083
1964-1973 0122442

Educ Dir Dent Aux
Educational directions for dental auxiliaries
0363-3888
Continued by: Educational directions in
dental hygiene.
1976-1985 7608320

Educ Dir Dent Hyg
Educational directions in dental hygiene
Continues: Educational directions for dental
auxiliaries.
1985-1986 8601514

Educ Health (Abingdon)
Education for health (Abingdon, England)
1357-6283 1469-5804
Continues: Annals of community-oriented
education.
1996 9607101

Educ Ind Telev
Educational & industrial television
0046-1466
Continues: Educational television. Continued
in June 1983 by: E-ITV.
1972-1983 0345573

Educ Med Salud
Educación médica y salud
0013-1091
Absorbed by: Revista panamericana de salud
pública. 1997
1966-1995 0070163

EEG EMG Z Elektroenzephalogr Elektromyogr Verwandte Geb
EEG-EMG Zeitschrift für
Elektroenzephalographie,
Elektromyographie und verwandte Gebiete
0012-7590
Continued by: Klinische Neurophysiologie.
1970-1997 0264413

Eff Clin Pract
Effective clinical practice: ECP
1099-8128 1538-9685
Continues: HMO practice.
1998-2002 9815774

Eff Health Care
Effective health care
0167-871X
1983-1985 8309796

Egeszsegtudomany
Egészségtudomány
0013-2268
1957 0375342

Egypt Dent J
Egyptian dental journal
0070-9484
1955-1995 0373212

Egypt J Bilharz
Egyptian journal of bilharziasis
0301-8849
Continued by: Egyptian journal of
schistosomiasis and endemic infectious
diseases.
1974-1999   **0415526**

Egypt J Immunol
The Egyptian journal of immunology /
Egyptian Association of Immunologists
1110-4902
199u   **9816016**

Egypt J Psychiatry
The Egyptian journal of psychiatry:
official journal of the Egyptian Psychiatric
Association
0254-136X
1978-1979   **8101154**

EHP Toxicogenomics
EHP toxicogenomics: journal of the National
Institute of Environmental Health Sciences
1542-4359   1542-4367
Absorbed by: Environmental health
perspectives.
2003-2003   **101167559**

Eicosanoids
Eicosanoids
0934-9820
1988-1992   **8906009**

Eisei Shikenjo Hokoku
Eisei Shikenjo hōkoku. Bulletin of National
Institute of Hygienic Sciences
0077-4715
Continues Eisei shikenjo iho. Continued by:
Kokuritsu Iyakuhin Shokuhin Eisei Kenkyūjo
hōkoku.
1950-1996   **0421152**

EITV
E-ITV
0743-7773
Continues: Educational & industrial
television.
1983-1988   **8309795**

Ekologiia
Ėkologiia
0367-0597
1970   **7611750**

Eksp Khir Anesteziol
Eksperimental'naia khirurgiia i
anesteziologiia
0013-3329
Continues Eksperimental'naia khirurgiia.
Continued by Anesteziologiia i
reanimatologiia.
1961-1976   **0373214**

Eksp Khirurgiia
Eksperimental'naia khirurgiia
Continued by Eksperimental'naia khirurgiia i
anesteziologiia.
1956-1960   **16720270R**

Eksp Klin Farmakol
Eksperimental'naia i klinicheskaia
farmakologiia
0869-2092
Continues: Farmakologiia i toksikologiia.
1992   **9215981**

Eksp Klin Gastroenterol
Ėksperimental'naiâ i klinicheskaiâ
gastroénterologiiâ = Experimental & clinical
gastroenterology
1682-8658
Continues: Rossiĭskiĭ gastroénterologicheskiĭ
zhurnal.
2002   **101144944**

Eksp Med Morfol
Eksperimentalna meditsina i morfologiia
0367-0643
Continued by: Molekuliarna meditsina.
1962-1994   **0007506**

Eksp Onkol
Eksperimental'naiâ onkologiiâ
0204-3564
Continued by: Experimental oncology.
1979-2004   **8406659**

Elder Care
Elderly care
1369-1856
Continues: Nursing the elderly. Continued by:
Nursing older people.
1993-2000   **9310629**

Electrodiagn Ther
Electrodiagnostic-Thérapie
0424-8120
1964-1981   **0033671**

Electroencephalogr Clin Neurophysiol
Electroencephalography and clinical
neurophysiology
0013-4694
Absorbed: Electroencephalography
and clinical neurophysiology. Index to
current literature. Continued by: Clinical
neurophysiology.
1949-1998   **0375035**

Electroencephalogr Clin Neurophysiol Suppl
Electroencephalography and clinical
neurophysiology. Supplement
0424-8155
Continued by: Supplements to Clinical
neurophysiology.
1950-1999   **0375036**

Electromagn Biol Med
Electromagnetic biology and medicine
1536-8378   1536-8386
Continues: Electro- and magnetobiology.
2002   **101133002**

Electromyogr Clin Neurophysiol
Electromyography and clinical
neurophysiology
0301-150X
Continues Electromyography.
1972   **0327533**

Electromyography
Electromyography
0013-4732
Continued by: Electromyography and clinical
neurophysiology.
1961-1971   **0330363**

Electron Microsc Rev
Electron microscopy reviews
0892-0354
Continues: Electron microscopy of proteins.
Merged with: Micron and microscopica acta,
to form: Micron (Oxford, England: 1993).
1988-1992   **8809169**

Electrophoresis
Electrophoresis
0173-0835   1522-2683
1980   **8204476**

Elektromed Biomed Tech
Elektro Medizin; Biomedizin und Technik
Continued by Biomedizinische Technik.
Biomedical engineering.
1955-1970   **1264714**

EMBO J
The EMBO journal
0261-4189   1460-2075
1982   **8208664**

EMBO Rep
EMBO reports
1469-221X   1469-3178
2000   **100963049**

Embryologia (Nagoya)
Embryologia
0367-0228
Continued by Development, growth &
differentiation.
1950-1969   **0225165**

Emerg Dep News
Emergency department news: EDN
0195-3281
Continued by: Emergency medicine &
ambulatory care news.
1979-1986   **8100351**

Emerg Health Serv Q
Emergency health services quarterly
0163-9358
Continued by: Emergency health services
review.
1980-1982   **8102105**

Emerg Health Serv Rev
Emergency health services review
0738-6192
Continues: Emergency health services
quarterly. Continued by: Journal of
ambulatory care marketing.
1983-1986   **8404925**

Emerg Infect Dis
Emerging infectious diseases
1080-6040   1080-6059
1995   **9508155**

Emerg Med
Emergency medicine
0013-6654
1969   **0214330**

Emerg Med (Fremantle)
Emergency medicine (Fremantle, W.A.)
1035-6851   1442-2026
Continues: Emergency doctor. Continued by:
Emergency medicine Australasia.
1989-2003   **9421464**

Emerg Med Australas
Emergency medicine Australasia: EMA
1742-6731   1742-6723
Continues: Emergency medicine (Fremantle,
W.A.).
2004   **101199824**

Emerg Med Clin North Am
Emergency medicine clinics of North
America
0733-8627
1983   **8219565**

Emerg Med J
Emergency medicine journal: EMJ
1472-0205   1472-0213
Continues: Journal of accident & emergency
medicine.
2001   **100963089**

Emerg Med Serv
Emergency medical services
0094-6575
Continued by: EMS magazine.
1972-2007   **0431735**

Emerg Nurse
Emergency nurse: the journal of the
RCN Accident and Emergency Nursing
Association
1354-5752
1992   **9208913**

Emerg Plann Dig
Emergency planning digest
0317-3518
Formed by the union of its EM0 national digest; ISSN 0012-7787 and its Bulletin national de l'O M U; ISSN 0576-1522 Continued by: Emergency preparedness digest.
1974-1986 9878434

Emerg Radiol
Emergency radiology
1070-3004 1438-1435
1994 9431227

Emergency
Emergency
0162-5942
Continues Emergency product news.
1978-1998 7910894

Emotion
Emotion (Washington, D.C.)
1528-3542
2001 101125678

Emphasis Nurs
Emphasis, nursing / Los Angeles County, Harbor-UCLA Medical Center, Nursing Department
0886-7143
1985-1995 8509371

Empl Benefits J
Employee benefits journal
0361-4050
Merged with: International Foundation of Employee Benefit Plans. Digest; to form: Benefits & compensation digest.
1975-2004 7703664

Empl Health Fit
Employee health & fitness
0199-6304
Absorbed by: Occupational health management.
19uu-uuuu 9878622

Employ Relat Today
Employment relations today
0745-7790
Continues: EEO today.
1983 9884311

Employee Benefit Plan Rev
Employee benefit plan review
0013-6808
Absorbed: Compensation & benefits management. Aug. 2002
1946 7703663

Employee Relat Law J
Employee relations law journal
0098-8898
1975 9877772

EMS Mag
EMS magazine
Continues: Emergency medical services.
2007 101466002

EMT J
The EMT journal
1977-1981 7705464

Enantiomer
Enantiomer
1024-2430
1996-2002 9612491

Encephale
L'Encéphale
0013-7006
1906 7505643

Endeavour
Endeavour
0160-9327 1873-1929
1942 0375037

ENDO
Endo: revue française d'endodontie: publication officielle de la Société française d'endodontie
1168-5476
Continues: Revue française d'endodontie.
1992-1996 9212291

Endocr Dev
Endocrine development
1421-7082 1662-2979
1999 101138956

Endocr J
Endocrine journal
0918-8959 1348-4540
Continues: Endocrinologia japonica.
1993 9313485

Endocr Metab Immune Disord Drug Targets
Endocrine, metabolic & immune disorders drug targets
1871-5303
Continues: Current drug targets. Immune, endocrine and metabolic disorders.
2006 101269157

Endocr Pathol
Endocrine pathology
1046-3976 1559-0097
1990 9009288

Endocr Pract
Endocrine practice: official journal of the American College of Endocrinology and the American Association of Clinical Endocrinologists
1530-891X 1934-2403
1995 9607439

Endocr Regul
Endocrine regulations
1210-0668 1336-0329
Continues: Endocrinologia experimentalis.
1991 9112018

Endocr Relat Cancer
Endocrine-related cancer
1351-0088 1479-6821
Continues: Reviews on endocrine-related cancer.
1994 9436481

Endocr Res
Endocrine research
0743-5800 1532-4206
Continues: Endocrine research communications.
1984 8408548

Endocr Res Commun
Endocrine research communications
0093-6391
Continued by Endocrine research.
1974-1983 0426337

Endocr Rev
Endocrine reviews
0163-769X 1945-7189
Absorbed: Recent progress in hormone research. 2005
1980 8006258

Endocr Terap
Endocrinologia y terapéutica
0013-7243
1935-1972 16730260R

Endocrine
Endocrine
0969-711X 15599-010
Continues: Endocrine journal.
1994 9434444

Endocrinol Exp
Endocrinologia experimentalis
0013-7200
Supersedes Endocrinologia experimentalis, published 1964-66. Continued by: Endocrine regulations.
1967-1990 0125712

Endocrinol Jpn
Endocrinologia japonica
0013-7219
Continued by: Endocrine journal.
1954-1992 0376546

Endocrinol Metab Clin North Am
Endocrinology and metabolism clinics of North America
0889-8529 1558-4410
Continues in part: Clinics in endocrinology and metabolism.
1987 8800104

Endocrinol Sci Cost
Endocrinologia e scienza della costituzione
0013-7197
Continues: Endocrinologia e patologia costituzionale.
1942-1973 0071535

Endocrinologie
Endocrinologie
0253-1801
Continues in part Revue roumaine de médecine. Continued by: Romanian journal of endocrinology.
1975-1995 7509386

Endocrinology
Endocrinology
0013-7227 1945-7170
Absorbed in part: Transactions of the American Goiter Association. American Goiter Association. 1957
1917 0375040

Endod Dent Traumatol
Endodontics & dental traumatology
0109-2502
Continued by: Dental traumatology.
1985-2000 8508054

Endod Prac
Endodontic practice
1465-9417
1998 100887863

Endod Rep
The Endodontic report
0899-8973
1987-1993 8804061

Endodoncia
Endodoncia (Madrid, Spain)
1130-9903
Continues: Revista española de endodoncia.
1990 9103345

Endodoncia (Mex)
Endodoncia
0071-0261
1966-1967 0125466

Endokrinologie
Endokrinologie
0013-7251
Continued by Experimental and clinical endocrinology.
1928-1982 0370675

Endokrynol Diabetol Chor Przemiany Materii Wieku Rozw
Endokrynologia, diabetologia i choroby przemiany materii wieku rozwojowego: organ Polskiego Towarzystwa Endokrynologów Dziecięcych
1234-625X
1995   100892008

Endokrynol Pol
Endokrynologia Polska
0423-104X
1950   0370674

Endosc Surg Allied Technol
Endoscopic surgery and allied technologies
0942-6027
  Merged with: Minimally invasive therapy. to form: Minimally invasive therapy & allied technologies.
1993-1995   9412631

Endoscopy
Endoscopy
0013-726X   1438-8812
1969   0215166

Endothelium
Endothelium: journal of endothelial cell research
1062-3329   1029-2373
1993   9412590

Enfance
Enfance; psychologie, pédagogie, neuropsychiatrie, sociologie
0013-7545
1948   0370676

Enferm Clin
Enfermería clínica
1130-8621   1579-2013
1991   101190915

Enferm Infecc Microbiol Clin
Enfermedades infecciosas y microbiología clínica
0213-005X   1578-1852
  Continues: Enfermedades infecciosas.
1984   9104081

Enferm Intensiva
Enfermería intensiva / Sociedad Española de Enfermería Intensiva y Unidades Coronarias
1130-2399
1988   9517771

Enferm Torax
Enfermedades del tórax
0423-121X
1952-1982   0413665

Enfermeria
Enfermeria
0378-6285
1965-1984   7701824

Enfoque
Enfoque
0101-3408
1974   9879302

Eng Med
Engineering in medicine
0046-2039
  Continued by: Proceedings of the Institution of Mechanical Engineers. Part H. Journal of engineering in medicine.
1971-1988   0322070

ENLB Emerg Nurse Leg Bull
ENLB. Emergency nurse legal bulletin
0098-1516
1975   7506581

ENO FO
Eno Fo
  Continued by: Fo. Facultad De Odontologia.
1974-1975   9878155

Entechnology
ENTechnology
0145-5613
19uu-1989   8605425

Entomol News
Entomological news
0013-872X
  Continues the Entomological news and proceedings of the Entomological Section of the Academy of Natural Sciences of Philadelphia.
1925   0007616

Entomon Int Z Gesamte Insektenkunde
Entomon; internationale Zeitschrift für die gesamte Insektenkunde
1949-1949   16740050R

Entret Bichat Med Entret Bichat
Les entretiens de Bichat. Médecine. Entretiens de Bichat
  Continued by: Entretiens de Bichat. Médecine et biologie. Entretiens de Bichat.
1947-1967   0241230

Environ Biol Med
Environmental biology and medicine
0046-2233
1971-1976   0372224

Environ Biosafety Res
Environmental biosafety research
1635-7922   1635-7930
2002   101172622

Environ Entomol
Environmental entomology
0046-225X
1972   7502320

Environ Geochem Health
Environmental geochemistry and health
0269-4042   1573-2983
  Continues: Minerals and the environment.
1985   8903118

Environ Health
Environmental health: a global access science source
    1476-069X
2002   101147645

Environ Health Perspect
Environmental health perspectives
0091-6765   1552-9924
  Absorbed: EHP toxicogenomics.
1972   0330411

Environ Health Ser [Radiol Health]
Environmental health series. [RH] Radiological health
0071-0911
  Continues Environmental health series. [R] Radiological health.
1964-1970   0216004

Environ Int
Environment international
0160-4120   1873-6750
1978   7807270

Environ Lett
Environmental letters
0013-9300
  Continued by Journal of environmental science and health. issued in three separate parts: Pt. A: Environmental science and engineering: Pt. B: Pesticides. food contaminants. and agricultural wastes: Pt. C:Environmental health sciences.
1971-1975   7610448

Environ Manage
Environmental management
0364-152X   1432-1009
1976   7703893

Environ Microbiol
Environmental microbiology
1462-2912   1462-2920
1999   100883692

Environ Mol Mutagen
Environmental and molecular mutagenesis
0893-6692   1098-2280
  Continues: Environmental mutagenesis.
1987   8800109

Environ Monit Assess
Environmental monitoring and assessment
0167-6369   1573-2959
1981   8508350

Environ Mutagen
Environmental mutagenesis
0192-2521
  Continued by: Environmental and molecular mutagenesis.
1979-1987   7909737

Environ Physiol Biochem
Environmental physiology & biochemistry
0300-5429
  Continues Environmental physiology.
1972-1975   7610449

Environ Pollut
Environmental pollution (Barking, Essex: 1987)
0269-7491   1873-6424
  Formed by the union of: Environmental pollution. Series A. Ecological and biological and: Environmental pollution. Series B. Chemical and physical.
1987   8804476

Environ Qual Saf
Environmental quality and safety
0300-824X
1972-1976   0332077

Environ Qual Saf Suppl
Environmental quality and safety. Supplement
0340-4714
1975-1976   7512713

Environ Res
Environmental research
0013-9351   1096-0953
1967   0147621

Environ Sci
Environmental sciences: an international journal of environmental physiology and toxicology
0915-955X
1991   9209787

Environ Sci Pollut Res Int
Environmental science and pollution research international
0944-1344   1614-7499
1994   9441769

Environ Sci Technol
Environmental science & technology
0013-936X
  Absorbed: Environmental buyers' guide. 1994
1967   0213155

Environ Technol
Environmental technology
0959-3330
  Continues: Environmental technology letters.
1990   9884939

Environ Toxicol
Environmental toxicology
1520-4081   1522-7278
Continues: Environmental toxicology and
water quality.
1999   100885357

Environ Toxicol Chem
Environmental toxicology and chemistry /
SETAC
0730-7268   1552-8618
1982   8308958

Enzyme
Enzyme
0013-9432
Continues Enzymologia biologica et clinica.
Continued by: Enzyme & protein.
1971-1992   1262265

Enzyme Microb Technol
Enzyme and microbial technology
0141-0229
1979   8003761

Enzyme Protein
Enzyme & protein
1019-6773
Continues: Enzyme.
1993-1996   9422761

Enzymol Biol Clin (Basel)
Enzymologia biologica et clinica
0425-1423
Continued by Enzyme.
1961-1970   1262560

Enzymologia
Enzymologia
0013-9424
Continued by: Molecular and cellular
biochemistry.
1936-1972   0427141

Epatologia
Epatologia
0013-9475
1955-1984   0401042

Epheta
Epheta; revista de enfermería y acción social
0071-0970
1962-1971   0057376

Epidemiol Bull
Epidemiological bulletin
0256-1859
Supersedes Weekly epidemiological report.
1980   8011598

Epidemiol Community Health
Epidemiology and community health
0142-467X
Continues Journal of epidemiology and
community health. Continued by Journal of
epidemiology and community health.
1979-1979   7907645

Epidemiol Infect
Epidemiology and infection
0950-2688   1469-4409
Continues: The Journal of hygiene.
1987   8703737

Epidemiol Mikrobiol Imunol
Epidemiologie, mikrobiologie, imunologie:
casopis Spolecnosti pro epidemiologii a
mikrobiologii Ceské lékarské spolecnosti
J.E. Purkyne
1210-7913
Continues: Ceskoslovenská epidemiologie,
mikrobiologie, imunologie.
1994   9431736

Epidemiol Prev
Epidemiologia e prevenzione
1120-9763
1976   8902507

Epidemiol Psichiatr Soc
Epidemiologia e psichiatria sociale
1121-189X
1992   9501447

Epidemiol Rev
Epidemiologic reviews
0193-936X   1478-6729
1979   7910703

Epidemiol Vital Stat Rep
Epidemiological and vital statistics report.
Rapport épidémiologique et démographique
Continued by the World health statistics
report. Rapport de statistiques sanitaires
mondiales.
1947-1967   0161143

Epidemiology
Epidemiology (Cambridge, Mass.)
1044-3983   1531-5487
1990   9009644

Epigenetics
Epigenetics: official journal of the DNA
Methylation Society
1559-2294   1559-2308
2006   101265293

Epilepsia
Epilepsia
0013-9580   1528-1167
1909   2983306R

Epilepsy Behav
Epilepsy & behavior: E&B
1525-5050   1525-5069
2000   100892858

Epilepsy Res
Epilepsy research
0920-1211   1872-6844
Absorbed: Journal of epilepsy. 1999-
1987   8703089

Epilepsy Res Suppl
Epilepsy research. Supplement
0922-9833
1988-1996   8913231

Epileptic Disord
Epileptic disorders: international epilepsy
journal with videotape
1294-9361   1950-6945
1999   100891853

Epione
Epione
Absorbed by: Sairaanhoitaja.
1908-1965   0102642

Epithelial Cell Biol
Epithelial cell biology
0940-9912
1992-1995   9206038

Equine Vet J
Equine veterinary journal
0425-1644
1968   0173320

Equine Vet J Suppl
Equine veterinary journal. Supplement
1983   9614088

Erfahrungsheilkunde
Erfahrungsheilkunde
0014-0082
1951   2984752R

Ergeb Allg Pathol Pathol Anat
Ergebnisse der allgemeinen Pathologie und
pathologischen Anatomie
Continues: Ergebnisse der allgemeinen
Pathologie und pathologischen Anatomie
de Menschen und der Tiere. Continued by:
Current topics in pathology.
1954-1968   0244770

Ergeb Anat Entwicklungsgesch
Ergebnisse der Anatomie und
Entwicklungsgeschichte
0071-1098
Continued by: Advances in anatomy,
embryology, and cell biology.
1891-1973   0404053

Ergeb Biol
Ergebnisse der Biologie
1926-1964   16810110R

Ergeb Chir Orthop
Ergebnisse der Chirurgie und Orthopädie
0300-8681
1910-1971   7611997

Ergeb Enzymforsch
Ergebnisse der Enzymforschung
1932-1954   16810120R

Ergeb Gesamten Tuberkuloseforsch
Ergebnisse der gesamten
Tuberkuloseforschung
1930-1958   0330460

Ergeb Hyg Bakteriol Immunitatsforsch Exp Ther
Ergebnisse der Hygiene, Bakteriologie,
Immunitätsforschung und experimentellen
Therapie
Supersedes Jahresbericht über die
Ergebnisse der Immunitätsforschung.
Continued by Ergebnisse der Mikrobiologie,
Immunitätsforschung und experimentellen
Therapie.
1914-1955   16810160R

Ergeb Inn Med Kinderheilkd
Ergebnisse der inneren Medizin und
Kinderheilkunde
0071-111X
1908-1993   0370703

Ergeb Mikrobiol Immunitatsforsch Exp Ther
Ergebnisse der Mikrobiologie,
Immunitätsforschung und experimentellen
Therapie
0367-1003
Continues Ergebnisse der Hygiene,
Bakteriologie, Imunitätsforschung, und
experimentellen Therapie. Continued
by Current topics in microbiology and
immunology.
1957-1966   0111273

Ergeb Physiol
Ergebnisse der Physiologie, biologischen
Chemie und experimentellen Pharmakologie
0080-2042
Continued by Reviews of physiology,
biochemistry and pharmacology.
1902-1974   0434572

Ergonomics
Ergonomics
0014-0139   1366-5847
1957   0373220

Ernahrungsforsch Ber Mitt
Ernährungsforschung. Berichte und
Mitteilungen
Continued by: Ernährungsforschung.
1956-1974   101255809

Ernahrungsforschung
Ernährungsforschung
0071-1179
1974-2002   0416606

Ernst Schering Found Symp Proc
Ernst Schering Foundation symposium
proceedings
Continues: Ernst Schering Research
Foundation workshop.
2006   101312605

Ernst Schering Res Found Workshop
Ernst Schering Research Foundation
workshop
0947-6075
Continues: Schering Foundation workshop.
Continued by: Ernst Schering Foundation
symposium proceedings.
1994-2006   9422786

Esc Farm
La Escuela de farmacia
0367-0341
1938-1969   16810380R

Esencia Odontol
Esencia Odontologica
0716-9817
1984   9884322

Essays Biochem
Essays in biochemistry
0071-1365
1965   0043306

Essays Fundam Immunol
Essays in fundamental immunology
0301-4703
1973-1973   0402264

Essays Neurochem Neuropharmacol
Essays in neurochemistry and
neuropharmacology
0147-0205
1977-1981   7703003

Essent Psychopharmacol
Essential psychopharmacology
1087-495X
Continues: Directions in
psychopharmacology.
1996   9616904

Estodont Press
Estodont/press
1983-1983   8409411

Estomatol Cult
Estomatologia e cultura
0014-1364
Merged with: Revista da Faculdade de
Odontologia da Universidade de São Paulo.
and: Revista de Faculdade de Odontologia
de Ribeirão Prêto. to form: Revista de
odontologia da Universidade de São Paulo.
1967-1986   1275101

Estomatologia
Estomatologia
0014-1356
1963-1966   0033754

Estud Psiq
Estudos psíquicos
1940-1978   16820100R

ET J
ET journal
0195-9883
Continued by Journal of enterostomal therapy.
1974-1979   7906030

Ethics Sci Med
Ethics in science & medicine
0306-4581
Continues Science. medicine and man.
Continued by Social science & medicine. Part
F. Medical & social ethics.
1975-1980   7510822

Ethiop Med J
Ethiopian medical journal
0014-1755
1962   0373223

Ethn Dis
Ethnicity & disease
1049-510X
1991   9109034

Ethn Health
Ethnicity & health
1355-7858   1465-3419
1996   9608374

Etud Soins Serv Infirm
Etudes Sur Les Soins Et Le Service
Infirmier
0338-3989
1975   9879792

Etudes Neonatales
Etudes néo-natales. Neo-natal studies
Continued by Biologia neonatorum.
1952-1958   16820150R

Eugen Q
Eugenics quarterly
0097-2762
Supersedes Eugenical news. Continued by
Social biology.
1954-1968   0205544

Eugen Rev
The Eugenics review
1909-1968   0215413

Eugen Soc Symp
Eugenics Society symposia
0071-223X
1964-1967   7507110

Eugenesia
Eugenesia
Continues the Boletín of the Sociedad
Mexicana para el Mejoramiento de la Raza.
1932-19uu   16820170R

Eukaryot Cell
Eukaryotic cell
1535-9778   1535-9786
2002   101130731

Eur Addict Res
European addiction research
1022-6877   1421-9891
1995   9502920

Eur Ann Allergy Clin Immunol
European annals of allergy and clinical
immunology
1764-1489
Continues: Allergie et immunologie.
2003   101466614

Eur Arch Otorhinolaryngol Suppl
European archives of oto-rhino-laryngology.
Supplement
0942-8992
Continues: Archives of oto-rhino-laryngology.
Supplement.
1992-1996   9212295

Eur Arch Paediatr Dent
European archives of paediatric dentistry:
official journal of the European Academy of
Paediatric Dentistry
1818-6300
Separated from: European journal of
paediatric dentistry.
2006   101277157

Eur Arch Psychiatry Neurol Sci
European archives of psychiatry and
neurological sciences
0175-758X
Continues: Archiv für Psychiatrie und
Nervenkrankheiten. Continued by: European
archives of psychiatry and clinical neuroscience.
1984-1990   8411522

Eur Biophys J
European biophysics journal: EBJ
0175-7571   1432-1017
Continues: Biophysics of structure and
mechanism.
1984   8409413

Eur Cell Mater
European cells & materials
    1473-2262
2001   100973416

Eur Child Adolesc Psychiatry
European child & adolescent psychiatry
1018-8827   1435-165X
1992   9212296

Eur Cytokine Netw
European cytokine network
1148-5493
1990   9100879

Eur Eat Disord Rev
European eating disorders review: the
journal of the Eating Disorders Association
1072-4133   1099-0968
Continues: Eating disorders review
(Chichester. England).
1993   9436977

Eur Heart J
European heart journal
0195-668X   1522-9645
1980   8006263

Eur J Anaesthesiol
European journal of anaesthesiology
0265-0215   1365-2346
1984   8411711

Eur J Anaesthesiol Suppl
European journal of anaesthesiology.
Supplement
0952-1941
1987   8804068

Eur J Appl Physiol
European journal of applied physiology
1439-6319   1439-6327
Continues: European journal of applied
physiology and occupational physiology.
2000   100954790

Eur J Appl Physiol Occup Physiol
European journal of applied physiology and
occupational physiology
0301-5548
Continues: Internationale Zeitschrift für
angewandte Physiologie. einschliesslich
Arbeitsphysiologie. Continued by: European
journal of applied physiology.
1973-1999   0410266

Eur J Basic Appl Histochem
European journal of basic and applied
histochemistry
1121-4201
Continues: Basic and applied histochemistry.
Continued by: European journal of
histochemistry.
1991-1991   9109553

Eur J Biochem
European journal of biochemistry / FEBS
0014-2956   1432-1033
Continues: Biochemische Zeitschrift.
Continued by: FEBS journal.
1967-2004   0107600

Eur J Cancer
European journal of cancer
0014-2964
Continued by European journal of cancer & clinical oncology.
1965-1981   0074126

Eur J Cancer
European journal of cancer (Oxford, England: 1990)
0959-8049   1879-0852
Continues: European journal of cancer & clinical oncology. Continued in part by: European journal of cancer. Part B, Oral oncology.
1990   9005373

Eur J Cancer B Oral Oncol
European journal of cancer. Part B, Oral oncology
0964-1955
Separated from: European journal of cancer. Continued by: Oral oncology.
1992-1996   9214373

Eur J Cancer Care (Engl)
European journal of cancer care
0961-5423   1365-2354
1991   9301979

Eur J Cancer Clin Oncol
European journal of cancer & clinical oncology
0277-5379
Continues: European journal of cancer. Continued by: European journal of cancer (Oxford, England: 1990).
1981-1989   8112045

Eur J Cancer Prev
European journal of cancer prevention: the official journal of the European Cancer Prevention Organisation (ECP)
0959-8278   1473-5709
1991   9300837

Eur J Cardiol
European journal of cardiology
0301-4711
Continued by International journal of cardiology.
1973-1981   0404054

Eur J Cardiothorac Surg
European journal of cardio-thoracic surgery: official journal of the European Association for Cardio-thoracic Surgery
1010-7940   1873-734X
1987   8804069

Eur J Cardiovasc Nurs
European journal of cardiovascular nursing: journal of the Working Group on Cardiovascular Nursing of the European Society of Cardiology
1474-5151   1873-1953
2002   101128793

Eur J Cardiovasc Prev Rehabil
European journal of cardiovascular prevention and rehabilitation: official journal of the European Society of Cardiology, Working Groups on Epidemiology & Prevention and Cardiac Rehabilitation and Exercise Physiology
1741-8267   1741-8275
Continues: Journal of cardiovascular risk.
2003   101192000

Eur J Cell Biol Suppl
European journal of cell biology. Supplement
0724-5130
1983   8303754

Eur J Clin Chem Clin Biochem
European journal of clinical chemistry and clinical biochemistry: journal of the Forum of European Clinical Chemistry Societies
0939-4974
Continues: Journal of clinical chemistry and clinical biochemistry. Continued by: Clinical chemistry and laboratory medicine.
1991-1997   9105775

Eur J Clin Invest
European journal of clinical investigation
0014-2972   1365-2362
Supersedes Archiv für klinische Medizin.
1970   0245331

Eur J Clin Microbiol
European journal of clinical microbiology
0722-2211
Continued by: European journal of clinical microbiology & infectious diseases.
1982-1987   8219582

Eur J Clin Microbiol Infect Dis
European journal of clinical microbiology & infectious diseases: official publication of the European Society of Clinical Microbiology
0934-9723   1435-4373
Continues: European journal of clinical microbiology.
1988   8804297

Eur J Clin Nutr
European journal of clinical nutrition
0954-3007   1476-5640
Formed by the union of: Human nutrition. Clinical nutrition, and: Human nutrition. Applied nutrition.
1988   8804070

Eur J Clin Pharmacol
European journal of clinical pharmacology
0031-6970   1432-1041
Continues Pharmacologia clinica.
1970   1256165

Eur J Contracept Reprod Health Care
The European journal of contraception & reproductive health care: the official journal of the European Society of Contraception
1362-5187   1473-0782
1996   9712127

Eur J Dent Educ
European journal of dental education: official journal of the Association for Dental Education in Europe
1396-5883   1600-0579
1997   9712132

Eur J Dermatol
European journal of dermatology: EJD
1167-1122
1991   9206420

Eur J Disord Commun
European journal of disorders of communication: the journal of the College of Speech and Language Therapists, London
0963-7273
Continues: British journal of communication. Continued by: International journal of language & communication disorders.
1992-1997   9208302

Eur J Drug Metab Pharmacokinet
European journal of drug metabolism and pharmacokinetics
0398-7639
1976   7608491

Eur J Echocardiogr
European journal of echocardiography: the journal of the Working Group on Echocardiography of the European Society of Cardiology
1525-2167   1532-2114
2000   100890618

Eur J Emerg Med
European journal of emergency medicine: official journal of the European Society for Emergency Medicine
0969-9546   1473-5695
1994   9442482

Eur J Endocrinol
European journal of endocrinology / European Federation of Endocrine Societies
0804-4643   1479-683X
Continues: Acta endocrinologica.
1994   9423848

Eur J Epidemiol
European journal of epidemiology
0393-2990   1573-7284
1985   8508062

Eur J Gastroenterol Hepatol
European journal of gastroenterology & hepatology
0954-691X   1473-5687
1989   9000874

Eur J Gen Pract
The European journal of general practice
1381-4788   1751-1402
1995   9513566

Eur J Genet Soc
European journal of genetics in society: an ethical approach to genetics
1023-9022
Continued by: Human reproduction and genetic ethics.
1995-1997   9517856

Eur J Gynaecol Oncol
European journal of gynaecological oncology
0392-2936
1980   8100357

Eur J Haematol
European journal of haematology
0902-4441   1600-0609
Continues: Scandinavian journal of haematology.
1987   8703985

Eur J Health Econ
The European journal of health economics: HEPAC: health economics in prevention and care
1618-7598   1618-7601
Continues: Health economics in prevention and care.
2002   101134867

Eur J Health Law
European journal of health law
0929-0273
1994   9431861

Eur J Heart Fail
European journal of heart failure: journal of the Working Group on Heart Failure of the European Society of Cardiology
1388-9842   1879-0844
1999   100887595

Eur J Histochem
European journal of histochemistry: EJH
1121-760X
Continues: European journal of basic and applied histochemistry.
1992   9207930

Eur J Hum Genet
European journal of human genetics: EJHG
1018-4813   1476-5438
1992   9302235

Eur J Immunogenet
European journal of immunogenetics:
official journal of the British Society for
Histocompatibility and Immunogenetics
0960-7420   1365-2370
Continues: Journal of immunogenetics.
Continued by: International journal of
immunogenetics.
1991-2004   9106962

Eur J Immunol
European journal of immunology
0014-2980   1521-4141
1971   1273201

Eur J Intensive Care Med
European journal of intensive care medicine
0340-0964
Continued by: Intensive care medicine.
1975-1976   7504969

Eur J Intern Med
European journal of internal medicine
0953-6205
1989   9003220

Eur J Mass Spectrom (Chichester, Eng)
European journal of mass spectrometry
(Chichester, England)
1469-0667
Continues: European mass spectrometry.
2000   101124748

Eur J Med
The European journal of medicine
1165-0478
1992-1993   9209793

Eur J Med Chem
European journal of medicinal chemistry
0223-5234   1768-3254
Continues Chimica therapeutica.
1974   0420510

Eur J Med Genet
European journal of medical genetics
1769-7212   1878-0849
Continues: Annales de génétique.
2005   101247089

Eur J Med Res
European journal of medical research
0949-2321
1995   9517857

Eur J Morphol
European journal of morphology
0924-3860   1744-4241
Absorbed: European archives of biology.
1995 Apr. Continues: Acta morphologica
Neerlando-Scandinavica.
1990-2005   9011462

Eur J Neurol
European journal of neurology: the official
journal of the European Federation of
Neurological Societies
1351-5101   1468-1331
1994   9506311

Eur J Neurosci
The European journal of neuroscience
0953-816X   1460-9568
1989   8918110

Eur J Nucl Med
European journal of nuclear medicine
0340-6997
Continued by: European journal of nuclear
medicine and molecular imaging.
1976-2001   7606882

Eur J Nucl Med Mol Imaging
European journal of nuclear medicine and
molecular imaging
1619-7070   1619-7089
Continues: European journal of nuclear
medicine.
2002   101140988

Eur J Nutr
European journal of nutrition
1436-6207   1436-6215
Continues: Zeitschrift für
Ernährungswissenschaft.
1999   100888704

Eur J Obstet Gynecol Reprod Biol
European journal of obstetrics, gynecology,
and reproductive biology
0301-2115   1872-7654
Continues European journal of obstetrics and
gynecology.
1973   0375672

Eur J Oncol Nurs
European journal of oncology nursing:
the official journal of European Oncology
Nursing Society
1462-3889   1532-2122
Continues: Journal of cancer nursing.
1998   100885136

Eur J Ophthalmol
European journal of ophthalmology
1120-6721
1991   9110772

Eur J Oral Sci
European journal of oral sciences
0909-8836   1600-0722
Continues: Scandinavian journal of dental
research.
1995   9504563

Eur J Orthod
European journal of orthodontics
0141-5387   1460-2210
1979   7909010

Eur J Paediatr Dent
European journal of paediatric dentistry:
official journal of European Academy of
Paediatric Dentistry
1591-996X
Continues: Italian journal of paediatric
dentistry. Continued in part by: European
archives of paediatric dentistry.
2000   101121881

Eur J Paediatr Neurol
European journal of paediatric neurology:
EJPN: official journal of the European
Paediatric Neurology Society
1090-3798   1532-2130
1997   9715169

Eur J Pain
European journal of pain (London, England)
1090-3801   1532-2149
1997   9801774

Eur J Pediatr
European journal of pediatrics
0340-6199   1432-1076
Continues Zeitschrift für Kinderheilkunde.
Absorbed Acta paediatrica Belgica. Feb.
1982.
1975   7603873

Eur J Pediatr Surg
European journal of pediatric surgery:
official journal of Austrian Association of
Pediatric Surgery ... [et al] = Zeitschrift für
Kinderchirurgie
0939-7248   1439-359X
Formed by the union of: Zeitschrift für
Kinderchirurgie. and: Chirurgie pédiatrique.
1991   9105263

Eur J Pharm Biopharm
European journal of pharmaceutics and
biopharmaceutics: official journal of
Arbeitsgemeinschaft für Pharmazeutische
Verfahrenstechnik e.V
0939-6411   1873-3441
Continues: Acta pharmaceutica technologica.
1991   9109778

Eur J Pharm Sci
European journal of pharmaceutical
sciences: official journal of the European
Federation for Pharmaceutical Sciences
0928-0987   1879-0720
Absorbed: Acta pharmaceutica Fennica. and:
Acta pharmaceutica Nordica.
1993   9317982

Eur J Pharmacol
European journal of pharmacology
0014-2999   1879-0712
Absorbed: Acta physiologica et
pharmacologica Neerlandica. Continued
in part by: Environmental toxicology and
pharmacology.
1967   1254354

Eur J Phys Rehabil Med
European journal of physical and
rehabilitation medicine
1973-9087   1973-9095
Continues: Europa medicophysica.
2008   101465662

Eur J Prosthodont Restor Dent
The European journal of prosthodontics and
restorative dentistry
0965-7452
Continues: Restorative dentistry.
1992   9314899

Eur J Protistol
European journal of protistology
0932-4739   1618-0429
Continues: Protistologica.
1987   8917383

Eur J Public Health
European journal of public health
1101-1262   1464-360X
1991   9204966

Eur J Radiol
European journal of radiology
0720-048X   1872-7727
Absorbed: Journal of medical imaging. 1990
1981   8106411

Eur J Respir Dis
European journal of respiratory diseases
0106-4339
Formed by the union of Scandinavian journal
of respiratory diseases and Acta tuberculosea
et pneumologica Belgica. Merged with:
Bulletin européen de physiopathologie
respiratoire. to form: European respiratory
journal.
1980-1987   8006891

Eur J Respir Dis Suppl
European journal of respiratory diseases.
Supplement
0106-4347
Continues Scandinavian journal of respiratory
diseases. Supplementum. Continued by:
European respiratory journal. Supplement.
Supplement to: European journal of
respiratory diseases.
1980-1987   8010618

Eur J Rheumatol Inflamm
European journal of rheumatology and
inflammation
0140-1610
1978-1996   7805765

Eur J Surg
The European journal of surgery = Acta
chirurgica
1102-4151
Absorbed in 1992: Netherlands journal of
surgery. Absorbed by: British journal of
surgery. 2003
1991-2002   9105264

Eur J Surg Oncol
European journal of surgical oncology: the
journal of the European Society of Surgical
Oncology and the British Association of
Surgical Oncology
0748-7983   1532-2157
Continues: Clinical oncology.
1985   8504356

Eur J Surg Suppl
The European journal of surgery.
Supplement.: = Acta chirurgica. Supplement
1102-416X
Continues: Acta chirurgica Scandinavica.
Supplementum. Supplement to: European
journal of surgery.
1991-2003   9114489

Eur J Toxicol
European journal of toxicology
0021-8219
Continued by European journal of toxicology
and hygiene of environment.
1968-1972   0422351

Eur J Toxicol Environ Hyg
European journal of toxicology and
environmental hygiene. Journal européen de
toxicologie
0397-4693
Continues European journal of toxicology
and hygiene of environment. Superseded by
Toxicological European research. Recherche
européenne en toxicologie.
1974-1976   7501125

Eur J Toxicol Hyg Environ
European journal of toxicology and hygiene
of environment
0398-8023
Continues European journal of toxicology.
Continued by European journal of toxicology
and environmental hygiene.
1972-1973   7501126

Eur J Ultrasound
European journal of ultrasound: official
journal of the European Federation of Societies
for Ultrasound in Medicine and Biology
0929-8266
1994-2003   9440414

Eur J Vasc Endovasc Surg
European journal of vascular and
endovascular surgery: the official journal of
the European Society for Vascular Surgery
1078-5884   1532-2165
Continues: European journal of vascular
surgery.
1995   9512728

Eur J Vasc Surg
European journal of vascular surgery
0950-821X
Continued by: European journal of vascular
and endovascular surgery.
1987-1994   8709440

Eur Med (Paris)
Europa medica. [Edición española]
0375-8869
1964-1976   0106040

Eur Neurol
European neurology
0014-3022   1421-9913
Supersedes in part Psychiatria et neurologia.
1968   0150760

Eur Neuropsychopharmacol
European neuropsychopharmacology:
the journal of the European College of
Neuropsychopharmacology
0924-977X   1873-7862
1990   9111390

Eur Phys J E Soft Matter
The European physical journal. E, Soft
matter
1292-8941   1292-895X
Formerly issued as the section: Soft
condensed matter, in: European physical
journal. B, Condensed matter physics.
2000   101126530

Eur Psychiatry
European psychiatry: the journal of the
Association of European Psychiatrists
0924-9338
Continues: Psychiatrie & psychobiologie.
1991   9111820

Eur Qual Assur Netw Newsl
European Quality Assurance Network
newsletter / EuroQuan
199u-1995   9433395

Eur Radiol
European radiology
0938-7994   1432-1084
Absorbed: Diagnostic & interventional
radiology.
1991   9114774

Eur Respir J
The European respiratory journal: official
journal of the European Society for Clinical
Respiratory Physiology
0903-1936   1399-3003
Formed by the union of: Bulletin européen de
physiopathologie respiratoire, and: European
journal of respiratory diseases.
1988   8803460

Eur Respir J Suppl
The European respiratory journal.
Supplement
0904-1850
Continues: European journal of respiratory
diseases. Supplement.
1988   8910681

Eur Rev Med Pharmacol Sci
European review for medical and
pharmacological sciences
1128-3602
Continues: Rivista europea per le scienze
mediche e farmacologiche.
1997   9717360

Eur Spine J
European spine journal: official publication
of the European Spine Society, the European
Spinal Deformity Society, and the European
Section of the Cervical Spine Research
Society
0940-6719   1432-0932
1992   9301980

Eur Surg Res
European surgical research. Europäische
chirurgische Forschung. Recherches
chirurgicales européennes
0014-312X   1421-9921
1969   0174752

Eur Urol
European urology
0302-2838   1873-7560
1975   7512719

Eura Medicophys
Europa medicophysica
0014-2573   1827-1804
Continued by: European journal of physical
and rehabilitation medicine.
1965-2007   0071035

EURO Rep Stud
EURO reports and studies
0250-8710
1979-1989   8000103

Euro Surveill
Euro surveillance: bulletin européen sur
les maladies transmissibles = European
communicable disease bulletin
1025-496X   1560-7917
1995   100887452

EuroIntervention
EuroIntervention: journal of EuroPCR in
collaboration with the Working Group on
Interventional Cardiology of the European
Society of Cardiology
1774-024X
2005   101251040

Europace
Europace: European pacing, arrhythmias,
and cardiac electrophysiology: journal
of the working groups on cardiac pacing,
arrhythmias, and cardiac cellular
electrophysiology of the European Society of
Cardiology
1099-5129   1532-2092
1999   100883649

Eval Health Prof
Evaluation & the health professions
0163-2787
1978   7805992

Eval Program Plann
Evaluation and program planning
0149-7189   1873-7870
1978   7801727

Eval Rev
Evaluation review
0193-841X
Continues Evaluation quarterly.
1980   8004942

Evaluation
Evaluation
0090-4449
1972-1976   0415527

Evid Based Cardiovasc Med
Evidence-based cardiovascular medicine
1361-2611   1532-2173
1997   9709510

Evid Based Dent
Evidence-based dentistry
1462-0049   1476-5446
1998   100883603

Evid Based Med
Evidence-based medicine
1356-5524   1473-6810
Beginning 2000, some articles and abstracts
absorbed by: ACP journal club. Articles
published in ACP journal club have different
v. numbering and may have different titles
from what is published online.
1995   9608386

Evid Based Ment Health
Evidence-based mental health
1362-0347   1468-960X
1998   100883413

Evid Based Nurs
Evidence-based nursing
1367-6539   1468-9618
1998   9815947

Evid Rep Technol Assess (Full Rep)
Evidence report/technology assessment
1530-4396
1999   101082681

Evid Rep Technol Assess (Summ)
Evidence report/technology assessment
(Summary)
1530-440X
1998-2005   100890218

Evol Comput
Evolutionary computation
1063-6560   1530-9304
1993   9513581

Evol Dev
Evolution & development
1520-541X   1525-142X
1999   100883432

Evol Med
L' Evolution médicale
0014-3847
1957-1974   0370705

Evol Psychiatr (Paris)
L' Evolution psychiatrique
0014-3855
1925   0370706

Evolution
Evolution; international journal of organic
evolution
0014-3820   1558-5646
1947   0373224

Except Child
Exceptional children
0014-4029
Continues Journal of exceptional children.
1951   0375042

Excerpta Med (Dermatol)
Excerpta medica. Section 13, Dermatology
and venereology
0014-4177
1947   0175373

Excerpta Med (Ophthalmol)
Excerpta medica. Section 12, Ophthalmology
0014-4169
1947   0175372

Excerpta Med (Urol)
Excerpta medica. Section 28, Urology and
nephrology
0014-4320
Continues Excerpta medica. Section 28,
Urology.
1969   0217101

Excerpta Medica 15 Chest Dis
Excerpta medica. Section 15, Chest diseases
Continues: Excerpta medica. Section 15,
Tuberculosis and pulmonary diseases.
Continued by: Excerpta medica. Section
15. Chest diseases, thoracic surgery, and
tuberculosis.
1956-1965   0200317

Excerpta Medica 20 Gerontol Geriatr
Excerpta medica. Section 20, Gerontology
and geriatrics
0014-424X
1958   0200321

Exec Housekeep Today
Executive housekeeping today / the official
magazine of the National Executive
Housekeepers Association
0738-6583
1980   8915365

Exec Housekeeper
Executive housekeeper
0014-455X
19uu-1979   9876029

Exec Solut Healthc Manag
Executive solutions for healthcare
management
1099-193X
Continues: Health system leader.
1998-2000   9808647

Exerc Immunol Rev
Exercise immunology review
1077-5552
1995   9505535

Exerc Sport Sci Rev
Exercise and sport sciences reviews
0091-6331   1538-3008
1973   0375434

Exp Aging Res
Experimental aging research
0361-073X   1096-4657
1975   7603335

Exp Anim
Experimental animals / Japanese Association
for Laboratory Animal Science
1341-1357   1881-7122
Continues: Jikken dōbutsu.
1995   9604830

Exp Appl Acarol
Experimental & applied acarology
0168-8162   1572-9702
1985   8507436

Exp Biol
Experimental biology
0176-8638
Continues: Revue canadienne de biologie
expérimentale.
1984-1990   8503247

Exp Biol Med
Experimental biology and medicine
0071-3384
Continued by: Issues in biomedicine.
1967-1987   0114060

Exp Biol Med (Maywood)
Experimental biology and medicine
(Maywood, N.J.)
1535-3702   1535-3699
Continues: Proceedings of the Society for
Experimental Biology and Medicine. Society
for Experimental Biology and Medicine (New
York, N.Y.).
2001   100973463

Exp Brain Res
Experimental brain research.
Experimentelle Hirnforschung.
Expérimentation cérébrale
0014-4819   1432-1106
1966   0043312

Exp Cell Biol
Experimental cell biology
0304-3568
Continues Pathologia et microbiologia.
Merged with: Pathology and
immunopathology research, to form:
Pathobiology.
1976-1989   7701827

Exp Cell Res
Experimental cell research
0014-4827   1090-2422
1950   0373226

Exp Cell Res Suppl
Experimental cell research. Supplement
0099-9539
1949-1963   0375043

Exp Clin Endocrinol
Experimental and clinical endocrinology
0232-7384
Continues: Endokrinologie. Continued by:
Experimental and clinical endocrinology &
diabetes.
1983-1994   8302802

Exp Clin Endocrinol Diabetes
Experimental and clinical endocrinology &
diabetes: official journal, German Society
of Endocrinology [and] German Diabetes
Association
0947-7349   1439-3646
Continues: Experimental and clinical
endocrinology.
1995   9505926

Exp Clin Immunogenet
Experimental and clinical immunogenetics
0254-9670
1984-2002   8411714

Exp Clin Psychopharmacol
Experimental and clinical
psychopharmacology
1064-1297
1993   9419066

Exp Clin Transplant
Experimental and clinical transplantation:
official journal of the Middle East Society
for Organ Transplantation
1304-0855
2003   101207333

Exp Dermatol
Experimental dermatology
0906-6705   1600-0625
1992   9301549

Exp Diabesity Res
Experimental diabesity research
1543-8600   1543-8619
Continues: International journal of
experimental diabesity research. Continued
by: Experimental diabetes research.
2003-2004   101183590

Exp Diabetes Res
Experimental diabetes research
1687-5214   1687-5303
Continues: Experimental diabesity research.
2007   101274844

Exp Embryol Teratol
Experimental embryology and teratology
0306-2090
Supersedes Advances in teratology.
1974-1974   7513591

Exp Eye Res
Experimental eye research
0014-4835   1096-0007
1961   0370707

Exp Gerontol
Experimental gerontology
0531-5565   1873-6815
1964   0047061

Exp Hematol
Experimental hematology
0301-472X   1873-2399
Supersedes Experimental hematology,
published in Oak Ridge, Tenn.
1973   0402313

Exp Lung Res
Experimental lung research
0190-2148   1521-0499
1980   8004944

Exp Med Pathol Klin
Experimentelle Medizin, Pathologie und Klinik
0071-3430
1964-1972   0034007

Exp Med Surg
Experimental medicine and surgery
0014-4878
1943-1971   0435437

Exp Mol Med
Experimental & molecular medicine
1226-3613
Continues: Korean journal of biochemistry.
1996   9607880

Exp Mol Pathol
Experimental and molecular pathology
0014-4800   1096-0945
1962   0370711

Exp Mol Pathol Suppl
Experimental and molecular pathology.
Supplement
0531-5522
1963-1966   0007677

Exp Mycol
Experimental mycology
0147-5975
Continued by: Fungal genetics and biology.
1977-1995   8511210

Exp Nephrol
Experimental nephrology
1018-7782
Merged with part of: Nephron, to form:
Nephron. Experimental nephrology.
1993-2002   9302239

Exp Neurol
Experimental neurology
0014-4886   1090-2430
1959   0370712

Exp Neurol Suppl
Experimental neurology. Supplement
0531-559X
1964-19uu   0066741

Exp Oncol
Experimental oncology
1812-9269
Continues: Eksperimental'naiâ onkologiiâ.
2004   101230541

Exp Parasitol
Experimental parasitology
0014-4894   1090-2449
1951   0370713

Exp Pathol
Experimental pathology
0232-1513
Continues: Experimentelle Pathologie.
Continued by: Experimental and toxicologic
pathology.
1981-1991   8108218

Exp Pathol (Jena)
Experimentelle Pathologie
0014-4908
Continued by: Experimental pathology.
1967-1980   0113124

Exp Pathol Suppl
Experimental pathology. Supplement =
Experimentelle Pathologie. Supplement
0323-6102
1975-1989   8300901

Exp Physiol
Experimental physiology
0958-0670   1469-445X
Continues: Quarterly journal of experimental
physiology (Cambridge, England).
1990   9002940

Exp Psychol
Experimental psychology
1618-3169
Continues: Zeitschrift für experimentelle
Psychologie.
2002   101138477

Exp Toxicol Pathol
Experimental and toxicologic pathology:
official journal of the Gesellschaft für
Toxikologische Pathologie
0940-2993   1618-1433
Continues: Experimental pathology.
1992   9208920

Experientia
Experientia
0014-4754
Continued by: Cellular and molecular life
sciences.
1945-1996   0376547

Experientia Suppl
Experientia. Supplementum
0071-335X
Continued by: EXS.
1953-1989   0320043

Expert Opin Biol Ther
Expert opinion on biological therapy
1471-2598   1744-7682
2001   101125414

Expert Opin Drug Deliv
Expert opinion on drug delivery
1742-5247   1744-7593
2004   101228421

Expert Opin Drug Metab Toxicol
Expert opinion on drug metabolism &
toxicology
1742-5255   1744-7607
2005   101228422

Expert Opin Drug Saf
Expert opinion on drug safety
1474-0338   1744-764X
2002   101163027

Expert Opin Emerg Drugs
Expert opinion on emerging drugs
1472-8214   1744-7623
Continues: Emerging drugs.
2001   101135662

Expert Opin Investig Drugs
Expert opinion on investigational drugs
1354-3784   1744-7658
Continues: Current opinion in investigational
drugs.
1994   9434197

Expert Opin Pharmacother
Expert opinion on pharmacotherapy
1465-6566   1744-7666
1999   100897346

Expert Opin Ther Targets
Expert opinion on therapeutic targets
1472-8222   1744-7631
Continues: Emerging therapeutic targets.
2001   101127833

Expert Rev Anti Infect Ther
Expert review of anti-infective therapy
1478-7210   1744-8336
2003   101181284

Expert Rev Anticancer Ther
Expert review of anticancer therapy
1473-7140   1744-8328
2001   101123358

Expert Rev Cardiovasc Ther
Expert review of cardiovascular therapy
1477-9072   1744-8344
2003   101182328

Expert Rev Gastroenterol Hepatol
Expert review of gastroenterology &
hepatology
1747-4124   1747-4132
2007   101278199

Expert Rev Med Devices
Expert review of medical devices
1743-4440   1745-2422
2004   101230445

Expert Rev Mol Diagn
Expert review of molecular diagnostics
1473-7159   1744-8352
2001   101120777

Expert Rev Mol Med
Expert reviews in molecular medicine
    1462-3994
1997   100939725

Expert Rev Neurother
Expert review of neurotherapeutics
1473-7175   1744-8360
2001   101129944

Expert Rev Proteomics
Expert review of proteomics
1478-9450   1744-8387
2004   101223548

Expert Rev Vaccines
Expert review of vaccines
1476-0584   1744-8395
2002   101155475

Explore (NY)
Explore (New York, N.Y.)
1550-8307
2005   101233160

Explorer (Hayward)
Explorer
Continues: Sac Explorer. Continued by:
Southern Alameda County Explorer.
1969-1972   9875621

Explorer (Kansas City)
The Explorer: the journal of the School of
Dentistry of the University of Missouri at
Kansas City. University of Missouri--Kansas
City. School of Dentistry
University of Missouri at Kansas City
1970   9875622

Expos Annu Biochim Med
Exposés annuels de biochimie médicale
0300-9076
1938-1982   0071567

EXS
EXS
1023-294X
Continues: Experientia. Supplementum.
1989   9204529

Extremophiles
Extremophiles: life under extreme
conditions
1431-0651   1433-4909
1997   9706854

Eye
Eye (London, England)
0950-222X   1476-5454
Continues: Transactions of the
ophthalmological societies of the United
Kingdom.
1987   8703986

Eye Contact Lens
Eye & contact lens
1542-2321   1542-233X
Continues: CLAO journal.
2003   101160941

Eye Ear Nose Throat Mon
Eye, ear, nose & throat monthly
0014-5491
Absorbed: Diseases of the eye, ear, nose and
throat. Continued by: Ear, nose, & throat
journal.
1922-1976   0370714

F

Fa Yi Xue Za Zhi
Fa yi xue za zhi
1004-5619
1985   9426151

Fac Notes (New Orleans La)
Faculty notes (New Orleans, La.)
Continued by: HIV clinician.
19uu-1999   100893937

Fachbl Schweiz Heime Anst Rev Suisse Etabl Hosp Educ
Fachblatt für schweizerische Heime und
Anstalten. Revue suisse des établissements
hospitaliers et d'éducation
Continues Fachblatt für schweizerisches
Anstaltswesen. Continued by Hospitalis.
1946-1947   16910100R

Facial Orthop Temporomandibular Arthrol
Facial orthopedics and temporomandibular
arthrology
0749-0399
1984-1988   8510890

Facial Plast Surg
Facial plastic surgery: FPS
0736-6825   1098-8793
1983   8405303

Facial Plast Surg Clin North Am
Facial plastic surgery clinics of North
America
1064-7406   1558-1926
1993   9414907

Fact Sheet (Cent Home Care Policy Res)
Fact sheet (Center for Home Care Policy
and Research (U.S.))
Continued by: Policy brief (Center for Home
Care Policy and Research (U.S.)).
2000-2000   101285584

Factor Odontol
Factor odontológico
Continues: Revista científica, técnica y
cultural F.O.
1986   9108447

Fag Tidsskr Sykepleien
Fag tidsskriftet sykepleien
0802-9768
Continues in part: Sykepleien. Continued by:
Sykepleien. Fag.
1989-1992   9008896

Fam Cancer
Familial cancer
1389-9600   1573-7292
2000   100898211

Fam Community Health
Family & community health
0160-6379   1550-5057
1978   7809641

Fam Health
Family health
0014-7249
Absorbed Today's health, Apr. 1976.
Continued by Health (Family Media, Inc.).
1969-1981   7610780

Fam Med
Family medicine
0742-3225
Continues: Family medicine teacher.
1981   8306464

Fam Plann
Family planning
0014-7338
Continued by: Family planning today.
1952-1976   7703901

Fam Plann Perspect
Family planning perspectives
0014-7354
Continued by: Perspectives on sexual and
reproductive health.
1969-2001   0241370

Fam Pract
Family practice
0263-2136   1460-2229
1984   8500875

Fam Pract Manag
Family practice management
1069-5648
1993   9417533

Fam Pract Res J
The Family practice research journal
0270-2304
1981-1994   8208228

Fam Process
Family process
0014-7370   1545-5300
1962   0400666

FAO Food Nutr Pap
FAO food and nutrition paper
0254-4725
1977   8110156

FAO Food Nutr Ser
FAO food and nutrition series
1014-3181
1976   7804985

FAO Nutr Meet Rep Ser
FAO nutrition meetings report series
0071-707X
1948-1977   0373227

FAO Nutr Stud
FAO nutritional studies
0071-7088
Continued by: FAO food and nutrition series.
1948-1974   0373230

Faraday Discuss
Faraday discussions
1359-6640
Continues: Faraday discussions of the
Chemical Society.
1991   9212301

Faraday Discuss Chem Soc
Faraday discussions of the Chemical Society
0301-5696
Continues: Discussions of the Faraday
Society. Continued by: Faraday discussions.
1972-1991   7507112

Farm Glas
Farmaceutski glasnik
0014-8202
1945   0373232

Farm Hosp
Farmacia hospitalaria: órgano oficial de
expresión científica de la Sociedad Española
de Farmacia Hospitalaria
1130-6343
Continues: Revista de la Sociedad Española
de Farmacia Hospitalaria.
199u   9440679

Farm Nueva
Farmacia nueva
0367-2689
1934-1982   16920230R

Farm Obz
Farmaceutický obzor
0014-8172
Continues Farmácia.
1961   16920150R

Farm Pol
Farmacja polska
0014-8261
1945   0400670

Farm Revy
Farmacevtisk revy
0014-8210
1902   0400667

Farm Tid
Farmaceutisk tidende
0367-1720
Continues Blad for Pharmaceutisk
medhjaelperforening. Continued by:
Farmaceuten.
1895-1988   0407150

Farm Vestn
Farmacevtski vestnik
0014-8229
1950   0373233

Farm Zh
Farmatsevtychnyĭ zhurnal
0014-8342
1928   0374603

Farmaco
Farmaco (Società chimica italiana: 1989)
0014-827X
Formed by the union of: Farmaco (Edizione
pratica); and: Farmaco (Edizione scientifica).
Continued by: ChemMedChem.
1989-2005   8912641

Farmaco [Prat]
Il Farmaco; edizione pratica
0014-827X
Continues in part Il Farmaco; scienza e
tecnica. Merged with: Farmaco; edizione
scientifica, to form: Farmaco (Società chimica
italiana: 1989).
1953-1988   0376330

Farmaco [Sci]
Il Farmaco; edizione scientifica
0430-0920
Continues in part Il Farmaco; scienza e
tecnica. Merged with: Farmaco; edizione
practica, to form: Farmaco (Società chimica
italiana: 1989).
1953-1988   0370716

Farmacognosia
Farmacognosia; anales del Instituto José
Celestino Mutis
1942-1967   16920340R

Farmacoter Actual
Farmacoterapia actual
1944-1952   16920380R

Farmacoterapia
Farmacoterapia
1947-19uu   16920370R

Farmakol Toksikol
Farmakologiia i toksikologiia
0014-8318
Supersedes, in part, Farmatsiia
i farmakologiia. Continued by:
Eksperimental'naia i klinicheskaia
farmakologiia.
1938-1991   16920420R

Farmakoterapi
Farmakoterapi
0014-8326
Supersedes Nyconytt.
1945-1993 0400671

Farmalecta
Farmalecta
0325-8300
1946-1950 16920430R

Farmatsiia
Farmatsiia
0367-3014
Continues Aptechnoe delo.
1967 0136541

Farmatsiia (Sofia)
Farmatsiia
0428-0296
1951 0372770

FASEB J
The FASEB journal: official publication of
the Federation of American Societies for
Experimental Biology
0892-6638 1530-6860
Continues: Federation proceedings.
1987 8804484

Fasett
Fasett
0802-6939
1966 8502354

Fauchard
Fauchard
0533-0319
1970 9875646

Faulkner Grays Med Health
Faulkner & Gray's medicine & health
1047-8892
Continues: Medicine & health. Continued by:
Medicine & health (1997).
1989-1997 9001350

FDA Consum
FDA consumer
0362-1332
Continues: FDA papers.
1972 0344327

FDA Drug Bull
FDA drug bulletin
0361-4344
Continued by: FDA medical bulletin.
1971-1990 1302430

FDI World
FDI world
1025-403X
Continues: Dental world (London, England).
1994-2001 9432540

FEBS J
The FEBS journal
1742-464X 1742-4658
Continues: European journal of biochemistry.
2005 101229646

FEBS Lett
FEBS letters
0014-5793 1873-3468
1968 0155157

Fed Bull
Federation bulletin / Federation of State
Medical Boards of the United States
0014-9306
Continues: Monthly bulletin. Federation of
State Medical Boards of the United States.
Continued by: Journal of medical licensure
and discipline.
1921-2000 0375044

Fed Oper Dent
Federation of operative dentistry
1990 9885646

Fed Proc
Federation proceedings
0014-9446
Continues: Federation yearbook. Federation
of American Societies for Experimental
Biology. Continued by: FASEB journal.
1942-1987 0372771

Fed Proc Transl Suppl
Federation proceedings. Translation
supplement; selected translations from
medical-related science
0430-2494
1963-1966 16920890R

Fed Regist
Federal register
0097-6326
1936 7808722

Fegato
Il Fegato
0014-9659
Continued by: Fegato (San Donato Milanese,
Italy: 1994).
1955-1990 2984756R

Feldsher Akush
Feĭdsher i akusherka
0014-9772
Continues: Feĭdsher. Continues Fel'dsher.
Merged with: Meditŝinskaiâ sestra, to form:
Meditŝinskaiâ pomoshch.
1940-1992 16930040R

FEMS Immunol Med Microbiol
FEMS immunology and medical
microbiology
0928-8244 1574-695X
Continues: FEMS microbiology immunology.
1993 9315554

FEMS Microbiol Ecol
FEMS microbiology ecology
0168-6496 1574-6941
1985 8901229

FEMS Microbiol Immunol
FEMS microbiology immunology
0920-8534
Continued by: FEMS immunology and
medical microbiology.
1988-1992 8901230

FEMS Microbiol Lett
FEMS microbiology letters
0378-1097 1574-6968
1977 7705721

FEMS Microbiol Rev
FEMS microbiology reviews
0168-6445 1574-6976
1985 8902526

FEMS Yeast Res
FEMS yeast research
1567-1356 1567-1364
2001 101085384

Fen Zi Xi Bao Sheng Wu Xue Bao
Fen zi xi bao sheng wu xue bao = Journal
of molecular cell biology / Zhongguo xi bao
sheng wu xue xue hui zhu ban
1673-520X
Continues: Shi yan sheng wu xue bao.
2006 101249591

Fertil Steril
Fertility and sterility
0015-0282 1556-5653
1950 0372772

Fetal Diagn Ther
Fetal diagnosis and therapy
1015-3837 1421-9964
Continues: Fetal therapy.
1990 9107463

Fetal Pediatr Pathol
Fetal and pediatric pathology
1551-3815 1551-3823
Continues: Pediatric pathology & molecular
medicine.
2004 101230972

Fetal Ther
Fetal therapy
0257-2788
Continued by: Fetal diagnosis and therapy.
1986-1989 8700083

Feuill Prat
Feuillets du praticien
0426-0627
1937-1973 0174345

Fich Med Ter Puriss
Fichero médico terapéutico
0015-0606
1939-1971 16930130R

Fin Lakaresallsk Handl
Finska läkaresällskapets handlingar
0015-2501
1841 0371572

Find Brief
Findings brief: health care financing &
organization
 1553-0302
1996 101149237

Fire J
Fire journal (Boston, Mass.)
0015-2617
Continues: Quarterly of the National Fire
Protection Association. Merged with: Fire
command (Quincy, Mass.), to form: NFPA
journal.
1965-1990 9877774

Fire Technol
Fire technology
0015-2684
1965 9877775

Fish Physiol Biochem
Fish physiology and biochemistry
0920-1742 1573-5168
1986 100955049

Fish Shellfish Immunol
Fish & shellfish immunology
1050-4648 1095-9947
1991 9505220

Fission Prod Inhal Proj
Fission product inhalation project [technical
progress report]. Lovelace Foundation for
Medical Education and Research
1962-1969 21830910R

Fitoterapia
Fitoterapia
0367-326X 1873-6971
Continues: Estratti fluidi titolati.
1947 16930290R

Fiziol Cheloveka
Fiziologiia cheloveka
0131-1646
1975 7603567

Fiziol Norm Patol
Fiziologia normală şi patologică
0015-3281
Continues Revista de fiziologie normală şi
patologică.
1960-1973 7612005

Fiziol Zh
Fiziologicheskiĭ zhurnal
0201-8489
Continues Fiziolohichnyĭ zhurnal published 1955-77. Continued by: Fiziolohichnyĭ zhurnal (Kiev, Ukraine: 1994).
1978-1993   7806822

Fiziol Zh
Fiziolohichnyĭ zhurnal
0015-3311
Formed by the union of Medychnyĭ zhurnal and Voprosy fiziologii. Continued by Fiziologicheskiĭ zhurnal.
1955-1977   7806823

Fiziol Zh
Fiziolohichnyĭ zhurnal (Kiev, Ukraine: 1994)
Continues: Fiziologicheskiĭ zhurnal.
1994   9601541

Fiziol Zh Im I M Sechenova
Fiziologicheskiĭ zhurnal imeni I.M. Sechenova / Rossiĭskaia akademiia nauk
1027-3646
Continues: Fiziologicheskiĭ zhurnal SSSR im. I.M. Sechenova. Continued by: Rossiĭskaia fiziologicheskiĭ zhurnal.
1992-1996   9308360

Fiziol Zh SSSR Im I M Sechenova
Fiziologicheskiĭ zhurnal SSSR imeni I. M. Sechenova
0015-329X
Continues: Russkiĭ fiziologicheskiĭ zhurnal imeni I. M. Sechenova. Continued by: Fiziologicheskiĭ zhurnal imeni I.M. Sechenova.
1932-1991   0427673

Fla Dent J
Florida dental journal
0015-3990
Continues The Journal of the Florida State Dental Society. Merged with: Dental times dispatch, to form: Today's FDA.
1968-1989   7512730

Fla Health Notes
Florida health notes
0015-4105
Continued by Florida's health.
1892-1975   7606886

Fla Nurse
The Florida nurse
0015-4199
Continues the Bulletin of the Florida State Nurse's Association.
1955   16930510R

Fla Optom
Florida optometrist
Continued by the Journal of the Florida Optometric Association.
1929-1950   16930440R

Flash Inf
Flash-Informations
0771-8187
Continues: Fnib: Organe De La Federation Nationale Des Infirmier(e)s Belges. Continued by: Fnib Info.
1982-1988   9880024

Fly (Austin)
Fly
1933-6934
1933-6942
2007   101470897

FNIB
F.N.I.B.; organe de la Fédération nationale des infirmier(e)s belges
0301-0813
Continues L'Infirmière. Continued by: Flash-informations (Brussels, Belgium).
1972-1981   0366610

FNIB Info
FNIB info
0774-935X
Continues: Flash-informations (Brussels, Belgium).
1987-1998   9002951

FO
Fo. Facultad De Odontologia
Continues: Eno Fo.
1976-1980   9878156

Focus
Focus (San Francisco, Calif.)
1047-0719
1985   8911231

Focus AACN
Focus On Aacn
Continues: Focus. Continued by: Focus On Critical Care.
1980-1983   9879072

Focus Crit Care
Focus on critical care / American Association of Critical-Care Nurses
0736-3605
Continues: Focus on AACN.
1983-1992   8302805

Focus MDA
Focus MDA: the official publication of the Missouri Dental Association
Continues: Missouri dental journal.
1998   9815833

Focus Ohio Dent
Focus on Ohio dentistry
1042-2528
Continues the Newsnotes issues of Ohio dental journal. Vols. for 1994- include a section in the May and Nov. issues with title: Ohio dental journal. Continued by: ODA today.
1989-2001   9100050

Fogorv Sz
Fogorvosi szemle
0015-5314
Supersedes Magyar fogorvosok lapja, 1906-07.
1908   0374613

Fold Des
Folding & design
1359-0278
Merged with: Structure, to form: Structure with Folding & design.
1996-1998   9604387

Folha Med
Folha medica
0015-5454
1920-1998   0370720

Folia Allergol (Roma)
Folia allergologica
0015-5470
Supersedes I Quaderni dell'allergia. Continued by Folia allergologica et immunologica clinica.
1954-1973   7502074

Folia Biol (Krakow)
Folia biologica
0015-5497
1953   2984758R

Folia Biol (Praha)
Folia biologica
0015-5500
Supersedes in part: Ceskoslovenská biologie.
1955   0234640

Folia Cardiol
Folia cardiologica
0390-5756
Merged with Cuore e circolazione and Malattie cardiovascolari to form Giornale italiano di cardiologia.
1940-1969   1270452

Folia Clin Biol (Sao Paulo)
Folia clinica et biologica
0015-5519
1929-1974   0356575

Folia Clin Int (Barc)
Folia clínica internacional
0015-5527
1951-1976   2984759R

Folia Endocrinol
Folia endocrinologica
0015-5535
1948-1974   0417431

Folia Endocrinol Mens Incretologia Incretoterapia
Folia endocrinologica; mensile di incretologia e incretoterapia
1923-19uu   16940290R

Folia Gynaecol (1908)
Folia gynaecologica
1121-1199
1908-1949   16940300R

Folia Haematol (Frankf)
Folia haematologica; internationales Magazin für Blutforschung
0015-556X
Absorbed by Blut, 1965.
1956-1964   0140243

Folia Haematol Int Mag Klin Morphol Blutforsch
Folia haematologica (Leipzig, Germany: 1928)
0323-4347
Formed by the union of: Folia haematologica. 1. Teil. Archiv, and: Folia haematologica. 2. Teil. Zentral-Organ; and continues the vol. numbering of the first.
1927-1990   0374615

Folia Hered Pathol (Milano)
Folia hereditaria et pathologica
0015-5578
1951-1986   0417432

Folia Histochem Cytobiol
Folia histochemica et cytobiologica / Polish Academy of Sciences, Polish Histochemical and Cytochemical Society
0239-8508   1897-5631
Continues: Folia histochemica et cytochemica.
1984   8502651

Folia Histochem Cytochem (Krakow)
Folia histochemica et cytochemica
0015-5586
Continued by Folia histochemica et cytobiologica.
1963-1983   2984760R

Folia Med (Napoli)
Folia medica. Folia medica (Naples, Italy)
0015-5608
Continued by Rivista di medicina del lavoro ed igiene industriale.
1915-1974   2983161R

Folia Med (Plovdiv)
Folia medica
0204-8043
1959   2984761R

Folia Med Cracov
Folia medica Cracoviensia
0015-5616
1959   0374617

Folia Med Neerl
Folia medica Neerlandica
0015-5624
Continued by the Netherlands journal of medicine.
1958-1972   0354741

Folia Microbiol (Praha)
Folia microbiologica
0015-5632   1874-9356
Continues: Ceskoslovenská mikrobiologie.
1959   0376757

Folia Morphol (Praha)
Folia morphologica
0015-5640
Continues, in English, Ceskoslovenská morfologie. Continued by: Functional and developmental morphology.
1965-1990   0010076

Folia Morphol (Warsz)
Folia morphologica
0015-5659
1929   0374620

Folia Neuropathol
Folia neuropathologica / Association of Polish Neuropathologists and Medical Research Centre, Polish Academy of Sciences
1641-4640   1509-572X
Continues: Neuropatologia polska.
1994   9437431

Folia Parasitol (Praha)
Folia parasitologica
0015-5683
Continues: Ceskoslovenská parasitologie.
1966   0065750

Folia Phoniatr (Basel)
Folia phoniatrica
0015-5705
Continued by: Folia phoniatrica et logopaedica.
1947-1993   0424467

Folia Phoniatr Logop
Folia phoniatrica et logopaedica: official organ of the International Association of Logopedics and Phoniatrics (IALP)
1021-7762   1421-9972
Continues: Folia phoniatrica.
1994   9422792

Folia Primatol (Basel)
Folia primatologica; international journal of primatology
0015-5713   1421-9980
1963   0370723

Folia Psychiatr
Folia psychiatrica
Continued by Folia neuropsychiatrica.
1958-1966   0132463

Folia Psychiatr Neurol Jpn
Folia psychiatrica et neurologica japonica
0015-5721
Continued by: The Japanese journal of psychiatry and neurology.
1933-1985   0372774

Folia Psychiatr Neurol Neurochir Neerl
Folia psychiatrica, neurologica et neurochirurgica Neerlandica
Continues Psychiatrische en neurologische bladen. Continued by Psychiatria, neurologia, neurochirurgia.
1948-1959   16940420R

Folia Stomatol
Folia stomatologica
1940-1950   16940440R

Folia Vet Lat
Folia veterinaria Latina
0301-0724
1971-1977   0374246

Food Addit Contam
Food additives and contaminants
0265-203X   1464-5122
Split into: Food additives & contaminants. Part A, Chemistry, analysis, control, exposure & risk assessment, and: Food additives & contaminants. Part B, Surveillance.
1984-2007   8500474

Food Addit Contam Part A Chem Anal Control Expo Risk Assess
Food additives & contaminants. Part A, Chemistry, analysis, control, exposure & risk assessment
Continues in part: Food additives and contaminants.
2008   101485040

Food Addit Contam Part B Surveill
Food additives & contaminants. Part B, Surveillance
1939-3210   1939-3229
Continues in part: Food additives and contaminants.
2008   101317183

Food Cosmet Toxicol
Food and cosmetics toxicology
0015-6264
Continued by Food and chemical toxicology.
1963-1981   0374623

Food Drug Cosmet Law Q
Food, Drug, cosmetic law quarterly
Continued by: Food, drug, cosmetic law journal.
1946-1949   17010130R

Food Drug Law J
Food and drug law journal
1064-590X
Continues: Food, drug, cosmetic law journal.
1992   9215384

Food Ind
Food industries
0096-2236
Continued by Food engineering.
1928-1951   17010140R

Food Manage
Food management
0091-018X
Formed by the union of: Hospital & nursing home food management, and: School & college food management, continuing their vol. numbering.
1972   9877776

Food Microbiol
Food microbiology
0740-0020   1095-9998
1984   8601127

Food Nutr (Roma)
Food and nutrition
0304-8942
Supersedes Nutrition newsletter. Continued by: Food, nutrition, and agriculture.
1975-1987   7512731

Food Nutr Bull
Food and nutrition bulletin
0379-5721
Supersedes PAG bulletin.
1978   7906418

Food Res
Food research
Continued by Journal of food science.
1936-1960   0027704

Foodborne Pathog Dis
Foodborne pathogens and disease
1535-3141   1556-7125
2004   101120121

Foot Ankle
Foot & ankle
0198-0211
Continued by: Foot & ankle international.
1980-1993   8010104

Foot Ankle Clin
Foot and ankle clinics
1083-7515   1558-1934
1996   9615073

Foot Ankle Int
Foot & ankle international / American Orthopaedic Foot and Ankle Society [and] Swiss Foot and Ankle Society
1071-1007
Continues: Foot & ankle.
1994   9433869

Foot Ankle Surg
Foot and ankle surgery: official journal of the European Society of Foot and Ankle Surgeons
1268-7731   1460-9584
Continues: European journal of foot and ankle surgery.
1996   9609647

For Your Inf (Inst Health Rec Inf Manag)
For your information (Institute of Health Record & Information Management)
Continues: Journal (Institute of Health Record Information and Management). Continued by: New journal (Institute of Health Record & Information Management).
2004-2004   101284925

Forbes
Forbes
0015-6914
1917   9877777

Fordham Law Rev
Fordham law review / edited by Fordham law students
0015-704X
1914   9891707

Forensic Sci
Forensic science
0300-9432
Absorbed the Journal of forensic medicine. Continued by Forensic science international.
1972-1978   0330706

Forensic Sci Int
Forensic science international
0379-0738   1872-6283
Continues: Forensic science.
1978   7902034

Forensic Sci Int Genet
Forensic science international. Genetics
1872-4973   1878-0326
2007   101317016

Forensic Sci Med Pathol
Forensic science, medicine, and pathology
1547-769X   1556-2891
2005   101236111

Formulary
Formulary (Cleveland, Ohio)
1082-801X
Continues: Hospital formulary.
1995   9513311

Forsch Fortbild Chir Bewegungsappar
Forschung und Fortbildung in der Chirurgie
des Bewegungsapparates
1983-1992   8408562

Forsch Fortschr
Forschungen und Fortschritte;
Nachrichtenblatt der deutschen
Wissenschaft und Technik
1925-1967   0154621

Forsch Komplementarmed
Forschende Komplementärmedizin
1021-7096
Continued by: Forschende
Komplementärmedizin und klassische
Naturheilkunde.
1994-1999   9440428

Forsch Komplementarmed Klass Naturheilkd
Forschende Komplementärmedizin und
klassische Naturheilkunde = Research in
complementary and natural classical medicine
1424-7364
Continues: Forschende
Komplementärmedizin. Continued by:
Forschende Komplementärmedizin (2006).
2000-2005   100958201

Forsch Komplementmed
Forschende Komplementärmedizin (2006)
1661-4119   1661-4127
Continues: Forschende Komplementärmedizin
und klassische Naturheilkunde.
2006   101269884

Fortn Rev Chic Dent Soc
The Fortnightly review of the Chicago
Dental Society
0009-353X
Supersedes the society's Bulletin. Continued
by CDS review.
1941-1972   7503518

Fortschr Androl
Fortschritte der Andrologie
0301-5726
1970-1990   0410273

Fortschr Angew Radioisot Grenzgeb
Fortschritte der angewandten Radioisotopie
und Grenzgebiete
1957-1957   17010500R

Fortschr Arzneimittelforsch
Fortschritte der Arzneimittelforschung.
Progress in drug research. Progrès des
recherches pharmaceutiques
0071-786X
Continued by: Progress in drug research.
1959-1968   1303005

Fortschr Chem Org Naturst
Fortschritte der Chemie organischer
Naturstoffe. Progress in the chemistry of
organic natural products. Progrès dans la
chimie des substances organiques naturelles
0071-7886
1938   0370724

Fortschr Geb Rontgenstr
Fortschritte auf dem Gebiete der
Röntgenstrahlen
Continued by Fortschritte auf dem Gebiete
der Röntgenstrahlen und der Nuklearmedizin.
Absorbed Röntgenpraxis, Diagnostik.
Röntgen-, Radium-, Lichttherapie in Apr.
1949.
1897-1955   17010480R

Fortschr Geb Rontgenstr Nuklearmed
Fortschritte auf dem Gebiete der
Röntgenstrahlen und der Nuklearmedizin
0015-8151
Continues Fortschritte auf dem Gebiete der
Röntgenstrahlen. Continued by RöFo.
1956-1974   7507118

Fortschr Geb Rontgenstrahlen Neuen Bildgeb Verfahr Erganzungsbd
Fortschritte auf dem Gebiete der
Röntgenstrahlen und der neuen
bildgebenden Verfahren. Ergänzungsband
Continues: Fortschritte auf dem Gebiete der
Röntgenstrahlen und der Nuklearmedizin.
Ergänzungsband.
1992-1992   9316522

Fortschr Geb Rontgenstrahlen Nuklearmed Erganzungsbd
Fortschritte auf dem Gebiete der
Röntgenstrahlen und der Nuklearmedizin.
Ergänzungsband
0178-4609
Continues the Ergänzungsband of Fortschritte
auf dem Gebiete der Röntgenstrahlen.
Continued by: Fortschritte auf dem
Gebiete der Röntgenstrahlen und der neuen
bildgebenden Verfahren. Ergänzungsband.
1956-1988   0372776

Fortschr Geburtshilfe Gynakol
Fortschritte der Geburtshilfe und
Gynäkologie
0065-2997
Continues Fortschritte der Geburtshilfe und
Gynäkologie issued in the series Bibliotheca
gynaecologica. Superseded by Contributions
to gynecology and obstetrics.
1971-1975   7609286

Fortschr Hals Nasen Ohrenheilkd
Fortschritte der Hals-Nasen-Ohrenheilkunde
Continued by Advances in oto-rhino-
laryngology. Supplement to Practica oto-
rhino-laryngologica. 1953-65.
1953-1968   0242561

Fortschr Immunitatsforsch
Fortschritte der Immunitätsforschung
0071-7908
1959-1965   17010520R

Fortschr Kiefer Gesichtschir
Fortschritte der Kiefer- und Gesichts-
Chirurgie
0071-7916
Merged with: Deutsche Zeitschrift für Mund-,
Kiefer- und Gesichts-Chirurgie, to become:
Mund-, Kiefer- und Gesichtschirurgie.
1955-1996   0066413

Fortschr Kieferorthop
Fortschritte der Kieferorthopädie
0015-816X
Continued by: Journal of orofacial
orthopedics.
1952-1995   2984762R

Fortschr Med
Fortschritte der Medizin
0015-8178
Absorbed: Medizinische Praxis (Munich,
Germany). Merged with: MMW. Münchener
medizinische Wochenschrift, to form: MMW,
Fortschritte der Medizin.
1883-1999   2984763R

Fortschr Med Monogr
Fortschritte der Medizin. Monographie
0946-5634
1988-1994   9435833

Fortschr Med Orig
Fortschritte der Medizin. Originalien
199u   101120496

Fortschr Med Suppl
Fortschritte der Medizin. Supplement: die
Kongressinformation für die Praxis
0932-5611
1985-1999   9435801

Fortschr Neurol Psychiatr
Fortschritte der Neurologie-Psychiatrie
0720-4299   1439-3522
Continues: Fortschritte der Neurologie-
Psychiatrie und ihrer Grenzgebiete.
1981   8103137

Fortschr Neurol Psychiatr Grenzgeb
Fortschritte der Neurologie, Psychiatrie, und
ihrer Grenzgebiete
0015-8194
Continued by: Fortschritte der Neurologie,
Psychiatrie.
1929-1980   0370726

Fortschr Ophthalmol
Fortschritte der Ophthalmologie: Zeitschrift
der Deutschen Ophthalmologischen
Gesellschaft
0723-8045
Continues: Deutsche Ophthalmologische
Gesellschaft. Zusammenkunft. Bericht
über die Zusammenkunft. Split into:
German journal of ophthalmology, and:
Ophthalmologe.
1982-1991   8302807

Fortschr Psychosom Med
Fortschritte der psychosomatischen Medizin.
Advances in psychosomatic medicine
Continued by: Advances in psychosomatic
medicine.
1960-1964   0143116

Fortschr Tierphysiol Tierernahr
Fortschritte in der Tierphysiologie und
Tierernährung
0301-570X
Continued by: Advances in animal physiology
and animal nutrition.
1972-1991   0414664

Fortschr Verhaltensforsch
Fortschritte der Verhaltensforschung
0301-2808
1972-1984   0436651

Fortschr Zool
Fortschritte der Zoologie
0071-7991
Supersedes Ergebnisse und Fortschritte der
Zoologie.
1935-1996   0374625

Fortune
Fortune
0015-8259
1930   01920610R

Forum (Genova)
Forum (Genoa, Italy)
1121-8142   1970-0008
1991   9315183

Forum (Wash)
Forum (Washington, D.C.: 1977)
0160-7154
Supersedes Record.
1977-1981   7801061

Forum Med
Forum on medicine
0161-7478
Supersedes Bulletin of the American College
of Physicians. Continued by American
College of Physicians observer.
1978-1980   7805999

Forum Nutr
Forum of nutrition
1660-0347   1662-2987
Continues: Bibliotheca nutritio et dieta.
2003   101194770

Found News
Foundation news
0015-8976
Continued by: Foundation news & commentary.
1960-1994   0253250

Found News Comment
Foundation news & commentary
1076-3961
Continues: Foundation news.
1994   9438201

Fprc
FPRC [reports]. Great Britain. Flying Personnel Research Committee
0432-3726
19uu   23020660R

Fr Med
France Medecine
19uu   9879159

Fra Sundhedsstyr
Fra Sundhedsstyrelsen
0015-9263
1963-1974   1310313

Fracastoro
Il Fracastoro
0015-9271
Continued by: Quaderni de Il Fracastoro.
1905-1996   0401045

Frankf Z Pathol
Frankfurter Zeitschrift für Pathologie
0367-3480
Merged with Virchows Archiv für pathologische Anatomie un Physiologie und für klinische Medizin, to form Virchows Archiv. A: Pathology. Pathologische Anatomie; and Virchows Archiv. B: Cell Pathology.
1907-1967   0151576

Frater Psi Omega
The Frater of Psi Omega
0071-9285
1901   17020320R

Free Radic Biol Med
Free radical biology & medicine
0891-5849   1873-4596
Formed by the union of: Advances in free radical biology and medicine; and: Journal of free radicals in biology & medicine.
1987   8709159

Free Radic Res
Free radical research
1071-5762   1029-2470
Continues: Free radical research communications.
1994   9423872

Free Radic Res Commun
Free radical research communications
8755-0199
Continued by: Free radical research.
1985-1993   8709453

Freie Zahnarzt
Der Freie Zahnarzt
0340-1766
Continues Monatsschrift deutscher Zahnärzte: der freie Zahnarzt.
1971   7506270

Fresenius J Anal Chem
Fresenius' journal of analytical chemistry
0937-0633   1432-1130
Continues: Fresenius' Zeitschrift für analytische Chemie. Merged with: Analusis, and: Química analítica (Belaterra, Spain), to form: Analytical and bioanalytical chemistry.
1990-2001   9114077

Friuli Med
Il Friuli medico
0016-1535
1946-1995   0421045

Front Aging Ser
Frontiers in aging series
0271-955X
1980-1988   8006903

Front Biol
Frontiers of biology
0071-965X
1966-1979   0065035

Front Biosci
Frontiers in bioscience: a journal and virtual library
1093-9946   1093-4715
Continued in part by: Frontiers in bioscience (scholar edition). Continued in part by: Frontiers in bioscience (elite edition).
1996   9709506

Front Gastrointest Res
Frontiers of gastrointestinal research
0302-0665
Supersedes Bibliotheca gastroenterologica.
1975-2002   7510219

Front Health Policy Res
Frontiers in health policy research / National Bureau of Economic Research
1096-231X   1537-2634
1998   9815924

Front Health Serv Manage
Frontiers of health services management
0748-8157
1984   8501389

Front Horm Res
Frontiers of hormone research
0301-3073   1662-3762
1972   0320246

Front Med Biol Eng
Frontiers of medical and biological engineering: the international journal of the Japan Society of Medical Electronics and Biological Engineering
0921-3775
1988-2002   9011464

Front Neuroendocrinol
Frontiers in neuroendocrinology
0091-3022   1095-6808
1969   7513292

Front Neurol Neurosci
Frontiers of neurology and neuroscience
1660-4431   1662-2804
Continues: Monographs in clinical neuroscience.
2005   101274949

Front Nurs Serv Q Bull
Frontier Nursing Service quarterly bulletin
0016-2116
Continues the Quarterly bulletin of the Kentucky Committee for Mothers and Babies.
1928   7502563

Front Oral Biol
Frontiers of oral biology
1420-2433
Continues: Frontiers of oral physiology.
1998   9812095

Front Oral Physiol
Frontiers of oral physiology
0301-536X
Continued by: Frontiers of oral biology.
1974-1991   0425735

Front Radiat Ther Oncol
Frontiers of radiation therapy and oncology
0071-9676   1662-3789
1968   0125544

Ftiziologia
Ftiziologia
0016-2329
Continues Revista de ftiziologie. Continued by Revista de igienă, bacteriologie, virusologie, parazitologie, epidemiologie, pneumoftiziologie. Pneumoftiziologie.
1954-1974   7503784

Fukuoka Igaku Zasshi
Fukuoka igaku zasshi = Hukuoka acta medica
0016-254X
Continues: Zasshi. Fukuoka Ika Daigaku.
1940   9423321

Fukuoka Shika Daigaku Gakkai Zasshi
Fukuoka Shika Daigaku Gakkai zasshi
0385-0064
1974   8219599

Fukushima Igaku Zasshi
[Fukushima igaku zasshi] Fukushima medical journal
0016-2582
1951   17030120R

Fukushima J Med Sci
Fukushima journal of medical science
0016-2590
1954   0374626

Fulorrgegegyogyaszat
Fül-, orr-, gégegyógyázat
0016-237X
1955   0375047

Funct Dev Morphol
Functional and developmental morphology
0862-8416
Continues: Folia morphologica.
1991-1994   9200392

Funct Integr Genomics
Functional & integrative genomics
1438-793X   1438-7948
2000   100939343

Funct Neurol
Functional neurology
0393-5264
1986   8707746

Funct Orthod
The Functional orthodontist
8756-3150
1984   8502864

Fund Raising Manage
Fund raising management
0016-268X
1969   9877778

Fundam Appl Toxicol
Fundamental and applied toxicology: official journal of the Society of Toxicology
0272-0590
Absorbed: Toxicologist. 1995 Continued by: Toxicological sciences.
1981-1997   8200838

Fundam Clin Pharmacol
Fundamental & clinical pharmacology
0767-3981   1472-8206
Absorbed: Archives internationales de pharmacodynamie et de thérapie. Continues: Journal de pharmacologie, issued by Masson, Paris, France.
1987   8710411

Fungal Genet Biol
Fungal genetics and biology: FG & B
1087-1845   1096-0937
Continues: Experimental mycology.
1996   9607601

Future Child
The Future of children / Center for the
Future of Children, the David and Lucile
Packard Foundation
1054-8289   1550-1558
1991   9306342

Future Dent
Future dentistry
1985-1990   9100051

Future Microbiol
Future microbiology
1746-0913   1746-0921
2006   101278120

Future Oncol
Future oncology (London, England)
1479-6694   1744-8301
2005   101256629

Fysiatr Revmatol Vestn
Fysiatrický a reumatologický vestník
0072-0038
Continues: Fysiatrický věstník. Split into:
Rehabilitace a fyzikální lékařství. and: Ceská
revmatologie.
1966-1994   0047421

Fysiatr Vestn Cesk Fysiatr Spol
Fysiatrický věstník. Československá
fysiatrická spolecnost
Continues Věstník of the Ceskoslovenská
fysiatrická společnost. Continued by
Fysiatrický a reumatologický věstník.
1953-1965   0071530

G

G Anest Stomatol
Giornale di anestesia stomatologica =
Journal of dental anaesthesia / Associazione
italiana per il progresso dell'anestesia in
odontostomatologia
0391-5670
Continues: Giornale di narco-
odontostomatologia.
1978-1997   8604142

G Batteriol Immunol
Giornale di batteriologia e immunologia
Continued by the Giornale di batteriologia,
virologia, ed immunologia et annali
dell'Ospedale Maria Vittoria di Torino.
1926-1957   17130390R

G Batteriol Virol Immunol
Giornale di batteriologia, virologia ed
immunologia
0390-5462
Continues Giornale di batteriologia virologia
ed immunologia ed annali dell'Ospedale
Maria Vittoria di Torino. Parte 1: Sezione
microbiologica.
1974-1994   7510850

G Batteriol Virol Immunol
Giornale di batteriologia, virologia, ed
immunologia ed annali dell'Ospedale Maria
Vittoria di Torino
0017-0267
Continues Giornale di batteriologia e
immunologia.
1958-1970   0365561

G Batteriol Virol Immunol Clin
Giornale di batteriologia, virologia ed
immunologia ed annali dell'Ospedale Maria
Vittoria di Torino. Parte 2: Sezione clinica
0301-1445
Continues the Annali previously included
in Giornale di batteriologia. virologia ed
immunologia ed annali del'Ospedale Maria
Vittoria di Torino, v. 51-63, 1958-70.
Continued by Annali dell'Ospedale Maria
Vittoria de Torino.
1971-1973   7510849

G Batteriol Virol Immunol Microbiol
Giornale di batteriologia, virologia ed
immunologia ed annali dell'Ospedale
Maria Vittoria di Torino. Parte 1: Sezione
microbiologica
0301-1453
Continues in part Giornale di batteriologia,
virologia ed immunologia ed annali
dell'Ospedale Maria Vittoria di Torino.
Continued by Giornale di batteriologia.
virologia ed immunologia.
1971-1973   7510848

G Biochim
Giornale di biochimica
0434-0272
1951   2985106R

G Chir
Il Giornale di chirurgia
0391-9005
1980   9011768

G Clin Med
Giornale di clinica medica
0017-0275
Merged with: Basi razionali della terapia, to
form: G & B.
1920-1990   0413411

G E N
G.E.N
0016-3503
1946-2002   0374633

G Endodonzia
Giornale di endodonzia
Continued by: Giornale italiano di
endodonzia.
1987-1990   9201292

G Fis Sanit Prot Radiaz
Giornale di fisica sanitaria e protezione
contro le radiazioni. The journal of health
physics and radiation protection
0026-4768
Continues Minerva fisiconucleare. Merged
with Minerva ecologica e idroclimatologica to
form Minerva ecologica idroclimatologica e
fisiconucleare.
1968-1974   0376760

G Gerontol
Giornale di gerontologia
0017-0305
1953   0375343

G Gerontol Suppl
Giornale di gerontologia. Supplemento
0434-0280
1953-1976   0375344

G Ig Med Prev
Giornale di igiene e medicina preventiva
0017-0313
Continued by: Journal of preventive medicine
and hygiene.
1960-1988   0413666

G Ital Anestesiol
Giornale italiano di anestesiologia
Continues Giornale italiano di anestesia e di
analgesia. Continued by Minerva anestesiologica.
1949-1952   17140050R

G Ital Cardiol
Giornale italiano di cardiologia
0046-5968
Formed by the merger of: Cuore e
circolazione; Folia cardiologica; and: Malattie
cardiovascolari. Merged with: Cardiologia
(Rome. Italy); to form: Italian heart journal.
1971-1999   1270331

G Ital Cardiol (Rome)
Giornale italiano di cardiologia (2006)
1827-6806
Continues: Italian heart journal. Supplement.
2006   101263411

G Ital Chemioter
Giornale italiano di chemioterapia
0017-0445
1954-1992   17140055R

G Ital Chir
Giornale italiano di chirurgia
0017-0453
1945-1997   2985107R

G Ital Della Tuberc
Giornale italiano della tubercolosi
Continued by the Giornale italiano della
tubercolosi e delle malattie del torace.
1946-1956   17140020R

G Ital Dermatol
Giornale italiano di dermatologia
0376-0901
Continues Giornale italiano delle malattie
veneree e della pelle. Merged with Minerva
dermatologica to form Giornale italiano di
dermatologia - Minerva dermatologica.
1925-1968   0214141

G Ital Dermatol Minerva Dermatol
Giornale italiano di dermatolotia. Minerva
dermatologica
0300-1318
Formed by the union of: Giornale italiano di
dermatologia. and: Minerva dermatologica.
Continued by: Giornale italiano di
dermatologia e venereologia.
1969-1979   0353523

G Ital Dermatol Venereol
Giornale italiano di dermatologia e
venereologia: organo ufficiale, Società
italiana di dermatologia e sifilografia
0026-4741
Continues: Giornale italiano di dermatologia.
Minerva dermatologica.
1980   8102852

G Ital Endod
Giornale italiano di endodonzia
1121-4171
Continues: Giornale di endodonzia.
1990   9201293

G Ital Mal Torace
Giornale italiano delle malattie del torace
0017-0437
Continues Giornale italiano della tubercolosi
e delle malattie del torace.
1966-1994   0050772

G Ital Med Lav
Giornale italiano di medicina del lavoro
0391-9889
Continued by: Giornale italiano di medicina
del lavoro ed ergonomia.
1979-1996   8000112

G Ital Med Lav Ergon
Giornale italiano di medicina del lavoro ed
ergonomia
1592-7830
Continues: Giornale italiano di medicina del
lavoro.
1997   9712708

G Ital Nefrol
Giornale italiano di nefrologia: organo ufficiale della Società italiana di nefrologia
0393-5590
1984   9426434

G Ital Oftalmol
Giornale italiano di oftalmologia
0367-455X
1948-1964   17140060R

G Ital Oncol
Giornale italiano di oncologia
0392-128X
1981   8508370

G Ital Patol
Giornale italiano di patologia e di scienze affini
0017-047X
1954-1985   0370744

G Ital Tuberc Mal Torace
Giornale italiano della tubercolosi e delle malattie del torace
0367-4622
Continues the Giornale italiano della tubercolosi. Continued by the Giornale italiano delle malattie del torace.
1957-1965   0051104

G Mal Infett Parassit
Giornale di malattie infettive e parassitarie
0017-0321
Continued by: Giornale italiano di malattie infettive.
1949-1994   0421044

G Med Mil
Giornale di medicina militare
0017-0364
1851   0417723

G Pneumol
Giornale di pneumologia
0431-8889
Continued by Il Torace.
1957-1972   7511682

G Psichiatr Neuropatol
Giornale di psichiatria e di neuropatologia
0017-0399
Continues Giornale di psichiatria cinica e tecnica manicomiale.
1931-1970   0404427

G Sci Mediche
Supersedes Giornale veneto di scienze mediche. Continued by Giornale veneto di scienze mediche.
1946-1955   7701419

G Stomatol Ortognatodonzia
Giornale di stomatologia e di ortognatodonzia
1122-1038
1982-1993   8702086

G Veneto Sci Med
Giornale veneto di scienze mediche
0367-5475
Continues Giornale di scienze mediche.
1956-1989   0177054

Ga Hosp Today
Georgia hospitals today / GHA
0898-316X
Continues: Georgia hospital affairs. Continued by: GHA today.
1986-1997   8610313

Ga Nurse
Georgia nursing
0016-8335
1945   0047220

Gac Med (Guayaquil)
Gaceta médica
0367-3715
1946-1969   0423436

Gac Med Caracas
Gaceta médica de Caracas
0367-4762
1893   0374627

Gac Med Esp
Gaceta médica española
0016-3821
1926-1977   2984764R

Gac Med Lima
Gaceta médica de Lima
1944-1949   17030420R

Gac Med Mex
Gaceta médica de México
0016-3813
1864   0010333

Gac Med Norte
Gaceta médica del Norte
Continued by Gaceta médica de Bilbao.
1895-1970   1306142

Gac Med Occidente
Gaceta médica de occidente
1938-1980   17030450R

Gac Sanit
Gaceta sanitaria / S.E.S.P.A.S
0213-9111
Continues: Gaseta sanitària de Barcelona.
1987   8901623

Gait Posture
Gait & posture
0966-6362   1879-2219
1993   9416830

Galen Cas Med Farm Hem Srod Nauke
Galenika; časopis za medicinu, farmaciju, hemiju i srodne nauke
195u-19uu   17030660R

Galicia Clin
Galicia-clinica
0304-4866
1973-1995   0376551

Gall Biol Acta
Gallica biologica acta
1948-19uu   17040010R

Gamete Res
Gamete research
0148-7280
1978-1989   7806559

Gan
Gan. Gann; the Japanese journal of cancer research
0016-450X
Continued by Gann.
1907-1958   0151745

Gan No Rinsho
Gan no rinsho. Japan journal of cancer clinics
0021-4949
1954   1257753

Gan To Kagaku Ryoho
Gan to kagaku ryoho. Cancer & chemotherapy
0385-0684
1974   7810034

Ganka
Ganka. Ophthalmology
0016-4488
1959   2984765R

Gann
Gann = Gan
0016-450X
Continues: Gan. Continued by: Japanese journal of cancer research.
1959-1984   8214471

Gaoxiong Yi Xue Ke Xue Za Zhi
Gaoxiong yi xue ke xue za zhi = The Kaohsiung journal of medical sciences
0257-5655
Continued by: Kaohsiung journal of medical sciences.
1985-1995   8603880

Gastric Cancer
Gastric cancer: official journal of the International Gastric Cancer Association and the Japanese Gastric Cancer Association
1436-3291
1998   100886238

Gastroenterol Bohema
Gastroenterologia bohema
Continued by: Sborník pro pathofysiologii trávení a výživy.
1947-1950   17040180R

Gastroenterol Clin Biol
Gastroentérologie clinique et biologique
0399-8320
Formed by the union of Archives françaises des maladies de l'appareil digestif and Biologie et gastro-entérologie.
1977   7704825

Gastroenterol Clin North Am
Gastroenterology clinics of North America
0889-8553   1558-1942
Continues in part: Clinics in gastroenterology.
1987   8706257

Gastroenterol Fortbildungskurse Prax
Gastroenterologische Fortbildungskurse für die Praxis
0302-9255
Continues Fortbildungskurse für praktische Gastroenterologie.
1973-1975   0410443

Gastroenterol Hepatol
Gastroenterología y hepatología
0210-5705
1978   8406671

Gastroenterol J
Gastroenterologisches Journal: Organ der Gesellschaft für Gastroenterologie der DDR
0863-1743
Continues: Deutsche Zeitschrift für Verdauungs- und Stoffwechselkrankheiten.
1989-1991   8913769

Gastroenterol Jpn
Gastroenterologia Japonica
0435-1339
Continued by: Journal of gastroenterology.
1966-1993   0152744

Gastroenterol Nurs
Gastroenterology nursing: the official journal of the Society of Gastroenterology Nurses and Associates
1042-895X   1538-9766
Continues: SGA journal (Society of Gastrointestinal Assistants (U.S.)).
1989   8915377

Gastroenterologia
Gastroenterologia
0301-164X
Continues Archiv für Verdauungs-Krankheiten, Stoffwechselpathologie und Diätetik. Superseded by Digestion.
1939-1967   0151054

Gastroenterologist
The Gastroenterologist
1065-2477
    Absorbed by: Journal of clinical
    gastroenterology.
1993-1998   9308839

Gastroenterology
Gastroenterology
0016-5085   1528-0012
1943   0374630

Gastrointest Endosc
Gastrointestinal endoscopy
0016-5107   1097-6779
    Continues the Bulletin of gastrointestinal
    endoscopy.
1965   0010505

Gastrointest Endosc Clin N Am
Gastrointestinal endoscopy clinics of North
America
1052-5157   1558-1950
1991   9202792

Gastrointest Radiol
Gastrointestinal radiology
0364-2356
    Merged with: Urologic radiology: to form:
    Abdominal imaging.
1976-1992   7611134

Gaz Egypt Paediatr Assoc
The Gazette of the Egyptian Paediatric
Association
1110-6638
1952-1999   7509401

Gaz Hop Civ Mil Empire Ottoman
Gazette Des Hopitaux Civils Et Militaire De
L Empire Ottoman
1887-1?uu   9427844

Gaz Med Fr
Gazette médicale de France
0016-5557
    Continued by Gazette médicale (Paris.
    France).
1927-1983   0034270

Gaz Med Limousine (1908)
Gazette médicale limousine
0980-4463
    Absorbed the Caducée médical d'Aunis et
    Saintonge. Merged with: Revue de médecine
    du Limousin. to form: Médi centre, 1984.
1908-1980   17040390R

Gaz Med Lomb
Gazzetta medica lombarda
1958-1969   17040470R

Gaz Med Port
Gazeta médica portuguesa
1948-1964   17040250R

Gaz Woda Tech
Gaz, woda; technika sanitarna
0016-5352
1927   17040210R

Gazz Int Med Chir
Gazzetta internazionale di medicina e
chirurgia
0016-5662
1899-1972   0373000

Gazz Med Ital
Gazzetta medica italiana
0393-3660
    Continues Gazzetta medica lombarda.
    Absorbed: Archivio per le scienze mediche.
    Jan./Feb. 1984.
1936   0370730

Gazz Osp Clin
Gazzetta degli ospedali e delle cliniche
0433-2253
    Continues Gazzetta degli ospitali.
1894-1969   0415017

Gazz Sanit
Gazzetta sanitaria
0016-5697
1928-1980   0370731

Geburtshilfe Frauenheilkd
Geburtshilfe und Frauenheilkunde
0016-5751
    Absorbed: Zentralblatt für Gynäkologie.
1939   0370732

Gegenbaurs Morphol Jahrb
Gegenbaurs morphologisches Jahrbuch
0016-5840
    Continues Morphologisches Jahrbuch.
1903-1990   0370733

Geka Chiryo
Geka chiryo. Surgical therapy
0433-2644
1959   2985100R

Gem State RN News Lett
The Gem State RN news letter
0072-0569
    Continues The Gem State R. N. Superseded
    by RN Idaho.
1964-1977   7902818

Gematol Transfuziol
Gematologiia i transfuziologiia
0234-5730
    Continues: Problemy gematologii i
    perelivaniia krovi.
1983   8301796

Gen
GEN
0377-8290
1973-1983   7605615

Gen Comp Endocrinol
General and comparative endocrinology
0016-6480   1095-6840
1961   0370735

Gen Cytochem Methods
General cytochemical methods
0435-2467
1958-1961   7608331

Gen Dent
General dentistry
0363-6771
    Continues Journal - Academy of General
    Dentistry.
1976   7610466

Gen Diagn Pathol
General & diagnostic pathology
0947-823X
    Continues: Zentralblatt für Pathologie.
1995-1998   9511700

Gen Hosp Psychiatry
General hospital psychiatry
0163-8343   1873-7714
1979   7905527

Gen Pharmacol
General pharmacology
0306-3623
    Continues: Comparative and general
    pharmacology. Continued by: Vascular
    pharmacology.
1975-2001   7602417

Gen Physiol Biophys
General physiology and biophysics
0231-5882
1982   8400604

Gen Pract
General practice
    Continues the Family physician.
1946-1964   17110310R

Gen Pract Clin
General practice clinics
0097-1634
    Supersedes: Review of medicine. surgery and
    obstetrics-gynecology. Merged with: Medical
    record. to form: International record of
    medicine and general practice clinics.
1943-1950   17110330R

Gen Thorac Cardiovasc Surg
General thoracic and cardiovascular surgery
1863-6705   1863-6713
    Continues: Japanese journal of thoracic and
    cardiovascular surgery.
2007   101303952

Gencho Hiroshima Igaku
[Gencho Hiroshima igaku] The Hiroshima
medical journal
    Continues: Hiroshima igaku. gencho gō.
    Continued by: Hiroshima Daigaku igaku
    zasshi.
1956-1961   17110180R

Gend Med
Gender medicine: official journal of the
Partnership for Gender-Specific Medicine at
Columbia University
1550-8579
2004   101225178

Gene
Gene
0378-1119   1879-0038
1976   7706761

Gene Amplif Anal
Gene amplification and analysis
0275-2778
1981-1987   8101596

Gene Anal Tech
Gene analysis techniques
0735-0651
    Continued by: Genetic anaiysis.
1984-1989   8408118

Gene Expr
Gene expression
1052-2166
1991   9200651

Gene Expr Patterns
Gene expression patterns: GEP
1567-133X
    Continues: Brain research. Gene expression
    patterns.
2002   101167473

Gene Geogr
Gene geography: a computerized bulletin on
human gene frequencies
0394-249X
1987-1997   9100053

Gene Ther
Gene therapy
0969-7128   1476-5462
1994   9421525

Geneeskd Bl
Geneeskundige bladen uit kliniek en
laboratorium voor de praktijk
0016-6456
1894-1970   0370734

Geneeskd Gids
Geneeskundige gids
0016-6464
1923-1969   0225640

Genes Brain Behav
Genes, brain, and behavior
1601-1848   1601-183X
2002   101129617

Genes Cells
Genes to cells: devoted to molecular &
cellular mechanisms
1356-9597   1365-2443
1996   9607379

Genes Chromosomes Cancer
Genes, chromosomes & cancer
1045-2257   1098-2264
1989   9007329

Genes Dev
Genes & development
0890-9369   1549-5477
1987   8711660

Genes Funct
Genes and function
1360-7413
1997-1997   9706385

Genes Genet Syst
Genes & genetic systems
1341-7568   1880-5779
Continues: Japanese journal of genetics.
1996   9607822

Genes Immun
Genes and immunity
1466-4879   1476-5470
199u   100953417

Genesis
Genesis (New York, N.Y.: 2000)
1526-954X   1526-968X
Continues: Developmental genetics.
2000   100931242

Genet Anal
Genetic analysis: biomolecular engineering
Continues: Genetic analysis, techniques and
applications. Continued by: Biomolecular
engineering.
1995-1999   9509403

Genet Anal Tech Appl
Genetic analysis, techniques and
applications
1050-3862
Continues: Gene analysis techniques.
Continued by: Genetic analysis.
1990-1994   9004550

Genet Couns
Genetic counseling (Geneva, Switzerland)
1015-8146
Continues: Journal de génétique humaine.
1990   9015261

Genet Eng
Genetic engineering (Academic Press)
0887-8307
1981-1988   8302443

Genet Eng (N Y)
Genetic engineering
0196-3716
1979   7907340

Genet Epidemiol
Genetic epidemiology
0741-0395   1098-2272
1984   8411723

Genet Epidemiol Suppl
Genetic epidemiology. Supplement
1986-1986   8914640

Genet Med
Genetics in medicine: official journal of the
American College of Medical Genetics
1098-3600   1530-0366
1998   9815831

Genet Mol Res
Genetics and molecular research: GMR
1676-5680
2002   101169387

Genet Psychol Monogr
Genetic psychology monographs
0016-6677
Continued by: Genetic, social, and general
psychology monographs.
1926-1984   0370737

Genet Res
Genetical research
0016-6723   1469-5073
1960   0370741

Genet Sel Evol
Genetics, selection, evolution.: GSE
0999-193X   1297-9686
Continues: Génétique, sélection, évolution.
1989   9114088

Genet Soc Gen Psychol Monogr
Genetic, social, and general psychology
monographs
8756-7547
Continues: Genetic psychology monographs.
1985   8508368

Genetica
Genetica
0016-6707   1573-6857
1919   0370740

Genetics
Genetics
0016-6731
1916   0374636

Genetika
Genetika
0016-6758
1966   0047354

Genitourin Med
Genitourinary medicine
0266-4348
Continues: British journal of venereal
diseases. Continued by: Sexually transmitted
infections.
1985-1997   8503853

Genome
Genome / National Research Council
Canada = Génome / Conseil national de
recherches Canada
0831-2796   1480-3321
Continues: Canadian journal of genetics and
cytology.
1987   8704544

Genome Biol
Genome biology
1465-6906   1465-6914
2000   100960660

Genome Dyn
Genome dynamics
1660-9263   1662-3797
2006   101319425

Genome Inform
Genome informatics. International
Conference on Genome Informatics
0919-9454
Continues: Genome informatics. Workshop
on Genome Informatics.
2001   101280573

Genome Inform Ser Workshop Genome Inform
Genome informatics. Workshop on Genome
Informatics
0919-9454
Continued by: Genome informatics.
International Conference on Genome
Informatics.
199u-2000   9717234

Genome Res
Genome research
1088-9051   1549-5477
Continues: PCR methods and applications.
1995   9518021

Genomics
Genomics
0888-7543   1089-8646
1987   8800135

Genomics Proteomics Bioinformatics
Genomics, proteomics & bioinformatics /
Beijing Genomics Institute
1672-0229
Continues: Developmental & reproductive
biology.
2003   101197608

Geobiology
Geobiology
1472-4677   1472-4669
2003   101185472

Geogr Med
Geographia medica
0300-807X
Supersedes Geographia medica Hungarica.
Absorbed by: Health & place.
1970-1994   0356650

Geogr Med Suppl
Geographia medica. Supplement =
Geographia medica. Sonderband
0866-4323
1988-1992   9011764

Georgetown Dent J
Georgetown dental journal
0016-8084
Continued by: Mirror.
1933-1981   17120070R

Georgetown Med Bull
Georgetown medical bulletin
0016-8106
Continues the Bulletin of the Georgetown
University Medical Center.
1959   2985101R

Georgetown Univ Sch Dent Mirror
Mirror / Georgetown University School of
Dentistry
0730-0808
Continues: Georgetown dental journal.
1981-1988   9879908

Georgian Med News
Georgian medical news
1512-0112
1994   101218222

Geospat Health
Geospatial health
1827-1987   1970-7096
2006   101302943

Ger J Ophthalmol
German journal of ophthalmology
0941-2921
Continues in part: Fortschritte der
Ophthalmologie. Absorbed by: Graefe's
archive for clinical and experimental
ophthalmology.
1992-1997   9206441

Ger Med
German medicine
0046-5844
Supersedes German medical monthly.
1971-1973   1274101

Ger Med Mon
German medical monthly
0016-8785
1956-1970   1274100

Geriatr Gerontol Int
Geriatrics & gerontology international
1444-1586   1447-0594
2001   101135738

Geriatr Nephrol Urol
Geriatric nephrology and urology
0924-8455
Absorbed by: International urology and nephrology.
1991-1999   9112603

Geriatr Nurs
Geriatric nursing (New York, N.Y.)
0197-4572   1528-3984
1980   8309633

Geriatr Nurs (Lond)
Geriatric nursing (London, England)
0950-0448
Continued by: Geriatric nursing and home care.
1981-1986   8510067

Geriatr Nurs (Minneap)
Geriatric nursing
0435-5733
1965-1968   0046433

Geriatr Nurs Home Care
Geriatric nursing and home care
0269-9079
Continues: Geriatric nursing (London, England). Continued by: Nursing the elderly.
1986-1989   8701774

Geriatrics
Geriatrics
0016-867X   1936-5764
Continues: Patient care. 2008
1946   2985102R

Gerodontics
Gerodontics
0109-565X
1985-1988   8508083

Gerodontology
Gerodontology
0734-0664   1741-2358
1982   8215850

Geron
Geron
0072-4157
1949-1979   0374637

Gerontion
Gerontion
0829-8297
1986-1987   8608449

Gerontol Clin (Basel)
Gerontologia clinica
0016-8998
Merged with Gerontologia to form Gerontology.
1959-1975   7601653

Gerontol Geriatr Educ
Gerontology & geriatrics education
0270-1960   1545-3847
1980   8101294

Gerontologia
Gerontologia
0016-898X
Merged with Gerontologia clinica to form Gerontology.
1957-1975   7601654

Gerontologie
Gerontologie
0168-8774
Continues: Nederlands tijdschrift voor gerontologie.
1980-1981   8005608

Gerontologist
The Gerontologist
0016-9013   1758-5341
Continues: Newsletter. Gerontological Society.
1961   0375327

Gerontology
Gerontology
0304-324X   1423-0003
Formed by the union of Gerontologia and Gerontologia clinica. and continues the vol. numbering of the former.
1976   7601655

Gesnerus
Gesnerus
0016-9161
1943   1257130

Gesnerus Suppl
Gesnerus. Supplement
1017-3293
Continues: Veröffentlichungen der Schweizerischen Gesellschaft für Geschichte der Medizin und der Naturwissenschaften.
1990-2000   9101438

Gesund Ing
Gesundheits-Ingenieur
0016-9277
Continues der Rohrleger und Gesundheits-Ingenieur. Continued by Haustechnik. Bauphysik. Umwelttechnik.
1880-1978   0370743

Gesund Wohlfahrt
Gesundheit und Wohlfahrt. Revue suisse d'hygiène
0367-4274
Continues: Schweizerische Zeitschrift für Hygiene und Archiv für Wohlfahrtspflege. Continued by: Zeitschrift für Präventivmedizin.
1934-1955   17120620R

Gesundheit
Gesundheit (Derendingen, Switzerland)
1935-1957   9429876

Gesundheitswesen
Gesundheitswesen (Bundesverband der Ärzte des Öffentlichen Gesundheitsdienstes (Germany))
0941-3790   1439-4421
Continues: Öffentliche Gesundheitswesen.
1992   9204210

Gewina
Gewina
0928-303X
Continues: Tijdschrift voor de geschiedenis der geneeskunde. natuurwetenschappen. wiskunde en techniek. Merged with: Nieuwsbrief universiteitsgeschiedenis. and: Scientiarum historia. to form: Studium (Rotterdam. Netherlands).
1992-2007   9425368

GHA Today
GHA today
1551-8434
Continues: Georgia hospitals today.
1997   9715778

GHAA J
GHAA journal
0888-4250
Continues: The Group health journal.
1986-1989   8703123

Ghana Med J
Ghana medical journal
0016-9560
1962   0073210

Ghana Nurse
The Ghanaian nurse
1961-1970   0235326

Gifu Shika Gakkai Zasshi
Gifu Shika Gakkai zasshi = The Journal of Gifu Dental Society
0385-0072
1974   8109799

Gig Sanit
Gigiena i sanitariia
0016-9900
1936   0412700

Gig Tr Prof Zabol
Gigiena truda i professional'nye zabolevaniia
0016-9919
Continued by: Meditsina truda i promyshlennaia ekologiia.
1957-1992   2985104R

Ginecol
La Ginecologia
1904-1944   0011434

Ginecol Obstet Mex
Ginecología y obstetricia de México
0300-9041
1946   0376552

Ginecologia
Ginecología
1946-1964   17130250R

Ginekol Pol
Ginekologia polska
0017-0011
1922   0374641

Glas Belgrad Hig Inst NR Srb
Glasnik. Belgrad. Higijenski institut NR Srbije
0354-1169
Continues: Glasnik Centralnog higijenskog zavoda. Continued by: Glasnik of the Zavod za zdravstvenu zaštitu SR Srbije.
1952-1961   15510410R

Glas Srp Akad Nauka [Med]
Glas. Srpska akademija nauka i umetnosti. Odeljenje medicinskih nauka
0081-3966
Continues the Glas of the Odeljenje medicinskih nauka of the Srpska akademija nauka. Belgrad.
1960   0027437

Glasg Dent J
Glasgow dental journal
0046-600X
1969-1974   0434574

Glasgow Med J
Glasgow medical journal
1828-1955   17140140R

Glasnik
Glasnik (Srpska akademija nauka)
Continued by: Glasnik (Srpska akademija nauka i umetnosti).
1949-1959   59120140R

Glaxo Vol Occas Contrib Sci Art Med
The Glaxo volume; an occasional contribution
to the science and art of medicine
1948-1974   0374644

Glia
Glia
0894-1491   1098-1136
1988   8806785

Glob Public Health
Global public health
1744-1692   1744-1706
2006   101256323

Globe
Globe. International College of Dentists
Continues: Newsletter. International College
of Dentists.
1985-uuuu   9881896

Glycobiology
Glycobiology
0959-6658   1460-2423
1990   9104124

Glycoconj J
Glycoconjugate journal
0282-0080   1573-4986
Absorbed: Glycosylation & disease.
1984   8603310

GMDA Bull
GMDA bulletin
0884-6898
Continues: Greater Milwaukee dental bulletin.
Continued by: GMDA journal.
1981-1993   9879573

GMHC Treat Issues
GMHC treatment issues: the Gay Men's
Health Crisis newsletter of experimental
AIDS therapies
1077-1824
Continues: Treatment issues.
1994   9509489

God Vojnomed Akad
Godisnjak Vojnomedicinske akademije =
Annual of the Military Medical Academy
0352-664X
Continues: Vojnomedicinska akademija
(Yugoslavia). Zbornik.
1984-1989   8606929

God Zb Med Fak Skopje
Godišen zbornik na Medicinskiot fakultet
vo Skopje
0065-1214
1954   0414607

Gov Relat Note
Government relations note
Continued by: Washington report.
1975-1981   7808490

GP
GP
0016-3600
Merged with American family physician to
form American family physician/GP.
1950-1969   0230511

Grace Hosp Bul
The Grace Hospital bulletin
0093-3724
1916-1974   0414333

Graefes Arch Clin Exp Ophthalmol
Graefe's archive for clinical and
experimental ophthalmology = Albrecht
von Graefes Archiv für klinische und
experimentelle Ophthalmologie
0721-832X   1435-702X
Absorbed: German journal of ophthalmology.
1998 Continues: Albrecht von Graefes
Archiv für klinische und experimentelle
Ophthalmologie.
1982   8205248

Grants Mag
Grants magazine
0160-9734
1978-1989   7807279

Grantsmanship Cent News
Grantsmanship Center News
0364-3115
1973-1985   9877044

Gravit Space Biol Bull
Gravitational and space biology bulletin:
publication of the American Society for
Gravitational and Space Biology
1089-988X
Continues: ASGSB bulletin.
1996   9816128

Great Ormond St J
Great Ormond Street journal
1951-1956   17210300R

Greater Milw Dent Bull
The Greater Milwaukee dental bulletin
0017-3754
Continues: Bulletin of the Greater Milwaukee
Dental Association. Continued by: GMDA
bulletin.
1957-1981   17210340R

Greater St Louis Dent Soc Bull
The Greater St. Louis Dental Society
bulletin
0072-7369
Continues Bulletin - St. Louis Dental Society.
Continued by Bulletin - Greater St. Louis
Dental Society.
1960-1974   7513598

Grenzgeb Med
Grenzgebiete der Medizin
1948-1949   17210420R

Groene Witte Kruis
Het Groene en het Witte Kruis
Continued by Gezondheidszorg.
1904-1956   17210430R

Ground Water
Ground water
0017-467X   1745-6584
1963   9882886

Group Health J
The Group health journal
0196-6332
Continued by: GHAA journal.
1980-1985   8009788

Group Pract
Group practice
0017-4726
Continues American Association of Medical
Clinics. Bulletin. Continued by Group
Practice Journal.
1957-1979   0432550

Group Pract J
Group practice journal
0199-5103
Continues Group practice.
1980   8004962

Growth
Growth
0017-4793
Continued by: Growth, development, and
aging.
1937-1987   0205044

Growth Dev Aging
Growth, development, and aging: GDA
1041-1232
Continues: Growth.
1988-2008   8809704

Growth Factors
Growth factors (Chur, Switzerland)
0897-7194   1029-2292
1988   9000468

Growth Horm IGF Res
Growth hormone & IGF research: official
journal of the Growth Hormone Research
Society and the International IGF Research
Society
1096-6374   1532-2238
Merger of: Endocrinology and metabolism
(London, England); and: Growth regulation,
continuing the numbering of the latter.
1998   9814320

Growth Regul
Growth regulation
0956-523X
Merged with: Endocrinology and metabolism
(London, England), to become: Growth
hormone & IGF research.
1991-1997   9106990

Grud Serdechnososudistaia Khir
Grudnaia i serdechno-sosudistaia khirurgiia /
Ministerstvo zdravookhraneniia SSSR [i]
Vsesoiuznoe nauchnoe obshchestvo khirurgov
0236-2791
Continues: Grudnaia khirurgiia (Moscow,
Russia).
1990   9004552

Grudn Khir
Grudnaia khirurgiia (Moscow, Russia)
0017-4866
Continued by: Grudnaia i serdechno-
sosudistaia khirurgiia.
1959-1989   8708014

Grundfragen Silikoseforsch
Grundfragen aus der Silikoseforschung
1955-1963   24030350R

Gruzlica
Gruźlica (Warsaw, Poland: 1926)
0367-5149
Continued by: Gruźlica i choroby płuc.
1926-1961   8502658

Gruzlica
Gruźlica i choroby płuc; tuberculosis et
pneumonologia
0017-4955
Continues Gruźlica (Warsaw, Poland :1926).
Continued by Pneumonologia polska.
1962-1975   0167652

Guang Pu Xue Yu Guang Pu Fen Xi
Guang pu xue yu guang pu fen xi = Guang pu
1000-0593
1981   9424805

Guide Prat
Guide du praticien; édition du district
parisien
Continues Cahiers R. M. F.
1964-1968   17220100R

Guigoz Sci Rev
Scientific review
Absorbed by: Documents scientifiques
(Guigoz (Firm)).
1952-1963   17220170R

Guildcraft
Guildcraft
1928-1967   17220210R

Gunma J Med Sci
The Gunma journal of medical sciences
0017-565X
1952-1969   0234221

Gut
Gut
0017-5749   1468-3288
1960   2985108R

Guys Hosp Gaz
Guy's Hospital gazette
0017-5870
     Continued by: Guy's gazette.
1872-1989   0416610

Guys Hosp Rep
Guy's Hospital reports
0017-5889
1836-1974   7612021

Gyermekgyogyaszat
Gyermekgyógyászat: az Orvosegészségügyi
Szakszervezet Gyermekorvos
Szakcsoportjának folyóirata = Pediatriia
0017-5900
1950   9312065

Gynaecologia
Gynaecologia. International monthly
review of obstetrics and gynecology. Revue
internationale mensuelle d'obstétrique et de
gynécologie. Monatsschrift für Geburtshilfe
und Gynäkologie
0367-5513
     Continues: Monatsschrift für Geburtshülfe
     und Gynäkologie. Continued by: Gynecologic
     investigation.
1946-1969   0245617

Gynakol Geburtshilfliche Rundsch
Gynäkologisch-geburtshilfliche Rundschau
1018-8843   1423-0011
     Continues: Gynäkologische Rundschau.
1992   9212667

Gynakol Rundsch
Gynäkologische Rundschau
0017-6001
     Continued by:
     GynkÄàologischgeburtshilfliche Rundschau.
1964-1991   0011363

Gynakologe
Der Gynäkologe
0017-5994
1968   0410275

Gynecol Endocrinol
Gynecological endocrinology: the official
journal of the International Society of
Gynecological Endocrinology
0951-3590   1473-0766
1987   8807913

Gynecol Invest
Gynecologic investigation
0017-5986
     Supersedes Gynaecologia. Continued by
     Gynecologic and obstetric investigation.
1970-1977   0245073

Gynecol Obstet (Paris)
Gynécologie et obstétrique
0017-601X
     Formed by the union of Annales de
     gynécologie et d'obstétrique and Archives
     mensuelles d'obstétrique et de gynécologie.
1920-1971   17220330R

Gynecol Obstet Fertil
Gynécologie, obstétrique & fertilité
1297-9589
     Continues: Contraception, fertilité, sexualité
     (1992).
2000   100936305

Gynecol Obstet Invest
Gynecologic and obstetric investigation
0378-7346   1423-002X
     Continues: Gynecologic investigation.
1978   7900587

Gynecol Oncol
Gynecologic oncology
0090-8258   1095-6859
1972   0365304

Gynecol Prat
Gynécologie pratique
0017-6028
     Continued by Gynécologie.
1950-1972   0376763

Gynecologie
Gynécologie
0301-2204
     Continues Gynécologie pratique. Merged
     with: Revue du gynécologue obstétricien, to
     form: Gynécologie (Paris. France: 1993).
1973-1993   0376762

Gyogyszeresz
A Gyógyszerész
0200-1292
     Superseded by: Gyógyszerészet.
1946-1956   17220380R

Gyogyszereszet
Gyógyszerészet
0017-6036
     Supersedes: Gyógyazerész.
1957   2985090R

H

Haematol Blood Transfus
Haematology and blood transfusion
0171-7111
     Continues: Hämatologie und Bluttransfusion.
1977   101169459

Haematol Lat
Haematologica Latina
0017-6575
1958-1971   0373001

Haematol Pol
Haematologica Polonica
     Continues Haematologica Cracoviensia.
1959-19uu   0011517

Haematologia (Budap)
Haematologia
0017-6559
     Supersedes Haematologia Hungarica.
1967-2002   0130266

Haematologica
Haematologica
0390-6078   1592-8721
     Absorbed: Hematology journal. 2005
1920   0417435

Haemophilia
Haemophilia: the official journal of the
World Federation of Hemophilia
1351-8216   1365-2516
1995   9442916

Haemostasis
Haemostasis
0301-0147
     Supersedes: Coagulation. Continued by:
     Pathophysiology of haemostasis and thrombosis.
1972-2001   0371574

Hahnemann Mon
Hahnemann monthly
1866-18uu   0011620

Hahnemannian
The Hahnemannian
0017-6621
1865-1990   0011622

Hamatol Bluttransfus
Hämatologie und Bluttransfusion
0440-0607
     Continued by: Haematology and blood
     transfusion.
1962-1976   7804332

Hamb Arztebl
Hamburger Ärzteblatt
0017-6915
1947   17230310R

Hamostaseologie
Hämostaseologie
0720-9355
1981   8204531

Hand
The Hand
0072-968X
     Continued by: The Journal of hand surgery
     (Edinburgh. Scotland).
1969-1983   0231601

Hand Clin
Hand clinics
0749-0712   1558-1969
1985   8510415

Hand Surg
Hand surgery: an international journal
devoted to hand and upper limb surgery and
related research: journal of the Asia-Pacific
Federation of Societies for Surgery of the
Hand
0218-8104   1793-6535
1996   9602613

Handb Clin Neurol
Handbook of clinical neurology / edited by
P.J. Vinken and G.W. Bruyn
0072-9752
1968   0166161

Handb Exp Pharmacol
Handbook of experimental pharmacology
0171-2004
     Continues: Handbuch der experimentellen
     Pharmakologie. New series.
1978   7902231

Handchir Mikrochir Plast Chir
Handchirurgie, Mikrochirurgie, plastische
Chirurgie: Organ der Deutschsprachigen
Arbeitsgemeinschaft für Handchirurgie:
Organ der Deutschsprachigen
Arbeitsgemeinschaft für Mikrochirurgie
der Peripheren Nerven und Gefässe: Organ
der Vereinigung der Deutschen Plastischen
Chirurgen
0722-1819   1439-3980
     Formed by the union of: Zeitschrift für
     Plastische Chirurgie; and: Handchirurgie.
1982   8302815

Handchirurgie
Handchirurgie
0046-6794
     Merged with Zeitschrift für plastische
     Chirurgie to form Handchirurgie,
     Mikrochiruregie, plastische Chirurgie.
1969-1981   1252612

Hanguk Uiyak
[Hanguk uiyak] Korean journal of medicine
1958   17240010R

Hansenol Int
Hansenologia internationalis
0100-3283
Supersedes Revista brasileira de leprologia.
1976   7704131

Harb Dent Log
Harbor dental log
1963-1971   0316647

Harefuah
Harefuah
0017-7768
1924   0034351

Harlem Hosp Bull
The Harlem Hospital bulletin
1948-1959   0234223

Harlem Hosp Bull (N Y)
The Harlem Hospital bulletin
0438-6124
Supersedes a publication with the same title issued 1948-59.
1960-1961   0050435

Harofe Haivri Heb Med J
Harofé haivri. The Hebrew medical journal
Continues the Hebrew physician.
1937-1965   0212157

Harper Hosp Bull
Harper Hospital bulletin
1890-1968   17240050R

Hartford Hosp Bull
Hartford Hospital bulletin
0017-7970
1946-1984   0376554

Harv Bus Rev
Harvard business review
0017-8012
1922   9875796

Harv Dent Alumni Bull
Harvard dental alumni bulletin
0046-6891
Supersedes the Harvard dental record.
1940-1990   17240080R

Harv Dent Bull
Harvard dental bulletin
1062-029X
Continues: Harvard dental alumni bulletin.
1991   9103776

Harv Health Lett
Harvard health letter / from Harvard Medical School
1052-1577
Continues: Harvard Medical School health letter.
1990   9425764

Harv Heart Lett
Harvard heart letter: from Harvard Medical School
1051-5313
1990   9425723

Harv Law Rev
Harvard law review
0017-811X
1887   7703681

Harv Mens Health Watch
Harvard men's health watch
1089-1102
1996   9802701

Harv Ment Health Lett
The Harvard mental health letter / from Harvard Medical School
1057-5022
Continues: Harvard Medical School mental health letter.
1990   9417017

Harv Public Health Alumni Bull
Harvard public health alumni bulletin
0017-8152
1944-1986   0376555

Harv Rev Psychiatry
Harvard review of psychiatry
1067-3229   1465-7309
1993   9312789

Harv Womens Health Watch
Harvard women's health watch
1070-910X
1993   9423147

Harvey Lect
Harvey lectures
0073-0874
1905   0404252

HASL Rep
HASL [reports]. U.S. Atomic Energy Commission
0498-5214
1957-1977   21830400R

Hastane
Hastane
1947-1985   17240280R

Hastings Cent Rep
The Hastings Center report
0093-0334
Absorbed: Hastings Center studies.
1971   0410447

Hautarzt
Der Hautarzt; Zeitschrift für Dermatologie, Venerologie, und verwandte Gebiete
0017-8470   1432-1173
1950   0372755

Hawaii Acad Sci Honol
Proceedings of the annual meeting. Hawaiian Academy of Science, Honolulu
1925-1967   17240490R

Hawaii Dent J
Hawaii dental journal
0891-9933
Formed by the union of: Journal of the Hawaii Dental Association, and: Odontoscope.
1984   8502148

Hawaii Med J
Hawaii medical journal
0017-8594
Continues the Hawaii medical journal and inter-island nurses' bulletin.
1962   2984209R

Hawaii Nurse
The Hawaii nurse: the official monthly newsletter of the Hawaii Nurses' Association
1047-4749
Continues: Hawaii nurses pipeline. Continued by: Hawaii nurse (Honolulu, Hawaii: 1994).
1989-1994   8914865

Hawaii Nurse (Honol)
Hawaii nurse (Honolulu, Hawaii: 1994)
1047-4749
Continues publication with the same title.
1994-2000   101135199

Hawaii Nurses Pipeline
Hawaii nurses pipeline
0146-2784
Continued by: The Hawaii nurse.
1962-198u   7701836

HBI Rep
HBI report
1979   9892143

Head Face Med
Head & face medicine
    1746-160X
2005   101245792

Head Neck
Head & neck
1043-3074   1097-0347
Continues: Head & neck surgery.
1989   8902541

Head Neck Surg
Head & neck surgery
0148-6403
Continued by: Head & neck.
1978-1988   7909027

Headache
Headache
0017-8748   1526-4610
1961   2985091R

Heal Light
Healing Light
1981   9879426

Health
Health
Continues Michigan out of doors.
1934-1981   17310040R

Health (London)
Health (London, England: 1997)
1363-4593
1997   9800465

Health (N Y)
Health (Family Media, Inc.)
0279-3547
Continues: Family health. Merged with: In health, to form: Health (San Francisco, Calif.).
1981-1991   8302449

Health Aff
Health affairs
0092-8577
Continues Medical affairs.
1972-1985   0351302

Health Aff (Millwood)
Health affairs (Project Hope)
0278-2715   1544-5208
1981   8303128

Health Army
Health of the Army. United States. Surgeon-General's Office
Supersedes the Office's Health.
1946-1988   22310590R

Health Bull
Health bulletin
1916-1956   17310270R

Health Bull
Health bulletin. Kern Co., Calif. Dept. of Public Health
Supersedes the Kern County health bulletin.
1943-uuuu   22510640R

Health Bull (Edinb)
Health bulletin
0374-8014
1941   0012330

Health Bull (Melb)
Health bulletin
0311-9254
Continues: Health bulletin of the Dept. of Public Health, Victoria, Australia.
1944-1968   0405374

Health Bull (Raleigh)
The Health bulletin
0017-8934
Continues North Carolina. Board of Health. Bulletin.
1913-1973   0374645

Health Bull Teach
Health bulletin for teachers
1929-1965   17310290R

Health Care (Don Mills)
Health care
0226-5788
Continues Health care in Canada.
1979-1991   8000123

Health Care Anal
Health care analysis: HCA: journal of health philosophy and policy
1065-3058
1993   9432537

Health Care Can
Health care in Canada
0706-0726
Formed by the union of Hospital administration in Canada and of Health care digest. Continued by Health care.
1978-1979   7900777

Health Care Cost Reengineering Rep
Health care cost reengineering report
1088-4653
Continued by: Clinical resource management.
1996-1999   9707732

Health Care Dimen
Health care dimensions
0093-0628
1974-1976   7501325

Health Care Educ
Health care education
0160-7006
Continues In-service training and education.
1977-1981   7801070

Health Care Financ Rev
Health care financing review
0195-8631   1554-9887
Absorbed: Health care financing review. Annual supplement.
1979   7909994

Health Care Financ Rev Annu Suppl
Health care financing review. Annual supplement
1057-9389
Continued by: Health care financing review. Statistical supplement.
19uu-199u   9617613

Health Care Financ Rev Stat Suppl
Health care financing review. Statistical supplement
1553-0930
Continues: Health care financing review. Annual supplement.
1995   9617616

Health Care Financ Trends
Health care financing trends
0882-8946
1979-1982   8005827

Health Care Innov
Health care innovations: the journal of the American Association of Preferred Provider Organizations
1085-1089
Continues: AAPPO journal.
1995-1999   9506760

Health Care Law Mon
Health care law monthly
1526-0704
Continues: Bender's health care law monthly.
1998   9814757

Health Care Law Newsl
Health care law newsletter / Weissburg and Aronson, Inc
0893-6099
Continued by: Bender's health care law monthly.
1986-1995   8701070

Health Care Manag
Health care management (Philadelphia, Pa.)
1069-6571
1994-1996   9438798

Health Care Manag (Frederick)
The health care manager
1525-5794   1550-512X
Continues: Health care supervisor.
1999   100896672

Health Care Manag Sci
Health care management science
1386-9620
1998   9815649

Health Care Manage Rev
Health care management review
0361-6274   1550-5030
1976   7611530

Health Care Mark
Health care marketer
0896-1204
Continues: Health care marketer & target market. Merged with: Part A news, to form: Hospital revenue report.
1986-1990   8707757

Health Care Mark Target Market
Health care marketer & target market
0884-6596
Formed by the union of: Target market, and: Cost containment. Continued by: Health care marketer.
1986-1986   8612805

Health Care Newsl
Health care newsletter / National Safety Council
Continues: Hospital health care newsletter.
1978   9877954

Health Care Plann Mark
Health care planning & marketing: HCP&M
0271-1222
1981-1982   8200863

Health Care Reform Week
Health care reform week
1067-2214
Continues: Health policy week. Continued by: Managed medicare & medicaid news.
1992-1995   9304299

Health Care Secur Saf Manage
Health care security and safety management
0279-3466
Continued by: Hospital security and safety management.
1980-1982   8708284

Health Care Strateg Manage
Health care strategic management
0742-1478
1983   8405900

Health Care Superv
The Health care supervisor
0731-3381
Continued by: Health care manager.
1982-1999   8301065

Health Care Syst
Health care systems
0149-2888
Continues Management systems. Continued by: Healthcare information management.
1975-1987   7704274

Health Care Week
Health care week
0162-2307
Merged with Washington actions on health to form Washington actions on health & health care week.
1977-1979   7801750

Health Care Women Int
Health care for women international
0739-9332   1096-4665
Continues: Issues in health care of women.
1984   8411543

Health Cent J
The Health center journal
Continued by The Journal of the Ohio State University College of Medicine at Columbus.
1947-1963   17310320R

Health Commun
Health communication
1041-0236   1532-7027
1989   8908762

Health Commun Informatics
Health communications and informatics
0378-9845
Continues Biosciences communications.
1979-1980   7904272

Health Cost Manage
Health cost management
0740-2406
1983-1988   8604149

Health Data Manag
Health data management
1079-9869
Continues: Medical claims management.
1994   9512999

Health Devices
Health devices
0046-7022
1971   1262063

Health Econ
Health economics
1057-9230
1992   9306780

Health Econ Policy Law
Health economics, policy, and law
1744-1331   1744-134X
2006   101247224

Health Educ
Health education
0097-0050
Continues: School health review. Continued by: Journal of health education.
1975-1990   7512764

Health Educ Behav
Health education & behavior: the official publication of the Society for Public Health Education
1090-1981
Continues: Health education quarterly.
1997   9704962

Health Educ J
Health education journal
0017-8969
Supersedes: Health and Empire.
1943   0374646

Health Educ J
Health education journal
Continues Health education.
1943-1962   17320250R

Health Educ Monogr
Health education monographs
0073-1455
Continued by Health education quarterly.
1957-1979   0431135

Health Educ Q
Health education quarterly
0195-8402
Continues: Health education monographs.
Continued by: Health education & behavior.
1980-1996   8108606

Health Educ Q Suppl
Health education quarterly. Supplement
1993-1994   9515187

Health Educ Rep
Health education reports
0193-5232
1979-2004   7904999

Health Educ Res
Health education research
0268-1153   1465-3648
1986   8608459

Health Estate
Health estate
Continues: Health estate journal.
1998   100888268

Health Estate J
Health estate journal: journal of the
Institute of Hospital Engineering
0957-7742
Continues: Journal of the Institute of Hospital
Engineering. Continued by: Health estate.
1990-1997   9004555

Health Expect
Health expectations: an international
journal of public participation in health care
and health policy
1369-6513   1369-7625
1998   9815926

Health Facil Manage
Health facilities management
0899-6210
1988   8906517

Health Forum J
Health Forum journal
1527-3547
Continues: Healthcare Forum journal.
1999-2003   100884164

Health History
Health and history
1998   100888373

Health Horiz
Health horizon
1946-1963   17310500R

Health Hum Rights
Health and human rights
1079-0969
1994   9502498

Health Ind Today
Health industry today
0745-4678
Continues: Surgical business. Continues:
Surgical business.
1983-2001   8400108

Health Inf Manag
Health information management: journal
of the Health Information Management
Association of Australia
1322-4913
Continues: Australian medical record journal.
Continued by: HIM journal.
1994-2000   9438200

Health Inf Syst Telemed
Health information systems and telemedicine
1995-1996   9806447

Health Info Libr J
Health information and libraries journal
1471-1834   1471-1842
Continues: Health libraries review.
2001   100970070

Health Informatics J
Health informatics journal
1460-4582   1741-2811
Continues: Health informatics (Edinburgh,
Scotland).
1997   100883604

Health Lab Sci
Health laboratory science
0017-9035
1964-1978   0374650

Health Law Can
Health law in Canada
0226-8841
1980   8101300

Health Law J
Health law journal
1192-8336
1993   9804242

Health Law Proj Libr Bull
Health Law Project library bulletin
0163-3996
1970-1981   8002731

Health Law Vigil
Health law vigil
0270-3343
1978-1988   8004176

Health Libr Rev
Health libraries review
0265-6647   1365-2532
Continues: Newsletter - Medical, Health
and Welfare Libraries Group. Continued by:
Health information and libraries journal.
1984-2000   8607228

Health Manag Technol
Health management technology
1074-4770
Continues: Computers in healthcare.
1994   9423239

Health Manage Forum
Health management forum
0712-5046
Continued by: Healthcare management
forum.
1980-1987   8113011

Health Manage Q
Health management quarterly: HMQ
Continues: Hospital management quarterly.
1984-1994   8502875

Health Manpow Lit
Health manpower literature
0160-0222
1977-1981   9877997

Health Manpow Manage
Health manpower management
0955-2065
Continues: Health services manpower review.
Absorbed by: Journal of management in
medicine. 1999
1988-1998   8911894

Health Manpow Rep
Health manpower report
0161-6781
Merged with Health planning & manpower
reports to form Health Planning & manpower
report.
1972-1978   7801226

Health Mark Q
Health marketing quarterly
0735-9683   1545-0864
Continues: Health & medical care services
review.
1983   8306485

Health Matrix
Health matrix
0748-383X
Continued by: Health matrix (Cleveland,
Ohio: 1991).
1983-1990   8405332

Health Matrix Clevel
Health matrix (Cleveland, Ohio: 1991)
0748-383X
Continues: Health matrix.
1991   9311154

Health Med
Health & medicine: journal of the Health
and Medicine Policy Research Group
0741-2339
1982-1987   8307267

Health Med Care Serv Rev
Health & medical care services review
0160-7618
Continued by: Health marketing quarterly.
1978-1982   7806285

Health N Hav
Health
Continues the Monthly bulletin of the New
Haven Dept. of Health.
1924-uuuu   22521080R

Health News
Health news (Waltham, Mass.)
1081-5880
1992   9800495

Health PAC Bull
Health PAC bulletin
0017-9051
1968-1993   1255014

Health People
The Health of the people
0301-0384
Formed by the merger of Occupational health
New Zealand and Community health, and
assumes the numbering of the former.
1972-1974   0366537

Health Perspect
Health perspectives
0097-0069
Merged with Quarterly - Consumer
Commission on the Accreditation of
Health Services to form Consumer health
perspectives.
1973-1977   7503531

Health Phys
Health physics
0017-9078   1538-5159
1958   2985093R

Health Place
Health & place
1353-8292
Continues: Geographia medica.
1995   9510067

Health Plann Manpow Rep
Health planning & manpower report
Formed by the union of Health manpower
report and Health planning & manpower
reports. Continued by: Health professions
report.
1978-1984   7806574

Health Plann Manpow Rep
Health planning & manpower reports
0362-3165
Merged with Health manpower report to form
Health planning & manpower report.
1976-1978   7610479

Health Policy
Health policy (Amsterdam, Netherlands)
0168-8510
Continues: Health policy and education.
1984   8409431

Health Policy Educ
Health policy and education
0165-2281
Continued by: Health policy (Amsterdam,
Netherlands).
1979-1983   7909999

Health Policy Plan
Health policy and planning
0268-1080   1460-2237
1986   8610614

Health Policy Q
Health policy quarterly
0163-5107
1981-1982   8109813

Health Policy Week
Health policy week: HPW
0732-7439
Continues: Morris report on federal health
policy. Continued by: Health care reform
week.
1982-1992   8917069

Health Popul Perspect Issues
Health and population; perspectives and
issues
0253-6803
Formed by the union of NIHAE bulletin and
Journal of population research.
1978   7909318

Health Pract Physician Assist
Health practitioner. Physician assistant
0192-7310
Formed by the union of Health practitioner
and Physician assistant. Continued by:
Physician assistant, health practitioner.
1978-1979   7904275

Health Prog
Health progress (Saint Louis, Mo.)
0882-1577
Continues: Hospital progress.
1984   8500263

Health Promot
Health promotion (Oxford, England)
0268-1099
Continued by: Health promotion
international.
1986-1989   8700098

Health Promot Int
Health promotion international
0957-4824   1460-2245
Continues: Health promotion (Oxford,
England).
1990   9008939

Health Promot J Austr
Health promotion journal of Australia:
official journal of Australian Association of
Health Promotion Professionals
1036-1073
1991   9710936

Health Promot Pract
Health promotion practice
1524-8399
2000   100890609

Health Psychol
Health psychology: official journal of the
Division of Health Psychology, American
Psychological Association
0278-6133
1982   8211523

Health Qual Life Outcomes
Health and quality of life outcomes
     1477-7525
2003   101153626

Health Rays
Health Rays
1936-1957   17320350R

Health Rep
Health reports / Statistics Canada, Canadian
Centre for Health Information = Rapports
sur la santé / Statistique Canada, Centre
canadien d'information sur la santé
0840-6529
1989   9012854

Health Serv J
The Health service journal
0952-2271
Continues: Health and social service journal.
1986   8605800

Health Serv J
Health services journal
Continued by Health services.
1946-1972   0323673

Health Serv Manage
Health services management
0953-8534
Continues: Hospital and health services
review.
1988-1994   8809216

Health Serv Manage Res
Health services management research:
an official journal of the Association
of University Programs in Health
Administration / HSMC, AUPHA
0951-4848
1988   8811549

Health Serv Manager
Health services manager
0363-020X
Continues Hospital supervision.
1976-1982   7607516

Health Serv Manpow Rev
Health services manpower review
0306-0233
Continued by: Health manpower
management.
1975-1988   8103581

Health Serv Rep
Health services reports
0090-2918
Continues: HSMHA health reports.
Continued by: Public health reports
(Washington, D.C.: 1974).
1972-1974   0430452

Health Serv Res
Health services research
0017-9124   1475-6773
1966   0053006

Health Soc Care Community
Health & social care in the community
0966-0410   1365-2524
1993   9306359

Health Soc Serv J
Health and social service journal
0300-8347
Continues British hospital journal and social
service review. Continued by: The Health
service journal.
1973-1986   0361025

Health Soc Work
Health & social work
0360-7283
1976   7611528

Health Stat Q
Health statistics quarterly / Office for
National Statistics
1465-1645
1999   100886205

Health Syst Lead
Health system leader
1075-1807
Continued by: Executive solutions for
healthcare management.
1994-1998   9442811

Health Syst Manage
Health systems management
0361-0195
1974-1985   7603078

Health Syst Rev
Health systems review
1055-7466
Continues: Review (Federation of American
Health Systems). Continued by: Hospital
outlook. Merged with: Hotline (Federation of
American Health Systems), to form: Hospital
outlook.
1991-1997   9103399

Health Technol
Health technology
0891-1924
Formed by the union of: Journal of health
care technology, and: Issues in health care
technology.
1987-1989   8705905

Health Technol Assess
Health technology assessment (Winchester,
England)
1366-5278
1997   9706284

Health Technol Assess (Rockv)
Health technology assessment
Continues: Health technology assessment
reports (Irregular).
1994   9501929

Health Technol Assess Rep
Health technology assessment reports
8755-9765
Continued by: Health technology assessment.
1981-1991   8607675

Health Transit Rev
Health transition review: the cultural, social,
and behavioural determinants of health
1036-4005
1991-1997   9114114

Health Trends
Health trends
0017-9132
1969-1999   0233525

Health Values
Health values
0147-0353
Continued by: American journal of health behavior.
1977-1995   7801228

Health Visit
Health visitor
0017-9140
Continues: Woman health officer. Continued by: Community practitioner.
1964-1998   17320470R

Healthc Ala
Healthcare Alabama / Alabama Hospital Association
1062-0257
1988-2000   9200409

Healthc Benchmarks
Healthcare benchmarks
1091-6768
Continues: Hospital benchmarks. Absorbed: Outpatient benchmarks. 199<6> Merged with: QI/TQM, to form: Healthcare benchmarks and quality improvement.
1996-2002   9800467

Healthc Bottom Line
Healthcare bottom line
1062-032X
Continues: Hospital bottom line.
1986-1996   9001373

Healthc Comput Commun
Healthcare computing & communications
8750-149X
Continued by: U.S. healthcare.
1984-1988   8503108

Healthc Demand Dis Manag
Healthcare demand & disease management
1094-2521
Continues: Healthcare demand management. Continued by: Disease management advisor.
1997-2000   9891547

Healthc Exec
Healthcare executive
0883-5381
1985   8612808

Healthc Exec Curr
Healthcare executive currents
0898-1647
Continues: Hospital administration currents.
1988-1991   9004556

Healthc Facil Manag Ser
Healthcare facilities management series
Continues: Technical document series.
1992   9716571

Healthc Financ Manage
Healthcare financial management: journal of the Healthcare Financial Management Association
0735-0732
Continues: Hospital financial management.
1982   8215859

Healthc Foodserv
Healthcare foodservice
Continued by: Healthcare foodservice magazine.
19uu-199u   9888383

Healthc Foodserv Mag
Healthcare foodservice magazine: the international trade publication for the healthcare foodservice industry
Continues: Healthcare foodservice.
199u-2003   100954799

Healthc Forum
Healthcare forum
0885-257X
Continues: Hospital forum. Continued by: Healthcare Forum journal.
1985-1987   8511257

Healthc Forum J
The Healthcare Forum journal
0899-9287
Continues: Healthcare forum. Continued by: Health Forum journal.
1987-1998   8801357

Healthc Hazard Manage Monit
Healthcare hazard management monitor: HHMM: the newsletter of the Center for Healthcare Environmental Management
1532-3633
Continues: Healthcare hazardous materials management.
2000   100955103

Healthc Hazard Mater Manage
Healthcare hazardous materials management: HHMM
1050-575X
Continues: Hospital hazardous materials management. Continued by: Healthcare hazard management monitor.
1990-2000   9014236

Healthc Hum Resour
Healthcare human resources
1060-9253
1992-1994   9212326

Healthc Hum Resour Spec Rep
Healthcare human resources. Special report
1076-8157
1992-1992   9416012

Healthc Inf Manage
Healthcare information management: journal of the Healthcare Information and Management Systems Society of the American Hospital Association
1066-906X
Continues: Health care systems. Continued by: Journal of healthcare information management.
1987-199u   8806584

Healthc Inform
Healthcare informatics: the business magazine for information and communication systems
1050-9135
Continues: U.S. healthcare.
1990   9004557

Healthc Leadersh Manag Rep
Healthcare leadership & management report
1533-2292
Continues: Integrated healthcare report. Continued by: Healthcare leadership report.
2000-2003   100958264

Healthc Leadersh Rep
Healthcare leadership report
1551-8906
Continues: Healthcare leadership & management report.
2004-2004   101209410

Healthc Manage Forum
Healthcare management forum / Canadian College of Health Service Executives = Forum gestion des soins de santé / Collège canadien des directeurs de services de santé
0840-4704
Continues: Health management forum.
1988   8805307

Healthc Pap
HealthcarePapers
1488-917X
1999   100961305

Healthc Prot Manage
Healthcare protection management
1980-1983   9878882

Healthc Q
Healthcare quarterly (Toronto, Ont.)
1710-2774
Continues: Hospital quarterly.
2004   101208192

Healthc Strateg
The healthcare strategist
1097-0819
1997-2000   9891985

Healthc Syst Strategy Rep
Healthcare systems strategy report
Continues: Health care competition week. Absorbed by: Health system leader.
1994-1996   9442118

Healthc Trends Transit
Healthcare trends & transition
1047-7276
1989-1995   9425861

Healthcare Benchmarks Qual Improv
Healthcare benchmarks and quality improvement
1541-1052
Merger of: Healthcare benchmarks, and: QI/TQM.
2002   101151031

Healthmarketing
HealthMarketing
0745-4538
Continues: Hospital management communications. Continued by: HealthService leader.
1982-1992   8403803

Healthplan
Healthplan
1087-3678
Continues: HMO. Continued by: AHIP coverage.
1996-2004   9707233

Healthspan
HealthSpan
0883-0452
Continues: HealthScan.
1985-1995   8507456

Healthtexas
HealthTexas / Texas Hospital Association
1048-4167
Continues: Texas Hospitals.
1989-1996   8903882

Healthy People 2000 Stat Notes
Healthy People 2000 statistical notes / National Center for Health Statistics
Continued by: Healthy People 2010 statistical notes.
1991-2000   9315564

Healthy People 2000 Stat Surveill
Healthy People 2000 statistics and surveillance / National Center for Health Statistics
1991-1998   9315565

Healthy People 2010 Stat Notes
Healthy People 2010 statistical notes: from the Centers for Disease Control and Prevention/ National Center for Health Statistics
Continues: Healthy People 2000 statistical notes. Continued by: Healthy people statistical notes.
2001-2004   101126643

Healthy People Stat Notes
Healthy people statistical notes / Healthy People 2010
Continues: Healthy People 2010 statistical notes.
2008   101482652

Hear News (Washington)
Hearing news
Continued by Hearing & speech news.
1935-1965   17320580R

Hear Res
Hearing research
0378-5955
1978   7900445

Heart
Heart (British Cardiac Society)
1355-6037   1468-201X
Continues: British heart journal.
1996   9602087

Heart Advis
Heart advisor / the Cleveland Clinic
1523-9004
Continues: Heartline (Cleveland. Ohio).
1998   9892190

Heart Bull
The Heart bulletin
0017-9248
1952-1971   7600720

Heart Cent Bull (Roslyn)
Bulletin. Roslyn, N. Y. St. Francis Hospital and Sanatorium for Cardiac Children
Continues the Bulletin of the hospital under its earlier name: St. Francis Sanatorium for Cardiac Children.
1954-1969   20440140R

Heart Dis
Heart disease (Hagerstown, Md.)
1521-737X   1533-3973
1999-2003   100887299

Heart Dis Stroke
Heart disease and stroke: a journal for primary care physicians
1058-2819
1992-1994   9210156

Heart Fail Clin
Heart failure clinics
1551-7136
2005   101231934

Heart Fail Monit
Heart failure monitor
1470-8590
2000   101140283

Heart Fail Rev
Heart failure reviews
1382-4147
1996   9612481

Heart Lung
Heart & lung: the journal of critical care
0147-9563   1527-3288
1972   0330057

Heart Lung Circ
Heart, lung & circulation
1443-9506   1444-2892
Continues: Asia Pacific heart journal.
2000   100963739

Heart Rhythm
Heart rhythm: the official journal of the Heart Rhythm Society
1547-5271   1556-3871
2004   101200317

Heart Surg Forum
The heart surgery forum
1098-3511   1522-6662
1998   100891112

Heart Vessels
Heart and vessels
0910-8327
1985   8511258

Heart Vessels Suppl
Heart and vessels. Supplement
0935-736X
1985   8810802

Heartbeat
Heartbeat (San Francisco, Calif.)
1057-0438
1990-2001   9104930

Heat Piping Air Cond
Heating, piping, and air conditioning
0017-940X
Absorbed: Aerologist. Apr. 1937 Journal of the American Society of Heating and Ventilating Engineers. Continued in part by: Journal of the American Society of Heating and Air-Conditioning Engineers. American Society of Heating and Air-Conditioning Engineers. Continued by: Heating/piping/air conditioning engineering.
1929-1999   9877468

HEC Forum
HEC forum: an interdisciplinary journal on hospitals' ethical and legal issues
0956-2737
1989   8917455

Hefte Unfallheilkd
Hefte zur Unfallheilkunde
0085-1469
Continued by: Heft zur Zeitschrift "Der Unfallchirurg".
1929-1992   7504994

Heilkd Heilwege
Heilkunde - Heilwege
Merged with Gesundes Leben; medizinalpolitische Rundschau to form Gesundes Leben vereinigt mit Heilkunde-Heilwege.
1951-1964   0254146

Heilkunst
Die Heilkunst
0017-9639
Continues Arzt und Patient.
1951-1993   0377243

Heilpadagog Werkbl
Heilpädagogische Werkblätter
Continued by Vierteljahresschrift für Heilpädagogik und ihre Nachbargebiete (VHN).
1932-1970   1301763

Helicobacter
Helicobacter
1083-4389   1523-5378
1996   9605411

Hell Adelphe
Hellenis adelphe
0301-5157
Continued by: Noséleutiké.
1965-1978   0377562

Hell Cheirourgike
Hellēnikē cheirourgikē. Acta chirurgica Hellenica
0018-0092
1954   17330220R

Hell Iatr
Hellenike iatrike
0258-2694
1927   0373002

Hell J Nucl Med
Hellenic journal of nuclear medicine
1790-5427
Continues: Hellēnikē pyrēnikē iatrikē.
2004   101257471

Hell Period Stomat Gnathopathoprosopike Cheir
To Hellēniko periodiko gia stomatikē & gnathoprosōpikē cheirourgikē / epísēmo organo tēs Hetaireias Stomatognathoprosōpikēs Cheirourgikēs = The Greek journal of oral & maxillofacial surgery
1105-1124
1986-2001   9001934

Hell Stomatol Chron
Hellenika stomatologika chronika. Hellenic stomatological annals
1011-4181
Continues: Stomatologika chronika.
1970   0322305

Hellenic J Cardiol
Hellenic journal of cardiology: HJC = Hellēnikē kardiologikē epitheōrēsē
1109-9666
2002   101257381

Helv Chim Acta
Helvetica chimica acta
0018-019X
1918   2985094R

Helv Chir Acta
Helvetica chirurgica acta
0018-0181
Merged with: Zeitschrift für Unfallchirurgie und Versicherungsmedizin. to form: Swiss surgery. Continues surgical section of Helvetica medica acta. and assumes its volume numbering.
1945-1994   2985095R

Helv Chir Acta Suppl
Helvetica chirurgica acta. Supplementum
0377-9440
1946-1981   2985096R

Helv Med Acta
Helvetica medica acta
0018-0203
1934-1974   0401174

Helv Med Acta Suppl
Helvetica medica acta. Supplementum
0367-5971
1937-1972   7706034

Helv Odontol Acta
Helvetica odontologica acta
0018-0211
Absorbed by: Schweizerische Monatsschrift für Zahnheilkunde.
1957-1975   7610480

Helv Paediatr Acta
Helvetica paediatrica acta
0018-022X
1945-1988   0373005

Helv Paediatr Acta Suppl
Helvetica paediatrica acta. Supplementum
0073-1811
1945-1989   0373006

Helv Physiol Pharmacol Acta
Helvetica physiologica et pharmacologica acta
0367-6242
1943-1969   17330350R

Helv Physiol Pharmacol Acta Suppl 1
Helvetica physiologica et pharmacologica
acta. Supplementum
1943-1967   17330360R

Hematol Cell Ther
Hematology and cell therapy
1269-3286
  Continues: Nouvelle revue française
  d'hematologie. Absorbed by: Annals of
  hematology.
1996-2000   9613253

Hematol J
The hematology journal: the official journal
of the European Haematology Association
/ EHA
1466-4860
  Absorbed by: Haematologica.
2000-2005   100965523

Hematol Oncol
Hematological oncology
0278-0232
1983   8307268

Hematol Oncol Clin North Am
Hematology/oncology clinics of North
America
0889-8588
  Formed by the union of: Clinics in
  haematology, in part, and: Clinics in
  oncology.
1987   8709473

Hematol Pathol
Hematologic pathology
0886-0238
  Continued by: Hematopathology and
  molecular hematology.
1987-1995   8707764

Hematology
Hematology (Amsterdam, Netherlands)
1024-5332   1607-8454
1996   9708388

Hematology Am Soc Hematol Educ Program
Hematology / the Education Program of the
American Society of Hematology. American
Society of Hematology. Education Program
1520-4391   1520-4383
  Continues: Education Program. American
  Society of Hematology. Education Program.
1980   100890099

Hematopathol Mol Hematol
Hematopathology and molecular hematology
1082-8893
  Continues: Hematologic pathology.
1996-1998   9608785

Hemodial Int
Hemodialysis international. International
Symposium on Home Hemodialysis
1492-7535
  Continues: Home hemodialysis international.
  International Symposium on Home
  Hemodialysis.
2000   101093910

Hemoglobin
Hemoglobin
0363-0269   1532-432X
1976   7705865

Hemostase
Hémostase
1961-1966   0156010

Henry E Sigerist Suppl Bull Hist Med
The Henry E. Sigerist supplements to the
Bulletin of the history of medicine
0194-1100
  Supersedes Bulletin of the history of medicine.
  Supplements which was published 1943-51.
1978-1985   7905538

Henry Ford Hosp Med Bull
Henry Ford Hospital medical bulletin
  Continued by the Henry Ford Hospital
  medical journal.
1953-1967   0124331

Henry Ford Hosp Med J
Henry Ford Hospital medical journal
0018-0416
  Continues the Henry Ford Hospital medical
  bulletin.
1967-1992   0122304

Hepatobiliary Pancreat Dis Int
Hepatobiliary & pancreatic diseases
international: HBPD INT
1499-3872
2002   101151457

Hepatogastroenterology
Hepato-gastroenterology
0172-6390
  Continues: Acta hepato-gastroenterologica.
1980   8007849

Hepatology
Hepatology (Baltimore, Md.)
0270-9139   1527-3350
1981   8302946

Hereditas
Hereditas
0018-0661   1601-5223
1920   0374654

Heredity
Heredity
0018-067X   1365-2540
1947   0373007

Hernia
Hernia: the journal of hernias and
abdominal wall surgery
1265-4906   1248-9204
1997   9715168

Herpes
Herpes: the journal of the IHMF
0969-7667
199u   9801722

Herz
Herz
0340-9937
1976   7801231

Herzschrittmacherther Elektrophysiol
Herzschrittmachertherapie &
Elektrophysiologie
0938-7412   1435-1544
1990   9425873

Hifu
[Hifu] Skin research
0018-1390
  Continued by: Hifu no kagaku.
195u-2001   17340020R

Hifu To Hinyo Dermatol Urol
Hifu to hinyo. The Dermatology and urology
  Continued by Nishi Nippon Hifuka and Nishi
  Hinyokika.
1933-1968   0213157

Hifuka Kiyo
Hifuka kiyo. Acta dermatologica
0065-1176
1923-1999   1305010

Hifuka No Rinsho
Hifuka no rinsho. Rinsho derma (Tokyo)
0018-1404
1959   7501807

Hig Cas Hig Mikrobiol Epidemiol Sanit Teh
Higijena; časopis za higijenu,
mikrobiologiju, epidemiologiju i sanitarnu
tehniku
0367-584X
1949-1965   17340330R

Hig Salubr
Higiene y salubridad
1947-1956   17340310R

Hig Sanit
Higiene sanitaria
1931-19uu   17340300R

Higashi Nippon Shigaku Zasshi
Higashi Nihon shigaku zasshi
0910-9722
  Continued by: Hokaidō Iryō Daigaku
  Shigakkai zasshi..
1982-2004   8703497

High Alt Med Biol
High altitude medicine & biology
1527-0297
2000   100901183

Higiene
Higiene
0437-4495
1948-1969   0060440

Hillside J Clin Psychiatry
The Hillside journal of clinical psychiatry
0193-5216
  Continues: Journal of the Hillside Hospital.
1979-1989   7905001

HIM J
The HIM journal
1833-3583   1833-3575
  Continues: Health information management.
2001   101122643

Hindsight
Hindsight (Saint Louis, Mo.)
  Continues: Newsletter of the Optometric
  Historical Society.
1992   9431605

Hindustan Antibiot Bull
Hindustan antibiotics bulletin
0018-1935
1958   2985097R

Hinyokika Kiyo
Hinyokika kiyo. Acta urologica Japonica
0018-1994
1955   0421145

Hip
The Hip
0095-7216
1973-1987   7511195

Hip Int
Hip international: the journal of clinical and
experimental research on hip pathology and
therapy
1120-7000   1724-6067
1991   9200413

Hippocampus
Hippocampus
1050-9631   1098-1063
1991   9108167

Hippokrates
Hippokrates
0018-2001
1928-1978   0413670

Hiroshima Daigaku Shigaku Zasshi
Hiroshima Daigaku shigaku zasshi. The
Journal of Hiroshima University Dental
Society
0046-7472
1969   0224555

Hiroshima J Med Sci
Hiroshima journal of medical sciences
0018-2052
1951   0421060

Hisp Med
Hispalis médica; revista sevillana de
medicina y cirugia
0018-2125
1943-1992   0373011

Hist Biol
Historical biology
0891-2963
1988   9426321

Hist Bull (Calgary)
Historical bulletin; notes and abstracts
dealing with medical history
1936-1958   17340510R

Hist Cienc Saude Manguinhos
História, ciências, saúde--Manguinhos
0104-5970
1994   9513999

Hist Hosp
Historia hospitalium
0440-9043
1966   7507133

Hist Med Vet
Historia medicinae veterinariae
0105-1423
1976   7700207

Hist Philos Life Sci
History and philosophy of the life sciences
0391-9714
    Absorbed: Episteme. Continues in part:
    Pubblicazioni. Stazione zoologica di Napoli.
1979   8003052

Hist Psychiatry
History of psychiatry
0957-154X
1990   9013819

Hist Psychol
History of psychology
1093-4510
1998   9808650

Hist Sci
History of science; an annual review of
literature, research and teaching
0073-2753
1962   17340520R

Hist Sci (Tokyo)
Historia scientiarum: international journal
of the History of Science Society of Japan
0285-4821
    Continues: Japanese studies in the history of
    science.
1980   8201528

Hist Sci Med
Histoire des sciences médicales
0440-8888
1967   0225346

Histochem Cell Biol
Histochemistry and cell biology
0948-6143   1432-119X
    Continues: Histochemistry.
1995   9506663

Histochem J
The Histochemical journal
0018-2214
    Continued by: Journal of molecular histology.
1968-2003   0163161

Histochemie
Histochemie. Histochemistry. Histochimie
0018-2222
    Continues the Abteilung Histochemie
    of the Zeitschrift für Zellforschung und
    mikroskopische Anatomie. Continued by
    Histochemistry.
1964-1973   0411277

Histochemistry
Histochemistry
0301-5564
    Continues: Histochemie. Continued by:
    Histochemistry and cell biology.
1974-1994   0411300

Histol Histopathol
Histology and histopathology
0213-3911   1699-5848
1986   8609357

Histopathology
Histopathology
0309-0167   1365-2559
1977   7704136

HIV AIDS Policy Law Rev
HIV/AIDS policy & law review / Canadian
HIV/AIDS Legal Network
1712-624X
    Continues: Canadian HIV/AIDS policy & law
    review.
2004   101249725

HIV AIDS Surveill Rep
HIV/AIDS surveillance report (Atlanta, Ga.)
1048-759X
    Continues: HIV/AIDS surveillance.
1993   9517597

HIV Capsule Rep
HIV capsule report
1992-1996   9417025

HIV Clin
HIV clinician / Delta Region AIDS
Education & Training Center
1551-885X
    Continues: Faculty notes (New Orleans, La.).
1999   101122284

HIV Clin Trials
HIV clinical trials
1528-4336
2000   100936377

HIV Hotline
HIV hotline
1991-1998   9200421

HIV Inside
HIV inside: a newsletter for correctional
professionals
1551-9066
uuuu   101150647

HIV Med
HIV medicine
1464-2662   1468-1293
1999   100897392

HIV Prev Plus
HIV prevention plus!
1488-3694   1488-3708
    Continues: Canadian AIDS news.
1999   100954637

HMO
HMO
1091-0506
    Continues: HMO magazine. Continued by:
    Healthplan.
1994-1996   9506687

HMO Pract
HMO practice / HMO Group
0891-6624
    Continued by: Effective clinical practice.
1987-1998   8710832

HNO
HNO
0017-6192   1433-0458
1947   2985099R

Hoitotiede
Hoitotiede
0786-5686
    Continues: Sairaanhoidon vuosikirja.
1989   9104138

Hoja Tisiol
Hoja tisiológica
0018-3326
1941-1971   0011672

Hokenfu Zasshi
[Hokenfu zasshi] The Japanese journal for
public health nurse
0047-1844
    Continued by: Hokenshi jānaru.
1951-2003   17410240R

Hokkaido Igaku Zasshi
[Hokkaido igaku zasshi] The Hokkaido
journal of medical science
0367-6102
1923   17410290R

Hokkaido Shika Ishikai Shi
Hokkaido Shika Ishikai shi
0073-2915
1948   7502572

Holist Nurs Pract
Holistic nursing practice
0887-9311   1550-5138
    Continues: Topics in clinical nursing.
1986   8702105

Holistic Assertive Nurse
Holistic Assertive Nurse
    Continues: Assertive Nurse.
1981-1981   9879074

Home Care Econ
Home care economics
0891-9364
1987-1988   8707765

Home Care Manag
Home care manager
1094-0375
    Continued by: Home healthcare nurse
    manager.
1997-1998   9809996

Home Care Provid
Home care provider
1084-628X
1996-2001   9605410

Home Health Care Serv Q
Home health care services quarterly
0162-1424   1545-0856
1979   8000128

Home Health J
Home health journal
0734-7588
1980-1987   8612812

Home Health Rev
Home health review
0193-2683
1977-1982   7909326

Home Healthc Nurse
Home healthcare nurse
0884-741X   1539-0713
Absorbed: Nephrology nurse.
1983   8403379

Home Healthc Nurse Manag
Home healthcare nurse manager
1520-5657
Continues: Home care manager.
1998-2000   100884165

Homeopath Bull
Homoeopathic bulletin
1928-1976   17410500R

Homeopathy
Homeopathy: the journal of the Faculty of
Homeopathy
1475-4916   1476-4245
Continues: British homoeopathic journal.
2002   101140517

Homeost Health Dis
Homeostasis in health and disease:
international journal devoted to integrative
brain functions and homeostatic systems
0960-7560
Continues: Activitas nervosa superior.
1991   9206066

Homo
Homo: internationale Zeitschrift für die
vergleichende Forschung am Menschen
0018-442X
1949   0374655

Homoeopath Rec
The Homoeopathic recorder
Supersedes Boericke and Tafel's bulletin of
homoeopathic news. Merged with the Journal
of the American Institute of Homeopathy to
form the Journal of the American Institute of
Homeopathy; with the homeopathic recorder.
1886-1959   17410540R

Hong Kong Med J
Hong Kong medical journal = Xianggang
yi xue za zhi / Hong Kong Academy of
Medicine
1024-2708
Continues: Journal of the Hong Kong
Medical Association.
1995   9512509

Honvedorvos
Honvédorvos
0133-879X
1949-1990   17410690R

Hoosier Health Her
Hoosier health herald
1919-1968   17410710R

Hopital
L' Hôpital
Merged with L'Information thérapeutique to
form L'Hôpital information thérapeutique.
1913-1966   1301165

Hopkins HIV Rep
The Hopkins HIV report: a bimonthly
newsletter for healthcare providers / Johns
Hopkins University AIDS Service
1551-8396
Continues: Moore news for care providers.
1996   9614441

Hoppe Seylers Z Physiol Chem
Hoppe-Seyler's Zeitschrift für
physiologische Chemie
0018-4888
Continues Zeitschrift für physiologische
chemie. Continued by Biological chemistry
Hoppe-Seyler.
1895-1984   2985060R

Horiz Biochem Biophys
Horizons in biochemistry and biophysics
0096-2708
1974-1989   7502793

Horiz Med
Horizons médicaux
0437-8849
1953-1975   17420040R

Horm Behav
Hormones and behavior
0018-506X   1095-6867
1969   0217764

Horm Metab Res
Hormone and metabolic research. Hormon-
und Stoffwechselforschung. Hormones et
métabolisme
0018-5043
1969   0177722

Horm Metab Res Suppl
Hormone and metabolic research.
Supplement series
0170-5903
1969-1995   0330417

Horm Res
Hormone research
0301-0163   1423-0046
Continues Hormones.
1973   0366126

Hormoner
Hormoner
1936-1969   17420080R

Hormones
Hormones
0018-5051
Supersedes European journal of
endocrinology. Continued by Hormone
research.
1970-1972   0366127

Hormones (Athens)
Hormones (Athens, Greece)
1109-3099
2002   101142469

Hormoon
Het Hormoon
0168-6860
1931-1963   8306251

Horumon To Rinsho
Horumon to rinsho. Clinical endocrinology
0045-7167
1953   0420561

Hosp (Lond)
The Hospital
0018-5477
Continues: Hospital gazette. Absorbed the
Journal of the Incorporated Association of
Clerks and Stewards of Mental Hospitals in
Oct. 1942. Continued by: Hospital and health
services review.
1930-1971   0332425

Hosp Adm (Chic)
Hospital administration
0018-5523
Continued by: Hospital & health services
administration.
1956-1975   9427237

Hosp Adm (New Delhi)
Hospital administration
0018-5531
1964   0037362

Hosp Adm Can
Hospital administration in Canada
0018-554X
Continues Hospital administration and
construction. Merged with Health care digest
to form Health care in Canada.
1961-1978   0373014

Hosp Admin Curr
Hospital administration currents
0046-7952
Continues Currents in hospital administration.
Continued by: Healthcare executive currents.
1968-1988   0262165

Hosp Admitting Mon
Hospital admitting monthly
0745-1466
Continued by: Hospital access management.
1982-1993   8302821

Hosp Aviat
Hospital aviation
0740-8315
Merged with: AeroMedical journal, to form:
Journal of air medical transport.
1982-1989   8906078

Hosp Bond Rev
Hospital bond review
19uu   9892141

Hosp Cap Finance
Hospital capital finance American Hospital
Association, Division of Hospital Planning
and Capital Finance
0742-5708
1984-1986   8410882

Hosp Case Manag
Hospital case management: the monthly
update on hospital-based care planning and
critical paths
1087-0652
1993   9603097

Hosp Community Psychiatry
Hospital & community psychiatry
0022-1597
Continues Mental hospitals. Continued by:
Psychiatric services (Washington, D.C.).
1966-1994   0040250

Hosp Corps Q
Hospital Corps quarterly
1917-1949   17420450R

Hosp Cost Manag Account
Hospital cost management and accounting
1045-1765
Continues: Hospital cost accounting advisor.
1989-1997   9201993

Hosp Counc Bull
Hospital Council bulletin
1935-1950   17420460R

Hosp Dev
Hospital development
0300-5720
Supersedes Hospital building & engineering.
1973   0361026

Hosp Employee Health
Hospital employee health
0744-6470
1982   8510434

Hosp Eng
Hospital engineering
Continues HE. Hospital engineering.
Continued by: Journal of the Institute of
Hospital Engineering.
1977-1987 **7805786**

Hosp Entrep Newsl
Hospital entrepreneurs' newsletter
8756-7253
Continued by: Hospital strategy report.
1985-1988 **8712401**

Hosp Equip Supplies
Hospital equipment & supplies
0018-5620
Continues: Hospital equipment news.
Continued by: Healthcare equipment &
supplies.
1968-200u **0152562**

Hosp Ethics
Hospital ethics / American Hospital
Association
8756-8519
1985-1995 **8602397**

Hosp Financ Manage
Hospital financial management
0018-5639
Continues Hospital accounting. Continued by
Healthcare financial management.
1968-1982 **0227500**

Hosp Food Nutr Focus
Hospital food & nutrition focus
0747-7376
Continued by: Health care food & nutrition
focus.
1984-1996 **8703500**

Hosp Formul
Hospital formulary
0098-6909
Continues: Hospital formulary management.
Continued by: Formulary (Cleveland. Ohio).
1975-1995 **7508609**

Hosp Forum
Hospital forum
0018-5663
Continued by: Healthcare forum.
1958-1985 **0376561**

Hosp Gen (Madr)
Hospital general
0018-5698
1961-1980 **0401046**

Hosp Gift Shop Manage
Hospital gift shop management
0738-7946
1983 **9880319**

Hosp Guest Relations Rep
Hospital guest relations report
0899-8957
Continued by: Hospital patient relations
report.
1986-1989 **8802247**

Hosp Hazard Mater Manage
Hospital hazardous materials management
0895-7169
Continued by: Healthcare hazardous materials
management.
1987-1990 **9008949**

Hosp Health Manag
Hospital and health management
Continues: Hospital and nursing home
management.
1946-1964 **17420260R**

Hosp Health Netw
Hospitals & health networks / AHA
1068-8838
Continues: Hospitals.
1993 **9312077**

Hosp Health Netw 360
Hospitals & health networks 360°: H&HN
360°
1999-1999 **100892665**

Hosp Health Serv Adm
Hospital & health services administration
8750-3735
Continues: Hospital administration.
Continued by: Journal of healthcare
management.
1976-1997 **7611540**

Hosp Health Serv Rev
The Hospital and health services review
0308-0234
Continues The Hospital. Continued by:
Health services management.
1972-1988 **0332235**

Hosp Infect Control
Hospital infection control
0098-180X
Continued by: Hospital infection control &
prevention.
1974-2008 **7507137**

Hosp J
The Hospice journal
0742-969X
Merged with: Journal of pharmaceutical care
in pain & symptom control, to form: Journal
of pain & palliative care pharmacotherapy.
1985-2001 **8505218**

Hosp Libr
Hospital libraries
0145-8930
1976-1981 **7700322**

Hosp Manage
Hospital management
0018-5744
1916-1971 **0373016**

Hosp Manage Commun
Hospital management communications
0274-5429
Continued by: HealthMarketing.
1977-1982 **8202040**

Hosp Manage Q
Hospital management quarterly: HMQ
0891-9941
Continued by: Health management quarterly.
1979-1984 **8502526**

Hosp Manager
The Hospital manager / American Hospital
Association
0740-9982
Continues: Cross-reference on human
resources management.
1983-1986 **8400614**

Hosp Mater Manage
Hospital material[dollar sign] management
0888-3068
Continues: Hospital purchasing management.
1986 **8702109**

Hosp Mater Manage Q
Hospital materiel management quarterly
0192-2262
1979-2001 **7909330**

Hosp Med
Hospital medicine (London, England: 1998)
1462-3935
Continues: British journal of hospital
medicine. Continued by: British journal of
hospital medicine (London. England: 2005).
1998-2005 **9803882**

Hosp Med Staff
The Hospital medical staff
0090-0710
Continued by: Medical staff news.
1972-1985 **0350747**

Hosp Outlook
Hospital outlook
1098-8416
Merger of: Health systems review. and:
Hotline (Federation of American Health
Systems).
1998 **9805449**

Hosp Patient Relat Rep
Hospital patient relations report
1048-4477
Continues: Hospital guest relations report.
Merged with: Nursing recruitment &
retention, to form: Report on healthcare
management solutions.
1989-1994 **9013820**

Hosp Peer Rev
Hospital peer review
0149-2632
1976 **7706036**

Hosp Pharm
Hospital pharmacy
0018-5787
1966 **0043175**

Hosp Physician
Hospital physician
0888-2428
1965 **7600530**

Hosp Pract
Hospital practice
0018-5809
Split into: Hospital practice (Hospital ed.);
and. Hospital practice (Office ed.).
1966-1980 **0074404**

Hosp Pract (Hosp Ed)
Hospital practice (Hospital ed.)
8755-4542
Continues in part: Hospital practice.
198u **9880471**

Hosp Pract (Minneap)
Hospital practice (1995)
Formed by the union of: Hospital practice
(Family practice ed.); Hospital practice
(Hospital ed.); and: Hospital practice (Office
ed.).
1995-2001 **101268948**

Hosp Pract (Off Ed)
Hospital practice (Office ed.)
8750-2836
Contents of feature articles are identical
to Hospital practice (Hospital ed.), but
pagination. advertisements and editorials
differ slightly. Occasionally contains
supplemental articles that do not appear in the
hospital ed. Merged with: Hospital practice
(Family practice ed.), and Hospital practice
(Hospital ed.), to form: Hospital practice
(1995).
1981-1995 **8404149**

Hosp Prog
Hospital progress
0018-5817
Continued by: Health progress (Saint Louis,
Mo.).
1920-1984 **0374656**

Hosp Purch Manage
Hospital purchasing management
0163-1322
    Continued by: Hospital material management.
1976-1986   **7804118**

Hosp Q
Hospital quarterly
1480-221X
    Continued by: Healthcare quarterly.
1997-2003   **100883480**

Hosp Rec Study
Hospital record study: a joint study by
CPHA and IMS America Ltd. / IMS
America
0891-8538
1960   **8508098**

Hosp Revenue Rep
Hospital revenue report
1052-8733
    Formed by the union of: Part A news, and:
    Health care marketer. Continued by: Hospital
    networker insider.
1990-1993   **9014460**

Hosp Risk Manage
Hospital risk management
0199-6312
    Continued by: Healthcare risk management.
1979-1994   **8100790**

Hosp Secur Saf Manage
Hospital security and safety management
0745-1148
    Continues: Health care security and safety
    management.
1982-2002   **8708292**

Hosp Strategy Rep
Hospital strategy report
1040-6263
    Continues: Hospital entrepreneurs' newsletter.
    Continued by: Russ Coile's health trends.
1988-1995   **8903894**

Hosp Superv
Hospital supervision
0018-5841
    Continued by: Health services manager.
1967-1975   **9876115**

Hosp Superv Bull
Hospital supervisor's bulletin
0018-585X
    Continued by: Leadership edge.
1965-1993   **0236624**

Hosp Technol Ser
Hospital technology series
0888-711X
    Continues: AHA hospital technology series.
1983-1997   **8500896**

Hosp Top
Hospital topics
0018-5868
    Absorbed: Hospital digest. Continues:
    Hospital topics and buyer's guide.
1951   **0411772**

Hosp Trustee
Hospital trustee
0704-0407
    Merged with: Dimensions in health service,
    to form: Leadership in health services.
1977-1991   **7810267**

Hospital
El Hospital; la revista interamericana de
hospitales
0018-5485
1945   **0373020**

Hospital (Rio J)
Hospital (Rio de Janeiro, Brazil)
0018-5469
    Continues: Revista. Rio de Janeiro. Hospital
    São Francisco de Assis. Sociedade Médica.
1931-19uu   **9427238**

Hospitalia
Hospitalia
    Continued by L'Hôpital.
1939-1947   **17430270R**

Hospitalis
Hospitalis
0018-5930
    Continues: Fachblatt für schweizerische
    Heime und Anstalten.
1948   **0373015**

Hospitalist
The hospitalist
1553-085X
1997   **100964619**

Hospitals
Hospitals
0018-5973
    Continues: Bulletin of the American Hospital
    Association. Absorbed: MULTIs. Continued
    by: Hospitals & health networks.
1936-1993   **0374657**

Hospitals (Lond)
Hospitals
1940-194u   **0050430**

Hotetsu Rinsho
Hotetsu rinsho. Practice in prosthodontics
0018-6341
1968   **1254114**

How Eval Health Programs
How to: Evaluate health programs
0191-3727
1978-1980   **7901130**

HPB Surg
HPB surgery: a world journal of hepatic,
pancreatic and biliary surgery
0894-8569   **1607-8462**
1988   **9002972**

HPN Hosp Purch News
Hospital purchasing news: HPN
0279-4799
    Continues: Purchasing administration.
    Continued by: Healthcare purchasing news.
1981-1994   **9426503**

HRMAGAZINE
HRMagazine: on human resource
management
1047-3149
    Continues: Personnel administrator.
1990   **9011800**

HRSA Careaction
HRSA careaction
                    1551-8868
1998   **100969580**

HSMHA Health Rep
HSMHA health reports
0083-1204
    Continues: Public health reports. Continued
    by: Health services reports.
1971-1972   **0323220**

Hu Li Yan Jiu
Hu li yan jiu = Nursing research
1022-6265
    Continues in part: Hu li za zhi. Continued by:
    Journal of nursing research.
1993-2001   **9712938**

Hu Li Za Zhi
Hu li za zhi The journal of nursing
0047-262X
    Continued in part by: Hu li yan jiu.
1954   **0073267**

Hua Xi Kou Qiang Yi Xue Za Zhi
Hua xi kou qiang yi xue za zhi = Huaxi
kouqiang yixue zazhi = West China journal
of stomatology
1000-1182
1983   **9422648**

Hua Xi Yi Ke Da Xue Xue Bao
Hua xi yi ke da xue xue bao = Journal of
West China University of Medical Sciences =
Huaxi yike daxue xuebao / [bian ji zhe, Hua
xi yi ke da xue xue bao bian wei hui]
0257-7712
    Continues: Sichuan yi xue yuan xue bao.
    Continued by: Sichaun da xue xue bao. Yi
    xue ban.
1986-2002   **8609552**

Huan Jing Ke Xue
Huan jing ke xue= Huanjing kexue / [bian
ji, Zhongguo ke xue yuan huan jing ke xue
wei yuan hui "Huan jing ke xue" bian ji wei
yuan hui.]
0250-3301
1978   **8405344**

Hudson Cty Health Rec
Hudson County health record [monthly]
    Supersedes the board's Monthly report.
1934-uuuu   **22730300R**

Hum Antibodies
Human antibodies
1093-2607
    Continues: Human antibodies and hybridomas.
1997   **9711270**

Hum Antibodies Hybridomas
Human antibodies and hybridomas
0956-960X
    Continued by: Human antibodies.
1990-1996   **9014461**

Hum Biol
Human biology; an international record of
research
0018-7143
1929   **0116717**

Hum Biol Oceania
Human biology in Oceania
0046-8142
1971-1973   **0347221**

Hum Brain Mapp
Human brain mapping
1065-9471   **1097-0193**
1993   **9419065**

Hum Cell
Human cell: official journal of Human Cell
Research Society
0914-7470
1988   **8912329**

Hum Dev
Human development
0018-716X   **1423-0054**
    Continues Vita humana.
1965   **0012445**

Hum Exp Toxicol
Human & experimental toxicology
0960-3271   **1477-0903**
    Continues: Human toxicology.
1990   **9004560**

Hum Factors
Human factors
0018-7208
1958   **0374660**

Hum Fertil (Camb)
Human fertility (Cambridge, England)
1464-7273
Continues: Journal of the British Fertility
Society.
1998   100888143

Hum Gene Ther
Human gene therapy
1043-0342   1557-7422
1990   9008950

Hum Genet
Human genetics
0340-6717   1432-1203
Continues Humangenetik.
1976   7613873

Hum Genet Suppl
Human genetics. Supplement
0172-7699
1978-1981   7809212

Hum Genomics
Human genomics
1473-9542   1479-7364
2003   101202210

Hum Health Care Int
Humane health care international
Continues: Humane medicine. Beginning
in 2001. available only online with title:
Humane health care.
1996-1997   9607656

Hum Hered
Human heredity
0001-5652   1423-0062
Continues Acta genetica et statistica medica.
1969   0200525

Hum Immunol
Human immunology
0198-8859
1980   8010936

Hum Mol Genet
Human molecular genetics
0964-6906   1460-2083
1992   9208958

Hum Mov Sci
Human movement science
0167-9457
1982   8300127

Hum Mutat
Human mutation
1059-7794   1098-1004
1992   9215429

Hum Neurobiol
Human neurobiology
0721-9075
1982-1988   8211530

Hum Nutr Appl Nutr
Human nutrition. Applied nutrition
0263-8495
Continues in part: Journal of human nutrition.
Continued in part by: Journal of human
nutrition and dietetics. and in part merged
with: Human nutrition. Clinical nutrition: to
become: European Journal of clinical nutrition.
1982-1987   8207515

Hum Nutr Clin Nutr
Human nutrition. Clinical nutrition
0263-8290
Continues in part: Journal of human nutrition.
Merged with part of: Human nutrition.
Applied nutrition, to form: European journal
of clinical nutrition.
1982-1987   8207516

Hum Organ
Human organization
0018-7259
Continues Applied anthropology.
1949   0412703

Hum Pathol
Human pathology
0046-8177   1532-8392
1970   9421547

Hum Physiol
Human physiology
0362-1197
1975   7605014

Hum Psychopharmacol
Human psychopharmacology
0885-6222   1099-1077
1986   8702539

Hum Reprod
Human reproduction (Oxford, England)
0268-1161   1460-2350
Continued in part by: Human reproduction
update.
1986   8701199

Hum Reprod Genet Ethics
Human reproduction and genetic ethics
1028-7825
Continues: European journal of genetics in
society.
1998   9815992

Hum Reprod Update
Human reproduction update
1355-4786   1460-2369
Merger of: Bibliography of reproduction, and:
Oxford reviews of reproductive biology.
1995   9507614

Hum Res Rep
Human research report
0885-0615
1986   9105327

Hum Resour Manage
Human resource management
0090-4848
Continues: Management of personnel
quarterly.
1972   9877746

Hum Toxicol
Human toxicology
0144-5952
Continued by: Human & experimental
toxicology.
1981-1989   8206759

Hum Vaccin
Human vaccines
1554-8600   1554-8619
2005   101265291

Humangenetik
Humangenetik
0018-7348
Supersedes Zeitschrift für menschliche
Vererbungs- und Konstitutionslehre.
Continued by Human genetics.
1964-1975   7607154

Hunan Yi Ke Da Xue Xue Bao
**Hunan yi ke da xue xue bao = Hunan yike
daxue xuebao = Bulletin of Hunan Medical
University**
1000-5625
Continues: Hunan yi xue yuan xue bao.
Continued by: Zhong nan da xue xue bao.
1989-2003   9424769

Hung Acta Physiol
Hungarica acta physiologica
1946-1949   17440280R

HW SA US At Energy Comm
**HW-SA [reports]. U.S. Atomic Energy
Commission**
1964   0111357

Hybrid Hybridomics
Hybridoma and hybridomics
1536-8599
Continues: Hybridoma. Continued by:
Hybridoma.
2001-2004   101131136

Hybridoma
Hybridoma
0272-457X
Absorbed: Monoclonal antibodies. Continued
by: Hybridoma and hybridomics.
1981-2001   8202424

Hybridoma (Larchmt)
Hybridoma (2005)
1554-0014   1557-8348
Continues: Hybridoma and hybridomics.
2005   101241539

Hydrother Physiother
Hydrotherapie-Physiotherapie
1955-1956   17440330R

Hyg Ment
L'Hygiéne mentale
0073-4241
Continues l'Informateur des aliénistes et des
neurologistes. Supplement to L'Encéphale.
1925-1973   0374661

Hyg Revy
Hygienisk revy
0018-8255
Continued by Hygien & miljö.
1912-1973   7606913

Hygie
Hygie
0751-7149
Continues: International journal of health
education. Continued by: Promotion &
education.
1982-1993   8304186

Hypertens Pregnancy
**Hypertension in pregnancy: official journal
of the International Society for the Study of
Hypertension in Pregnancy**
1064-1955   1525-6065
Continues: Clinical and experimental
hypertension. Part B, Hypertension in
pregnancy.
1993   9421297

Hypertens Res
**Hypertension research: official journal of
the Japanese Society of Hypertension**
0916-9636   1348-4214
Continues: Kōketsuatsu.
1992   9307690

Hypertension
Hypertension
0194-911X   1524-4563
Supersedes Hypertension which was issued as
pt. 2 of Circulation research.
1979   7906255

I

IADS Newsl
IADS newsletter
0301-5831
1972-1984   0351477

IAL News
IAL news
1955   17510040R

IAPAC Mon
IAPAC monthly
1545-1089
Continues: Journal of the International
Association of Physicians in AIDS Care.
2000   **101087241**

IARC Monogr Eval Carcinog Risk Chem Hum
IARC monographs on the evaluation of the
carcinogenic risk of chemicals to humans
0250-9555
Continues IARC monographs on the
evaluation of carcinogenic risk of chemicals
to man. Continued by: IARC monographs
on the evaluation of carcinogenic risks to
humans.
1978-1987   **7902489**

**IARC Monogr Eval Carcinog Risk Chem Hum
Suppl**
IARC monographs on the evaluation of the
carcinogenic risk of chemicals to humans.
Supplement
1014-4307
Continued by: IARC monographs on the
evaluation of carcinogenic risks to humans.
Supplement.
1979-1985   **8002508**

IARC Monogr Eval Carcinog Risk Chem Man
IARC monographs on the evaluation of
carcinogenic risk of chemicals to man
0301-3944
Continued by IARC monographs on the
evaluation of carcinogenic risk of
chemicals to humans.
1972-1978   **0402626**

IARC Monogr Eval Carcinog Risks Hum
IARC monographs on the evaluation of
carcinogenic risks to humans / World Health
Organization, International Agency for
Research on Cancer
1017-1606
Continues: IARC monographs on the
evaluation of carcinogenic risk of
chemicals to humans.
1988   **8907342**

IARC Monogr Eval Carcinog Risks Hum Suppl
IARC monographs on the evaluation of
carcinogenic risks to humans. Supplement
/ World Health Organization, International
Agency for Research on Cancer
1014-711X
Continues: IARC monographs on the
evaluation of the carcinogenic risk of
chemicals to humans. Supplement.
Supplement to: IARC monographs on the
evaluation of carcinogenic risks to humans.
1987-1989   **8907341**

IARC Publ
IARC publications
0254-2730
Continues IARC scientific publications.
Continued by IARC scientific publications.
1979-1979   **8002749**

IARC Sci Publ
IARC scientific publications
0300-5038
Continues IARC publications.
1979   **8009542**

IARC Sci Publ
IARC scientific publications
0300-5038
Continued by IARC publications.
1971-1979   **0364347**

IAVI Rep
IAVI report: newsletter on international
AIDS vaccine research
1816-6253   1816-6261
1996   **9810937**

ICD Sci Educ J
Icd Scientific And Educational Journal
Continues: Scientific And Educational
Journal.
1974-1978   **9877655**

ICRS J Int Res Commun
IRCS journal of international research
communications
0300-5569
Continued by IRCS journal of medical
science.
1973-1974   **7505550**

ICRS Med Rep
I. C. R. S. medical reports
1959-1964   **59430280R**

Icsu Rev
ICSU review
Continued by ICSU review of world science.
1959-1962   **17510090R**

IDAA Commun
I.D.A.A. communique
0360-7224
196u-1980   **7601701**

Ideggyogy Sz
Ideggyógyászati szemle
0019-1442
Absorbed: Neurobiology (Budapest,
Hungary). 2002
1955   **17510500R**

IDO Rep
IDO [reports]. U.S. Atomic Energy
Commission
194u-1970   **21830410R**

IDrugs
IDrugs: the investigational drugs journal
1369-7056
1998   **100883655**

IEE Proc Nanobiotechnol
IEE proceedings. Nanobiotechnology
1478-1581   1740-9748
Continued by: IET nanobiotechnology.
2003-2006   **101188789**

IEEE Comput Graph Appl
IEEE computer graphics and applications
0272-1716
1981   **9881869**

IEEE Eng Med Biol Mag
IEEE engineering in medicine and biology
magazine: the quarterly magazine of the
Engineering in Medicine & Biology Society
0739-5175   1558-1756
Continues: Engineering in medicine &
biology.
1982   **8305985**

IEEE Trans Biomed Eng
IEEE transactions on bio-medical
engineering
0018-9294   1558-2531
Continues IEEE transactions on bio-medical
electronics.
1964   **0012737**

IEEE Trans Image Process
IEEE transactions on image processing: a
publication of the IEEE Signal Processing
Society
1057-7149   **9886191**
1992

IEEE Trans Inf Technol Biomed
IEEE transactions on information
technology in biomedicine: a publication
of the IEEE Engineering in Medicine and
Biology Society
1089-7771   1558-0032
1997   **9712259**

IEEE Trans Med Imaging
IEEE transactions on medical imaging
0278-0062   1558-0062
1982   **8310780**

IEEE Trans Nanobioscience
IEEE transactions on nanobioscience
1536-1241   1558-2639
2002   **101152869**

IEEE Trans Neural Netw
IEEE transactions on neural networks / a
publication of the IEEE Neural Networks
Council
1045-9227   1941-0026
1990   **101211035**

IEEE Trans Neural Syst Rehabil Eng
IEEE transactions on neural systems and
rehabilitation engineering: a publication
of the IEEE Engineering in Medicine and
Biology Society
1534-4320   1558-0210
Continues: IEEE transactions on
rehabilitation engineering.
2001   **101097023**

IEEE Trans Pattern Anal Mach Intell
IEEE transactions on pattern analysis and
machine intelligence
0162-8828
1979   **9885960**

IEEE Trans Rehabil Eng
IEEE transactions on rehabilitation
engineering: a publication of the IEEE
Engineering in Medicine and Biology Society
1063-6528
Continued by: IEEE transactions on neural
systems and rehabilitation engineering.
1993-2000   **9413994**

IEEE Trans Syst Man Cybern
IEEE transactions on systems, man, and
cybernetics
0018-9472
Formed by the merger of IEEE transactions
on systems science and cybernetics and the
IEEE transactions on man-machine systems.
Split into: IEEE transactions on systems,
man and and cybernetics. Part A, systems and
humans; and: IEEE transactions on systems,
man and cybernetics. Part B, Cybernetics.
1971-1995   **1274320**

IEEE Trans Syst Man Cybern B Cybern
IEEE transactions on systems, man,
and cybernetics. Part B, Cybernetics: a
publication of the IEEE Systems, Man, and
Cybernetics Society
1083-4419   1941-0492
Continues in part: IEEE transactions on
systems, man, and cybernetics.
1996   **9890044**

IEEE Trans Ultrason Ferroelectr Freq Control
IEEE transactions on ultrasonics,
ferroelectrics, and frequency control
0885-3010   1525-8955
Continues: IEEE transactions on sonics and
ultrasonics.
1986   **9882735**

IEEE Trans Vis Comput Graph
IEEE transactions on visualization and
computer graphics
1077-2626
1995   **9891704**

IEEE/ACM Trans Comput Biol Bioinform
IEEE/ACM transactions on computational
biology and bioinformatics / IEEE, ACM
1545-5963   1557-9964
2004   **101196755**

IET Nanobiotechnol
IET nanobiotechnology / IET
1751-8741   1751-875X
Continues: IEE proceedings. Nanobiotechnology.
2007   101303205

IET Syst Biol
IET systems biology
1751-8849
Continues: Systems biology.
2007   101301198

Ig Mod
L'igiene moderna
0019-1655
1908   9427236

Ig Sanita Pubbl
Igiene e sanità pubblica
0019-1639
1945   0373022

Ig Sanita Pubblica Collana Monogr
Igiene e sanitá pubblica. Collana di
monografie
1946-19uu   17520220R

Igaku
[Igaku] [Medicine]
1946-1953   17520040R

Igaku Butsuri
Igaku butsuri: Nihon Igaku Butsuri Gakkai
kikanshi = Japanese journal of medical
physics: an official journal of Japan Society
of Medical Physics
1345-5354
Continues: Hōshasen igaku butsuri.
2000   101125977

Igaku Kenkyu
Igaku kenkyu. Acta medica
0076-597X
1927-1993   0421144

Igaku To Seibutsugaku
Igaku to seibutsugaku. Medicine and biology
0019-1604
1942   0417441

Igiena
Igiena
0019-1620
Continued by Revista de igienă. bacteriologie.
virusologie. parazitologie. epidemiologie.
pneumoftiziologie. Seria: Igiena.
1952-1974   7502094

IHRIM
IHRIM: the journal of the Institute
of Health Record Information and
Management
1364-6974
Continues: AMRO. Continued by: Journal
(Institute of Health Record Information and
Management).
1994-2000   9439766

ILAR J
ILAR journal / National Research Council,
Institute of Laboratory Animal Resources
1084-2020
Continues: ILAR news.
1995   9516416

Ill Dent J
Illinois dental journal
0019-1973
Supersedes: Bulletin. Illinois State Dental
Society. Continued by: Illinois dental news.
1931-1995   0374667

Ill Med J
The Illinois medical journal
0019-2120
Continued by: IMJ. Illinois medical journal.
1899-1962   7703926

Illum Eng
Illuminating engineering
0019-2333
Continues the Transactions of the
Illuminating Engineering Society.
1940-1971   17520760R

IMA J Math Appl Med Biol
IMA journal of mathematics applied in
medicine and biology
0265-0746
Continued by: Mathematical medicine and
biology.
1984-2002   8704892

Image (IN)
Image
0363-2792
Continued by Image--the journal of nursing
scholarship.
1967-1982   0435746

Image J Nurs Sch
Image--the journal of nursing scholarship
0743-5150
Continues: Image. Continued by: Journal of
nursing scholarship.
1983-1999   8400753

Images Marquette Univ Dent Reflections
Images; Marquette University dental
reflections
Continued by Dental images.
1961-1967   0253702

IMJ Ill Med J
IMJ. Illinois medical journal
0019-2120
Continues: Illinois medical journal.
Continued by: Illinois medicine.
1963-1988   7703940

Immun Infekt
Immunität und Infektion
0340-1162
Continued by: Immunität und Infektion
(1997).
1973-1995   7505519

Immunitatsforschung
Die Immunitätsforschung ...
1947-1951   17530110R

Immunity
Immunity
1074-7613
1994   9432918

Immunobiol Suppl
Immunobiology. Supplement
0722-6365
Continues: Zeitschrift für
Immunitätsforschung. Immunobiology.
Supplemente.
1987-1989   8804308

Immunobiology
Immunobiology
0171-2985
Continues Zeitschrift für
Immunitätsforschung. Immunobiology.
1979   8002742

Immunochemistry
Immunochemistry
0019-2791
Continued by Molecular immunology.
1964-1978   0010301

Immunodefic Rev
Immunodeficiency reviews
0893-5300
Continued by: Immunodeficiency.
1988-1992   9001383

Immunodeficiency
Immunodeficiency
1067-795X
Continues: Immunodeficiency reviews.
1993-199u   9418574

Immunogenetics
Immunogenetics
0093-7711   1432-1211
1974   0420404

Immunohematology
Immunohematology / American Red Cross
0894-203X
1984   8806387

Immunol Allergy Clin North Am
Immunology and allergy clinics of North
America
0889-8561
Continues in part: Clinics in immunology and
allergy.
1987   8805635

Immunol Cell Biol
Immunology and cell biology
0818-9641   1440-1711
Continues: The Australian journal of
experimental biology and medical science.
1987   8706300

Immunol Commun
Immunological communications
0090-0877
Continued by Immunological investigations.
1972-1984   0353016

Immunol Invest
Immunological investigations
0882-0139   1532-4311
Beginning with v. 15. no. 3 (1986).
occasional special issues called: Clinical
immunology reviews (formerly an
independent publication).
1985   8504629

Immunol Lett
Immunology letters
0165-2478
1979   7910006

Immunol Res
Immunologic research
0257-277X   1559-0755
Continues: Survey of immunologic research.
1986   8611087

Immunol Rev
Immunological reviews
0105-2896   1600-065X
Continues Transplantation reviews.
1977   7702118

Immunol Ser
Immunology series
0092-6019
1973-1994   0404721

Immunol Suppl
Immunology. Supplement
0953-4954
1988   8807494

Immunol Today
Immunology today
0167-5699
Continued by: Trends in immunology.
1980-2000   8008346

Immunology
Immunology
0019-2805   1365-2567
1958   0374672

Immunomethods
ImmunoMethods
1058-6687
1992-1994   9306032

Immunopharmacol Immunotoxicol
Immunopharmacology and
immunotoxicology
0892-3973   1532-2513
Continues: Journal of immunopharmacology.
1987   8800150

Immunopharmacology
Immunopharmacology
0162-3109
Merged with: International journal of
immunopharmacology, to form: International
immunopharmacology.
1978-2000   7902474

Immunotechnology
Immunotechnology: an international journal
of immunological engineering
1380-2933
Absorbed by: Journal of immunological
methods.
1995-1999   9511979

Impact Sci Soc
Impact of science on society
0019-2872
1950-1992   17530130R

Implant Dent
Implant dentistry
1056-6163   1538-2982
1992   9206481

Implant Soc
The Implant Society: [periodical]
1059-3489
1990-1996   9109589

Implantologist
Implantologist
0190-2024
Continued by: International journal of oral
implantology.
1976-1987   7806013

Important Adv Oncol
Important advances in oncology
0883-5896
1985-1996   8505229

Imprensa Medica
Imprensa médica
1925-1957   17530180R

Impressions (Orange)
Impressions
Continues: Orange County Dental Society
Bulletin.
1979   9878816

Imprint
Imprint
0019-3062
Continues NSNA news letter.
1968   0163356

IMS Ind Med Surg
IMS, Industrial medicine and surgery
0019-8536
Continues Industrial medicine & surgery.
Continued by the International journal of
occupational health & safety.
1968-1973   0414123

In Pract
In practice
0263-841X
1979   8106445

In Silico Biol
In silico biology
1386-6338
1998   9815902

In Vitr Mol Toxicol
In vitro & molecular toxicology
1097-9336
Continues: In vitro toxicology.
1998-2001   9808800

In Vitro
In vitro
0073-5655
Continued by: In vitro cellular &
developmental biology.
1965-1984   0063733

In Vitro Cell Dev Biol
In vitro cellular & developmental biology:
journal of the Tissue Culture Association
0883-8364
Continues: In vitro. Split into: In vitro
cellular & developmental biology. Plant, in
1991, and: In vitro cellular & developmental
biology. Animal, in Mar. 1993.
1985-1993   8506951

In Vitro Cell Dev Biol Anim
In vitro cellular & developmental biology.
Animal
1071-2690
Continues in part: In vitro cellular &
developmental biology.
1993   9418515

In Vitro Monogr
In vitro. Monograph
0363-521X
1970-1984   7607749

In Vivo
In vivo (Athens, Greece)
0258-851X
1987   8806809

Ind Eng
Industrial engineering (American Institute
of Industrial Engineers)
0019-8234
Continues: Journal of industrial engineering.
Continued by: Industrial engineering
(Institute of Industrial Engineers (1981-)).
1969-1981   9877779

Ind Health
Industrial health
0019-8366   1880-8026
Continues: Kenkyu hokoku.
1963   2985065R

Ind Health Bull
Industrial health bulletin
Continued by Occupational health bulletin.
1944-1952   17540520R

Ind Health Care
Industry and health care
0887-1086
1978-1980   7902844

Ind Health Care (Cambridge Ma)
Industry and health care (Ballinger
Publishing Co.)
0887-1086
Continues: Industry and health care.
1983   100960888

Ind Health Mon
Industrial health monthly
Continues Industrial hygiene newsletter.
Continued by Occupational health.
1951-1951   17540540R

Ind Health Rev
Industrial health review
0317-4301
Continued by: Occupational health review.
1949-1952   17540550R

Ind Hyg Newsl
Industrial hygiene newsletter
Continued by Industrial health monthly.
1940-1951   17540640R

Ind Labor Relat Rev
Industrial & labor relations review
0019-7939
1947   9875079

Ind Med Gaz
Indian medical gazette
0019-5863
1961   7501544

Ind Med Surg
Industrial medicine & surgery
0019-8536
Continues Industrial medicine. Absorbs the
Industrial doctor and International journal of
industrial medicine and surgery. Continued by
IMS, Industrial medicine and surgery.
1949-1967   0414125

Ind Nurs
Industrial nursing
Continues Industrial nurse, issued quarterly as
a section in Industrial medicine, Nov. 1941-
Nov. 1942. Absorbed by: Trained nurse and
hospital review.
1943-1949   17540660R

Ind Saf Surv
Industrial safety survey ...
1925-1950   17540670R

Indent [Engl]
Indent; Journal Of International Dentistry;
English Edition
19uu   9875623

India J Med Sci
The India journal of medical science
1834-1835   0163321

Indian Heart J
Indian heart journal
0019-4832
1949   0374675

Indian Heart J Teach Ser
Indian heart journal: teaching series
0378-6315
1976-1981   7703235

Indian J Anim Sci
The Indian journal of animal sciences
0367-8318
Continues The Indian journal of veterinary
science and animal husbandry.
1969   0221656

Indian J Biochem
Indian journal of biochemistry
0019-5081
Supersedes the Annals of biochemistry
and experimental medicine. Continued by
Indian journal of biochemistry & biophysics.
"Enzyme nomenclature [partial reprint of]
recommendations of the International Union
of Biochemistry" included as a supplement to
v. 2, no. 3.
1964-1970   1306642

Indian J Biochem Biophys
Indian journal of biochemistry & biophysics
0301-1208
Continues: Indian journal of biochemistry.
1971   0310774

Indian J Cancer
Indian journal of cancer
0019-509X
1963   0112040

Indian J Chem
Indian journal of chemistry
0019-5103
Split into: Indian journal of chemistry.
Section A: Inorganic, physical, theoretical &
analytical, and: Indian journal of chemistry.
Section B: Organic including medicinal.
1963-1975   7613423

Indian J Chest Dis
The Indian journal of chest diseases
0019-5111
Continued by The Indian journal of chest
diseases & allied sciences.
1959-1975   7612045

Indian J Chest Dis Allied Sci
The Indian journal of chest diseases & allied
sciences
0377-9343
Continues: Indian journal of chest diseases.
1976   7612044

Indian J Child Health
The Indian journal of child health
Merged with: Journal of the Indian Pediatric
Society, to form: Indian pediatrics.
1952-1963   17530370R

Indian J Dent Res
Indian journal of dental research: official
publication of Indian Society for Dental
Research
0970-9290
1989   9202990

Indian J Dermatol
Indian journal of dermatology
0019-5154   1998-3611
1955   0370750

Indian J Dermatol Venereol Leprol
Indian journal of dermatology, venereology
and leprology
0378-6323   0973-3922
Continues: Indian journal of dermatology and
venereology.
1976   7701852

Indian J Environ Health
Indian journal of environmental health
0367-827X
Continues: Environmental health. Continued
by: Journal of enviornmental science &
engineering.
1971-2003   0335007

Indian J Exp Biol
Indian journal of experimental biology
0019-5189
Supersedes Journal of scientific & industrial
research. C. Biological sciences.
1963   0233411

Indian J Gastroenterol
Indian journal of gastroenterology:
official journal of the Indian Society of
Gastroenterology
0254-8860
1982   8409436

Indian J Lepr
Indian journal of leprosy
0254-9395
Continues: Leprosy in India.
1984   8409173

Indian J Malariol
Indian journal of malariology
0367-8326
Continues: Journal of the Malaria Institute of
India. Continued by: Journal of vector borne
diseases.
1947-2002   17540010R

Indian J Med Ethics
Indian journal of medical ethics
Continues: Issues in medical ethics.
2004   101214913

Indian J Med Microbiol
Indian journal of medical microbiology
0255-0857
1983   8700903

Indian J Med Res
The Indian journal of medical research
0971-5916
Supersedes Paludism and Scientific memoirs
by officers of the Medical and Sanitary
Departments of the Government of India.
1913   0374701

Indian J Med Sci
Indian journal of medical sciences
0019-5359
Supersedes: Medical bulletin, Bombay.
1947   0373023

Indian J Med Surg
The Indian journal of medicine & surgery
0019-5367
Continues the Punjab medical journal.
1948-1977   0374702

Indian J Ophthalmol
Indian journal of ophthalmology
0301-4738
Continues: Journal of the All-India
Ophthalmological Society.
1971   0405376

Indian J Otolaryngol
Indian journal of otolaryngology
0019-5421
Continued by: Indian journal of
otolaryngology, and head, and neck.
1949-1991   0374705

Indian J Pathol Bacteriol
Indian journal of pathology & bacteriology
0019-5448
Continued by Indian journal of pathology &
microbiology.
1958-1975   7605903

Indian J Pathol Microbiol
Indian journal of pathology & microbiology
0377-4929
Continues Indian journal of pathology &
bacteriology.
1975   7605904

Indian J Pediatr
Indian journal of pediatrics
0019-5456   0973-1679
1933   0417442

Indian J Pharm
The Indian journal of pharmacy
0019-5472
Continued by Indian journal of
paharmaceutical sciences.
1939-1978   0262422

Indian J Physiol Pharmacol
Indian journal of physiology and
pharmacology
0019-5499
1957   0374707

Indian J Public Health
Indian journal of public health
0019-557X
1957   0400673

Indian J Tuberc
The Indian journal of tuberculosis
0019-5707
1953   0373027

Indian J Vener Dis Dermatol
Indian journal of venereal diseases and
dermatology
Continued by the Indian journal of
dermatology and venereology.
1935-1955   17540060R

Indian Med J
Indian medical journal
0019-5871
Continues: All-India Hospital Assistants'
journal.
1910   9705769

Indian Pediatr
Indian pediatrics
0019-6061
Formed by the merger of: Indian journal
of child health, and: Journal of the Indian
Pediatric Society.
1964   2985062R

Indian Physician
The Indian physician
1942-1952   17540160R

Indian Pract
The Indian practitioner
0019-6169
Continues the Indian medical guide.
1952   0370753

Indian Vet J
The Indian veterinary journal
0019-6479
1924   0374710

Indiana Med
Indiana medicine: the journal of the Indiana
State Medical Association
0746-8288
Continues: The Journal of the Indiana State
Medical Association.
1984-1996   8401780

Indiana Nurse
The Indiana nurse
0019-6681
Continues: Lamp. Continued by: ISNA
bulletin.
1951-1971   17540290R

Indiana Pharm
The Indiana pharmacist
1882   17540320R

Indicator
Indicator (Minnesota Mining and
Manfuacturing Company)
0898-5308
Continues: Infection control rounds. With:
Journal of hospital supply, processing,
and distribution. v. 1, no. 1-4; Journal of
healthcare materiel management, Sept./Oct.
1985- .
1985-1985   8507466

Individ Psychol Bull
Individual psychology bulletin
Continues: Individual psychology news.
Continued by: American journal of individual
psychology.
1941-1951   17540450R

Indoor Air
Indoor air
0905-6947
1991   9423515

Inf Dent
L' Information dentaire
0020-0018
Continues Semaine dentaire.
1938   0370756

Inf Manage
Information management (PTN Publishing Corporation)
0739-9049
Continues: Information & records management. Merged with: Office administration and automation, to form: Administrative management (New York, N.Y.: 1985).
1983-1985   9875395

Inf Med
L'Informatore medico
1946-1963   17610210R

Inf Med Paramed (Montreal)
L' Information médicale et paramédicale
0020-014X
1948-1980   0370757

Inf Medicas
Informaciones médicas
1936-1951   17610110R

Inf Odontostomatol
Informatore Odonto-Stomatologico
0020-0751
1965   9875610

Inf Orthod Kieferorthop
Informationen aus Orthodontie und Kieferorthopädie: mit Beiträgen aus der internationalen Literatur
0020-0336
1969   1300712

Inf Process Med Imaging
Information processing in medical imaging: proceedings of the ... conference
1011-2499
198u   9216871

Inf Psychiatr
L'Information psychiatrique
0020-0204
19uu   9705768

Infant Behav Dev
Infant behavior & development
0163-6383   1934-8800
1978   7806016

Infanz Anorm
Infanzia anormale
Continues the Bolletino dell' Associazione romana per la cura medico-pedagogica dei fanciulli anomali e deficienti poveri. Continued by Neuropsichiatria infantile.
1911-1968   0220203

Infect Agents Dis
Infectious agents and disease
1056-2044
1992-1996   9209834

Infect Control
Infection control: IC
0195-9417
Continued by: Infection control and hospital epidemiology.
1980-1987   8008357

Infect Control Can
Infection control Canada
0833-076X
Continued by: Canadian journal of infection control.
1986-1990   8703508

Infect Control Dig
Infection control digest
0275-0236
1980-1986   8011626

Infect Control Hosp Epidemiol
Infection control and hospital epidemiology: the official journal of the Society of Hospital Epidemiologists of America
0899-823X   1559-6834
Continues: Infection control.
1988   8804099

Infect Control Rounds
Infection control rounds
0272-1619
Continued by Indicator (Saint Paul, Minn.).
1977-1983   8007156

Infect Control Urol Care
Infection control & urological care
0740-3615
Continues: Infection control in urological care.
1977-1983   7903304

Infect Dis
Infectious diseases
1971-1987   1302451

Infect Dis Clin North Am
Infectious disease clinics of North America
0891-5520
1987   8804508

Infect Dis Obstet Gynecol
Infectious diseases in obstetrics and gynecology
1064-7449   1098-0997
1993   9318481

Infect Disord Drug Targets
Infectious disorders drug targets
1871-5265
Continues: Current drug targets. Infectious disorders.
2006   101269158

Infect Genet Evol
Infection, genetics and evolution: journal of molecular epidemiology and evolutionary genetics in infectious diseases
1567-1348
2001   101084138

Infect Immun
Infection and immunity
0019-9567   1098-5522
1970   0246127

Infection
Infection
0300-8126
1973   0365307

Infez Med
Le infezioni in medicina: rivista periodica di eziologia, epidemiologia, diagnostica, clinica e terapia delle patologie infettive
1124-9390
1993   9613961

Infirm Aux
L'Infirmière auxiliaire: revue de la Corporation professionnelle des infirmières et infirmiers auxiliaires du Québec
0822-8558
Continues: L'Auxiliare.
1982-1999   8410629

Infirm Can
L' Infirmière canadienne
0019-9605
1959-1985   0042116

Infirm Fr
L'Infirmière francaise
0019-9613
Continued by: Lettre de l'infirmière française.
1923-1985   0400674

Infirm Haiti
L' Infirmiere haïtienne
1967-1971   0174016

Infirm Que
L'Infirmière du Québec: revue officielle de l'Ordre des infirmières et infirmiers du Québec
1195-2695
Continues: Nursing Québec. Continued by: Perspective infirmière.
1993-2003   9430795

Infirmiere
L' Infirmière
0019-9591
Continued by F. N. I. B.
1923-1971   0366542

Infirmiers
Infirmiers
0180-2224
Continues: Revue de l infirmier d Afrique Noire.
1977-1993   7804334

Inflamm Allergy Drug Targets
Inflammation & allergy drug targets
1871-5281
Continues: Current drug targets. Inflammation and allergy.
2006   101266886

Inflamm Bowel Dis
Inflammatory bowel diseases
1078-0998   1536-4844
1995   9508162

Inflamm Res
Inflammation research: official journal of the European Histamine Research Society ... [et al.]
1023-3830   1420-908X
Continues: Agents and actions.
1995   9508160

Inflammation
Inflammation
0360-3997
1975   7600105

Inflammopharmacology
Inflammopharmacology
0925-4692
1991   9112626

Infocare
InfoCare: information strategies for healthcare networks
1090-4522
1994-1998   9504687

Inform
Inform (Silver Spring, Md.)
0892-3876
Continues: Journal of information and image management. Merged with: Document world, to form: E-doc.
1987-2000   9882762

Inform Health Soc Care
Informatics for health & social care
1753-8157   1753-8165
Continues: Medical informatics and the Internet in medicine.
2008   101475011

Inform Prim Care
Informatics in primary care
1476-0320   1475-9985
Continues: Journal of informatics in primary
care.
200u   101150138

Infort Traumatol Lav
Infortunistica e traumatologia del lavoro
0390-9417
Absorbed by: Minerva chirurgica.
1935-1948   17610250R

Inforum
Inforum (Adelaide, S. Aust.)
0812-9304
1980-1993   8807312

Infusionsther Klin Ernahr
Infusionstherapie und klinische Ernährung
0378-0791
Continues: Die Infusionstherapie. Continued
by: Infusionstherapie (Basel. Switzerland).
1975-1987   7613112

Infusionsther Klin Ernahr Sonderh
Infusionstherapie und klinische Ernährung.
Sonderheft
0379-4938
Continues: Die Infusionstherapie. Sonderheft.
Continued by: Beiträge zu Infusionstherapie
und klinische Ernährung.
1975-1975   7705430

Infusionsther Transfusionsmed
Infusionstherapie und Transfusionsmedizin
1019-8466   1424-5493
Continues: Infusionstherapie (Basel.
Switzerland). Continued by: Transfusion
medicine and hemotherapy.
1992-2002   9209406

Infusionstherapie
Die Infusionstherapie
0301-3243
Continued by Infusionstherapie und klinische
Ernährung.
1973-1974   7613113

Infusionstherapie
Infusionstherapie (Basel, Switzerland)
1011-6966
Continues: Infusionstherapie und klinische
Ernährung. Continued by: Infusiontherapie
und Transfusionsmedizin.
1988-1991   9001943

Inhal Toxicol
Inhalation toxicology
0895-8378   1091-7691
1989   8910739

Inhaled Part
Inhaled particles
0301-1577
Continues: Inhaled particles and vapours.
1970-1977   0320346

Inj Control Saf Promot
Injury control and safety promotion
1566-0974
Continues: International journal for
consumer and product safety. Continued by:
International journal of injury control and
safety promotion.
2000-2004   100941859

Inj Prev
Injury prevention: journal of the
International Society for Child and
Adolescent Injury Prevention
1353-8047
1995   9510056

Injury
Injury
0020-1383   1879-0267
1969   0226040

Innate Immun
Innate immunity
1753-4259   1753-4267
Continues: Journal of endotoxin research.
2008   101469670

Innovations
Innovations
0095-4519
1973-1980   7503029

Inorg Chem
Inorganic chemistry
0020-1669   1520-510X
1962   0366543

Inquiry
Inquiry: a journal of medical care
organization, provision and financing
0046-9580
1963   0171671

Insect Biochem Mol Biol
Insect biochemistry and molecular biology
0965-1748
Continues: Insect biochemistry.
1992   9207282

Insect Mol Biol
Insect molecular biology
0962-1075   1365-2583
1992   9303579

Insight
Insight (American Society of Ophthalmic
Registered Nurses)
1060-135X
1976   9111431

Inst Vol Feed
Institutions/volume feeding
0094-6745
Continues: Institutions and volume feeding
management. Continued by: Institutions.
1971-1978   9877756

Institutions
Institutions
Continues: Institutions volume feeding.
Continued by: Restaurants & institutions.
1978-1980   9878212

Instr Course Lect
Instructional course lectures
0065-6895
1943   7507149

Int Abstr Surg
International abstracts of surgery
1913-1963   60020060R

Int Adv Surg Oncol
International advances in surgical oncology
0190-1575
Continued by Seminars in surgical oncology.
1978-1984   7806861

Int Anesthesiol Clin
International anesthesiology clinics
0020-5907   1537-1913
Absorbed: Problems in anesthesia. 2002
1962   0370760

Int Angiol
International angiology: a journal of the
International Union of Angiology
0392-9590
1982   8402693

Int Arch Allergy Appl Immunol
International archives of allergy and applied
immunology
0020-5915
Continued by: International archives of
allergy and immunology.
1950-1991   0404561

Int Arch Allergy Immunol
International archives of allergy and
immunology
1018-2438   1423-0097
Continues: International archives of allergy
and applied immunology.
1992   9211652

Int Arch Arbeitsmed
Internationales Archiv für Arbeitsmedizin
0020-5923
Continues Internationales Archiv für
Gewerbepathologie und Gewerbehygiene.
Continued by International archives of
occupational and environmental health.
1970-1975   7512135

Int Arch Gewerbepathol Gewerbehyg
Internationales Archiv für
Gewerbepathologie und Gewerbehygiene
Continues Archiv für Gewerbepathologie
und Gewerbehygiene. Continued by
Internationales Archiv für Arbeitsmedizin.
1962-1969   0251374

Int Arch Occup Environ Health
International archives of occupational and
environmental health
0340-0131   1432-1246
Continues: Internationales Archiv für
Arbeitsmedizin.
1975   7512134

Int Braz J Urol
International braz j urol: official journal of
the Brazilian Society of Urology
1677-5538   1677-6119
Continues: Brazilian journal of urology.
2002   101158091

Int Clin Psychopharmacol
International clinical psychopharmacology
0268-1315
1986   8609061

Int Dent J
International dental journal
0020-6539
1950   0374714

Int Dig Health Legis
International digest of health legislation
0020-6563
Continues: Bulletin mensuel de l'office
international d'hygiène publique. Supersedes
in part the Bulletin mensuel de l'office
international d'hygiène publique.
1948-1999   2985068R

Int Disabil Stud
International disability studies
0259-9147
Continues: International rehabilitation
medicine. Continued by: Disability and
rehabilitation.
1987-1991   8710422

Int Emerg Nurs
International emergency nursing
1755-599X
Continues: Accident and emergency nursing.
2008   101472191

Int Endod J
International endodontic journal
0143-2885   1365-2591
Continues Journal of the British Endodontic
Society.
1980   8004996

Int Fam Plan Perspect
International family planning perspectives
0190-3187
Continues International family planning
perspectives and digest.
1979   7907371

Int Fam Plann Dig
International family planning digest
0362-4056
Continued by International family planning
perspectives and digest.
1975-1977   7610494

Int Heart J
International heart journal
1349-2365   1349-3299
Continues: Japanese heart journal.
2005   101244240

Int Hist Nurs J
**International history of nursing journal:
IHNJ**
1360-1105
Continues: History of Nursing Society
journal.
1995-2003   9608372

Int Immunol
International immunology
0953-8178   1460-2377
1989   8916182

Int Immunopharmacol
International immunopharmacology
1567-5769
Formed by the union of:
Immunopharmacology, and: International
journal of immunopharmacology.
2001   100965259

Int J Addict
The International journal of the addictions
0020-773X
Continued by: Substance use & misuse.
1966-1995   0123640

Int J Adolesc Med Health
**International journal of adolescent medicine
and health**
0334-0139
1985   8506960

Int J Adult Orthodon Orthognath Surg
**The International journal of adult
orthodontics and orthognathic surgery**
0742-1931
1986-2002   8610335

Int J Aging Hum Dev
**International journal of aging & human
development**
0091-4150
Continues Aging & human development.
1973   0370033

Int J Air Pollut
International journal of air pollution
Continued by The International journal of air
and water pollution.
1958-1960   17630120R

Int J Air Water Pollut
**International journal of air and water
pollution**
Continues the International journal of air
pollution. Continued by Air and water
pollution.
1961-1962   17630130R

Int J Alcohol Alcohol
**International journal on alcohol and
alcoholism**
0535-1073
1955-1957   17630240R

Int J Androl
International journal of andrology
0105-6263   1365-2605
1978   8000141

Int J Anesth
International journal of anesthesia
1953-1960   17630140R

Int J Antimicrob Agents
International journal of antimicrobial agents
0924-8579
Continues: Antimicrobial agents annual
(Amsterdam, Netherlands).
1991   9111860

Int J Appl Radiat Isot
**The International journal of applied
radiation and isotopes**
0020-708X
Continued by: International journal of
radiation applications and instrumentation.
Part A, Applied radiation and isotopes.
1956-1985   0374715

Int J Artif Organs
The International journal of artificial organs
0391-3988
1978   7802649

Int J Audiol
International journal of audiology
1499-2027   1708-8186
Merger of: Audiology; British journal of
audiology; and: Scandinavian audiology.
2002   101140017

Int J Behav Med
International journal of behavioral medicine
1070-5503   1532-7558
1994   9421097

Int J Biochem
The International journal of biochemistry
0020-711X
Continued by: International journal of
biochemistry & cell biology.
1970-1994   0250365

Int J Biochem Cell Biol
**The international journal of biochemistry &
cell biology**
1357-2725
Continues: International journal of
biochemistry.
1995   9508482

Int J Bioinform Res Appl
**International journal of bioinformatics
research and applications**
1744-5485   1744-5493
2005   101253758

Int J Biol Macromol
**International journal of biological
macromolecules**
0141-8130
1979   7909578

Int J Biol Markers
**The International journal of biological
markers**
0393-6155   1724-6008
1986   8712411

Int J Biol Res Pregnancy
**International journal of biological research
in pregnancy**
0173-8593
Continued by biological research in
pregnancy and perinatology.
1980-1982   8011123

Int J Biol Sci
International journal of biological sciences
                                     1449-2288
2004   101235568

Int J Biomed Comput
**International journal of bio-medical
computing**
0020-7101
Continued by: International journal of
medical informatics.
1970-1996   0252005

Int J Biometeorol
International journal of biometeorology
0020-7128   1432-1254
Continues: International journal of
bioclimatology and biometeorology.
1961   0374716

Int J Cancer
**International journal of cancer. Journal
international du cancer**
0020-7136   1097-0215
Absorbed: Radiation oncology investigations.
2000 Supersedes the Acta of the International
Union Against Cancer.
1966   0042124

Int J Cancer Suppl
**International journal of cancer. Supplement
= Journal international du cancer.
Supplement**
0898-6924
1987-2002   8710267

Int J Card Imaging
International journal of cardiac imaging
0167-9899
Continued by: International journal of
cardiovascular imaging.
1985-2000   8600426

Int J Cardiol
International journal of cardiology
0167-5273   1874-1754
Continues: European journal of cardiology.
1981   8200291

Int J Cardiovasc Imaging
**The international journal of cardiovascular
imaging**
1569-5794
Continues: International journal of cardiac
imaging.
2001   100969716

Int J Cardiovasc Intervent
**International journal of cardiovascular
interventions**
1462-8848
Continued by: Acute cardiac care.
1998-2005   9815622

Int J Cell Cloning
International journal of cell cloning
0737-1454
Continued by: Stem cells (Dayton, Ohio).
1983-1992   8308172

Int J Chron Obstruct Pulmon Dis
**International journal of chronic obstructive
pulmonary disease**
1176-9106   1178-2005
2006   101273481

Int J Chronobiol
International journal of chronobiology
0300-9998
Absorbed by: Life chemistry reports.
1973-1983   0367714

Int J Circumpolar Health
International journal of circumpolar health
1239-9736
Continues: Arctic medical research.
1997   9713056

Int J Clin Exp Hypn
The International journal of clinical and experimental hypnosis
0020-7144 1744-5183
 Continues: Journal of clinical and experimental hypnosis.
1959 0376166

Int J Clin Lab Res
International journal of clinical & laboratory research
0940-5437
 Continues: Ricerca in clinica e in laboratorio. Merged with: Research in experimental medicine, to form: Clinical and experimental medicine.
1991-2000 9206491

Int J Clin Monit Comput
International journal of clinical monitoring and computing
0167-9945
 Merged with: Journal of clinical monitoring, to form: Journal of clinical monitoring and computing.
1984-1997 8601284

Int J Clin Oncol
International journal of clinical oncology / Japan Society of Clinical Oncology
1341-9625
1996 9616295

Int J Clin Pharmacol
International journal of clinical pharmacology, therapy and toxicology
0300-9718
 Continues Internationale Zeitschrift für klinische Pharmakologie, Therapie und Toxikologie. Continued by International journal of clinical pharmacology and biopharmacy.
1972-1974 7505528

Int J Clin Pharmacol Biopharm
International journal of clinical pharmacology and biopharmacy
0340-0026
 Continues International journal of clinical pharmacology, therapy and toxicology. Continued by International journal of clinical pharmacology, therapy, and toxicology.
1975-1979 7505527

Int J Clin Pharmacol Res
International journal of clinical pharmacology research
0251-1649
1981 8110183

Int J Clin Pharmacol Ther
International journal of clinical pharmacology and therapeutics
0946-1965
 Continues: International journal of clinical pharmacology, therapy, and toxicology.
1994 9423309

Int J Clin Pharmacol Ther Toxicol
International journal of clinical pharmacology, therapy, and toxicology
0174-4879
 Continues International journal of clinical pharmacology and biopharmacy. Continued by: International journal of clinical pharmacology and therapeutics.
1980-1993 8003415

Int J Clin Pract
International journal of clinical practice
1368-5031 1742-1241
 Continues: British journal of clinical practice.
1997 9712381

Int J Clin Pract Suppl
International journal of clinical practice. Supplement
1368-504X
 Continues: British journal of clinical practice. Supplement.
1997 9712380

Int J Colorectal Dis
International journal of colorectal disease
0179-1958
1986 8607899

Int J Comput Dent
International journal of computerized dentistry
1463-4201
1998 100891504

Int J Cosmet Sci
International journal of cosmetic science
0142-5463 1468-2494
1979 8007161

Int J Data Min Bioinform
International journal of data mining and bioinformatics
1748-5673 1748-5681
2006 101279469

Int J Dent Hyg
International journal of dental hygiene
1601-5029 1601-5037
2003 101168070

Int J Dent Symp
International journal of dental symposia
 Continues: Journal of dental symposia.
1994 9889472

Int J Dermatol
International journal of dermatology
0011-9059 1365-4362
 Continues Dermatologia internationalis.
1970 0243704

Int J Dev Biol
The International journal of developmental biology
0214-6282
 Continues: Anales del desarrollo.
1989 8917470

Int J Dev Neurosci
International journal of developmental neuroscience: the official journal of the International Society for Developmental Neuroscience
0736-5748
1983 8401784

Int J Drug Policy
The International journal on drug policy
0955-3959 1873-4758
 Continues: Mersey drugs journal.
1989 9014759

Int J Eat Disord
The International journal of eating disorders
0276-3478 1098-108X
1981 8111226

Int J Electron Healthc
International journal of electronic healthcare
1741-8453 1741-8461
2004 101227192

Int J Emerg Ment Health
International journal of emergency mental health
1522-4821
1999 100888872

Int J Environ Anal Chem
International journal of environmental analytical chemistry
0306-7319 1029-0397
1971 0331757

Int J Environ Health Res
International journal of environmental health research
0960-3123 1369-1619
1991 9106628

Int J Environ Res Public Health
International journal of environmental research and public health
1661-7827 1660-4601
2004 101238455

Int J Epidemiol
International journal of epidemiology
0300-5771 1464-3685
1972 7802871

Int J Equilib Res
International journal of equilibrium research
0303-7223
1971-1975 7501152

Int J Exp Diabetes Res
International journal of experimental diabetes research
1560-4284
 Continued by: International journal of experimental diabesity research.
2000-2002 100962067

Int J Exp Pathol
International journal of experimental pathology
0959-9673 1365-2613
 Continues: Journal of experimental pathology (Oxford, England).
1990 9014042

Int J Fertil
International journal of fertility
0020-725X
 Continued by: International journal of fertility and menopausal studies.
1955-1992 0374717

Int J Fertil Menopausal Stud
International journal of fertility and menopausal studies
1069-3130
 Continues: International journal of fertility. Continued by: International journal of fertility and women's medicine.
1993-1996 9309760

Int J Fertil Womens Med
International journal of fertility and women's medicine
1534-892X
 Continues: International journal of fertility and menopausal studies.
1997 9706778

Int J Food Microbiol
International journal of food microbiology
0168-1605
1984 8412849

Int J Food Sci Nutr
International journal of food sciences and nutrition
0963-7486 1465-3478
 Continues: Food sciences and nutrition.
1992 9432922

Int J Forensic Dent
The International journal of forensic dentistry
0306-9419
 Continues: Journal of the American Society of Forensic Odontology.
1973-1977 7507151

Int J Gastrointest Cancer
International journal of gastrointestinal cancer
1537-3649   1559-0739
Continues: International journal of pancreatology. Continued by: Journal of gastrointestinal cancer.
2001-2006   101135379

Int J Geriatr Psychiatry
International journal of geriatric psychiatry
0885-6230   1099-1166
1986   8710629

Int J Group Psychother
International journal of group psychotherapy
0020-7284
1951   0374720

Int J Gynaecol Obstet
International journal of gynaecology and obstetrics: the official organ of the International Federation of Gynaecology and Obstetrics
0020-7292
Continues: Journal of the International Federation of Gynaecology and Obstetrics. Has supplement: Supplement to International journal of gynecology and obstetrics, 1989, suppl. 1-3. Later v. with this title are numbered as suppls. to individual v. of the parent serial and shelved with it at NLM.
1969   0210174

Int J Gynecol Cancer
International journal of gynecological cancer: official journal of the International Gynecological Cancer Society
1048-891X   1525-1438
1991   9111626

Int J Gynecol Pathol
International journal of gynecological pathology: official journal of the International Society of Gynecological Pathologists
0277-1691   1538-7151
1982   8214845

Int J Health Care Finance Econ
International journal of health care finance and economics
1389-6563
2001   101132988

Int J Health Care Qual Assur
International journal of health care quality assurance
0952-6862
1988   8916799

Int J Health Care Qual Assur Inc Leadersh Health Serv
International journal of health care quality assurance incorporating Leadership in health services
1366-0756
Also issued without the section Leadership in health services as: International journal of health care quality assurance.
1997-2006   9711269

Int J Health Educ
International journal of health education
0020-7306
Continued by Hygie.
1958-1981   0374721

Int J Health Geogr
International journal of health geographics
1476-072X
19uu   101152198

Int J Health Plann Manage
The International journal of health planning and management
0749-6753
1985   8605825

Int J Health Serv
International journal of health services: planning, administration, evaluation
0020-7314
1971   1305035

Int J Hematol
International journal of hematology
0925-5710
Continues: Nippon Ketsueki Gakkai zassh.
1991   9111627

Int J Hyg Environ Health
International journal of hygiene and environmental health
1438-4639
Continues: Zentralblatt für Hygiene und Umweltmedizin.
2000   100898843

Int J Hyperthermia
International journal of hyperthermia: the official journal of European Society for Hyperthermic Oncology, North American Hyperthermia Group
0265-6736   1464-5157
1985   8508395

Int J Immunogenet
International journal of immunogenetics
1744-3121   1744-313X
Continues: European journal of immunogenetics.
2005   101232337

Int J Immunopathol Pharmacol
International journal of immunopathology and pharmacology
0394-6320
1988   8911335

Int J Immunopharmacol
International journal of immunopharmacology
0192-0561
Merged with: Immunopharmacology, to form: International imunopharmacology.
1979-2000   7904799

Int J Impot Res
International journal of impotence research
0955-9930   1476-5489
1989   9007383

Int J Infect Dis
International journal of infectious diseases: IJID: official publication of the International Society for Infectious Diseases
1201-9712   1878-3511
1996   9610933

Int J Inj Contr Saf Promot
International journal of injury control and safety promotion
1745-7300
Continues: Injury control and safety promotion.
2005   101247254

Int J Instr Media
International journal of instructional media
0092-1815
1973   9877780

Int J Lab Hematol
International journal of laboratory hematology
1751-5521   1751-553X
Continues: Clinical and laboratory haematology.
2007   101300213

Int J Lang Commun Disord
International journal of language & communication disorders / Royal College of Speech & Language Therapists
1368-2822   1460-6984
Continues: European journal of disorders of communication.
1998   9803709

Int J Law Psychiatry
International journal of law and psychiatry
0160-2527
1978   7806862

Int J Legal Med
International journal of legal medicine
0937-9827
Continues: Zeitschrift für Rechtsmedizin.
1990   9101456

Int J Lepr
International journal of Leprosy
0020-7349
Continued by International journal of leprosy and other mycobacterial diseases.
1933-1965   2985070R

Int J Lepr Other Mycobact Dis
International journal of leprosy and other mycobacterial diseases: official organ of the International Leprosy Association
0148-916X   1544-581X
Continues: International journal of leprosy.
1966-2005   8505819

Int J Low Extrem Wounds
The international journal of lower extremity wounds
1534-7346   1552-6941
2002   101128359

Int J Med Inform
International journal of medical informatics
1386-5056
Continues: International journal of bio-medical computing.
1997   9711057

Int J Med Microbiol
International journal of medical microbiology: IJMM
1438-4221   1618-0607
Continues: Zentralblatt für Bakteriologie.
2000   100898849

Int J Med Robot
The international journal of medical robotics + computer assisted surgery: MRCAS
1478-5951   1478-596X
2004   101250764

Int J Med Sci
International journal of medical sciences
        1449-1907
2004   101213954

Int J Ment Health Nurs
International journal of mental health nursing
1445-8330
Continues: Australian and New Zealand journal of mental health nursing.
2002   101140527

Int J Methods Psychiatr Res
International journal of methods in psychiatric research
1049-8931
1991   9111433

Int J Microcirc Clin Exp
International journal of microcirculation, clinical and experimental / sponsored by the European Society for Microcirculation
0167-6865
Absorbed by: Journal of vascular research.
1982-1997   8400122

Int J Mol Med
International journal of molecular medicine
1107-3756   1791-244X
1998   9810955

Int J Nanomedicine
International journal of nanomedicine
1176-9114   1178-2013
2006   101263847

Int J Neural Syst
International journal of neural systems
0129-0657
1989   9100527

Int J Neurol
International journal of neurology
0020-7446
1959-1992   0374722

Int J Neuropharmacol
International journal of neuropharmacology
0375-9458
    Continued by: Neuropharmacology.
1962-1969   9421557

Int J Neuropsychiatry
International journal of neuropsychiatry
    Supersedes the Journal of neuropsychiatry.
1965-1968   0243214

Int J Neuropsychopharmacol
The international journal of
neuropsychopharmacology / official scientific
journal of the Collegium Internationale
Neuropsychopharmacologicum (CINP)
1461-1457   1469-5111
1998   9815893

Int J Neurosci
The International journal of neuroscience
0020-7454   1563-5279
1970   0270707

Int J Nucl Med Biol
International journal of nuclear medicine
and biology
0047-0740
    Continued by: International journal of
    radiation applications and instrumentation.
    Part B. Nuclear medicine and biology.
1973-1986   0360047

Int J Nurs Educ Scholarsh
International journal of nursing education
scholarship
                                   1548-923X
2004   101214977

Int J Nurs Pract
International journal of nursing practice
1322-7114   1440-172X
1995   9613615

Int J Nurs Stud
International journal of nursing studies
0020-7489
1963   0400675

Int J Nurs Terminol Classif
International journal of nursing
terminologies and classifications: the official
journal of NANDA International
1541-5147   1744-618X
    Continues: Nursing diagnosis.
2002   101155367

Int J Obes
International journal of obesity
0307-0565
    Continued by: International journal of obesity
    and related metabolic disorders.
1977-1991   7703240

Int J Obes (Lond)
International journal of obesity (2005)
0307-0565   1476-5497
    Continues: International journal of obesity
    and related metabolic disorders.
2005   101256108

Int J Obes Relat Metab Disord
International journal of obesity and
related metabolic disorders: journal of the
International Association for the Study of
Obesity
0307-0565
    Continues: International journal of obesity.
    Continued by: International journal of
    obesity.
1992-2004   9313169

Int J Obstet Anesth
International journal of obstetric anesthesia
0959-289X   1532-3374
1991   9200430

Int J Occup Environ Health
International journal of occupational and
environmental health
1077-3525
1995   9505217

Int J Occup Health Saf
The International journal of occupational
health & safety
0093-2205
    Continues IMS. Industrial medicine and
    surgery. Continued by Occupational health &
    safety (Waco, Tex.).
1974-1975   7910014

Int J Occup Med Environ Health
International journal of occupational
medicine and environmental health
1232-1087
    Continues: Polish journal of occupational
    medicine and environmental health.
1994   9437093

Int J Occup Saf Ergon
International journal of occupational safety
and ergonomics: JOSE
1080-3548
1995   9507598

Int J Offender Ther Comp Criminol
International journal of offender therapy
and comparative criminology
0306-624X
    Continues International journal of offender
    therapy.
1972   0333601

Int J Oncol
International journal of oncology
1019-6439   1791-2423
1992   9306042

Int J Oral Implantol
The International journal of oral
implantology: implantologist
1048-1842
    Continues: Implantologist. Continued by:
    Implant dentistry.
1987-1991   9002981

Int J Oral Maxillofac Implants
The International journal of oral &
maxillofacial implants
0882-2786   1942-4434
1986   8611905

Int J Oral Maxillofac Surg
International journal of oral and
maxillofacial surgery
0901-5027   1399-0020
    Continues: International journal of oral
    surgery.
1986   8605826

Int J Oral Myol
The International journal of oral myology
0360-4004
    Continued by The International journal of
    orofacial myology.
1975-1980   7600106

Int J Oral Surg
International journal of oral surgery
0300-9785
    Continued by: International journal of oral
    and maxillofacial surgery.
1972-1985   0334641

Int J Orofacial Myology
The International journal of orofacial
myology: official publication of the
International Association of Orofacial
Myology
0735-0120
    Continues: The International journal of oral
    myology.
1980   8207532

Int J Orthod
International journal of orthodontics
0020-7500
1962-1991   0055653

Int J Orthod Milwaukee
International journal of orthodontics
(Milwaukee, Wis.)
1539-1450
    Continues: Journal of general orthodontics.
2002   101147228

Int J Paediatr Dent
International journal of paediatric dentistry
/ the British Paedodontic Society [and] the
International Association of Dentistry for
Children
0960-7439   1365-263X
    Formed by the union of: Journal of paediatric
    dentistry, and: Journal of the International
    Association of Dentistry for Children.
1991   9107511

Int J Palliat Nurs
International journal of palliative nursing
1357-6321
1995   9506762

Int J Pancreatol
International journal of pancreatology:
official journal of the International
Association of Pancreatology
0169-4197
    Continued by: International journal of
    gastrointestinal cancer.
1986-2001   8703511

Int J Parasitol
International journal for parasitology
0020-7519   1879-0135
1971   0314024

Int J Partial Hosp
International journal of partial
hospitalization
0272-4308
1982-1992   8208732

Int J Pediatr Nephrol
The International journal of pediatric
nephrology
0391-6510
    Continued by: Child nephrology and urology.
1980-1987   8007162

Int J Pediatr Obes
International journal of pediatric obesity:
IJPO: an official journal of the International
Association for the Study of Obesity
1747-7166   1747-7174
2006   101256330

Int J Pediatr Otorhinolaryngol
International journal of pediatric
otorhinolaryngology
0165-5876
1979   8003603

Int J Pept Protein Res
International journal of peptide and protein
research
0367-8377
 Continues: International journal of protein
 research. Title varies slightly. Merged with:
 Peptide research, to form: The journal of
 peptide research
1972-1996   0330420

Int J Periodontics Restorative Dent
The International journal of periodontics &
restorative dentistry
0198-7569
1981   8200894

Int J Pharm
International journal of pharmaceutics
0378-5173
1978   7804127

Int J Phytoremediation
International journal of phytoremediation
1522-6514   1549-7879
1999   101136878

Int J Prison Health
International journal of prisoner health
1744-9200   1744-9219
2005   101255940

Int J Prosthodont
The International journal of prosthodontics
0893-2174
1988   8900938

Int J Protein Res
International journal of protein research
0020-7551
 Continued by: International journal of peptide
 and protein research.
1969-1972   0330421

Int J Psychiatr Nurs Res
The international journal of psychiatric
nursing research
0968-0624
1994   9508871

Int J Psychiatry
International journal of psychiatry
0020-756X
 Absorbed by: International journal of
 psychoanalytic psychotherapy in 1974.
1965-1973   0243036

Int J Psychiatry Med
International journal of psychiatry in
medicine
0091-2174
 Continues Psychiatry in medicine.
1973   0365646

Int J Psychoanal
The International journal of psycho-analysis
0020-7578
 Absorbed: International review of psychoanalysis. 1994
1920   2985179R

Int J Psychoanal Psychother
International journal of psychoanalytic
psychotherapy
0091-0600
 Absorbed International journal of
 psychiatry, and International journal of child
 psychotherapy in 1974.
1972-1986   0364543

Int J Psychol
International journal of psychology: Journal
international de psychologie
0020-7594   1464-066X
 In 1993, Cahiers de psychologie cognitive
 (CPC) was merged with International journal
 of psychology. In 1994, CPC resumed
 publication with a new English title: Current
 psychology of cognition.
1966   0107305

Int J Psychophysiol
International journal of psychophysiology:
official journal of the International
Organization of Psychophysiology
0167-8760
1983   8406214

Int J Psychosom
International journal of psychosomatics:
official publication of the International
Psychosomatics Institute
0884-8297
 Continues: The Journal of the American
 Society of Psychosomatic Dentistry and
 Medicine.
1984-1995   8409613

Int J Public Health
International journal of public health
1661-8556   1661-8564
 Continues: Sozial- und Präventivmedizin.
2007   101304551

Int J Qual Health Care
International journal for quality in health
care: journal of the International Society for
Quality in Health Care / ISQua
1353-4505   1464-3677
 Continues: Quality assurance in health care.
1994   9434628

Int J Rad Appl Instrum B
International journal of radiation
applications and instrumentation. Part B,
Nuclear medicine and biology
0883-2897
 Continues: International journal of nuclear
 medicine and biology. Continued by: Nuclear
 medicine and biology.
1986-1992   8611098

Int J Rad Appl Instrum [A]
International journal of radiation
applications and instrumentation. Part A,
Applied radiation and isotopes
0883-2889
 Continues: International journal of applied
 radiation and isotopes. Continued by: Applied
 radiation and isotopes.
1986-1992   8611097

Int J Radiat Biol
International journal of radiation biology
0955-3002   1362-3095
 Continues: International journal of radiation
 biology and related studies in physics,
 chemistry, and medicine.
1988   8809243

Int J Radiat Biol Relat Stud Phys Chem Med
International journal of radiation biology
and related studies in physics, chemistry,
and medicine
0020-7616
 Continued by International journal of
 radiation biology.
1959-1988   0374725

Int J Radiat Oncol Biol Phys
International journal of radiation oncology,
biology, physics
0360-3016   1879-355X
1975   7603616

Int J Rehabil Res
International journal of rehabilitation
research. Internationale Zeitschrift
für Rehabilitationsforschung. Revue
internationale de recherches de réadaptation
0342-5282
1978   7805421

Int J Soc Psychiatry
The International journal of social
psychiatry
0020-7640   1741-2854
1955   0374726

Int J Sport Nutr
International journal of sport nutrition
1050-1606
 Continued by: International journal of sport
 nutrition and exercise metabolism.
1991-1999   9307702

Int J Sport Nutr Exerc Metab
International journal of sport nutrition and
exercise metabolism
1526-484X
 Continues: International journal of sport
 nutrition.
2000   100939812

Int J Sports Med
International journal of sports medicine
0172-4622
1980   8008349

Int J Sports Physiol Perform
International journal of sports physiology
and performance
1555-0265   1555-0273
2006   101276430

Int J STD AIDS
International journal of STD & AIDS
0956-4624   1758-1052
1990   9007917

Int J Stroke
International journal of stroke: official
journal of the International Stroke Society
1747-4930   1747-4949
2006   101274068

Int J Surg
International journal of surgery (London,
England)
1743-9191   1743-9159
 Continues: Journal of surgery (London,
 England).
2004   101228232

Int J Surg Investig
International journal of surgical
investigation
1028-5229
1999-2001   100965774

Int J Surg Pathol
International journal of surgical pathology
1066-8969
1993   9314927

Int J Syst Bacteriol
International journal of systematic
bacteriology
0020-7713
 Continues: International bulletin of
 bacteriological nomenclature and taxonomy.
 Continued by: International journal of
 systematic and evolutionary microbiology.
1966-1999   0042143

Int J Syst Evol Microbiol
International journal of systematic and
evolutionary microbiology
1466-5026   1466-5034
 Continues: International journal of systematic
 bacteriology.
2000   100899600

Int J Technol Assess Health Care
International journal of technology
assessment in health care
0266-4623
1985   8508113

Int J Tissue React
International journal of tissue reactions
0250-0868
   Continues: International journal on tissue
   reactions.
1980   8302116

Int J Toxicol
International journal of toxicology
1091-5818   1092-874X
   Continues: Journal of the American College
   of Toxicology.
1997   9708436

Int J Trauma Nurs
International journal of trauma nursing
1075-4210
   Continued by: Disaster management &
   response.
1995-2002   9506955

Int J Tuberc Lung Dis
The international journal of tuberculosis
and lung disease: the official journal of the
International Union against Tuberculosis
and Lung Disease
1027-3719   1815-7920
1997   9706389

Int J Urol
International journal of urology: official
journal of the Japanese Urological Association
0919-8172   1442-2042
1994   9440237

Int J Vitam Nutr Res
International journal for vitamin and
nutrition research. Internationale Zeitschrift
für Vitamin- und Ernährungsforschung.
Journal international de vitaminologie et de
nutrition
0300-9831
   Continues: Internationale Zeitschrift für
   Vitaminforschung.
1971   1273304

Int J Vitam Nutr Res Suppl
International journal for vitamin and
nutrition research. Supplement =
Internationale Zeitschrift für Vitamin- und
Ernährungsforschung. Supplement
0373-0883
   Continues: Internationale Zeitschrift für
   Vitamin- und Ernährungsforschung. Beiheft.
1982-1989   9211653

Int J Zoonoses
International journal of zoonoses
0377-0168
1974-1986   7505008

Int Marit Health
International maritime health
1641-9251
   Continues: Bulletin of the Institute of
   Maritime and Tropical Medicine in Gdynia.
1999   100958373

Int Med Abstr Rev
International medical abstracts & reviews
   Continued by the Journal of medecine and
   international medical abstracts & reviews.
1947-1955   17630280R

Int Microbiol
International microbiology: the official
journal of the Spanish Society for
Microbiology
1139-6709
   Continues: Microbiología (Madrid, Spain).
1998   9816585

Int MS J
International MS journal / MS Forum
1352-8963
1994   9804403

Int Nurs Rev
International nursing review
0020-8132   1466-7657
   Supersedes The International nursing bulletin.
   Absorbed ICN calling in 1972.
1954   7808754

Int Ophthalmol
International ophthalmology
0165-5701
1978   7904294

Int Ophthalmol Clin
International ophthalmology clinics
0020-8167   1536-9617
1961   0374731

Int Orthop
International orthopaedics
0341-2695   1432-5195
1977   7705431

Int Pharmacopsychiatry
International pharmacopsychiatry
0020-8272
   Absorbed by: Neuropsychobiology, 1983.
1968-1982   0135645

Int Psychiatry Clin
International psychiatry clinics
0020-8426
1964-1972   0401660

Int Psychogeriatr
International psychogeriatrics / IPA
1041-6102
1989   9007918

Int Q Community Health Educ
International quarterly of community health
education
0272-684X   1541-3519
1981   8010942

Int Rec Med
International record of medicine
0096-0632
   Continues: International record of medicine
   and general practice clinics. Absorbed by:
   Antibiotics & chemotherapy.
1957-1961   9427061

Int Rec Med Gen Pract Clin
International record of medicine and
general practice clinics
0097-1650
   Merger of: Medical record, and: General
   practice clinics. Absorbed: Quarterly
   review of medicine: Quarterly review of
   ophthalmology in Sept. 1952: Pan American
   medical woman's journal in Nov. 1952; and
   Quarterly review of otorhinolaryngology
   and bronchoesophagology in Feb. 1953.
   Issues for July 1952-53 include a separate
   section: Quarterly review of psychiatry and
   neurology. Continued by: International record
   of medicine.
1951-1956   9881794

Int Rehabil Med
International rehabilitation medicine
0379-0797
   Continued by: International disability studies.
1978-1987   7911315

Int Rescuer
International rescuer
0020-8515
   Continued by: International rescuer
   newsletter.
1957-199u   0056013

Int Rev Cell Mol Biol
International review of cell and molecular
biology
1937-6448
   Continues: International review of cytology.
2008   101475846

Int Rev Connect Tissue Res
International review of connective tissue
research
0074-767X
1963-1983   0374736

Int Rev Cytol
International review of cytology
0074-7696
   Continued by: International review of cell and
   molecular biology.
1952-2008   2985180R

Int Rev Cytol Suppl
International review of cytology. Supplement
0074-770X
1969-1987   0177061

Int Rev Exp Pathol
International review of experimental
pathology
0074-7718
1962-1996   0374737

Int Rev Immunol
International reviews of immunology
0883-0185   1563-5244
1986   8712260

Int Rev Neurobiol
International review of neurobiology
0074-7742
1959   0374740

Int Rev Neurobiol Suppl
International review of neurobiology.
Supplement
0091-5432
1972-1972   0372105

Int Rev Physiol
International review of physiology
0363-3918
   Continues: Physiology.
1976-1983   7608349

Int Rev Psychiatry
International review of psychiatry
(Abingdon, England)
0954-0261   1369-1627
1989   8918131

Int Rev Trop Med
International review of tropical medicine
0074-7777
1961-1971   7511476

Int Ser Monogr Oral Biol
International series of monographs on oral
biology
1961-1964   17640070R

Int Surg
International surgery
0020-8868
   Absorbed: International surgery bulletin.
   Continues: Journal of the International
   College of Surgeons.
1966   0043524

Int Symp Fluorid Prev Dent
International Symposium On Fluoridation
And Preventive Dentistry
19uu-19uu   9881598

Int Tinnitus J
The international tinnitus journal
0946-5448
1995   9612993

Int Urogynecol J Pelvic Floor Dysfunct
International urogynecology journal and
pelvic floor dysfunction
0937-3462 1433-3023
Continues: International urogynecology
journal.
1995 9514583

Int Urol Nephrol
International urology and nephrology
0301-1623
Absorbed: Geriatric nephrology and urology.
Continues: Urology and nephrology.
1970 0262521

Int Wound J
International wound journal
1742-4801 1742-481X
2004 101230907

Int Z Angew Physiol
Internationale Zeitschrift für
angewandte Physiologie, einschliesslich
Arbeitsphysiologie
0020-9376
Formed by the union of: Arbeitsphysiologie,
and: Luftfahrtmedizin. Continued by:
European journal of applied physiology and
occupational physiology.
1955-1973 0410302

Int Z Klin Pharmakol Ther Toxikol
Internationale Zeitschrift für klinische
Pharmakologie, Therapie, und Toxikologie.
International journal of clinical
pharmacology, therapy, and toxicology
0020-9392
Continued by International journal of clinical
pharmacology, therapy, and toxicology.
1967-1972 0340713

Int Z Phys Med Rehabil
Internationale Zeitschrift für physikalische
Medizin und Rehabilitation, mit Zentralblatt
für die gesamte Rehabilitation
Continues Internationale Rundschau für
physikalische Medizin. Continued by
Rehabilitation; internationale Zeitschrift für
physikalische Medizin und Rehabilitation mit
Zentralblatt.
1960-1961 21350220R

Int Z Vitam Ernahrungsforsch Beih
Internationale Zeitschrift für Vitamin- und
Ernährungsforschung. Beiheft
0300-9831
Continues: Internationale Zeitschrift für
Vitaminforschung. Beiheft. Continued by:
International journal for vitamin and nutrition
research. Supplement.
1972-1981 0332153

Int Z Vitaminforsch
Internationale Zeitschrift für
Vitaminforschung. Internätional journal of
vitamin research. Journal international de
vitaminologie
0020-9406
Continues Zeitschrift für Vitaminforschung.
Continued by International journal for
vitamin and nutrition research.
1947-1970 1274010

Int Z Vitaminforsch Beih
Internationale Zeitschrift für
Vitaminforschung. Beiheft
Continues Zeitschrift für Vitaminforschung.
Beihefte. Continued by Internationale
Zeitschrift für Vitamin- und
Ernährungsforschung. Beiheft.
1948-1968 0331132

Integr Cancer Ther
Integrative cancer therapies
1534-7354
2002 101128834

Integr Environ Assess Manag
Integrated environmental assessment and
management
1551-3777 1551-3793
2005 101234521

Integr Healthc Rep
Integrated healthcare report
Continued by: Healthcare leadership &
management report.
1992-1999 9318485

Integr Physiol Behav Sci
Integrative physiological and behavioral
science: the official journal of the Pavlovian
Society
1053-881X
Continues: Pavlovian journal of biological
science. Continued by: Integrative
psychological & behavioral science.
1991-2005 9105843

Integr Psychol Behav Sci
Integrative psychological & behavioral
science
1932-4502 1936-3567
Continues: Integrative physiological and
behavioral science.
2007 101319534

Intellect Dev Disabil
Intellectual and developmental disabilities
1934-9491 1934-9556
Continues: Mental retardation.
2007 101299965

Intensive Care Med
Intensive care medicine
0342-4642 1432-1238
Continues European journal of intensive care
medicine.
1977 7704851

Intensive Care Nurs
Intensive care nursing
0266-612X
Continued by: Intensive & critical care
nursing.
1985-1991 8507471

Intensive Care World
Intensive care world
0266-7037
Continues: Critical care international.
1984-uuuu 8600423

Intensive Crit Care Nurs
Intensive & critical care nursing: the official
journal of the British Association of Critical
Care Nurses
0964-3397
1992 9211274

Intensivmed Prax
Intensivmedizinische Praxis
0173-2315
Supersedes Anästhesiologische und
intensivmedizinische Praxis. Supplement to
Chirurgische Praxis.
1979-1983 8009540

Inter Des
Interior design (New York, N.Y.)
0020-5508
Continues: Interior design and decoration.
1950 9877782

Interact Cardiovasc Thorac Surg
Interactive cardiovascular and thoracic
surgery
1569-9293 1569-9285
2002 101158399

Intercamb Urol Corresp
Intercambio urológico por correspondencia
1131-3277
1949-1952 17620410R

Intercom (Des Moines)
Intercom
0273-9127
19uu 9880227

Interdiscip Top Gerontol
Interdisciplinary topics in gerontology
0074-1132 1662-3800
1968 0135125

Interexter
Inter-exter
0245-9205
Continued by Inter-fac.
1947-1962 17620430R

Interferon
Interferon
0276-1076
1979-1987 8003803

Interiors
Interiors (New York, N.Y.: 1978)
0164-8470
Continues: Contract interiors.
1978-2001 9878226

Intern Emerg Med
Internal and emergency medicine
1828-0447 1970-9366
Continues: Annali italiani di medicina interna.
2006 101263418

Intern Med
Internal medicine (Tokyo, Japan)
0918-2918 1349-7235
Continues: Japanese journal of medicine.
1992 9204241

Intern Med J
Internal medicine journal
1444-0903 1445-5994
Continues: Australian and New Zealand
journal of medicine.
2001 101092952

Interne
The interne
Absorbed: Journal of the Association of
Medical Students.
1935-1952 0374745

Internist
The Internist
0020-9546
Continued by: Today's internist.
1970-1996 1251744

Internist (Berl)
Der Internist
0020-9554 1432-1289
Continues: Aerztliche Wochenschrift.
1960 0264620

Internist Prax
Internistische Praxis
0020-9570
1961 0165250

Interstudy Qual Edge
The Interstudy quality edge: measurement
and management of clinical outcomes
1056-9618
1991-1993 9203358

Interuniv Fac Work Conf
Inter-University Faculty Work Conference
1964-1966 100961282

Intervirology
Intervirology
0300-5526 1423-0100
1973 0364265

InTouch
InTouch (Melville, N.Y.)
1522-7510
1999-2002　　　　　100888431

Invasion Metastasis
Invasion & metastasis
0251-1789
1981-1999　　　　　8202435

Invert Neurosci
Invertebrate neuroscience: IN
1354-2516　　　　　1439-1104
1995　　　　　　　　9602489

Invest Cell Pathol
Investigative & cell pathology
0146-7611
Continued by Diagnostic histopathology.
1978-1980　　　　　**7805425**

Invest Clin
Investigación clínica
0535-5133
1960　　　　　　　　0421531

Invest New Drugs
Investigational new drugs
0167-6997　　　　　1573-0646
1983　　　　　　　　8309330

Invest Ophthalmol
Investigative ophthalmology
0020-9988
Continued by Investigative ophthalmology & visual science.
1962-1976　　　　　0374730

Invest Ophthalmol Vis Sci
Investigative ophthalmology & visual science
0146-0404　　　　　1552-5783
Continues Investigative ophthalmology.
1977　　　　　　　　7703701

Invest Radiol
Investigative radiology
0020-9996　　　　　1536-0210
1966　　　　　　　　0045377

Invest Urol
Investigative urology
0021-0005
1963-1981　　　　　0374747

Investig Urol (Berl)
Investigative urology (Berlin, Germany)
1987-1994　　　　　9104156

Investor Owned Hosp Rev
The Investor-owned hospital review
0093-7312
Continues The FAH review. Continued by Review - Federation of American Hospitals.
1973-1976　　　　　7613884

Ion Channels
Ion channels
1059-7514
1988-1996　　　　　9004840

Ion Exch Membr
Ion exchange and membranes
0091-0619
1972-1975　　　　　0364544

Iowa Dent Bull
The Iowa dental bulletin
0021-048X
Continued by the Iowa dental journal.
1915-1954　　　　　**17710060R**

Iowa Dent Bull
Iowa Dental Bulletin
1967-1976　　　　　9877968

Iowa Dent J
The Iowa dental journal / Iowa State Dental Society
0021-0498
Continues: Iowa dental bulletin.
1955　　　　　　　　9301639

Iowa Med
Iowa medicine: journal of the Iowa Medical Society
0746-8709
Continues: Journal of the Iowa Medical Society.
1984　　　　　　　　8403404

Iowa Orthop J
The Iowa orthopaedic journal
1541-5457　　　　　1555-1377
1981　　　　　　　　8908272

Iowa State Coll J Sci
Iowa State College journal of science
Continues: Iowa state journal of science.
1926-1959　　　　　17710130R

Iowa State Univ Vet
Iowa State University veterinarian
0099-5851
Continues the Iowa State College veterinarian.
1959-2001　　　　　17710170R

Ir J Med Sci
Irish journal of medical science
0021-1265
Supersedes: Irish journal of medical science.
1971　　　　　　　　7806864

Ir J Med Sci
Irish journal of medical science
0021-1265
Continues Dublin journal of medical science. Superseded by Irish journal of medical science.
1922-1970　　　　　7806865

Ir Med J
Irish medical journal
0332-3102
Continues: Journal of the Irish Medical Association.
1974　　　　　　　　0430275

Ir Nurs Hosp World
Irish nursing and hospital world
0790-7702
Formed by union of: Irish nurses' journal.
1931-1968　　　　　0323465

Ir Nurs News
The Irish nursing news
0021-1354
1922　　　　　　　　17710360R

Ir Nurses J
Irish nurses' journal
0021-1346
Supersedes Irish nurse. Absorbed Irish nursing and hospital world in April 1968. Superseded by World of Irish nursing.
1968-1971　　　　　0323464

Iran Biomed J
Iranian biomedical journal
1028-852X
1997　　　　　　　　9814853

Iran J Allergy Asthma Immunol
Iranian journal of allergy, asthma, and immunology
1735-1502　　　　　1735-5249
2000　　　　　　　　101146178

Iran J Immunol
Iranian journal of immunology: IJI
1735-1383　　　　　1735-367X
2004　　　　　　　　101282932

Iraqi Dent J
Iraqi Dental Journal
1972-198u　　　　　9883855

IRB
IRB
0193-7758
1979　　　　　　　　7906878

IRCS J Med Sci
IRCS journal of medical science
0305-6481
Continues: IRCS journal of international research communication.
1975-1986　　　　　7505551

Ire Trans Biomed Electron
IRE transactions on bio-medical electronics
0096-1884
Continues IRE transactions on medical electronics. Continued by IEEE transactions on bio-medical electronics.
1961-1962　　　　　17510200R

IRE Trans Med Electron
IRE transactions on medical electronics
Continued by IRE transactions on bio-medical electronics.
1953-1960　　　　　17510210R

Iryo
Iryo
0021-1699
1946　　　　　　　　0413672

ISA Trans
ISA transactions
0019-0578
1962　　　　　　　　0374750

Isis
Isis; an international review devoted to the history of science and its cultural influences
0021-1753　　　　　1545-6994
1913　　　　　　　　2985182R

ISME J
The ISME journal
1751-7362　　　　　1751-7370
2007　　　　　　　　101301086

Isotopes Environ Health Stud
Isotopes in environmental and health studies
1025-6016
Continues: Isotopenpraxis.
1995　　　　　　　　9602611

Isozymes Curr Top Biol Med Res
Isozymes
0160-3787
1977-1987　　　　　7706779

Isr Ann Psychiatr Relat Discip
The Israel annals of psychiatry and related disciplines
0021-1958
Continued by The Israel journal of psychiatry and related sciences.
1963-1979　　　　　0374751

Isr J Dent Sci
Israel journal of dental sciences
0792-5999
1983-19uu　　　　　8811620

Isr J Exp Med
Israel journal of experimental medicine
0535-806X
Continues: Bulletin of the Research Council of Israel. Section E. Experimental medicine. Merged with: Israel medical journal, to form: Israel journal of medical sciences.
1963-1964　　　　　0013104

Isr J Med Sci
Israel journal of medical sciences
0021-2180
Formed by the union of: Israel medical journal, and: Israel journal of experimental medicine. Continued by: Israel Medical Association journal.
1965-1997   0013105

Isr J Psychiatry Relat Sci
The Israel journal of psychiatry and related sciences
0333-7308
Continues: The Israel annals of psychiatry and related disciplines.
1981   8108287

Isr J Zool
Israel journal of zoology
0021-2210
Continues: Bulletin of the Research Council of Israel. Section B, Zoology. Continued by: Israel journal of ecology & evolution.
1963-2005   0404433

Isr Med Assoc J
The Israel Medical Association journal: IMAJ
1565-1088
Continues: Israel journal of medical sciences.
1999   100930740

Isr Med J
Israel medical journal
0368-0150
Continues Acta medica orientalia. Merged with Israel journal of experimental medicine to form Israel journal of medical sciences.
1958-1964   0117447

Issled Genet
Issledovaniia po genetike
0578-9508
1961-1979   17710500R

Issue Brief (Commonw Fund)
Issue brief (Commonwealth Fund)
1558-6847
19uu   101087100

Issue Brief (George Wash Univ Med Cent Ensuring Solut Alcohol Probl)
Issue brief (George Washington University. Medical Center. Ensuring Solutions to Alcohol Problems)
2002   101174923

Issue brief (Grantmakers Health)
Issue brief (Grantmakers in Health)
1559-5609
1999   101161182

Issue Brief (Inst Health Care Costs Solut)
Issue brief (Institute on Health Care Costs and Solutions)
2002   101178232

Issue Brief (Mass Health Policy Forum)
Issue brief (Massachusetts Health Policy Forum)
1998   101178227

Issue Brief (Public Policy Inst (Am Assoc Retired Pers))
Issue Brief (Public Policy Institute (American Association of Retired Persons))
1063-3189
1991   100898603

Issue Brief Cent Medicare Educ
Issue brief (Center for Medicare Education)
2000-2004   101132264

Issue Brief Cent Stud Health Syst Change
Issue brief (Center for Studying Health System Change)
1996   9806954

Issue Brief George Wash Univ Cent Health Serv Res Policy
Issue brief (George Washington University. Center for Health Services Research and Policy)
1998   101133095

Issue Brief Health Policy Track Serv
Issue brief (Health Policy Tracking Service)
19uu   9812946

Issue Brief Natl Health Policy Forum
Issue brief (George Washington University. National Health Policy Forum)
Continued by: NHPF issue brief.
19uu-2001   9888076

Issues
Issues (National Council of State Boards of Nursing (U.S.))
0885-0046
1980   8505238

Issues Brief (Alan Guttmacher Inst)
Issues in brief (Alan Guttmacher Institute)
19uu   101095748

Issues Compr Pediatr Nurs
Issues in comprehensive pediatric nursing
0146-0862   1521-043X
1976   7702326

Issues Emerg Health Technol
Issues in emerging health technologies
1488-6324
1997   100886782

Issues Health Care
Issues in health care (Philadelphia, Pa.)
0885-0054
1980-1995   9879293

Issues Health Care Women
Issues in health care of women
0161-5246
Continued by: Health care for women international.
1978-1983   7908143

Issues Law Med
Issues in law & medicine
8756-8160
1985   8511295

Issues Ment Health Nurs
Issues in mental health nursing
0161-2840   1096-4673
1978   7907126

Issues Sci Technol
Issues in science and technology
0748-5492
1984   8502534

Istanbul Univ Dishekim Fak Derg
İstanbul Üniversitesi Dişhekimliği Fakültesi dergisi = The journal of the Dental Faculty of Istanbul
0257-8212
1967   9425140

Ital Gen Rev Dermatol
Italian general review of dermatology
0021-292X
1959-1992   0163320

Ital Gen Rev Otorhinolaryngol
Italian general review of oto-rhino-laryngology. Revue générale italienne d'oto-rhino-laryngologie
1959-1962   17720130R

Ital Heart J
Italian heart journal: official journal of the Italian Federation of Cardiology
1129-471X
Formed by the union of: Cardiologia (Rome, Italy), and: Giornale italiano di cardiologia. Continued by: Journal of cardiovascular medicine (Hagerstown, Md.).
2000-2005   100909716

Ital Heart J Suppl
Italian heart journal. Supplement: official journal of the Italian Federation of Cardiology
1129-4728
Continued by: Giornale italiano di cardiologia (2006).
2000-2005   101223651

Ital J Anat Embryol
Italian journal of anatomy and embryology = Archivio italiano di anatomia ed embriologia
1122-6714
Continues: Archivio italiano di anatomia e di embriologia.
1992   9612303

Ital J Biochem
The Italian journal of biochemistry
0021-2938
1957   0376564

Ital J Gastroenterol
The Italian journal of gastroenterology
0392-0623
Continues: Rendiconti di gastro-enterologia. Continued by: Italian journal of gastroenterology and hepatology.
1978-1996   8000544

Ital J Gastroenterol Hepatol
Italian journal of gastroenterology and hepatology
1125-8055
Continues: Italian journal of gastroenterology. Continued by: Digestive and liver disease.
1997-1999   9711056

Ital J Neurol Sci
Italian journal of neurological sciences
0392-0461
Continued by: Neurological sciences.
1979-1999   8006502

Ital J Orthop Traumatol
Italian journal of orthopaedics and traumatology
0390-5489
Supersedes Orthopaedica italica.
1975-1993   7511480

Ital J Orthop Traumatol Suppl
Italian journal of orthopaedics and traumatology. Supplementum
1975-1978   7801241

Ital J Surg Sci
The Italian journal of surgical sciences / sponsored by Società italiana di chirurgia
0392-3525
Continues: Surgery in Italy.
1981-1989   8213451

Itogi Nauk
Itogi nauki
1957-1960   17720300R

IUBMB Life
IUBMB life
1521-6543   1521-6551
Continues: Biochemistry and molecular biology international.
1999   100888706

Iugosl Physiol Pharmacol Acta
Iugoslavica physiologica et pharmacologica acta
0021-3225
Continued by: Acta physiologica et pharmacologica Serbica.
1965-2006   0133265

Iyodenshi To Seitai Kogaku
Iyō denshi to seitai kōgaku. Japanese journal of medical electronics and biological engineering
0021-3292
Continued by: Seitai ikōgaku.
1963-1995   17720370R

Izv Akad Nauk Kirg Ssr [Biol]
Izvestiia Akademii nauk Kirgizskoĭ SSR. Seriia biologicheskikh nauk
0568-5168
Supersedes in part the academy's Izvestiia.
1959-1964   7507161

Izv Akad Nauk Ser Biol
Izvestiia Akademii nauk. Seriia biologicheskaia / Rossiĭskaia akademiia nauk
1026-3470
Continues: Ivestiia Akademii nauk SSSR. Seriia biologicheskaia.
1992   9300152

Izv Akad Nauk SSSR Biol
Izvestiia Akademii nauk SSSR. Seriia biologicheskaia
0002-3329
Continues Izvestiia Akademii nauk SSSR. Otdelenie matematicheskikh i estestvennykh nauk. Seriia biologicheskaia. Continued by: Izvestiia Akademii nauk. Seriia bibliogicheskaia.
1939-1992   7505543

Izv Akad Nauk Sssr Otdelenie Khim Nauk
Izvestiia Akademii nauk SSSR, Otdelenie khimicheskikh nauk
Continues the Academy's Izvestiia. Otdelenie matematicheskikh i estestvennykh nauk. Seriia khimicheskaia, 1936-38. Continued by Izvestiia Akademii nauk SSSR. Seriia khimicheskaia.
1940-1963   7505545

Izv Bulg Akad Naukite Sofia
Nauchnoizsledovatelski Inst protivorak antibiot
Izvestiia. Bŭlgarska akademiia na naukite, Sofia. Nauchnoizsledovatelski institut za protivorakovi antibiotitsi
1961-19uu   15751090R

Izv Inst Fiziol (Sofiia)
Izvestiia na Instituta po fiziologiia
0068-3922
Continues the Izvestiia of the academy's Institut po eksperimentalna meditsina. Superseded by Acta physiologica et pharmacologica Bulgarica.
1960-1974   7503809

Izv Meditsinskite Inst Bulg Akad Naukite Sofia Otd Biol Meditsinski Nauki
Izvestiia na meditsinskite instituti. [Bulletin des instituts de médecine]. Bŭlgarska akademiia na naukite, Sofia. Otdelenie za biologicheski i meditsinski nauki
Supersedes Izvestiia of the Academy's Institut za sotsialna meditsina. Continued by Izvestiia of the academy's Institut za klinichna i sotsialna meditsina.
1951-1957   15751080R

Izv Mikrobiol Inst (Sofiia)
Izvestiia na Mikrobiologicheskiia institut
0068-3957
Continued by: Acta microbiologica, virologica et immunologica.
1950-1974   7600108

Izv Ser Fiziol Meditsiny Qazaq SSR Ghylym Akademiiasy
Izvestiia. Seriia fiziologii i meditsiny. Qazaq SSR ghylym akademiiâsy
1952-1961   0025001R

Izv Seriia Fiziol Meditsiny Qazaq SSR Ghylum Akad
Izvestiia. Seriia fiziologii i meditsiny. Qazaq SSR Ghylym Akademiiasy
1952-1961   14710270R

J

J AAPOS
Journal of AAPOS: the official publication of the American Association for Pediatric Ophthalmology and Strabismus / American Association for Pediatric Ophthalmology and Strabismus
1091-8531   1528-3933
1997   9710011

J Abnorm Child Psychol
Journal of abnormal child psychology
0091-0627
1973   0364547

J Abnorm Psychol
Journal of abnormal psychology
0021-843X   1939-1846
Continues the Journal of abnormal and social psychology.
1965   0034461

J Abnorm Soc Psychol
Journal of abnormal and social psychology
0096-851X
Continues: Journal of abnormal psychology and social psychology. Continued in part by: Journal of abnormal psychology. ISSN 0021-843X, and Superseded in part by: Journal of personality and social psychology. ISSN 0022-3514.
1925-1964   0014016

J Acad Gen Dent
Journal - Academy of General Dentistry
0001-4265
Continues Bulletin of the Academy of General Dentistry. Continued by General dentistry.
1969-1975   7610507

J Acad Hosp Adm
Journal (Academy of Hospital Administration (India))
0970-9452
1989   9109129

J Accid Emerg Med
Journal of accident & emergency medicine
1351-0622
Continues: Archives of emergency medicine. Continued by: Emergency medicine journal.
1994-2000   9433751

J Acoust Soc Am
The Journal of the Acoustical Society of America
0001-4966   1520-8524
1929   7503051

J Acquir Immune Defic Syndr
Journal of acquired immune deficiency syndromes
0894-9255
Continued by: Journal of acquired immune deficiency syndromes and human retrovirology.
1988-1994   8812597

J Acquir Immune Defic Syndr
Journal of acquired immune deficiency syndromes (1999)
1525-4135
Continues: Journal of acquired immune deficiency syndromes and human retrovirology.
1999   100892005

J Acquir Immune Defic Syndr Hum Retrovirol
Journal of acquired immune deficiency syndromes and human retrovirology: official publication of the International Retrovirology Association
1077-9450
Continues: Journal of acquired immune deficiency syndromes. Continued by: Journal of acquired immune deficiency syndromes (1999).
1995-1999   9501482

J Addict Dis
Journal of addictive diseases
1055-0887   1545-0848
Continues: Advances in alcohol & substance abuse.
1991   9107051

J Adhes Dent
The journal of adhesive dentistry
1461-5185
1999   100888552

J Adolesc
Journal of adolescence
0140-1971
1978   7808986

J Adolesc Health
The Journal of adolescent health: official publication of the Society for Adolescent Medicine
1054-139X
Continues: Journal of adolescent health care.
1991   9102136

J Adolesc Health Care
Journal of adolescent health care: official publication of the Society for Adolescent Medicine
0197-0070
Continued by: Journal of adolescent health.
1980-1990   8100395

J Adv Med Surg Nurs
Journal of advanced medical-surgical nursing
0897-2869
1988-1989   8901657

J Adv Nurs
Journal of advanced nursing
0309-2402   1365-2648
1976   7609811

J Aerosol Med
Journal of aerosol medicine: the official journal of the International Society for Aerosols in Medicine
0894-2684   1557-9026
Continued by: Journal of aerosol medicine and pulmonary drug delivery.
1988-2007   8809251

J Aerosol Med Pulm Drug Deliv
Journal of aerosol medicine and pulmonary drug delivery
1941-2711   1941-2703
Continues: Journal of aerosol medicine.
2008   101475057

J Affect Disord
Journal of affective disorders
0165-0327
1979   7906073

J Aging Health
Journal of aging and health
0898-2643
1989   8912686

J Aging Phys Act
Journal of aging and physical activity
1063-8652   1543-267X
1993   9415639

J Aging Soc Policy
Journal of aging & social policy
0895-9420   1545-0821
1989   8914669

J Agric Food Chem
Journal of agricultural and food chemistry
0021-8561   1520-5118
1953   0374755

J Agric Saf Health
Journal of agricultural safety and health
1074-7583
1995   9613956

J Agromedicine
Journal of agromedicine
1059-924X   1545-0813
1994   9421530

J AHIMA
Journal of AHIMA / American Health
Information Management Association
1060-5487
   Continues: Journal (American Medical
   Records Association).
1991   9202024

J Air Med Transp
The Journal of air medical transport
1046-9095
   Formed by the union of: AeroMedical
   journal, and: Hospital aviation. Continued by:
   Air medical journal.
1989-1992   9002199

J Air Pollut Control Assoc
Journal of the Air Pollution Control
Association
0002-2470
   Continues Air repair. Absorbed the APCA
   news, Jan. 1960. Continued by: JAPCA.
1955-1986   7505567

J Air Waste Manag Assoc
Journal of the Air & Waste Management
Association (1995)
1096-2247
   Continues: Air & waste.
1995   9503111

J Air Waste Manage Assoc
Journal of the Air & Waste Management
Association
1047-3289
   Continues: JAPCA. Continued by: Air &
   waste.
1990-1992   9002202

J Ala Dent Assoc
Journal - Alabama Dental Association
0002-4198
   Continues Bulletin of the Alabama Dental
   Association.
1958-1997   7505557

J Albert Einstein Med Cent (Phila)
The Journal of the Albert Einstein Medical
Center, Philadelphia
0002-4708
1952-1972   7503053

J All India Dent Assoc
The Journal of the All India Dental Association
0377-0516
   Continued by: Journal of the Indian Dental
   Association.
1947-1966   7503054

J All India Ophthalmol Soc
Journal of the All-India Ophthalmological
Society
0044-7307
   Continues: Indian journal of ophthalmology.
   Continued by: Indian journal of ophthalmology.
1953-1970   7503055

J Allergy
The Journal of allergy
0021-8707
   Continued by: Journal of allergy and clinical
   immunology.
1929-1971   1305603

J Allergy Clin Immunol
The Journal of allergy and clinical
immunology
0091-6749   1097-6825
   Continues: Journal of allergy.
1971   1275002

J Allied Health
Journal of allied health
0090-7421
1972   0361603

J Altern Complement Med
Journal of alternative and complementary
medicine (New York, N.Y.)
1075-5535   1557-7708
1995   9508124

J Alzheimers Dis
Journal of Alzheimer's disease: JAD
1387-2877
1998   9814863

J Am Acad Appl Nutr
Journal of the American Academy of
Applied Nutrition. American Academy of
Applied Nutrition
0095-9839
   Continued by: Journal of applied nutrition.
1947-1952   101469829

J Am Acad Audiol
Journal of the American Academy of
Audiology
1050-0545
1990   9114646

J Am Acad Child Adolesc Psychiatry
Journal of the American Academy of Child
and Adolescent Psychiatry
0890-8567   1527-5418
   Continues: Journal of the American Academy
   of Child Psychiatry.
1987   8704565

J Am Acad Child Psychiatry
Journal of the American Academy of Child
Psychiatry
0002-7138
   Continued by: Journal of the American
   Academy of Child and Adolescent Psychiatry.
1962-1986   7505568

J Am Acad Dermatol
Journal of the American Academy of
Dermatology
0190-9622   1097-6787
1979   7907132

J Am Acad Gnathol Orthop
Journal (American Academy of Gnathologic
Orthopedics)
0886-1064
1984   8709880

J Am Acad Gold Foil Oper
The Journal of the American Academy of
Gold Foil Operators
0002-7146
   Continued by: Operative dentistry.
1958-1975   7605632

J Am Acad Nurse Pract
Journal of the American Academy of Nurse
Practitioners
1041-2972   1745-7599
1989   8916634

J Am Acad Orthop Surg
The Journal of the American Academy of
Orthopaedic Surgeons
1067-151X
1993   9417468

J Am Acad Psychiatry Law
The journal of the American Academy of
Psychiatry and the Law
1093-6793
   Continues: Bulletin of the American Academy
   of Psychiatry and the Law.
1997   9708963

J Am Acad Psychoanal
The Journal of the American Academy of
Psychoanalysis
0090-3604
   Continued by: Journal of the American
   Academy of Psychoanalysis and Dynamic
   Psychiatry.
1973-2002   7505570

J Am Acad Psychoanal Dyn Psychiatry
The journal of the American Academy of
Psychoanalysis and Dynamic Psychiatry
1546-0371
   Continues: Journal of the American Academy
   of Psychoanalysis.
2003   101177980

J Am Anim Hosp Assoc
Journal of the American Animal Hospital
Association
0587-2871   1547-3317
   Continues: Animal hospital.
1968   0415027

J Am Assoc Gynecol Laparosc
The Journal of the American Association of
Gynecologic Laparoscopists
1074-3804
   Continued by: Journal of minimally invasive
   gynecology.
1993-2004   9417443

J Am Assoc Lab Anim Sci
Journal of the American Association for
Laboratory Animal Science: JAALAS
1559-6109
   Continues: Contemporary topics in laboratory
   animal science.
2006   101269489

J Am Assoc Med Rec Libr
Journal. American Association of Medical
Record Librarians
   Continues the association's Bulletin.
   Continued by the Medical record news.
1944-1961   14740580R

J Am Assoc Med Transcr
Journal (American Association for Medical
Transcription)
0745-2624
   Continued by: JAAMT.
1982-2000   8400760

J Am Assoc Nephrol Nurses Tech
The Journal of the American Association of
Nephrology Nurses & Technicians
0360-7615
1974-1980   7601746

J Am Assoc Nurse Anesth
The Journal of the American Association of
Nurse Anesthetists
0002-7448
   Continues: Bulletin of the American
   Association of Nurse Anesthetists. Continued
   by: AANA journal.
1945-1973   0431453

J Am Aud Soc
Journal of the American Auditory Society
0164-5080
Continues Journal of the American Audiology Society. Superseded by Ear and hearing.
1978-1979   7907691

J Am Audiol Soc
Journal of the American Audiology Society
0360-9294
Continued by Journal of the American Auditory Society.
1975-1978   7602679

J Am Board Fam Med
Journal of the American Board of Family Medicine: JABFM
1557-2625
Continues: Journal of the American Board of Family Practice.
2006   101256526

J Am Board Fam Pract
The Journal of the American Board of Family Practice / American Board of Family Practice
0893-8652   1544-8770
Continued by: Journal of the American Board of Family Medicine.
1988-2005   8807505

J Am Chem Soc
Journal of the American Chemical Society
0002-7863   1520-5126
Absorbed: American chemical journal. Jan. 1914 Journal of analytical and applied chemistry. July 1893
1879   7503056

J Am Coll Cardiol
Journal of the American College of Cardiology
0735-1097   1558-3597
1983   8301365

J Am Coll Dent
The Journal of the American College of Dentists
0002-7979
1934   7503057

J Am Coll Health
Journal of American college health: J of ACH
0744-8481
Continues: Journal of the American College Health Association.
1982   8214119

J Am Coll Health Assoc
Journal of the American College Health Association
0002-7944
Continues Student medicine. Continued by Journal of American college health.
1962-1982   7503059

J Am Coll Neuropsychiatr
Journal of the American College of Neuropsychiatrists
0517-0613
Continued by: Journal of the American College of neuropsychiatrists (1986).
1962-1964   7503058

J Am Coll Nutr
Journal of the American College of Nutrition
0731-5724   1541-1087
1982   8215879

J Am Coll Radiol
Journal of the American College of Radiology: JACR
1546-1440   1558-349X
2004   101190326

J Am Coll Surg
Journal of the American College of Surgeons
1072-7515
Vols. for 2002- include supplement with title Surgical forum, which was formerly issued separately.
1994   9431305

J Am Dent Assoc
Journal of the American Dental Association (1939)
0002-8177
Continues: Journal of the American Dental Association and the dental cosmos.
1939   7503060

J Am Dent Assoc (Ed Ital)
Journal Of The American Dental Association (Edizione Italiana)
0393-5388
1985   9881715

J Am Dent Hyg Assoc
The Journal of the American Dental Hygienists' Association
0002-8185
Continued by Dental hygiene
1927-1972   7505571

J Am Dent Soc Anesthesiol
Journal of the American Dental Society of Anesthesiology
Continues: News monthly. American Dental Society of Anesthesiology. Continued by: Anesthesia progress.
1958-1965   7505572

J Am Diet Assoc
Journal of the American Dietetic Association
0002-8223
Supersedes: Bulletin of the American Dietetic Association.
1925   7503061

J Am Geriatr Soc
Journal of the American Geriatrics Society
0002-8614   1532-5415
1953   7503062

J Am Health Care
The journal of American health care
1078-6856
Continues: Journal of American health policy.
1994-1994   9442073

J Am Health Care Assoc
Journal - American Health Care Association
0360-4969
Supersedes Governing Council report - American Health Care Association. Continued by: Provider (Washington, D.C.).
1975-1986   7600544

J Am Health Policy
The Journal of American health policy
1055-324X
Continued by: Journal of American health care.
1991-1994   9110832

J Am Inst Homeopath
Journal of the American Institute of Homeopathy
0002-8967
Supersedes the Transactions of the American Institute of Homeopathy. Absorbed the Homeopathic recorder in 1959. Continued by: American journal of homeopathy.
1909-2002   7507175

J Am Inst Plann
Journal of the American Institute of Planners
0002-8991
Continues: Planners' journal. Continued by: Journal of the American Planning Association.
1944-1978   9877929

J Am Insur
Journal of American insurance
0021-874X
1924-1990   0254060

J Am Intraocul Implant Soc
Journal - American Intra-Ocular Implant Society
0146-2776
Continues Newsletter - American Intra-Ocular Implant Society. Continued by: Journal of cataract and refractive surgery.
1976-1985   7701858

J Am Med Dir Assoc
Journal of the American Medical Directors Association
1525-8610   1538-9375
2000   100893243

J Am Med Inform Assoc
Journal of the American Medical Informatics Association: JAMIA
1067-5027   1527-974X
1994   9430800

J Am Med Rec Assoc
Journal (American Medical Record Association)
0273-9976
Continues: Journal of the American Medical Record Association. Continued by: Journal of AHIMA.
1983-1991   8406720

J Am Med Rec Assoc
Journal of the American Medical Record Association
0273-9976
Continues: Medical record news. Continued by: Journal (American Medical Record Association).
1980-1982   8215880

J Am Med Womens Assoc
Journal of the American Medical Women's Association
0091-7427
Continues: Women in medicine. Continued by: Woman physician.
1946-1969   9810653

J Am Med Womens Assoc
Journal of the American Medical Women's Association (1972)
0098-8421   1551-8221
Continues: Woman physician.
1972-2005   7503064

J Am Mosq Control Assoc
Journal of the American Mosquito Control Association
8756-971X
Continues: Mosquito news. Absorbed: Journal of the American Mosquito Control Association. Supplement. Mosquito systematics.
1985   8511299

J Am Mosq Control Assoc Suppl
Journal of the American Mosquito Control Association. Supplement
1046-3607
Absorbed by: Journal of the American Mosquito Control Association.
1988-1990   8904843

J Am Oil Chem Soc
Journal of the American Oil Chemists' Society
0003-021X
Continues Oil and soap.
1947   7505574

J Am Optom Assoc
Journal of the American Optometric
Association
0003-0244
Continues: A.O.A. organizer. Continued by:
Optometry (St. Louis, Mo.).
1930-1999 **7505575**

J Am Osteopath Assoc
The Journal of the American Osteopathic
Association
0098-6151
1901 **7503065**

J Am Paraplegia Soc
The Journal of the American Paraplegia
Society
0195-2307
Continued by: Journal of spinal cord
medicine.
1978-1994 **8303486**

J Am Pharm Assoc
Journal of the American Pharmaceutical
Association
0003-0465
Supersedes American Pharmaceutical
Association. Journal. Practical pharmacy ed.
Continued by American pharmacy.
1961-1977 **7505576**

J Am Pharm Assoc (2003)
Journal of the American Pharmacists
Association: JAPhA
1544-3191 1544-3450
Continues: Journal of the American
Pharmaceutical Association.
2003 **101176252**

J Am Pharm Assoc (Wash)
Journal of the American Pharmaceutical
Association (Washington,D.C.: 1996)
1086-5802
Continues: American pharmacy. Continued
by: Journal of the American Pharmacists
Association.
1996-2003 **9601004**

J Am Pharm Assoc Am Pharm Assoc
Journal of the American Pharmaceutical
Association. American Pharmaceutical
Association
Merged with: Drug standards, to form:
Journal of pharmaceutical sciences.
1940-1960 **14840180R**

J Am Pharm Assoc Am Pharm Assoc (Baltim)
Journal of the American Pharmaceutical
Association. American Pharmaceutical
Association
Supersedes, in part, the association's Journal.
Superseded by the association's Journal, new
ser.
1940-1960 **14840170R**

J Am Phys Ther Assoc
Journal of the American Physical Therapy
Association
Continues: Physical therapy review.
Continued by: Physical therapy.
1962-1963 **0001556**

J Am Plann Assoc
Journal of the American Planning
Association. American Planning Association
0194-4363
Continues: Journal of the American Institute
of Planners.
1979 **9878432**

J Am Podiatr Med Assoc
Journal of the American Podiatric Medical
Association
8750-7315
Continues: Journal of the American Podiatry
Association.
1985 **8501423**

J Am Podiatry Assoc
Journal of the American Podiatry
Association
0003-0538
Continues The Journal of the National
Association of Chiropodists. Continued by
Journal of the American Podiatric Medical
Association.
1958-1984 **7505577**

J Am Psychoanal Assoc
Journal of the American Psychoanalytic
Association
0003-0651 1941-2460
1953 **7505579**

J Am Soc Echocardiogr
Journal of the American Society of
Echocardiography: official publication of the
American Society of Echocardiography
0894-7317 1097-6795
1988 **8801388**

J Am Soc Geriatr Dent
The Journal of the American Society for
Geriatric Dentistry
0003-1054
Merged with Journal of hospital dental
practice, and, Journal of dentistry for the
handicapped, to form: Special care in
dentistry.
1966-1979 **7503066**

J Am Soc Inf Sci
Journal of the American Society for
Information Science. American Society for
Information Science
0002-8231
Continues American documentation.
Continued by: Journal of the American
Society for Information Science and
Technology (Print).
1970-2000 **0232761**

J Am Soc Mass Spectrom
Journal of the American Society for Mass
Spectrometry
1044-0305
1990 **9010412**

J Am Soc Nephrol
Journal of the American Society of
Nephrology: JASN
1046-6673 1533-3450
1990 **9013836**

J Am Soc Prev Dent
The Journal of the American Society for
Preventive Dentistry
0093-4518
1970-1977 **0415031**

J Am Soc Psych Res
The Journal of the American Society for
Psychical Research
0003-1070
1907 **7505580**

J Am Soc Psychosom Dent Med
The Journal of the American Society of
Psychosomatic Dentistry and Medicine
0003-1194
Continues the Journal of the American
Society of Psychosomatic Dentistry.
Continued by International journal of
psychosomatics.
1958-1983 **7505581**

J Am Soc Study Orthod
Journal of the American Society for the
Study of Orthodontics. American Society for
the Study of Orthodontics
0003-1089
1963-1967 **9875580**

J Am Vener Dis Assoc
Journal of the American Venereal Disease
Association
0095-148X
Continued by Sexually Transmitted diseases.
1974-1976 **7500328**

J Am Vet Med Assoc
Journal of the American Veterinary Medical
Association
0003-1488
Continues: American veterinary review.
Absorbed: Scientific proceedings of the
American Veterinary Medical Association.
1915 **7503067**

J Ambul Care Manage
The Journal of ambulatory care
management
0148-9917 1550-3267
1978 **7802876**

J Ambul Care Mark
Journal of ambulatory care marketing
0886-9723
Continues: Emergency health services review.
1987-1995 **8710130**

J Anal Psychol
The Journal of analytical psychology
0021-8774
1955 **0376573**

J Anal Toxicol
Journal of analytical toxicology
0146-4760
1977 **7705085**

J Anat
Journal of anatomy
0021-8782 1469-7580
Continues: Journal of anatomy and
physiology.
1916 **0137162**

J Anat Soc India
Journal of the Anatomical Society of India
0003-2778
1952 **7505583**

J Androl
Journal of andrology
0196-3635
1980 **8106453**

J Anesth
Journal of anesthesia
0913-8668
1987 **8905667**

J Anglocont Dent Soc
Journal (Anglo-Continental Dental Society)
0003-3324
1962-1980 **8301204**

J Anim Breed Genet
Journal of animal breeding and genetics
= Zeitschrift für Tierzüchtung und
Züchtungsbiologie
0931-2668 1439-0388
Continues: Zeitschrift für Tierzüchtung und
Züchtungsbiologie.
1986 **100955807**

J Anim Ecol
The Journal of animal ecology
0021-8790 1365-2656
1932 **0376574**

J Anim Physiol Anim Nutr (Berl)
Journal of animal physiology and animal
nutrition
0931-2439 1439-0396
Continues: Zeitschrift für Tierphysiologie,
Tierernährung und Futtermittelkunde.
2001 **101126979**

J Anim Sci
Journal of animal science
0021-8812   1525-3163
Supersedes: Record of proceedings of the
annual meeting - American Society of Animal
Production.
1942   8003002

J Anti Aging Med
Journal of anti-aging medicine
1094-5458
Continued by: Rejuvenation research.
1998-2003   9815684

J Antibiot (Tokyo)
The Journal of antibiotics
0021-8820
Continues in part the same title with text in
Japanese.
1953   0151115

J Antibiot [B]
The Journal of antibiotics. Ser. B
0447-8991
Continues in part the Journal of antibiotics.
Continued by the Japanese journal of
antibiotics.
1953-1967   0154411

J Antimicrob Chemother
The Journal of antimicrobial chemotherapy
0305-7453   1460-2091
1975   7513617

J Anxiety Disord
Journal of anxiety disorders
0887-6185
1987   8710131

J AOAC Int
Journal of AOAC International
1060-3271
Continues: Journal - Association of Official
Analytical Chemists.
1992   9215446

J APDSA (Tokyo)
Journal Of Apdsa; Asian Pacific Dental
Student Association
0571-2912
1968-1978   9875625

J Appl Anim Welf Sci
Journal of applied animal welfare science:
JAAWS
1088-8705   1532-7604
Continues: Humane innovations and
alternatives.
1998   9804404

J Appl Bacteriol
The Journal of applied bacteriology
0021-8847
Continues: Proceedings. Society for Applied
Bacteriology. Continued by: Journal of
applied microbiology.
1954-1996   7503050

J Appl Behav Anal
Journal of applied behavior analysis
0021-8855
1968   0174763

J Appl Behav Sci
The Journal of applied behavioral science
0021-8863
1965   0060433

J Appl Biochem
Journal of applied biochemistry
0161-7354
Continued by: Biotechnology and applied
biochemistry.
1979-1985   7908148

J Appl Biomater
Journal of applied biomaterials: an official
journal of the Society for Biomaterials
1045-4861
Absorbed by: Journal of biomedical materials
research.
1990-1995   9011484

J Appl Biomech
Journal of applied biomechanics
1065-8483
Continues: International journal of sport
biomechanics.
1993   9315240

J Appl Clin Med Phys
Journal of applied clinical medical physics /
American College of Medical Physics
                             1526-9914
2000   101089176

J Appl Genet
Journal of applied genetics
1234-1983
Continues: Genetica polonica.
1995   9514582

J Appl Gerontol
Journal of applied gerontology: the official
journal of the Southern Gerontological
Society
0733-4648   1552-4523
1982   8606502

J Appl Meas
Journal of applied measurement
1529-7713
Absorbed: Journal of outcome measurement.
2000   101084377

J Appl Microbiol
Journal of applied microbiology
1364-5072   1365-2672
Continues: Journal of applied bacteriology.
1997   9706280

J Appl Nutr
The Journal of applied nutrition
0021-8960
Continues the Journal of the American
Academy of Applied Nutrition.
1953   0404726

J Appl Oral Sci
Journal of applied oral science: revista FOB
1678-7757   1678-7765
Continues: Revista da Faculdade de
Odontologia de Bauru, USP.
2003   101189774

J Appl Physiol
Journal of applied physiology
0021-8987
Continued by: Journal of applied physiology:
respiratory, environmental and exercise
physiology.
1948-1976   0376576

J Appl Physiol
Journal of applied physiology (Bethesda,
Md.: 1985)
8750-7587   1522-1601
Continues: Journal of applied physiology:
respiratory, environmental and exercise
physiology.
1985   8502536

J Appl Physiol
Journal of applied physiology: respiratory,
environmental and exercise physiology
0161-7567
Continues: Journal of applied physiology.
Continued by: Journal of applied physiology
(Bethesda, Md.: 1985).
1977-1984   7801242

J Appl Psychol
The Journal of applied psychology
0021-9010
1917   0222526

J Appl Toxicol
Journal of applied toxicology: JAT
0260-437X
1981   8109495

J Aquat Anim Health
Journal of aquatic animal health
0899-7659   1548-8667
1989   9884881

J Ark Med Soc
The Journal of the Arkansas Medical Society
0004-1858
Continues: Monthly bulletin of the Arkansas
Medical Society.
1906   7503069

J Arthroplasty
The Journal of arthroplasty
0883-5403   1532-8406
1986   8703515

J Artif Organs
Journal of artificial organs: the official journal
of the Japanese Society for Artificial Organs
1434-7229
Continues: Artificial organs today.
1998   9815648

J Asian Nat Prod Res
Journal of Asian natural products research
1028-6020
1998   100888334

J Assist Reprod Genet
Journal of assisted reproduction and
genetics
1058-0468
Continues: Journal of in vitro fertilization and
embryo transfer.
1992   9206495

J Assoc Acad Minor Phys
Journal of the Association for Academic
Minority Physicians: the official publication
of the Association for Academic Minority
Physicians
1048-9886
1989   9113765

J Assoc Adv Med Instrum
JAAMI; journal of the Association for the
Advancement of Medical Instrumentation
0004-5446
Continued by Medical instrumentation.
1966-1972   1275534

J Assoc Am Med Coll
Journal. Association of American Medical
Colleges
0095-9545
Continues: Bulletin of the Association of
American Medical Colleges. Continued by:
Medical education (Chicago, Ill.).
1929-1950   15340090R

J Assoc Care Child Health
Journal of the Association for the Care of
Children's Health
0274-8916
Continues: Journal of the Association for the
Care of Children in Hospitals. Continued by:
Children's health care.
1980-1980   8101321

J Assoc Care Child Hosp
Journal of the Association for the Care of
Children in Hospitals
0145-3351
Continued by Journal of the Association for
the Care of Children's Health.
1972-1980   7613888

J Assoc Healthc Philanthr
Journal (Association for Healthcare
Philanthropy (U.S.))
1061-7655
Continues: Journal (National Association for
Hospital Development (U.S.)). Continued by:
AHP journal.
1991-2001   9202815

J Assoc Hosp Med Educ
Journal - Association for Hospital Medical
Education
0148-4869
Supersedes AHME journal.
1976-1978   7705084

J Assoc Med Illus
Journal of the Association of Medical
Illustrators
0098-8456
Continues Graphics. Continued by Medical
art.
1953-1964   7503072

J Assoc Nurses AIDS Care
The Journal of the Association of Nurses in
AIDS Care: JANAC
1055-3290   1552-6917
1989   9111870

J Assoc Off Anal Chem
Journal - Association of Official Analytical
Chemists
0004-5756
Continues: Journal of the Association of
Official Agricultural Chemists. Continued by:
Journal of AOAC International.
1966-1991   7505559

J Assoc Pediatr Oncol Nurses
Journal of the Association of Pediatric
Oncology Nurses
0748-1802
Continues: APON newsletter. Continued by:
Journal of pediatric oncology nursing.
1984-1989   8410048

J Assoc Phys Ment Rehabil
Journal of the Association for Physical and
Mental Rehabilitation
0098-8448
Continued by American corrective therapy
journal.
1947-1967   7503071

J Assoc Physicians India
The Journal of the Association of Physicians
of India
0004-5772
1953   7505585

J Assoc Res Otolaryngol
Journal of the Association for Research in
Otolaryngology: JARO
1525-3961   1438-7573
2000   100892857

J Asthma
The Journal of asthma: official journal of
the Association for the Care of Asthma
0277-0903   1532-4303
Continues: Journal of asthma research.
1981   8106454

J Asthma Res
The Journal of asthma research
0021-9134
Supersedes Children's Asthma Research
Institute and Hospital, Denver. Journal.
Continued by The Journal of asthma.
1963-1980   0376577

J Atheroscler Res
Journal of atherosclerosis research
0368-1319
Continued by Atherosclerosis.
1961-1969   0242574

J Atheroscler Thromb
Journal of atherosclerosis and thrombosis
1340-3478   1880-3873
Absorbed: Dōmyaku kōka.
1994   9506298

J Athl Train
Journal of athletic training
1062-6050
Continues: Athletic training.
1992   9301647

J Atten Disord
Journal of attention disorders
1087-0547
1996   9615686

J Aud Res
The Journal of auditory research
0021-9177
1960-1987   0014024

J Aud Res Suppl
Journal of auditory research. Supplement
0096-2724
1974-1981   7512800

J Audiov Media Med
The Journal of audiovisual media in
medicine
0140-511X   1465-3494
Supersedes: Medical & biological
illustration. Continued by: Journal of visual
communication in medicine.
1978-2004   7803121

J Aust Inst Surg Dent Tech
Journal Of The Australian Institute
Of Surgical And Dental Technicians
(Melbourne)
0313-8356
1974   9883613

J Autism Child Schizophr
Journal of autism and childhood
schizophrenia
0021-9185
Continued by Journal of autism and
developmental disorders.
1971-1978   1264240

J Autism Dev Disord
Journal of autism and developmental
disorders
0162-3257   1573-3432
Continues: Journal of autism and childhood
schizophrenia.
1979   7904301

J Autoimmun
Journal of autoimmunity
0896-8411
1988   8812164

J Auton Nerv Syst
Journal of the autonomic nervous system
0165-1838
Continued by: Autonomic neuroscience.
1979-2000   8003419

J Auton Pharmacol
Journal of autonomic pharmacology
0144-1795   1365-2680
Continued by: Autonomic & autacoid
pharmacology.
1980-2001   8106455

J Aux Odontol
Journal Das Auxiliares Odontologicas
1980-2001   9875624

J Avian Med Surg
Journal of avian medicine and surgery
1082-6742
Continues: Journal of the Association of
Avian Veterinarians.
1995   9512497

J Aviat Med
The Journal of aviation medicine
0095-991X
Continued by Aerospace medicine.
1930-1959   14640090R

J Ayub Med Coll Abbottabad
Journal of Ayub Medical College,
Abbottabad: JAMC
1025-9589   1819-2718
1988   8910750

J Bacteriol
Journal of bacteriology
0021-9193   1098-5530
1916   2985120R

J Baltimore Coll Dent Surg
Journal of the Baltimore College of Dental
Surgery
0067-3072
1937-1985   7505588

J Basic Clin Physiol Pharmacol
Journal of basic and clinical physiology and
pharmacology
0792-6855
Continues: Reviews in clinical & basic
pharmacology.
1990   9101750

J Basic Microbiol
Journal of basic microbiology
0233-111X
Continues: Zeitschrift für allgemeine
Mikrobiologie.
1985   8503885

J Behav Health Serv Res
The journal of behavioral health services &
research
1094-3412   1556-3308
Continues: Journal of mental health
administration.
1998   9803531

J Behav Med
Journal of behavioral medicine
0160-7715   1573-3521
1978   7807105

J Behav Ther Exp Psychiatry
Journal of behavior therapy and
experimental psychiatry
0005-7916
1970   0245075

J Belge Med Phys
Journal belge de médecine physique.
Belgisch tijdschrift voor fysische
geneeskunde
0378-9500
Continues in part Journal belge de
rhumatologie et de médecine physique.
Belgisch tijdschrift voor reumatologie
en fysische geneeskunde. Superseded by
Journal belge de médecine physique et de
réhabilitation. Belgisch tijdschrift voor
fysische geneeskunde en rehabilitatie.
1977-1977   7903136

J Belge Med Phys Rehabil
Journal belge de médecine physique et de
réhabilitation. Belgisch tijdschrift voor
fysische geneeskunde en rehabilitatie
0250-4766
Supersedes Journal belge de médecine
physique. Belgisch tijdschrift voor fysische
geneeskunde. Continued by Acta Belgica.
Medica physica.
1978-1982   7903309

J Belge Med Phys Rhumatol
Journal belge de médecine physique et de
rhumatologie. Belgisch tijdschrift voor
fysische geneeskunde en reumatologie
0368-1459
Continues Acta physiotherapica et
rheumatologica Belgica. Continued by Journal
belge de rhumatologie et de médecine physique.
1956-1964   0071431

J Belge Neurol Psychiatr
Journal belge de neurologie et de psychiatrie
0368-1408
Continues Journal de neurologie et de
psychiatrie. Continued by Acta neurologica et
psychiatrica belgica.
1933-1947   17810480R

J Belge Radiol
Journal belge de radiologie
0021-7646
Continues: Journal de radiologie. Continued
by: JBR-BTR.
1924-1998   0420407

J Belge Rhumatol Med Phys
Journal belge de rhumatologie et de
médecine physique. Belgisch tijdschrift voor
reumatologie en fysische geneeskunde
0021-7654
Continues Journal belge de médecine
physique et de rhumatologie. Continued
in part by Journal belge de médecine
physique. Belgisch tijdschrift voor fysische
geneeskunde and Acta rhumatologie Belgica.
1964-1976   0071414

J Belge Urol
Journal belge d'urologie
Continued by Acta urologica Belgica.
1928-1954   17810500R

J Bergen Cty Dent Soc
The journal of the Bergen County Dental
Society. Bergen County Dental Society
0092-9832
Continues: Bulletin of the Bergen County
Dental Society. Continued by: Newsletter/
BCDS.
1973-1987   7507180

J Biochem
Journal of biochemistry
0021-924X
1922   0376600

J Biochem Biophys Methods
Journal of biochemical and biophysical
methods
0165-022X
Continued by: Journal of proteomics.
1979-2007   7907378

J Biochem Mol Biol
Journal of biochemistry and molecular
biology
1225-8687   0219-1024
Continues: Han æguk Saenghwahakhoe chi.
Han æguk Saenghwahakhoe. Continued by:
BMB reports.
1995-2007   9702084

J Biochem Mol Biol Biophys
Journal of biochemistry, molecular biology,
and biophysics: JBMBB: the official journal
of the Federation of Asian and Oceanian
Biochemists and Molecular Biologists
(FAOBMB)
1025-8140
1997-2002   9714994

J Biochem Mol Toxicol
Journal of biochemical and molecular
toxicology
1095-6670   1099-0461
Continues: Journal of biochemical toxicology.
1998   9717231

J Biochem Toxicol
Journal of biochemical toxicology
0887-2082
Continued by: Journal of biochemical and
molecular toxicology.
1986-1996   8700114

J Biocommun
The Journal of biocommunication
0094-2499
Absorbed: Journal of biological photography.
2000
1974   0425742

J Bioenerg
Journal of bioenergetics
0449-5705
Continued by Journal of bioenergetics and
biomembranes.
1970-1976   1301714

J Bioenerg Biomembr
Journal of bioenergetics and biomembranes
0145-479X
Continues Journal of bioenergetics.
1976   7701859

J Bioeng
Journal of bioengineering
0145-3068
Absorbed by: Annals of biomedical
engineering.
1976-1978   7801772

J Bioeth
Journal of bioethics
0278-9523
Continues: Bioethics quarterly. Continued
by: The journal of medical humanities and
bioethics.
1983-1984   8410621

J Bioinform Comput Biol
Journal of bioinformatics and computational
biology
0219-7200
2003   101187344

J Biol
Journal of biology
1478-5854   1475-4924
2002   101147570

J Biol Buccale
Journal de biologie buccale
0301-3952
1973-1992   0400336

J Biol Chem
The Journal of biological chemistry
0021-9258   1083-351X
1905   2985121R

J Biol Dyn
Journal of biological dynamics
1751-3758   1751-3766
2007   101299725

J Biol Inorg Chem
Journal of biological inorganic chemistry:
JBIC: a publication of the Society of
Biological Inorganic Chemistry
0949-8257   1432-1327
1996   9616326

J Biol Photogr
Journal of biological photography
0274-497X
Continues: Journal of the Biological
Photographic Association. Absorbed by:
Journal of biocommunication. 2000
1980-1999   8006504

J Biol Photogr Assoc
Journal of the Biological Photographic
Association
0006-3215
Continued by: Journal of biological
photography.
1932-1979   7503073

J Biol Regul Homeost Agents
Journal of biological regulators and
homeostatic agents
0393-974X
1987   8809253

J Biol Response Mod
Journal of biological response modifiers
0732-6580
Continued by: Journal of immunotherapy.
1982-1990   8219656

J Biol Rhythms
Journal of biological rhythms
0748-7304
1986   8700115

J Biol Stand
Journal of biological standardization
0092-1157
Continued by: Biologicals.
1973-1989   0400335

J Biolumin Chemilumin
Journal of bioluminescence and
chemiluminescence
0884-3996
Continued by: Luminescence.
1986-1998   8612490

J Biomater Appl
Journal of biomaterials applications
0885-3282
1986   8813912

J Biomater Dent
Journal de biomatériaux dentaires:
[publication du Collège français de
biomatériaux dentaires]
0295-6195
1985-2002   8612237

J Biomater Sci Polym Ed
Journal of biomaterials science. Polymer
edition
0920-5063
1989   9007393

J Biomech
Journal of biomechanics
0021-9290
1968   0157375

J Biomech Eng
Journal of biomechanical engineering
0148-0731
1977   7909584

J Biomed Biotechnol
Journal of biomedicine & biotechnology
1110-7243   1110-7251
2001   101135740

J Biomed Eng
Journal of biomedical engineering
0141-5425
Continued by: Medical engineering &
physics.
1979-1993   7906074

J Biomed Inform
Journal of biomedical informatics
1532-0464   1532-0480
Continues: Computers and biomedical
research.
2001   100970413

J Biomed Mater Res
Journal of biomedical materials research
0021-9304   1097-4636
Absorbed: Journal of applied biomaterials.
1996 Split into: Journal of biomedical
materials research. Part A; and: Journal
of biomedical materials research. Part B,
Applied biomaterials.
1967-2002   0112726

J Biomed Mater Res A
Journal of biomedical materials research.
Part A
1549-3296   1552-4965
Continues in part: Journal of biomedical
materials research.
2003   101234237

J Biomed Mater Res B Appl Biomater
Journal of biomedical materials research.
Part B, Applied biomaterials
1552-4973   1552-4981
Continues in part: Journal of biomedical
materials research.
2003   101234238

J Biomed Opt
Journal of biomedical optics
1083-3668
1996   9605853

J Biomed Sci
Journal of biomedical science
1021-7770   1423-0127
1994   9421567

J Biomol NMR
Journal of biomolecular NMR
0925-2738   1573-5001
1991   9110829

J Biomol Screen
Journal of biomolecular screening:
the official journal of the Society for
Biomolecular Screening
1087-0571
1996   9612112

J Biomol Struct Dyn
Journal of biomolecular structure &
dynamics
0739-1102   1538-0254
1983   8404176

J Biomol Tech
Journal of biomolecular techniques: JBT
1524-0215   1943-4731
Absorbed: ABRF news.
1998   100888641

J Biopharm Stat
Journal of biopharmaceutical statistics
1054-3406   1520-5711
1991   9200436

J Biophys Biochem Cytol
The Journal of biophysical and biochemical
cytology
0095-9901
Continued by the Journal of cell biology.
1955-1961   17840020R

J Biosci
Journal of biosciences
0250-5991
Continues: Proceedings, Experimental
Biology Section.
1979   8100809

J Biosci Bioeng
Journal of bioscience and bioengineering
1389-1723   1347-4421
Continues: Journal of fermentation and
bioengineering.
1999   100888800

J Biosoc Sci
Journal of biosocial science
0021-9320   1469-7599
1969   0177346

J Biosoc Sci Suppl
Journal of biosocial science. Supplement
0300-9645
1969-1989   0235416

J Biotechnol
Journal of biotechnology
0168-1656
1984   8411927

J Bodyw Mov Ther
Journal of bodywork and movement
therapies
1360-8592   1532-9283
1996   9700068

J Bone Joint Surg Am
The Journal of bone and joint surgery.
American volume
0021-9355   1535-1386
Continues in part: Journal of bone and joint
surgery.
1948   0014030

J Bone Joint Surg Br
The Journal of bone and joint surgery.
British volume
0301-620X
Continues in part: Journal of bone and joint
surgery.
1948   0375355

J Bone Miner Metab
Journal of bone and mineral metabolism
0914-8779   1435-5604
Continues in part: Nihon Kotsu Taisha Gakkai
zasshi. Absorbed: Nihon Kotsu Keisoku
Gakkai zasshi.
1988   9436705

J Bone Miner Res
Journal of bone and mineral research: the
official journal of the American Society for
Bone and Mineral Research
0884-0431   1523-4681
1986   8610640

J Bowman Gray Sch Med Wake For Coll
Journal. Bowman Gray School of Medicine
0099-6653
Continued by: Research and reviews.
1943-1961   0106577

J Br Endod Soc
Journal of the British Endodontic Society
0007-0653
Continued by International endodontic
journal.
1967-1979   7507181

J Br Menopause Soc
The journal of the British Menopause
Society
1362-1807
Continued by: Menopause international.
1995-2006   9815771

J Bras Doencas Torac
Jornal brasileiro de doenças torácicas
0047-2069
Supersedes the Revista brasileira de
tuberculose e doenças torácicas.
1965-1968   0071033

J Bras Med
Jornal brasileiro de medicina
0047-2077
Continued by JBM; jornal brasileiro de
medicina.
1959-1962   0173113

J Bras Neurol
Jornal brasileiro de neurologia
0021-7514
1949-1964   0077540

J Bras Pneumol
Jornal brasileiro de pneumologia:
publicaçaÃ£o oficial da Sociedade Brasileira
de Pneumologia e Tisiologia
1806-3713   1806-3756
Continues: Jornal de pneumologia.
2004   101222274

J Bras Psiquiatr
Jornal brasileiro de psiquiatria
0047-2085
Supersedes the Anais of the Instituto de
Psiquiatria, Universidade do Brasil.
1948   0413673

J BUON
Journal of B.U.ON.: official journal of the
Balkan Union of Oncology
1107-0625
199u   100883428

J Burn Care Rehabil
The Journal of burn care & rehabilitation
0273-8481
Continued by: Journal of burn care &
research.
1980-2005   8110188

J Burn Care Res
Journal of burn care & research: official
publication of the American Burn
Association
1559-047X   1559-0488
Continues: Journal of burn care &
rehabilitation.
2006   101262774

J Bus Strategy
The Journal of business strategy
0275-6668
Absorbed: Journal of European business.
1980   9879872

J Calif Dent Assoc
Journal - California Dental Association
0008-0977
Continues Journal of the California State
Dental Association and the Nevada State
Dental Society. Superseded by CDA Journal.
1961-1973   7507164

J Calif Dent Assoc
Journal of the California Dental Association
1043-2256
Continues: CDA journal.
1988   8905668

J Calif State Dent Assoc Nev State Dent Soc
The journal of the California State Dental
Association and the Nevada State Dental
Society
0099-4502
Continues: Bulletin of the California State
Dental Association. Continued by: Journal -
California Dental Association.
1917-1960   16020250R

J Can Assoc Radiol
Journal of the Canadian Association of
Radiologists
0008-2902
Continued by: Canadian Association of
Radiologists journal.
1950-1985   7505589

J Can Dent Assoc
Journal (Canadian Dental Association)
0709-8936   1488-2159
Continues: Dental journal.
1979   7907605

J Can Dent Assoc (Tor)
Journal of the Canadian Dental Association
0008-3372
  Supersedes: Dominion dental journal.
  Absorbed: Bulletin. Canadian Dental
  Association. Continued by: Dental journal.
  1935-1973   **7505590**

J Can Diet Assoc
Journal of the Canadian Dietetic Association
0008-3399
  Continued by: Canadian journal of dietetic
  practice and research.
  1939-1998   **0415554**

J Cancer Educ
Journal of cancer education: the official
journal of the American Association for
Cancer Education
0885-8195   1543-0154
  1986   **8610343**

J Cancer Epidemiol Prev
Journal of cancer epidemiology and
prevention
1476-6647   1476-6655
  Continues: Journal of epidemiology and
  biostatistics.
  2002-2002   **101141610**

J Cancer Res Clin Oncol
Journal of cancer research and clinical
oncology
0171-5216
  Continues Zeitschrift für Krebsforschung und
  klinische Onkologie. Cancer research and
  clinical oncology.
  1979   **7902060**

J Cancer Res Ther
Journal of cancer research and therapeutics
0973-1482   1998-4138
  2005   **101249598**

J Cancer Surviv
Journal of cancer survivorship: research
and practice
1932-2259   1932-2267
  2007   **101307557**

J CANNT
Le Journal CANNT = CANNT journal:
the journal of the Canadian Association of
Nephrology Nurses and Technicians
1483-698X
  Continued by: CANNT Journal.
  1990-1995   **9013563**

J Capill Electrophor Microchip Technol
Journal of capillary electrophoresis and
microchip technology
  Continues: Journal of capillary
  electrophoresis.
  1999   **101294946**

J Capillary Electrophor
Journal of capillary electrophoresis
1079-5383
  Continued by: Journal of capillary
  electrophoresis and microchip technology.
  1994-1998   **9507610**

J Card Fail
Journal of cardiac failure
1071-9164   1532-8414
  1994   **9442138**

J Card Surg
Journal of cardiac surgery
0886-0440   1540-8191
  1986   **8908809**

J Cardiogr
Journal of cardiography
0386-2887
  Continues Rinsho shin'onzu. Cardiovascular
  sound bulletin. Continued by: Journal of
  cardiology.
  1976-1986   **7801085**

J Cardiogr Suppl
Journal of cardiography. Supplement
0386-2887
  Continued by: Journal of cardiology.
  Supplement. Supplement to: Journal of
  cardiography.
  1984-1987   **9002200**

J Cardiol
Journal of cardiology
0914-5087
  Supplement to v. for 1987-1994? have its
  own numbering system and was cataloged
  separately: supplement to v. for 1995?-
  included in the numbering of the journal.
  1987   **8804703**

J Cardiol Suppl
Journal of cardiology. Supplement
  Continues: Journal of cardiography.
  Supplement. Absorbed by: Journal of
  cardiology.
  1987-1994   **9001403**

J Cardiometab Syndr
Journal of the cardiometabolic syndrome
1559-4564   1559-4572
  2006   **101284690**

J Cardiopulm Rehabil
Journal of cardiopulmonary rehabilitation
0883-9212   1539-0691
  Continues: Journal of cardiac rehabilitation.
  Continued by: Journal of cardiopulmonary
  rehabilitation and prevention.
  1985-2006   **8511296**

J Cardiopulm Rehabil Prev
Journal of cardiopulmonary rehabilitation
and prevention
1932-7501   1932-751X
  Continues: Journal of cardiopulmonary
  rehabilitation.
  2007   **101291247**

J Cardiothorac Anesth
Journal of cardiothoracic anesthesia
0888-6296
  Continued by: Journal of cardiothoracic and
  vascular anesthesia.
  1987-1990   **8709732**

J Cardiothorac Surg
Journal of cardiothoracic surgery
                                             1749-8090
  2006   **101265113**

J Cardiothorac Vasc Anesth
Journal of cardiothoracic and vascular
anesthesia
1053-0770   1532-8422
  Continues: Journal of cardiothoracic
  anesthesia.
  1991   **9110208**

J Cardiovasc Comput Tomogr
Journal of cardiovascular computed
tomography
1934-5925   1876-861X
  2007   **101308347**

J Cardiovasc Electrophysiol
Journal of cardiovascular electrophysiology
1045-3873   1540-8167
  Continues: Journal of electrophysiology.
  1990   **9010756**

J Cardiovasc Magn Reson
Journal of cardiovascular magnetic
resonance: official journal of the Society for
Cardiovascular Magnetic Resonance
1097-6647   1532-429X
  Absorbed: Critical reviews in computed
  tomography.
  1998   **9815616**

J Cardiovasc Med (Hagerstown)
Journal of cardiovascular medicine
(Hagerstown, Md.)
1558-2027   1558-2035
  Continues: Italian heart journal.
  2006   **101259752**

J Cardiovasc Nurs
The Journal of cardiovascular nursing
0889-4655   1550-5049
  1986   **8703516**

J Cardiovasc Pharmacol
Journal of cardiovascular pharmacology
0160-2446   1533-4023
  1979   **7902492**

J Cardiovasc Pharmacol Ther
Journal of cardiovascular pharmacology
and therapeutics
1074-2484   1940-4034
  1996   **9602617**

J Cardiovasc Risk
Journal of cardiovascular risk
1350-6277
  Continued by: European journal of
  cardiovascular prevention and rehabilitation.
  1994-2003   **9436980**

J Cardiovasc Surg (Torino)
The Journal of cardiovascular surgery
0021-9509
  1960   **0066127**

J Case Manag
Journal of case management
1061-3706
  Merged with: Journal of long term home
  health care. to form: Care management
  journals.
  1992-1998   **9301156**

J Cataract Refract Surg
Journal of cataract and refractive surgery
0886-3350
  Absorbed: European journal of implant
  and refractive surgery. Continues: Journal -
  American Intra-Ocular Implant Society.
  1986   **8604171**

J Cathol Nurses Guild Engl Wales
Journal of the Catholic Nurses Guild of
England and Wales
19uu   **9880621**

J Cell Biochem
Journal of cellular biochemistry
0730-2312   1097-4644
  Continues: Journal of supramolecular
  structure and cellular biochemistry.
  1982   **8205768**

J Cell Biochem Suppl
Journal of cellular biochemistry.
Supplement
0733-1959
  Continues: Journal of supramolecular
  structure and cellular biochemistry.
  Supplement.
  1982   **8207539**

J Cell Biol
The Journal of cell biology
0021-9525   1540-8140
  Continues the Journal of biophysical and
  biochemical cytology.
  1962   **0375356**

J Cell Comp Physiol
Journal of cellular and comparative physiology
0095-9898
Continued by Journal of cellular physiology.
1932-1965 0165540

J Cell Mol Med
Journal of cellular and molecular medicine
1582-1838
Continues: Journal of medicine and biochemistry.
2000 101083777

J Cell Physiol
Journal of cellular physiology
0021-9541 1097-4652
Continues Journal of Cellular and comparative physiology.
1966 0050222

J Cell Physiol Suppl
Journal of cellular physiology. Supplement
0737-1462
1982-1987 8300145

J Cell Sci
Journal of cell science
0021-9533 1477-9137
Supersedes the Quarterly journal of microscopical science.
1966 0052457

J Cell Sci Suppl
Journal of cell science. Supplement
0269-3518
1984-1995 8502898

J Cereb Blood Flow Metab
Journal of cerebral blood flow and metabolism: official journal of the International Society of Cerebral Blood Flow and Metabolism
0271-678X 1559-7016
1981 8112566

J Charles H. Tweed Int Found
Journal of the Charles H. Tweed International Foundation
0885-3517
Continues: Journal of the Charles H. Tweed Foundation. Continued by: Bulletin of the Charles H. Tweed International Foundation.
1981-1992 9880032

J Chem Doc
Journal of chemical documentation
0021-9576
Continued by: Journal of chemical information and computer sciences.
1961-1974 7505011

J Chem Ecol
Journal of chemical ecology
0098-0331 1573-1561
1975 7505563

J Chem Educ
Journal of chemical education
0021-9584
1924 2985122R

J Chem Inf Comput Sci
Journal of chemical information and computer sciences
0095-2338
Continues: Journal of chemical documentation. Continued by: Journal of chemical information and modeling.
1975-2004 7505012

J Chem Inf Model
Journal of chemical information and modeling
1549-9596 1549-960X
Continues: Journal of chemical information and computer sciences.
2005 101230060

J Chem Neuroanat
Journal of chemical neuroanatomy
0891-0618
1988 8902615

J Chem Phys
The Journal of chemical physics
0021-9606 1089-7690
1933 0375360

J Chem Soc
Journal of the Chemical Society
Supersedes the society's Memoirs and proceedings.
1847-1965 7507187

J Chem Soc [Perkin 1]
Journal of the Chemical Society. Perkin transactions 1
0300-922X
Continues: Journal of the Chemical Society. C: Organic. Absorbed: Contemporary organic synthesis. Jan. 7, 1998 Absorbed in part: Acta chemica Scandinavica (Copenhapen, Denmark: 1989). Continued by: Perkin 1.
1972-1999 7505598

J Chem Technol Biotechnol
Journal of chemical technology and biotechnology (Oxford, Oxfordshire: 1986)
0268-2575
Formed by the union of: Journal of chemical technology and biotechnology. Chemical technology, and: Journal of chemical technology and biotechnology. Biotechnology.
1986 8711102

J Chemother
Journal of chemotherapy (Florence, Italy)
1120-009X 1973-9478
1989 8907348

J Chiba Med Soc
Chiba Igakkai zasshi. The Journal of Chiba Medical Society
0009-3459
Supersedes Chiba Igaku Senmongakko zasshi. Continued by Chiba igaku zasshi.
1923-1973 0425641

J Child Adolesc Psychiatr Ment Health Nurs
Journal of child and adolescent psychiatric and mental health nursing
0897-9685
Continued by: Journal of child and adolescent psychiatric nursing.
1988-1993 8812165

J Child Adolesc Psychiatr Nurs
Journal of child and adolescent psychiatric nursing: official publication of the Association of Child and Adolescent Psychiatric Nurses, Inc
1073-6077 1774-6171
Continues: Journal of child and adolescent psychiatric and mental health nursing.
1994 9431738

J Child Adolesc Psychopharmacol
Journal of child and adolescent psychopharmacology
1044-5463 1557-8992
1990 9105358

J Child Asthma Res Inst Hosp Denver
Journal. Children's Asthma Research Institute and Hospital, Denver
1961-1961 0006601

J Child Fam Nurs
Journal of child and family nursing
1098-7134
1998-2001 9892302

J Child Health Care
Journal of child health care: for professionals working with children in the hospital and community
1367-4935
1997 9806360

J Child Lang
Journal of child language
0305-0009
1974 0425743

J Child Neurol
Journal of child neurology
0883-0738 1708-8283
1986 8606714

J Child Psychiatry
The Journal of child psychiatry
1947-1956 17840100R

J Child Psychol Psychiatry
Journal of child psychology and psychiatry, and allied disciplines
0021-9630 1469-7610
1960 0375361

J Child Sex Abus
Journal of child sexual abuse
1053-8712 1547-0679
1992 9301157

J Chin Med Assoc
Journal of the Chinese Medical Association: JCMA
1726-4901
Continues: Zhonghua yi xue za zhi.
2003 101174817

J Chir (Paris)
Journal de chirurgie
0021-7697
Absorbed: Annales de chirurgie.
1908 0374754

J Christ Nurs
Journal of Christian nursing: a quarterly publication of Nurses Christian Fellowship
0743-2550
1984 8411743

J Chromatogr
Journal of chromatography
0021-9673
Absorbed: Chromatographic reviews. Split into: Journal of chromatography. A, Oct. 15, 1993; and: Journal of chromatography. B, Biomedical applications, Jan. 14, 1994.
1958-1994 0427043

J Chromatogr A
Journal of chromatography. A
0021-9673
Continues in part: Journal of chromatography.
1993 9318488

J Chromatogr B Analyt Technol Biomed Life Sci
Journal of chromatography. B, Analytical technologies in the biomedical and life sciences
1570-0232
Continues: Journal of chromatography. B, Biomedical sciences and applications.
2002 101139554

J Chromatogr B Biomed Appl
Journal of chromatography. B, Biomedical applications
1572-6495
Continues in part: Journal of chromatography. Continued by: Journal of chromatography. B, Biomedical sciences and applications.
1994-1996 9421796

J Chromatogr B Biomed Sci Appl
Journal of chromatography. B, Biomedical
sciences and applications
1387-2273
Continues: Journal of chromatography. B,
Biomedical applications. Continued by:
Journal of chromatography. B. Analytical
technologies in the biomedical and life
sciences.
1997-2001 9714109

J Chromatogr Sci
Journal of chromatographic science
0021-9665
Continues Journal of gas chromatography.
1969 0173225

J Chromatogr Suppl
Journal of chromatography. Supplementary
volume
0376-737X
1968-1976 7610816

J Chronic Dis
Journal of chronic diseases
0021-9681
Continues: American journal of syphilis,
gonorrhea, and venereal diseases. Continued
by: Journal of clinical epidemiology.
1955-1987 2985123R

J Clin Anesth
Journal of clinical anesthesia
0952-8180
1988 8812166

J Clin Apher
Journal of clinical apheresis
0733-2459 1098-1101
1982 8216305

J Clin Chem Clin Biochem
Journal of clinical chemistry and clinical
biochemistry. Zeitschrift für klinische
Chemie und klinische Biochemie
0340-076X
Continues Zeitschrift für klinische Chemie
und klinische Biochemie. Continued by:
European journal of clinical chemistry and
clinical biochemistry.
1976-1990 7701860

J Clin Child Adolesc Psychol
Journal of clinical child and adolescent
psychology: the official journal for the
Society of Clinical Child and Adolescent
Psychology, American Psychological
Association, Division 53
1537-4416 1537-4424
Continues: Journal of clinical child
psychology.
2002 101133858

J Clin Child Psychol
Journal of clinical child psychology
0047-228X
Supersedes Clinical child psychology
newsletter. Continued by: Journal of clinical
child and adolescent psychology.
1971-2001 7603095

J Clin Comput
Journal of clinical computing
0090-1091
1971-1999 0351310

J Clin Densitom
Journal of clinical densitometry: the official
journal of the International Society for
Clinical Densitometry
1094-6950
1998 9808212

J Clin Dent
The Journal of clinical dentistry
0895-8831
1988 8904411

J Clin Dysmorphol
The Journal of clinical dysmorphology
0736-4407
Continues: Syndrome identification.
Continued by: Dysmorphology and clinical
genetics.
1983-1985 8400758

J Clin Endocrinol Metab
The Journal of clinical endocrinology and
metabolism
0021-972X
Absorbed in part: Transactions of the
American Goiter Association. American
Goiter Association. Continues: Journal of
clinical endocrinology.
1952 0375362

J Clin Eng
Journal of clinical engineering
0363-8855
1976 7703941

J Clin Epidemiol
Journal of clinical epidemiology
0895-4356 1878-5921
Continues: Journal of chronic diseases.
1988 8801383

J Clin Ethics
The Journal of clinical ethics
1046-7890
1990 9114645

J Clin Exp Hematop
Journal of clinical and experimental
hematopathology: JCEH
1346-4280 1880-9952
Continues in part: Nihon Rinpa Mōnaikei
Gakkai kaishi.
2001 101141257

J Clin Exp Neuropsychol
Journal of clinical and experimental
neuropsychology
1380-3395 1744-411X
Continues: Journal of clinical
neuropsychology.
1985 8502170

J Clin Exp Psychopathol
Journal of clinical and experimental
psychopathology
Continues Journal of criminal
psychopathology.
1944-1953 17840130R

**J Clin Exp Psychopathol Q Rev Psychiatry
Neurol**
Journal of clinical and experimental
psychopathology & quarterly review of
psychiatry and neurology
0447-9122
1954-1962 17840140R

J Clin Forensic Med
Journal of clinical forensic medicine
1353-1131
Continues: Police surgeon. Continued by:
Journal of forensic and legal medicine.
1994-2006 9434927

J Clin Gastroenterol
Journal of clinical gastroenterology
0192-0790 1539-2031
1979 7910017

J Clin Hosp Pharm
Journal of clinical and hospital pharmacy
0143-3180
Continues Journal of clinical pharmacy.
Continued by: Journal of clinical pharmacy
and therapeutics.
1980-1986 8006505

J Clin Hypertens
Journal of clinical hypertension
0748-450X
Continued by: American journal of
hypertension.
1985-1987 8510461

J Clin Hypertens (Greenwich)
Journal of clinical hypertension (Greenwich,
Conn.)
1524-6175
1999 100888554

J Clin Immunol
Journal of clinical immunology
0271-9142
1981 8102137

J Clin Invest
The Journal of clinical investigation
0021-9738 1558-8238
Continued in part by: Clinical research.
1924 7802877

J Clin Lab Anal
Journal of clinical laboratory analysis
0887-8013 1098-2825
Absorbed: Diagnostic and clinical
immunology in 1989.
1987 8801384

J Clin Lab Immunol
Journal of clinical & laboratory immunology
0141-2760
1978 7808987

J Clin Laser Med Surg
Journal of clinical laser medicine & surgery
1044-5471
Continues: Laser medicine & surgery news.
Continued by: Photomedicine and laser
surgery.
1990-2004 9006547

J Clin Microbiol
Journal of clinical microbiology
0095-1137 1098-660X
1975 7505564

J Clin Monit
Journal of clinical monitoring
0748-1977
Merged with: International journal of clinical
monitoring and computing, to form: Journal
of clinical monitoring and computing.
1985-1997 8506707

J Clin Monit Comput
Journal of clinical monitoring and
computing
1387-1307
Merger of: International journal of clinical
monitoring and computing; and: Journal of
clinical monitoring.
1998 9806357

J Clin Neuromuscul Dis
Journal of clinical neuromuscular disease
1522-0443 1537-1611
1999 100887391

J Clin Neuroophthalmol
Journal of clinical neuro-ophthalmology
0272-846X
Continued by: Journal of neuro-
ophthalmology.
1981-1993 8109051

J Clin Neurophysiol
Journal of clinical neurophysiology:
official publication of the American
Electroencephalographic Society
0736-0258 1537-1603
Continues: Journal of the American EEG
Society.
1984 8506708

J Clin Neuropsychol
Journal of clinical neuropsychology
0165-0475
Continued by Journal of clinical and experimental neuropsychology.
1979-1984   8002260

J Clin Neurosci
Journal of clinical neuroscience: official journal of the Neurosurgical Society of Australasia
0967-5868
1994   9433352

J Clin Nurs
Journal of clinical nursing
0962-1067   1365-2702
Continued in part by: International journal of older people nursing.
1992   9207302

J Clin Nutr
The Journal of clinical nutrition
0095-9871
Continued by: American journal of clinical nutrition.
1952-1954   17840170R

J Clin Oncol
Journal of clinical oncology: official journal of the American Society of Clinical Oncology
0732-183X   1527-7755
1983   8309333

J Clin Orthod
Journal of clinical orthodontics: JCO
0022-3875
Continues: JPO.
1970   0243471

J Clin Pathol
Journal of clinical pathology
0021-9746   1472-4146
Absorbed: Molecular pathology. 2004
1947   0376601

J Clin Pathol Suppl (Assoc Clin Pathol)
Journal of clinical pathology. Supplement (Association of Clinical Pathologists)
0144-0349
1967-1980   0217241

J Clin Pathol Suppl (R Coll Pathol)
Journal of clinical pathology. Supplement (Royal College of Pathologists)
0144-0330
Continues: Journal of clinical pathology. Supplement (College of Pathologists).
1970-1980   8300543

J Clin Pathol Suppl Coll Pathol
Journal of clinical pathology. Supplement (College of Pathologists)
Continued by: Journal of clinical pathology. Supplement (Royal College of Pathologists).
1967-1969   101273195

J Clin Pediatr Dent
The Journal of clinical pediatric dentistry
1053-4628   1557-5268
Continues: Journal of pedodontics.
1990   9100079

J Clin Periodontol
Journal of clinical periodontology
0303-6979   1600-051X
1974   0425123

J Clin Pharm Ther
Journal of clinical pharmacy and therapeutics
0269-4727   1365-2710
Continues: Journal of clinical and hospital pharmacy.
1987   8704308

J Clin Pharmacol
Journal of clinical pharmacology
0091-2700   1552-4604
Continues Journal of clinical pharmacology and new drugs.
1973   0366372

J Clin Pharmacol J New Drugs
The Journal of clinical pharmacology and the journal of new drugs
0095-9863
Continues the Journal of new drugs. Continued by the Journal of clinical pharmacology and new drugs.
1967-1970   1255670

J Clin Pharmacol New Drugs
The Journal of clinical pharmacology and new drugs
0021-9754
Continues the Journal of clinical pharmacology and the journal of new drugs. Continued by the Journal of clinical pharmacology.
1971-1973   0366131

J Clin Psychiatry
The Journal of clinical psychiatry
0160-6689   1555-2101
Continues Diseases of the nervous system.
1978   7801243

J Clin Psychol
Journal of clinical psychology
0021-9762   1097-4679
Absorbed: In session (New York, N.Y.: 1995). Mar. 1999
1945   0217132

J Clin Psychol Med Settings
Journal of clinical psychology in medical settings
1068-9583   1573-3572
1994   9435680

J Clin Psychopharmacol
Journal of clinical psychopharmacology
0271-0749   1533-712X
1981   8109496

J Clin Rheumatol
Journal of clinical rheumatology: practical reports on rheumatic & musculoskeletal diseases
1076-1608   1536-7355
1995   9518034

J Clin Sleep Med
Journal of clinical sleep medicine: JCSM: official publication of the American Academy of Sleep Medicine
1550-9389   1550-9397
2005   101231977

J Clin Stomatol Conf
Journal of clinical stomatology conferences
1960-1966   17840200R

J Clin Ultrasound
Journal of clinical ultrasound: JCU
0091-2751   1097-0096
1973   0401663

J Clin Virol
Journal of clinical virology: the official publication of the Pan American Society for Clinical Virology
1386-6532
Continues: Clinical and diagnostic virology.
1998   9815671

J Cogn Neurosci
Journal of cognitive neuroscience
0898-929X   1530-8898
1989   8910747

J Coll Gen Pract
The Journal of the College of General Practitioners
0307-4749
Continues: Journal of the College of General Practitioners and research newsletter. Continued by: Journal of the Royal College of General Practitioners.
1960-1967   7503074

J Coll Physicians Surg Pak
Journal of the College of Physicians and Surgeons--Pakistan: JCPSP
1022-386X
1991   9606447

J Coll Radiol Australas
Journal of the College of Radiologists of Australasia
0374-8545
Continues Proceedings of the College of Radiologists of Australasia. Continued by Australasian radiology.
1960-1965   7507190

J Collect Negotiations Public Sect
Journal of collective negotiations in the public sector
0047-2301
1972   9877813

J Colloid Interface Sci
Journal of colloid and interface science
0021-9797   1095-7103
Continues Journal of colloid science.
1966   0043125

J Colloid Sci
Journal of colloid science
0095-8522
Continued by the Journal of colloid and interface science.
1946-1965   17840210R

J Colo Dent Assoc
Journal of the Colorado Dental Association
0010-1559
Continues the Journal of the Colorado State Dental Association.
1962   7507191

J Colo State Dent Assoc
Journal. Colorado State Dental Association
Continues the association's Bulletin. Continued by: Journal of the Colorado Dental Association.
1935-1962   16320380R

J Comb Chem
Journal of combinatorial chemistry
1520-4766   1520-4774
1999   100886263

J Commun
The Journal of communication
0021-9916
1951   0222527

J Commun Dis
The Journal of communicable diseases
0019-5138
Supersedes the Bulletin of the Indian Society for Malaria and Other Communicable Diseases.
1969   0261652

J Commun Disord
Journal of communication disorders
0021-9924   1460-6984
1967   0260316

J Community Health
Journal of community health
0094-5145
1975   7600747

J Community Health Nurs
Journal of community health nursing
0737-0016   1532-7655
1984   8411341

J Community Psychol
Journal of community psychology
0090-4392
  Supersedes in part Journal of clinical
  psychology.
1973   0367033

J Comp Neurol
The Journal of comparative neurology
0021-9967   1096-9861
  Continues: Journal of comparative neurology
  and psychology.
1911   0406041

J Comp Pathol
Journal of comparative pathology
0021-9975
  Continues the Journal of comparative
  pathology and therapeutics.
1965   0102444

J Comp Physiol A Neuroethol Sens Neural Behav Physiol
Journal of comparative physiology. A,
Neuroethology, sensory, neural, and
behavioral physiology
0340-7594
  Continues: Journal of comparative
  physiology. A. Sensory, neural, and
  behavioral physiology.
2001   101141792

J Comp Physiol Psychol
Journal of comparative and physiological
psychology
0021-9940
  Continues: Journal of comparative
  psychology. Split into: Journal of comparative
  psychology (Washington, D.C.: 1983) and:
  Behavioral neuroscience.
1947-1982   0414612

J Comp Physiol [A]
Journal of comparative physiology. A,
Sensory, neural, and behavioral physiology
0340-7594
  Continues in part: Journal of comparative
  physiology. Continued by: Journal of
  comparative physiology. A. Neuroethology,
  sensory. neural, and behavioral physiology.
1984-2001   8413199

J Comp Physiol [B]
Journal of comparative physiology. B,
Biochemical, systemic, and environmental
physiology
0174-1578
  Continues in part: Journal of comparative
  physiology.
1984   8413200

J Comp Psychol
Journal of comparative psychology
(Washington, D.C.: 1983)
0735-7036
  Continues in part: Journal of comparative and
  physiological psychology.
1983   8309850

J Compliance Health Care
The Journal of compliance in health care:
JCHC
0887-6509
1986-1989   8610641

J Comput Aided Mol Des
Journal of computer-aided molecular design
0920-654X
1987   8710425

J Comput Assist Tomogr
Journal of computer assisted tomography
0363-8715   1532-3145
1977   7703942

J Comput Biol
Journal of computational biology: a journal
of computational molecular cell biology
1066-5277   1557-8666
1994   9433358

J Comput Chem
Journal of computational chemistry
0192-8651   1096-987X
1980   9878362

J Comput Neurosci
Journal of computational neuroscience
0929-5313   1573-6873
1994   9439510

J Comput Tomogr
The Journal of computed tomography
0149-936X
  Continues: Computed axial tomography.
  Continued by: Clinical imaging.
1978-1988   7805373

J Conf Workshop
Journalism Conference And Workshop
1978-1988   9880680

J Conn State Dent Assoc
Journal - Connecticut State Dental
Association
0010-6232
  Continues the Bulletin of the Connecticut
  State Dental Association, issued 1925-May
  1948? (Material for 1948-51 issued in the
  New England dental journal).
1952-1999   7507166

J Consult Clin Psychol
Journal of consulting and clinical psychology
0022-006X   1939-2117
  Continues: Journal of consulting psychology.
1968   0136553

J Consult Psychol
Journal of consulting psychology
0095-8891
  Supersedes: Consulting psychologist.
  Continued by: Journal of consulting and
  clinical psychology.
1937-1967   0136646

J Contam Hydrol
Journal of contaminant hydrology
0169-7722
1986   8805644

J Contemp Dent Pract
The journal of contemporary dental practice
                             1526-3711
1999   101090552

J Contemp Health Law Policy
The Journal of contemporary health law
and policy
0882-1046
1985   8510462

J Contin Educ Health Prof
The Journal of continuing education in the
health professions
0894-1912   1708-8321
  Continues: Möbius.
1988   8805847

J Contin Educ Nurs
Journal of continuing education in nursing
0022-0124
1970   0262321

J Contra Costa Dent Soc
Journal / Contra Costa Dental Society
  Continues: Bulletin Of The Contra Costa
  Dental Society.
1968-1984   9883807

J Control Release
Journal of controlled release: official journal
of the Controlled Release Society
0168-3659   1873-4995
1984   8607908

J Cosmet Dermatol
Journal of cosmetic dermatology
1473-2130   1473-2165
2002   101130964

J Cosmet Laser Ther
Journal of cosmetic and laser therapy:
official publication of the European Society
for Laser Dermatology
1476-4172   1476-4180
  Continues: Journal of cutaneous laser therapy.
2001   101136419

J Cosmet Sci
Journal of cosmetic science
1525-7886
  Continues: Journal of the Society of Cosmetic
  Chemists.
1998   9814276

J Craniofac Genet Dev Biol
Journal of craniofacial genetics and
developmental biology
0270-4145
  Merged with: Clinical orthodontics and
  research. to form: Orthodontics & craniofacial
  research.
1981-2000   8109845

J Craniofac Genet Dev Biol Suppl
Journal of craniofacial genetics and
developmental biology. Supplement
0890-6661
1985-1986   8508398

J Craniofac Surg
The Journal of craniofacial surgery
1049-2275   1536-3732
1990   9010410

J Craniomandib Disord
Journal of craniomandibular disorders:
facial & oral pain
0890-2739
  Continued by: Journal of orofacial pain.
1987-1992   8709733

J Craniomandibular Pract
The Journal of cranio-mandibular practice
0734-5410
  Continued by: Cranio.
1982-1984   8301363

J Craniomaxillofac Surg
Journal of cranio-maxillo-facial surgery:
official publication of the European
Association for Cranio-Maxillo-Facial
Surgery
1010-5182
  Continues: Journal of maxillofacial surgery.
1987   8704309

J Craniomaxillofac Trauma
The Journal of cranio-maxillofacial trauma
1074-3219
1995-2001   9513587

J Crim Law Criminol (1931)
The Journal of criminal law and criminology, including the American journal of police science
0885-2731
Continues: Journal of the American Institute of Criminal Law and Criminology. Absorbed the American journal of police science in July 1932 and includes in v. 27 an index to material on police science in both periodicals from 1930-37. Continued by: Journal of criminal law, criminology, and police science.
1931-1951   17910010R

J Crit Care
Journal of critical care
0883-9441   1557-8615
Absorbed: Seminars in anesthesia perioperative medicine and pain.
1986   8610642

J Crit Illn
The Journal of critical illness
1040-0257
1986-2003   8608118

J Cross Cult Gerontol
Journal of cross-cultural gerontology
0169-3816
1986   8700909

J Cult Divers
Journal of cultural diversity
1071-5568
1994   9439196

J Cutan Laser Ther
Journal of cutaneous laser therapy
1462-883X
Continued by: Journal of cosmetic and laser therapy.
1999-2001   100890790

J Cutan Med Surg
Journal of cutaneous medicine and surgery
1203-4754   1615-7109
Absorbed: Medical & surgical dermatology. 2001
1996   9614685

J Cutan Pathol
Journal of cutaneous pathology
0303-6987   1600-0560
1974   0425124

J Cyclic Nucleotide Protein Phosphor Res
Journal of cyclic nucleotide and protein phosphorylation research
0746-3898
Continues: Journal of cyclic nucleotide research. Continued by: Second messengers and phosphoproteins.
1983-1987   8309334

J Cyclic Nucleotide Res
Journal of cyclic nucleotide research
0095-1544
Continued by Journal of cyclic nucleotide and protein phosphorylation research.
1975-1982   7511483

J Cyst Fibros
Journal of cystic fibrosis: official journal of the European Cystic Fibrosis Society
1569-1993
2002   101128966

J Dairy Res
The Journal of dairy research
0022-0299
1929   2985125R

J Dairy Sci
Journal of dairy science
0022-0302   1525-3198
1917   2985126R

J Deaf Stud Deaf Educ
Journal of deaf studies and deaf education
1081-4159   1465-7325
1996   9889915

J Dent
Journal of dentistry
0300-5712
Supersedes The Dental practitioner and dental record.
1972   0354422

J Dent Assoc S Afr
The Journal of the Dental Association of South Africa = Die Tydskrif van die Tandheelkundige Vereniging van Suid-Afrika
0011-8516
Continues: Dental Association of South Africa. Official journal. Continued by: SADJ.
1953-1998   7505600

J Dent Assoc Thai
The Journal of the Dental Association of Thailand
0045-9917
1949   7505601

J Dent Aux
The Journal of the dental auxiliaries, Malaya, Malaysia
0449-5144
1963-1971   0322313

J Dent Belge
Le Journal dentaire belge. Belgisch blad voor tandheelkunde
Merged with Revue belge de science dentaire to form Revue belge de médecine dentaire.
1909-1961   17820240R

J Dent Child
Journal of dentistry for children
0022-0353
Continues: Review of dentistry for children. Continued by: ASDC journal of dentistry for children.
1940-1968   0150034

J Dent Child (Chic)
Journal of dentistry for children (Chicago, Ill.)
1551-8949   1935-5068
Continues: ASDC journal of dentistry for children.
2003   101180951

J Dent Educ
Journal of dental education
0022-0337
1936   8000150

J Dent Guid Counc Handicap
Journal of the Dental Guidance Council on the Handicapped
0147-3972
Continues Bulletin of the Dental Guidance Council for Cerebral Palsy.
1975-1977   7703947

J Dent Handicap
Journal of dentistry for the handicapped
0163-8629
Merged with: Journal of hospital dental practice; and, Journal of the American Society for Geriatric Dentistry, to form: Special care in dentistry.
1974-1980   7807106

J Dent Hyg
Journal of dental hygiene: JDH / American Dental Hygienists' Association
1043-254X   1553-0205
Continues: Dental hygiene.
1988   8902616

J Dent Med
The Journal of dental medicine
0096-0241
Continued by Journal of oral medicine.
1946-1965   17910020R

J Dent Pract Adm
Journal of dental practice administration: JDPA: official publication of American Academy of Dental Practice Administration, Organization of Teachers of Dental Practice Administration, American Academy of Dental Group Practice
0741-8620
1984-1990   8410046

J Dent Que
Le Journal dentaire du Québec
0021-7999
Continued by: Journal de l'Ordre des dentistes du Québec.
1963-2006   0063015

J Dent Res
Journal of dental research
0022-0345   1544-0591
Absorbed: Critical reviews in oral biology and medicine. Continues: Journal of the Allied Dental Societies.
1919   0354343

J Dent Sch Natl Univ Iran
Journal of the Dental School, National University of Iran
1969-198u   9875626

J Dent Symp
The Journal of dental symposia
Continued by: International journal of dental symposia.
1993-1993   9416048

J Dent Technol
Journal of dental technology: the peer-reviewed publication of the National Association of Dental Laboratories
1088-3118
Continues: Trends & techniques in the contemporary dental laboratory.
1996   9610506

J Dermatol
The Journal of dermatology
0385-2407
Supersedes: Japanese journal of dermatology. Ser. B.
1974   7600545

J Dermatol Sci
Journal of dermatological science
0923-1811
1990   9011485

J Dermatol Surg
The Journal of dermatologic surgery
0097-9716
Continued by The Journal of dermatologic surgery and oncology.
1975-1976   7505013

J Dermatol Surg Oncol
The Journal of dermatologic surgery and oncology
0148-0812
Continues: Journal of dermatologic surgery. Continued by: Dermatologic surgery.
1977-1994   7707501

J Dermatolog Treat
The Journal of dermatological treatment
0954-6634   1471-1753
1989   8918133

J Dev Behav Pediatr
Journal of developmental and behavioral
pediatrics: JDBP
0196-206X   1536-7312
1980   8006933

J Dev Physiol
Journal of developmental physiology
0141-9846
1979-1993   7910737

J Diabet Complications
The Journal of diabetic complications
0891-6632
    Continues: Diabetic nephropathy. Continued
    by: Journal of diabetes and its complications.
1987-1991   8708656

J Diabetes Complications
Journal of diabetes and its complications
1056-8727   1873-460X
    Continues: Journal of diabetic complications.
1992   9204583

J Dial
Journal of dialysis
0362-8558
    Continued by Clinical and experimental
    dialysis and apheresis.
1976-1980   7612051

J Diarrhoeal Dis Res
Journal of diarrhoeal diseases research
0253-8768
    Continued by: Journal of health, population
    and nutrition.
1983-1999   8402695

J Dig Dis
Journal of digestive diseases
1751-2972   1751-2980
    Continues: Chinese journal of digestive diseases.
2007   101302699

J Digit Imaging
Journal of digital imaging: the official
journal of the Society for Computer
Applications in Radiology
0897-1889   1618-727X
1988   9100529

J Dist Columbia Dent Soc
District of Columbia Dental Society journal.
District of Columbia Dental Society
0012-4060
    Continues: Bulletin. District of Columbia
    Dental Society.
1936-1981   7507168

J Drug Educ
Journal of drug education
0047-2379
1971   1300031

J Drug Target
Journal of drug targeting
1061-186X   1029-2330
1993   9312476

J Drugs Dermatol
Journal of drugs in dermatology: JDD
1545-9616
2002   101160020

J Dtsch Dermatol Ges
Journal der Deutschen Dermatologischen
Gesellschaft = Journal of the German
Society of Dermatology: JDDG
1610-0379   1610-0387
    Continues: Zeitschrift für Hautkrankheiten.
2003   101164708

J Econ Bus
Journal of economics and business
0148-6195
    Continues: Economic and business bulletin.
1972   9878121

J Econ Entomol
Journal of economic entomology
0022-0493
1908   2985127R

J Econ Perspect
The journal of economic perspectives:
a journal of the American Economic
Association
0895-3309
1987   9885204

J Econ Soc Meas
Journal of economic and social measurement
0747-9662
    Continues: Review of public data use.
1985   9881985

J ECT
The journal of ECT
1095-0680   1533-4112
    Continues: Convulsive therapy.
1998   9808943

J Educ Psychol
Journal of education & psychology
0022-0590
1942   0047617

J Educ Psychol
Journal of educational psychology
0022-0663
1910   0135751

J Egypt Med Assoc
The Journal of the Egyptian Medical
Association
0013-2411
    Continues Revue médicale égyptienne.
1928-1994   0417734

J Egypt Natl Canc Inst
Journal of the Egyptian National Cancer
Institute
1110-0362
1982   9424566

J Egypt Public Health Assoc
The Journal of the Egyptian Public Health
Association
0013-2446
1926   7505602

J Egypt Soc Parasitol
Journal of the Egyptian Society of
Parasitology
0253-5890
1970   8102141

J Elder Abuse Negl
Journal of elder abuse & neglect
0894-6566   1540-4129
1989   8914370

J Electrocardiol
Journal of electrocardiology
0022-0736   1532-8430
1968   0153605

J Electromyogr Kinesiol
Journal of electromyography and
kinesiology: official journal of the
International Society of Electrophysiological
Kinesiology
1050-6411
1991   9109125

J Electron Microsc (Tokyo)
Journal of electron microscopy
0022-0744   1477-9986
    Absorbed: Denshi kenbikyō (Tokyo, Japan:
    1950). Continued in part by: Denshi kenbikyō
    (Tokyo, Japan: 1974).
1953   7611157

J Electron Microsc Tech
Journal of electron microscopy technique
0741-0581
    Continued by: Microscopy research and
    technique.
1984-1991   8502171

J Elisha Mitchell Sci Soc Chapel Hill N C
Journal. Elisha Mitchell Scientific Society,
Chapel Hill, N.C
0013-6220
    Continued by: Journal of the North Carolina
    Academy of Science.
1883-2001   16720410R

J Embryol Exp Morphol
Journal of embryology and experimental
morphology
0022-0752
    Continued by: Development (Cambridge,
    Cambridgeshire).
1953-1986   7906439

J Emerg Med
The Journal of emergency medicine
0736-4679   1090-1280
1983   8412174

J Emerg Nurs
Journal of emergency nursing: JEN: official
publication of the Emergency Department
Nurses Association
0099-1767   1527-2966
1975   7605913

J Endocrinol
The Journal of endocrinology
0022-0795   1479-6805
1939   0375363

J Endocrinol Invest
Journal of endocrinological investigation
0391-4097   1720-8386
1978   7806594

J Endod
Journal of endodontia
1946-1948   17910050R

J Endod
Journal of endodontics
0099-2399
1975   7511484

J Endotoxin Res
Journal of endotoxin research
0968-0519   1743-2839
    Continued by: Innate immunity.
1994-2007   9433350

J Endourol
Journal of endourology / Endourological
Society
0892-7790   1557-900X
1987   8807503

J Endovasc Surg
Journal of endovascular surgery: the official
journal of the International Society for
Endovascular Surgery
1074-6218
    Continued by: Journal of endovascular therapy.
1994-1999   9500580

J Endovasc Ther
Journal of endovascular therapy: an official
journal of the International Society of
Endovascular Specialists
1526-6028   1545-1550
    Continues: Journal of endovascular surgery.
2000   100896915

J Eng Psychol
Journal of engineering psychology
    Supersedes in part Engineering and industrial
    psychology.
1962-1966   7708242

J Enterostomal Ther
Journal of enterostomal therapy
0270-1170
Continues: ET journal. Continued by: Journal of ET nursing.
1980-1991   8003806

J Environ Biol
Journal of environmental biology / Academy of Environmental Biology, India
0254-8704
1980   8300544

J Environ Health
Journal of environmental health
0022-0892
Continues the Sanitarian's journal of environmental health.
1963   0405525

J Environ Manage
Journal of environmental management
0301-4797
1973   0401664

J Environ Monit
Journal of environmental monitoring: JEM
1464-0325   1464-0333
1999   100968688

J Environ Pathol Toxicol
Journal of environmental pathology and toxicology
0146-4779
Continued by Journal of environmental pathology, toxicology and oncology.
1977-1981   7801245

J Environ Pathol Toxicol Oncol
Journal of environmental pathology, toxicology and oncology: official organ of the International Society for Environmental Toxicology and Cancer
0731-8898
Continues: Journal of environmental pathology and toxicology.
1984   8501420

J Environ Qual
Journal of environmental quality
0047-2425
1972   0330666

J Environ Radioact
Journal of environmental radioactivity
0265-931X
1984   8508119

J Environ Sci (China)
Journal of environmental sciences (China)
1001-0742
1989   100967627

J Environ Sci Eng
Journal of environmental science & engineering
Continues: Indian journal of environmental health.
2004   101273917

J Environ Sci Health A Tox Hazard Subst Environ Eng
Journal of environmental science and health. Part A, Toxic/hazardous substances & environmental engineering
1093-4529   1532-4117
Continues: Journal of environmental science and health. Part A, Environmental science and engineering & toxic and hazardous substance control.
1998   9812551

J Environ Sci Health B
Journal of environmental science and health. Part. B, Pesticides, food contaminants, and agricultural wastes
0360-1234   1532-4109
Continues in part: Environmental letters.
1976   7607167

J Environ Sci Health C
Journal of environmental science and health. Part C: Environmental health sciences
0360-1242
Continues in part Environmental letters. Continued by Journal of environmental science and health. Part C, Environmental carcinogenesis reviews.
1978-1979   7804129

J Environ Sci Health C Environ Carcinog Ecotoxicol Rev
Journal of environmental science and health. Part C, Environmental carcinogenesis & ecotoxicology reviews
1059-0501   1532-4095
Continues: Environmental carcinogenesis reviews.
1991   9317093

J Enzyme Inhib
Journal of enzyme inhibition
8755-5093
Continued by: Journal of enzyme inhibition and medicinal chemistry.
1985-2001   8709734

J Enzyme Inhib Med Chem
Journal of enzyme inhibition and medicinal chemistry
1475-6366   1475-6374
Continues: Journal of enzyme inhibition.
2002   101150203

J Epidemiol
Journal of epidemiology / Japan Epidemiological Association
0917-5040   1349-9092
1991   9607688

J Epidemiol Biostat
Journal of epidemiology and biostatistics
1359-5229
Continued by: Journal of cancer epidemiology and prevention.
1996-2001   9611181

J Epidemiol Community Health
Journal of epidemiology and community health
0143-005X   1470-2738
Continues Epidemiology and community health.
1979   7909766

J Epidemiol Community Health
Journal of epidemiology and community health
0141-7681
Continues British journal of preventive & social medicine. Continued by Epidemiology and community health.
1978-1978   7806055

J Esthet Dent
Journal of esthetic dentistry
1040-1466
Continued by: Journal of esthetic and restorative dentistry.
1989-2000   9010411

J Esthet Restor Dent
Journal of esthetic and restorative dentistry: official publication of the American Academy of Esthetic Dentistry ... [et al.]
1496-4155   1708-8240
Continues: Journal of esthetic dentistry.
2001   101096515

J ET Nurs
Journal of ET nursing: official publication, International Association for Enterostomal Therapy
1055-3045
Continues: Journal of enterostomal therapy. Continued by: Journal of wound, ostomy, and continence nursing.
1991-1993   9109128

J Ethn Subst Abuse
Journal of ethnicity in substance abuse
1533-2640   1533-2659
Continues: Drugs & society (New York, N.Y.).
2002   101083217

J Ethnobiol Ethnomed
Journal of ethnobiology and ethnomedicine
1746-4269
2005   101245794

J Ethnopharmacol
Journal of ethnopharmacology
0378-8741
1979   7903310

J Eukaryot Microbiol
The Journal of eukaryotic microbiology
1066-5234   1550-7408
Continues: Journal of protozoology.
1993   9306405

J Eur Acad Dermatol Venereol
Journal of the European Academy of Dermatology and Venereology: JEADV
0926-9959   1468-3083
1992   9216037

J Eval Clin Pract
Journal of evaluation in clinical practice
1356-1294   1365-2753
1995   9609066

J Evid Based Dent Pract
The journal of evidence-based dental practice
1532-3382   1532-3390
2001   101083101

J Evid Based Soc Work
Journal of evidence-based social work
1543-3714   1543-3722
2004   101197676

J Evol Biol
Journal of evolutionary biology
1010-061X   1420-9101
1987   8809954

J Except Child
Journal of exceptional children
0887-5405
Continues Council review of the International Council for Exceptional Children. Continued by Exceptional children.
1935-1951   16830110R

J Existent
Journal of existentialism
0449-2498
Continues the Journal of existential psychiatry.
1964-1968   0014050

J Exp Anal Behav
Journal of the experimental analysis of behavior
0022-5002   1938-3711
1958   0203727

J Exp Anim Sci
Journal of experimental animal science
0939-8600
Continues: Zeitschrift für Versuchstierkunde.
1991   9103426

J Exp Biol
The Journal of experimental biology
0022-0949   1477-9145
Continues: British journal of experimental
biology.
1930   0243705

J Exp Bot
Journal of experimental botany
0022-0957   1460-2431
Vols. for <1985-> indexed in: European
journals of plant physiology. Subject index.
Absorbed: Flowering newsletter.
1950   9882906

J Exp Child Psychol
Journal of experimental child psychology
0022-0965   1096-0457
1964   2985128R

J Exp Clin Cancer Res
Journal of experimental & clinical cancer
research: CR
0392-9078   1756-9966
1982   8308647

J Exp Med
The Journal of experimental medicine
0022-1007   1540-9538
1896   2985109R

J Exp Med Sci
Journal of experimental medical sciences
0022-099X
1957-1968   0374761

J Exp Pathol
Journal of experimental pathology
0730-8485
1983-1992   8400623

J Exp Pathol (Oxford)
Journal of experimental pathology (Oxford,
England)
0958-4625
Continues: British journal of experimental
pathology. Continued by: International
journal of experimental pathology.
1990-1990   9004579

J Exp Psychol
Journal of experimental psychology
0022-1015
Superseded by: Journal of experimental
psychology. Animal behavior processes, and:
Journal of experimental psychology. General,
and: Journal of experimental psychology.
Human learning and memory, and: Journal of
experimental psychology. Human perception
and performance.
1916-1974   7502586

J Exp Psychol Anim Behav Process
Journal of experimental psychology. Animal
behavior processes
0097-7403
Supersedes in part Journal of experimental
psychology.
1975   7504289

J Exp Psychol Appl
Journal of experimental psychology. Applied
1076-898X
1995   9507618

J Exp Psychol Gen
Journal of experimental psychology. General
0096-3445
Continues in part Journal of experimental
psychology.
1975   7502587

J Exp Psychol Hum Percept Perform
Journal of experimental psychology. Human
perception and performance
0096-1523
Supersedes in part Journal of experimental
psychology.
1975   7502589

J Exp Psychol Learn Mem Cogn
Journal of experimental psychology.
Learning, memory, and cognition
0278-7393
Continues: Journal of experimental
psychology. Human learning and memory.
1982   8207540

J Exp Psychol [Hum Learn]
Journal of experimental psychology. Human
learning and memory
0096-1515
Supersedes in part Journal of experimental
psychology. Continued by Journal of
experimental psychology. Learning. memory,
and cognition.
1975-1981   7502588

J Exp Ther Oncol
Journal of experimental therapeutics &
oncology
1359-4117   1533-869X
1996   9604933

J Exp Zool
The Journal of experimental zoology
0022-104X   1097-010X
Split into: Journal of experimental zoology.
Part A. Comparative experimental biology,
and: Journal of experimental zoology. Part B.
Molecular and developmental evolution.
1904-2002   0375365

J Exp Zool Part A Ecol Genet Physiol
Journal of experimental zoology. Part A,
Ecological genetics and physiology
1932-5223   1932-5231
Continues: Journal of experimental zoology.
Part A. Comparative experimental biology.
2007   101297745

J Exp Zool Suppl
The Journal of experimental zoology.
Supplement: published under auspices of
the American Society of Zoologists and
the Division of Comparative Physiology
and Biochemistry / the Wistar Institute of
Anatomy and Biology
1059-8324
1987-1990   9005420

J Exp Zoolog A Comp Exp Biol
Journal of experimental zoology. Part A,
Comparative experimental biology
1548-8969   1552-499X
Absorbed in part: Journal of experimental
zoology. Continued by: Journal of
experimental zoology. Part A. Ecological
genetics and physiololgy.
2003-2006   101168223

J Exp Zoolog B Mol Dev Evol
Journal of experimental zoology. Part B.
Molecular and developmental evolution
1552-5007   1552-5015
Absorbed in part: Journal of experimental
zoology.
2003   101168228

J Expo Anal Environ Epidemiol
Journal of exposure analysis and
environmental epidemiology
1053-4245   1476-5519
Continued by: Journal of exposure science
and environmental epidemiology.
1991-2005   9111438

J Expo Sci Environ Epidemiol
Journal of exposure science &
environmental epidemiology
1559-0631   1559-064X
Continues: Journal of exposure analysis and
environmental epidemiology.
2006   101262796

J Extra Corpor Technol
The Journal of extra-corporeal technology
0022-1058
1968   0267637

J Fac Radiol
The Journal of the Faculty of Radiologists.
Faculty of Radiologists (Great Britain)
Continued by: Clinical radiology.
1949-1959   1306022

J Fam Health Care
The journal of family health care
1474-9114
Continues: Professional care of mother and
child.
2002   101142028

J Fam Hist
Journal of family history
0363-1990
1976   7701861

J Fam Nurs
Journal of family nursing
1074-8407   1552-549X
1995   9503761

J Fam Plann Reprod Health Care
The journal of family planning and
reproductive health care / Faculty of
Family Planning & Reproductive Health
Care, Royal College of Obstetricians &
Gynaecologists
1471-1893
Continues: British journal of family planning.
2001   101087687

J Fam Pract
The Journal of family practice
0094-3509   1533-7294
1974   7502590

J Fam Psychol
Journal of family psychology: JFP: journal
of the Division of Family Psychology of
the American Psychological Association
(Division 43)
0893-3200   1939-1293
1987   8802265

J Farm
Jornal dos farmacêuticos
Supersedes the Jornal of the Sindicato
Nacional dos Farmacêuticos. Superseded by
Revista portuguesa de farmácia.
1942-1950   17810400R

J Feline Med Surg
Journal of feline medicine and surgery
1098-612X
1999   100897329

J Fish Dis
Journal of fish diseases
0140-7775   1365-2761
1978   9881188

J Fla Med Assoc
The Journal of the Florida Medical
Association
0015-4148
Continues: JFMA. the Journal of the Florida
Medical Association. Florida Medical
Association.
1974   7505604

J Fla Med Assoc
The Journal of the Florida Medical Association. Florida Medical Association
0093-0970
Continued by: JFMA, the journal of the Florida Medical Association.
1914-1971   100964058

J Fla State Dent Soc
The Journal of the Florida State Dental Society
0360-1676
Continues Florida dental journal. Continued by Florida dental journal.
1937-1967   7512802

J Fluency Disord
Journal of fluency disorders
0094-730X   1873-801X
1974   7601744

J Fluoresc
Journal of fluorescence
1053-0509
1991   9201341

J Food Prot
Journal of food protection
0362-028X
Continues: Journal of milk and food technology.
1977   7703944

J Food Sci
Journal of food science
0022-1147   1750-3841
Continues: Food research.
1961   0014052

J Foot Ankle Surg
The Journal of foot and ankle surgery: official publication of the American College of Foot and Ankle Surgeons
1067-2516   1542-2224
Continues: Journal of foot surgery.
1993   9308427

J Foot Surg
The Journal of foot surgery
0449-2544
Continues the Journal of the American College of Foot Surgeons. Continued by: Journal of foot and ankle surgery.
1967-1992   0132575

J Forensic Leg Med
Journal of forensic and legal medicine
1752-928X
Continues: Journal of clinical forensic medicine.
2007   101300022

J Forensic Med
Journal of forensic medicine
0022-1171
Absorbed by: Forensic science.
1953-1971   0330423

J Forensic Nurs
Journal of forensic nursing
1556-3693
2005   101234500

J Forensic Odontostomatol
The Journal of forensic odonto-stomatology
0258-414X
1983   8501421

J Forensic Sci
Journal of forensic sciences
0022-1198   1556-4029
1956   0375370

J Forensic Sci Soc
Journal - Forensic Science Society
0015-7368
Continued by: Science & justice.
1960-1994   7505560

J Formos Med Assoc
Journal of the Formosan Medical Association = Taiwan yi zhi
0929-6646
Continues: Taiwan yi xue hui za zhi.
1991   9214933

J Fr Med Chir Thorac
Journal français de médecine et chirurgie thoraciques
0021-8324
Supersedes Archives médico-chirurgicales de l'appareil respiratoire.
1947-1972   0376571

J Fr Ophtalmol
Journal français d'ophtalmologie
0181-5512   1773-0597
Formed by the union of: Annales d'oculistique and Archives d'ophtalmologie.
1978   7804128

J Fr Otorhinolaryngol Audiophonol Chir Maxillofac
Journal français d'oto-rhino-laryngologie, audio-phonologie et chirurgie maxillo-faciale
0021-8332
Continues: Journal français d'oto-rhino-laryngologie et chirurgie maxillo-faciale. Continued by: JFORL; journal français d'oto-rhino laryngologie, audiophonologie et chirurgie maxillo-faciale.
1967-1971   0320134

J Fr Otorhinolaryngol Audiophonol Chir Maxillofac
Journal français d'oto-rhino-laryngologie; audiophonologie, chirurgie maxillo-faciale
0398-9771
Continues: JFORL. Journal français d'oto-rhino-laryngologie; audiophonologie et chirurgie maxillo-faciale. Absorbed by: Annales d'oto-laryngologie et de chirurgie cervico faciale.
1977-2003   7703703

J Fr Otorhinolaryngol Chir Maxillofac
Journal français d'oto-rhino-laryngologie et chirurgie maxillo-faciale
Supersedes Bulletin of the Société d'oto-rhino-laryngologie de Lyon et de la région. Continued by Journal français d'oto-rhino-laryngologie audio-phonologie et chirurgie maxillo-faciale.
1952-1966   0120644

J Franklin Inst
Journal of the Franklin Institute
0016-0032
Continues: Franklin journal and American mechanics' magazine.
1828   7503075

J Free Radic Biol Med
Journal of free radicals in biology & medicine
0748-5514
Merged with: Advances in free radical biology and medicine, to form: Free radical biology & medicine.
1985-1986   8508399

J Ga Dent Assoc
Journal of the Georgia Dental Association
0016-819X
Continues: Journal of the Georgia State Dental Association.
1944-1981   7505605

J Gambl Stud
Journal of gambling studies / co-sponsored by the National Council on Problem Gambling and Institute for the Study of Gambling and Commercial Gaming
1050-5350   1573-3602
Continues: Journal of gambling behavior.
1990   9425991

J Gastroenterol
Journal of gastroenterology
0944-1174
Continues: Gastroenterologia Japonica.
1994   9430794

J Gastroenterol Hepatol
Journal of gastroenterology and hepatology
0815-9319   1440-1746
1986   8607909

J Gastrointest Cancer
Journal of gastrointestinal cancer
1941-6628   1941-6636
Continues: International journal of gastrointestinal cancer.
2007   101479627

J Gastrointest Surg
Journal of gastrointestinal surgery: official journal of the Society for Surgery of the Alimentary Tract
1091-255X   1873-4626
1997   9706084

J Gastrointestin Liver Dis
Journal of gastrointestinal and liver diseases: JGLD
1841-8724
Continues: Romanian journal of gastroenterology.
2006   101272825

J Gen Appl Microbiol
The Journal of general and applied microbiology
0022-1260   1349-8037
1955   0165543

J Gen Intern Med
Journal of general internal medicine: official journal of the Society for Research and Education in Primary Care Internal Medicine
0884-8734   1525-1497
1986   8605834

J Gen Microbiol
Journal of general microbiology
0022-1287
Continued by: Microbiology (Reading, England).
1947-1993   0375371

J Gen Orthod
Journal of general orthodontics
1048-1990
Continued by: International journal of orthodontics (Milwukee, Wis.).
1990-2001   9100530

J Gen Physiol
The Journal of general physiology
0022-1295   1540-7748
1918   2985110R

J Gen Psychol
The Journal of general psychology
0022-1309
1928   2985111R

J Gen Virol
The Journal of general virology
0022-1317   1465-2099
1967   0077340

J Gend Specif Med
The journal of gender-specific medicine: JGSM: the official journal of the Partnership for Women's Health at Columbia
1523-7036
1998-2003   100887298

J Gene Med
The journal of gene medicine
1099-498X   1521-2254
1999   9815764

J Genet
Journal of genetics
0022-1333
1910 2985113R

J Genet Couns
Journal of genetic counseling
1059-7700 1573-3599
1992 9206865

J Genet Genomics
Journal of genetics and genomics = Yi chuan
xue bao
1673-8527
Continues: Acta genetica Sinica.
2007 101304616

J Genet Hum
Journal de génétique humaine
0021-7743
Continued by: Genetic counseling (Geneva,
Switzerland).
1952-1989 2983308R

J Genet Psychol
The Journal of genetic psychology
0022-1325
Continues: Pedagogical seminary and journal
of genetic psychology.
1954 2985112R

J Geriatr Phys Ther
Journal of geriatric physical therapy (2001)
1539-8412
Continues: Issues on aging.
2001 101142169

J Geriatr Psychiatry
Journal of geriatric psychiatry
0022-1414
1967-2002 0255141

J Geriatr Psychiatry Neurol
Journal of geriatric psychiatry and
neurology
0891-9887
Continues: Massachusetts General Hospital
newsletter. Topics in geriatrics.
1988 8805645

J Germantown Hosp
Journal of the Germantown Hospital
0433-6445
1960-1968 0412711

J Gerontol
Journal of gerontology
0022-1422
Split into: Journals of gerontology. Series A.
Biological sciences and medical sciences.
and: Journals of gerontology. Series B.
Psychological sciences and social sciences.
1946-1994 0374762

J Gerontol A Biol Sci Med Sci
The journals of gerontology. Series A,
Biological sciences and medical sciences
1079-5006
Continues in part: Journal of gerontology.
1995 9502837

J Gerontol B Psychol Sci Soc Sci
The journals of gerontology. Series B,
Psychological sciences and social sciences
1079-5014
Continues in part: Journal of gerontology.
1995 9508483

J Gerontol Nurs
Journal of gerontological nursing
0098-9134
1975 7510258

J Gerontol Soc Work
Journal of gerontological social work
0163-4372 1540-4048
1978 7903311

J Glaucoma
Journal of glaucoma
1057-0829 1536-481X
1992 9300903

J Gnathol
The Journal of gnathology
0891-8171
1982-199u 8508120

J Gravit Physiol
Journal of gravitational physiology: a
journal of the International Society for
Gravitational Physiology
1077-9248
1994 9437868

J Gt Houst Dent Soc
The Journal of the Greater Houston Dental
Society
1062-0265
Continues: Houston District Dental Society.
Journal.
1989 8917480

J Gynecol Obstet Biol Reprod (Paris)
Journal de gynécologie, obstétrique et
biologie de la reproduction
0368-2315
Supersedes Gynécologie et obstétrique and
the Bulletin of the Fédération des sociétés
de gynécologie et d'obstétrique de langue
française.
1972 0322206

J Gynecol Surg
Journal of gynecologic surgery
1042-4067
Continues: Colposcopy & gynecologic laser
surgery.
1989 9000936

J Hand Surg Eur Vol
The Journal of hand surgery, European
volume
1753-1934
Continues: Journal of hand surgery
(Edinburgh, Scotland).
2007 101315820

J Hand Surg [Am]
The Journal of hand surgery
0363-5023 1531-6564
1976 7609631

J Hand Surg [Br]
Journal of hand surgery (Edinburgh,
Scotland)
0266-7681 1532-2211
Continues: Hand. Continued by: Journal of
hand surgery. European volume.
1984-2006 8403839

J Hand Ther
Journal of hand therapy: official journal of
the American Society of Hand Therapists
0894-1130
1987 8806591

J Hawaii Dent Assoc
Journal of the Hawaii Dental Association
0017-8616
Continues the Journal of the Hawaii
State Dental Association. Merged with
Odontoscope to form Hawaii dental journal.
Continued by Hawaii dental journal.
1970-1983 7507197

J Hawaii State Dent Assoc
Journal of the Hawaii State Dental
Association
0092-5578
Continues: Aloha-Dontia. Continued by:
Journal of the Hawaii Dental Association.
1967-1969 7507198

J Hazard Mater
Journal of hazardous materials
0304-3894
1975 9422688

J Head Trauma Rehabil
The Journal of head trauma rehabilitation
0885-9701 1550-509X
1986 8702552

J Headache Pain
The journal of headache and pain
1129-2369 1129-2377
2000 100940562

J Health Adm Educ
The Journal of health administration
education
0735-6722
Continues: Program notes - Association
of University Programs in Health
Administration.
1983 8403840

J Health Care Benefits
Journal of health care benefits
1057-5073
1991-1995 9204247

J Health Care Chaplain
Journal of health care chaplaincy
0885-4726 1528-6916
1987 8800764

J Health Care Finance
Journal of health care finance
1078-6767
Continues: Topics in health care financing.
1994 9503024

J Health Care Inter Des
Journal of health care interior design:
proceedings from the ... Annual National
Symposium on Health Care Interior Design.
National Symposium on Health Care
Interior Design (U.S.)
1068-1132
Continued by: Symposium on Health Care
Interior Design. Journal of health care interior
design.
1989-1989 9318047

J Health Care Inter Des
Journal of health care interior design:
proceedings from the ... Symposium on
Health Care Interior Design. Symposium on
Health Care Interior Design
1068-1132
Continues: National Symposium on Health
Care Interior Design (U.S.). Journal of
health care interior design. Continued by:
Symposium on Healthcare Design. Journal of
healthcare design.
1990-1991 9318489

J Health Care Mark
Journal of health care marketing
0737-3252
Continued by: Marketing health services.
1981-1996 9875249

J Health Care Poor Underserved
Journal of health care for the poor and
underserved
1049-2089 1548-6869
1990 9103800

J Health Care Technol
Journal of health care technology
0748-075X
Merged with: Issues in health care
technology, to form: Health technology.
1984-1986 8504411

J Health Commun
Journal of health communication
1081-0730   1087-0415
1996   9604100

J Health Econ
Journal of health economics
0167-6296
1982   8410622

J Health Hosp Law
Journal of health and hospital law: a
publication of the American Academy of
Hospital Attorneys of the American Hospital
Association
1046-4360
Continues: Hospital law. Continued by:
Journal of health law.
1988-1998   8807932

J Health Hum Behav
Journal of health and human behavior
Continued by: Journal of health & social
behavior.
1960-1966   2985114R

J Health Hum Resour Adm
Journal of health and human resources
administration
0160-4198
Continued by: Journal of health and human
services administration.
1978-1994   7900790

J Health Hum Serv Adm
Journal of health and human services
administration
1079-3739
Continues: Journal of health and human
resources administration.
1994   9501928

J Health Law
Journal of health law
1526-2472
Continues: Journal of health and hospital
law. Continued by: Journal of health & life
sciences law.
1998-2007   100883816

J Health Life Sci Law
Journal of health & life sciences law
1942-4736
Continues: Journal of health law.
2007   101464667

J Health Organ Manag
Journal of health organization and
management
1477-7266
Continues: Journal of management in
medicine.
2003   101179473

J Health Phys Educ
The Journal of health and physical
education
Formed by the union of the American
physical education review and the Pentathlon.
Continued by the Journal of the American
Association for Health, Physical Education
and Recreation.
1930-1948   17910130R

J Health Polit Policy Law
Journal of health politics, policy and law
0361-6878   1527-1927
1976   7609331

J Health Popul Nutr
Journal of health, population, and nutrition
1606-0997
Continues: Journal of diarrhoeal diseases
research.
2000   100959228

J Health Psychol
Journal of health psychology
1359-1053
1996   9703616

J Health Serv Res Policy
Journal of health services research & policy
1355-8196
1996   9604936

J Health Soc Behav
Journal of health and social behavior
0022-1465
Continues the Journal of health and human
behavior.
1967   0103130

J Health Soc Policy
Journal of health & social policy
0897-7186
Continued by: Social work in public health.
1989-2006   9000937

J Healthc Des
Journal of healthcare design: proceedings
from the ... Symposium on Healthcare
Design. Symposium on Healthcare Design
1068-1124
Continues: Symposium on Health Care
Interior Design. Journal of health care interior
design.
1992-1998   9318490

J Healthc Educ Train
Journal of healthcare education and
training: the journal of the American
Society for Healthcare Education and
Training / American Hospital Association
0898-2740
1986-1995   8610643

J Healthc Inf Manag
Journal of healthcare information
management: JHIM
1099-811X
Continues: Healthcare information
management.
1998   9815773

J Healthc Manag
Journal of healthcare management /
American College of Healthcare Executives
1096-9012
Continues: Hospital & health services
administration.
1998   9803529

J Healthc Mater Manage
Journal of healthcare materiel management
0889-2482
Continues: Journal of hospital supply,
processing, and distribution. Continued by:
Journal of healthcare resource management.
1985-1994   8601287

J Healthc Prot Manage
Journal of healthcare protection
management: publication of the
International Association for Hospital
Security
0891-7930
1984   8506548

J Healthc Qual
Journal for healthcare quality: official
publication of the National Association for
Healthcare Quality
1062-2551
Continues: Journal of quality assurance.
1992   9202994

J Healthc Resour Manag
Journal of healthcare resource management
1078-9537
Continues: Journal of healthcare materiel
management.
1995-1998   9504369

J Healthc Risk Manag
Journal of healthcare risk management:
the journal of the American Society for
Healthcare Risk Management
1074-4797
Continues: Perspectives in healthcare risk
management.
1992   9305245

J Heart Lung Transplant
The Journal of heart and lung
transplantation: the official publication
of the International Society for Heart
Transplantation
1053-2498   1557-3117
Continues: Journal of heart transplantation.
1991   9102703

J Heart Transplant
The Journal of heart transplantation
0887-2570
Continues: Heart transplantation. Continued
by: Journal of heart and lung transplantation.
1984-1990   8604172

J Heart Valve Dis
The Journal of heart valve disease
0966-8519
1992   9312096

J Helminthol
Journal of helminthology
0022-149X   1475-2697
1923   2985115R

J Hematother
Journal of hematotherapy
1061-6128
Continued by: Journal of hematotherapy &
stem cell research.
1992-1999   9306048

J Hematother Stem Cell Res
Journal of hematotherapy & stem cell
research
1525-8165
Continues: Journal of hematotherapy.
Continued by: Stem cells and development.
1999-2003   100892915

J Hepatobiliary Pancreat Surg
Journal of hepato-biliary-pancreatic surgery
0944-1166
1993   9431940

J Hepatol
Journal of hepatology
0168-8278
Absorbed: Journal of hepatology.
Supplement.
1985   8503886

J Hepatol Suppl
Journal of hepatology. Supplement / EASL
0169-5185
Absorbed by: Journal of hepatology.
1985-1985   8505239

J Herb Pharmacother
Journal of herbal pharmacotherapy
1522-8940   1522-9106
2001   100888586

J Hered
The Journal of heredity
0022-1503   1465-7333
Continues: American breeders magazine.
1914   0375373

J Hillside Hosp
Journal of the Hillside Hospital
0440-8152
1952-1969   7507199

J Hirnforsch
Journal für Hirnforschung
0021-8359
1954-1999   0421521

J Hist Behav Sci
Journal of the history of the behavioral
sciences
0022-5061   1520-6696
1965   18020010R

J Hist Biol
Journal of the history of biology
0022-5010
1968   0202503

J Hist Dent
Journal of the history of dentistry
1089-6287
Continues: Bulletin of the history of dentistry.
1996   9609747

J Hist Ideas
Journal of the history of ideas
0022-5037   1086-3222
1940   00140360R

J Hist Med
Jornal de historia da medicina
1956-1962   17810380R

J Hist Med Allied Sci
Journal of the history of medicine and allied
sciences
0022-5045   1468-4373
1946   0413415

J Hist Neurosci
Journal of the history of the neurosciences
0964-704X   1744-5213
1992   9441330

J Histochem Cytochem
The journal of histochemistry and
cytochemistry: official journal of the
Histochemistry Society
0022-1554   1551-5044
1953   9815334

J HIV Ther
Journal of HIV therapy
1462-0308
Absorbed: HIV & AIDS current trends. 2005
Continues: Journal of HIV combination
therapy.
1998   101088049

J Holist Nurs
Journal of holistic nursing: official journal
of the American Holistic Nurses' Association
0898-0101   1552-5724
1983   8506709

J Homosex
Journal of homosexuality
0091-8369   1540-3602
1974   7502386

J Hosp Admit Manage
The Journal for hospital admitting
management: official publication of the
National Association of Hospital Admitting
Managers / NAHAM
0894-1068
Continues: NAHAM admitting bulletin.
Continued by: Admitting management
journal.
1983-1988   8704017

J Hosp Dent Pract
Journal of hospital dental practice
0022-1600
Merged with: The Journal of the American
Society for Geriatric Dentistry; and, Journal
of dentistry for the handicapped, to form:
Special care in dentistry.
1967-1980   1265125

J Hosp Infect
The Journal of hospital infection
0195-6701
1980   8007166

J Hosp Mark
Journal of hospital marketing
0883-7570
Continued by: Journal of hospital marketing
& public relations.
1986-1999   8708320

J Hosp Mark Public Relations
Journal of hospital marketing & public
relations
1539-0942   1539-0934
Continues: Journal of hospital marketing.
2001   101121477

J Hosp Med
Journal of hospital medicine (Online)
1553-5592   1553-5606
2006   101271025

J Hosp Supply Process Distrib
Journal of hospital supply, processing, and
distribution
0738-2928
Continued by: Journal of health care materiel
management. With: Indicator (Minnesota
Mining and Manufacturing Company)
1983-1985   8507483

J Houston Dist Dent Soc
Journal. Houston District Dental Society
Continues the Journal of the Houston Dental
Society. Continued by: Journal of the Greater
Houston Dental Society.
1938-1989   17430410R

J Huazhong Univ Sci Technolog Med Sci
Journal of Huazhong University of Science
and Technology. Medical sciences = Hua
zhong ke ji da xue xue bao. Yi xue Ying De
wen ban = Huazhong keji daxue xuebao.
Yixue Yingdewen ban
1672-0733
Continues: Journal of Tongji Medical
University.
2002   101169627

J Hum Ergol (Tokyo)
Journal of human ergology
0300-8134
1972   0364267

J Hum Evol
Journal of human evolution
0047-2484
1972   0337330

J Hum Genet
Journal of human genetics
1434-5161   1435-232X
Continues: Japanese journal of human
genetics.
1998   9808008

J Hum Hypertens
Journal of human hypertension
0950-9240
1987   8811625

J Hum Lact
Journal of human lactation: official journal
of International Lactation Consultant
Association
0890-3344
1985   8709498

J Hum Nutr
Journal of human nutrition
0308-4329
Continues: Nutrition. Split into: Human
nutrition. Applied nutrition; and, Human
nutrition. Clinical nutrition.
1976-1981   7702659

J Hum Nutr Diet
Journal of human nutrition and dietetics:
the official journal of the British Dietetic
Association
0952-3871   1365-277X
Continues in part: Human nutrition. Applied
nutrition.
1988   8904840

J Hum Resour
The Journal of human resources
0022-166X
1966   0235700

J Hum Virol
Journal of human virology
1090-9508
1997-2002   9805755

J Human Stress
Journal of human stress
0097-840X
Continued by: Behavioral medicine
(Washington, D.C.).
1975-1987   7602457

J Hyg (Lond)
The Journal of hygiene
0022-1724
Continued by: Epidemiology and infection.
1901-1986   0375374

J Hyg Epidemiol Microbiol Immunol
Journal of hygiene, epidemiology,
microbiology, and immunology
0022-1732
Continued by: Central European journal of
public health.
1957-1992   2985116R

J Hypertens
Journal of hypertension
0263-6352
1983   8306882

J Hypertens Suppl
Journal of hypertension. Supplement:
official journal of the International Society
of Hypertension
0952-1178
1983   8501422

J Image Guid Surg
Journal of image guided surgery
1078-7844
Continued by: Computer aided surgery.
1995-1995   9508564

J Immigr Health
Journal of immigrant health
1096-4045   1573-3629
Continued by: Journal of immigrant and
minority health.
1999-2005   9815654

J Immigr Minor Health
Journal of immigrant and minority health /
Center for Minority Public Health
1557-1912   1557-1920
Continues: Journal of immigrant health.
2006   101256527

J Immunoassay
Journal of immunoassay
0197-1522
Continued by: Journal of immunoassay &
immunochemistry.
1980-2000   8007167

J Immunoassay Immunochem
Journal of immunoassay &
immunochemistry
1532-1819   1532-4230
Continues: Journal of immunoassay.
2001   100963688

J Immunogenet
Journal of immunogenetics
0305-1811
Continued by: European journal of immunogenetics.
1974-1990　　　　0425125

J Immunol
Journal of immunology (Baltimore, Md.: 1950)
0022-1767　　　1550-6606
Continues: Journal of immunology, virus research and experimental chemotherapy.
1950　　　　2985117R

J Immunol Methods
Journal of immunological methods
0022-1759
Absorbed: Immunotechnology.
1971　　　　1305440

J Immunopharmacol
Journal of immunopharmacology
0163-0571
Continued by: Immunopharmacology and immunotoxicology.
1978-1986　　　　7901853

J Immunother
Journal of immunotherapy (Hagerstown, Md.: 1997)
1524-9557　　　1537-4513
Continues: Journal of immunotherapy with emphasis on tumor immunology.
1997　　　　9706083

J Immunother (1991)
Journal of immunotherapy: official journal of the Society for Biological Therapy
1053-8550
Continues: Journal of biological response modifiers. Continued by: Journal of immunotherapy with emphasis on tumor immunology.
1991-1992　　　　9102704

J Immunother Emphasis Tumor Immunol
Journal of immunotherapy with emphasis on tumor immunology: official journal of the Society for Biological Therapy
1067-5582
Continues: Journal of immunotherapy. Continued by: Journal of immunotherapy (Hagerstown, Md.: 1997).
1993-1996　　　　9418950

J Immunotoxicol
Journal of immunotoxicology
1547-691X　　　1547-6901
2004　　　　101201960

J In Vitro Fert Embryo Transf
Journal of in vitro fertilization and embryo transfer: IVF
0740-7769
Continued by: Journal of assisted reproduction and genetics.
1984-1991　　　　8412594

J Ind Hyg Toxicol
The Journal of industrial hygiene and toxicology
0095-9030
1919-1949　　　　17920050R

J Ind Microbiol
Journal of industrial microbiology
0169-4146
Continued by: Journal of industrial microbiology & biotechnology.
1986-1996　　　　8610887

J Ind Microbiol Biotechnol
Journal of industrial microbiology & biotechnology
1367-5435
Continues: Journal of industrial microbiology.
1996　　　　9705544

J Indian Acad Dent
Journal of the Indian Academy of Dentistry
0019-4255
1960-1971　　　　7505606

J Indian Dent Assoc
Journal of the Indian Dental Association
0019-4611
Continues the Journal of the All India Dental Association.
1966-1996　　　　7507202

J Indian Med Assoc
Journal of the Indian Medical Association
0019-5847
Continues: Indian medical world.
1931　　　　7505608

J Indian Med Prof
Journal of the Indian medical profession
0019-588X
1954-1982　　　　0376341

J Indian Orthod Soc
The Journal of Indian Orthodontic Society
0301-5742
1968-1981　　　　7503130

J Indian Soc Pedod Prev Dent
Journal of the Indian Society of Pedodontics and Preventive Dentistry
0970-4388　　　1998-3905
1983　　　　8710631

J Indiana Dent Assoc
Journal (Indiana Dental Association)
0019-6568
Continues: The Journal of the Indiana Dental Association.
1974　　　　8502537

J Indiana Dent Assoc
The Journal of the Indiana Dental Association
0019-6568
Continues The Journal of the Indiana State Dental Association. Continued by Journal (Indiana Dental Association).
1968-1973　　　　7507203

J Indiana State Dent Assoc
The Journal of the Indiana State Dental Association
0092-6116
Continues the association's Bulletin. Continued by the Journal of the Indiana Dental Association.
1933-1968　　　　7505609

J Indiana State Med Assoc
The Journal of the Indiana State Medical Association
0019-6770
Formed by the merger of: Fort Wayne medical journal-magazine; and, Transactions of the Indiana State Medical Association. Continued by: Indiana medicine.
1908-1983　　　　7505610

J Indianap Dist Dent Soc
Journal. Indianapolis District Dental Society
Continues the society's Bulletin.
1957-1976　　　　17540400R

J Individ Psychol
Journal of individual psychology
0022-1805
Continues the American journal of individual psychology. Merged with Individual psychologist to form Individual psychology.
1957-1981　　　　0400026

J Inf Image Manage
The Journal of information and image management: JIIM
0745-9963
Continues: Journal of micrographics. Continued by: Inform (Silver Spring, Md.).
1983-1986　　　　9880303

J Infect
The Journal of infection
0163-4453　　　1532-2742
1979　　　　7908424

J Infect Chemother
Journal of infection and chemotherapy: official journal of the Japan Society of Chemotherapy
1341-321X
1995　　　　9608375

J Infect Dis
The Journal of infectious diseases
0022-1899　　　1537-6613
1904　　　　0413675

J Inflamm
Journal of inflammation
1078-7852
Continues: Circulatory shock.
1995-1998　　　　9511967

J Infus Chemother
The Journal of infusional chemotherapy
1060-0051
1991-1996　　　　9306406

J Infus Nurs
Journal of infusion nursing: the official publication of the Infusion Nurses Society
1533-1458　　　1539-0667
Continues: Journal of intravenous nursing.
2001　　　　101124170

J Inherit Metab Dis
Journal of inherited metabolic disease
0141-8955　　　1573-2665
1978　　　　7910918

J Inorg Biochem
Journal of inorganic biochemistry
0162-0134　　　1873-3344
Continues: Bioinorganic chemistry.
1979　　　　7905788

J Insect Physiol
Journal of insect physiology
0022-1910
1957　　　　2985080R

J Insect Sci
Journal of insect science (Online)
　　　　　　　1536-2442
2001　　　　101096396

J Inst Hosp Eng
The Journal of the Institute of Hospital Engineering
0953-1211
Continues: Hospital engineering. Continued by: Health estate journal.
1987-1989　　　　8807313

J Inst Sanit Eng Lond
Journal. Institution of Sanitary Engineers, London
Continues Institute of Sanitary Engineers. Journal. Continued by the Journal of the Institution of Public Health Engineers, London.
1916-1955　　　　17620180R

J Inst Sterile Serv Manage
Journal (Institute of Sterile Services Management)
0951-2578
Continues: Journal of sterile services management. Continued by: ISSM journal.
1988-1996　　　　8915209

J Insur Med
Journal of insurance medicine
Absorbed by: Insurance index. Oct. 1951
1946-1951   **17920070R**

J Insur Med
Journal of insurance medicine (New York, N.Y.)
0743-6661
Continues: Insurance medicine.
1979   **8401468**

J Int Acad Periodontol
Journal of the International Academy of Periodontology
1466-2094
1999   **100888553**

J Int Assoc Dent Child
Journal of the International Association of Dentistry for Children
0309-6858
Merged with: Journal of paediatric dentistry, to form: International journal of paediatric dentistry.
1970-1990   **7613434**

J Int Assoc Physicians AIDS Care
Journal of the International Association of Physicians in AIDS Care
1081-454X
Continues: Journal of the Physicians Association for AIDS Care. Continued by: IAPAC monthly.
1995-2000   **9508185**

J Int Assoc Physicians AIDS Care (Chic Ill)
Journal of the International Association of Physicians in AIDS Care (Chicago, Ill.: 2002)
1545-1097   **1557-0886**
2002   **101185740**

J Int Assoc Physicians AIDS Care (Chic)
Journal of the International Association of Physicians in AIDS Care. Supplement: JIAPAC
2001   **101096587**

J Int Bioethique
Journal international de bioéthique = International journal of bioethics
1145-0762
Absorbed: Ethique. 1997 Continues: Cahier de droit médical et d'éthique médicale.
1990   **9015754**

J Int Chir
Journal international de chirurgie
Continued by the Bulletin of the International Society of Surgery in 1955.
1936-1953   **17640210R**

J Int Coll Dent (Jpn)
Journal Of The International College Of Dentists; Japan Section
0912-1471
1970   **9875608**

J Int Coll Surg
The Journal of the International College of Surgeons
0096-557X
Continued by International surgery.
1938-1965   **7507208**

J Int Fed Clin Chem
Journal of the International Federation of Clinical Chemistry / IFCC
1051-2292
Continued by: EJIFCC.
1989-1999   **9318491**

J Int Med Res
The Journal of international medical research
0300-0605   **1473-2300**
1972   **0346411**

J Int Neuropsychol Soc
Journal of the International Neuropsychological Society: JINS
1355-6177   **1469-7661**
1995   **9503760**

J Integr Neurosci
Journal of integrative neuroscience
0219-6352
2002   **101156357**

J Integr Plant Biol
Journal of integrative plant biology
1672-9072   **1744-7909**
Continues: Acta botanica sinica.
2005   **101250502**

J Intellect Dev Disabil
Journal of intellectual & developmental disability
1366-8250   **1469-9532**
Continues: Australia and New Zealand journal of developmental disabilities.
1996   **9610837**

J Intellect Disabil
Journal of intellectual disabilities: JOID
1744-6295   **1744-6309**
Continues: Journal of learning disabilities (London. England).
2005   **101229024**

J Intellect Disabil Res
Journal of intellectual disability research: JIDR
0964-2633   **1365-2788**
Continues: Journal of mental deficiency research.
1992   **9206090**

J Intensive Care Med
Journal of intensive care medicine
0885-0666   **1525-1489**
1986   **8610344**

J Interferon Cytokine Res
Journal of interferon & cytokine research: the official journal of the International Society for Interferon and Cytokine Research
1079-9907   **1557-7465**
Formed by the union of: Journal of interferon research; and: Lymphokine and cytokine research. and continues the numbering of the former.
1995   **9507088**

J Interferon Res
Journal of interferon research
0197-8357
Merged with: Lymphokine and cytokine research, to form: Journal of interferon & cytokine research.
1980-1994   **8100396**

J Intern Med
Journal of internal medicine
0954-6820   **1365-2796**
Continues: Acta medica Scandinavica.
1989   **8904841**

J Intern Med Suppl
Journal of internal medicine. Supplement
0955-7873
Continues: Acta medica Scandinavica. Supplementum. Supplement to: Journal of internal medicine.
1989   **8912975**

J Interpers Violence
Journal of interpersonal violence
0886-2605
1986   **8700910**

J Interprof Care
Journal of interprofessional care
1356-1820   **1469-9567**
Continues: Holistic medicine.
1992   **9205811**

J Interv Card Electrophysiol
Journal of interventional cardiac electrophysiology: an international journal of arrhythmias and pacing
1383-875X
Absorbed: Cardiac electrophysiology review. 2004
1997   **9708966**

J Interv Cardiol
Journal of interventional cardiology
0896-4327   **1540-8183**
1988   **8907826**

J Intraven Nurs
Journal of intravenous nursing: the official publication of the Intravenous Nurses Society
0896-5846
Continues: NITA. Continued by: Journal of infusion nursing.
1988-2001   **8804311**

J Invasive Cardiol
The Journal of invasive cardiology
1042-3931   **1557-2501**
1988   **8917477**

J Invertebr Pathol
Journal of invertebrate pathology
0022-2011   **1096-0805**
Continues Journal of insect pathology.
1965   **0014067**

J Invest Dermatol
The Journal of investigative dermatology
0022-202X   **1523-1747**
Absorbed: Advances in biology of skin.
1938   **0426720**

J Invest Surg
Journal of investigative surgery: the official journal of the Academy of Surgical Research
0894-1939   **1521-0553**
1988   **8809255**

J Investig Allergol Clin Immunol
Journal of investigational allergology & clinical immunology: official organ of the International Association of Asthmology (INTERASMA) and Sociedad Latinoamericana de Alergia e Inmunología
1018-9068
1991   **9107858**

J Investig Dermatol Symp Proc
The journal of investigative dermatology. Symposium proceedings / the Society for Investigative Dermatology, Inc. [and] European Society for Dermatological Research
1087-0024   **1529-1774**
1996   **9609059**

J Investig Med
Journal of investigative medicine: the official publication of the American Federation for Clinical Research
1081-5589   **1708-8267**
Continues: Clinical research.
1994   **9501229**

J Iowa Med Soc
Journal of the Iowa Medical Society
0021-0587
Continues Journal of the Iowa State Medical Society. Continued by Iowa medicine.
1961-1983   **7507210**

J Iowa State Med Soc
Journal. Iowa State Medical Society
0096-6983
Continued by the Journal of the Iowa Medical Society.
1911-1961   **17710080R**

J Ir Dent Assoc
Journal of the Irish Dental Association
0021-1133
Continues the Irish dental review.
1965   **7507211**

J Ir Med Assoc
Journal of the Irish Medical Association
0021-129X
Continues: Journal. Medical Association of Eire. Continued by: Irish medical journal.
1951-1974   **0430304**

J Jj Group Hosp Grant Med Coll
Journal of J. J. Group of Hospitals and Grant Medical College
1956   **0403467**

J Jpn Obstet Gynecol Soc
Journal of the Japanese Obstetrical & Gynecological Society
0388-0486
Continued by Acta obstetrica et gynaecologica Japonica.
1954-1968   **7507212**

J Kans City Mo Southwest Clin Soc
Journal. Kansas City (Mo.) Southwest Clinical Society
1924-1961   **18110710R**

J Kans Dent Assoc
Journal of the Kansas Dental Association
0888-7063
Continues: The Journal of the Kansas State Dental Association.
1981   **8408586**

J Kans Med Soc
The Journal of the Kansas Medical Society
0022-8699
Absorbed: Western medical journal. Wichita journal. Continued by: Kansas medicine.
1901-1984   **7505612**

J Kans State Dent Assoc
The Journal of the Kansas State Dental Association
0022-8796
Continues Bulletin of the Kansas State Dental Association. Continued by Journal of the Kansas Dental Association.
1933-1981   **7505613**

J Knee Surg
The journal of knee surgery
1538-8506
Continues: American journal of knee surgery.
2002   **101137599**

J Korean Acad Nurs
Journal of Korean Academy of Nursing
2005-3673
Continues: Taehan Kanho Hakhoe chi.
2008   **101488689**

J Korean Am Med Assoc
Journal of Korean American Medical Association
Continues: KAMA.
200u   **101156817**

J Korean Med Sci
Journal of Korean medical science
1011-8934   1598-6357
1986   **8703518**

J Korean Res Soc Dent Hypn
Journal Of The Korean Research Society For Dental Hypnosis
19uu-uuuu   **9875594**

J Ky Dent Assoc
Journal of the Kentucky Dental Association
0023-0162
Continues Journal of the Kentucky State Dental Association Continued by Kentucky dental journal.
1957-1981   **7505614**

J Ky Med Assoc
The Journal of the Kentucky Medical Association
0023-0294
Continues: Journal of the Kentucky State Medical Association.
1950   **7505615**

J La Dent Assoc
Journal of the Louisiana Dental Association
0024-6786
Continues the Journal of the Louisiana State Dental Society, issued 1943?-57? Continued by LDA journal.
1957-1972   **7503078**

J La State Med Soc
The Journal of the Louisiana State Medical Society: official organ of the Louisiana State Medical Society
0024-6921
Continues: New Orleans medical and surgical journal.
1953   **7505618**

J Lab Clin Med
The Journal of laboratory and clinical medicine
0022-2143   1532-6543
Continued by: Translational research.
1915-2006   **0375375**

J Lancet
The Journal-lancet
0096-0233
Continues: Journal of the Minnesota State Medical Association and the Northwestern lancet.
1912-1968   **17830080R**

J Laparoendosc Adv Surg Tech A
Journal of laparoendoscopic & advanced surgical techniques. Part A
1092-6429
Absorbed: Pediatric endosurgery & innovative techniques. 2005 Continues in part: Journal of laparoendoscopic surgery.
1997   **9706293**

J Laparoendosc Surg
Journal of laparoendoscopic surgery
1052-3901
Split into: Journal of laparoendoscopic & advanced surgical techniques. Part A; and: Pediatric endosurgery & innovative techniques.
1990-1996   **9109598**

J Laryngol Otol
The Journal of laryngology and otology
0022-2151   1748-5460
Continues: Journal of laryngology, rhinology, and otology.
1921   **8706896**

J Laryngol Otol Suppl
The Journal of laryngology and otology. Supplement
0144-2945
1978   **7809663**

J Laser Appl
Journal of laser applications
1042-346X
1988   **9208015**

J Law Ethics Dent
Journal of law and ethics in dentistry
0894-8879
1988-1991   **8812167**

J Law Health
Journal of law and health
1044-6419
1986   **8918134**

J Law Med
Journal of law and medicine
1320-159X
1993   **9431853**

J Law Med Ethics
The Journal of law, medicine & ethics: a journal of the American Society of Law, Medicine & Ethics
1073-1105   1748-720X
Continues: Law, medicine & health care.
1993   **9315583**

J Learn Disabil
Journal of learning disabilities
0022-2194   1538-4780
1968   **0157312**

J Leg Med
The Journal of legal medicine
0194-7648   1521-057X
1979   **8000151**

J Leg Med (N Y)
The Journal of legal medicine
0093-1748
Continued by Legal aspects of medical practice.
1973-1977   **0367344**

J Lesbian Stud
Journal of lesbian studies
1089-4160   1540-3548
1997   **9891002**

J Leukoc Biol
Journal of leukocyte biology
0741-5400
Continues: Journal of the Reticuloendothelial Society.
1984   **8405628**

J Leukoc Biol Suppl
Journal of leukocyte biology. Supplement
1990   **9207303**

J LGBT Health Res
Journal of LGBT health research
1557-4091   1557-4105
Continues: Journal of neuro-AIDS.
2007   **101254470**

J Lipid Mediat
Journal of lipid mediators
0921-8319
Continued by: Journal of lipid mediators and cell signalling.
1989-1993   **8913460**

J Lipid Mediat Cell Signal
Journal of lipid mediators and cell signalling
0929-7855
Continues: Journal of lipid mediators. Merged with: Prostaglandins, to form: Prostaglandins & other lipid mediators.
1994-1997   **9430888**

J Lipid Res
Journal of lipid research
0022-2275
1959   **0376606**

J Liposome Res
Journal of liposome research
0898-2104   1532-2394
1988   9001952

J Lithotr Stone Dis
The Journal of lithotripsy & stone disease
1040-2152
    Continued by: Journal of stone disease.
1989-1991   8912687

J Long Term Care Adm
The Journal of long term care administration
0093-4445
    Continues the Journal of the American College of Nursing Home Administrators. Merged with: Long-term care administrator; and: College notes, to form: Balance (Alexandria, Va.).
1973-1997   0415026

J Long Term Eff Med Implants
Journal of long-term effects of medical implants
1050-6934
1991   9110830

J Long Term Home Health Care
The Journal of long term home health care: The PRIDE Institute journal
1072-4281
    Continues: Pride Institute journal of long term home health care. Merged with: Journal of case management, to form: Care management journals.
1994-1998   9423871

J Low Genit Tract Dis
Journal of lower genital tract disease
1089-2591   1526-0976
    Continues: Colposcopist.
1997   9704963

J Macomb Dent Soc
Journal Of The Macomb Dental Society
0744-9682
1964   9878331

J Magn Reson
Journal of magnetic resonance (San Diego, Calif.: 1997)
1090-7807   1557-8968
    Merger of: Journal of magnetic resonance. Series A. and: Journal of magnetic resonance. Series B. continuing the numbering of the former.
1997   9707935

J Magn Reson B
Journal of magnetic resonance. Series B
1064-1866
    Continues in part: Journal of magnetic resonance. Merged with: Journal of magnetic resonance. Series A. to form: Journal of magnetic resonance (San Diego. Calif.: 1997).
1993-1996   9309764

J Magn Reson Imaging
Journal of magnetic resonance imaging: JMRI
1053-1807
1991   9105850

J Maine Dent Assoc
Journal / Maine Dental Association
1977-1979   9875005

J Maine Med Assoc
The Journal of the Maine Medical Association
0025-0694
1911-1980   7505619

J Mal Vasc
Journal des maladies vasculaires
0398-0499
1976   7707965

J Mammal
Journal of mammalogy
0022-2372
1919   2985081R

J Mammary Gland Biol Neoplasia
Journal of mammary gland biology and neoplasia
1083-3021   1573-7039
1996   9601804

J Manag Care Pharm
Journal of managed care pharmacy: JMCP
1083-4087
1995   9605854

J Manag Med
Journal of management in medicine
0268-9235
    Absorbed: Health manpower management. 1999 Continued by: Journal of health organization and management.
1987-2002   8705942

J Manipulative Physiol Ther
Journal of manipulative and physiological therapeutics
0161-4754   1532-6586
1978   7807107

J Marital Fam Ther
Journal of marital and family therapy
0194-472X
    Continues: Journal of marriage and family counseling.
1979   7904614

J Mark Ment Health
Journal of marketing for mental health
0883-7589
    Continued by: Journal of nonprofit and public sector marketing..
1986-1990   8708658

J Mark Prof
Journal of marketing for professions
1980-19uu   9878859

J Marmara Univ Dent Fac
Journal of Marmara University Dental Faculty
1018-5992
1990-2001   9114162

J Mass Dent Soc
Journal of the Massachusetts Dental Society
0025-4800
1952   7503082

J Mass Spectrom
Journal of mass spectrometry: JMS
1076-5174
    Merger of: OMS. Organic mass spectrometry; and: Biological mass spectrometry. continuing the numbering of the former.
1995   9504818

J Mater Sci Mater Med
Journal of materials science. Materials in medicine
0957-4530
1990   9013087

J Matern Fetal Med
The Journal of maternal-fetal medicine
1057-0802
    Merged with: Prenatal and neonatal medicine, to form: Journal of maternal-fetal and neonatal medicine
1992-2001   9211288

J Matern Fetal Neonatal Med
The journal of maternal-fetal & neonatal medicine: the official journal of the European Association of Perinatal Medicine, the Federation of Asia and Oceania Perinatal Societies, the International Society of Perinatal Obstetricians
1476-7058   1476-4954
    Merger of: Journal of maternal-fetal medicine: and: Prenatal and neonatal medicine, and continues the numbering of the former.
2002   101136916

J Math Biol
Journal of mathematical biology
0303-6812
1974   7502105

J Maxillofac Orthop
Journal of maxillofacial orthopedics
0022-2534
1968-1972   7511218

J Maxillofac Surg
Journal of maxillofacial surgery
0301-0503
    Continued by: Journal of cranio-maxillo-facial surgery.
1973-1986   0370036

J Md State Dent Assoc
Journal of the Maryland State Dental Association
0025-4355
    Continued by: MSDA journal.
1958-1994   7503081

J Mechanochem Cell Motil
Journal of mechanochemistry & cell motility
0091-6552
1971-1977   0372277

J Med
Journal of medicine
0025-7850
    Continues: Medicina experimentalis.
1970   7505566

J Med (Oporto)
Jornal do médico
0021-7573
1940-1992   0374753

J Med Assoc Eire
Journal. Medical Association of Eire
0368-2986
    Continues the Journal of the Irish Free State Medical Union. Continued by the Journal of the Irish Medical Association.
1941-1950   18510260R

J Med Assoc Ga
Journal of the Medical Association of Georgia
0025-7028
1911   7505620

J Med Assoc State Ala
Journal of the Medical Association of the State of Alabama
0025-7044
    Supersedes the association's Transactions. Continued by Alabama medicine.
1931-1983   7503083

J Med Assoc Thai
Journal of the Medical Association of Thailand = Chotmaihet thangphaet
0125-2208
    Continues: Chotmāihet thāngphaet khong Phaetthaya Samākhom haeng Prathēt Thai.
1967   7507216

J Med Biogr
Journal of medical biography
0967-7720
1993   9308895

J Med Bord
Journal de médecine de Bordeaux et du
Sud-Ouest
0368-3001
1878-1967   0161067

J Med Chem
Journal of medicinal chemistry
0022-2623   1520-4804
Continues: Journal of medicinal and
pharmaceutical chemistry.
1963   9716531

J Med Chir Prat
Journal de médecine et de chirurgie
pratiques
0021-7913
1830-1988   2985083R

J Med Cuneif
Le journal des médecines cunéiformes
1761-0583
2003   101185239

J Med Dent Sci
Journal of medical and dental sciences
1342-8810
Continues: Bulletin of Tokyo Medical and
Dental University.
1997   9717112

J Med Educ
Journal of medical education
0022-2577
Continues: Medical education (Chicago, Ill.).
Continued by: Academic medicine.
1951-1988   0375377

J Med Eng Technol
Journal of medical engineering & technology
0309-1902   1464-522X
Supersedes: Biomedical engineering.
1977   7702125

J Med Entomol
Journal of medical entomology
0022-2585
1964   0375400

J Med Entomol Suppl
Journal of medical entomology. Supplement
0146-6631
1976-1983   7902862

J Med Ethics
Journal of medical ethics
0306-6800   1473-4257
Continued in part by: Medical humanities,
which split off in June 2000 and assumed vol.
numbering beginning with v. 26.
1975   7513619

J Med Food
Journal of medicinal food
1096-620X   1557-7600
1998   9812512

J Med Genet
Journal of medical genetics
0022-2593   1468-6244
1964   2985087R

J Med Humanit
The Journal of medical humanities
1041-3545
Continues: Journal of medical humanities and
bioethics.
1989   8917478

J Med Humanit Bioeth
The Journal of medical humanities and
bioethics
0882-6498
Continues: The Journal of bioethics.
Continued by: Journal of medical humanities.
1985-1988   8507484

J Med Imaging Radiat Oncol
Journal of medical imaging and radiation
oncology
1754-9477   1754-9485
Continues: Australasian radiology.
2008   101469340

J Med Internet Res
Journal of medical Internet research
                       1438-8871
1999   100959882

J Med Invest
The journal of medical investigation: JMI
1343-1420   1349-6867
Continues: Tokushima journal of
experimental medicine.
1997   9716841

J Med Lab Technol
The Journal of medical laboratory
technology
0368-3109
Continues the Laboratory journal. Continued
by Medical laboratory technology.
1951-1970   1263574

J Med Liban
Le Journal médical libanais. The Lebanese
medical journal
0023-9852
Continues La Revue médicale libanaise.
1950   0375352

J Med Libr Assoc
Journal of the Medical Library Association:
JMLA
1536-5050   1558-9439
Continues: Bulletin of the Medical Library
Association.
2002   101132728

J Med Lyon
Journal de médecine de Lyon
0021-7883
1920-2002   2985084R

J Med Microbiol
Journal of medical microbiology
0022-2615   1473-5644
1968   0224131

J Med Nantes
Journal de médecine de Nantes
1961-1969   17820050R

J Med Paris
Journal de médecine de Paris
1881-1968   2985085R

J Med Pernamb
Jornal de medicina de Pernambuco
1905-1954   2985187R

J Med Philos
The Journal of medicine and philosophy
0360-5310   1744-5019
1976   7610512

J Med Pract Manage
The Journal of medical practice
management: MPM
8755-0229
Absorbed in part by: Medical practice
management news.
1985   8605494

J Med Primatol
Journal of medical primatology
0047-2565
1972   0320626

J Med Screen
Journal of medical screening
0969-1413   1475-5793
1994   9433359

J Med Soc N J
The Journal of the Medical Society of New
Jersey
0025-7524
Continued by: New Jersey medicine.
1904-1985   7503084

J Med Syst
Journal of medical systems
0148-5598
Supersedes Journal of medical systems.
1977   7806056

J Med Toxicol
Journal of medical toxicology: official journal
of the American College of Medical Toxicology
1556-9039
2005   101284598

J Med Vet Mycol
Journal of medical and veterinary mycology:
bi-monthly publication of the International
Society for Human and Animal Mycology
0268-1218
Continues: Sabouraudia. Continued by:
Medical mycology.
1986-1997   8605493

J Med Virol
Journal of medical virology
0146-6615   1096-9071
1977   7705876

J Medicaid Manage
Journal for Medicaid management
0147-6726
Superseded by: Perspectives on Medicaid
management..
1977-1977   7800045

J Membr Biol
The Journal of membrane biology
0022-2631
1969   0211301

J Ment Defic Res
Journal of mental deficiency research
0022-264X
Continued by: Journal of intellectual
disability research.
1957-1991   0375401

J Ment Defic Res [Monogr Ser]
Journal of mental deficiency research.
Monograph series
0301-0600
1972-19uu   0372300

J Ment Health Adm
Journal of mental health administration
0092-8623
Continued by: Journal of behavioral health
services & research.
1972-1997   0351035

J Ment Health Policy Econ
The journal of mental health policy and
economics
1091-4358   1099-176X
1998   9815374

J Ment Sci
The Journal of mental science
0368-315X
Continues: Asylum journal of mental science.
Continued by: British journal of psychiatry.
1857-1962   0014157

J Mercer Dent Soc
Journal. Mercer Dental Society, Trenton
0025-9861
1940-1977   18640710R

J Mich Dent Assoc
The Journal of the Michigan Dental
Association
0026-2102
Continues the Journal of the Michigan State
Dental Association.
1968   7505621

J Mich State Dent Assoc
The Journal of the Michigan State Dental
Association
0098-7107
Continues the Journal of the Michigan State
Dental Society. Continued by the Journal of
the Michigan Dental Association.
1951-1968   7503085

J Mich State Dent Soc
Journal. Michigan State Dental Society
Continues: Bulletin of the Michigan State
Dental Society. Continued by: Journal of the
Michigan State Dental Association.
1932-1951   18710160R

J Mich State Med Soc
Journal - Michigan State Medical Society
0098-7522
Supersedes the Transactions of the Michigan
State Medical Society. Continued by
Michigan medicine.
1902-1964   7503038

J Microbiol
Journal of microbiology (Seoul, Korea)
1225-8873
Continues: Misaengmul Hakhoe chi.
Continued in part by: Misaengmul Hakhoe
chi (Seoul, Korea: 1997).
1995   9703165

J Microbiol Biotechnol
Journal of microbiology and biotechnology
1017-7825   1738-8872
1991   9431852

J Microbiol Epidemiol Immunobiol
Journal of microbiology, epidemiology and
immunobiology. Zhurnal mikrobiologii,
epidemiologii i immunobiologii
1957-1961   17920150R

J Microbiol Immunol Infect
Journal of microbiology, immunology, and
infection = Wei mian yu gan ran za zhi
1684-1182
Continues: Zhonghua Minguo wei sheng wu
ji mian yi xue za zhi.
1998   100956211

J Microbiol Methods
Journal of microbiological methods
0167-7012
1983   8306883

J Microencapsul
Journal of microencapsulation
0265-2048   1464-5246
1984   8500513

J Microgr
The Journal of micrographics
0022-2712
Continues NMA journal. Continued by: Journal
of information and image management..
1969-1983   0240227

J Microsc
Journal of microscopy
0022-2720   1365-2818
Continues the Journal of the Royal
Microscopical Society.
1969   0204522

J Microsc (Paris)
Journal de microscopie
0021-7921
Continued by Journal de microscopie et de
biologie cellulaire. Continued in part by:
Journal de microscopie et de spectroscopie
électroniques.
1962-1974   7512145

J Microsc Biol Cell
Journal de microscopie et de biologie
cellulaire
0395-9260
Continues Journal de microscopie. Continued
by Biologie cellulaire.
1975-1976   7512144

J Microsurg
Journal of microsurgery
0191-3239
Merged with: International journal of
microsurgery, to form: Microsurgery.
1979-1982   8005001

J Microw Power
The Journal of microwave power
0022-2739
Continued by: Journal of microwave power
and electromagnetic energy.
1966-1984   0332155

J Microw Power Electromagn Energy
The Journal of microwave power and
electromagnetic energy: a publication of the
International Microwave Power Institute
0832-7823
Continues: The Journal of microwave power.
1985   8706313

J Midwifery Womens Health
Journal of midwifery & women's health
1526-9523   1542-2011
Continues: Journal of nurse-midwifery.
2000   100909407

J Minim Invasive Gynecol
Journal of minimally invasive gynecology
1553-4650   1553-4669
Continues: Journal of the American
Association of Gynecologic Laparoscopists.
2005   101235322

J Miss Dent Assoc
Journal - Mississippi Dental Association
0047-7532
Continued by Mississippi Dental Association
journal.
1943-1974   7513940

J Miss State Med Assoc
Journal of the Mississippi State Medical
Association
0026-6396
Absorbed the Mississippi doctor.
1960   7505622

J Mo Dent Assoc
Journal of the Missouri Dental Association
0273-3463
Continues MDA journal. Continued by
Missouri dental journal.
1980-1984   8010650

J Mo Dent Assoc
Journal of the Missouri Dental Association
0026-6523
Continues The Journal of the Missouri State
Dental Association. Continued by MDA
journal.
1961-1979   7503087

J Mo State Dent Assoc
Journal. Missouri State Dental Association
1041-1178
Continued by the Journal of the Missouri
Dental Association.
1934-1961   18740050R

J Mol Appl Genet
Journal of molecular and applied genetics
0271-6801
1981-1985   8109497

J Mol Biol
Journal of molecular biology
0022-2836   1089-8638
1959   2985088R

J Mol Cell Cardiol
Journal of molecular and cellular cardiology
0022-2828   1095-8584
1970   0262322

J Mol Cell Immunol
The Journal of molecular and cellular
immunology: JMCI
0724-6803
1983-1990   8405005

J Mol Diagn
The Journal of molecular diagnostics: JMD
1525-1578
1999   100893612

J Mol Endocrinol
Journal of molecular endocrinology
0952-5041   1479-6813
1988   8902617

J Mol Evol
Journal of molecular evolution
0022-2844   1432-1432
1971   0360051

J Mol Graph
Journal of molecular graphics
0263-7855
Continued by: Journal of molecilar graphics
& modelling.
1983-1996   9014762

J Mol Graph Model
Journal of molecular graphics & modelling
1093-3263   1873-4243
Continues: Journal of molecular graphics.
1997   9716237

J Mol Histol
Journal of molecular histology
1567-2379
Continues: Histochemical journal.
2004   101193653

J Mol Med
Journal of molecular medicine (Berlin,
Germany)
0946-2716   1432-1440
Continues: Clinical investigator.
1995   9504370

J Mol Microbiol Biotechnol
Journal of molecular microbiology and
biotechnology
1464-1801   1660-2412
1999   100892561

J Mol Model
Journal of molecular modeling
1610-2940   0948-5023
1995   9806569

J Mol Neurosci
Journal of molecular neuroscience: MN
0895-8696   1559-1166
Absorbed: Molecular and chemical
neuropathology. 1999-
1989   9002991

J Mol Recognit
Journal of molecular recognition: JMR
0952-3499
1988   9004580

J Morphol
Journal of morphology
0362-2525   1744-4241
1887   0406125

J Mot Behav
Journal of motor behavior
0022-2895
1969   0236512

J Mt Sinai Hosp N Y
Journal of the Mount Sinai Hospital, New York
0099-9695
Continued by The Mount Sinai journal of medicine, New York.
1934-1969   0242260

J Muscle Res Cell Motil
Journal of muscle research and cell motility
0142-4319
1980   8006298

J Musculoskelet Neuronal Interact
Journal of musculoskeletal & neuronal interactions
1108-7161
2000   101084496

J Music Ther
Journal of music therapy
0022-2917
Supersedes: Bulletin of NAMT.
1964   0014162

J N C Dent Soc
The Journal of the North Carolina Dental Society
0029-2443
Continues Bulletin of the North Carolina Dental Society. Continued by North Carolina dental journal.
1951-1972   7505625

J N H Dent Soc
Journal (New Hampshire Dental Society)
1044-4114
1973-1991   8901297

J N J Dent Assoc
Journal of the New Jersey Dental Association
0093-7347
Continues the Journal of the New Jersey State Dental Society.
1970   0420021

J N J Dent Hyg Assoc
Journal Of The New Jersey Dental Hygienists Association
0028-5641
Continued by: Wisdom Tooth.
1964-1979   9875595

J N J State Dent Soc
The Journal of the New Jersey State Dental Society
0028-596X
Continues the New Jersey state dental journal. Continued by the Journal of the New Jersey Dental Association.
1938-1970   0420022

J N Y State Nurses Assoc
The Journal of the New York State Nurses' Association
0028-7644
Supersedes New York State nurse.
1970   7507218

J N Y State Sch Nurse Teach Assoc
The Journal of the New York State School Nurse Teachers Association
0191-3751
Continues: NYSSNTA journal.
1977-1978   7901144

J N Y State Sch Nurse Teach Assoc
Journal of the New York State School Nurse-Teachers Association
0036-1755
Continued by: NYSSNTA journal.
1969-1975   7609158

J N Z Soc Periodontol
Journal of the New Zealand Society of Periodontology
0111-1485
Continues Bulletin - The N. Z. Society of Periodontology
1977   7809869

J Nanosci Nanotechnol
Journal of nanoscience and nanotechnology
1533-4880   1533-4899
2001   101088195

J Nat Prod
Journal of natural products
0163-3864   1520-6025
Continues: Lloydia.
1979   7906882

J Nat Toxins
Journal of natural toxins
1058-8108
1992-2002   9208016

J Natl Analg Soc
Journal. National Analgesia Society
Supersedes Journal of the Rocky Mountain Analgesia Society.
1972-1977   0330010

J Natl Assoc Chirop
Journal of the National Association of Chiropodists
0360-1684
Continues Pedic items. Continued by Journal of the American Podiatry Association.
1921-1957   7600748

J Natl Assoc Hosp Dev
Journal (National Association for Hospital Development (U.S.))
0196-4933
Continued by: Journal (Association for Healthcare Philanthropy (U.S.))
1971-1990   7511919

J Natl Assoc Priv Psychiatr Hosp
Journal - National Association of Private Psychiatric Hospitals
0027-8629
Continued by The Psychiatric hospital.
1969-1981   7503039

J Natl Assoc Seventh Day Advent Dent
Journal Of The National Association Of Seventh-Day Adventist Dentists
1959-1966   9883819

J Natl Black Nurses Assoc
Journal of National Black Nurses' Association: JNBNA
0885-6028
1986   8703519

J Natl Cancer Inst
Journal of the National Cancer Institute
0027-8874   1460-2105
Absorbed: Cancer treatment reports.
1940   7503089

J Natl Cancer Inst Monogr
Journal of the National Cancer Institute. Monographs
1052-6773   1745-6614
Continues NCI monographs.
1990   9011255

J Natl Compr Canc Netw
Journal of the National Comprehensive Cancer Network: JNCCN
1540-1405   1540-1413
2003   101162515

J Natl Malar Soc
Journal. National Malaria Society
Merged with the American journal of tropical medicine to form the American journal of tropical medicine and hygiene.
1942-1951   18930020R

J Natl Med Assoc
Journal of the National Medical Association
0027-9684
1909   7503090

J Natl Proctol Assoc
Journal. National Proctologic Association
Continues: Journal of the American College of Proctology.
1940-1949   0375310

J Nebr Dent Assoc
The Journal of the Nebraska Dental Association
0028-1832
Continues the Nebraska dental news.
1931-1985   7503091

J Negat Results Biomed
Journal of negative results in biomedicine
                             1477-5751
2002   101152210

J Nephrol
Journal of nephrology
1121-8428   1724-6059
1988   9012268

J Nephrol Nurs
Journal of nephrology nursing
0748-5328
1984-1986   8502669

J Nerv Ment Dis
The Journal of nervous and mental disease
0022-3018   1539-736X
Continues: Chicago journal of nervous and mental disease.
1876   0375402

J Neural Eng
Journal of neural engineering
1741-2560
2004   101217933

J Neural Transm
Journal of neural transmission
0300-9564
Continues Journal of neuro-visceral relations. Split into: Journal of neural transmission. General section, and: Journal of neural transmission. Parkinson's disease and dementia section.
1972-1989   0337042

J Neural Transm
Journal of neural transmission (Vienna, Austria: 1996)
0300-9564   1435-1463
Merger of: Journal of neural transmission. General section, and: Journal of neural transmission. Parkinson's disease and dementia section, continuing the numbering of the former.
1996   9702341

J Neural Transm Gen Sect
Journal of neural transmission. General section
0300-9564
Continues in part: Journal of neural transmission. Merged with: Journal of neural transmission. Parkinson's disease and dementia section, to form: Journal of neural transmission (Vienna, Austria: 1996).
1989-1995   9002201

J Neural Transm Park Dis Dement Sect
Journal of neural transmission. Parkinson's disease and dementia section
0936-3076
Continues in part: Journal of neural transmission. Merged with: Journal of neural transmission. General section, to form: Journal of neural transmission (Vienna, Austria: 1996).
1989-1995   8914371

J Neural Transm Suppl
Journal of neural transmission. Supplementum
0303-6995
Continues: Journal of neuro-visceral relations. Supplementum.
1974   0425126

J Neural Transplant
Journal of neural transplantation
1352-237X
Continued by: Journal of neural transplantation & plasticity.
1989-1989   9104162

J Neural Transplant Plast
Journal of neural transplantation & plasticity
0792-8483
Continues: Journal of neural transplantation. Continued by: Neural plasticity.
1991-1997   9104161

J NeuroAIDS
Journal of neuro-AIDS
1069-7438
Continued by: Journal of LGBT health research.
1996-2004   9613966

J Neurobiol
Journal of neurobiology
0022-3034   1097-4695
Continued by: Developmental neurobiology.
1969-2006   0213640

J Neurochem
Journal of neurochemistry
0022-3042   1471-4159
1956   2985190R

J Neurocytol
Journal of neurocytology
0300-4864
Continued by: Brain cell biology.
1972-2005   0364620

J Neuroendocrinol
Journal of neuroendocrinology
0953-8194   1365-2826
1989   8913461

J Neuroeng Rehabil
Journal of neuroengineering and rehabilitation
                   1743-0003
2004   101232233

J Neurogenet
Journal of neurogenetics
0167-7063   1563-5260
1983   8406473

J Neuroimaging
Journal of neuroimaging: official journal of the American Society of Neuroimaging
1051-2284   1552-6569
1991   9102705

J Neuroimmune Pharmacol
Journal of neuroimmune pharmacology: the official journal of the Society on NeuroImmune Pharmacology
1557-1890   1557-1904
2006   101256586

J Neuroimmunol
Journal of neuroimmunology
0165-5728
1981   8109498

J Neuroimmunol Suppl
Journal of neuroimmunology. Supplement
0169-5088
1982   8219171

J Neuroinflammation
Journal of neuroinflammation
                   1742-2094
2004   101222974

J Neurol
Journal of neurology
0340-5354
Continues Zeitschrift für Neurologie.
1974   0423161

J Neurol Neurosurg Psychiatry
Journal of neurology, neurosurgery, and psychiatry
0022-3050   1468-330X
Continues: Journal of neurology and psychiatry.
1944   2985191R

J Neurol Phys Ther
Journal of neurologic physical therapy: JNPT
1557-0576   1557-0584
Continues: Neurology report.
2003   101193365

J Neurol Sci
Journal of the neurological sciences
0022-510X
1964   0375403

J Neurooncol
Journal of neuro-oncology
0167-594X   1573-7373
1983   8309335

J Neuroophthalmol
Journal of neuro-ophthalmology: the official journal of the North American Neuro-Ophthalmology Society
1070-8022   1536-5166
Continues: Journal of clinical neuro-ophthalmology.
1994   9431308

J Neuropathol Exp Neurol
Journal of neuropathology and experimental neurology
0022-3069
1942   2985192R

J Neurophysiol
Journal of neurophysiology
0022-3077   1522-1598
1938   0375404

J Neuropsychiatr
Journal of neuropsychiatry
1959-1964   0070073

J Neuropsychiatry Clin Neurosci
The Journal of neuropsychiatry and clinical neurosciences
0895-0172   1545-7222
1989   8911344

J Neuropsychol
Journal of neuropsychology
1748-6645   1748-6653
2007   101468753

J Neuroradiol
Journal of neuroradiology. Journal de neuroradiologie
0150-9861
Continues Journal de neuroradiologie.
1976   7705086

J Neurosci
The Journal of neuroscience: the official journal of the Society for Neuroscience
0270-6474   1529-2401
1981   8102140

J Neurosci Methods
Journal of neuroscience methods
0165-0270
1979   7905558

J Neurosci Nurs
The Journal of neuroscience nursing: journal of the American Association of Neuroscience Nurses
0888-0395
Continues: Journal of neurosurgical nursing.
1986   8603596

J Neurosci Res
Journal of neuroscience research
0360-4012   1097-4547
1975   7600111

J Neurosurg
Journal of neurosurgery
0022-3085   1933-0693
Vols. for 2004-Dec. 2007 have supplement with title: Journal of neurosurgery. Pediatrics, which became an independent journal with Vol. 1, no. 1 (Jan. 2008). Vols. for 1999-May 2004 have supplement with title: Journal of neurosurgery. Spine, which became a separate journal with Vol. 1, no. 1 (July 2004).
1944   0253357

J Neurosurg Anesthesiol
Journal of neurosurgical anesthesiology
0898-4921   1537-1921
1989   8910749

J Neurosurg Nurs
Journal of neurosurgical nursing
0047-2603
Continued by: The Journal of neuroscience nursing.
1969-1985   1300146

J Neurosurg Pediatrics
Journal of neurosurgery. Pediatrics
1933-0707   1933-0715
Formerly published as a supplement to: Journal of neurosurgery.
2008   101463759

J Neurosurg Sci
Journal of neurosurgical sciences
0390-5616
Absorbed: Rivista di neuroscienze pediatriche. Continues Minerva neurochirurgica.
1973   0432557

J Neurosurg Spine
Journal of neurosurgery. Spine
1547-5654   1547-5646
Formerly published as a supplement to: Journal of neurosurgery.
2004   101223545

J Neurotrauma
Journal of neurotrauma
0897-7151
Continues: Central nervous system trauma.
1988   8811626

J Neurovirol
Journal of neurovirology
1355-0284   1538-2443
1995   9508123

J Neurovisc Relat
Journal of neuro-visceral relations
0075-4323
Continues Acta neurovegetativa. Continued by Journal of neural transmission.
1968-1972   0337043

J New Drugs
The Journal of new drugs
0096-0284
　Continued by the Journal of clinical
　pharmacology and the journal of new drugs.
1961-1966　　　　　　　　　0101352

J Newark Beth Isr Hosp
Journal - Newark Beth Israel Hospital
0549-0650
　Continued by Journal of the Newark Beth
　Israel Medical Center.
1950-1968　　　　　　　　　7503040

J Niger Assoc Dent Stud
Journal Of The Nigeria Association Of
Dental Students
0331-8699
1977　　　　　　　　　　　　9878250

J Nihon Univ Sch Dent
The Journal of Nihon University School of
Dentistry
0029-0432
　Continued by: Journal of oral science.
1958-1997　　　　　　　　　7509209

J Nippon Med Sch
Journal of Nippon Medical School = Nihon
Ika Daigaku zasshi
1345-4676　　　　　　　　　1347-3409
　Continues: Nippon Ika Daigaku zasshi.
　Continued in part by: Nihon Ika Daigaku
　Igakkai zasshi.
2000　　　　　　　　　　　100935589

J Nucl Biol Med
The Journal of nuclear biology and medicine
0449-2846
　Continues in part Minerva nucleare.
　Continued by The Journal of nuclear
　medicine and allied sciences.
1966-1976　　　　　　　　　0103164

J Nucl Biol Med
Journal of nuclear biology and medicine
(Turin, Italy: 1991)
0368-3249
　Continues: Journal of nuclear medicine and
　allied sciences. Continued by: Quarterly
　journal of nuclear medicine.
1991-1994　　　　　　　　　9110209

J Nucl Cardiol
Journal of nuclear cardiology: official
publication of the American Society of
Nuclear Cardiology
1071-3581　　　　　　　　　1532-6551
1994　　　　　　　　　　　　9423534

J Nucl Med
Journal of nuclear medicine: official
publication, Society of Nuclear Medicine
0161-5505　　　　　　　　　1535-5667
1960　　　　　　　　　　　　0217410

J Nucl Med Allied Sci
The Journal of nuclear medicine and allied
sciences
0392-0208
　Continues The Journal of nuclear biology and
　medicine.
1977-1990　　　　　　　　　7708412

J Nucl Med Technol
Journal of nuclear medicine technology
0091-4916　　　　　　　　　1535-5675
1973　　　　　　　　　　　　0430303

J Nurs Adm
The Journal of nursing administration
0002-0443　　　　　　　　　1539-0721
1971　　　　　　　　　　　　1263116

J Nurs Care
The Journal of nursing care
0162-7155
　Continues Nursing care.
1978-1982　　　　　　　　　7806870

J Nurs Care Qual
Journal of nursing care quality
1057-3631　　　　　　　　　1550-5065
　Continues: Journal of nursing quality
　assurance.
1991　　　　　　　　　　　　9200672

J Nurs Educ
The Journal of nursing education
0148-4834
1962　　　　　　　　　　　　7705432

J Nurs Ethics
Journal Of Nursing Ethics
　Continues: Update On Ethics.
1978-1978　　　　　　　　　9875515

J Nurs Hist
Journal of nursing history: a publication of
the Nursing Archives Associates at Boston
University
0888-5796
1985-1988　　　　　　　　　8605835

J Nurs Manag
Journal of nursing management
0966-0429　　　　　　　　　1365-2834
1993　　　　　　　　　　　　9306050

J Nurs Meas
Journal of nursing measurement
1061-3749
1993　　　　　　　　　　　　9318902

J Nurs Qual Assur
Journal of nursing quality assurance
0889-4647
　Continued by: Journal of nursing care quality.
1986-1991　　　　　　　　　8703781

J Nurs Res
The journal of nursing research: JNR
1682-3141
　Continues: Hu li yan jiu.
2001　　　　　　　　　　　101128757

J Nurs Scholarsh
Journal of nursing scholarship: an
official publication of Sigma Theta Tau
International Honor Society of Nursing /
Sigma Theta Tau
1527-6546　　　　　　　　　1547-5069
　Continues: Image--the journal of nursing
　scholarship.
2000　　　　　　　　　　　100911591

J Nurs Staff Dev
Journal of nursing staff development: JNSD
0882-0627
　Continued by: Journal for nurses in staff
　development.
1985-1998　　　　　　　　　8601288

J Nurse Midwifery
Journal of nurse-midwifery
0091-2182
　Continues: Bulletin of the American College
　of Nurse-Midwives. Continued by: Journal of
　midwifery & women's health.
1973-1999　　　　　　　　　0365647

J Nurses Staff Dev
Journal for nurses in staff development:
JNSD: official journal of the National
Nursing Staff Development Organization
1098-7886　　　　　　　　　1538-9049
　Continues: Journal of nursing staff
　development.
1998　　　　　　　　　　　　9809908

J Nutr
The Journal of nutrition
0022-3166　　　　　　　　　1541-6100
1928　　　　　　　　　　　　0404243

J Nutr Biochem
The Journal of nutritional biochemistry
0955-2863
　Continues: Nutrition reports international.
1990　　　　　　　　　　　　9010081

J Nutr Educ
Journal of nutrition education
0022-3182
　Continued by: Journal of nutrition education
　and behavior.
1969-2001　　　　　　　　　0246004

J Nutr Educ Behav
Journal of nutrition education and behavior
1499-4046　　　　　　　　　1708-8259
　Continues: Journal of nutrition education.
2002　　　　　　　　　　　101132622

J Nutr Elder
Journal of nutrition for the elderly
0163-9366　　　　　　　　　1540-8566
1980　　　　　　　　　　　　8208739

J Nutr Health Aging
The journal of nutrition, health & aging
1279-7707
1997　　　　　　　　　　　100893366

J Nutr Sci Vitaminol (Tokyo)
Journal of nutritional science and
vitaminology
0301-4800
　Continues: Journal of Vitaminology.
1973　　　　　　　　　　　　0402640

J Obstet Gynaecol
Journal of obstetrics and gynaecology
(Tokyo, Japan)
1340-9654
　Continues: Asia-Oceania journal of obstetrics
　and gynaecology. Continued by: Journal of
　obstetrics and gynaecology.
1995-1995　　　　　　　　　9515066

J Obstet Gynaecol
Journal of obstetrics and gynaecology: the
journal of the Institute of Obstetrics and
Gynaecology
0144-3615　　　　　　　　　1364-6893
1980　　　　　　　　　　　　8309140

J Obstet Gynaecol Br Commonw
The Journal of obstetrics and gynaecology of
the British Commonwealth
0022-3204
　Continues: Journal of obstetrics and
　gynaecology of the British Empire. Continued
　by: British journal of obstetrics and
　gynaecology.
1961-1974　　　　　　　　　7512801

J Obstet Gynaecol Can
Journal of obstetrics and gynaecology
Canada: JOGC = Journal d'obstétrique et
gynécologie du Canada: JOGC
1701-2163
　Continues: Journal SOGC.
2001　　　　　　　　　　　101126664

J Obstet Gynaecol Res
The journal of obstetrics and gynaecology
research
1341-8076
　Continues: Journal of obstetrics and
　gynaecology (Tokyo, Japan).
1996　　　　　　　　　　　　9612761

J Obstet Gynecol Neonatal Nurs
Journal of obstetric, gynecologic, and
neonatal nursing: JOGNN / NAACOG
0884-2175   1552-6909
　　Absorbed: AWHONN's clinical issues
　　in perinatal and women's health nursing.
　　Continues: JOGN nursing.
1985   8503123

J Occup Environ Hyg
Journal of occupational and environmental
hygiene
1545-9624   1545-9632
　　Formed by the union of: AIHA journal: and:
　　Applied occupational and environmental
　　hygiene.
2004   101189458

J Occup Environ Med
Journal of occupational and environmental
medicine / American College of
Occupational and Environmental Medicine
1076-2752   1536-5948
　　Continues: Journal of occupational medicine.
1995   9504688

J Occup Health
Journal of occupational health
1341-9145   1348-9585
　　Continues in part: Sangyō eiseigaku zasshi.
1996   9616320

J Occup Health Psychol
Journal of occupational health psychology
1076-8998
1996   9612485

J Occup Med
Journal of occupational medicine.: official
publication of the Industrial Medical
Association
0096-1736
　　Continued by: Journal of occupational and
　　environmental medicine.
1959-1994   7502807

J Occup Rehabil
Journal of occupational rehabilitation
1053-0487
1991   9202814

J Ocul Pharmacol
Journal of ocular pharmacology
8756-3320
　　Continued by: Journal of ocular
　　pharmacology and therapeutics.
1985-1994   8511297

J Ocul Pharmacol Ther
Journal of ocular pharmacology and
therapeutics: the official journal of the
Association for Ocular Pharmacology and
Therapeutics
1080-7683   1557-7732
　　Continues: Journal of ocular pharmacology.
1995   9511091

J Odontol Conserv
Journal d'odontologie conservatrice /
CNEOC
0756-1911
1983-1989   8804107

J Okla Dent Assoc
Journal - Oklahoma Dental Association
0164-9442
　　Continues Your Oklahoma Dental Association
　　journal.
1978   7905263

J Okla State Dent Assoc
Journal - Oklahoma State Dental Association
0030-1868
　　Continues Oklahoma State Dental
　　Association. Bulletin. Continued by Your
　　Oklahoma Dental Association journal.
1951-1974   7503042

J Okla State Med Assoc
The Journal of the Oklahoma State Medical
Association
0030-1876
1908   7503043

J Oleo Sci
Journal of oleo science
1345-8957   1347-3352
　　Continues in part: Nihon Yuka Gakkai shi.
2001   101175339

J Omaha Midwest Clin Soc
Journal. Omaha Mid-West Clinical Society
　　Continued by: Newsletter. Omaha Midwest
　　Clinical Society.
1940-1968   19330960R

J Oncol Pharm Pract
Journal of oncology pharmacy practice:
official publication of the International
Society of Oncology Pharmacy Practitioners
1078-1552   1477-092X
1995   9511372

J Ont Dent Assoc
The Journal of the Ontario Dental
Association
0030-2864
　　Continues the Booster. Continued by Ontario
　　dentist.
1931-19uu   7503096

J Oper Res Soc
The Journal of the Operational Research
Society
0160-5682
　　Continues Operational Research Quarterly.
1978   7804132

J Oper Room Res Inst
The Journal of the Operating Room
Research Institute: JORRI
0276-6353
1980-1983   8204894

J Ophthalmic Nurs Technol
Journal of ophthalmic nursing & technology
0744-7132
1982-2000   8219658

J Opioid Manag
Journal of opioid management
1551-7489
2005   101234523

J Opt Soc Am
Journal of the Optical Society of America
0030-3941
　　Continues in part Journal of the Optical
　　Society of America and review of scientific
　　instruments. Split into: Journal of the Optical
　　Society of America. A. Optics and image
　　science. and: Journal of the Optical Society of
　　America. B. Optical physics.
1930-1983   7503097

J Opt Soc Am A
Journal of the Optical Society of America. A,
Optics and image science
0740-3232
　　Continues in part: Journal of the Optical
　　Society of America. Continued by: Journal
　　of the Optical Society of America. A. Optics.
　　image science, and vision.
1984-1993   8402086

J Opt Soc Am A Opt Image Sci Vis
Journal of the Optical Society of America. A,
Optics, image science, and vision
1084-7529
　　Continues: Journal of the Optical Society of
　　America. A. Optics and image science.
1993   9800943

J Or State Dent Assoc
Journal. Oregon State Dental Association
　　Continued by the Oregon state dental journal.
1932-1949   19420380R

J Oral Implant Transplant Surg
The Journal of oral implant and transplant
surgery
　　Continues: Journal of implant dentistry.
1964-1966   0256541

J Oral Implantol
The Journal of oral implantology
0160-6972
　　Continues Oral implantology.
1977   7801086

J Oral Maxillofac Surg
Journal of oral and maxillofacial surgery:
official journal of the American Association
of Oral and Maxillofacial Surgeons
0278-2391   1531-5053
　　Continues: Journal of oral surgery (American
　　Dental Association: 1965).
1982   8206428

J Oral Med
Journal of oral medicine
0022-3247
　　Continues Journal of dental medicine.
1966-1987   0045507

J Oral Pathol
Journal of oral pathology
0300-9777
　　Continued by: Journal of oral pathology &
　　medicine.
1972-1988   0342050

J Oral Pathol Med
Journal of oral pathology & medicine:
official publication of the International
Association of Oral Pathologists and the
American Academy of Oral Pathology
0904-2512   1600-0714
　　Continues: Journal of oral pathology.
1989   8911934

J Oral Rehabil
Journal of oral rehabilitation
0305-182X   1365-2842
1974   0433604

J Oral Sci
Journal of oral science
1343-4934   1880-4926
　　Continues: Journal of Nihon University
　　School of Dentistry.
1998   9808942

J Oral Surg
Journal of oral surgery (American Dental
Association: 1965)
0022-3255
　　Continues: Journal of oral surgery, anesthesia
　　and hospital dental service. Continued by:
　　Journal of oral and maxillofacial surgery.
1965-1981   8302454

J Oral Surg (Chic)
Journal of oral surgery
0146-1575
　　Continued by: Journal of oral surgery,
　　anesthesia, and hospital dental service.
1943-1958   0234121

J Oral Surg Anesth Hosp Dent Serv
Journal of oral surgery, anesthesia, and
hospital dental service
0095-9618
　　Continues and continued by Journal of oral
　　surgery.
1959-1964   0234122

J Oral Ther Pharmacol
Journal of oral therapeutics and
pharmacology
0449-2889
1964-1968   17930060R

J Oreg Dent Assoc
The Journal of the Oregon Dental
Association
0030-4670
Continues the Oregon state dental journal.
Continued by: Membership matters (Portland,
Or.: 1995).
1968-1995   7503098

J Org Chem
The Journal of organic chemistry
0022-3263   1520-6904
1936   2985193R

J Orofac Orthop
Journal of orofacial orthopedics =
Fortschritte der Kieferorthopädie: Organ/
official journal Deutsche Gesellschaft für
Kieferorthopädie
1434-5293
Continues: Fortschritte der Kieferorthopädie.
1996   9713484

J Orofac Pain
Journal of orofacial pain
1064-6655
Continues: Journal of craniomandibular
disorders.
1993   9418507

J Orthod
Journal of orthodontics
1465-3125   1465-3133
Continues: British journal of orthodontics.
2000   100957268

J Orthop Res
Journal of orthopaedic research: official
publication of the Orthopaedic Research
Society
0736-0266   1554-527X
1983   8404726

J Orthop Sci
Journal of orthopaedic science: official
journal of the Japanese Orthopaedic
Association
0949-2658
1996   9604934

J Orthop Sports Phys Ther
The Journal of orthopaedic and sports
physical therapy
0190-6011
Formed by the union of the Bulletin of the
Orthopaedic Section and the Bulletin of the
Sports Medicine Section of the American
Physical Therapy Association.
1979   7908150

J Orthop Surg (Hong Kong)
Journal of orthopaedic surgery (Hong Kong)
1022-5536
Continues: Journal of the Western Pacific
Orthopaedic Association.
1993   9440382

J Orthop Trauma
Journal of orthopaedic trauma
0890-5339   1531-2291
1987   8807705

J Osaka Dent Univ
Journal of Osaka Dental University
0475-2058
1967   7507225

J Osaka Univ Dent Sch
The Journal of Osaka University Dental
School
0473-4599
Supersedes Dental bulletin of Osaka Daigaku.
1961-1995   7503132

J Oslo City Hosp
Journal of the Oslo city hospitals
0030-6207
1951-1989   7908151

J Osteopath (Kirksvill)
The Journal of osteopathy
1894-1964   0014167

J Otolaryngol
The Journal of otolaryngology
0381-6605   1708-833X
Continues: Canadian journal of
otolaryngology. Continued by: Journal of
otolaryngology - head & neck surgery.
1976-2007   7610513

J Otolaryngol Head Neck Surg
Journal of otolaryngology - head &
neck surgery = Le Journal d'oto-rhino-
laryngologie et de chirurgie cervico-faciale
1916-0216
Continues: Journal of otolaryngology.
2008   101479544

J Otolaryngol Soc Aust
Journal of the Oto-laryngological Society of
Australia
0030-6614
Continued by: Australian journal of otolaryngology.
1961-1991   7503099

J Otolaryngol Suppl
The Journal of otolaryngology. Supplement
0707-7270
Continues Canadian journal of
otolaryngology. Journal canadien
d'otolaryngologie. Supplement.
1977-1986   7708963

J Outcome Meas
Journal of outcome measurement
1090-655X
Absorbed by: Journal of applied
measurement.
1997-2002   9710385

J Paediatr Child Health
Journal of paediatrics and child health
1034-4810   1440-1754
Continues: Australian paediatric journal.
1990   9005421

J Paediatr Dent
Journal of paediatric dentistry
0267-2073
Continues: Proceedings of the British
Paedodontic Society. Merged with: Journal
of the International Association of Dentistry
for Children, to form: International journal of
paediatric dentistry.
1985-1990   8508400

J Pain
The journal of pain: official journal of the
American Pain Society
1526-5900   1528-8447
Continues: Pain forum.
2000   100898657

J Pain Palliat Care Pharmacother
Journal of pain & palliative care
pharmacotherapy
1536-0288   1536-0539
Merger of: Hospice journal, and: Journal
of pharmaceutical care in pain & symptom
control.
2002   101125608

J Pain Symptom Manage
Journal of pain and symptom management
0885-3924   1873-6513
Continues: PRN forum.
1986   8605836

J Pak Med Assoc
JPMA. The Journal of the Pakistan Medical
Association
0030-9982
Continues Journal of the Pakistan Medical
Association.
1974   7501162

J Palest Arab Med Assoc
Journal. Palestine Arab Medical Association
1945-1947   19520010R

J Palliat Care
Journal of palliative care
0825-8597
1985   8610345

J Palliat Med
Journal of palliative medicine
1096-6218   1557-7740
1998   9808462

J Parapsychol
The Journal of parapsychology
0022-3387
1937   0413414

J Parasitol
The Journal of parasitology
0022-3395
1914   7803124

J Parenter Drug Assoc
Journal of the Parenteral Drug Association
0161-1933
Continues Bulletin of the Parenteral Drug
Association. Continued by Journal of
parenteral science and technology.
1978-1980   7803538

J Parenter Sci Technol
Journal of parenteral science and
technology: a publication of the Parenteral
Drug Association
0279-7976
Continues: Journal of the Parenteral Drug
Association. Continued by: Journal of
pharmaceutical science and technology.
1981-1993   8103145

J Parodontol
Journal de parodontologie
0750-1838
Continued by: Journal de paradontologie &
d'implantologie orale.
1982-1993   8506963

J Pastoral Care
Journal of pastoral care
0022-3409
Absorbed the Journal of clinical pastoral
work in 1950. Continued by: Journal of
pastoral care & counseling.
1947-2001   17930120R

J Pastoral Care Counsel
The journal of pastoral care & counseling:
JPCC
1542-3050
Continues: Journal of pastoral care.
2002   101144384

J Pathol
The Journal of pathology
0022-3417   1096-9896
Absorbed: Diagnostic histopathology. 1984
Continues in part: Journal of pathology and
bacteriology.
1969   0204634

J Pathol Bacteriol
The Journal of pathology and bacteriology
0368-3494
Continued by the Journal of pathology and
the Journal of medical microbiology.
1892-1968   0204750

J Patient Acc Manage
Journal of patient account management
0890-6068
19uu   9878499

J Pediatr
The Journal of pediatrics
0022-3476   1097-6833
Continues: Transactions. American Academy
of Pediatrics.
1932   0375410

J Pediatr (Rio J)
Jornal de pediatria
0021-7557   1678-4782
1934   2985188R

J Pediatr Adolesc Gynecol
Journal of pediatric and adolescent gynecology
1083-3188   1873-4332
Continues: Adolescent and pediatric
gynecology.
1996   9610774

J Pediatr Endocrinol
The Journal of pediatric endocrinology
0334-018X
Continued by: Journal of pediatric
endocrinology and metabolism.
1985-1994   8510464

J Pediatr Endocrinol Metab
Journal of pediatric endocrinology &
metabolism: JPEM
0334-018X
Continues: Journal of pediatric endocrinology.
1995   9508900

J Pediatr Gastroenterol Nutr
Journal of pediatric gastroenterology and
nutrition
0277-2116   1536-4801
1982   8211545

J Pediatr Health Care
Journal of pediatric health care: official
publication of National Association of
Pediatric Nurse Associates & Practitioners
0891-5245
1987   8709735

J Pediatr Hematol Oncol
Journal of pediatric hematology/oncology:
official journal of the American Society of
Pediatric Hematology/Oncology
1077-4114   1563-5309
Continues: American journal of pediatric
hematology/oncology.
1995   9505928

J Pediatr Nurs
Journal of pediatric nursing
0882-5963   1532-8449
1986   8607529

J Pediatr Oncol Nurs
Journal of pediatric oncology nursing:
official journal of the Association of
Pediatric Oncology Nurses
1043-4542   1532-8457
Continues: Journal of the Association of
Pediatric Oncology Nurses.
1989   8917825

J Pediatr Ophthalmol
Journal of pediatric ophthalmology
0022-345X
Continued by Journal of pediatric
ophthalmology and strabismus.
1964-1977   0044350

J Pediatr Ophthalmol Strabismus
Journal of pediatric ophthalmology and
strabismus
0191-3913
Continues Journal of pediatric ophthalmology.
1978   7901143

J Pediatr Orthop
Journal of pediatric orthopedics
0271-6798   1539-2570
1981   8109053

J Pediatr Orthop B
Journal of pediatric orthopaedics. Part B /
European Paediatric Orthopaedic Society,
Pediatric Orthopaedic Society of North
America
1060-152X   1473-5865
1992   9300904

J Pediatr Perinat Nutr
Journal of pediatric & perinatal nutrition
8756-6206
1987-1990   8712414

J Pediatr Psychol
Journal of pediatric psychology
0146-8693   1465-735X
Supersedes Pediatric psychology.
1976   7801773

J Pediatr Surg
Journal of pediatric surgery
0022-3468   1531-5037
1966   0052631

J Pediatr Urol
Journal of pediatric urology
1477-5131   1873-4898
2005   101233150

J Pedod
The Journal of pedodontics
0145-5508
Continued by: Journal of clinical pediatric
dentistry.
1976-1990   7702327

J Pept Res
The journal of peptide research: official
journal of the American Peptide Society
1397-002X   1399-3011
Merger of: International journal of peptide
& protein research. and: Peptide research,
continuing the numbering of the former.
Continued by: Chemical biology & drug
design.
1997-2005   9707067

J Pept Sci
Journal of peptide science: an official
publication of the European Peptide Society
1075-2617
1995   9506309

J Perianesth Nurs
Journal of perianesthesia nursing: official
journal of the American Society of
PeriAnesthesia Nurses / American Society of
PeriAnesthesia Nurses
1089-9472   1532-8473
Continues: Journal of post anesthesia nursing.
1996   9610507

J Perinat Med
Journal of perinatal medicine
0300-5577
1973   0361031

J Perinat Neonatal Nurs
The Journal of perinatal & neonatal nursing
0893-2190   1550-5073
1987   8801387

J Perinatol
Journal of perinatology: official journal of
the California Perinatal Association
0743-8346   1476-5543
Continues: Journal of the California Perinatal
Association.
1984   8501884

J Periodontal Res
Journal of periodontal research
0022-3484   1600-0765
1966   0055107

J Periodontal Res Suppl
Journal of periodontal research. Supplement
0075-4331
1967-1986   0101604

J Periodontol
Journal of periodontology
0022-3492
Continues Journal of periodontology-
periodontics.
1970   8000345

J Periodontol
The Journal of periodontology
Merged with Periodontics to form Journal of
periodontology-periodontics.
1930-1968   0173665

J Perioper Pract
Journal of perioperative practice
1750-4589
Continues: British journal of perioperative
nursing.
2006   101271023

J Peripher Nerv Syst
Journal of the peripheral nervous system:
JPNS
1085-9489   1529-8027
1996   9704532

J Pers
Journal of personality
0022-3506   1467-6494
Continues: Character and personality.
1945   2985194R

J Pers Assess
Journal of personality assessment
0022-3891   1532-7752
Continues: Journal of projective techniques &
personality assessment.
1971   1260201

J Pers Disord
Journal of personality disorders
0885-579X
1987   8710838

J Pers Soc Psychol
Journal of personality and social psychology
0022-3514
Supersedes in part the Journal of abnormal
and social psychology.
1965   0014171

J Pharm Belg
Journal de pharmacie de Belgique
0047-2166
1919   0375351

J Pharm Biomed Anal
Journal of pharmaceutical and biomedical
analysis
0731-7085
1983   8309336

J Pharm Mark Manage
Journal of pharmaceutical marketing &
management
0883-7597
1986   8709879

J Pharm Pharm Sci
Journal of pharmacy & pharmaceutical
sciences: a publication of the Canadian
Society for Pharmaceutical Sciences, Société
canadienne des sciences pharmaceutiques
1482-1826
1998   9807281

J Pharm Pharmacol
The Journal of pharmacy and pharmacology
0022-3573
Absorbed: Pharmacy and pharmacology
communications, Jan. 2001.
1949   0376363

J Pharm Sci
Journal of pharmaceutical sciences
0022-3549   1520-6017
Formed by the merger of: American
Pharmaceutical Association. Journal of
the American Pharmaceutical Association.
Scientific edition, and: Drug standards, and
continues the numbering of the former.
1961   2985195R

J Pharm Sci Technol
Journal of pharmaceutical science and
technology: the official journal of PDA
1076-397X
Continues: Journal of parenteral science and
technology. Continued by: PDA journal of
pharmaceutical science and technology.
1994-1994   9432967

J Pharm Technol
The Journal of pharmacy technology: jPT:
official publication of the Association of
Pharmacy Technicians
8755-1225
1985   8504643

J Pharmacobiodyn
Journal of pharmacobio-dynamics
0386-846X
Continued by: Biological & pharmaceutical
bulletin.
1978-1992   7901854

J Pharmacokinet Biopharm
Journal of pharmacokinetics and
biopharmaceutics
0090-466X
Continued by: Journal of pharmacokinetics
and pharmacodynamics,.
1973-1999   0357115

J Pharmacokinet Pharmacodyn
Journal of pharmacokinetics and
pharmacodynamics
1567-567X
Continues: Journal of pharmacokinetics and
biopharmaceutics.
2001   101096520

J Pharmacol
Journal de pharmacologie
0021-793X
Continued by: Fundamental & clinical
pharmacology.
1970-1986   1247760

J Pharmacol Exp Ther
The Journal of pharmacology and
experimental therapeutics
0022-3565   1521-0103
Vols. 1-2 of: Pharmacological reviews issued
as supplements in v. 95-100, consisting of pt.
2 of Apr., Aug., and Dec. issues.
1909   0376362

J Pharmacol Methods
Journal of pharmacological methods
0160-5402
Continued by: Journal of pharmacological
and toxicological methods.
1978-1991   7806596

J Pharmacol Sci
Journal of pharmacological sciences
1347-8613   1347-8648
Continues: Japanese journal of pharmacology.
2003   101167001

J Pharmacol Toxicol Methods
Journal of pharmacological and toxicological
methods
1056-8719   1873-488X
Continues: Journal of pharmacological
methods.
1992   9206091

J Phila Cty Dent Soc
The journal of the Philadelphia County
Dental Society
1523-5238
Continues: Bulletin of the Philadelphia
County Dental Society (1965).
1983   9880286

J Philipp Dent Assoc
The Journal of the Philippine Dental
Association
0031-7497
1948-1999   7505626

J Philipp Fed Priv Med Pract
Journal of the Philippine Federation of
Private Medical Practitioners
0031-7535
Continues: Philippine medical world.
1952-1967   7503101

J Philipp Med Assoc
Journal of the Philippine Medical
Association
Continues the Journal of the Philippine
Islands Medical Association.
1940-1996   7503102

J Philos Sci Law
The journal of philosophy, science & law
1549-8549
2001   101197577

J Photochem Photobiol B
Journal of photochemistry and photobiology.
B, Biology
1011-1344
Continued in part by: Journal of
photochemistry.
1987   8804966

J Phys Act Health
Journal of physical activity & health
1543-3080   1543-5474
2004   101189457

J Phys Chem
The Journal of physical chemistry
0022-3654
Continues: Journal of physical & colloid
chemistry. Split into: Journal of physical
chemistry. A ; and: Journal of physical
chemistry. B.
1952-1996   0406042

J Phys Chem A
The journal of physical chemistry. A
1089-5639   1520-5215
Continues in part: Journal of physical
chemistry (1952).
1997   9890903

J Phys Chem B
The journal of physical chemistry. B
1520-6106   1520-5207
Continues in part: Journal of physical
chemistry (1952).
1997   101157530

J Phys Colloid Chem
The Journal of physical and colloid chemistry
0092-7023
Continues: Journal of physical chemistry
(1896). Continued by: Journal of physical
chemistry (1952).
1947-1951   0405527

J Phys Educ
Journal of physical education
Continues Journal of physical education
and school hygiene. Continued by Physical
education.
1945-1954   17930170R

J Phys Educ
Journal of physical education (Dayton, Ohio)
0022-3662
Continues: Physical training. Continued by:
Journal of physical education and program.
1927-1981   8405946

J Phys [E]
Journal of physics E: Scientific instruments
0022-3735
Continues the Journal of scientific
instruments. Continued by: Measurement
science & technology.
1970-1989   1276760

J Physical Soc Japan
Journal Of The Physical Society Of Japan
1946   9877151

J Physicians Assoc AIDS Care
Journal of the Physicians Association for
AIDS Care
1074-2395
Continues: PAACnotes. Continued by:
Journal of the International Association of
Physicians in AIDS Care.
1994-1995   9431848

J Physiol
The Journal of physiology
0022-3751   1469-7793
1878   0266262

J Physiol (Paris)
Journal de physiologie
0021-7948
Continues: Journal de physiologie et de
pathologie générale. Continued by: Journal of
physiology, Paris.
1947-1991   9309350

J Physiol Anthropol
Journal of physiological anthropology
1880-6791   1880-6805
Continues: Journal of physiological
anthropology and applied human science.
2006   101269653

J Physiol Anthropol Appl Human Sci
Journal of physiological anthropology and
applied human science
1345-3475   1347-5355
Continues: Applied human science.
Continued by: Journal of physiological
anthropology.
2000-2005   100930389

J Physiol Biochem
Journal of physiology and biochemistry
1138-7548
Continues: Revista española de fisiología.
1998   9812509

J Physiol Paris
Journal of physiology, Paris
0928-4257
Continues: Journal de physiologie.
1992   9309351

J Physiol Pharmacol
Journal of physiology and pharmacology: an official journal of the Polish Physiological Society
0867-5910   1899-1505
Continues: Acta physiologica polonica.
1991   9114501

J Physiol Sci
The journal of physiological sciences: JPS
1880-6546   1880-6562
Continues: Japanese journal of physiology.
2006   101262417

J Physiol Suppl (Paris)
Journal de physiologie. Supplément
0449-1939
1959-1967   0427151

J Pierre Fauchard Acad
Journal of Pierre Fauchard Academy (Pierre Fauchard Academy. India Section)
0970-2199
1987   8712416

J Pineal Res
Journal of pineal research
0742-3098   1600-079X
1984   8504412

J Plant Physiol
Journal of plant physiology
0176-1617
Absorbed: Biochemie und Physiologie der Pflanzen. Continues: Zeitschrift für Pflanzenphysiologie.
1984   9882059

J Plant Res
Journal of plant research
0918-9440   1618-0860
Continues: Botanical magazine. Tokyo.
1993   9887853

J Plast Reconstr Aesthet Surg
Journal of plastic, reconstructive & aesthetic surgery: JPRAS
1748-6815
Continues: British journal of plastic surgery.
2006   101264239

J Plast Reconstr Surg Nurs
The Journal of plastic and reconstructive surgical nursing: official organ of the American Society of Plastic and Reconstructive Surgical Nurses
0273-3285
Continued by: Plastic surgical nursing.
1981-1982   8301364

J Policy Anal Manage
Journal of policy analysis and management: [the journal of the Association for Public Policy Analysis and Management]
0276-8739   1520-6688
Formed by the union of: Policy analysis. ISSN 0098-2067; and: Public policy. ISSN 0033-3646.
1981   8214851

J Polym Sci A
Journal of polymer science: Part A, General papers
0449-2951
Supersedes in part Journal of polymer science. Continued by Journal of polymer sciences: Part A-1. Polymer chemistry and Journal of polymer science: Part A-2. Polymer physics.
1963-1965   0165253

J Polym Sci [A1]
Journal of polymer science. Part A-1, Polymer chemistry
0449-296X
Continues in part Journal of polymer science: Part A. General papers. Continued by Journal of polymer science. Polymer chemistry edition.
1966-1972   0050636

J Polym Sci [B]
Journal of polymer science. Part B: Polymer letters
0449-2986
Supersedes in part Journal of polymer science. Continued by Journal of polymer science. Polymer letters edition.
1963-1972   7610515

J Post Anesth Nurs
Journal of post anesthesia nursing
0883-9433
Continues: Journal of perianesthesia nursing.
1986-1996   8609069

J Postgrad Med
Journal of postgraduate medicine
0022-3859
1955   2985196R

J Pract Nurs
The Journal of practical nursing
0022-3867
Continues Practical nursing.
1963   0376610

J Prat Rev Gen Clin Ther
Journal des praticiens; revue générale de clinique et de thérapeutique
Merged with Paris médical to form Revue du praticien.
1887-1951   17820280R

J Prev Dent
The Journal of preventive dentistry
0096-2732
Continued by: Clinical preventive dentistry.
1974-1980   7502591

J Prev Interv Community
Journal of prevention & intervention in the community
1085-2352   1540-7330
Continues: Prevention in human services.
1996   9702085

J Prev Med Hyg
Journal of preventive medicine and hygiene
1121-2233
Continues: Giornale di igiene e medicina preventiva.
1989   9214440

J Prev Med Public Health
Journal of preventive medicine and public health = Yebang ŭihakhoe chi
1975-8375
Continues: Yebang ŭihakhoe chi.
2004   101242972

J Prim Prev
The journal of primary prevention
0278-095X
Continues: Journal of prevention.
1981   8213457

J Prof Nurs
Journal of professional nursing: official journal of the American Association of Colleges of Nursing
8755-7223   1532-8481
1985   8511298

J Prof Serv Mark
Journal of professional services marketing
0748-4623
1986   9881815

J Proj Tech
Journal of projective techniques
Continues Rorschach research exchange and journal of projective techniques. Continued by the Journal of projective techniques & personality assessment.
1950-1963   0052130

J Proj Tech Pers Assess
Journal of projective techniques & personality assessment
0091-651X
Continues Journal of projective techniques. Continued by Journal of personality assessment.
1963-1970   1260202

J Prosthet Dent
The Journal of prosthetic dentistry
0022-3913   1097-6841
1951   0376364

J Prosthodont
Journal of prosthodontics: official journal of the American College of Prosthodontists
1059-941X   1532-849X
1992   9301275

J Protein Chem
Journal of protein chemistry
0277-8033
Continued by: Protein journal.
1982-2003   8217321

J Proteome Res
Journal of proteome research
1535-3893   1535-3907
2002   101128775

J Proteomics
Journal of proteomics
1874-3919
Continues: Journal of biochemical and biophysical methods.
2008   101475056

J Protozool
The Journal of protozoology
0022-3921
Continued by: Journal of eukaryotic microbiology.
1954-1992   2985197R

J Psychedelic Drugs
Journal of psychedelic drugs
0022-393X
Continued by Journal of psychoactive drugs.
1967-1980   0203241

J Psychiatr Ment Health Nurs
Journal of psychiatric and mental health nursing
1351-0126   1365-2850
1994   9439514

J Psychiatr Nurs
Journal of psychiatric nursing
Continued by: Journal of psychiatric nursing and mental health services.
1963-1966   7900452

J Psychiatr Nurs Ment Health Serv
Journal of psychiatric nursing and mental health services
0360-5973
Continues Journal of psychiatric nursing. Continued by Journal of psychosocial nursing and mental health services.
1967-1981   0141401

J Psychiatr Pract
Journal of psychiatric practice
1527-4160   1528-1145
Continues: Journal of practical psychiatry and behavioral health.
2000   100901141

J Psychiatr Res
Journal of psychiatric research
0022-3956
1961   0376331

J Psychiatr Soc Work
Journal of psychiatric social work
Continues the News-letter of the American
Association of Psychiatric Social Workers.
Superseded by Social work.
1947-1955   17940070R

J Psychiatry Neurosci
Journal of psychiatry & neuroscience: JPN
1180-4882   1488-2434
Continues: Psychiatric journal of the
University of Ottawa.
1991   9107859

J Psychoactive Drugs
Journal of psychoactive drugs
0279-1072
Continues: Journal of psychedelic drugs.
1981   8113536

J Psychohist
The Journal of psychohistory
0145-3378
Absorbed: Journal of psychoanalytic
anthropology. Continues: History of
childhood quarterly.
1976   7613887

J Psychol
The Journal of psychology
0022-3980
1935   0376332

J Psychol Norm Pathol (Paris)
Journal de psychologie normale et
pathologique
0021-7956
1904-1987   2985198R

J Psycholinguist Res
Journal of psycholinguistic research
0090-6905
1971   0333506

J Psychopharmacol
Journal of psychopharmacology (Oxford,
England)
0269-8811
1987   8907828

J Psychosoc Nurs Ment Health Serv
Journal of psychosocial nursing and mental
health services
0279-3695
Continues: Journal of psychiatric nursing and
mental health services.
1981   8200911

J Psychosoc Oncol
Journal of psychosocial oncology
0734-7332   1540-7586
1983   8309337

J Psychosom Obstet Gynaecol
Journal of psychosomatic obstetrics and
gynaecology
0167-482X
1982   8308648

J Psychosom Res
Journal of psychosomatic research
0022-3999
1956   0376333

J Psychother Pract Res
The Journal of psychotherapy practice and
research
1055-050X
Absorbed by: American journal of
psychotherapy.
1992-2001   9206496

J Public Health (Bangkok)
Journal of public health
0125-1678
1900   7705878

J Public Health (Oxf)
Journal of public health (Oxford, England)
1741-3842   1741-3850
Continues: Journal of public health medicine.
2004   101188638

J Public Health Dent
Journal of public health dentistry
0022-4006
Continues: Public health dentistry.
1965   0014207

J Public Health Manag Pract
Journal of public health management and
practice: JPHMP
1078-4659   1550-5022
1995   9505213

J Public Health Med
Journal of public health medicine
0957-4832   1464-3782
Continues: Community medicine. Continued
by: Journal of public health (Oxford,
England).
1990-2003   9011205

J Public Health Policy
Journal of public health policy
0197-5897
1980   8006508

J Qual Assur
Journal of quality assurance: a publication
of the National Association of Quality
Assurance Professionals
1062-0273
Continued by: Journal for healthcare quality.
1979-1991   8809256

J Qual Clin Pract
Journal of quality in clinical practice
1320-5455   1440-1762
Continues: Australian clinical review.
1994-2001   9430670

J R Army Med Corps
Journal of the Royal Army Medical Corps
0035-8665
1903   7505627

J R Army Vet Corps
The Journal of the Royal Army Veterinary
Corps
0035-8681
1929-1971   7503106

J R Coll Gen Pract
The Journal of the Royal College of General
Practitioners
0035-8797
Continues: Journal of the College of General
Practitioners. Continued by: British journal of
general practice.
1967-1989   7503107

J R Coll Gen Pract Occas Pap
The Journal of the Royal College of General
Practitioners. Occasional paper
0309-6300
Continued by: Occasional paper (Royal
College of General Practitioners).
1976-1988   7805797

J R Coll Physicians Edinb
The journal of the Royal College of
Physicians of Edinburgh
1478-2715
Continues: Proceedings of the Royal College
of Physicians of Edinburgh.
2002   101144324

J R Coll Physicians Lond
Journal of the Royal College of Physicians
of London
0035-8819
Continued by: Clinical medicine (London,
England).
1966-2000   7503108

J R Coll Surg Edinb
Journal of the Royal College of Surgeons of
Edinburgh
0035-8835
Continued by: Surgeon.
1955-2002   7503110

J R Fac Med Iraq
The Journal of the Royal Faculty of
Medicine of Iraq
0303-1608
Continued by the Journal of the Faculty of
Medicine, Baghdad.
1935-1948   0417270

J R I State Dent Soc
Journal of the Rhode Island State Dental
Society
0035-4643
Continued by Rhode Island dental journal.
1968-1972   7503103

J R Microsc Soc
Journal. Royal Microscopical Society (Great
Britain)
0368-3974
Supersedes the Monthly microscopical
journal. Continued by the Journal of
microscopy.
1878-1968   0204543

J R Nav Med Serv
Journal of the Royal Naval Medical Service
0035-9033
1915   7503111

J R Sanit Inst
Journal. Royal Sanitary Institute (Great
Britain)
Continues the Journal of the Sanitary Institute
of Great Britain. Continued by the Journal
of the Royal Society for the Promotion of
Health, London.
1904-1955   20440840R

J R Soc Health
Journal of the Royal Society of Health
0264-0325   1476-9042
Continues: Royal Society of Health journal.
1983   8303144

J R Soc Interface
Journal of the Royal Society, Interface / the
Royal Society
1742-5689   1742-5662
2004   101217269

J R Soc Med
Journal of the Royal Society of Medicine
0141-0768   1758-1095
Continues Proceedings of the Royal Society
of Medicine.
1978   7802879

J Radiat Res (Tokyo)
Journal of radiation research
0449-3060
1960   0376611

J Radiol
Journal de radiologie
0221-0363
Continues Journal de radiologie,
d'électrologie, et de médecine nucléaire.
1979   7906266

J Radiol Electrol Arch Electr Medicale
Journal de radiologie, d'électrologie &
archives d'électricité médicale
Continued by the Journal de radiologie.
d'électrologie et de médecine nucléaire.
1947-1957   0013747

J Radiol Electrol Med Nucl
Journal de radiologie, d'électrologie, et de
médecine nucléaire
0368-3966
Continues Journal de radiologie.
d'électrologie & archives d'électricité
médicale. Continued by Journal de radiologie.
1957-1978   7610508

J Radiol Prot
Journal of radiological protection: official
journal of the Society for Radiological
Protection
0952-4746   1361-6498
Continues: Journal of the Society for
Radiological Protection.
1988   8809257

J Recept Res
Journal of receptor research
0197-5110
Merged with: Second messengers and
phosphoproteins, to form: Journal of receptor
and signal transduction research.
1980-1994   8008358

J Recept Signal Transduct Res
Journal of receptor and signal transduction
research
1079-9893   1532-4281
Formed by the union of: Second messengers
and phosphoproteins; and: Journal of receptor
research, continuing the numbering of the latter.
1995   9509432

J Reconstr Microsurg
Journal of reconstructive microsurgery
0743-684X
1984   8502670

J Refract Corneal Surg
Journal of refractive and corneal surgery
1081-0803
Continues: Refractive & corneal surgery.
Continued by: Journal of refractive surgery
(Thorofare, N.J.: 1995).
1994-1994   9431306

J Refract Surg
Journal of refractive surgery (Thorofare,
N.J.: 1995)
1081-597X
Continues: Journal of refractive and corneal
surgery.
1995   9505927

J Rehabil
Journal of rehabilitation
0022-4154
Continues National rehabilitation news.
1945   0411775

J Rehabil Med
Journal of rehabilitation medicine: official
journal of the UEMS European Board of
Physical and Rehabilitation Medicine
1650-1977   1651-2081
Continues: Scandinavian journal of
rehabilitation medicine.
2001   101088169

J Rehabil R D
Journal of rehabilitation R&D / Veterans
Administration, Department of Medicine
and Surgery, Rehabilitation R&D Service
0742-3241
Continues: Bulletin of prosthetics research.
Continued by: Journal of rehabilitation
research and development.
1983-1983   8307649

J Rehabil Res Dev
Journal of rehabilitation research and
development
0748-7711
Continues: Journal of rehabilitation R&D.
1984   8410047

J Rehabil Res Dev Clin Suppl
Journal of rehabilitation research and
development. Clinical supplement / Veterans
Administration
0898-2732
1985-1990   8604381

J Relig Health
Journal of religion and health
0022-4197   1573-6571
1961   2985199R

J Ren Care
Journal of renal care
1755-6678   1755-6686
Continues: EDTNA/ERCA journal (English
ed.).
2006   101392167

J Ren Nutr
Journal of renal nutrition: the official
journal of the Council on Renal Nutrition of
the National Kidney Foundation
1051-2276   1532-8503
1991   9112938

J Renin Angiotensin Aldosterone Syst
Journal of the renin-angiotensin-aldosterone
system: JRAAS
1470-3203   1752-8976
2000   100971636

J Reprod Dev
The Journal of reproduction and
development
0916-8818   1348-4400
Continues: Japanese journal of animal
reproduction.
1992   9438792

J Reprod Fertil
Journal of reproduction and fertility
0022-4251
Supersedes: Studies on fertility. Merged
with: Reviews of reproduction, to form:
Reproduction (Cambridge, England).
Formerly included proceedings of the Society
for the Study of Fertility, later published in:
Journal of reproduction & fertility. Abstract
series.
1960-2000   0376367

J Reprod Fertil Abstr Ser
Journal of reproduction & fertility. Abstract
series
0954-0725
Continued by: Reproduction (Cambridge,
England). Abstract series.
1988-2000   8808774

J Reprod Fertil Suppl
Journal of reproduction and fertility.
Supplement
0449-3087
Continued by: Reproduction (Cambridge,
England). Supplement.
1966-2001   0225652

J Reprod Immunol
Journal of reproductive immunology
0165-0378
1979   8001906

J Reprod Med
The Journal of reproductive medicine
0024-7758
Continues Lying-in.
1969   0173343

J Res Natl Bur Stand (1934)
Journal of research of the National Bureau
of Standards
0091-0635
Continues: Bureau of Standards journal of
research. Continued in part by: Journal of
research of the National Bureau of Standards.
D, Radio propagation. Continued in part
by: Journal of research of the National
Bureau of Standards. C, Engineering and
instrumentation. Continued in part by:
Journal of research of the National Bureau of
Standards. Section A. Physics and chemistry.
Continued in part by: Journal of research
of the National Bureau of Standards. B,
Mathematics and mathematical physics.
1934-1959   0364550

J Reticuloendothel Soc
Journal of the Reticuloendothelial Society
0033-6890
Abstracts of papers for the National Meeting
of the Reticuloendothelial Society is included,
1974-1983? as a part of a regular issue of the
journal or as a supplement to it. Continued by
Journal of leukocyte biology.
1964-1983   0206462

J Rheumatol
The Journal of rheumatology
0315-162X
1974   7501984

J Rheumatol Suppl
The Journal of rheumatology. Supplement
0380-0903
1974   7806058

J Risk Insur
The Journal of risk and insurance
0022-4367
Continues: Journal of insurance
(Bloomington, Ill.).
1964   9877928

J Rocky Mt Analg Soc
Journal of the Rocky Mountain Analgesia
Society
0048-8488
Continued by: Journal of the National
Analgesia Society.
1969-1971   7503104

J Rural Health
The Journal of rural health: official journal of
the American Rural Health Association and
the National Rural Health Care Association
0890-765X   1748-0361
Continues: American journal of rural health.
1985   8508122

J S Afr Logop Soc
Journal of the South African Logopedic
Society
0081-2471
Continued by Journal of the South African
Speech and Hearing Association.
1948-1970   7503121

J S Afr Speech Hear Assoc
Journal of the South African Speech and
Hearing Association
0300-9874
Continues Journal of the South African
Logopedic Society. Continued by The
South African journal of communication
disorders. Die Suid-Afrikaanse tydskrif vir
Kommunikasieafwykings.
1971-1976   7505628

J S Afr Vet Assoc
Journal of the South African Veterinary
Association
1019-9128
Continues: Journal of the South African
Veterinary Medical Association.
1972   7503122

J S Afr Vet Med Assoc
Journal of the South African Veterinary
Medical Association
0038-2809
Continued by: Journal of the South African
Veterinary Association.
1927-1971   7503123

J S C Med Assoc
Journal of the South Carolina Medical
Association (1975)
0038-3139   1544-4910
Continues: Journal (South Carolina Medical
Association).
1975   7503045

J Safety Res
Journal of safety research
0022-4375
1969   1264241

J San Antonio Dent Soc
Journal. San Antonio District Dental Society
0036-3979
Continued by: Newsletter (San Antonio
District Dental Society).
1946-1971   20530710R

J Sch Health
The Journal of school health
0022-4391   1746-1561
Continues the School physicians' bulletin.
1937   0376370

J Sch Nurs
The Journal of school nursing: the official
publication of the National Association of
School Nurses
1059-8405   1546-8364
Continues: School nurse.
1991   9206498

J Sch Psychol
Journal of school psychology
0022-4405   1873-3506
1963   0050303

J Sci Food Agric
Journal of the science of food and
agriculture
0022-5142
1950   0376334

J Sci Ind Res (C)
Journal of scientific & industrial research.
C. Biological sciences
1955-1962   0034470

J Sci Instrum
Journal of scientific instruments
0950-7671
Continued by the Journal of physics E:
Scientific instruments.
1923-1969   1276761

J Sci Med Lille
Journal des sciences médicales de Lille
0021-8111
1878-1981   0413413

J Sci Med Sport
Journal of science and medicine in sport /
Sports Medicine Australia
1440-2440
Continues: Australian journal of science and
medicine in sport.
1998   9812598

J Seattle Dist Dent Soc
Journal of the Seattle District Dental Society
0037-0452
Continued by Journal - Seattle-King County
Dental Society.
1962-1970   7507222

J Seattle King Cty Dent Soc
Journal - Seattle-King County Dental
Society
0037-0452
Continues Journal of the Seattle District
Dental Society.
1970   7503044

J Sep Sci
Journal of separation science
1615-9306   1615-9314
Absorbed: Journal of microcolumn
separations. Jan. 2002 Continues: Journal of
high resolution chromatography.
2001   101088554

J Sex Marital Ther
Journal of sex & marital therapy
0092-623X   1521-0715
1974   7502387

J Sex Med
The journal of sexual medicine
1743-6095   1743-6109
2004   101230693

J Sex Res
Journal of sex research
0022-4499
1965   0062647

J Shoulder Elbow Surg
Journal of shoulder and elbow surgery /
American Shoulder and Elbow Surgeons ...
[et al.]
1058-2746   1532-6500
1992   9206499

J Singapore Paediatr Soc
The Journal of the Singapore Paediatric
Society
0037-5683
Continues: Proceedings of the Singapore
Paediatric Society. Continued by: Singapore
paediatric journal.
1959-1994   7507223

J Sleep Res
Journal of sleep research
0962-1105   1365-2869
1992   9214441

J Small Anim Pract
The Journal of small animal practice
0022-4510
1960   0165053

J Smooth Muscle Res
Journal of smooth muscle research = Nihon
Heikatsukin Gakkai kikanshi
0916-8737
Continues: Nippon Heikatsukin Gakkai
zasshi. Beginning 1997, articles in Japanese
published in: Journal of smooth muscle
research. Japanese section.
1991   9211664

J Soc Biol
Journal de la Société de biologie
1295-0661
Continues: Comptes rendus des séances de la
Société de biologie et de ses filiales.
1999   100890617

J Soc Casework
Journal of social casework
8755-4879
Continues: Family (New York, N.Y. 1920).
Continued by: Social casework.
1920-1949   17940210R

J Soc Cienc Med Lisb
Jornal da Sociedade das Ciências Médicas
de Lisboa
0304-4769
Continued by: Jornal das ciências médicas.
1835-1982   7503552

J Soc Gynecol Investig
Journal of the Society for Gynecologic
Investigation
1071-5576   1556-7117
Continued by: Reproductive sciences.
1994-2006   9433806

J Soc Health Syst
Journal of the Society for Health Systems
1043-1721
1989-1997   9112311

J Soc Hyg
Journal of social hygiene
Continues Social hygiene.
1922-1954   17940220R

J Soc Integr Oncol
Journal of the Society for Integrative
Oncology
1715-894X
Continues: Journal of cancer integrative
medicine.
2005   101262057

J Soc Occup Med
The Journal of the Society of Occupational
Medicine
0301-0023
Continues Transactions of the Society of
Occupational Medicine. Continued by:
Occupational medicine (Oxford, England).
1973-1991   7503120

J Soc Pediatr Nurs
Journal of the Society of Pediatric Nurses:
JSPN
1088-145X
Continues: Maternal-child nursing journal.
Continued by: Journal for specialist in
pediatric nursing.
1996-2001   9615684

J Soc Policy
Journal of social policy
0047-2794
1972   7806597

J Soc Psychol
The Journal of social psychology
0022-4545
1930   0376372

J Soc Work Disabil Rehabil
Journal of social work in disability &
rehabilitation
1536-710X   1536-7118
2002   101132991

J Soc Work End Life Palliat Care
Journal of social work in end-of-life &
palliative care
1552-4256   1552-4264
Continues: Loss, grief & care.
2005   101235219

J South Calif Dent Assistants Assoc
Journal (Southern California Dental
Assistants Association)
0738-7970
19uu   9879183

J South Calif Dent Assoc
Journal - Southern California Dental
Association
0098-843X
Continues Journal - Southern California State
Dental Association. Merged with Composite
to form CDA journal. Superseded by CDA
journal.
1967-1973   7503046

J South Calif State Dent Assoc
Journal - Southern California State Dental
Association
0098-7115
Continued by: Journal of the California
Dental Association.
1934-1966   7503047

J South Calif State Dent Hyg Assoc
Journal of the Southern California Dental
Hygienists' Association
0038-3899
1958-1984   7503124

J South Orthop Assoc
Journal of the Southern Orthopaedic
Association
1059-1052
Continued by: Journal of surgical orthopaedic
advances.
1992-2003   9211289

J Spec Pediatr Nurs
Journal for specialists in pediatric nursing:
JSPN
1539-0136   1744-6155
Continues: Journal of the Society of Pediatric
Nurses.
2002   101142025

J Speech Disord
The Journal of speech disorders
Continued by the Journal of speech and
hearing disorders.
1936-1947   18010030R

J Speech Hear Disord
The Journal of speech and hearing disorders
0022-4677
Continues the Journal of speech disorders.
1948-1990   0376335

J Speech Hear Disord Monogr Suppl
Journal of speech and hearing disorders.
Monograph supplement
Continued by ASHA monographs.
1950-1963   0234123

J Speech Hear Res
Journal of speech and hearing research
0022-4685
Continued by: Journal of speech. language.
and hearing research.
1958-1996   0376336

J Speech Lang Hear Res
Journal of speech, language, and hearing
research: JSLHR
1092-4388
Continues: Journal of speech and hearing
research.
1997   9705610

J Spinal Cord Med
The journal of spinal cord medicine
1079-0268
Continues: Journal of the American
Paraplegia Society.
1995   9504452

J Spinal Disord
Journal of spinal disorders
0895-0385
Continued by: Journal of spinal disorders &
techniques.
1988-2001   8904842

J Spinal Disord Tech
Journal of spinal disorders & techniques
1536-0652   1539-2465
Continues: Journal of spinal disorders.
2002   101140323

J Sport Exerc Psychol
Journal of sport & exercise psychology
0895-2779   1543-2904
Continues: Journal of sport psychology.
1988   8809258

J Sport Rehabil
Journal of sport rehabilitation
1056-6716   1543-3072
1992   9206500

J Sports Med
The Journal of sports medicine
0090-4201
Continued by The American journal of sports
medicine.
1972-1975   7609632

J Sports Med Phys Fitness
The Journal of sports medicine and physical
fitness
0022-4707
1961   0376337

J Sports Sci
Journal of sports sciences
0264-0414   1466-447X
1983   8405364

J State Gov
The Journal of state government / National
Conference of State Legislatures [and] the
Council of State Governments
1043-2248
Continues: State government (Denver. Colo.).
Continued by: Spectrum (Lexington. Ky.).
1986-1992   9883142

J Sterile Serv Manage
Journal of sterile services management
0951-2578
Continues: Sterile world. Continued
by: Journal (Institute of Sterile Services
Management).
1983-198u   9880290

J Steroid Biochem
Journal of steroid biochemistry
0022-4731
Continued by: Journal of steroid biochemistry
and molecular biology.
1969-1990   0260125

J Steroid Biochem Mol Biol
The Journal of steroid biochemistry and
molecular biology
0960-0760
Continues: Journal of steroid biochemistry.
1990   9015483

J Stomatol Belg
Journal de stomatologie de Belgique
1959-1965   0050076

J Stone Dis
The Journal of stone disease
1059-9509
Continues: Journal of lithotripsy & stone
disease.
1992-1993   9204584

J Strength Cond Res
Journal of strength and conditioning
research / National Strength & Conditioning
Association
1064-8011   1533-4287
Continues: Journal of applied sport science
research.
1993   9415084

J Stroke Cerebrovasc Dis
Journal of stroke and cerebrovascular
diseases: the official journal of National
Stroke Association
1052-3057   1532-8511
1991   9111633

J Struct Biol
Journal of structural biology
1047-8477   1095-8657
Continues: Journal of ultrastructure and
molecular structure research.
1990   9011206

J Struct Funct Genomics
Journal of structural and functional
genomics
1345-711X
2000   101128185

J Stud Alcohol
Journal of studies on alcohol
0096-882X
Continues: Quarterly journal of studies on
alcohol. Continued by: Journal of studies on
alcohol and drugs.
1975-2006   7503813

J Stud Alcohol Drugs
Journal of studies on alcohol and drugs
1937-1888   1938-4114
Continues: Journal of studies on alcohol.
2007   101295847

J Stud Alcohol Suppl
Journal of studies on alcohol. Supplement
0363-468X
Continues Quarterly journal of studies on
alcohol. Supplement.
1975   7609332

J Submicrosc Cytol
Journal of submicroscopic cytology
0022-4782
Continued by: Journal of submicroscopic
cytology and pathology.
1969-1987   0235232

J Submicrosc Cytol Pathol
Journal of submicroscopic cytology and
pathology
1122-9497
Continues: Journal of submicroscopic
cytology.
1988   8804312

J Subst Abuse
Journal of substance abuse
0899-3289
1988-2001   9001404

J Subst Abuse Treat
Journal of substance abuse treatment
0740-5472   1873-6483
1984   8500909

J Support Oncol
The journal of supportive oncology
1544-6794
2003   101181305

J Supramol Struct
Journal of supramolecular structure
0091-7419
Continued by: Journal of Supramolecular
structure and cellular biochemistry.
1972-1980   0330464

J Supramol Struct Cell Biochem
Journal of supramolecular structure and
cellular biochemistry
0275-3723
Continues: Journal of supramolecular
structure. Continued by: Journal of cellular
biochemistry.
1981-1981   8106911

J Supramol Struct Cell Biochem Suppl
Journal of supramolecular structure and
cellular biochemistry. Supplement
0730-6652
Continues: Journal of supramolecular
structure. Supplement. Continued by: Journal
of cellular biochemistry. Supplement.
1981-1981   8109846

J Supramol Struct Suppl
Journal of supramolecular structure. Supplement
0161-3294
Continued by: Journal of supramolecular structure and cellular biochemistry. Supplement.
1976-1980   7708965

J Surg Educ
Journal of surgical education
1931-7204
Continues: Current surgery.
2007   101303204

J Surg Oncol
Journal of surgical oncology
0022-4790   1096-9098
1969   0222643

J Surg Oncol Suppl
Journal of surgical oncology. Supplement
1046-7416
1989   8912976

J Surg Orthop Adv
Journal of surgical orthopaedic advances
1548-825X
Continues: Journal of the Southern Orthopaedic Association.
2003   101197881

J Surg Res
The Journal of surgical research
0022-4804   1095-8673
1961   0376340

J Sykepleien
Journalen sykepleien
0802-9776
Continues in part: Sykepleien. Merged with: Sykepleien. Fag, to become: Tidsskriftet sykepleien.
1989-1995   9008978

J Synchrotron Radiat
Journal of synchrotron radiation
0909-0495
1994   9888878

J Telemed Telecare
Journal of telemedicine and telecare
1357-633X   1758-1109
1995   9506702

J Tenn Acad Sci
Journal. Tennessee Academy of Science
0040-313X
Supersedes the Transactions of the Tennessee Academy of Science.
1926   21130160R

J Tenn Dent Assoc
The Journal of the Tennessee Dental Association
0040-3385
Continues: Journal - Tennessee State Dental Association.
1970   7503125

J Tenn Med Assoc
Journal of the Tennessee Medical Association
0040-3318
Continues: Journal of the Tennessee State Medical Association. Continued by: Tennessee medicine.
1963-1996   7505629

J Tenn State Dent Assoc
Journal - Tennessee State Dental Association
0091-3987
Continued by the Journal of the Tennessee Dental Association.
1919-1970   7503048

J Texas Dent Hyg Assoc
The Journal of the Texas Dental Hygienists' Association. Texas Dental Hygienists' Association
0040-4276
19uu   9875596

J Theor Biol
Journal of theoretical biology
0022-5193   1095-8541
1961   0376342

J Thorac Cardiovasc Surg
The Journal of thoracic and cardiovascular surgery
0022-5223   1097-685X
Continues: Journal of thoracic surgery.
1959   0376343

J Thorac Imaging
Journal of thoracic imaging
0883-5993   1536-0237
1985   8606160

J Thorac Oncol
Journal of thoracic oncology: official publication of the International Association for the Study of Lung Cancer
1556-0864   1556-1380
2006   101274235

J Thorac Surg
The Journal of thoracic surgery
0096-5588
Continued by the Journal of thoracic and cardiovascular surgery.
1931-1959   18030030R

J Thromb Haemost
Journal of thrombosis and haemostasis: JTH
1538-7933   1538-7836
2003   101170508

J Thromb Thrombolysis
Journal of thrombosis and thrombolysis
0929-5305
1994   9502018

J Tissue Eng Regen Med
Journal of tissue engineering and regenerative medicine
1932-6254   1932-7005
2007   101308490

J Tissue Viability
Journal of tissue viability
0965-206X
Continues: Care (Salisbury, England).
1991   9306822

J Tn State Med Assoc
The Journal of the Tennessee State Medical Association. Tennessee State Medical Association
0735-7338
Continued by: Journal of the Tennessee Medical Association.
1908-1963   21130210R

J Tongji Med Univ
Journal of Tongji Medical University = Tong ji yi ke da xue xue bao
0257-716X
Continues: Acta Academiae Medicinae Wuhan. Continued by: Journal of Huazhong University of Science and Technology. Medical sciences.
1986-2001   8605495

J Toxicol Clin Exp
Journal de toxicologie clinique et expérimentale
0753-2830
Continues: Journal de toxicologie médicale.
1985-1992   8606713

J Toxicol Clin Toxicol
Journal of toxicology. Clinical toxicology
0731-3810   1097-9875
Continues: Clinical toxicology. Continued by: Clinical toxicology (Philadelphia, Pa.).
1982-2004   8213460

J Toxicol Environ Health
Journal of toxicology and environmental health
0098-4108
Split into: Journal of toxicology and environmental health. Part A; and: Journal of toxicology and environmental health. Part B, Critical reviews.
1975-1997   7513622

J Toxicol Environ Health A
Journal of toxicology and environmental health. Part A
1528-7394
Continues in part: Journal of toxicology and environmental health.
1998   100960995

J Toxicol Environ Health B Crit Rev
Journal of toxicology and environmental health. Part B, Critical reviews
1093-7404   1521-6950
Absorbed: Comments on toxicology. Continues in part: Journal of toxicology and environmental health.
1998   9802627

J Toxicol Environ Health Suppl
Journal of toxicology and environmental health. Supplement
0161-5548
1976-1977   7801250

J Toxicol Sci
The Journal of toxicological sciences
0388-1350   1880-3989
1976   7805798

J Trace Elem Electrolytes Health Dis
Journal of trace elements and electrolytes in health and disease
0931-2838
Continued by: Journal of trace elements in medicine and biology.
1987-1994   8807101

J Trace Elem Med Biol
Journal of trace elements in medicine and biology: organ of the Society for Minerals and Trace Elements (GMS)
0946-672X
1995   9508274

J Tradit Chin Med
Journal of traditional Chinese medicine = Chung i tsa chih ying wen pan / sponsored by All-China Association of Traditional Chinese Medicine, Academy of Traditional Chinese Medicine
0254-6272
1981   8211546

J Transcult Nurs
Journal of transcultural nursing: official journal of the Transcultural Nursing Society / Transcultural Nursing Society
1043-6596
1989   9001407

J Transl Med
Journal of translational medicine
    1479-5876
2003   101190741

J Transpl Coord
Journal of transplant coordination: official publication of the North American Transplant Coordinators Organization (NATCO)
0905-9199
Continued by: Progress in transplantation (Aliso Viejo, Calif.).
1991-1999 9111439

J Trauma
The Journal of trauma
0022-5282 1529-8809
1961 0376373

J Trauma Dissociation
Journal of trauma & dissociation: the official journal of the International Society for the Study of Dissociation (ISSD)
1529-9732 1529-9740
2000 100898209

J Trauma Nurs
Journal of trauma nursing: the official journal of the Society of Trauma Nurses
1078-7496
Continues: STN's journal of trauma nursing.
1994 9512997

J Trauma Stress
Journal of traumatic stress
0894-9867 1573-6598
1988 8809259

J Travel Med
Journal of travel medicine: official publication of the International Society of Travel Medicine and the Asia Pacific Travel Health Association
1195-1982 1708-8305
1994 9434456

J Trop Med Hyg
The Journal of tropical medicine and hygiene
0022-5304
Continues the Journal of tropical medicine. Merged with: Tropical and geographical medicine; Tropical medicine and parasitology; and: Annales de la Société belge de médecine tropicale: to form: Tropical medicine & international health.
1907-1995 0406044

J Trop Pediatr
Journal of tropical pediatrics
Continues: Journal of tropical pediatrics and African child health. Continued by: Journal of tropical pediatrics and environmental child health.
1967-1970 0311070

J Trop Pediatr
Journal of tropical pediatrics
0142-6338 1465-3664
Continues The Journal of tropical pediatrics and environmental child health.
1980 8010948

J Trop Pediatr (Lond)
Journal of tropical pediatrics (London, England: 1955)
0449-3281
Continued in Dec. 1959 by: Journal of tropical pediatrics and African child health.
1955-1959 101177115

J Trop Pediatr Afr Child Health
The Journal of tropical pediatrics and African child health
0368-4512
Continues: Journal of tropical pediatrics. Continued by: Journal of tropical pediatrics.
1959-1967 0166276

J Trop Pediatr Environ Child Health
The Journal of tropical pediatrics and environmental child health
0300-9920
Continues Journal of tropical pediatrics. Continued by Journal of tropical pediatrics.
1971-1979 0311071

J Ultrasound Med
Journal of ultrasound in medicine: official journal of the American Institute of Ultrasound in Medicine
0278-4297 1550-9613
1982 8211547

J Ultrastruct Mol Struct Res
Journal of ultrastructure and molecular structure research
0889-1605
Continues: Journal of ultrastructure research. Continued by: Journal of structural biology.
1986-1989 8612238

J Ultrastruct Res
Journal of ultrastructure research
0022-5320
Continued by: Journal of ultrastructure and molecular structure research.
1957-1985 0376344

J Ultrastruct Res Suppl
Journal of ultrastructure research. Supplement
0075-4404
1959-1973 0376345

J UOEH
Journal of UOEH
0387-821X
1979 7909645

J Urban Health
Journal of urban health: bulletin of the New York Academy of Medicine
1099-3460 1468-2869
Continues: Bulletin of the New York Academy of Medicine.
1998 9809909

J Urol
The Journal of urology
0022-5347 1527-3792
1917 0376374

J Urol (Paris)
Journal d'urologie
0248-0018
Continues in part Journal d'urologie et de néphrologie.
1980-1997 8006503

J Urol Medicale Chir
Journal d'urologie médicale et chirurgicale
0368-4679
Continued by the Journal d'urologie et de néphrologie.
1912-1960 17820300R

J Urol Nephrol (Paris)
Journal d'urologie et de néphrologie
0021-8200
Continues Journal d'urologie médicale et chirurgicale. Continued by Journal d'urologie and by Néphrologie. Continued in part by: Néphrologie. Continued in part by: Journal d'urologie.
1961-1979 7802652

J Vasc Access
The journal of vascular access
1129-7298 1724-6032
2000 100940729

J Vasc Interv Radiol
Journal of vascular and interventional radiology: JVIR
1051-0443 1535-7732
1990 9203369

J Vasc Nurs
Journal of vascular nursing: official publication of the Society for Peripheral Vascular Nursing
1062-0303 1532-6578
Continues: SPVN.
1990 9014475

J Vasc Res
Journal of vascular research
1018-1172 1423-0135
Absorbed: International journal of microcirculation, clinical and experimental. Continues: Blood vessels.
1992 9206092

J Vasc Surg
Journal of vascular surgery: official publication, the Society for Vascular Surgery [and] International Society for Cardiovascular Surgery, North American Chapter
0741-5214 1097-6809
1984 8407742

J Vector Borne Dis
Journal of vector borne diseases
0972-9062
Continues: Indian journal of malariology.
2003 101212761

J Vector Ecol
Journal of vector ecology: journal of the Society for Vector Ecology
1081-1710
Continues: Bulletin of the Society for Vector Ecology.
1995 9512496

J Vener Dis Inf
The Journal of venereal disease information
Continues: Venereal disease information. Absorbed by: Public health reports.
1945-1951 18030040R

J Vestib Res
Journal of vestibular research: equilibrium & orientation
0957-4271
1991 9104163

J Vet Cardiol
Journal of veterinary cardiology: the official journal of the European Society of Veterinary Cardiology
1760-2734 1875-0834
1999 101163270

J Vet Dent
Journal of veterinary dentistry
0898-7564
Continues: Veterinary dentistry.
1988 9426426

J Vet Diagn Invest
Journal of veterinary diagnostic investigation: official publication of the American Association of Veterinary Laboratory Diagnosticians, Inc
1040-6387
1989 9011490

J Vet Intern Med
Journal of veterinary internal medicine / American College of Veterinary Internal Medicine
0891-6640
1987 8708660

J Vet Med A Physiol Pathol Clin Med
Journal of veterinary medicine. A,
Physiology, pathology, clinical medicine
0931-184X   1439-0442
Continues: Zentralblatt für Veterinärmedizin.
Reihe A. Continued by: Transboundary and
emerging diseases.
2000-2007   100955112

J Vet Med B Infect Dis Vet Public Health
Journal of veterinary medicine. B, Infectious
diseases and veterinary public health
0931-1793   1439-0450
Continues: Zentralblatt für Veterinärmedizin.
Reihe B. Continued by: Zoonoses and public
health.
2000-2006   100955260

J Vet Med Educ
Journal of veterinary medical education
0748-321X
1974   7610519

J Vet Med Sci
The Journal of veterinary medical science /
the Japanese Society of Veterinary Science
0916-7250   1347-7439
Continues: Nippon juigaku zasshi.
1991   9105360

J Vet Pharmacol Ther
Journal of veterinary pharmacology and
therapeutics
0140-7783   1365-2885
1978   7910920

J Vet Sci
Journal of veterinary science (Suwŏn-si,
Korea)
1229-845X
2000   100964185

J Viral Hepat
Journal of viral hepatitis
1352-0504   1365-2893
1994   9435672

J Virol
Journal of virology
0022-538X   1098-5514
1967   0113724

J Virol Methods
Journal of virological methods
0166-0934
1980   8005839

J Vis
Journal of vision
    1534-7362
2001   101147197

J Vis Commun Med
Journal of visual communication in medicine
1745-3054   1745-3062
Continues: Journal of audiovisual media in
medicine.
2005   101254059

J Vis Exp
Journal of visualized experiments: JoVE
    1940-087X
2006   101313252

J Vitaminol (Kyoto)
The Journal of vitaminology
0022-5398
Continued by: Journal of nutritional science
and vitaminology.
1954-1972   0402374

J Voice
Journal of voice: official journal of the Voice
Foundation
0892-1997   1557-8658
1987   8712262

J Volunt Adm
The Journal of volunteer administration
0733-6535
Continues: Volunteer administration.
1982   9879615

J Water Health
Journal of water and health
1477-8920
2003   101185420

J Water Pollut Control Fed
Journal - Water Pollution Control
Federation
0043-1303
Continues Sewage and industrial wastes.
1960-1989   7505562

J West Aust Nurses
Journal of the West Australian Nurses
0022-5177
1935-1971   18030020R

J West Soc Periodontol Periodontal Abstr
The Journal of the Western Society of
Periodontology/Periodontal abstracts
0148-4893
Continues Periodontal abstracts.
1976   7705433

J Wildl Dis
Journal of wildlife diseases
0090-3558
Continues: Bulletin of the Wildlife Disease
Association.
1970   0244160

J Wis Dent Assoc
The Journal of the Wisconsin Dental
Association
0091-4185
Continues the Journal of the Wisconsin State
Dental Society. Continued by: Wisconsin
Dental Association journal.
1973-1985   7503127

J Wis State Dent Soc
The Journal of the Wisconsin State Dental
Society
0043-6674
Continues the Wisconsin dental review.
Continued by the Journal of the Wisconsin
Dental Association.
1938-1973   7503128

J Women Aging
Journal of women & aging
0895-2841   1540-7322
1988   8916635

J Womens Health
Journal of women's health / the official
publication of the Society for the
Advancement of Women's Health Research
1059-7115
Continued by: Journal of women's health &
gender-based medicine.
1992-1999   9208978

J Womens Health (Larchmt)
Journal of women's health (2002)
1540-9996   1931-843X
Continues: Journal of women's health &
gender-based medicine.
2002   101159262

J Womens Health Gend Based Med
Journal of women's health & gender-based
medicine
1524-6094
Continues: Journal of women's health.
Continued by: Journal of women's health
(2002).
1999-2002   100888719

J Wound Care
Journal of wound care
0969-0700
1992   9417080

J Wound Ostomy Continence Nurs
Journal of wound, ostomy, and continence
nursing: official publication of The Wound,
Ostomy and Continence Nurses Society /
WOCN
1071-5754   1528-3976
Continues: Journal of ET nursing.
1994   9435679

J Zhejiang Univ Sci
Journal of Zhejiang University. Science
1009-3095
Split into: Journal of Zhejiang University.
Science A, and: Journal of Zhejiang
University. Science. B.
2000   100954270

J Zhejiang Univ Sci B
Journal of Zhejiang University. Science. B
1673-1581
Continues in part: Journal of Zhejiang
University. Science.
2005   101236535

J Zoo Wildl Med
Journal of zoo and wildlife medicine: official
publication of the American Association of
Zoo Veterinarians
1042-7260
Continues: Journal of zoo animal medicine.
1989   8915208

J Zool
Journal of zoology
0022-5460
Continues the Proceedings of the Zoological
Society of London. Split into: Journal
of zoology. Series A, Proceedings of the
Zoological Society of London; and: Journal
of zoology. Series B.
1966-1984   0142477

JAAPA
JAAPA: official journal of the American
Academy of Physician Assistants
1547-1896
Continues: Journal of the American Academy
of Physician Assistants.
1994   9513102

Jaarb Kankeronderz Kankerbestrijd Ned
Jaarboek van kankeronderzoek en
kankerbestrijding in Nederland. Yearbook
for cancer research and fight against cancer
in the Netherlands
0446-3471
Continues Vereeniging het Nederlandsch
Kankerinstituut, Amsterdam. Jaarboek.
1952-1974   17730040R

JACEP
JACEP
0361-1124
Continued by Annals of emergency medicine.
1972-1979   0317011

Jackson Clin Bull
The Jackson Clinic bulletin
1939-1958   17730050R

Jahrb Volksgesundh
Jahrbuch Volksgesundheit
Supersedes Volksgesundheitskalender of the
Schweizerischer Verein für Volksgesundheit.
1947   0165372

Jahresber Schweiz Akad Med Wiss
Jahresbericht (Schweizerische Akademie der
Medizinischen Wissenschaften: 1988)
1016-1562
Continues: Bulletin der Schweizerischen
Akademie der Medizinischen Wissenschaften.
1988   8916516

Jam Public Health
Jamaica public health
1926-1969   9426543

JAMA
JAMA: the journal of the American Medical Association
0098-7484   1538-3598
Continues: Journal of the American Medical Association.
1960   7501160

Jamaican Nurse
The Jamaican nurse
0021-4140
1961   0203020

JAPCA
JAPCA
0894-0630
Continues: Journal of the Air Pollution Control Association. Continued by: Jounrnal of the Air & Waste Management Association.
1987-1989   8802680

JBR-BTR
JBR-BTR: organe de la Société royale belge de radiologie (SRBR) = orgaan van de Koninklijke Belgische Vereniging voor Radiologie (KBVR)
0302-7430
Continues: Journal belge de radiologie.
1999   100888280

JCAH Perspect
JCAH perspectives. Joint Commission on Accreditation of Hospitals
0277-8327
Continues: Perspectives on accreditation. Continued by: Joint Commission on Accreditation of Healthcare Organizations. Joint Commission perspectives.
1981-1987   8208742

Jefferson-Hillman Hosp Bull
The Jefferson-Hillman hospital bulletin
1947-1950   17740380R

JEMS
JEMS: a journal of emergency medical services
0197-2510
Continues: Paramedics international.
1980   8102138

Jena Z Med Naturwiss
Jenaische Zeitschrift für Medicin und Naturwissenschaft
1864-1947   17740420R

Jew Mem Hosp Bull
The Jewish Memorial Hospital bulletin
0021-6585
1955-1973   0414131

JFMA
JFMA, the Journal of the Florida Medical Association. Florida Medical Association
0091-6757
Continues the Journal of the Florida Medical Association, published 1914-71, and is continued by the Journal of the Florida Medical Association, published 1974- .
1972-1973   0417646

JFORL J Fr Otorhinolaryngol Audiophonol Chir Maxillofac
JFORL. Journal français d'oto-rhino-laryngologie; audiophonologie et chirurgie maxillo-faciale
Continues Journal français d'oto-rhino-laryngologie, audio-phonologie et chirurgie maxillo-faciale. Continued by Journal français d'oto-rhino-laryngologie: audiophonologie, chirurgie maxillo-faciale.
1972-1976   0320133

Ji Sheng Chong Xue Yu Ji Sheng Chong Bing Za Zhi
Ji sheng chong xue yu ji sheng chong bing za zhi = Journal of parasitology & parasitic diseases
1000-1808
Continued by: Zhongguo ji sheng chong xue yu ji sheng chong bing za zhi.
1983-1986   8404889

Jibiinkoka
Jibi inkōka Otolaryngology
0386-9679
Continued by: Jibi inkōka tōkeibu geka (Igaku Shoin).
1928-1987   0417444

Jika Shinryo
[Jika shinryō] Journal for pediatric praxis
Continued by: Shōnika shinryō.
1935-1953   20730870R

Jikeikai Med J
Jikeikai medical journal
0021-6968
1954   2985186R

Jikken Dobutsu
Jikken dobutsu. Experimental animals
0007-5124
Continues: Jikken dobutsu iho. Continued by: Experimental animals.
1957-1995   1256412

Jikoketsu Yuketsu
Jikoketsu yuketsu: Nihon Jikoketsu Yuketsu Gakkai kaishi = Journal of Japanese Society of Autologous Blood Transfusion
0915-0188
Continues: Kaishūshiki jiko yuketsu.
1989   100899988

Jinrui Idengaku Zasshi
Jinrui idengaku zasshi. The Japanese journal of human genetics
0021-5074
Continued by: Japanese journal of human genetics.
1956-1991   0420105

JNMA J Nepal Med Assoc
JNMA; journal of the Nepal Medical Association
0028-2715   1815-672X
1963   0045233

JOGN Nurs
JOGN nursing; journal of obstetric, gynecologic, and neonatal nursing
0090-0311
Continued by Journal of obstetric, gynecologic, and neonatal nursing.
1972-1984   0347421

Johns Hopkins Med J
The Johns Hopkins medical journal
0021-7263
Continues the Bulletin of the Johns Hopkins Hospital.
1967-1982   0072456

Johns Hopkins Med J Suppl
Johns Hopkins medical journal. Supplement
0091-7400
1972-1976   0334432

Johns Hopkins Med Lett Health After 50
The Johns Hopkins medical letter health after 50
1042-1882
1989   9802902

Johns Hopkins Nurses Alumnae Mag
The Johns Hopkins nurses alumnae magazine
Continued by the association's Alumnae magazine.
1901-1956   17810130R

Johns Hopkins Nurses Alumni Mag
The Johns Hopkins Nurses' alumni magazine
Continues: Alumni magazine. Continued by: Vigilando.
1987-1989   9318900

Joint Bone Spine
Joint, bone, spine: revue du rhumatisme
1297-319X   1778-7254
Continues: Revue du rhumatisme.
2000   100938016

JONAS Healthc Law Ethics Regul
JONA'S healthcare law, ethics and regulation
1520-9229   1539-073X
1999   100888423

JOP
JOP: Journal of the pancreas
    1590-8577
2000   101091810

Jordan Dent J
The Jordan dental journal
0258-4638
Continues: Majallat Niqābat Attibā' al-Asnān al-Urdunīyah.
1984-2002   8411106

Jordemodern
Jordemodern
0021-7468
1888   17810330R

Jordmorbladet
Jordmorbladet: bilag til tidsskriftet Sykepleien
0805-0562
1994-2001   9500811

Jorn Med
Jornada médica
1947-1974   17810340R

Josai Shika Daigaku Kiyo
Jōsai Shika Daigaku kiyō. The Bulletin of the Josai Dental University
0301-2662
Continued by: Neikai Daigaku shigaku zasshi.
1972-1987   0377752

Josanpu Zasshi
Josanpu zasshi = The Japanese journal for midwife
0047-1836
Continued by: Josan zasshi.
1952-2002   17810430R

Journ Annu Diabetol Hotel Dieu
Journées annuelles de diabétologie de l'Hôtel-Dieu
0075-4439
1961   0424745

Journal (Inst Health Rec Inf Manag)
Journal (Institute of Health Record Information and Management)
Continues: IHRIM. Continued by: For your information (Institute of Health Record & Information Management).
2000-2003   101284924

JPEN J Parenter Enteral Nutr
JPEN. Journal of parenteral and enteral nutrition
0148-6071
1977   7804134

Jpn Circ J
Japanese circulation journal
0047-1828   1347-4839
Absorbed: Nippon junkankigaku shi. Continued by: Circulation journal.
1960-2001   7806868

Jpn Dent J
Japanese dental journal
Continued by: Dentistry in Japan.
1964-1967   0226646

Jpn Heart J
Japanese heart journal
0021-4868   1348-673x
Continued by: International heart journal.
1960-2004   0401175

Jpn Hosp
Japan-hospitals: the journal of the Japan
Hospital Association
0910-1004
1982   8301814

Jpn J Antibiot
The Japanese journal of antibiotics
0368-2781
Continues the Journal of antibiotics. Ser. B.
1968   0154402

Jpn J Cancer Res
Japanese journal of cancer research: Gann
0910-5050
Continues: Gann. Continued by: Cancer
science.
1985-2002   8509412

Jpn J Clin Oncol
Japanese journal of clinical oncology
0368-2811   1465-3621
1971   0313225

Jpn J Dermatol B
The Japanese journal of dermatology. Ser. B
0368-282X
Continues: Japanese Journal of Dermatology.
Continued by: Journal of Dermatology.
1963-1972   7600543

Jpn J Exp Med
The Japanese journal of experimental
medicine
0021-5031
Continues: Scientific reports. Tōkyō Daigaku.
Densenbyo Kenkyūjo. Continued by: Annual
report. Tōkyō Daigaku. Ikagaku Kenkyūjo.
1928-1990   9800765

Jpn J Genet
Idengaku zasshi
0021-504X   1880-5787
Continued by: Genes & genetic systems.
1921-1995   9301272

Jpn J Hum Genet
The Japanese journal of human genetics
0916-8478
Continues: Jinrui idengaku zasshi. Continued
by: Journal of human genetics.
1992-1997   9213239

Jpn J Infect Dis
Japanese journal of infectious diseases
1344-6304
Continues: Japanese journal of medical
science & biology.
1999   100893704

Jpn J Med
Japanese journal of medicine
0021-5120
Continues: Abstracts of papers of the Journal
of Japanese Society of Internal Medicine.
Nihon Naika Gakkai. Continued by: Internal
medicine (Tokyo, Japan)..
1962-1991   0247713

Jpn J Med Sci Biol
Japanese journal of medical science & biology
0021-5112
Continues: Japanese medical journal.
Continued by: Japanese journal of infectious
diseases.
1952-1998   0243706

Jpn J Microbiol
Japanese journal of microbiology
0021-5139
Continued by Microbiology and immunology.
1957-1976   0376565

Jpn J Ophthalmol
Japanese journal of ophthalmology
0021-5155
1957   0044652

Jpn J Pharmacol
Japanese journal of pharmacology
0021-5198   1347-3506
Continues: Japanese journal of medical
sciences,. Continued by: Journal of
pharmacological sciences.
1951-2002   2983305R

Jpn J Physiol
The Japanese journal of physiology
0021-521X
Continues: Japanese journal of medical
sciences. III. Biophysics. Continued by:
Journal of physiological sciences.
1950-2005   2985184R

Jpn J Psychiatry Neurol
The Japanese journal of psychiatry and
neurology
0912-2036
Continues: Folia psychiatrica et neurologica
japonica. Continued by: Psychiatry and
clinical neurosciences.
1986-1994   8610886

Jpn J Surg
The Japanese journal of surgery
0047-1909
Continued by: Surgery today.
1971-1991   1302176

Jpn J Thorac Cardiovasc Surg
The Japanese journal of thoracic and
cardiovascular surgery: official publication
of the Japanese Association for Thoracic
Surgery = Nihon Kyōbu Geka Gakkai zasshi
1344-4964
Continues: Zasshi. Nihon Kyōbu Geka
Gakkai. Continued by: General thoracic and
cardiovascular surgery.
1998-2006   100884261

Jpn J Tuberc
The Japanese journal of tuberculosis
Continued by the Japanese journal of
tuberculosis and chest diseases.
1953-1967   0235076

Jpn J Tuberc Chest Dis
The Japanese journal of tuberculosis and
chest diseases
0021-5279
Continues the Japanese journal of
tuberculosis.
1968-1978   0235077

Jpn J Vet Res
The Japanese journal of veterinary research
0047-1917
Continues Juigaku kenkyu.
1954   0376567

Jpn Med J
[Nippon iji shinpō] Japanese medical journal
0385-9215
Absorbed Iji eisei in hachigatsu 1940.
1921   19130030R

Jpn Med J (Natl Inst Health Jpn)
Japanese medical journal
0368-3095
Continued by: Japanese journal of medical
science and biology.
1948-1951   17740340R

JPO J Pract Orthod
JPO: the journal of practical orthodontics
8755-4852
Continued by: Journal of clinical orthodontics.
1967-1969   2985200R

JSLS
JSLS: Journal of the Society of
Laparoendoscopic Surgeons / Society of
Laparoendoscopic Surgeons
1086-8089   1938-3797
1997   100884618

Jt Comm J Qual Improv
The Joint Commission journal on quality
improvement
1070-3241
Continues: QRB. Quality review bulletin.
Continued by: Joint Commission journal on
quality and safety.
1993-2002   9315239

Jt Comm J Qual Patient Saf
Joint Commission journal on quality and
patient safety / Joint Commission Resources
1553-7250
Continues: Joint Commission journal on
quality and safety.
2005   101238023

Jt Comm J Qual Saf
Joint Commission journal on quality and
safety
1549-3741   1549-425X
Continues: Joint Commission journal on
quality improvement. Continued by: Joint
Commission journal on quality and patient
safety.
2003-2004   101166696

Jt Comm Perspect
Joint Commission perspectives. Joint
Commission on Accreditation of Healthcare
Organizations
1044-4017
Continues: Joint Commission on
Accreditation of Hospitals. JCAH
perspectives.
1987   8812163

Jt Meet Abstr Am Dairy Sci Assoc
Joint meeting abstracts / American Dairy
Science Association & American Society of
Animal Science. American Dairy Science
Association. Meeting
Continues: Program and abstracts. American
Dairy Science Association. Meeting.
199u   101319133

Jugosl Ginekol Opstet
Jugoslavenska ginekologija i opstetricija
0017-002X
Continues: Jugoslavenska ginekologija i
opstetricija, ISSN 0017-002X, published
1969-7. Continued by: Jugoslavenska
ginekologija i perinatologija.
1970-1984   7608510

Jugosl Ginekol Perinatol
Jugoslavenska ginekologija i perinatologija
0352-5562
Continues: Jugoslavenska ginekologija i
opstetricija.
1985   8601606

Julk Suom Naishammaslaak Ryhma
Julkaisu. Suomen Naishammaslääkärit
ryhmä, Helsingfors
1953-1968   21030350R

Justus Liebigs Ann Chem
Justus Liebigs Annalen der Chemie
0075-4617
Continues Justus Liebig's Annalen der
Chemie und Pharmacie. Continued by Liebigs
Annalen der Chemie.
1874-1978   0400657

K

K Rep
K [reports]. U.S. Atomic Energy Commission
194u-1968   21830460R

Kagaku
[Kagaku] [Science]
0022-7625
1931   18110020R

Kagakushi Kenkyu
Kagakushi kenkyu. [Journal of the history of science, Japan
0022-7692
1941   0326141

Kaibogaku Zasshi
Kaibogaku zasshi. Journal of anatomy
0022-7722
Continued in part by: Anatomical science international.
1928   0413526

Kaiin Dayori Nippon Kontakuto Renzu Gakkai
Kaiin dayori. [Membership news]. Nippon Kontakuto Renzu Gakkai
0374-9851
1960   0057120

Kaku Igaku
Kaku igaku. The Japanese journal of nuclear medicine
0022-7854
1964   2985202R

Kanagawa Shigaku
Kanagawa shigaku. The Journal of the Kanagawa Odontological Society
0454-8302
1967   0164673

Kango
[Kango] Japanese journal of nursing
0022-8362
1949   18110540R

Kango Gijutsu
[Kango gijutsu]: [Nursing technique]
0449-752X
1953   18110565R

Kango Kenkyu
Kango kenkyu. The Japanese journal of nursing research
0022-8370
1968   0133626

Kango Kyoiku
[Kango kyōiku] Japanese journal of nurses' education
0047-1895
1960   18110570R

Kango Kyoshitsu
Kango kyoshitsu. [Nursing classroom]
0451-3347
1957-1976   1305441

Kango Tenbo
Kango tenbō. The Japanese journal of nursing science
0385-549X
1976   7810064

Kangogaku Zasshi
[Kangogaku zasshi] The Japanese journal of nursing
0386-9830   1345-2746
1946   18110590R

Kanho Hakhoe Chi
Kanho Hakhoe chi [The Journal of Nurses Academic Society]
0378-004X
Continued by: Taehan Kanho Hakhoe chi.
1970-199u   7601750

Kanhohak Tamgu
Kanhohak t'amgu
1992-1994   9500886

Kans Med
Kansas medicine: the journal of the Kansas Medical Society
8755-0059
Continues: Journal of the Kansas Medical Society.
1985-1998   8501226

Kans Nurse
The Kansas nurse
0022-8710
Continues the Bulletin of the Kansas State Nurses' Association.
1941   18110790R

Kansenshogaku Zasshi
Kansenshōgaku zasshi. The Journal of the Japanese Association for Infectious Diseases
0387-5911
Continues Nippon Densenbyō Gakkai zasshi.
1970   0236671

Kaohsiung J Med Sci
The Kaohsiung journal of medical sciences
1607-551X
Continues: Gaoxiong yi xue ke xue za zhi.
1996   100960562

Kardiol Pol
Kardiologia polska
0022-9032
Continues: Kardiologia polska.
1957   0376352

Kardiologiia
Kardiologiia
0022-9040
1961   0376351

Kassenzahnarzt Colloq Med Dent
Der Kassenzahnarzt; Colloquium med. dent
Continued by Der Zahnarzt; Colloquium med. dent.
1957-1968   0213515

Kathmandu Univ Med J (KUMJ)
Kathmandu University medical journal (KUMJ)
1812-2027   1812-2078
2003   101215359

Katilolehti
Kätilölehti
0022-9415
1896   0153272

Keio J Med
The Keio journal of medicine
0022-9717   1880-1293
1952   0376354

Keisei Geka
Keisei geka. Plastic & reconstructive surgery
0021-5228
Continues: Keisei biyōgeka.
1962   0413676

Kekkaku
Kekkaku: [Tuberculosis]
0022-9776
1923   0422132

Kennedy Inst Ethics J
Kennedy Institute of Ethics journal
1054-6863   1086-3249
1991   9109135

Kenya Nurs J
Kenya nursing journal
0301-0333
1972   0371210

Khimiia Meditsina
Khimiia i meditsina
0450-2132
1954-1961   0416615

Khirurgiia (Mosk)
Khirurgiia
0023-1207
Continues: Sovetskaia khirurgiia.
1937   0412765

Khirurgiia (Sofiia)
Khirurgiia
0450-2167
Continues Khirurgiia i ortopediia.
1951   0376355

Kidney Blood Press Res
Kidney & blood pressure research
1420-4096   1423-0143
Continues: Renal physiology and biochemistry.
1996   9610505

Kidney Int
Kidney international
0085-2538   1523-1755
1972   0323470

Kidney Int Suppl
Kidney international. Supplement
0098-6577
1974   7508622

Kinderarztl Prax
Kinderärztliche Praxis
0023-1495
Absorbed by: Sozialpädiatrie und Kinderärztliche Praxis.
1930-1993   0376356

Kinderkrankenschwester
Kinderkrankenschwester: Organ der Sektion Kinderkrankenpflege / Deutsche Gesellschaft für Sozialpädiatrie und Deutsche Gesellschaft für Kinderheilkunde
0723-2276
1982   8305989

King Faisal Spec Hosp Med J
The King Faisal Specialist Hospital medical journal
0253-4770
Continued by: Annals of Saudi medicine.
1981-1985   8208745

Kings Coll Hosp Gaz
King's College Hospital gazette
0309-7366
Continued by King's gazette.
1921-1967   7903314

Kisaengchunghak Chapchi
Kisaengch'unghak chapchi. The Korean journal of parasitology
Continues the Chapchi of the Taehan Kisaengch'ung Hakhoe. Continued by: Korean journal of parasitology.
1964-1992   0366132

Kisechugaku Zasshi
Kiseichugaku zasshi. Japanese journal of parasitology
0021-5171
Continued by: Parasitology international.
1951-1996   0417450

Kiserl Orvostud
Kísérletes orvostudomány
0023-1878
1949-1990   0376357

Kita Kanto Igaku
Kita Kantō igaku. Kitakanto medical journal
1343-2826   1881-1191
1951   0413530

Kitasato Arch Exp Med
  The Kitasato archives of experimental
  medicine
  0023-1924
  1917-1993   0376613

Klin Anasthesiol Intensivther
  Klinische Anästhesiologie und
  Intensivtherapie
  0341-5023
    Continues: Klinische Anästhesiologie.
  1974-1995   7605042

Klin Khir
  Klinicheskaia khirurgiia
  0023-2130
    Continues Novyĭ khirurgicheskiĭ arkhiv.
    Continued by: Klinichna khirurhiia.
  1962-1994   0376360

Klin Khir
  Klinichna khirurhiia / Ministerstvo
  okhorony zdorov'ia Ukraïny, Naukove
  tovarystvo khirurhiv Ukraïny
  0023-2130
    Continues: Klinicheskaia khirurgiia.
  1995   9516872

Klin Lab Diagn
  Klinicheskaia laboratornaia diagnostika
  0869-2084
    Continues: Laboratornoe delo.
  1992   9432021

Klin Lech Zlokach Novoobraz
  Klinika i lechenie zlokachestvennykh
  novoobrazovaniĭ
    Continues Voprosy kliniki i lecheniia
    zlokachestvennykh novoobrazovaniĭ.
  1963-1968   0152601

Klin Med (Mosk)
  Klinicheskaia meditsina
  0023-2149
  1923   2985204R

Klin Med Osterr Z Wiss Prakt Med
  Klinische Medizin; österreichische
  Zeitschrift für wissenschaftliche und
  praktische Medizin
  0368-6132
  1946-1967   18140020R

Klin Mikrobiol Infekc Lek
  Klinická mikrobiologie a infekční lékařství
  1211-264X
  1995   101189112

Klin Monatsbl Augenheilkd
  Klinische Monatsblätter für Augenheilkunde
  0023-2165   1439-3999
    Continues: Klinische Monatsblätter für
    Augenheilkunde und für augenärztliche
    Fortbildung.
  1963   0014133

Klin Monatsblatter Augenheilkd Augenarztl Fortbild
  Klinische Monatsblätter für Augenheilkunde
  und für augenärztliche Fortbildung
  0344-6360
    Continues: Klinische Monatsblätter für
    Augenheilkunde. Continued by: Klinische
    Monatsblätter für Augenheilkunde (1963).
  1925-1962   101288212

Klin Oczna
  Klinika oczna
  0023-2157
    Continues Postęp okulistyczny.
  1923   0376614

Klin Onkol
  Klinická onkologie: casopis Ceské a
  Slovenské onkologické spolecnosti
  0862-495X   1802-5307
  1988   9425213

Klin Padiatr
  Klinische Pädiatrie
  0300-8630
    Continues Archiv für Kinderheilkunde.
  1972   0326144

Klin Sygepleje
  Klinisk sygepleje
  0902-2767
  1987   9425346

Klin Wochenschr
  Klinische Wochenschrift
  0023-2173
    Formed by the union of Berliner klinische
    Wochenschrift and Therapeutische
    Halbmonatshefte. Continued by: Clinical
    investigation.
  1922-1991   2985205R

Knappschaftsarzt
  Der Knappschaftsarzt
  0450-4178
    Continues Medizinische wissenschaftliche
    Beiträge.
  1956-1970   0376777

Knee
  The Knee
  0968-0160
  1994   9430798

Knee Surg Sports Traumatol Arthrosc
  Knee surgery, sports traumatology,
  arthroscopy: official journal of the ESSKA
  0942-2056   1433-7347
  1993   9314730

Kobe Daigaku Igakubu Kiyo
  Kobe Daigaku Igakubu kiyo. Medical
  journal of Kobe University
  0075-6431
    Continues Kobe Ika Daigaku kiyo.
  1968   7507234

Kobe Ika Daigaku Kiyo
  Kobe Ika Daigaku kiyo
    Continues the Kiyo of Hyogo Kenritsu
    Ika Daigaku. Continued by Kobe Igakubu
    Daigaku kiyo.
  1952-1967   7502599

Kobe J Med Sci
  The Kobe journal of medical sciences
  0023-2513   1883-0498
  1951   0413531

Koku Eisei Gakkai Zasshi
  Koku Eisei Gakkai zasshi
  0023-2831
  1952   7502602

Kokubyo Gakkai Zasshi
  Kōkūbyō Gakkai zasshi. The Journal of the
  Stomatological Society, Japan
  0300-9149
  1927   0413677

Kokuritsu Iyakuhin Shokuhin Eisei Kenkyusho Hokoku
  Kokuritsu Iyakuhin Shokuhin Eisei
  Kenkyūjo hōkoku = Bulletin of National
  Institute of Health Sciences
  1343-4292
    Continues: Eisei Shikenjo hōkoku.
  1997   9807834

Kokyu To Junkan
  Kokyu to junkan. Respiration & circulation
  0452-3458
  1953   0413532

Kokyuki Shinryo
  [Kokyūki shinryō] Clinics of respiratory
  organs
    Continues Kekkaku shinryō.
  1956-1961   18140450R

Kongressbd Dtsch Ges Chir Kongr
  Kongressband / Deutsche Gesellschaft
  für Chirurgie. Deutsche Gesellschaft für
  Chirurgie. Kongress
                               1868-1050
    Continues: Langenbecks Archiv für Chirurgie.
    Supplement. Kongressband. Deutsche
    Gesellschaft für Chirurgie. Kongress.
  1999   100959225

Korean J Gastroenterol
  The Korean journal of gastroenterology =
  Taehan Sohwagi Hakhoe chi
  1598-9992
    Continues: Taehan Sohwagibyŏng Hakhoe
    chapchi.
  2003   101189416

Korean J Hepatol
  The Korean journal of hepatology
  1738-222X
    Continues: Taehan Kan Hakhoe chi.
  2004   101211947

Korean J Intern Med
  The Korean journal of internal medicine
  1226-3303
  1986   8712418

Korean J Lab Med
  The Korean journal of laboratory medicine
  1598-6535
    Continues: Taehan Chindan Kŏmsa ŭihakhoe
    chi.
  2006   101322822

Korean J Ophthalmol
  Korean journal of ophthalmology: KJO
  1011-8942
  1987   8804513

Korean J Parasitol
  The Korean journal of parasitology
  0023-4001   1738-0006
    Continues: Kisaengch'unghak chapchi.
  1993   9435800

Korean J Radiol
  Korean journal of radiology: official journal
  of the Korean Radiological Society
  1229-6929
  2000   100956096

Korot
  Korot
  0023-4109
  1952   2985207R

Kos
  KOS
  0393-2095
  1984   9424952

Kosei kagaku Jpn J Public Health
  [Kōsei kagaku] The Japanese journal of
  public health
  1940-1950   18210040R

Kosm Biol Aviakosm Med
  Kosmicheskaia biologiia i aviakosmicheskaia
  meditsina
  0321-5040
    Continues Kosmicheskaia biologiia i
    meditsina. Continued by: Aviakosmicheskaia
    i ekologicheskaia meditsina.
  1974-1991   0417736

Kosm Biol Med
  Kosmicheskaia biologiia i meditsina
  0023-4192
    Continued by Kosmicheskaia biologiia i
    aviakosmicheskaia meditsina.
  1967-1973   0412766

Kosm Ser A Biol
Kosmos. Seria A, Biologia / Polskie
Towarzystwo Przyrodników im. Kopernika
0023-4249
Continued by: Kosmos (Warsaw, Poland).
1952-1983 9892261

Krankengymnastik
Krankengymnastik
1614-0397
1949 7801777

Krankenpfl J
Krankenpflege Journal
0174-108X
Continues Schwestern Revue.
1980 8006304

Krankenpfl Soins Infirm
Krankenpflege. Soins infirmiers
0253-0465
Continues Zeitschrift für Krankenpflege.
Revue suisse des infirmières.
1979 8000153

Krankenpflege (Frankf)
Krankenpflege (Frankfurt am Main, Germany)
0002-1008
Continues: Agnes Karllschwester. der
Krankenpfleger. Continued by: Pflege aktuell.
1972-1993 0321505

Krankenschwester
Die Krankenschwester
0029-9480
Continued by Oesterreichische
Schwesternzeitung.
1948-1966 0425135

Krebsarzt
Der Krebsarzt
0368-6698
Continued by Oesterreichische Zeitschrift
für Erforschung und Bekämpfung der
Krebskrankheit.
1946-1969 0251004

Krebsforsch Krebsbekampf
Krebsforschung und Krebsbekämpfung
0075-7098
1955-1966 7808996

Kritiek
Kritiek (Ravels, Belgium)
0774-5346
1982-1991 8609082

Kroc Found Ser
Kroc Foundation series
0361-0489
Continues Kroc Foundation symposia.
1975-1985 7611160

Kulak Burun Bogaz Ihtis Derg
Kulak burun boğaz ihtisas dergisi: KBB =
Journal of ear, nose, and throat
1300-7475
1991 100899230

Kult Fiz
Kultura fizyczna
0137-7671
1947 18220190R

Kumamoto Igakkai Zasshi
Kumamoto Igakkai zasshi. The Journal of
the Kumamoto Medical Society
0300-919X
1925-2000 0413701

Kumamoto Med J
The Kumamoto medical journal
0023-5326
1938-1999 0376615

Kurinikaru Sutadi
Kurinikaru sutadī = Clinical study
0388-5585
1980 8302118

Kurume Med J
The Kurume medical journal
0023-5679 1881-2090
1954 2985210R

Kwart Hist Nauki Tech
Kwartalnik historii nauki i techniki:
Kwartal'nyĭ zhurnal istorii nauki i tekhniki
-
0023-589X
Continues: Studia i materialy do dziejow
nauki polskiej.
1956 0065346

Ky Dent J
Kentucky dental journal
0744-396X
Continues: Journal of the Kentucky Dental
Association. Continued by: KDA today.
1982-1998 9879657

Ky Hosp Mag
Kentucky hospitals magazine
1062-0354
Continues: Kentucky hospitals.
1989-1995 9206095

Ky Med J
Kentucky medical journal
Continues the Bulletin of the Kentucky
State Medical Association. Continued by
the Journal of the Kentucky State Medical
Association.
1904-1950 18120750R

Ky Nurse
Kentucky nurse
0742-8367
Continues: Kentucky Nurses Association.
Newsletter.
1983 8309653

KY Rep
KY [reports]. U.S. Atomic Energy
Commission
1962-1970 21830470R

Kybernetik
Kybernetik
0023-5946
Continued by Biological cybernetics.
1961-1974 7502604

Kyobu Geka
Kyobu geka. The Japanese journal of
thoracic surgery
0021-5252
1948 0413533

Kyoto Daigaku Kekkaku Kenkyusho Kiyo
Kiyo. [Reports]. Kyoto Daigaku. Kekkaku
Kenkyusho
0452-9839
1953-1967 0157752

Kyoto Daigaku Kokukagaku Kiyo
Kyoto Daigaku kokukagaku kiyo. Bulletin of
stomatology, Kyoto University
0023-6039
1959-1979 0152332

Kyushu J Med Sci
Kyushu journal of medical science
0453-0330
Continues Kyushu memoirs of medical
sciences.
1955-1964 0234040

L

LA Rep
LA [reports]. U.S. Atomic Energy
Commission
194u-1977 21830480R

Lab Anim
Laboratory animals
0023-6772
1967 0112725

Lab Anim (NY)
Lab animal
0093-7355
1972 0417737

Lab Anim Care
Laboratory animal care
0094-5331
Continues the Proceedings of the Animal
Care Panel.
1963-1970 0015266

Lab Anim Sci
Laboratory animal science
0023-6764
Continues: Laboratory animal care.
Continued by: Comparative medicine.
1971-1999 1266503

Lab Chip
Lab on a chip
1473-0197 1473-0189
2001 101128948

Lab Delo
Laboratornoe delo
0023-6748
Continued by: Klinicheskaia laboratornaia
diagnostika.
1955-1991 18230140R

Lab Dig
The Laboratory digest
0023-6799
Continues: Gradwohl laboratory digest.
1943-1975 18230150R

Lab Hematol
Laboratory hematology: official publication
of the International Society for Laboratory
Hematology
1080-2924 1523-6528
1995 9615688

Lab Invest
Laboratory investigation; a journal of
technical methods and pathology
0023-6837 1530-0307
Supersedes the Bulletin of the International
Association of Medical Museums.
1952 0376617

Lab Pract
Laboratory practice
0023-6853
1952-1992 0376620

Lab Res Methods Biol Med
Laboratory and research methods in biology
and medicine
0160-8584
1977-1984 7707818

Labor Law J
Labor law journal
0023-6586
1949 9877924

Laboratorio
"Laboratorio;" análisis clínicos,
bacteriología, inmunología, parasitología,
hematología, anatomía patológica, química
clínica
0023-6691
1946-1987 0376616

Laboratory
The Laboratory
0023-6748
1928-19uu 2985211R

Laeknabladid
Læknabladid
0023-7213   1670-4959
1915   7901326

Lahey Clin Bull
The Lahey Clinic bulletin
Continued by the Bulletin of the Lahey Clinic
Foundation.
1938-1964   0015312

Lahey Clin Found Bull
Lahey Clinic Foundation bulletin
0023-7299
Continues The Lahey Clinic bulletin.
1964-1983   7502608

Lait
Le Lait
0023-7302
Continues: Revue générale du lait. Continued
by: Dairy science & technology.
1921-2007   **18230280R**

Lakartidningen
Läkartidningen
0023-7205
Continues Svenska läkartidningen.
1965   0027707

Lamp
The Lamp
0047-3936
1944   0015376

Lampada
Lampada
0266-8769
1984-1990   8511320

Lancet
Lancet
0140-6736   1474-547X
1823   2985213R

Lancet Infect Dis
The Lancet infectious diseases
1473-3099
2001   101130150

Lancet Neurol
Lancet neurology
1474-4422   1474-4465
2002   101139309

Lancet Oncol
The lancet oncology
1470-2045   1474-5488
2000   100957246

Landarzt
Der Landarzt
0023-7728
Continued by Zeitschrift für
Allgemeinmedizin.
1919-1968   0173426

Lang Speech
Language and speech
0023-8309
1958   2985214R

Lang Speech Hear Serv Sch
Language, speech, and hearing services in
schools
0161-1461
Continues: Speech and hearing services in
schools.
1971   0323431

Langenbecks Arch Chir
Langenbecks Archiv für Chirurgie
0023-8236
Continues: Langenbecks Archiv für klinische
Chirurgie. Continued by: Langenbeck's
archives of surgery.
1969-1997   0204167

Langenbecks Arch Chir Suppl II Verh Dtsch Ges Chir
Langenbecks Archiv für Chirurgie.
Supplement II, Verhandlungen der
Deutschen Gesellschaft für Chirurgie.
Deutsche Gesellschaft für Chirurgie.
Kongress
0173-0541
Supplement to: Langenbecks Archiv
für Chirurgie. Continued by: Deutsche
Gesellschaft für Chirurgie. Kongress.
Langenbecks Archiv für Chirurgie.
Supplement, Kongressband.
1988-1990   9200455

Langenbecks Arch Chir Suppl Kongressbd
Langenbecks Archiv für Chirurgie.
Supplement. Kongressband. Deutsche
Gesellschaft für Chirurgie. Kongress
0942-2854
Continues: Langenbecks Archiv für Chirurgie.
Supplement II, Verhandlungen der Deutschen
Gesellschaft für Chirurgie. Deutsche
Gesellschaft für Chirurgie. Kongress.
Continued by: Kongressband. Deutsche
Gesellschaft für Chirurgie. Kongress.
1991-1998   9200456

Langenbecks Arch Klin Chir Ver Dtsch Z Chir
Langenbecks Archiv für klinische Chirurgie
... vereinigt mit Deutsche Zeitschrift für
Chirurgie
Continued by Langenbecks Archiv für
klinische Chirurgie.
1947-1964   0171206

Langenbecks Arch Surg
Langenbeck's archives of surgery / Deutsche
Gesellschaft für Chirurgie
1435-2443   1435-2451
Continues: Langenbecks Archiv für Chirurgie.
1998   9808285

Langmuir
Langmuir: the ACS journal of surfaces and
colloids
0743-7463   1520-5827
1985   9882736

Languedoc Med
Languedoc médical
Supersedes Le Languedoc médico-chirurgical.
1918-1970   1272344

Lar Do Med
O Lar do médico
1943-1947   18240290R

LARC Med
LARC médical
0242-9462
Continues: Lille médical. Continued by: Lille
médical (1987).
1981-1986   8203246

Laryngol Rhinol Otol (Stuttg)
Laryngologie, Rhinologie, Otologie
0340-1588
Formed by the union of Laryngologie,
Rhinologie, Otologie und ihre Grenzgebiete
and Monatsschrift für Ohrenheilkunde und
Laryngo-Rhinologie, and continues the vol.
numbering of the former. Continued by:
Laryngo- rhino- otologie.
1975-1988   7513628

Laryngol Rhinol Otol (Stuttg)
Laryngologie, Rhinologie, Otologie und ihre
Grenzgebiete
0302-9379
Continues Zeitschrift für Laryngologie,
Rhinologie, Otologie und ihre Grenzgebiete.
Merged with Monatsschrift für
Ohrenheilkunde und Laryngo-Rhinologie to
form Laryngologie, Rhinologie, Otologie.
1974-1974   7513627

Laryngorhinootologie
Laryngo- rhino- otologie
0935-8943
Continues: Laryngologie, Rhinologie,
Otologie.
1989   8912371

Laryngoscope
The Laryngoscope
0023-852X   1531-4995
1896   8607378

Laser Nurs
Laser nursing
0888-6075
Continued by: Minimally invasive surgical
nursing.
1987-1992   8711105

Lasers Med Sci
Lasers in medical science
0268-8921   1435-604X
1986   8611515

Lasers Surg Med
Lasers in surgery and medicine
0196-8092   1096-9101
1980   8007168

Lasers Surg Med Suppl
Lasers in surgery and medicine. Supplement
1050-9267
1989   9005665

Laterality
Laterality
1357-650X   1464-0678
1996   9609064

Lattante
Il Lattante
0023-8864
1930-1974   2985216R

Laund News
Laundry news
0164-5765
Continued by: American laundry news.
19uu-1996   9877785

Lav Ist Anat Istol Patol Univ Studi Perugia
Lavori dell'Istituto di anatomia e istologia
patologica, Università degli studi di Perugia
0041-8943
1940-1978   7505645

Lav Um
Lavoro umano
0023-9127
Continued by: Archivio di scienze del Lavoro,
in 1985.
1940-1984   0404434

Laval Med
Laval médical
0023-9046
Supersedes: Bulletin de la Société médical
des hôpitaux universitaires de Québec.
Superseded by: Vie médicale au Canada
français.
1936-1971   2985217R

Law Contemp Probl
Law and contemporary problems
0023-9186
1933   9875488

Law Hum Behav
Law and human behavior
0147-7307
1977   7801255

Law Hum Genome Rev
Law and the human genome review =
Revista de derecho y genoma humano /
Chair in Law and the Human Genome,
BBV Foundation-Provincial Government of
Biscay, University of Deusto
1134-7708
1994   9700234

Law Med Health Care
Law, medicine & health care: a publication
of the American Society of Law & Medicine
0277-8459
Formed by the union of: Medicolegal news,
and: Nursing law & ethics and continues
the numbering of the former. Continued by:
Journal of law, medicine & ethics.
1981-1992   8205794

LDA J
LDA journal
0092-4458
Continues Journal of the Louisiana Dental
Association.
1973   0403231

LDI Issue Brief
LDI issue brief
1553-0671
1994   9815837

Leadersh Health Serv
Leadership in health services = Leadership
dans les services de santé
1188-3669
Formed by the union of: Dimensions in health
service, and: Hospital trustee. Continued as a
separately paged section within: International
journal of health care quality assurance
incorporating Leadership in health services.
1992-1996   9211318

Leadersh Health Serv (Bradf Engl)
Leadership in health services (Bradford,
England)
1751-1879   1751-1887
Separated from: International journal of
health care quality assurance incorporating
Leadership in health services.
2007   101464443

League Exch
League exchange
0077-5134
1952-1982   7507243

League Lines
League lines
1955-1969   0102673

Learn Behav
Learning & behavior: a Psychonomic
Society publication
1543-4494   1543-4508
Continues: Animal learning & behavior.
2003   101155056

Learn Mem
Learning & memory (Cold Spring Harbor,
N.Y.)
1072-0502   1549-5485
1994   9435678

Leban Pharm J
The Lebanese pharmaceutical journal. La
Revue pharmaceutique libanaise
1953-1975   18310190R

Lebensversicher Med
Lebensversicherungs Medizin
0024-0044
Continued by: Versicherungsmedizin.
1949-1987   2985219R

Leber Magen Darm
Leber, Magen, Darm
0300-8622
Absorbed: Innere Medizin in 1992.
1971-2000   0311747

Lect Sci Basis Med
Lectures on the scientific basis of medicine
Continued by the Scientific basis of medicine;
annual reviews.
1951-1959   0243575

Leech
The Leech
0457-3277
Supersedes: Leech.
194u-1969   18310430R

Leeds Dent J
Leeds Dental Journal
0024-0265
1962-1968   9881977

Leg Aspects Med Pract
Legal aspects of medical practice
0190-2350
Continues The Journal of legal medicine.
1977-1989   7801257

Leg Med
Legal medicine
0197-9981
Continues Legal medicine annual.
1980-1995   8003226

Leg Med (Tokyo)
Legal medicine (Tokyo, Japan)
1344-6223
Continues English language articles formerly
published in: Nippon hōigaku zasshi.
1999   100889186

Leg Med Annu
Legal medicine annual
0075-8590
Continued by Legal medicine.
1969-1978   0206765

Leg Med Q
Legal medical quarterly
0703-1211
1977-2001   7810301

Lege Artis Med
Lege artis medicinae: új magyar orvosi
hírmondó
0866-4811
1991   9425319

Lek List
Lékařské listy
Continued by: Vnitřní lékařství.
1946-1954   18310680R

Lek Pr
Lekárske práce
1961-1987   0260743

Lek Veda Zahr
Lékařská věda v zahraničí
0139-889X
1957-1967   1306751

Lek Wojsk
Lekarz wojskowy
0024-0745
1920   18310760R

Lens Eye Toxic Res
Lens and eye toxicity research
1042-6922
Continues: Lens research.
1989-1992   8916639

Lepr India
Leprosy in India
0024-1024
Continued by Indian journal of leprosy.
1929-1983   0376624

Lepr Rev
Leprosy review
0305-7518
Supersedes Leprosy notes.
1930   0243711

Lett Appl Microbiol
Letters in applied microbiology
0266-8254   1472-765X
1985   8510094

Leuk Lymphoma
Leukemia & lymphoma
1042-8194   1029-2403
1989   9007422

Leuk Res
Leukemia research
0145-2126   1873-5835
1977   7706787

Leukemia
Leukemia: official journal of the Leukemia
Society of America, Leukemia Research
Fund, U.K
0887-6924   1476-5551
1987   8704895

Libr J
Library journal
0363-0277
1876   57630670R

Libr Resour Tech Serv
Library resources & technical services
0024-2527
Supersedes the Journal of cataloging and
classification and Serial slants. Continued in
part by: New directions in technical services.
1957   57920670R

Libr Technol Rep
Library technology reports
0024-2586
1976   57630720R

Licentiate
The Licentiate; a monthly journal of
medicine and surgery
0457-7795
1951-1951   2985220R

Liet Tsr Aukst Mokyklu Mokslo Darb
Lietuvos TSR aukštuÃßjuÃß mokykluÃß
mokslo darbai: Biologija
0459-3383
1961-199u   0142735

Life Sci
Life sciences
0024-3205
Formed by the union of Life sciences. Part
1, Physiology and pharmacology; and: Life
sciences. Part 2, Biochemistry, general and
molecular biology.
1973   0375521

Life Sci I
Life sciences. Pt. 1: Physiology and
pharmacology
0300-9653
Continues in part Life sciences. Merged with
Life sciences. Pt. 2: Biochemistry, general
and molecular biology to form Life sciences.
1970-1973   0375522

Life Sci II
Life sciences. Pt. 2: Biochemistry, general
and molecular biology
0300-9637
Continues in part Life sciences. Merged
with Life sciences. Pt. 1: Physiology and
pharmacology to form Life sciences.
1970-1973   0375523

Life Sci Space Res
Life sciences and space research
0075-9422
Absorbed by: Advances in space research.
1962-1980   1250331

Life Support Biosph Sci
Life support & biosphere science:
international journal of earth space
1069-9422
Continued by: Habitation (Elmsford, N.Y.).
1994-2002   9431217

Life Support Syst
Life support systems: the journal of the
European Society for Artificial Organs
0261-989X
1983-1987   8219681

Life Threat Behav
Life-threatening behavior
0047-4592
Continued by Suicide.
1971-1974   7610536

Lifelong Learn Adult Years
Lifelong learning, the adult years / Adult
Education Association of the United States
of America
0148-2165
Continues: Adult leadership. Continued by:
Lifelong learning (Washington, D.C.).
1977-1983   9877808

Lifetime Data Anal
Lifetime data analysis
1380-7870
1995   9516348

Ligament
Ligament
1963   9880095

Lijec Vjesn
Liječnički vjesnik
0024-3477
1877   0074253

Lik Sprava
Likars'ka sprava / Ministerstvo okhorony
zdorov'ia Ukraïny
1019-5297
Continues: Vrachebnoe delo.
1992   9601540

Lille Chir
Lille chirurgical
0024-3493
1946-1987   0376625

Lille Med
Lille médical: journal de la Faculté de
médecine et de pharmacie de l'Université
de Lille
0024-3507
Continues: L'Écho médical du Nord.
Continued by: LARC médical.
1956-1981   8203780

Lin Chuang Er Bi Yan Hou Ke Za Zhi
Lin chuang er bi yan hou ke za zhi =
Journal of clinical otorhinolaryngology
1001-1781
Continued by: Lin chuang er bi yan hou tou
jing wai ke za zhi.
1987-2006   9426080

Lin Chung Er Bi Yan Hou Tou Jing Wai Ke Za Zhi
Lin chuang er bi yan hou tou jing
wai ke za zhi = Journal of clinical
otorhinolaryngology, head, and neck surgery
Continues: Lin chuang er bi yan hou ke za zhi.
2007   101303164

Linacre Q
The Linacre quarterly
0024-3639
1932   2985221R

Linen Supply News
Linen supply news
0024-3825
Continued by: Textile rental.
19uu-197u   9877786

Lipids
Lipids
0024-4201
1966   0060450

Lipids Health Dis
Lipids in health and disease
                             1476-511X
2002   101147696

Lippincott Health Promot Lett
The Lippincott health promotion letter
1089-9693
1997   9715780

Lippincotts Case Manag
Lippincott's case management: managing
the process of patient care
1529-7764
Continues: Nursing case management.
Absorbed: Inside case management. 2004
Continued by: Professional case management.
2000-2006   100961551

Lippincotts Prim Care Pract
Lippincott's primary care practice
1088-5471
1997-2000   9706704

Lit Med
Literature and medicine
0278-9671   1080-6571
1982   8309346

Liver
Liver
0106-9543   1600-0676
Continued by: Liver international.
1981-2002   8200939

Liver Int
Liver international: official journal of the
International Association for the Study of
the Liver
1478-3223   1478-3231
Continues: Liver.
2003   101160857

Liver Transpl
Liver transplantation: official publication of
the American Association for the Study of
Liver Diseases and the International Liver
Transplantation Society
1527-6465   1527-6473
Continues: Liver transplantation and surgery.
2000   100909185

Liver Transpl Surg
Liver transplantation and surgery: official
publication of the American Association
for the Study of Liver Diseases and the
International Liver Transplantation Society
1074-3022
Continued by: Liver transplanation.
1995-1999   9502504

Lloydia
Lloydia
0024-5461
Continued by: Journal of natural products.
1938-1978   0376626

LMT
LMT: Lab management today
1058-7845
Continues: Dental lab management today.
1991   9211328

Local Popul Stud
Local population studies
0143-2974
1968   0211167

Log
The Log
Supersedes the Harbor dental log, with
caption title still carrying that name.
1971-1980   0316657

Logoped Phoniatr Vocol
Logopedics, phoniatrics, vocology
1401-5439
Merger of: Scandinavian journal of
logopedics & phoniatrics, and: Voice
(London, England).
1996   9617311

Loma Linda Univ Dent Mag
Loma Linda University Dentist Magazine
1962-1967   9883833

Lond Clin Med J
London Clinic medical journal
0024-6018
1960-1971   0413706

Lond Hosp Gaz
The London Hospital gazette
0024-6050
1894-1975   0015362

Lond Sch Hyg Trop Med
Report of the ... meeting of the Ross
institute Industrial advisory committee ...
London School of Hygiene and Tropical
Medicine. Ross Institute of Tropical Hygiene
(East Africa Branch)
1928-19uu   18340170R

Long Range Plann
Long range planning
0024-6301
1968   9878044

Long Term Care (Don Mills)
Long term care (Don Mills, Ont.)
0831-5035
1985-1986   8503900

Long Term Care Health Serv Adm Q
Long term care and health services
administration quarterly
0161-6773
1977-1980   7801260

Long Term Care Q
Long-term care quarterly
0891-8104
1986-1986   8608499

Longevita
Longevita
1952-19uu   18340330R

Lotta Contro Tuberc Malat Polm Sociali
Lotta contro la tubercolosi e le malattie
polmonari sociali
6368-7546
Continues Lotta contro la tubercolosi.
Continued by: Prevenzione respiratoria.
1972-1999   0333116

Lotta Tuberc
Lotta contro la tubercolosi
0024-6638
Continued by Lotta contro la tubercolosi e le malattie polmonari sociali.
1930-1971   0333115

Lovelace Clin Rev
The Lovelace Clinic review
1961-1966   18340750R

Lucina
Lucina
1934   18340860R

Luminescence
Luminescence: the journal of biological and chemical luminescence
1522-7235   1522-7243
Continues: Journal of bioluminescence and chemiluminescence.
1999   100889025

Lung
Lung
0341-2040
Continues Pneumonologie. Pneumonology.
1976   7701875

Lung Cancer
Lung cancer (Amsterdam, Netherlands)
0169-5002
1985   8800805

Lupus
Lupus
0961-2033
1991   9204265

Lutte Cancer
La Lutte contre le cancer
0024-7642
Continued by: Vivre (Paris, France).
1923-1980   9003285

Luzif Amor
Luzifer-Amor: Zeitschrift zur Geschichte der Psychoanalyse
0933-3347
1988   9214703

Lymphat Res Biol
Lymphatic research and biology
1539-6851
2003   101163587

Lymphokine Cytokine Res
Lymphokine and cytokine research
1056-5477
Continues: Lymphokine research. Merged with: Journal of interferon research. to form: Journal of interferon & cytokine research.
1991-1994   9107882

Lymphokine Res
Lymphokine research
0277-6766
Continued by: Lymphokine and cytokine research.
1982-1990   8308208

Lymphology
Lymphology
0024-7766
1968   0155112

Lyon Chir
Lyon chirurgical
0024-7782
Absorbed by: Annales de chirurgie.
1908-1997   0376627

Lyon Med
Lyon médical
0024-7790
Formed by the union of Gazette médicale de Lyon and Journal de médecine de Lyon. Absorbed La Revue lyonnaise de médecine. Jan. 1971.
1869-1985   0335015

M

M B Pharm Bull
M & B pharmaceutical bulletin
0460-2390
1952-1979   18410020R

M S C Vet
M. S. C. veterinarian
Continued by: MSU veterinarian.
1940-1955   18410180R

Ma Zui Xue Za Zhi
Ma zui xue za zhi = Anaesthesiologica Sinica
0254-1319
Continued by: Acta anaesthesiologica Sinica.
1960-1993   8200948

Maandschr Kindergeneeskd
Maandschrift voor kindergeneeskunde
0024-869X
Supersedes Nederlandsch maandschrift voor geneeskunde. Continued by Tijdschrift voor kindergeneeskunde.
1931-1975   7704293

Macromol Biosci
Macromolecular bioscience
1616-5187   1616-5195
2001   101135941

Macromolecules
Macromolecules
0024-9297
1968   0365316

Madj Persat Dokt Gigi Indones
Madjalah Persatuan Dokter Gigi Indonesia. Journal Of The Indonesian Dental Association
0024-9548
Continued by: Majalah Pdgi.
1961-1963   9430140

Madjalah Kedokt Indones
Madjalah Kedokteran Indonesia
0464-3186
Continued by Majalah Kedokteran Indonesia.
1951-1970   7507251

Mag Camb Univ Med Soc
Magazine. Cambridge University Medical Society
Continued by Murmur.
1922-1963   16020600R

Mag R Free Hosp (Lond Engl)
Magazine. Royal Free Hospital (London, England). School of Medicine
0144-2198
Continued by: Journal. Royal Free Hospital (London. England). School of Medicine.
1895-1958   18340100R

MAGMA
Magma (New York, N.Y.)
0968-5243
1993   9310752

Magn Reson Annu
Magnetic resonance annual
8756-9787
Continued by: Magnetic resonance quarterly.
1985-1988   8409187

Magn Reson Chem
Magnetic resonance in chemistry: MRC
0749-1581   1097-458X
Continues: OMR. Organic magnetic resonance.
1985   9882600

Magn Reson Imaging
Magnetic resonance imaging
0730-725X
1982   8214883

Magn Reson Imaging Clin N Am
Magnetic resonance imaging clinics of North America
1064-9689
1993   9422762

Magn Reson Med
Magnetic resonance in medicine: official journal of the Society of Magnetic Resonance in Medicine / Society of Magnetic Resonance in Medicine
0740-3194   1522-2594
1984   8505245

Magn Reson Med Sci
Magnetic resonance in medical sciences: MRMS: an official journal of Japan Society of Magnetic Resonance in Medicine
1347-3182   1880-2205
2002   101153368

Magn Reson Q
Magnetic resonance quarterly
0899-9422
Continues: Magnetic resonance annual.
1989-1995   8910769

Magnes Res
Magnesium research: official organ of the International Society for the Development of Research on Magnesium
0953-1424
1988   8900948

Magnes Trace Elem
Magnesium and trace elements
1015-3845
Continues: Magnesium.
1990-1992   9005667

Magnesium
Magnesium
0252-1156
Continued by: Magnesium and trace elements.
1982-1989   8219687

Magy Belorv Arch
Magyar belorvosi archivum
0133-5464
1947   0417742

Magy Noorv Lapja
Magyar nöorvosok lapja
0025-021X
1938   0016262

Magy Onkol
Magyar onkologia
0025-0244
1957   9313833

Magy Radiol
Magyar radiologia
0025-0287
Continues Radiologia Hungarica.
1950-1990   20010350R

Magy Seb
Magyar sebészet
0025-0295
Absorbed: Acta chirurgica Hungarica. 2000 Continues: Archivum chirurgicum..
1949   18420110R

Magy Traumatol Orthop Helyreallito Seb
Magyar traumatológia, orthopaedia és
helyreállító sebészet
0025-0317
Continues Traumatológiai és orthopaediai
közlemények. Continued by: Magyar
traumatológia, ortopédia, kézsebészet,
plasztikai sebészet.
1960-1992   0074071

Magy Traumatol Ortop Kezseb Plasztikai Seb
Magyar traumatológia, ortopédia,
kézsebészet, plasztikai sebészet
Continues: Magyar traumatológia.
orthopaedia és helyreállító sebészet.
1992   9313834

Magy Tud
Magyar tudomány: [a Magyar Tudományos
Akadémia Értesítője]
0025-0325
Continues: Akadémiai értesítő.
1956   0417650

Maine Nurse
Maine nurse
0025-0767
1969   1300152

Mainlines
MainLines: the newsletter for the Midwest
Alliance in Nursing
0278-9450
1980-1999   9310753

Majallah Jamia Dandan Pazshki
Majallah-i Jāmiah-i Dandānpizishkī-i
Īrān = The journal of the Iranian Dental
Association
19uu-19uu   9440736

Majallat Niqabat Attiba Alasnnan Alurduniyah
Majallat Niqābat Attibā' al-Asnān
al-Urdunīyah
Continued by: The Jordan dental journal.
1960-1983   7507213

Majallat Tibb Alasnan Alsuriyah
Majallat tibb al-asnān al-Sūrīyah
0586-349X
1965-1975   7808298

Majallat Tibb Alfamm Alsuriyah
Majallat tibb al-famm al-Sūrīyah
Continues: Majallat tibb al-asnān al-Sūrīyah.
19uu   9500584

Major Probl Clin Pediatr
Major problems in clinical pediatrics
0076-2865
1964-1988   0243601

Major Probl Clin Surg
Major problems in clinical surgery
0025-1062
1964-1984   1271453

Major Probl Intern Med
Major problems in internal medicine
0090-6956
1971-1985   1262076

Major Probl Obstet Gynecol
Major problems in obstetrics and
gynecology
0076-2873
1970-1982   0261660

Major Probl Pathol
Major problems in pathology
0076-2881
1970   0261661

Makedon Med Pregl
Makedonski medicinski pregled. Revue
médicale macedonienne
0025-1097
1946   18420240R

Mal Cardiovasc
Malattie cardiovascolari
0542-268X
Merged with Cuore e circolazione and Folia
cardiologica to form Giornale italiano di
cardiologia.
1960-1969   1270355

Malacologia
Malacologia
0076-2997
1962   0400677

Malar J
Malaria journal
                                             1475-2875
2002   101139802

Malawi Med J
Malawi medical journal: the journal of
Medical Association of Malawi
1995-7262   1995-7270
Continues: Medical quarterly (Blantyre,
Malawi).
1990   9500170

Malays Dent J
Malaysian dental journal
Continues Malayan dental journal.
1965-1967   0105614

Malays J Pathol
The Malaysian journal of pathology
0126-8635
1978   8101177

Male Nurses J
The male nurses' journal
1944-19uu   0073774

Mali Med
Le Mali médical
0464-7874   1993-0836
1963   18420390R

Mamm Genome
Mammalian genome: official journal of the
International Mammalian Genome Society
0938-8990   1432-1777
Absorbed: Mouse genome. Jan. 1998
1991   9100916

Mammalia
Mammalia
0025-1461
1936   7508250

Man (Lond)
Man; a monthly record of anthropological
science
0025-1496
1901-1965   0073340

Man Med
Man and medicine
0145-9783
1975-1980   7606743

Man Ther
Manual therapy
1356-689X   1532-2769
1995   9610924

Manag Care
Managed care (Langhorne, Pa.)
1062-3388
1992   9303583

Manag Care Interface
Managed care interface
1096-5645
Continues: Medical interface.
1997   9715194

Manag Care Q
Managed care quarterly
1064-5454
1993   9308935

Manag Care Strateg
Managed care strategies (Atlanta, Ga.)
Continues: Hospital managed care strategies.
Absorbed by: Physician's managed care
report. 1999
1997-1998   9709416

Manag Compliance Ser
Management and compliance series /
American Society for Hospital Engineering
of the American Hospital Association
1987   9104196

Manag Medicare Medicaid News
Managed medicare & medicaid news
1085-0317
Continues: Health care reform week.
Absorbed by: Part B news. Sept. 1997
1995-1997   9514312

Manage Focus
Management focus
0193-8266
Continues: Management controls. Absorbed
in May 1985 by: World.
1978-1985   9877904

Manage Rev
Management review
0025-1895
Continues American management review.
1926-2000   18420420R

Manage World
Management world
0090-3825
1972-1992   9877903

Manch Med Gaz
The Manchester medical gazette
0025-2018
Continues: Manchester University Medical
School gazette. Continued by: Mediscope
(Manchester, England).
1960-1979   9804133

Manch Univ Med Sch Gaz
Manchester University Medical School
gazette
Continued by: Manchester medical gazette.
1921-1960   0324110

Manedsskr Prakt Laegegern
Maanedsskrift for praktisk Laegegerning og
social Medicin
0373-2746
1922   18410260R

Manit Med Rev
Manitoba medical review
0025-2255
Continues the Manitoba Medical Association
review.
1939-1971   0410760

Mar Biotechnol (NY)
Marine biotechnology (New York, N.Y.)
1436-2228   1436-2236
Formed by the merger of: Journal of marine
biotechnology, and: Molecular marine
biology and biotechnology.
1999   100892712

Mar Drugs
Marine drugs
1660-3397
2003   101213729

Mar Environ Res
Marine environmental research
0141-1136
1978   9882895

Mar Pollut Bull
Marine pollution bulletin
0025-326X
1970   0260231

Marbg Schrift Medgesch
Marburger Schriften zur Medizingeschichte
0721-3859
1981   8413234

Marg Otolaryngol
Marginalia otolaryngologica
1939-19uu   18420710R

Marginalia Dermatol
Marginalia dermatologica
1941-1952   18420700R

Mark Health Serv
Marketing health services
1094-1304
  Continues: Journal of health care marketing.
1997   9891646

Maroc Med
al-Maghrib al-ṭibbī. Maroc médical
0253-4053
  Supersedes: Maroc médical. ISSN 0025-388X, published 1921-75 with differing numbering designation.
1978-2001   7902084

Maroc Med
Maroc médical
0025-388X
  Continued by: Maroc médical.
1921-1975   0421062

Marquette Med Rev
Marquette medical review
1936-1969   18430020R

Mars Chir
Marseille chirurgical
0025-4045
  Absorbed by: Mediterranée médicale.
1949-1972   0414134

Mars Med
Marseille médical
0025-4053
  Continues Union médicale de la Provence. Merged with Nice médical: and. Journal de médecine de Montpellier: to form. Revue méditerranéenne des sciences médicales.
1869-1975   2985228R

MASA Rev
MASA review: journal of the Medical Association of the State of Alabama
1092-1850
  Continues: Alabama medicine.
1996-1999   9813470

Mass Nurse
The Massachusetts nurse
0163-0784
  Continues: Bulletin of the Massachusetts Nurses Association.
1976   7803548

Mass Spectrom Rev
Mass spectrometry reviews
0277-7037   1098-2787
1982   8219702

Masui
Masui. The Japanese journal of anesthesiology
0021-4892
1952   0413707

Mater Manag Health Care
Materials management in health care
1059-4531
1992   9304859

Mater Med Nordmark
Materia medica Nordmark
0025-5238
1931-1986   0400704

Mater Med Pol
Materia medica Polona. Polish journal of medicine and pharmacy
0025-5246
1969-1998   0236526

Mater Ther
Materia therapeutica: aus Klinik und Praxis für Klinik und Praxis
  Continues: Materia therapeutica Dr. Kutiak.
1964-1971   9508118

Matern Child Health J
Maternal and child health journal
1092-7875
1997   9715672

Matern Child Nurs J
Maternal-child nursing journal
0090-0702
  Continued by: Journal of the Society of Pediatric Nurses.
1972-1996   0350761

Matern Child Nutr
Maternal & child nutrition
1740-8695   1740-8709
2005   101201025

Matern Infanc (Sao Paulo)
Maternidade e infância; arquivos médicos-sociais
0025-5491
1945-1976   18430590R

Matern Infanz (1926)
Maternita e infanzia
1720-9579
1926-1975   18430600R

Maternite
Maternité; revue pratique d'obstétrique et de puériculture
0543-081X
1952-1968   18430610R

Math Biosci
Mathematical biosciences
0025-5564
1967   0103146

Math Biosci Eng
Mathematical biosciences and engineering: MBE
1547-1063   1551-0018
2004   101197794

Math Med Biol
Mathematical medicine and biology: a journal of the IMA
1477-8599   1477-8602
  Continues: IMA journal of mathematics applied in medicine and biology.
2003   101182345

Matrix
Matrix (Stuttgart, Germany)
0934-8832
  Continues: Collagen and related research.
  Continued by: Matrix biology.
1989-1993   8906139

Matrix Biol
Matrix biology: journal of the International Society for Matrix Biology
0945-053X
  Continues: Matrix (Stuttgart, Germany).
1994   9432592

Matrix Suppl
Matrix (Stuttgart, Germany). Supplement
0940-1199
1992-1992   9312140

Maturitas
Maturitas
0378-5122
  Absorbed: European menopause journal.
  1998
1978   7807333

Mayan
The Mayan
0543-176X
1965-1967   0104141

Mayo Clin Health Lett
Mayo Clinic health letter (English ed.)
0741-6245
1983   8507508

Mayo Clin Proc
Mayo Clinic proceedings. Mayo Clinic
0025-6196   1942-5546
  Continues: Proceedings of the staff meetings of the Mayo Clinic.
1964   0405543

Mayo Clin Womens Healthsource
Mayo Clinic women's healthsource
1091-0220
1997   9891120

Mcgill Dent Rev
The McGill dental review
0024-9025
1934-1983   18410300R

Mcgraw Hills Med Health
McGraw-Hill's medicine & health
0891-737X
  Continues: McGraw-Hill's Washington report on medicine & health. Continued by: Medicine & health.
1986-1989   8611912

Mcgraw Hills Wash Rep Med Health
McGraw-Hill's Washington report on medicine & health
0043-0730
  Continues: Washington report on medicine & health. Continued by: McGraw-Hill's medicine & health.
1986-1986   8611913

McGregor Clin Bull
McGregor Clinic bulletin
1939-1964   18410310R

MCN Am J Matern Child Nurs
MCN. The American journal of maternal child nursing
0361-929X   1539-0683
1976   7605941

MD
MD medical newsmagazine
0024-8010
1957-1994   18410070R

MD Comput
M.D. computing: computers in medical practice
0724-6811
1984-2001   8408946

Md Health Bull
Maryland health bulletin
Continues and is continued by the Monthly bulletin of the Maryland State Dept. of Health.
1945-1953   **22620100R**

Md Med
Maryland medicine: MM: a publication of MEDCHI, the Maryland State Medical Society
1538-2656
Merger of: Maryland medical journal (Baltimore, Md.: 1985), and: Montgomery medicine.
2000   **100931679**

Md Med J
Maryland medical journal (Baltimore, Md.: 1985)
0886-0572
Continues: Maryland state medical journal. Merged with: Montgomery medicine, to form: Maryland medicine.
1985-1999   **8506985**

Md Nurs News
Maryland nursing news
Superseded by: Maryland nurses.
1931-1969   **1246143**

Md Nurse
The Maryland nurse
0047-6080
Supersedes Maryland nursing news. Continued by: Maryland nurse (Linthicum Heights, Md.: 1999).
1970-1999   **1246142**

Md State Med J
Maryland state medical journal
0025-4363
Supersedes Medical and Chirurgical Faculty of the State of Maryland. Bulletin. Incorporates Medical and Chirurgical Faculty of the State of Maryland. News letter. Continued by Maryland medical journal (Baltimore, Md.: 1985).
1952-1984   **2985229R**

Mead Johnson Symp Perinat Dev Med
Mead Johnson Symposium on Perinatal and Developmental Medicine
0190-0749
1972-1979   **7806609**

Mech Ageing Dev
Mechanisms of ageing and development
0047-6374
Continued in part by: Ageing research reviews.
1972   **0347227**

Mech Chem Biosyst
Mechanics & chemistry of biosystems: MCB
1546-2048   **1546-2056**
Continued by: Molecular & cellular biomechanics.
2004-2005   **101258184**

Mech Dev
Mechanisms of development
0925-4773   **1872-6356**
Continues: Cell differentiation and development.
1990   **9101218**

Med Aeronaut
La Médecine aéronautique
1946-1959   **18440230R**

Med Aeronaut Spat
Médecine aéronautique et spatiale
0294-0817
Continues in part: Médecine aéronautique et spatiale, médecine subaquatique et hyperbare.
1982   **8609124**

Med Aff
Medical affairs
0025-6951
Continued by: Health affairs (Philadelphia, Pa.).
1959-1972   **0352131**

Med Afr Noire
Médecine d'Afrique noire
0047-6404
1954   **9427297**

Med Ann Dist Columbia
The Medical annals of the District of Columbia
0025-6986
Supersedes Washington medical annals and Bulletin of the Medical Society of the District of Columbia.
1932-1974   **7612076**

Med Anthropol
Medical anthropology
0145-9740   **1545-5882**
1977   **7707343**

Med Anthropol Q
Medical anthropology quarterly
0745-5194
Continues: Medical anthropology newsletter.
1983   **8405037**

Med Arh
Medicinski arhiv
0350-199X
1947   **0400722**

Med Art
Medical art
0076-5902
1965-1972   **0425576**

Med Arts Sci
Medical arts and sciences
0025-6994
1947-1974   **0400712**

Med Aspects Hum Sex
Medical aspects of human sexuality
0025-7001
1967-1992   **0117251**

Med Audio Vis
Médecine et audio vision
0543-2251
Continues Revue médicale internationale de photo, cinéma, télévision.
1966-1967   **0060560**

Med Bild Dienst
Medizinischer Bild-Dienst
195u-1966   **18630210R**

Med Biol
Medical biology
0302-2137
Continues Annales medicinae experimentalis et biologiae Fenniae. Merged with: Annals of clinical research, to form: Annals of medicine.
1974-1987   **0417300**

Med Biol Eng
Medical & biological engineering
0025-696X
Continues Medical electronics & biological engineering. Continued by Medical & biological engineering & computing.
1966-1976   **0043417**

Med Biol Eng Comput
Medical & biological engineering & computing
0140-0118   **1741-0444**
Absorbed: Cellular engineering. Continues: Medical & biological engineering.
1977   **7704869**

Med Biol Illus
Medical & biological illustration
0025-6978
Continued by: Journal of audiovisual media in medicine.
1951-1977   **0400710**

Med Bogota Colomb
Medicina (Bogotá, Colombia)
19uu-19uu   **100927874**

Med Bohringer (Overseas)
Medico Boehringer: overseas ed
Continues Die Therapie des Monats. Overseas ed. Continued by Medico: international ed.
1961-1962   **18610690R**

Med Bookm Hist
Medical bookman and historian
0266-8645
Continued by: Medicine illustrated.
1947-1948   **101281329**

Med Br (Lond)
Medica Britannica
Continued by Africa medical practitioner.
1961-1965   **0017240**

Med Bull
The Medical bulletin
Continued by Lycoming Medicine.
1911-1964   **0034640**

Med Bull (Ann Arbor)
Medical bulletin (Ann Arbor, Mich.)
0196-5336
Absorbed: Bulletin of the Pharmacy and Therapeutics Committee. University of Michigan. University Hospital. Continues: University Hospital bulletin. Continued by: University of Michigan Medical Center journal.
1950-1963   **9427052**

Med Bull (NY)
The Medical bulletin
0098-5252
1932-1983   **18510390R**

Med Bull Harrisburg Polyclin Hosp
Medical bulletin. Harrisburg Polyclinic Hospital
1957-1964   **2985234R**

Med Bull St Louis Univ
Medical bulletin. St. Louis University
Continues St. Louis University. Hospital. Bulletin.
1952-1953   **20520670R**

Med Bull U S Army Army 1st
Medical bulletin. United States. Army. Army, 1st
Supersedes U. S. Army Service Forces. Second Service Command. Medical bulletin.
1946-uuuu   **22210405R**

Med Bull U S Army Eur Command Med Div
Medical bulletin. United States. Army. European Command. Medical Division
Continues U. S. Army. European Command. Office of the Chief Surgeon. Medical bulletin. Continued by U. S. Army, Europe. Medical Division. Medical bulletin of the U. S. Army, Europe.
1948-1952   **22210300R**

Med Bull U S Army Force Europe Theater Off Theater Chief Surg
Medical bulletin. United States. Army. Forces in the European Theater. Office of the Theater Chief Surgeon
Supersedes U. S. Army. European Theater of Operations. Medical bulletin. Continued by U. S. Army. European Command. Office of the Chief Surgeon. Medical bulletin.
1946-1947   **22210280R**

Med Bull US
The Medical bulletin of the U. S. Army Far East
1952-1954   22210480R

Med Bull US Army Eur
Medical bulletin of the U. S. Army, Europe. United States. Army, Europe. Medical Division
Continues: United States. Army. European Command. Medical Division. Medical bulletin. Continued by: Medical bulletin (United States. Army. Medical Command. 7th).
1952-1970   22210310R

Med Bull Vet Adm
Medical bulletin. United States. Veterans Administration. Dept. of Medicine and Surgery
1957-1966   22110150R

Med Care
Medical care
0025-7079   1537-1948
1963   0230027

Med Care Res Rev
Medical care research and review: MCRR
1077-5587
Continues: Medical care review.
1995   9506850

Med Care Rev
Medical care review
0025-7087
Continues: Public health economics and medical care abstracts. Continued by: Medical care research and review.
1967-1994   0073130

Med Chem
Medicinal chemistry (Shāriqah (United Arab Emirates))
1573-4064
2005   101240303

Med Chir Dig
Médecine & chirurgie digestives
0047-6412
Supersedes Revue médico-chirurgicale des maladies du foie.
1972-1999   0331257

Med Cir (Bogota)
Medicina y cirugía
1932-1979   18610320R

Med Cir Farm
Medicina, cirurgia, farmácia
1934-1963   18540370R

Med Cir Guerra
Medicina y cirugía de guerra
0212-3584
Continues Revista española de medicina y cirugía de guerra.
1946-1971   0404435

Med Claims Manag
Medical claims management
1069-5699
Continued by: Health data management.
1993-1993   9515688

Med Clin (Barc)
Medicina clínica
0025-7753
1943   0376377

Med Clin North Am
The Medical clinics of North America
0025-7125
Continues: Medical clinics of Chicago.
1917   2985236R

Med Clin Sper
Medicina clinica e sperimentale
0025-7761
1960-1970   0421050

Med Colon
La Medicina colonial
0368-931X
Continued by La Medicina tropical.
1943-1956   18610270R

Med Comment
The Medical comment
1919-1983   18510510R

Med Confl Surviv
Medicine, conflict, and survival
1362-3699
Continues: Medicine and war.
1996   9612305

Med Contemp
Medicina contemporânea (Lisbon, Portugal)
0025-777X
1883-1974   0400720

Med Cutan Ibero Lat Am
Medicina cutánea ibero-latino-americana
0210-5187
Formed by the union of Dermatologia ibero latino-americana and Medicina cutánea.
1973   7601805

Med Decis Making
Medical decision making: an international journal of the Society for Medical Decision Making
0272-989X
1981   8109073

Med Dent Bull
The Medical and dental bulletin
Continues the Bulletin of the Polish Medical and Dental Association of America. Continued by Bulletin - National Medical and Dental Association of America.
1935-1953   1255176

Med Dent J
Medical/dental journal
0149-2624
1976-1977   7706056

Med Deporte Trab
Medicina del deporte y del trabajo
Continues the Revista de medicina aplicada a los deportes. educación física y trabajo. Continued by Medicina del trabajo. Occupational medicine.
1946-1957   18540440R

Med Des Mater
Medical design and material
1051-984X
1991-1991   9886071

Med Device Technol
Medical device technology
1048-6690
1990   9215490

Med Dig
Medical digest
0025-7184
1933-1967   2985238R

Med Dir Chic
Medical directory of Chicago (including Cook Co.)
1801   27310340R

Med Dok
Medizinische Dokumentation
Continues Dokumentation in Medizin und Biologie. Superseded by: Methods of information in medicine.
1960-1961   58230450R

Med Dosim
Medical dosimetry: official journal of the American Association of Medical Dosimetrists
0958-3947   1873-4022
Continues: Journal (American Association of Medical Dosimetrists).
1987   8908862

Med Dosw
Medycyna doświadczalna
0025-8598
Continues: Prace. Poznańskie Towarzystwo Przyjaciół Nauk. Komisja Medycyny Doświadczalnej.
1962-1973   0216750

Med Dosw Mikrobiol
Medycyna doświadczalna i mikrobiologia
0025-8601
1949   0210575

Med Econ
Medical economics
0025-7206
1923   2985239R

Med Educ
Medical education
0308-0110   1365-2923
British journal of medical education.
1976   7605655

Med Egypte
Médecine d'Egypte
1952-1964   18440270R

Med Electron
Medical electronics
0149-9734
Includes a section with its own volume numbering called: The Heart watcher. Continues MED. Medical electronics & data. Part 1 issued also separately as Medical electronic products. Continued by: Medical electronics and equipment manufacturing.
1977-1998   7801790

Med Electron Biol Eng
Medical electronics & biological engineering
0368-9271
Continued by Medical & biological engineering.
1963-1965   18520120R

Med Electron Microsc
Medical electron microscopy: official journal of the Clinical Electron Microscopy Society of Japan
0918-4287
Continues in part: Nihon Rinshō Denshi Kenbikyō Gakkai shi. Continued by: Medical molecular morphology.
1993-2004   9430789

Med Eng Phys
Medical engineering & physics
1350-4533
Continues: Journal of biomedical engineering.
1994   9422753

Med Esp
Medicina española
0025-7842
1938-1985   2985243R

Med Exp Int J Exp Med
Medicina experimentalis. International journal of experimental medicine
0258-2589
Superseded by: Journal of medicine.
1959-1969   1246320

Med Fis Rehabil
Medicina física y rehabilitación
0374-9045
Continues Kinesiología, 1939-1./2. trimestre
1949.
1949-1966   **18540550R**

Med Foren Tidskr
Medicinska föreningens tidskrift
0301-6498
Continues Meddelanden från medicinska
föreningen. Continued by MFT.
1928-1960   **0414415**

Med Forum
Medicinsk Forum
0025-8040
1948-1988   **18610520R**

Med Fr (Bombay)
La Médecine en France
0465-4684
1953   **18440290R**

Med Gen Fr
Le Médecin généraliste de France
Supersedes Bulletin d'information des
omnipracticiens du Rhône, du Sud-est, de
la Seine et Ile-de-France. Absorbed by:
Médecine humaine et sociale.
1962-1969   **7508660**

Med Ges
Medizin und Gesellschaft
0323-6153
Continues: Zeitschrift für ärztliche
Fortbildung. Beiheft.
1977-1989   **7806079**

Med Ges Gesch
Medizin, Gesellschaft, und Geschichte:
Jahrbuch des Instituts für Geschichte der
Medizin der Robert Bosch Stiftung
0939-351X
Continues: Jahrbuch des Instituts für
Geschichte der Medizin der Robert Bosch
Stiftung.
1989   **9214715**

Med Glas
Medicinski glasnik
0025-8091
1946-r   **0400723**

Med Group Manage
Medical group management
0025-7257
Continues the Bulletin of the National
Association of Clinic Managers. Continued
by: Medical group management journal.
1960-1987   **0346073**

Med Group Manage J
Medical group management journal /
MGMA
0899-8949
Continues: Medical group management.
Continued by: MGMA connexion.
1987-2001   **8804124**

Med Gynaecol Androl Sociol
Medical gynaecology, andrology, and
sociology
0300-5828
Continues Medical gynaecology and
sociology.
1972-1974   **0362525**

Med Health
Medicine & health
1047-8884
Continues: McGraw-Hill's medicine &
health. Continued by: Faulkner & Gray's
medicine & health.
1989-1989   **9001428**

Med Health
Medicine & health (1997)
1548-9825
Absorbed: Health alliance alert. Continues:
Faulkner & Gray's medicine & health.
1997   **9801557**

Med Health Care Philos
Medicine, health care, and philosophy
1386-7423   1572-8633
Continues: European philosophy of medicine
and health care.
1998   **9815900**

Med Health R I
Medicine and health, Rhode Island
1086-5462
Continues: Rhode Island medicine.
1996   **9603446**

Med Hist
Medical history
0025-7273
1957   **0401052**

Med Hist (Barc)
Medicina e historia
0300-8169
1964   **0361435**

Med Hist Suppl
Medical history. Supplement
0950-5571
1981   **8411123**

Med Humanit Rev
Medical humanities review
0892-2772
1987   **8710646**

Med Hyg (Geneve)
Médecine et hygiène
0025-6749
Merged with: Revue médicale de la Suisse
romande, to form: Revue médicale suisse.
1943-2004   **9427226**

Med Hypotheses
Medical hypotheses
0306-9877
1975   **7505668**

Med Illus
Medicine illustrated
0266-982X
Continues: Medical bookman and historian.
Continued by: British journal of clinical
practice.
1949-1956   **18610450R**

Med Image Anal
Medical image analysis
1361-8415   1361-8423
1996   **9713490**

Med Image Comput Comput Assist Interv Int
Conf Med Image Comput Comput Assist Interv
Medical image computing and computer-
assisted intervention: MICCAI ...
International Conference on Medical
Image Computing and Computer-Assisted
Intervention
1998   **101249582**

Med Infant
Medicina infantil
1958-1960   **18540600R**

Med Infant (Paris)
La Médecine infantile
0025-6773
1897-1993   **2985233R**

Med Inform (Lond)
Medical informatics = Médecine et
informatique
0307-7640
Continued by: Medical informatics and the
Internet in medicine.
1976-1998   **7612096**

Med Inform Internet Med
Medical informatics and the Internet in
medicine
1463-9238
Continues: Medical informatics. Continued
by: Informatics for health & social care.
1999-2007   **100883495**

Med Instrum
Medical instrumentation
0090-6689
Continues JAAMI: journal of the
Association for the Advancement of Medical
Instrumentation. Merged with: Biomedical
technology today, to form: Biomedical
instrumentation & technology.
1973-1988   **0361136**

Med Int
Medicine international (UK ed.)
0144-0403
Continues Medicine, published London:
Medical Education (International) Ltd., 1972-
1980. Continued by: Medicine (Abingdon,
England: UK ed.).
1981-1994   **8105721**

Med Int (Milano)
La Medicina internazionale
1893-19uu   **2985244R**

Med Intensiva
Medicina intensiva / Sociedad Española de
Medicina Intensiva y Unidades Coronarias
0210-5691
197u   **9207689**

Med Interface
Medical interface
0896-4831
Continued by: Managed care interface.
1988-1997   **8916855**

Med Interna
Medicină internă (Bucharest, Romania:
1991)
1220-5818
Continues: Revista de medicină internă,
neurologie, psihiatrie, neurochirurgie,
dermato-venerologie. Medicină internă.
1991-1993   **9431273**

Med Interna (Bucur)
Medicină internă
0025-7869
Continues: Revista științelor medicale:
medicina internă. Continued by: Revista
de medicină internă, neurologie, psihiatrie,
neurochirurgie, dermato-venerologie.
Medicină internă.
1955-1974   **7503144**

Med Interne
Médecine interne
0377-1202
Continues in part Revue roumaine de
médecine. Continued by: Romanian journal
of internal medicine.
1975-1990   **7506353**

Med Ital
La Medicina italiana
Merged with Policlinico infantile and La
Pediatria del medico pratico to form Minerva
pediatrica.
1920-1948   **18540620R**

Med J Aust
The Medical journal of Australia
0025-729X 1326-5377
Formed by the union of the Australasian medical gazette and the Australian medical journal.
1914 0400714

Med J Egypt Armed Forces
The Medical journal of the Egyptian Armed Forces
Continued by Armed Forces medical journal. A. R. E.
1955-1960 7705894

Med J Malaya
The Medical journal of Malaya
0025-7303
Supersedes the Journal of the Malaya Branch of the British Medical Association. Continued by the Medical journal of Malaysia.
1946-1972 0361546

Med J Malaysia
The Medical journal of Malaysia
0300-5283
Continues the Medical journal of Malaya.
1972 0361547

Med J Osaka Univ
Medical journal of Osaka University
0030-6169
1949 0135201

Med J Southwest
The Medical journal of the South-West
0369-0458
Continues: Bristol medico-chirurgical journal (1883). Continued by: Bristol medico-chirurgical journal (1963).
1953-1962 18520390R

Med J Zambia
Medical journal of Zambia
0047-651X
1967 0251103

Med Klin
Medizinische Klinik
0025-8458
Split into: Medizinische Klinik (Klinik-Ausg.). and: Medizinische Klinik (Praxis-Ausg.).
1946-1981 0376637

Med Klin (Munich)
Medizinische Klinik (Munich, Germany: 1983)
0723-5003
Continues: Medizinische Klinik (Klinik-Ausg.).
1983 8303501

Med Klin Suppl
Medizinische Klinik (Munich, Germany: 1983). Supplement
0931-2595
1985-1986 8611127

Med Klin [Klin]
Medizinische Klinik (Klinik-Ausg.)
0722-9321
Continues in part: Medizinische Klinik (1947). Continued by: Medizinische Klinik (Munich, Germany: 1983).
1982-1982 8302967

Med Klin [Prax]
Medizinische Klinik (Praxis-Ausg.)
0722-933X
Continues in part: Medizinische Klinik (1947). Continued by: Medizinische Klinik & Praxis.
1982-1982 8302966

Med Lab
Médecine et laboratoire
1950-1964 18440320R

Med Lab (Stuttg)
Das Medizinische Laboratorium
0025-8466
Continues in part Röntgen- und Laboratoriumspraxis.
1963-1982 0375264

Med Lab Prog
Medicine and laboratory progress ...
1940-19uu 18610420R

Med Lab Sci
Medical laboratory sciences
0308-3616
Continues Medical laboratory technology. Continued by: British journal of biomedical science.
1976-1992 7609161

Med Lab Technol
Medical laboratory technology
0022-2607
Continues The Journal of medical laboratory technology. Continued by Medical laboratory sciences.
1971-1975 7609162

Med Lat
Medicina latina; revista médica de colaboración científica
1942-1960 18610010R

Med Lav
La Medicina del lavoro
0025-7818
Continues: Il Lavoro (Clinica delle malattie professionali di Milano).
1925 0401176

Med Law
Medicine and law
0723-1393
1982 8218185

Med Law Rev
Medical law review
0967-0742 1464-3790
1993 9308945

Med Leg Bull
Medico-legal bulletin
0025-8164
Continues Bulletin of the Office of the Chief Medical Examiner. Virginia.
1959-1990 0376631

Med Leg Dommage Corpor
Médecine légale et dommage corporel
0025-679X
Supersedes Annales de médecine légale.
1968-1974 7513649

Med Leg J
The Medico-legal journal
0025-8172
Continues: Medico-legal and criminological review.
1947 0412004

Med Lett Drugs Ther
The Medical letter on drugs and therapeutics
0025-732X 1523-2859
1959 2985240R

Med Libre
Le Médecin libre
Continues Le Médecin chez lui.
1940-1962 18440200R

Med Maandbl
Medisch maandblad
Supersedes Geneeskundig tijdschrift voor Nederlandsch-Indië.
1946-1950 18620430R

Med Mal Infect
Médecine et maladies infectieuses
0399-077X
1971 0311416

Med Malpract Cost Containment J
The Medical malpractice cost containment journal
0194-7400
1979-1980 7910744

Med Manag Netw
Medical management network
1097-0835
Continues: Patient care management abstracts.
1997-1999 9801899

Med Mark Media
Medical marketing & media
0025-7354
Continues Pharmaceutical marketing & media.
1969 0261537

Med Microbiol Immunol
Medical microbiology and immunology
0300-8584 1432-1831
Continues Zeitschrift für medizinische Mikrobiologie und Immunologie.
1971 0314524

Med Mol Morphol
Medical molecular morphology
1860-1480 1860-1499
Continues: Medical electron microscopy.
2005 101239023

Med Monatsschr
Medizinische Monatsschrift
0025-8474
Continued by: Medizinische Monatsschrift für Pharmazeuten.
1947-1977 0375265

Med Monatsschr Pharm
Medizinische Monatsschrift für Pharmazeuten
0342-9601
Supersedes Medizinische Monatsschrift.
1978 7802665

Med Monde
Médecine dans le monde
1953-1966 18440250R

Med Mycol
Medical mycology: official publication of the International Society for Human and Animal Mycology
1369-3786
Continues: Journal of medical and veterinary mycology.
1998 9815835

Med Nachr Ver Staaten
Medizinische Nachrichten aus den Vereinigten Staaten
1946-1949 18630110R

Med Netw Strategy Rep
Medical network strategy report
1079-3003
Continues: Medical staff strategy report. Continued by: Physician performance & payment report.
1994-1999 9442877

Med News Lett Aviat Suppl
Medical news letter. Aviation supplement.
United States. Navy Dept. Bureau of
Medicine and Surgery. Division of Aviation
Medicine
    Continues BuMed news letter, Aviation
    supplement.
    1948-1952   **22420420R**

Med Newsl (Lond)
Medical newsletter
0309-2569
    Continued by Fertility and contraception.
    1958-1976   **7606227**

Med Nov
Medizinische Novitäten
1uuu-19uu   **9429506**

Med Nowozytna
Medycyna nowozytna: studia nad historia
medycyny / Polska Akademia Nauk, Instytut
Historii Nauki
1231-1960
1994   **9442133**

Med Oncol
Medical oncology (Northwood, London,
England)
1357-0560   **1559-131X**
    Continues: Medical oncology and tumor
    pharmacotherapy.
    1994   **9435512**

Med Oncol Tumor Pharmacother
Medical oncology and tumor
pharmacotherapy
0736-0118
    Continued by: Medical oncology (Northwood,
    London, England).
    1984-1993   **8405039**

Med Oral
Medicina oral: órgano oficial de la Sociedad
Española de Medicina Oral y de la
Academia Iberoamericana de Patología y
Medicina Bucal
1137-2834
    Continued by: Medicina oral, patología oral y
    cirugía bucal.
    1996-2004   **9815821**

Med Oral Patol Oral Cir Bucal
Medicina oral, patología oral y cirugía bucal
1698-4447   **1698-6946**
    Continues: Medicina oral.
    2004   **101231694**

Med Panam
Medicina panamericana
1953-1965   **18610080R**

Med Parazitol (Mosk)
Meditsinskaia parazitologiia i parazitarnye
bolezni
0025-8326
    Continues: Tropicheskaiâ meditŝina i
    veterinariiâ.
    1932   **0376635**

Med Pediatr Oncol
Medical and pediatric oncology
0098-1532   **1096-911X**
    Continued by: Pediatric blood & cancer.
    1975-2003   **7506654**

Med Pediatr Oncol Suppl
Medical and pediatric oncology. Supplement
0740-8226
1982   **8305678**

Med Periskop Ingelheim
Das Medizinische Periskop Ingelheim
1950-1970   **1277203**

Med Pharmacol Exp Int J Exp Med
Medicina et pharmacologia experimentalis.
International journal of experimental
medicine
0543-3002
    Continues Medicina experimentalis.
    Split into: Medicina experimentalis, and:
    Pharmacology.
    1965-1967   **0152106**

Med Phys
Medical physics
0094-2405
1974   **0425746**

Med Pr
Medycyna pracy
0465-5893
1948   **0376642**

Med Pract
El Medico práctico
1945-1973   **18620270R**

Med Pract (Zaragoza)
Medicina práctica
1943-19uu   **18610130R**

Med Pregl
Medicinski pregled
0025-8105
1948   **2985249R**

Med Press
The Medical press
1866-1961   **0017457**

Med Princ Pract
Medical principles and practice:
international journal of the Kuwait
University, Health Science Centre
1011-7571   **1423-0151**
1988   **8901334**

Med Proc (Johannesb)
Medical proceedings: a South African
journal for the advancement of medical
science = Mediese bydraes: 'n Suid-
Afrikaanse tydskrif vir die bevordering van
die geneeskunde
0025-7443
    1955-1979   **2985242R**

Med Prod Sales
Medical products sales: MPS: the official
journal of the American Surgical Trade
Association
0279-4802
    Continues: MPS. Medical products salesman.
    Continued by: Healtcare products today
    magazine.
    1981-2001   **8202448**

Med Prog
Medical progress; a review of medical
advances
1952-1957   **18530170R**

Med Prog Technol
Medical progress through technology
0047-6552
1972-1997   **0331260**

Med Prom SSSR
Meditsinskaia promyshlennost' SSSR
1947-1966   **1305622**

Med Psicosom
Medicina psicosomatica
0025-7893
1956   **2985246R**

Med Radiogr
Medical radiographer
0377-9289
1974-1980   **7604235**

Med Radiogr Photogr
Medical radiography and photography
0025-746X
    Continues: Radiography and clinical
    photography.
    1947-1988   **0412772**

Med Radiol
Medical radiology
1958-1962   **18530220R**

Med Radiol (Mosk)
Meditsinskaia radiologiia
0025-8334
    Continued by: Meditsinskaia radiologiia i
    radiatsionnaia bezopasnost ū.
    1956-1993   **2984767R**

Med Rec
Medical record
0363-0803
    Continues: Medical journal and record.
    Absorbed the Medical herald in Feb. 1934.
    Merged with: General practice clinics, to
    form: International record of medicine and
    general practice clinics.
    1934-1950   **18530250R**

Med Rec Health Care Inf J
Medical record and health care information
journal
0950-5539
    Continues: Medical record. Continued by:
    AMRO.
    1977-1988   **8405388**

Med Rec News
Medical record news
0025-7486
    Continues Journal of the American
    Association of Medical Record Librarians.
    Continued by Journal of the American
    Medical Record Association.
    1962-1980   **0400715**

Med Rec Read Pa
Medical record (Reading, Pa.)
    Continues: Bulletin of the Berks County
    Medical Society. Continued by: Berks County
    medical record.
    1955-1981   **0100043**

Med Ref Serv Q
Medical reference services quarterly
0276-3869   **1540-9597**
1982   **8219208**

Med Res Eng
Medical research engineering
0025-7508
    Continues the American journal of medical
    electronics.
    1966-1980   **0051420**

Med Res Rev
Medicinal research reviews
0198-6325   **1098-1128**
1981   **8103150**

Med Reserve (Paris)
Le Médecin de réserve
0397-9172
1960   **0421063**

Med Rev
Medicina em revista
1945-1968   **18540530R**

Med Sachverstand
Der Medizinische Sachverständige
0025-8490
    Continues Aerztliche Sachverständigen-
    Zeitung. issued 1895-1944.
    1954   **0375266**

Med Sci
Medical science
1957-1968 0142012

Med Sci (Paris)
Médecine sciences: M/S
0767-0974
1985 8710980

Med Sci Law
Medicine, science, and the law
0025-8024
1960 0400721

Med Sci Monit
Medical science monitor: international
medical journal of experimental and clinical
research
1234-1010 1643-3750
1995 9609063

Med Sci Sports
Medicine and science in sports
0025-7990
 Continued by: Medicine and science in sports
 and exercise.
1969-1979 0203246

Med Sci Sports Exerc
Medicine and science in sports and exercise
0195-9131 1530-0315
 Continues: Medicine and science in sports.
1980 8005433

Med Secoli
Medicina nei secoli
0394-9001
 Supersedes Collana storico-scientifica.
1964 0176472

Med Sect Proc
Medical Section proceedings: the ...
annual Meeting of the Medical Section of
the American Council of Life Insurance.
American Council of Life Insurance.
Medical Section. Meeting
 Continues: Proceedings, the annual meeting
 of the Medical Section of the American
 Council of Life Insurance.
1983-1995 9710573

Med Segur Trab (Madr)
Medicina y seguridad del trabajo
0465-546X
 Absorbed: Notas y documentos sobre
 prevención de riesgos profesionales.
1952 0413536

Med Serv
Medical service
0008-8102
1944-1983 0221461

Med Serv J Can
Medical services journal, Canada
0368-9204
 Continues the Canadian services medical
 journal.
1958-1967 0236073

Med Sestra
Meditŝinskaiâ sestra
0025-8342
 Merged with: Feĭdsher i akusherka. to form:
 Meditŝinskaiâ pomoshch.
1942-1992 18620490R

Med Soc (Berkeley)
Medicine and society
1988 9005153

Med Soc Report
Medical Society reporter
 Continued by Lackawanna medicine.
1910-1967 0205360

Med Sport (Roma)
Medicina dello sport; rivista di fisiopatologia
dello sport
0025-7826
1961 18540470R

Med Sport Sci
Medicine and sport science
0254-5020 1662-2812
 Continues: Medicine and sport.
1984 8402440

Med Staff Couns
The Medical staff counselor
0899-8981
1987-1993 8804138

Med Teach
Medical teacher
0142-159X 1466-187X
1979 7909593

Med Tech (Stuttg)
Medizinische Technik
0025-8504
 Supersedes Medizinmechanik. Continued by
 Medizintechnik.
1947-1977 7806081

Med Techn Bull
Medical technicians bulletin
0543-2898
 Supplement to the United States Armed
 Forces medical journal. Supersedes the
 Hospital Corps bulletin.
1950-1959 21410760R

Med Tekh
Meditsinskaia tekhnika
0025-8075
 Supersedes Meditsinskaia promyshlennost'
 SSSR.
1967 1305457

Med Thorac
Medicina thoracalis
0368-9220
 Continues Schweizerische Zeitschrift für
 Tuberkulose und Pneumonologie. Continued
 by Respiration.
1962-1967 0134451

Med Times
Medical times
0025-7583
 Continues the New York medical times.
1897-1990 0406055

Med Toxicol
Medical toxicology
0112-5966
 Continued by: Medical toxicology and
 adverse drug experience.
1986-1986 8606184

Med Toxicol Adverse Drug Exp
Medical toxicology and adverse drug
experience
0112-5966
 Continues: Medical toxicology. Continued by:
 Drug safety.
1987-1989 8709214

Med Tr Prom Ekol
Meditsina truda i promyshlennaia ekologiia
1026-9428
 Continues: Gigiena truda i professional'nve
 zabolevaniia.
1993 9434213

Med Trial Tech Q
Medical trial technique quarterly
0025-7591
1954 2984464R

Med Trop (Madr)
La Medicina tropical
0025-7958
 Continues La Medicina colonial.
1957-1973 0416617

Med Trop (Mars)
Médecine tropicale: revue du Corps de santé
colonial
0025-682X
 Continues: Annales de médecine et pharmacie
 coloniales.
1941 8710146

Med Usine Rev Hyg Ind Mal Prof
Le Médecin d'usine; revue d'hygiène
industrielle et des maladies professionnelles
 Continues Société médicale des hygiénistes
 du travail et de l'industrie. Bulletin.
1938-1957 18440190R

Med Vet Entomol
Medical and veterinary entomology
0269-283X 1365-2915
1987 8708682

Med War
Medicine and war
0748-8009
 Continues: Journal of the Medical Association
 for Prevention of War. Continued by:
 Medicine, conflict, and survival.
1985-1995 8508146

Med Waste Anal
Medical waste analyst
1072-6039
 Continues: Regulatory analyst. Medical
 waste.
1993-1994 9434066

Med Way
The Medical way
 Continues the Journal of the Medical Society
 of Cape May County.
1944-1961 0017615

Med Welt
Die Medizinische Welt
0025-8512
 Absorbed: Medwelt compact. 1992
 Continues: Medizinische.
1960 0376641

Med Weter
Medycyna weterynaryjna
0025-8628
1945 0413416

Med Wieku Rozwoj
Medycyna wieku rozwojowego
1428-345X
 Continues: Problemy medycyny wieku
 rozwojowego.
1997 100928610

Med Womans J
Medical woman's journal
 Continued by Pan American medical
 woman's journal.
1920-1952 18540150R

Med World
Medical world
 Merged with MPU newsletter to form
 Medical world and newsletter.
1913-1968 0170272

Med World (Lond)
Medical world
0025-7621
 Continues Medical world and newsletter.
 Absorbed The Journal of hospital pharmacy.
 Jan. 1976.
1969-1987 0211170

Med World (New York)
The Medical world
1883-1948   18540200R

Med World News
Medical world news
0025-763X
1960-1994   1275246

Med Year
Medicine of the year
1949-1952   18610500R

Med Zh Uzb
Meditsinskii zhurnal Uzbekistana
0025-830X
Continues Za sotsialisticheskoe
zdravookhranenie Uzbekistana.
1957   0376636

Med Zhurnal
Medychnyĭ zÕ°hurnal
Continues: ZÕ°hurnal medychnoho tŝyklu.
Merged with: Voprosy fiziologii, to form:
Fiziolohichnyĭ zÕ°hurnal.
1933-1954   9430263

Medd Flyg Navalmed Namnd Statens Namnd For
Flyg Navalmed Forsk Forsoksvererksamhet
Meddelanden från Flyg- och
navalmedicinska nämnden. Statens nämnd
för flyg- och navalmedicinsk forsknings- och
försöksverksamhet
1952-1963   0150176

Medd Nor Farm Selsk
Meddelelser fra Norsk farmaceutisk selskap
0029-1927
Continued by: Norvegica pharmaceutica acta.
1939-1982   19210370R

Medd Sundhedsstyr Beredskabsafdelingen
Meddelelser. Denmark. Sundhedsstyrelsen.
Beredskabsafdelingen
1951-1962   1310310

Meded Rijksuniv Gent Fak Landbouwkd Toegep
Biol Wet
Mededelingen (Rijksuniversiteit te Gent.
Fakulteit van de Landbouwkundige en
Toegepaste Biologische Wetenschappen)
1373-7503
Continues: Mededelingen - Faculteit
Landbouwwetenschappen, Rijksuniversiteit
Gent. Rijksuniversiteit te Gent. Faculteit van
de Landbouwwetenschappen. Continued by:
Communications in agricultural and applied
biological sciences.
1993-2002   100967625

MedGenMed
MedGenMed: Medscape general medicine
1531-0132
Absorbed: Medscape women's health. 2002
Continued by: Medscape journal of medicine.
1999-2007   100894134

Medi-Cal Policy Inst Issue Brief
Medi-Cal Policy Institute issue brief
1999   101149467

Mediators Inflamm
Mediators of inflammation
0962-9351   1466-1861
1992   9209001

Medica
Médica
Supersedes another periodical with same title,
issued 1921-30?
1942-1954   0421064

Medicamenta (Madr)
Medicamenta
0025-7648
1943-1975   0400716

Medicamundi
Medicamundi
0025-7664
1955   18540250R

Medicare Brief
Medicare brief / National Academy of Social
Insurance
1997   100899263

Medicina
Medicina
Continues the Ingham County Medical
Society bulletin.
1960   18540310R

Medicina (B Aires)
Medicina
0025-7680
1940   0204271

Medicina (Firenze)
Medicina (Florence, Italy)
0392-6516
1981-1990   8813280

Medicina (Kaunas)
Medicina (Kaunas, Lithuania)
1010-660X   1648-9144
1920   9425208

Medicina (Madr)
Medicina
0025-7710
1930-1978   0400717

Medicina (Mex)
Medicina
0025-7702
1920-1978   0417453

Medicinar
Medicinar
0025-7966
1946-1993   18610390R

Medicine
Medicine
0190-051X
Supersedes Symposium on Advanced
Medicine.
1976-1978   7806078

Medicine (Baltimore)
Medicine
0025-7974   1536-5964
1922   2985248R

Medico
El Médico
0461-6367
1951-1976   2985250R

Medico (Eur)
Medico; Europa Ausg
Continues Medico Boehringer: Europa Ausg.
1963-1964   0016603

Medico (Int)
Medico; international ed
Continues Medico Boehringer: overseas ed.
1963-1968   0016604

Medico (Porto)
O Medico; semanario de assuntos médicos e
paramédicos
0461-6375
1950-1993   0376633

Medicoleg News
Medicolegal news
0097-0085
Merged with Nursing law & ethics, to form
Law, medicine & health care.
1973-1981   7506659

Medicus
The Medicus
1950-1972   0375261

Medicus
Medicus
1945-1950   18620340R

Medika (Zagreb)
Medika; informativni časopis farmaceutiskih
poduzeća NRH
1948-1962   18620380R

Medinfo
Medinfo. MEDINFO
1974   7600347

Medizinhist J
Medizinhistorisches Journal
0025-8431
1966   0051574

Medscape J Med
Medscape journal of medicine
     1934-1997
Continues: MedGenMed.
2008   101462763

Medscape Womens Health
Medscape women's health
     1521-2076
Absorbed by: MedGenMed.
199u-2002   100844142

Medsurg Nurs
Medsurg nursing: official journal of the
Academy of Medical-Surgical Nurses
1092-0811
1992   9300545

Meharri Dent
The Meharri-Dent
0025-8725
1942-1976   18630360R

Meikai Daigaku Shigaku Zasshi
Meikai Daigaku shigaku zasshi = The
Journal of Meikai University School of
Dentistry
0916-0701
Continues: Jōsai Shika Daigaku kiyō.
Continued by: Meikai shika igaku.
1988-2005   8904891

Melanoma Res
Melanoma research
0960-8931   1473-5636
1991   9109623

Mem Acad Chir (Paris)
Mémoires. Académie de chirurgie (France)
0368-8291
Continues Bulletins et mémoires of the
Société de chirurgie de Paris. Continued
by Chirurgie; mémoires de l'Académie de
chirurgie.
1935-1969   0236701

Mem Acad R Med Belg
Mémoires de l'Académie royale de médecine
de Belgique
0065-0595
Merged with the Bulletin de l'Académie
royale de médecine de Belgique to form the
Bulletin et mémoires de l'Académie royale de
médecine de Belgique.
1848-1974   7608529

Mem Cognit
Memory & cognition
0090-502X
Supersedes in part Psychonomic science.
1973   0357443

Mem Inst Butantan
Memórias do Instituto Butantan
0073-9901
1918   7502618

Mem Inst Oswaldo Cruz
Memórias do Instituto Oswaldo Cruz
0074-0276   1678-8060
1909   7502619

Membr Biochem
Membrane biochemistry
0149-046X
Continued by: Molecular membrane biology.
1978-1993   7804153

Membr Cell Biol
Membrane & cell biology
1023-6597
Continues: Biologicheskie membrany.
English. Biological membranes.
1995-2001   9517472

Membranes
Membranes
0076-6356
1972-1975   0340707

Memo Med Res Counc
Medical Research Council memorandum
Continues: War memorandum.
1948-1976   7801273

Memo Rep Nav Med Res Inst (US)
Memorandum report. Naval Medical
Research Institute (U.S.)
1950-19uu   22420750R

Memory
Memory (Hove, England)
0965-8211   1464-0686
1993   9306862

Memphis Med J
Memphis medical journal
Continued by Memphis and Mid-South
medical journal.
1924-1960   18640100R

Memphis Mid South Med J
Memphis and Mid-South medical journal
Continues Memphis medical journal.
1960-1969   18640070R

Mendel Newsl
The Mendel newsletter; archival resources
for the history of genetics & allied sciences
0025-9241
1968   0202216

Menopause
Menopause (New York, N.Y.)
1072-3714   1530-0374
1994   9433353

Menopause Int
Menopause international
1754-0453   1754-0461
Continues: Journal of the British Menopause
Society.
2007   101303618

Mens Ondernem
Mens en onderneming
0025-9470
1947-1977   7806372

Ment Health Bull
Mental health bulletin
1923-1954   18640370R

Ment Health Bull (Danville)
Mental health bulletin
1921-1959   18640380R

Ment Health Care
Mental health care
1368-1230
Continued by: Mental health & learning
disabilities care.
1997-1999   9801603

Ment Health Learn Disabil Care
Mental health & learning disabilities care
1466-8785
Continues: Mental health care. Continued by:
Mental health today (Brighton. England).
1999-2001   101133624

Ment Health Nurs
Mental health nursing: journal of the
Psychiatric Nurses Association / PNA
0957-0780
1987-1989   8804998

Ment Health Serv Res
Mental health services research
1522-3434
Absorbed by: Administration and policy in
mental health.
1999-2005   9815815

Ment Health Soc
Mental health and society
0302-2811
1974-1978   7502128

Ment Health Stat Note
Mental health statistical note
0361-9311
Continues National Institute of Mental Health.
Survey and Reports Branch. Statistical note.
1976-1995   7605931

Ment Health Today
Mental health today (Brighton, England)
1474-5186
Continues: Mental health & learning
disabilities care.
2001   101133625

Ment Hosp
Mental hospitals
Continues the A. P. A. Mental Hospital
Service bulletin of the American Psychiatric
Association. Continued by Hospital &
community psychiatry.
1951-1965   14840420R

Ment Hyg
Mental hygiene
0025-9683
Continued by: MH.
1917-1972   0360401

Ment Phys Disabil Law Rep
Mental and physical disability law reporter
0883-7902
Continues: Mental disability law reporter.
1984   8502923

Ment Retard
Mental retardation
0047-6765   1931-1338
Continued by: Intellectual and developmental
disabilities.
1963-2006   18640670R

Ment Retard Abstr
Mental retardation abstracts
0025-9691
Continued by Mental retardation &
developmental disabilities abstracts.
1964-1973   7607558

Ment Retard Dev Disabil Res Rev
Mental retardation and developmental
disabilities research reviews
1080-4013   1098-2779
Continued by: Developmental disabilities
research reviews.
1995-2007   9517974

Mentalis
Mentalis
0360-7232
1971   7601813

Mercer Dent Soc Newsl
Mercer Dental Society Newsletter
Continues: Journal Of The Mercer Dental
Society.
1977   9877610

Merck Rep
The Merck report
1892-1956   18650050R

Mese Sanit
Mese sanitario
1949-1966   18650190R

Met Ions Biol Syst
Metal ions in biological systems
0161-5149
1973   0406332

Metab Bone Dis Relat Res
Metabolic bone disease & related research
0221-8747
Continued by Bone.
1978-1984   7900146

Metab Brain Dis
Metabolic brain disease
0885-7490
1986   8610370

Metab Eng
Metabolic engineering
1096-7176   1096-7184
1999   9815657

Metab Ophthalmol
Metabolic ophthalmology, pediatric and
systemic
0883-9522
Continues: Metabolic, pediatric, and systemic
ophthalmology. Continued by: Metabolic,
pediatric, and systemic ophthalmology (New
York, N.Y.: 1985).
1984-1984   8500744

Metab Pediatr Ophthalmol
Metabolic and pediatric ophthalmology
0191-2771
Continues: Metabolic ophthalmology.
Continued by: Metabolic, pediatric, and
systemic ophthalmology.
1979-1981   8001472

Metab Pediatr Syst Ophthalmol
Metabolic, pediatric, and systemic
ophthalmology
0277-9382
Continues: Metabolic and pediatric
ophthalmology. Continued by: Metabolic
ophthalmology, pediatric and systemic.
1982-1983   8214904

Metab Pediatr Syst Ophthalmol
Metabolic, pediatric, and systemic
ophthalmology (New York, N.Y.: 1985)
0882-889X
Continues: Metabolic ophthalmology,
pediatric and systemic.
1985-2000   8800197

Metab Syndr Relat Disord
Metabolic syndrome and related disorders
1540-4196   1557-8518
2003   101150318

Metabolism
Metabolism: clinical and experimental
0026-0495   1532-8600
1952   0375267

Methods
Methods (San Diego, Calif.)
1046-2023   1095-9130
1990   9426302

Methods Achiev Exp Pathol
Methods and achievements in experimental pathology
0076-681X
1966-1991   0204174

Methods Biochem Anal
Methods of biochemical analysis
0076-6941
1954   0376644

Methods Cell Biol
Methods in cell biology
0091-679X
Continues Methods in cell physiology.
1973   0373334

Methods Cell Sci
Methods in cell science: an official journal of the Society for In Vitro Biology
1381-5741
Continues: Journal of tissue culture methods.
Absorbed by: Cytotechnology.
1995-2003   9515839

Methods Enzymol
Methods in enzymology
0076-6879   1557-7988
1955   0212271

Methods Find Exp Clin Pharmacol
Methods and findings in experimental and clinical pharmacology
0379-0355
1979   7909595

Methods Inf Med
Methods of information in medicine
0026-1270
Supplements to v. 45 (2006)- issued as Yearbook of medical informatics. Supersedes Medizinische Dokumentation.
1962   0210453

Methods Inf Med Suppl
Methods of information in medicine. Supplement
0580-9525
1966-1978   0207712

Methods Med Res
Methods in medical research
0094-9590
1948-1970   0436274

Methods Mol Biol
Methods in molecular biology (Clifton, N.J.)
1064-3745
1984   9214969

Methods Mol Med
Methods in molecular medicine
1543-1894
1996   101123138

Mex Farm
México farmacético
1935-1965   0017172

MGMA Connex
MGMA connexion / Medical group Management Association
1537-0240
Continues: Medical group management journal.
2001   101127723

MH
MH
0090-6670
Continues Mental hygiene.
1972-1977   0365565

Mich Health Hosp
Michigan health & hospitals
Continues: Michigan hospitals.
1995-2003   9503636

Mich Hosp
Michigan hospitals
0026-220X
Continued by: Michigan health & hospitals.
1965-1994   1267473

Mich Law Rev
Michigan law review
0026-2234
1902   7703728

Mich Med
Michigan medicine
0026-2293
Continues the Journal of the Michigan State Medical Society. Includes, 1964- Annual directory of Michigan State Medical Society members, issued separately as supplement to some numbers. Continued in part by: Medigram (East Lansing, Mich.: 1985).
1964   0017314

Mich Nurse
The Michigan nurse
0026-2366
1928   1260337

Mich Public Health
Michigan public health
Continues Public health. Continued by Michigan's health.
1922-1951   18710430R

Microb Comp Genomics
Microbial & comparative genomics
1090-6592
Continues: Genome science & technology.
Continued by: Omics.
1996-2000   9616596

Microb Drug Resist
Microbial drug resistance (Larchmont, N.Y.)
1076-6294   1931-8448
1995   9508567

Microb Ecol
Microbial ecology
0095-3628   1432-184X
1974   7500663

Microb Pathog
Microbial pathogenesis
0882-4010
1986   8606191

Microb Releases
Microbial releases: viruses, bacteria, fungi
0940-9653
1992-1994   9301294

Microbes Infect
Microbes and infection / Institut Pasteur
1286-4579
Formed by the union of: Research in immunology; Research in virology; and: Bulletin de l'Institut Pasteur.
1999   100883508

Microbiol Esp
Microbiología española
0026-2595
1947-1986   0375271

Microbiol Immunol
Microbiology and immunology
0385-5600   1348-0421
Continues Japanese journal of microbiology.
1977   7703966

Microbiol Mol Biol Rev
Microbiology and molecular biology reviews: MMBR
1092-2172   1098-5557
Continues: Microbiological reviews.
1997   9706653

Microbiol Parazitol Epidemiol (Bucur)
Microbiologia, parazitologia, epidemiologia
0026-2609
Continued by Bacteriologia, virusologia, parazitologia, epidemiologia.
1956-1973   0420151

Microbiol Res
Microbiological research
0944-5013
Continues: Zentralblatt für Mikrobiologie.
1994   9437794

Microbiol Rev
Microbiological reviews
0146-0749
Continues: Bacteriological reviews.
Continued by: Microbiology and molecular biology reviews.
1978-1996   7806086

Microbiol Sci
Microbiological sciences
0265-1351
1984-1988   8510101

Microbiologia
Microbiología (Madrid, Spain)
0213-4101
Continued by: International microbiology.
1985-1997   8904895

Microbiologica
Microbiologica
0391-5352
Continued by: New microbiologica.
1978-1992   7902903

Microbiology
Microbiology (Reading, England)
1350-0872   1465-2080
Continues: Journal of general microbiology.
1994   9430468

Microbios
Microbios
0026-2633
1969-2001   0207257

Microcirc Endothelium Lymphatics
Microcirculation, endothelium, and lymphatics
0740-9451
1984-1991   8505251

Microcirculation
Microcirculation (New York, N.Y.: 1994)
1073-9688   1549-8719
1994   9434935

Microentomology
Microentomology
0893-3227
1936-1963   18710480R

Microgravity Q
Microgravity quarterly: MGQ
0958-5036
1990-1997   100971563

Microgravity Sci Technol
Microgravity science and technology
0938-0108   1875-0494
Continues: Applied microgravity technology.
1990   100971602

Micron
Micron (Oxford, England: 1993)
0968-4328
Merger of: Micron and microscopica acta,
and: Electron microscopy reviews.
1993   9312850

Microsc Acta
Microscopica acta
0044-376X
Continues Zeitschrift für Wissenschaftliche
Mikroskopie und mikroskopische Technik.
Merged with Micron to form Micron and
microscopica acta.
1971-1983   1306037

Microsc Acta Suppl
Microscopica acta. Supplement
0342-958X
1977-1983   7910933

Microsc Electron Biol Celular
Microscopía electrónica y biología
celular: organo oficial de las Sociedades
Latinoamericana de Microscopía Electrónica
e Iberoamericana de Biología Celular
0326-3142
Continues: Revista de microscopía
electrónica. Continued by: Biocell.
1980-1993   8612496

Microsc Microanal
Microscopy and microanalysis: the official
journal of Microscopy Society of America,
Microbeam Analysis Society, Microscopical
Society of Canada
1431-9276   1435-8115
Vol. 8, suppl. 2 (2002)- have title:
Proceedings: microscopy and microanalysis
and constitute the proceedings of the 60th-
Annual Meeting of the Microscopy Society of
America, plus those of meetings held jointly
with other organizations. These proceedings
were formerly published separately.
1997   9712707

Microsc Res Tech
Microscopy research and technique
1059-910X   1097-0029
Continues: Journal of electron microscopy
technique.
1992   9203012

Microsurgery
Microsurgery
0738-1085   1098-2752
Formed by the union of: Journal of
microsurgery, and: International journal of
microsurgery.
1983   8309230

Microvasc Res
Microvascular research
0026-2862   1095-9319
1968   0165035

Middle East Dent Oral Health
Middle East dentistry & oral health
0266-8874
1984-1986   8605523

Middle East Health
Middle East health
0263-1016
Continues: MEH. Middle East health supply
& service.
1981-1991   8202450

Middle East J Anaesthesiol
Middle East journal of anaesthesiology
0544-0440
Continued by: Middle East journal of
anesthesiology.
1966-1982   0074405

Middle East J Anesthesiol
Middle East journal of anesthesiology
0544-0440
Continues: Middle East journal of
anaesthesiology.
1983   8604187

Middle East Med J
The Middle East medical journal
1962-1965   18710550R

Middx Hosp J
The Middlesex Hospital journal
0026-3222
Continued by: Charles Bell journal.
1897-1987   0413710

Midwest Alliance Nurs J
Midwest Alliance in Nursing journal / MAIN
1048-499X
1989-1992   9306096

Midwest Dent
Midwestern dentist
0026-3478
Continues the Journal of the Kansas City
(Mo.) District Dental Society.
1959   18110700R

Midwife Health Visit
Midwife and health visitor
0026-3516
Continued by: Midwife, health visitor &
community nurse.
1965-1974   7504095

Midwife Health Visit Community Nurse
Midwife, health visitor & community nurse
0306-9699
Continues Midwife and health visitor.
Continued by: Professional care of mother
and child.
1975-1991   7504096

Midwifery
Midwifery
0266-6138
1985   8510930

Midwifery Today Childbirth Educ
Midwifery today and childbirth education
1522-2888
Continues: Midwifery today. Absorbed:
International midwife. Continued by:
Midwifery today with international midwife.
1989-1997   9303318

Midwifery Today Int Midwife
Midwifery today with international midwife
1551-8892
Continues: Midwifery today and childbirth
education.
1997   100888783

Midwives
Midwives
Continues: RCM midwives.
2008   101472618

Midwives
Midwives: official journal of the Royal
College of Midwives
1355-8404
Continues: Midwives chronicle. Continued
by: RCM midwives journal.
1995-1997   9506689

Midwives Chron
Midwives chronicle
0026-3524
Continued by: Midwives.
1945-1994   18710610R

Mie Med J
Mie medical journal
0026-3532
Continues the Journal of Mie Ika Daigaku,
Tsu, Japan.
1952-2001   0376650

Mikrobiol Z
Mikrobiolohichnyĭ zhurnal (Kiev, Ukraine:
1993)
1028-0987
Continues: Mikrobiologicheskiĭ zhurnal.
1993   9318954

Mikrobiol Zh
Mikrobiologicheskiĭ zhurnal
0201-8462
Continues Mikrobiolohichnyĭ zhurnal.
1978-1993   7909597

Mikrobiol Zh
Mikrobiolohichnyĭ zhurnal
0026-3664
Continued by Mikrobiologicheskiĭ zhurnal.
1934-1977   7910045

Mikrobiologiia
Mikrobiologiia
0026-3656
1932   0376652

Mikrobiyol Bul
Mikrobiyoloji bülteni
0374-9096
1966   7503830

Mikrochemie
Mikrochemie
0369-0261
1923-1938   0017501

Mikrochim Acta
Mikrochimica acta
0026-3672   1436-5073
Continues Mikrochimica et ichnoanalytica acta.
1966   7808782

Mikrochim Ichnoanal Acta
Mikrochimica et ichnoanalytica acta
0369-0504
Continues Mikrochimica acta. Continued by
Mikrochimica acta.
1963-1965   0145623

Mikroskopie
Mikroskopie
0026-3702
1946-1985   0376654

Mil Med
Military medicine
0026-4075   1930-613X
Continues: Military surgeon.
1955   2984771R

Mil Surg
Military surgeon
Continues the Journal of the Association of
Military Surgeons of the United States.
1907-1954   18720210R

Milbank Mem Fund Q
The Milbank Memorial Fund quarterly
0026-3745
Continues: Milbank Memorial Fund quarterly
bulletin. Continued by: Milbank Memorial
Fund quarterly: health and society.
1934-1972   0377263

Milbank Mem Fund Q Health Soc
The Milbank Memorial Fund quarterly.
Health and society
0160-1997
Continues the Milbank Memorial Fund
quarterly. Continued by: The Milbank
quarterly.
1973-1985   0400166

Milbank Q
The Milbank quarterly
0887-378X   1468-0009
1986   8607003

Militaerlaegen
Militaerlaegen
0026-3834
1893-1971   0017523

Militarsanitat
Militärsanität
1919-194u   18720190R

Miner Electrolyte Metab
Mineral and electrolyte metabolism
0378-0392
1978-1999   7802196

Minerva Anestesiol
Minerva anestesiologica
0375-9393   1827-1596
Continues: Giornale italiano di anestesiologia.
1953   0375272

Minerva Cardioangiol
Minerva cardioangiologica
0026-4725   1827-1618
1953   0400725

Minerva Cardioangiol Eur
Minerva cardioangiologica Europea
1958-1961   0376400

Minerva Chir
Minerva chirurgica
0026-4733   1827-1626
Absorbed: Infortunistica e traumatologia del
lavoro.
1946   0400726

Minerva Dermatol
Minerva dermatologica
Continues Dermosifilografo. Merged with
Giornale italiano di dermatologia to form
Giornale italiano di dermatologia - Minerva
dermatologica.
1951-1968   0216424

Minerva Dietol
Minerva dietologica
0026-475X
Merged with Minerva gastroenterologica to
form Minerva dietologica e gastroenterologica.
1961-1977   0400727

Minerva Dietol Gastroenterol
Minerva dietologica e gastroenterologica
0391-1993
Formed by the union of Minerva dietologica
and Minerva gastroenterologica. Continued
by: Minerva gastroenterologica e dietologica.
1977-1990   7708555

Minerva Ecol Idroclimatol Fis Sanit
Minerva ecologica idroclimatologica
fisicosanitaria
0391-1624
Continues Minerva ecologica
idroclimatologica e fisiconucleare.
1975-1977   7703967

Minerva Ecol Idroclimatol Fisiconucl
Minerva ecologica idroclimatologica e
fisiconucleare
0391-4852
Formed by the union of Minerva ecologica
e idroclimatologica and Giornale di
fisica sanitaria e protezione contro le
radiazioni. Continued by Minerva ecologica
idroclimatologica fisicosanitaria.
1975-1975   7802197

Minerva Endocrinol
Minerva endocrinologica
0391-1977   1827-1634
1976   8406505

Minerva Farm
Minerva farmaceutica
1952-1964   0205061

Minerva Fisiconucl
Minerva fisiconucleare
0026-4768
Continues in part Minerva nucleare.
Continued by Giornale di fisica sanitaria e
protezione contro le radiazioni.
1966-1967   0377005

Minerva Fisioter Radiobiol
Minerva fisioterapica e radiobiologica
Continued by Minerva radiologica,
fisioterapica e radiobiologica. Supplement to
Minerva medica, 1956-luglio - ag. 1957.
1956-1962   0031734

Minerva Gastroenterol
Minerva gastroenterologica
0026-4776
Merged with Minerva dietologica to form
Minerva dietologica e gastroenterologica.
Issued as a supplement to Minerva medica
1955-62.
1955-1977   0400730

Minerva Gastroenterol Dietol
Minerva gastroenterologica e dietologica
1121-421X   1827-1642
Continues: Minerva dietologica e
gastroenterologica.
1991   9109791

Minerva Ginecol
Minerva ginecologica
0026-4784   1827-1650
Formed by the union of: Folia gynaecologica,
and: Ginecologia.
1949   0400731

Minerva Med
Minerva medica
0026-4806   1827-1669
1909   0400732

Minerva Medicoleg
Minerva medicolegale; archivio di
antropologia criminale, psichiatria, e
medicina legale
0026-4849   1827-1677
Continues: Archivio di antropologia
criminale, psichiatria, e medicina legale.
1950   0400734

Minerva Nefrol
Minerva nefrologica
0026-4873
Merged with Minerva urologica, to form
Minerva urologica e nefrologica. A
supplement to Minerva medica.
1954-1983   0400735

Minerva Neurochir
Minerva neurochirurgica
0026-4881
Issued 1957-61 as supplement to Minerva
chirurgica. Continued by Journal of
neurosurgical sciences.
1957-1972   0432565

Minerva Nipiol
Minerva nipiologica
0026-489X
Supersedes Nipiopedologia. Continued by
Revista di pediatria preventiva e sociale,
nipiologia.
1951-1979   0400736

Minerva Nucl
Minerva nucleare
0369-0288
Continued by the Journal of nuclear biology
and medicine and Minerva fisiconucleare.
1957-1965   0103071

Minerva Oftalmol
Minerva oftalmologica
0026-4903   1827-1685
1959   0400737

Minerva Ortognatod
Minerva ortognatodontica
0394-168X   1827-1693
1983   8809304

Minerva Ortop
Minerva ortopedica
0026-4911
Continued by: Minerva ortopedica e
traumatologica.
1950-1986   2984772R

Minerva Otorinolaringol
Minerva otorinolaringologica
0026-4938
Merged with Nuovo archivio italiano di
otologia, rinologia e laringologia; Bollettino
delle malattie dell'orecchio, della gola, del
naso; and L'Oto-rino-laringologia italiana, to
form Otorinolaringologia.
1951-1980   0375274

Minerva Pediatr
Minerva pediatrica
0026-4946   1827-1715
Absorbed: Rivista di clinica pediatrica. 1974
Formed by the union of Medicina italiana,
Policlinico infantile, and La Pediatria del
medico pratico.
1949   0400740

Minerva Psichiatr
Minerva psichiatrica
0374-9320
Continues Minerva psichiatrica e psicologica.
1976   7707981

Minerva Radiol
Minerva radiologica
0026-4962
Continues: Minerva radiologica, fisioterapica
e radiobiologica. Absorbed by: Radiologia
medica.
1968-1970   7612089

Minerva Radiol Fisioter Radiobiol
Minerva radiologica, fisioterapica e
radiobiologica
0544-2656
Continues Minerva fisioterapica e
radiobiologica. Continued by Minerva
radiologica.
1963-1967   0151766

Minerva Stomatol
Minerva stomatologica
0026-4970
1952   0421071

Minerva Urol
Minerva urologica
0026-4989
Merged with Minerva nefrologica, to form
Minerva urologica e nefrologica.
1949-1983   0375275

Minerva Urol Nefrol
Minerva urologica e nefrologica = The
Italian journal of urology and nephrology
0393-2249
Formed by the union of: Minerva urologica,
and: Minerva nefrologica.
1984   8503649

Mini Rev Med Chem
Mini reviews in medicinal chemistry
1389-5575
2001   101094212

Minim Invasive Neurosurg
Minimally invasive neurosurgery: MIN
0946-7211
Continues: Neurochirurgia.
1994 **9440973**

Minim Invasive Surg Nurs
Minimally invasive surgical nursing
1068-5685
Continues: Laser nursing.
1993-1997 **9317135**

Minim Invasive Ther Allied Technol
Minimally invasive therapy & allied
technologies: MITAT: official journal of the
Society for Minimally Invasive Therapy
1364-5706 1365-2931
Merger of: Endoscopic surgery and allied
technologies, and: Minimally invasive
therapy.
1996 **9612996**

Minn Med
Minnesota medicine
0026-556X
1918 **8000173**

Minn Nurs Accent
Minnesota nursing accent
0026-5586
Continues: Minnesota registered nurse.
Continued by: MNA accent. Minnesota
Nurses Association.
1962-1977 **0067406**

Minn Welfare
Minnesota welfare
0026-5705
Supersedes Social welfare review. Merged
with Minnesota mental health/mental
retardation newsletter, and Rap. to form
People.
1945-1973 **8006323**

Minneap Dist Dent J
The Minneapolis district dental journal
0026-5365
1917-1979 **18730030R**

Minor Nurse Newsl
Minority nurse newsletter
1071-9946
1994 **9422780**

Mises Point Accouch Pediatre
Mises au point de l'accoucheur et du
pédiatre
1961-1966 **0067713**

Miss Dent Assoc J
Mississippi Dental Association journal
0098-4329
Continues Journal - Mississippi Dental
Association.
1974 **7513995**

Miss Doct
The Mississippi doctor
Absorbed by: Journal of the Mississippi State
Medical Association.
1922-1959 **18730470R**

Miss RN
Mississippi RN
0026-6388
194u **0044610**

Miss Valley Med J
Mississippi Valley medical journal
0096-5480
Continues Radiological review and
Mississippi Valley medical journal. Absorbed
by Clinical medicine in Sept. 1960.
1939-1960 **18730540R**

Mitochondrion
Mitochondrion
1567-7249
2001 **100968751**

Mitt Dtsch Pharm Ges Pharm Ges DDR
Mitteilungen. Deutsche Pharmazeutische
Gesellschaft
0012-0561
1924-1971 **0326216**

Mitt Geb Lebensmittelunters Hyg
Mitteilungen aus dem Gebiete der
Lebensmittel-untersuchung un Hygiene =
Travaux de chimie alimentaire et d'hygiène
0026-6841
Continued by: Mitteilungen aus
Lebensmitteluntersuchung und Hygiene.
1910-1998 **0017767**

Mitt Lebensmittelunters Hyg
Mitteilungen aus Lebensmitteluntersuchung
und Hygiene = Travaux de chimie
alimentaire et d'hygiène
1424-1307
Continues: Mitteilungen aus dem Gebiete der
Lebensmitteluntersuchung und Hygiene.
1999-2006 **100893464**

Mitt Med Abt Schweiz Unfallversicherunst
Mitteilungen. Schweizerische
Unfallversicherungsanstalt. Medizinische
Abteilung
Continued by: Medizinische Mitteilungen
(Lucern, Switzerland).
1900-1987 **2984773R**

MLM Rep
MLM [reports]. U.S. Atomic Energy
Commission
194u-1973 **21830530R**

MLN Bull
MLN bulletin
0047-7508
1952-1974 **0070743**

MLO Med Lab Obs
MLO: medical laboratory observer
0580-7247
1969 **0225602**

MMW Fortschr Med
MMW Fortschritte der Medizin
1438-3276
Merger of: Fortschritte der Medizin,
and: MMW. Münchener medizinische
Wochenschrift, continuing the numbering of
the latter.
1999 **100893959**

MMW Munch Med Wochenschr
MMW, Münchener medizinische
Wochenschrift
0341-3098
Continues: Münchener medizinische
Wochenschrift (1950). Merged with:
Fortschritte der Medizin, to form: MMW,
Fortschritte der Medizin.
1974-1999 **7801805**

MMWR CDC Surveill Summ
MMWR. CDC surveillance summaries:
Morbidity and mortality weekly report.
CDC surveillance summaries / Centers for
Disease Control
0892-3787
Continues: Morbidity and mortality weekly
report. Surveillance summaries. Continued
by: MMWR. Surveillance summaries.
1983-2001 **8407977**

MMWR Morb Mortal Wkly Rep
MMWR. Morbidity and mortality weekly
report
0149-2195 1545-861X
Continues Morbidity and mortality; weekly
report.
1976 **7802429**

MMWR Recomm Rep
MMWR. Recommendations and reports:
Morbidity and mortality weekly report.
Recommendations and reports / Centers for
Disease Control
1057-5987 1545-8601
Continues: Morbidity and mortality weekly
report. Supplement.
1989 **101124922**

MMWR Surveill Summ
MMWR. Surveillance summaries:
Morbidity and mortality weekly report.
Surveillance summaries / CDC
1546-0738 1545-8636
Continues: MMWR. CDC surveillance
summaries.
2002 **101142015**

MNA Accent
MNA accent / Minnesota Nurses Association
0026-5586
Continues: Minnesota nursing accent.
Continued by: Minnesota nursing accent
(1999).
1978-1999 **9210216**

Mo Dent J
Missouri dental journal (Jefferson City,
Mo.)
0887-4646
Continues: Journal of the Missouri Dental
Association. Continued by: Focus MDA.
1985-1997 **8502925**

Mo Med
Missouri medicine
0026-6620
Continues: Journal. Missouri State Medical
Association.
1953 **0400744**

Mo Nurse
The Missouri nurse
0026-6655
1932 **18740120R**

Mobius
Möbius
0272-3425
Continued by: Journal of continuing
education in the health professions.
1981-1987 **8200998**

Mod Concepts Cardiovasc Dis
Modern concepts of cardiovascular disease
0026-7600
1932-1991 **0400745**

Mod Dent Pract
Modern dental practice
0894-7953
1988-1988 **8805002**

Mod Healthc
Modern healthcare
0160-7480
Formed by union of: Modern healthcare.. and:
Modern healthcare..
1977 **7801798**

Mod Healthc (Short Term Care)
Modern healthcare. [Short-term care ed.]
0093-7061
Supersedes Modern hospital. Merged with
Modern healthcare. [Long-term care ed.] to
form Modern healthcare.
1974-1976 **0417653**

Mod Hosp
Modern hospital
0026-783X
Continued by: Modern healthcare [Short-term care ed.].
1913-1974 0417654

Mod Med
Modern medicine
0026-8070
1932-2000 0375300

Mod Med Asia
Modern medicine of Asia
0377-1504
Continues Asian journal of modern medicine.
1975-1981 7513643

Mod Med Can
Modern medicine of Canada
0026-8097
1946-1991 0375301

Mod Midwife
Modern midwife
0963-276X
Continued by: Practising midwife.
1991-1997 9443126

Mod Nurs Home
Modern nursing home
0026-8178
Continues Modern nursing home administration. Superseded by Modern healthcare [Long-term care ed.]
1967-1974 0420172

Mod Pathol
Modern pathology: an official journal of the United States and Canadian Academy of Pathology, Inc
0893-3952 1530-0285
1988 8806605

Mod Pharm
Modern pharmacy
1904-1959 18740620R

Mod Probl Ophthalmol
Modern problems in ophthalmology
0077-0078
Continues Problèmes actuels d'ophtalmologie. Merged with: Advances in ophthalmology, and: Bibliotheca ophthalmologia, to form: Developments in ophthalmology.
1971-1979 1270475

Mod Probl Paediatr
Modern problems in paediatrics
0303-884X
Continues Moderne Probleme der Pädiatrie. Merged with: Monographs in paediatrics, to form: Pediatric and adolescent medicine.
1972-1989 7502628

Mod Rheumatol
Modern rheumatology / the Japan Rheumatism Association
1439-7595
Continues: Japanese journal of rheumatology.
2000 100959226

Mod Treat
Modern treatment
0026-8526
1964-1972 7511504

Mod Treat Yearb
Modern treatment yearbook
1934-1962 18750030R

Mod Trends Hum Reprod Physiol
Modern trends in human reproductive physiology
0077-0140
1963-1963 0375304

Mod Trends Immunol
Modern trends in immunology
0544-6848
1963-1967 0375305

Mod Trends Med Virol
Modern trends in medical virology
0544-6856
1967-1974 0076444

Mod Trends Neurol
Modern trends in neurology
0544-6872
Continued by: Butterworths international medical reviews. Neurology.
1951-1975 0075472

Mod Trends Orthop
Modern trends in orthopaedics
0077-0159
1950-1972 0035777

Mod Trends Plast Surg
Modern trends in plastic surgery
0544-6929
1964-1966 18750050R

Mod Trends Radiother
Modern trends in radiotherapy
0544-6937
1967-1972 0076450

Mod Trends Rheumatol
Modern trends in rheumatology
0544-6945
1966-1971 0073315

Mod Trends Surg
Modern trends in surgery
0544-6953
1962-1971 0400747

Mod Vet Pract
Modern veterinary practice
0362-8140
Continues MVP. Modern veterinary practice.
1973-1994 7802904

Mol Aspects Med
Molecular aspects of medicine
0098-2997
1975 7603128

Mol Biochem Parasitol
Molecular and biochemical parasitology
0166-6851
1980 8006324

Mol Biol
Molecular biology
0026-8933 1608-3245
1967 0131463

Mol Biol (Mosk)
Molekuliarnaia biologiia
0026-8984
1967 0105454

Mol Biol Biochem Biophys
Molecular biology, biochemistry, and biophysics
0077-0221
1967-1987 0173540

Mol Biol Cell
Molecular biology of the cell
1059-1524 1939-4586
Continues: Cell regulation.
1992 9201390

Mol Biol Evol
Molecular biology and evolution
0737-4038 1537-1719
1983 8501455

Mol Biol Med
Molecular biology & medicine
0735-1313
1983-1991 8403879

Mol Biol Rep
Molecular biology reports
0301-4851
1973 0403234

Mol Biosyst
Molecular bioSystems
1742-206X 1742-2051
2005 101251620

Mol Biotechnol
Molecular biotechnology
1073-6085 1559-0305
Separated from: Applied biochemistry and biotechnology.
1994 9423533

Mol Biother
Molecular biotherapy
0952-8172
1988-1992 8904897

Mol Cancer
Molecular cancer
1476-4598
2002 101147698

Mol Cancer Res
Molecular cancer research: MCR
1541-7786
Continues: Cell growth & differentiation.
2002 101150042

Mol Cancer Ther
Molecular cancer therapeutics
1535-7163 1538-8514
2001 101132535

Mol Carcinog
Molecular carcinogenesis
0899-1987 1098-2744
1988 8811105

Mol Cell
Molecular cell
1097-2765 1097-4164
1997 9802571

Mol Cell Biochem
Molecular and cellular biochemistry
0300-8177
Supersedes Enzymologia.
1973 0364456

Mol Cell Biol
Molecular and cellular biology
0270-7306 1098-5549
1981 8109087

Mol Cell Biol Hum Dis Ser
Molecular and cell biology of human diseases series
1470-0573
1992-1995 9217079

Mol Cell Biol Res Commun
Molecular cell biology research communications: MCBRC
1522-4724 1522-4732
Continues in part: Biochemical and biophysical research communications. Absorbed by: Archives of biochemistry and biophysics, Nov. 2001.
1999-2001 100889076

Mol Cell Biomech
Molecular & cellular biomechanics: MCB
1556-5297 1556-5300
Continues: Mechanics & chemistry of biosystems.
2005 101253756

Mol Cell Endocrinol
Molecular and cellular endocrinology
0303-7207
1974   7500844

Mol Cell Neurosci
Molecular and cellular neurosciences
1044-7431   1095-9327
1990   9100095

Mol Cell Probes
Molecular and cellular probes
0890-8508
1987   8709751

Mol Cell Proteomics
Molecular & cellular proteomics: MCP
1535-9476   1535-9484
2002   101125647

Mol Cells
Molecules and cells
1016-8478
1990   9610936

Mol Chem Neuropathol
Molecular and chemical neuropathology /
sponsored by the International Society for
Neurochemistry and the World Federation
of Neurology and research groups on
neurochemistry and cerebrospinal fluid
1044-7393
Continues: Neurochemical pathology.
Absorbed by: Journal of molecular
neuroscience.
1989-1998   8910358

Mol Diagn
Molecular diagnosis: a journal devoted to
the understanding of human disease through
the clinical application of molecular biology
1084-8592
Merged with: American journal of
pharmacogenomics, to form: Molecular
diagnosis & therapy.
1996-2005   9614965

Mol Diagn Ther
Molecular diagnosis & therapy
1177-1062
Merger of: Molecular diagnosis; and:
American journal of pharmacogenomics,
continuing the numbering of the former.
2006   101264260

Mol Divers
Molecular diversity
1381-1991
1995   9516534

Mol Ecol
Molecular ecology
0962-1083   1365-294X
1992   9214478

Mol Endocrinol
Molecular endocrinology (Baltimore, Md.)
0888-8809
1987   8801431

Mol Gen Genet
Molecular & general genetics: MGG
0026-8925
Continues: Zeitschrift für Vererbungslehre.
Continued by: Molecular genetics and
genomics.
1967-2001   0125036

Mol Gen Mikrobiol Virusol
Molekuliarnaia genetika, mikrobiologiia i
virusologiia
0208-0613
1983   9315607

Mol Genet Genomics
Molecular genetics and genomics: MGG
1617-4615   1617-4623
Continues: Molecular & general genetics.
2001   101093320

Mol Genet Med
Molecular genetic medicine
1057-2805
Absorbed by: Advances in genetics.
1991-1994   9114827

Mol Genet Metab
Molecular genetics and metabolism
1096-7192   1096-7206
Continues: Biochemical and molecular
medicine.
1998   9805456

Mol Hum Reprod
Molecular human reproduction
1360-9947   1460-2407
1995   9513710

Mol Imaging
Molecular imaging: official journal of the
Society for Molecular Imaging
1535-3508   1536-0121
2001   101120118

Mol Imaging Biol
Molecular imaging and biology: MIB:
the official publication of the Academy of
Molecular Imaging
1536-1632   1860-2002
Continues: Clinical positron imaging.
2002   101125610

Mol Immunol
Molecular immunology
0161-5890
Continues Immunochemistry.
1979   7905289

Mol Interv
Molecular interventions
1534-0384
2001   101093789

Mol Mar Biol Biotechnol
Molecular marine biology and biotechnology
1053-6426
Merged with: Journal of marine
biotechnology, to form: Marine biotechnology
(New York, N.Y.)
1991-1998   9205135

Mol Med
Molecular medicine (Cambridge, Mass.)
1076-1551   1528-3658
1994   9501023

Mol Med (Sofia)
Molekuliarna meditsina = Molecular
medicine / Nauchno sdruzhenie
"Molekuliarna meditsina"
1310-7798
Continues: Eksperimentalna meditsina i
morfologiia.
1996-1996   9615138

Mol Med Today
Molecular medicine today
1357-4310
Continued by: Trends in molecular medicine.
1995-2000   9508560

Mol Membr Biol
Molecular membrane biology
0968-7688   1464-5203
Continues: Membrane biochemistry.
1994   9430797

Mol Microbiol
Molecular microbiology
0950-382X   1365-2958
1987   8712028

Mol Neurobiol
Molecular neurobiology
0893-7648   1559-1182
1987   8900963

Mol Nutr Food Res
Molecular nutrition & food research
1613-4125   1613-4133
Continues: Nahrung.
2004   101231818

Mol Pain
Molecular pain
                                        1744-8069
2005   101242662

Mol Pathol
Molecular pathology: MP
1366-8714   1472-4154
Continues: Clinical molecular pathology.
Absorbed by: Journal of clinical pathology.
1997-2003   9706282

Mol Pharm
Molecular pharmaceutics
1543-8384   1543-8392
2004   101197791

Mol Pharmacol
Molecular pharmacology
0026-895X   1521-0111
1965   0035623

Mol Phylogenet Evol
Molecular phylogenetics and evolution
1055-7903   1095-9513
1992   9304400

Mol Plant Microbe Interact
Molecular plant-microbe interactions:
MPMI
0894-0282
1988   9107902

Mol Plant Pathol
Molecular plant pathology
1464-6722   1364-3703
Continues the Internet journal, Molecular
plant pathology online.
2000   100954969

Mol Psychiatry
Molecular psychiatry
1359-4184   1476-5578
1996   9607835

Mol Reprod Dev
Molecular reproduction and development
1040-452X   1098-2795
1988   8903333

Mol Syst Biol
Molecular systems biology
                                        1744-4292
2005   101235389

Mol Ther
Molecular therapy: the journal of the
American Society of Gene Therapy
1525-0016   1525-0024
2000   100890581

Mol Toxicol
Molecular toxicology
0883-9492
1987-1989   8711544

Mol Urol
Molecular urology
1091-5362
1997-2001   9709255

Mol Vis
Molecular vision
                                        1090-0535
1995   9605351

Molecules
Molecules (Basel, Switzerland)
1420-3049
1996 100964009

Mon Bull Indiana State Board Health
Monthly bulletin. Indiana State Board of Health
0019-6754
Continued by: Indiana State Board of Health bulletin.
1899-1964 0220077

Mon Bull Minist Health Public Health Lab Serv
Monthly bulletin of the Ministry of Health and the Public Health Laboratory Service
0368-881X
Continues Monthly bulletin of the Ministry of Health and the Emergency Public Health Laboratory Service.
1947-1967 7502630

Mon Health Rep U S Army
Monthly health report. United States. Army. Military District of Washington
1948-1952 22230660R

Mon Heath Bull
Monthly health bulletin. United States. Army. Army, Second
1946-1952 22310410R

Mon Labor Rev
Monthly labor review / U.S. Department of Labor, Bureau of Labor Statistics
0098-1818
Continues: Monthly review of the U.S. Bureau of Labor Statistics.
1918 9108232

Mon Rev New York State Dep Labor Div Ind Hyg
Monthly review - New York State Department of Labor, Division of Industrial Hygiene
0361-9346
Continues Industrial hygiene. Superseded by Industrial hygiene review.
1946-1957 7600777

Mon Vital Stat Rep
Monthly vital statistics report
0364-0396
Formed by the merger of the National Office of Vital Statistics' Current mortality analysis, its Monthly marriage report and its Monthly vital statistics bulletin. Continued by: National vital statistics report.
1952-1998 0043110

Monaldi Arch Chest Dis
Monaldi archives for chest disease = Archivio Monaldi per le malattie del torace / Fondazione clinica del lavoro, IRCCS [and] Istituto di clinica tisiologica e malattie apparato respiratorio, Università di Napoli, Secondo ateneo
1122-0643
Continues: Archivio Monaldi per le malattie del torace.
1993 9307314

Monash Bioeth Rev
Monash bioethics review
1321-2753
Continues: Bioethics news.
1994 100973394

Monatsh Tierheilkd
Monatshefte für Tierheilkunde
Continues Monatshefte für praktische Tierheilkunde.
1953-1963 18750330R

Monatsh Veterinarmed
Monatshefte für Veterinärmedizin
0026-9263
1946-1994 2984796R

Monatskurse Arztl Fortbild [Bildbeil]
Monatskurse für die ärztliche Fortbildung. Bildbeilage; Farbige Medizin
0540-6234
1961-1963 18750340R

Monatsschr Dtsch Zahnarzte Freie Zahnarzt
Monatsschrift deutscher Zahnärzte: der freie Zahnarzt
0047-7842
Continued by Der Freie Zahnarzt.
1958-1971 7506349

Monatsschr Kinderheilkd
Monatsschrift für Kinderheilkunde
0026-9298
Continued by Monatsschrift Kinderheilkunde.
1902-1980 0400751

Monatsschr Kinderheilkd
Monatsschrift Kinderheilkunde: Organ der Deutschen Gesellschaft für Kinderheilkunde
0026-9298
Continues: Monatsschrift für Kinderheilkunde.
1980 8206462

Monatsschr Kriminol
Monatsschrift für Kriminologie und Strafrechtsreform
0026-9301
1904 18750460R

Monatsschr Ohrenheilkd Laryngorhinol
Monatsschrift für Ohrenheilkunde und Laryngo-Rhinologie
0026-9328
Merged with Laryngologie, Rhinologie, Otologie und ihre Grenzgebiete to form Laryngologie, Rhinologie, Otologie.
1867-1974 7513648

Monatsschr Psychiatr Neurol
Monatsschrift für Psychiatrie und Neurologie
Continued by: Psychiatria et neurologia.
1897-1956 18750490R

Monatsschr Tuberkulosebekampf
Monatsschrift für Tuberkulosebekämpfung
0323-8393
Continued by Monatsschrift für Lungenkrankheiten und Tuberkulosebekämpfung.
1958-1967 7501857

Monatsschr Unfallheilkd
Monatsschrift für Unfallheilkunde
0340-1669
Continues Monatsschrift für Unfallheilkunde, Versicherungs-, Versorgungs- und Verkehrsmedizin. Continued by Unfallheilkunde.
1975-1975 7611599

Monatsschr Unfallheilkd Versicher Versorg Verkehrsmed
Monatsschrift für Unfallheilkunde, Versicherungs-, Versorgungs- und Verkehrsmedizin
0026-9336
Continues: Monatsschrift für Unfallheilkunde und Versicherungsmedizin. Continued by: Monatsschrift für Unfallheilkunde.
1963-1974 7505682

Monatsschr Unfallheilkd Versicherungsmed
Monatsschrift für Unfallheilkunde und Versicherungsmedizin
0373-5222
Continued by: Monatsschrift für Unfallheilkunde, Versicherungs-, Versorgungs- und Verkehrsmedizin.
1894-1963 7505680

Monde Dent
Le monde dentaire
Continues: Nouvelles DDM.
1949-19uu 9427225

Monde Med
Monde médical
0397-9229
1891-1975 0400753

Mondo Odontostomatol
Mondo odontostomatologico
0026-9565
1959-1987 0421073

Mondo Ortod
Mondo ortodontico
0391-2000
1976 7703267

Monit Farm Ter
Monitor de la farmacía y de la terapéutica
0463-1536
1895-1993 18810080R

Monit Ostet Ginecol Endocrinol Metab
Monitore ostetrico-ginecologico di endocrinologia e del metabolismo
Continues Monitore ostetrico-ginecologico.
1959-1971 0400754

Monit Ostet Ginecolog
Monitore ostetrico-ginecologico
Continued by Monitore ostetrico-ginecologico di endocrinologia e del metabolismo.
1929-1958 18810180R

Monogr Allergy
Monographs in allergy
0077-0760
1966-1996 0077707

Monogr Am Assoc Ment Defic
Monograph of the American Association of Mental Deficiency
0098-7123
Continues: Monographs of the American Association on Mental Deficiency. Continued by: Monographs of the American Association on Mental Deficiency (1982).
1976-1981 8206810

Monogr Am Assoc Ment Defic
Monographs of the American Association on Mental Deficiency
0098-7123
Continued by Monograph of the American Association of Mental Deficiency.
1973-1973 7509014

Monogr Am Assoc Ment Defic
Monographs of the American Association on Mental Deficiency (1982)
0098-7123
Continues: Monograph of the American Association of Mental Deficiency. Continued by: Monographs of the American Association on Mental Retardation.
1982-1987 8301655

Monogr Am Assoc Ment Retard
Monographs of the American Association on Mental Retardation
0895-8009
Continues: Monographs of the American Association on Mental Deficiency (1982).
1987-1992 8801432

Monogr Atheroscler
Monographs on atherosclerosis
0077-099X
1969-1990 0362400

Monogr Clin Cytol
Monographs in clinical cytology
0077-0809 1662-3827
Continues Clinical cytology.
1969 0370161

Monogr Dev Biol
Monographs in developmental biology
0077-0825
1969-1992 0207715

Monogr Endocrinol
Monographs on endocrinology
0077-1015
1967-1989   0113567

Monogr Gesamtgeb Neurol Psychiatr
Monographien aus dem Gesamtgebiete der
Neurologie und Psychiatrie
0376-0464
1912-1970   1301562

Monogr Gesamtgeb Psychiatr Psychiatry Ser
Monographien aus dem Gesamtgebiete der
Psychiatrie
0077-0671
    Supersedes in part Monographien aus
    dem Gesamtgebiete der Neurologie und
    Psychiatrie.
1970   0251404

Monogr Hum Genet
Monographs in human genetics
0077-0876
1966   7600568

Monogr Neoplast Dis Var Sites
Neoplastic disease at various sites
0463-2036
1958-1970   0400755

Monogr Neural Sci
Monographs in neural sciences
0300-5186
    Continued by: Monographs in clinical
    neuroscience.
1973-1995   0357002

Monogr Oral Sci
Monographs in oral science
0077-0892   1662-3843
1971   0327545

Monogr Paediatr
Monographs in paediatrics
0077-0914
    Supersedes Bibliotheca paediatrica. Merged
    with: Modern problems in paediatrics. to
    form: Pediatric and adolescent medicine.
1971-1986   1264740

Monogr Pathol
Monographs in pathology
0077-0922
1960-1997   0416716

Monogr Physiol Soc
Monographs of the Physiological Society
0079-2020
1953   0401222

Monogr Popul Biol
Monographs in population biology
0077-0930
1967   0151324

Monogr Ser World Health Organ
Monograph series. World Health
Organization
0512-3038
1951   0413612

Monogr Soc Res Child Dev
Monographs of the Society for Research in
Child Development
0037-976X   1540-5834
1936   7508397

Monogr Sov Med Sci
Monographs in Soviet medical sciences
1962-1964   18810520R

Monogr Surg Sci
Monographs in the surgical sciences
1964-1967   0133452

Monogr Virol
Monographs in virology
0077-0965
1968   0124434

Montp Med
Montpellier médical
    Continues Nouveau Montpellier médical.
    Superseded by Journal de médecine de
    Montpellier.
1902-1965   18820540R

Montreal Med
Montréal médical
    Continues Revue médicale U de M.
    Superseded by Québec médical.
1957-1970   0253210

Morb Mortal Wkly Rep Surveill Summ
Morbidity and mortality weekly report.
Surveillance summaries: MMWR / Centers
for Disease Control
    Continued by: MMWR. CDC surveillance
    summaries.
1983-1983   8400155

Morfologiia
Morfologiia (Saint Petersburg, Russia)
1026-3543
    Continues: Arkhiv anatomii. gistologii i
    émbriologii.
1992   9317610

Morphol Embryol (Bucur)
Morphologie et embryologie
0377-5038
    Continues in part Revue roumaine de
    morphologie et de physiologie. Continued
    by: Romanian journal of morphology and
    embryology.
1975-1990   7512183

Morphol Igazsagugyi Orv Sz
Morphologiai és igazságügyi orvosi szemle
0540-889X
1961-1990   0400757

Morphol Med
Morphologia medica
0172-9187
1981-1983   8204929

Morphologie
Morphologie: bulletin de l'Association des
anatomistes
1286-0115
    Continues: Bulletin de l'Association des
    anatomistes.
1997   9814314

Mosq News
Mosquito news
0027-142X
    Continued by: Journal of the American
    Mosquito Control Association.
1941-1984   0400760

Mother Child
Mother and child
0027-1519
    Supersedes National health. Absorbed
    Maternity and child welfare in Oct. 1934.
1930-1974   18830500R

Motor Control
Motor control
1087-1640
1997   9706297

Mouth
Mouth (American Student Dental
Association)
1529-5044
    Continues: Dentistry (American Student
    Dental Association).
1999   100939354

Mouth Mirror
The Mouth mirror
    Absorbed by: British dental journal.
1904-1949   18830640R

Mov Disord
Movement disorders: official journal of the
Movement Disorder Society
0885-3185   1531-8257
1986   8610688

MPS
MPS. Medical products salesman
0192-432X
    Continues: Medical products salesman.
    Absorbed: American surgical dealer. July
    1975 Continued by: Medical products sales.
1974-1981   7905032

MSDA J
MSDA journal: journal of the Maryland
State Dental Association
    Continues: Journal of the Maryland State
    Dental Association.
1995-1998   9616365

Mt Sinai J Med
The Mount Sinai journal of medicine, New York
0027-2507   1931-7581
    Continues the Journal of the Mount Sinai
    Hospital. New York.
1970   0241032

Mucosal Immunol
Mucosal immunology
1933-0219   1935-3456
2008   101299742

Mult Scler
Multiple sclerosis (Houndmills, Basingstoke,
England)
1352-4585
1995   9509185

Multis
MULTIs
0749-1611
    Absorbed by: Hospitals. Jan. 5. 1986.
1983-1985   8405401

Munca Sanit
Munca sanitară
0027-318X
    Continued by: Viaţa medicală.
1952-1974   7609371

Munch Med Wochenschr
Münchener medizinische Wochenschrift
(1950)
0027-2973
    Continues in part: Medizinische Zeitschrift.
    Continued by: MMW, Münchener
    medizinische Wochenschrift.
1950-1973   7801802

Mund Kiefer Gesichtschir
Mund-, Kiefer- und Gesichtschirurgie:
MKG
1432-9417
    Merger of: Fortschritte der Kiefer- und
    Gesichts-Chirurgie; and: Deutsche Zeitschrift
    für Mund-, Kiefer- und Gesichts-Chirurgie.
    Continued by: Oral and maxillofacial surgery.
1997-2007   9716576

Mundo Med
Mundo Medico
1927-1940   9427816

Munnpleien
Munnpleien
0047-8377
1916   18840110R

Muscle Biol
Muscle biology
0090-0532
1972-1972   0350127

Muscle Nerve
Muscle & nerve
0148-639X   1097-4598
1978   7803146

Muscle Nerve Suppl
Muscle & nerve. Supplement
1994   9517433

Musculoskeletal Care
Musculoskeletal care
1478-2189
2003   101181344

Mutagenesis
Mutagenesis
0267-8357   1464-3804
1986   8707812

Mutat Res
Mutation research
0027-5107
Continued in part by: DNA repair.
1964   0400763

Mycol Res
Mycological research
0953-7562
Continues: Transactions of the British
Mycological Society.
1989   8913481

Mycologia
Mycologia
0027-5514   1557-2536
Formed by the merger of: Mycological
bulletin, and: Journal of mycology.
1909   0400764

Mycopathol Mycol Appl
Mycopathologia et mycologia applicata
0027-5530
Continues and is continued by
Mycopathologia.
1950-1974   7505688

Mycopathologia
Mycopathologia
0369-299X
Continued by Mycopathologia et mycologia
applicata.
1938-1949   0405402

Mycopathologia
Mycopathologia
0301-486X
Continues Mycopathologia et mycologia
applicata.
1975   7505689

Mycorrhiza
Mycorrhiza
0940-6360   1432-1890
1991   100955036

Mycoses
Mycoses
0933-7407   1439-0507
Continues: Mykosen.
1988   8805008

Mykosen
Mykosen
0027-5557
Continued by: Mycoses.
1957-1987   0400765

Mykosen Suppl
Mykosen. Supplement
0344-7677
1978-1988   8702151

Mymensingh Med J
Mymensingh medical journal: MMJ
1022-4742
1992   9601799

N

N Biotechnol
New biotechnology
1871-6784
Continues: Biomolecular engineering.
2008   101465345

N C Dent Gaz
North Carolina dental gazette: a publication
of North Carolina Dental Society
1979   9879671

N C Dent J
North Carolina dental journal
0091-164X
Continues: Journal of the North Carolina
Dental Society.
1973-1980   0365327

N C Med J
North Carolina medical journal
0029-2559
1940   2984805R

N Engl Dent J
New England dental journal
1075-1297
1948-1951   19020390R

N Engl J Hum Serv
New England journal of human services
0277-996X
1981-1994   8207591

N Engl J Med
The New England journal of medicine
0028-4793   1533-4406
Continues: Boston medical and surgical
journal.
1928   0255562

N Engl Reg Allergy Proc
New England and regional allergy proceedings
0742-2814
Continues: The New England Society of
Allergy proceedings. Continued by: Allergy
proceedings.
1983-1988   8306562

N HC Perspect Community
N & HC perspectives on community: official
publication of the National League for
Nursing
1081-8731
Continues: Nursing & health care. Continued
by: Nursing and health care perspectives.
1995-1997   9504562

N J Healthc
New Jersey healthCare
1047-4765
Continues: NJHA reporter..
1988-1990   8916654

N J League Nurs News
New Jersey League for Nursing news
0047-9780
1952   7507308

N J Med
New Jersey medicine: the journal of the
Medical Society of New Jersey
0885-842X
Continues: Journal of the Medical Society of
New Jersey.
1985-2005   8511653

N J Nurse
New Jersey nurse
0196-4895
Continues NJSNA newsletter.
1978   7907163

N M Dent J
New Mexico dental journal
0028-6176
Continues The New Mexico State dental
journal.
1957   7512900

N M Nurse
New Mexico nurse
0028-6273
Continues Newsletter - New Mexico State
Nurses' Association.
1949   7806629

N S Med Bull
The Nova Scotia medical bulletin
0029-5094
Continues the Bulletin of the Medical Society
of Nova Scotia. Continued by: Nova Scotia
medical journal.
1925-1987   0404445

N S W Public Health Bull
New South Wales public health bulletin
1034-7674
1990   9712270

N Y J Dent
The New York journal of dentistry
0028-7296
Continues: Bulletin. First District Dental
Society of the State of New York.
1931-1991   0401062

N Y Med Coll News Notes
New York Medical College news & notes
1960   7507309

N Y Physician
The New York physician
Continues Private hospitals.
1934-1969   0150004

N Y State Dent J
The New York state dental journal
0028-7571
Continues: Journal of the Dental Society of
the State of New York.
1947   0414634

N Y State J Med
New York state journal of medicine
0028-7628
Absorbed: Transactions of the Medical
Society of the State of New York. Medical
Society of the State of New York. Continues:
Transactions of the New York State Medical
Association for the year ....
1901-1993   0401064

N Y State Nurse
New York state nurse
Continues: Quarterly news from the New
York State Nurses' Association, New York
League of Nursing Education, New York
State Organization for Public Health Nursing.
Continued by: Journal of the New York State
Nurses' Association.
1938-1969   0247735

N Y State Pharm
New York state pharmacist
0028-7660
Continues The New York pharmacist.
Continued by N. Y. state pharmacist.
1935-1977   7804165

N Y Times Mag
The New York times magazine
0028-7822
1896   9877816

N Y Univ J Dent
New York University journal of dentistry
0028-7865
Continues: New York University dental journal.
1946-1969   19110650R

N Y Univ Med Q
New York University medical quarterly
0028-7903
Continued by The NYU physician.
1945-1980   19110670R

N Z Dent J
The New Zealand dental journal
0028-8047
1905   0401065

N Z Health Hospital
New Zealand health & hospital
0114-3727
Continues: New Zealand hospital.
1989   8911454

N Z Hosp
New Zealand hospital
0111-4042
Continues NZ hospital. Continued by: New
Zealand health & hospital.
1975-1989   7613464

N Z Med J
The New Zealand medical journal
0028-8446   1175-8716
1887   0401067

N Z Nurs Forum
New Zealand nursing forum
0110-7968
Continues: Nursing forum.
1977-199u   7802207

N Z Nurs J
The New Zealand nursing journal. Kai tiaki
0028-8535
Merged with: NZNU news, to form: Nursing
New Zealand.
1908-1993   19110850R

N Z Sch Dent Serv Gaz
New Zealand School Dental Service gazette
0110-327X
Continues School Dental Service gazette.
New Zealand.
1971-1991   7703975

N Z Vet J
New Zealand veterinary journal
0048-0169
1952   0021406

NAACOG Newsl
NAACOG newsletter
0889-0579
Continues: Bulletin; news of the Nurses
Association of ACOG. Continued by:
AWHONN voice.
1982-1992   9107925

NAACOG Tech Bull
NAACOG technical bulletin
0198-9227
1977-1981   8002791

NAACOGS Clin Issu Perinat Womens Health Nurs
NAACOG's clinical issues in perinatal and
women's health nursing
1046-7475
Continued by: AWHONN's clinical issues in
perinatal and women's health nursing.
1990-1992   9010476

NACDL J
NACDL journal
0027-5735
Continues and is continued by NADL journal.
1966-1971   0333617

NADC MA United States Nav Air Dev Cen Johnsville Pa Aviat Med Accel Lab
NADC-MA-. United States. Naval Air
Development Center, Johnsville, Pa. Aviation
Medical Acceleration Laboratory
1900-uuuu   22420610R

NADC-AC
NADC-AC. United States. Naval Air
Development Center, Johnsville, Pa.
Aeronautical Computer Laboratory
1967-1971   22420600R

NADC-ML Rep
NADC-ML [reports]. United States. Naval
Air Development Center, Johnsville, Pa.
Aviation Medical Acceleration Laboratory
1965-1965   0047423

NADC-MR Rep
NADC-MR [reports]. United States. Naval
Air Development Center, Johnsville, Pa.
Aerospace Medical Research Dept
1965-1971   0047422

NADL J
NADL journal
0360-5361
1954-1983   0333620

Nagasaki Igakkai Zasshi
Nagasaki Igakkai zasshi = Nagasaki medical
journal
0369-3228
Supersedes Zasshi of Kenkyokai, Nagasaki
Igaku Senmongakko.
1923   0413711

Nagoya J Med Sci
Nagoya journal of medical science
0027-7622
Continues Aichi journal of experimental
medicine.
1927   0412011

Nagoya Med J
Nagoya medical journal
0027-7649
1953   0413417

NAHAM Access Manag J
NAHAM access management journal
1534-9861
Continues: NAHAM management journal.
Continued by: Access management journal.
199u-2002   101125179

NAHAM Manage J
The NAHAM management journal
1057-3526
Continues: Admitting management journal.
Continued by: NAHAM access management
journal.
1991-199u   9102192

Nahrung
Die Nahrung
0027-769X   1521-3803
Continued by: Molecular nutrition & food
research.
1957-2004   0142530

Naika
Naika. Internal medicine
0022-1961
1958   0413541

Naika Hokan
Naika hokan. Japanese archives of internal
medicine
0021-4809
1954-1996   0417455

Nakadori Byoin Iho
Nakadori Byoin iho. Nakadori Hospital
medical bulletin]
0389-9411
1960-1992   1303255

Nan Fang Yi Ke Da Xue Xue Bao
Nan fang yi ke da xue xue bao = Journal of
Southern Medical University
1673-4254
Continues: Di 1 jun yi da xue xue bao.
2005   101266132

Nano Lett
Nano letters
1530-6984   1530-6992
2001   101088070

Nanomed
Nanomedicine (London, England)
1743-5889   1748-6963
2006   101278111

Nanomedicine
Nanomedicine: nanotechnology, biology, and
medicine
1549-9634   1549-9642
2005   101233142

NANR News
Nanr News
Continued by: Recruitment Directions.
1977-1984   9879596

NAPT Bull
NAPT bulletin
Continued by the Chest and heart bulletin.
1938-1958   16130230R

Nar Zdrav
Narodno zdravlje
0027-8025
1945-1977   0404440

NASA Contract Rep NASA CR
NASA contractor report. NASA CR. United
States. National Aeronautics and Space
Administration
0565-7059
1964-1973   21930160R

NASA Tech Memo
NASA technical memorandum
1959-1974   0053235

Nasnewsletter
NASNewsletter
1047-4757
1985   8912016

Nassau Med News
Nassau medical news
1927-1972   18910590R

Nasu Suteshon
Nāsu sutēshon: NS = Nurses' station
quarterly
0387-351X
1971-1990   8608530

Nat Biotechnol
Nature biotechnology
1087-0156   1546-1696
Continues: Bio/technology (Nature Publishing
Company).
1996   9604648

Nat Cell Biol
Nature cell biology
1465-7392   1476-4679
1999   100890575

Nat Chem Biol
Nature chemical biology
1552-4450   1552-4469
2005   101231976

Nat Clin Pract Cardiovasc Med
Nature clinical practice. Cardiovascular
medicine
1743-4297   1743-4300
2004   101226507

Nat Clin Pract Endocrinol Metab
Nature clinical practice. Endocrinology &
metabolism
1745-8366   1745-8374
2005   101261798

Nat Clin Pract Gastroenterol Hepatol
Nature clinical practice. Gastroenterology &
hepatology
1743-4378   1743-4386
2004   101226510

Nat Clin Pract Nephrol
Nature clinical practice. Nephrology
1745-8323   1745-8331
2005   101261800

Nat Clin Pract Neurol
Nature clinical practice. Neurology
1745-834X   1745-8358
2005   101261799

Nat Clin Pract Oncol
Nature clinical practice. Oncology
1743-4254   1743-4262
2004   101226509

Nat Clin Pract Rheumatol
Nature clinical practice. Rheumatology
1745-8382   1745-8390
2005   101261802

Nat Clin Pract Urol
Nature clinical practice. Urology
1743-4270   1743-4289
2004   101226508

Nat Genet
Nature genetics
1061-4036   1546-1718
1992   9216904

Nat Immun
Natural immunity
1018-8916
Continues: Natural immunity and cell growth
regulation.
1992-1998   9206126

Nat Immun Cell Growth Regul
Natural immunity and cell growth
regulation
0254-7600
Continues: Stem cells. Continued by: Natural
immunity.
1984-1991   8407979

Nat Immunol
Nature immunology
1529-2908   1529-2916
2000   100941354

Nat Mater
Nature materials
1476-1122
2002   101155473

Nat Med
Nature medicine
1078-8956   1546-170X
1995   9502015

Nat Med (Tokyo)
Natural medicines = Shōyakugaku zasshi /
The Japanese Society of Pharmacognosy
1340-3443   1861-0293
Continues: Shōyakugaku zasshi.
1994   9441222

Nat Methods
Nature methods
1548-7091   1548-7105
2004   101215604

Nat Nanotechnol
Nature nanotechnology
1748-3387   1748-3395
2006   101283273

Nat Neurosci
Nature neuroscience
1097-6256   1546-1726
1998   9809671

Nat New Biol
Nature: New biology
0090-0028
Continues in part and is continued by Nature.
1971-1973   0410463

Nat Prod Lett
Natural product letters
1057-5634
Continued by: Natural product research.
1992-2002   9315615

Nat Prod Rep
Natural product reports
0265-0568   1460-4752
Formed by the union of: Alkaloids;
Biosynthesis; Aliphatic and related natural
product chemistry; and: Terpenoids and
steroids.
1984   8502408

Nat Prod Res
Natural product research
1478-6419   1478-6427
Continues: Natural product letters.
2003   101167924

Nat Protoc
Nature protocols
1754-2189   1750-2799
2006   101284307

Nat Rev Cancer
Nature reviews. Cancer
1474-175X   1474-1768
2001   101124168

Nat Rev Drug Discov
Nature reviews. Drug discovery
1474-1776   1474-1784
2002   101124171

Nat Rev Genet
Nature reviews. Genetics
1471-0056   1471-0064
2000   100962779

Nat Rev Immunol
Nature reviews. Immunology
1474-1733   1474-1741
2001   101124169

Nat Rev Microbiol
Nature reviews. Microbiology
1740-1526   1740-1534
2003   101190261

Nat Rev Mol Cell Biol
Nature reviews. Molecular cell biology
1471-0072   1471-0080
2000   100962782

Nat Rev Neurosci
Nature reviews. Neuroscience
1471-003X   1471-0048
2000   100962781

Nat Struct Biol
Nature structural biology
1072-8368
Continued by: Nature structural & molecular
biology.
1994-2003   9421566

Nat Struct Mol Biol
Nature structural & molecular biology
1545-9993   1545-9985
Continues: Nature structural biology.
2004   101186374

Nat Toxins
Natural toxins
1056-9014
1992-1999   9212382

Nations Bus
Nation's business
0028-047X
1912-1999   9876356

Natl Bur Econ Res Bull Aging Health
National Bureau of Economic Research
bulletin on aging and health
2002   101215702

Natl Cancer Inst Monogr
National Cancer Institute monograph
0083-1921
Merged with: Cancer treatment symposia; to
form: NCI monographs.
1959-1986   0216026

Natl Cancer Inst Res Rep
National Cancer Institute research report
1962-1967   7509223

Natl Conf Dent Public Relat
National Conference on Dental Public
Relations
196u-uuuu   100961269

Natl Dent Assoc J
National Dental Association journal
1050-530X
Continues: Quarterly of the National Dental
Association, Inc.. Continued by: NDA
journal.
1984-1994   8502932

Natl Eng
The National engineer
0027-9218
1897   9877852

Natl Health Stat Report
National health statistics reports
Continues: Advance data.
2008   101479519

Natl Hosp Health Care
National hospital and health care
0312-794X
Formed by the union of National hospital
and of Hospital & health care administration.
Superseded by Australian hospital. Continued
by: Australian hospital.
1975-1976   7513650

Natl Inst Anim Health Q (Tokyo)
National Institute of Animal Health
quarterly
0027-951X
Absorbed by: Nōrin Suisanshō Kachiku Eisei
Shikenjō kenkyū hōkoku.
1961-1983   0413132

Natl Inst Drug Abuse Res Monogr Ser
National Institute on Drug Abuse research
monograph series
0361-8595
Continued by: NIDA research monograph.
1975-1976   7610559

Natl Inst Health Consens Dev Conf Consens Statement
National Institutes of Health consensus
development conference consensus statement
1048-566X
Continues: National Institutes of Health
consensus development conference summary.
Continued by: National Institutes of Health
Consensus Development Conference.
Consensus statement.
1984-1989   8500356

Natl Inst Health Consens Dev Conf Summ
National Institutes of Health consensus
development conference summaries
0195-6213
Consists of the annual cumulation of: NIH
consensus development conference summary.
1977-1979   7905296

Natl Inst Health Consens Dev Conf Summ
National Institutes of Health consensus
development conference summary
Continues: NIH consensus development
conference summary. Continued by: National
Institutes of Health consensus development
conference consensus statement.
1980-1984   **8301658**

Natl J (Wash)
National journal
0360-4217
Continues: National journal reports.
1975   **9876352**

Natl Med Care Util Expend Surv B
National Medical Care Utilization and
Expenditure Survey (Series). Series B,
Descriptive report
0895-2728
1986-1987   **8710665**

Natl Med Care Util Expend Surv C
National Medical Care Utilization and
Expenditure Survey (Series). Series C,
Analytical report
0895-2671
1985-1990   **8710854**

Natl Med J India
The National medical journal of India
0970-258X
1988   **8809315**

Natl Med Leg J
National medical-legal journal
1052-309X
Continued by online format: Legal nurse
consulting ezine.
1990-2000   **9106697**

Natl Netw
National network (Dallas, Tex.)
1075-3753
Continues: Newsletter (Medical Library
Association. Hospital Library Section).
1990   **9507560**

Natl Nosocomial Infect Study Rep
National Nosocomial Infections Study report
0147-443X
Continues: National Nosocomial Infections
Study (1971).
1974-1979   **8008548**

Natl Rep Subacute Care
National report on subacute care
1073-2551
Continued by: LTC regulatory risk & liability
advisor.
1993-2000   **9418980**

Natl Saf News
National safety news
0028-0100
Continued by National Safety and health
news.
1919-1985   **18930380R**

Natl Toxicol Program Genet Modif Model Rep
National Toxicology Program genetically
modified model report
1556-522X   **1556-5246**
2005   **101469988**

Natl Toxicol Program Tech Rep Ser
National Toxicology Program technical
report series
0888-8051
Continues: National Cancer Institute
carcinogenesis technical report series.
1982   **8500747**

Natl Underwrit [Life Health]
The National underwriter. Life & health
insurance edition
0028-033X
Continues: National underwriter (Life
insurance edition). Continued by: National
underwriter (Life. health/financial services
ed.).
1971-1986   **7909783**

Natl Vital Stat Rep
National vital statistics reports: from the
Centers for Disease Control and Prevention,
National Center for Health Statistics,
National Vital Statistics System
1551-8922   **1551-8930**
Continues: Monthly vital statistics report.
1998   **9814753**

NATNEWS
NATNews
0027-6049
Continued by: British journal of theatre
nursing.
1964-1991   **1251427**

Nature
Nature
0028-0836   **1476-4687**
1869   **0410462**

Nature (Paris, France)
Nature (Paris, France)
0369-3322
Continued by: Nature. science. progrès.
1873-1960   **18940010R**

Naturheikunde
Die Naturheilkunde
1903-1956   **18940150R**

Naturwissenschaften
Die Naturwissenschaften
0028-1042   **1432-1904**
Continues: Naturwissenschaftliche
Rundschau (Braunschweig. Germany).
Max-Planck-Gesellschaft zur Förderung der
Wissenschaften. Tätigkeitsbericht, continued
by: Max-Planck-Gesellschaft zur Förderung
der Wissenschaften. Jahresbericht.
1913   **0400767**

Nauchni Tr Med Acad Vulko Chervenkov
Nauchni trudove na Meditsinskata
akademiia "Vŭlko Chervenkov"
0489-6408
Supersedes Godishnik na Meditsinskata
akademiia "Vŭlko Chervenkov". Annuaire de
l'Academie de médecine "V. Tchervenkov".
Continued by Nauchni trudove na Visshiia
meditsinski institut. Sofiia.
1953-1953   **7902529**

Nauchni Tr Nauchnoizsled Stomatol Inst (Sofiia)
Nauchni trudove. Sofia. Nauchno-
izsledovatelski stomatologichen institut
0548-0191
1953-1969   **20910490R**

Nauchni Tr Vissh Med Inst Sofiia
Nauchni trudove na Visshiia meditsinski
institut, Sofiia
0525-0889
Continues: Nauchni trudove na Meditsinskata
akademiia "Vŭlko Chervenkov".
1954-1972   **7902092**

Nauchnye Doki Vyss Shkoly Biol Nauki
Nauchnye doklady vyssheĭ shkoly.
Biologicheskie nauki
0470-4606
1958-1993   **0020417**

Naunyn Schmiedebergs Arch Exp Pathol
Pharmakol
Naunyn-Schmiedebergs Archiv
für experimentelle Pathologie und
Pharmakologie
Continues Archiv für experimentelle
Pathologie und Pharmakologie. Continued
by Naunyn-Schmiedebergs Archiv für
Pharmakologie und experimentelle
Pathologie.
1926-1966   **0054224**

Naunyn Schmiedebergs Arch Pharmacol
Naunyn-Schmiedeberg's archives of
pharmacology
0028-1298   **1432-1912**
Continues: Naunyn-Schmiedebergs Archiv für
Pharmakologie.
1972   **0326264**

Naunyn Schmiedebergs Arch Pharmakol
Naunyn-Schmiedebergs Archiv für
Pharmakologie
Continues Naunyn-Schmiedebergs Archiv
für Pharmakologie und experimentelle
Pathologie. Continued by Naunyn-
Schmiedeberg's archives of pharmacology.
1969-1971   **0326263**

Naunyn Schmiedebergs Arch Pharmakol Exp
Pathol
Naunyn-Schmiedebergs Archiv für
Pharmakologie und experimentelle
Pathologie
0365-5423
Continues Naunyn-Schmiedebergs
Archiv für experimentelle Pathologie und
Pharmakologie. Continued by Naunyn-
Schmiedebergs Archiv für Pharmakologie.
1966-1969   **0214725**

Navy Med
Navy medicine
0895-8211
Continues: U. S. Navy medicine.
1987   **8708694**

NCI Monogr
NCI monographs: a publication of the
National Cancer Institute
0893-2751
Formed by the union of: National Cancer
Institute monograph; and: Cancer treatment
symposia. Continued by: Journal of the
National Cancer Institute. Monographs.
1986-1990   **8610384**

NCSDHA Dent Hyg
The NCSDHA dental hygienist
0275-486X
1970-1984   **8012076**

NCSL Legisbrief
NCSL legisbrief
1068-2716
1993   **101092658**

NDA J
NDA journal
1524-4938
Continues: National Dental Association
journal.
1994-1997   **9711435**

Nebr Med J
The Nebraska medical journal
0091-6730
Continues the Nebraska state medical journal.
1971-1996   **0326156**

Nebr Nurse
Nebraska nurse
0028-1921
1947   **19010060R**

Nebr State Med J
The Nebraska state medical journal
0028-1956
Continued by: Nebraska medical journal.
1916-1971   0326157

Nebr Symp Motiv
Nebraska Symposium on Motivation.
Nebraska Symposium on Motivation
0146-7875
Continues: Current theory and research in
motivation.
1954   0315565

Ned Milit Geneeskd Tijdschr
Nederlands militair geneeskundig tijdschrift
0028-2103
1947   0413420

Ned Tandartsenbl
Nederlands tandartsenblad
0028-2111
Continues Mededelingenblad of the
Nederlandse Maatschappij tot Bevordering
der Tandheelkunde.
1955   2984801R

Ned Tijdschr Geneeskd
Nederlands tijdschrift voor geneeskunde
0028-2162
Continues Nederlandsch tijdschrift voor
geneeskunde.
1957   0400770

Ned Tijdschr Gerontol
Nederlands tijdschrift voor gerontologie
0378-1186
Continued by Gerontologie.
1970-1979   0246274

Ned Tijdschr Natuurkd (Den Haag 1934)
Nederlands tijdschrift voor natuurkunde
0028-2189
Continues in part: Nederlandsch tijdschrift
voor natuurkunde. Split into: Nederlands
tijdschrift voor natuurkunde. A and:
Nederlands tijdschrift voor natuurkunde. B.
1948-1976   19010110R

Ned Tijdschr Psychol
Nederlands tijdschrift voor de psychologie
en haar grensgebieden
0028-2235
Continues Nederlandsch tijdschrift voor
de psychologie en haar grensgebieden.
Continued by: Netherlands journal of
psychology.
1946-2006   0375313

Ned Tijdschr Tandheelkd
Nederlands tijdschrift voor tandheelkunde
0028-2200
Continues Tijdschrift voor tandheelkunde.
1962   0400771

Ned Tijdschr Verloskd Gynaecol
Nederlandsch tijdschrift voor verloskunde
en gynaecologie
0301-2247
Superseded by: European journal of obstetrics
and gynecology.
1889-1970   0375707

Nefrologia
Nefrología: publicación oficial de la
Sociedad Española Nefrologia
0211-6995   1989-2284
1981   8301215

NEHW Health Watch
NEHW health watch
8756-0356
198u-1995   8812669

Neirofiziologiia
Neĭrofiziologiia = Neurophysiology
0028-2561
1969   0231364

Neonatal Intensive Care
Neonatal intensive care: the journal of
perinatology-neonatology
1062-2454
1988   9007473

Neonatal Netw
Neonatal network: NN
0730-0832   1539-2880
1981   8503921

Neonatal Pharmacol Q
Neonatal pharmacology quarterly
1056-8956
1992-1993   9216087

Neonatology
Neonatology
1661-7800   1661-7819
Continues: Biology of the neonate.
2007   101286577

Neoplasia
Neoplasia (New York, N.Y.)
1522-8002   1476-5586
1999   100886622

Neoplasma
Neoplasma
0028-2685
Continues Ceskoslovenská onkológia.
1957   0377266

Neopsichiatria
Neopsichiatria (U.S.L. n. 15)
1978-1999   8813288

Neotrop Entomol
Neotropical entomology
1519-566X
Continues: Anais da Sociedade Entomológica
do Brasil. Sociedade Entomológica do Brasil.
2001   101189728

Nepal Med Coll J
Nepal Medical College journal: NMCJ
1998   101129937

Nepegeszseguegy
Népegészségügy
0369-3805
1920-2000   19010500R

Nephrol Dial Transplant
Nephrology, dialysis, transplantation: official
publication of the European Dialysis and
Transplant Association - European Renal
Association
0931-0509   1460-2385
Continues: Proceedings of the European
Dialysis and Transplant Association -
European Renal Association. European
Dialysis and Transplant Association -
European Renal Association. Congress.
1986   8706402

Nephrol News Issues
Nephrology news & issues
0896-1263
1987   8709753

Nephrol Nurs J
Nephrology nursing journal: journal of the
American Nephrology Nurses' Association
1526-744X
Continues: ANNA journal.
2000   100909377

Nephrol Nurse
Nephrology nurse
0164-4386
Absorbed by: Home healthcare nurse.
1979-1983   7909387

Nephrol Ther
Néphrologie & thérapeutique
1769-7255
Continues: Néphrologie.
2005   101248950

Nephrologie
Néphrologie
0250-4960
Continues in part: Journal d'urologie et de
néphrologie. Continued by: Néphrologie &
thérapeutique.
1980-2004   8011169

Nephrology (Carlton)
Nephrology (Carlton, Vic.)
1320-5358   1440-1797
1995   9615568

Nephron
Nephron
0028-2766   1423-0186
1964   0331777

Nephron Clin Pract
Nephron. Clinical practice
1660-8151   1660-2110
2003   101159763

Nephron Exp Nephrol
Nephron. Experimental nephrology
1660-8151   1660-2129
Merger of: Experimental nephrology, and part
of: Nephron.
2003   101159770

Nephron Physiol
Nephron. Physiology
1660-8151   1660-2137
2003   101159772

Nerv Child
The Nervous child
1941-1956   19010560R

Nerv Sist
Nervnaia sistema / Leningradskiĭ ordena
Lenina gosudarstvennyĭ universitet imeni
A.A. Zhdanova, Fiziologicheskiĭ institut
imeni akad. A.A. Ukhtomskogo
0470-6625
1960   8209802

Nervenarzt
Der Nervenarzt
0028-2804
1928   0400773

Nestle Nutr Workshop Ser Clin Perform Programme
Nestlé Nutrition workshop series. Clinical &
performance programme
1422-7584   1662-386X
Continues in part: Nestlé Nutrition workshop
series.
1999   101121826

Nestle Nutr Workshop Ser Pediatr Program
Nestlé Nutrition workshop series. Paediatric
programme
1661-6677   1662-3878
Continues in part: Nestlé Nutrition workshop
series.
1999   101244056

Neth J Med
The Netherlands journal of medicine
0300-2977
Continues Folia medica Neerlandica.
1973   0356133

Neth J Surg
The Netherlands journal of surgery
0167-2487
Continues Archivum chirurgicum
Neerlandicum. Absorbed in 1992 by:
European journal of surgery.
1980-1991   8005043

Network
Network (Bristol, England)
0954-898X   1361-6536
1990   9431867

Neue Munch Beitr Gesch Med Naturwiss
Neue Münchner Beiträge zur Geschichte
der Medizin und Naturwissenschaften.
Naturwissenschaftshistorische Reihe
1969-1981   0334007

**Neue Munch Beitr Gesch Med Naturwiss
Medizinhist Reihe**
Neue Münchner Beiträge zur Geschichte
der Medizin und Naturwissenschaften.
Medizinhistorische Reihe
0300-8371
1970-1979   0332363

Neue Osterr Z Kinderheilkd
Neue österreichische Zeitschrift für
Kinderheilkunde
Supersedes die Osterreichische Zeitschrift
für Kinderheilkunde und Kinderfürsorge.
Superseded by Pädiatrie und Pädologie.
1955-1963   19010760R

Neuere Med Wiss Quellen Stud
Neuere Medizin- und
Wissenschaftsgeschichte
1995   9605423

Neumol Cir Torax
Neumologia y cirugía de tórax
0028-3746
Continues the Revista mexicana de
tuberculosis y enfermedades del aparato
respiratorio.
1962   19020050R

Neural Comput
Neural computation
0899-7667   1530-888X
1989   9426182

Neural Develop
Neural development
    1749-8104
2006   101286574

Neural Netw
Neural networks: the official journal of the
International Neural Network Society
0893-6080
1988   8805018

Neural Plast
Neural plasticity
    1687-5443
Continues: Journal of neural transplantation
& plasticity.
1998   100883417

Neuro Endocrinol Lett
Neuro endocrinology letters
0172-780X
1979   8008373

Neuro Oncol
Neuro-oncology
1522-8517   1523-5866
1999   100887420

Neurobehav Toxicol
Neurobehavioral toxicology
0191-3581
Continued by Neurobehavioral toxicology
and teratology.
1979-1980   8001482

Neurobehav Toxicol Teratol
Neurobehavioral toxicology and teratology
0275-1380
Continues: Neurobehavioral toxicology.
Continued by: Neurotoxicology and
teratology.
1981-1986   8104162

Neurobiol Aging
Neurobiology of aging
0197-4580   1558-1497
1980   8100437

Neurobiol Dis
Neurobiology of disease
0969-9961   1095-953X
1994   9500169

Neurobiol Learn Mem
Neurobiology of learning and memory
1074-7427   1095-9564
Continues: Behavioral and neural biology.
1995   9508166

Neurobiology
Neurobiology
0300-8819
1971-1975   7610562

Neurobiology (Bp)
Neurobiology (Budapest, Hungary)
1216-8068
Continues: Acta biochimica et biophysica
Hungarica. Absorbed by: Ideggyógyászati
szemle.
1993-2001   9312159

Neurocase
Neurocase: case studies in neuropsychology,
neuropsychiatry, and behavioural neurology
1355-4794   1465-3656
1995   9511374

Neurochem Int
Neurochemistry international
0197-0186
1980   8006959

Neurochem Pathol
Neurochemical pathology
0734-600X
Continued by: Molecular and chemical
neuropathology.
1983-1988   8310818

Neurochem Res
Neurochemical research
0364-3190   1573-6903
1976   7613461

Neurochirurgia (Stuttg)
Neurochirurgia
0028-3819
Continued by: Minimally invasive
neurosurgery.
1958-1993   0400774

Neurochirurgie
Neuro-Chirurgie
0028-3770
1955   0401057

Neurocirugia
Neurocirugia
0047-9411
1939-1980   19020070R

Neurocirugia (Astur)
Neurocirugía (Asturias, Spain)
1130-1473
Continues: Neurocirugia luso-española.
19uu   9425251

Neurocrit Care
Neurocritical care
1541-6933   1556-0961
2004   101156086

Neurodegener Dis
Neuro-degenerative diseases
1660-2854   1660-2862
2004   101189034

Neurodegeneration
Neurodegeneration: a journal
for neurodegenerative disorders,
neuroprotection, and neuroregeneration
1055-8330
1992-1996   9209022

Neuroendocrinology
Neuroendocrinology
0028-3835   1423-0194
1965   0035665

Neuroepidemiology
Neuroepidemiology
0251-5350   1423-0208
1982   8218700

Neurofibromatosis
Neurofibromatosis
1010-5662
1988-1989   8807525

Neurogastroenterol Motil
Neurogastroenterology and motility:
the official journal of the European
Gastrointestinal Motility Society
1350-1925   1365-2982
Continues: Journal of gastrointestinal
motility.
1994   9432572

Neurogenetics
Neurogenetics
1364-6745   1364-6753
1997   9709714

Neuroimage
NeuroImage
1053-8119   1095-9572
1992   9215515

Neuroimaging Clin N Am
Neuroimaging clinics of North America
1052-5149
1991   9211377

Neuroimmunomodulation
Neuroimmunomodulation
1021-7401   1423-0216
1994   9422763

Neuroinformatics
Neuroinformatics
1539-2791   1559-0089
2002   101142069

Neurol Clin
Neurologic clinics
0733-8619
1983   8219232

Neurol Clin Neurophysiol
Neurology & clinical neurophysiology: NCN
1538-4098   1526-8748
Continues: Journal of contemporary
neurology. Continued by: Neurology,
neurophysiology, and neuroscience.
2000-2006   100972440

Neurol Croat
Neurologia croatica: glasilo Udruzenja
neurologa Jugoslavije = official journal of
Yugoslav Neurological Association
0353-8842
Continues: Neurologija.
1991   9109632

Neurol India
Neurology India
0028-3886   1998-4022
Continues: Neurology.
1964   0042005

Neurol Med Chir (Tokyo)
Neurologia medico-chirurgica
0470-8105   1349-8029
1959   0400775

Neurol Neurochir Pol
Neurologia i neurochirurgia polska
0028-3843
    Continues: Neurologia, neurochirurgia i
    psychiatria polska.
1967   0101265

Neurol Neurochir Psychiatr Pol
Neurologia, neurochirurgia i psychiatria
polska
    Formed by the union of Neurologia polska
    and Rocznik psychiatryczny. Continued
    by Neurologia i neurochirurgia polska and
    Psychiatria polska.
1951-1966   2984836R

Neurol Neurocir Psiquiatr
Neurología, neurocirugía, psiquiatría
0028-3851
1959   0106331

Neurol Neurophysiol Neurosci
Neurology, neurophysiology, and
neuroscience
    1933-1266
    Continues: Neurology & clinical
    neurophysiology (Online).
2006   101287847

Neurol Psihiatr Neurochir
Neurologia, psihiatria, neurochirurgia
0028-386X
    Continued by Revista de medicina-interna,
    neurologie, psihiatrie, neurochirurgie,
    dermato-venerologie. Neurologie, psihiatrie,
    neurochirurgie.
1956-1974   7503838

Neurol Psychiatr (Bucur)
Neurologie et psychiatrie
0377-502X
    Continues in part Revue roumaine de
    médecine. Continued by: Romanian journal
    of neurology and psychiatry.
1975-1989   7506358

Neurol Psychiatr Ceskoslov
Neurologie a psychiatrie československá
    Supersedes Revue v neurologii a psychiatrii.
    Continued by Ceskoslovenská neurologie.
1938-1955   19020140R

Neurol Res
Neurological research
0161-6412   1743-1328
1979   7905298

Neurol Sci
Neurological sciences: official journal of
the Italian Neurological Society and of the
Italian Society of Clinical Neurophysiology
1590-1874
    Continues: Italian journal of neurological
    sciences.
2000   100959175

Neurologia
Neurología (Barcelona, Spain)
0213-4853   1578-1968
1986   9005460

Neurologija
Neurologija
0350-9559
    Continues Neuropsihijatrija. Continued by:
    Neurolgia croatia.
1977-1990   7808791

Neurologist
The neurologist
1074-7931
1995   9503763

Neurology
Neurology
0028-3878   1526-632X
1951   0401060

Neuromolecular Med
Neuromolecular medicine
1535-1084   1559-1174
2002   101135365

Neuromuscul Disord
Neuromuscular disorders: NMD
0960-8966
1991   9111470

Neuron
Neuron
0896-6273   1097-4199
1988   8809320

Neuron Glia Biol
Neuron glia biology
1740-925X   1741-0533
2004   101217278

Neuronio
Neurônio
1939-1974   0401061

Neuropadiatrie
Neuropädiatrie
0028-3797
    Continued by: Neuropediatrics.
1969-1980   0260671

Neuropathol Appl Neurobiol
Neuropathology and applied neurobiology
0305-1846   1365-2990
1975   7609829

Neuropathology
Neuropathology: official journal of the
Japanese Society of Neuropathology
0919-6544   1440-1789
    Continues: Shinkei byōrigaku.
1993   9606526

Neuropatol Pol
Neuropatologia polska
0028-3894
    Continued by: Folia neuropathologica.
1963-1993   0020712

Neuropediatrics
Neuropediatrics
0174-304X
    Continues: Neuropädiatrie.
1980   8101187

Neuropeptides
Neuropeptides
0143-4179
1980   8103156

Neuropharmacology
Neuropharmacology
0028-3908
    Continues the International journal of
    neuropharmacology.
1970   0236217

Neurophysiol Clin
Neurophysiologie clinique = Clinical
neurophysiology
0987-7053
    Continues: Revue d'électroencéphalographie
    et de neurophysiologie clinique.
1988   8804532

Neuropsichiatria
Neuropsichiatria
0028-3916
1929-1978   0404442

Neuropsihijatrija
Neuropsihijatrija
0047-9438
    Continued by Neurologija.
1953-1976   0400776

Neuropsychiatr
Neuropsychiatrie: Klinik, Diagnostik,
Therapie und Rehabilitation: Organ der
Gesellschaft Österreichischer Nervenärzte
und Psychiater
0948-6259
1986   9440588

Neuropsychiatr Enfance Adolesc
Neuropsychiatrie de l'enfance et de
l'adolescence
0222-9617
    Continues: Revue de neuropsychiatrie
    infantile et d'hygiène mentale de l'enfance.
1979   7905300

Neuropsychiatry
Neuropsychiatry
0467-1066
1951-1960   19020190R

Neuropsychiatry Neuropsychol Behav Neurol
Neuropsychiatry, neuropsychology, and
behavioral neurology
0894-878X   1537-0887
    Continued by: Cognitive and behavioral
    neurology.
1988-2002   8811108

Neuropsychobiology
Neuropsychobiology
0302-282X   1423-0224
    Absorbed: International pharmacopsychiatry,
    1983.
1975   7512895

Neuropsychol Dev Cogn B Aging Neuropsychol Cogn
Neuropsychology, development, and
cognition. Section B, Aging, neuropsychology
and cognition
1382-5585   1744-4128
    Continues: Neuropsychology, development,
    and cognition. Section B, Aging and
    cognition.
1996   9614434

Neuropsychol Rehabil
Neuropsychological rehabilitation
0960-2011
1991   9112672

Neuropsychol Rev
Neuropsychology review
1040-7308
1990   9009029

Neuropsychologia
Neuropsychologia
0028-3932
1963   0020713

Neuropsychology
Neuropsychology
0894-4105
1987   8904467

Neuropsychopharmacol Hung
Neuropsychopharmacologia Hungarica: a
Magyar Pszichofarmakológiai Egyesület
lapja = official journal of the Hungarian
Association of Psychopharmacology
1419-8711
1999   100961631

Neuropsychopharmacology
Neuropsychopharmacology: official
publication of the American College of
Neuropsychopharmacology
0893-133X   1470-634X
1987   8904907

Neuroradiology
Neuroradiology
0028-3940 1432-1920
1970 1302751

Neurorehabil Neural Repair
Neurorehabilitation and neural repair
1545-9683
Continues: Journal of neurologic rehabilitation.
1999 100892086

NeuroRehabilitation
NeuroRehabilitation
1053-8135
1991 9113791

Neuroreport
Neuroreport
0959-4965 1473-558X
1990 9100935

NeuroRx
NeuroRx: the journal of the American Society for Experimental NeuroTherapeutics
1545-5343 1545-5351
Continued by: Neurotherapeutics.
2004-2006 101189456

Neurosci Behav Physiol
Neuroscience and behavioral physiology
0097-0549
Continues Neuroscience translations.
1972 0330471

Neurosci Biobehav Rev
Neuroscience and biobehavioral reviews
0149-7634
Continues Biobehavioral reviews.
1978 7806090

Neurosci Bull
Neuroscience bulletin
1673-7067
Continues: Zhongguo shen jing ke xue za zhi.
2005 101256850

Neurosci Lett
Neuroscience letters
0304-3940
1975 7600130

Neurosci Lett Suppl
Neuroscience letters. Supplement
0167-6253
1978 7908180

Neurosci Res
Neuroscience research
0168-0102
1984 8500749

Neurosci Res (N Y)
Neurosciences research
0077-7846
1968-1973 0435453

Neurosci Res Program Bull
Neurosciences Research Program bulletin
0028-3967
1963-1982 7509226

Neurosci Res Suppl
Neuroscience research. Supplement: the official journal of the Japan Neuroscience Society
0921-8696
1985 8508422

Neuroscience
Neuroscience
0306-4522
1976 7605074

Neuroscientist
The Neuroscientist: a review journal bringing neurobiology, neurology and psychiatry
1073-8584 1089-4098
1995 9504819

Neurosignals
Neuro-Signals
1424-862X 1424-8638
Continues: Biological signals and receptors.
2002 101134359

Neurosurg Clin N Am
Neurosurgery clinics of North America
1042-3680 1558-1349
1990 9008004

Neurosurg Focus
Neurosurgical focus
1092-0684
1996 100896471

Neurosurg Rev
Neurosurgical review
0344-5607 1437-2320
1978 7908181

Neurosurgery
Neurosurgery
0148-396X 1524-4040
1977 7802914

Neurotherapeutics
Neurotherapeutics: the journal of the American Society for Experimental NeuroTherapeutics
1933-7213
Continues: NeuroRx.
2007 101290381

Neurotox Res
Neurotoxicity research
1029-8428 1476-3524
1999 100929017

Neurotoxicol Teratol
Neurotoxicology and teratology
0892-0362
Continues: Neurobehavioral toxicology and teratology.
1987 8709538

Neurotoxicology
Neurotoxicology
0161-813X
1979 7905589

Neurotoxins
Neurotoxins
1357-7115
1994-1994 9508903

Neurourol Urodyn
Neurourology and urodynamics
0733-2467 1520-6777
1982 8303326

Nev Nurses Assoc Q Newsl
Nevada Nurses Association Quarterly Newsletter
Continued by: Nevada Rnformation.
1969-1970 9875612

Nev Rnformation
Nevada RNformation
0273-4117
1972 9878814

Nevrone Period Neurol Psichiatr Sci Affin
Nevrone; periodico di neurologia, psichiatria e scienze affini
1953-19uu 19020280R

Nevropatol Psikhiatriia
Nevropatologiia i psikhiatriia
Continues: Sovetskaia nevropatologiia, psikhiatriia i psikhogigiena. Continued by: Zhurnal nevropatologii i psikhiatrii imeni S.S. Korsakova (Moscow, Russia: 1952).
1935-1951 21820270R

New Biol
The New biologist
1043-4674
1989-1992 9000976

New Dent
The New dentist: the official journal of the American Student Dental Association
0161-8431
Continues: ASDA news. Continued by: ASDA news (American Student Dental Association: 1981)
1979-1981 8109096

New Dir Child Adolesc Dev
New directions for child and adolescent development
1520-3247 1534-8687
Continues: New directions for child development.
1998 100886823

New Dir Child Dev
New directions for child development
0195-2269
Continued by: New directions for child and adolescent development.
1978-1998 8104414

New Dir Ment Health Serv
New directions for mental health services
0193-9416
Continued by: New directions for youth development.
1979-2001 7905590

New Dir Youth Dev
New directions for youth development
1533-8916 1537-5781
Continues: New directions for mental health services.
2002 101090644

New Era Nurs Image Int
New era nursing image international: NENI
0794-4373
1984-1989 8612860

New Health
New health
1926-1967 19020680R

New Horiz
New horizons (Baltimore, Md.)
1063-7389
1993-1999 9416195

New Istanbul Contrib Clin Sci
New Istanbul contribution to clinical science
0028-5447
Continues: Istanbul contribution to clinical science. Continued by: Turkish journal of haematology.
1954-1982 0377267

New J (Inst Health Rec Inf Manag)
New journal (Institute of Health Record & Information Management)
Continues: For your information (Institute of Health Record & Information Management).
2005 101284929

New Microbiol
The new microbiologica: official journal of the Italian Society for Medical, Odontoiatric, and Clinical Microbiology (SIMMOC)
1121-7138
Continues: Microbiologica.
1993 9516291

New Orleans Med Surg J
The New Orleans medical and surgical journal
0097-1790
Continued by the Journal of the Louisiana State Medical Society. Absorbed: American journal of tropical diseases and preventive medicine.
1844-1952　　　　　19030340R

New Physician
The New physician
0028-6451
Continues the Journal of the Student American Medical Association. Beginning with v.15, 1966- includes: Doctor and the law, which retains separate vol. numbering.
1957　　　　　0377016

New Phytol
The New phytologist
0028-646X　　　　　1469-8137
1902　　　　　9882884

New Sci
New scientist (1971)
0262-4079
Continues: New scientist and science journal.
1971　　　　　9815377

New Solut
New solutions: a journal of environmental and occupational health policy: NS
1048-2911　　　　　1541-3772
1990　　　　　9100937

New World Ir Nurs
The New world of Irish nursing: official journal of Irish Nurses Organisation and National Council of Nurses
Continues: World of Irish nursing. Continued by: World of Irish nursing (Dublin, Ireland: 1995).
1993-1994　　　　　9312538

Newcastle Med J
Newcastle medical journal
0028-887X
Continues the Newcastle-upon-Tyne and Northern Counties medical journal.
1920-1971　　　　　0405552

News Bull Indian Dent Assoc
News Bulletin - Indian Dental Association
1970-19uu　　　　　9877634

News Lett Florence Nightingale Int Nurs Assoc
News Letter; Florence Nightingale International Nurses Association
1968-19uu　　　　　9875611

News Lett Maine State Nurses Assoc
News letter. Maine State Nurses' Association
Continued by: News letter. Main State Nurses' Association. Continued by: Maine R. N..
1955-1966　　　　　1300154

News Lett Maine State Nurses Assoc
News letter. Maine State Nurses' Association
0464-5855
Supersedes a publication with the same title.
1966-1983　　　　　1300155

News Notes Ohio Dent J
News Notes / Ohio Dental Journal
1040-4945
Continued by: Focus On Ohio Dentistry.
1973-1988　　　　　9875297

News Physiol Sci
News in physiological sciences: an international journal of physiology produced jointly by the International Union of Physiological Sciences and the American Physiological Society
0886-1714　　　　　1522-161X
Continued by: Physiology (Bethesda, Md.).
1986-2004　　　　　8609378

News Views
News & Views: Rhode Island Nursing Magazine
Continues: Professional flashes.
19uu-uuuu　　　　　9878932

Newsette
Newsette - Department of Health National League of Nurses, Manila, Philippines
0418-7199
1961-1986　　　　　7507318

Newsl Am Acad Health Adm
Newsletter - American Academy of Health Administration. American Academy of Health Administration
0196-450X
Continues Association of Management in Public Health. Newsletter.
1970-1978　　　　　7906915

Newsl Am Acad Implant Dent
Newsletter. American Academy of Implant Dentistry
Absorbed by: Oral implantology.
1967-1969　　　　　0256711

Newsl Am Soc Anesthesiol
Newsletter - American Society of Anesthesiologists
Continues Newsletter - American Society of Anesthetists. Continued by ASA newsletter. Continued by: ASA newsletter.
1945-1965　　　　　7507319

Newsl Biomed Saf Stand
The Newsletter of biomedical safety & standards
1080-9775
Continued by: Biomedical safety & standards.
1971-1984　　　　　0352003

Newsl Inst Interam Aff
Newsletter / Health and Sanitation Division, the Institute of Inter-American Affairs. Institute of Inter-American Affairs (U.S.). Health and Sanitation Division
Continues: Health and Sanitation Division newsletter. United States. Office of the Coordinator of Inter-American Affairs. Health and Sanitation Division.
1945-1950　　　　　100901388

Newsl Int Acad Periodontol
Newsletter (International Academy of Periodontology)
0963-5742
1991-1993　　　　　9211941

Newsl Int Coll Dent India Sect
Newsletter. International College of Dentists. India Section
1965-19uu　　　　　1260704

Newsl Ky Nurses Assoc
Newsletter. Kentucky Nurses Association
0023-0316
Continued by Kentucky nurse
1953-1982　　　　　0045354

Newsl Scand Soc Forensic Odontol
News letter. Scandinavian Society of Forensic Odontology
0581-9504
1967-1972　　　　　0100712

Newsl Soc Welf Hist Group
Newsletter-Social Welfare History Group. Social Welfare History Group
0560-3870
1956-19uu　　　　　9883135

Newsl Springfield Dent Soc
Newsletter - Springfield Dental Society
Continued by: Greater Ozarks Dental Health Newsletter.
1976-1980　　　　　9877609

Newsl Suffolk Cty Med Soc
News letter. Suffolk County Medical Society
Continued by the society's Bulletin.
1922-1948　　　　　0234146

Newsl Wis League Nurs
Newsletter. Wisconsin League for Nursing
1959-197u　　　　　0242753

Newsline People AIDS Coalit N Y
Newsline (People with AIDS Coalition of New York)
Continues: PWAC NY newsline.
199u-1999　　　　　9603145

Newsweek
Newsweek
0028-9604
1933　　　　　9877127

NFPA J
NFPA journal: the official magazine of the National Fire Protection Association
1054-8793
Formed by the union of: Fire journal (Boston, Mass.), and: Fire command (Quincy, Mass.).
1991　　　　　9885590

NHPF Issue Brief
NHPF issue brief / National Health Policy Forum, George Washington University
Continues: Issue brief (George Washington University. National Health Policy Forum).
2002　　　　　101142615

NIAID AIDS Agenda
NIAID AIDS agenda / National Institute of Allergy and Infectious Diseases
199u-1998　　　　　9432911

Nicar Med
Nicaragua médica
0028-968X
1937-1972　　　　　0404443

Nicar Odontol
Nicaragua Odontologica
1937-1972　　　　　9875613

Nichidai Koko Kagaku
Nichidai kōkū kagaku = Nihon University journal of oral science
0385-0145
1975　　　　　9425106

Nicotine Tob Res
Nicotine & tobacco research: official journal of the Society for Research on Nicotine and Tobacco
1462-2203　　　　　1469-994X
1999　　　　　9815751

NIDA Res Monogr
NIDA research monograph
1046-9516
Continues: National Institute on Drug Abuse research monograph series.
1976　　　　　8811762

Niedersachs Zahnarztebl
Niedersächsisches Zahnärzteblatt
0173-6868
Continued by: Zahnärzteblatt Niedersachsen.
1966-2005　　　　　7907434

Nig Q J Hosp Med
Nigerian quarterly journal of hospital medicine
0189-2657
19uu 9713944

Niger Dent J
Nigerian Dental Journal
0189-1006
1980-1983 9880153

Niger J Clin Pract
Nigerian journal of clinical practice
1119-3077
1998 101150032

Niger J Med
Nigerian journal of medicine: journal of the National Association of Resident Doctors of Nigeria
1115-2613
1990 100888321

Niger J Physiol Sci
Nigerian journal of physiological sciences: official publication of the Physiological Society of Nigeria
0794-859X
1983 8811109

Niger Med J
Nigerian medical journal: journal of the Nigeria Medical Association
0300-1652
Continues: Journal of the Nigeria medical Association.
1971 0315137

Niger Nurse
The Nigerian nurse
0331-4448
1968-1985 0225531

Niger Postgrad Med J
The Nigerian postgraduate medical journal
1117-1936
1994 9613595

NIH Consens State Sci Statements
NIH consensus and state-of-the-science statements
1553-0957 1553-0779
Merger of: NIH consensus statement. and: Technology assessment statements.
2002 101160100

NIH Consens Statement
NIH consensus statement
1080-1707
Continues: National Institutes of Health Consensus Development Conference. Consensus statement. Merged with: State-of-the-science statements. to form: NIH consensus and state-of-the-science statements.
1992-2001 9308532

NIH Guide Grants Contracts
NIH guide for grants and contracts (Online)
1551-8965
Continues the print version in 1997.
19uu 9810664

NIH Guide Grants Contracts
NIH guide for grants and contracts / U.S. Department of Health, Education, and Welfare
1050-9364
Beginning with Oct. 1, 1997 available only in HTML format.
19uu-1997 9004625

NIHAE Bull
NIHAE bulletin
0378-6196
Merged with Journal of population research to form Health and population: perspectives and issues.
1968-1977 7909392

Nihon Ago Kansetsu Gakkai Zasshi
Nihon Ago Kansetsu Gakkai Zasshi
0915-3004
1989 9885488

Nihon Arukoru Yakubutsu Igakkai Zasshi
Nihon Arukōru Yakubutsu Igakkai zasshi = Japanese journal of alcohol studies & drug dependence
1341-8963
Continues: Arukōru kenkyū to yakubutsu izon.
1996 9612304

Nihon Eiyo Shokuryo Gakkai Shi
Nihon Eiyō Shokuryō Gakkai shi = Nippon Eiyō Shokuryō Gakkaishi = Journal of Japanese Society of Nutrition and Food Science
0287-3516 1883-2849
Continues: Eiyō to shokuryō.
1983 9318973

Nihon Hansenbyo Gakkai Zasshi
Nihon Hansenbyō Gakkai zasshi = Japanese journal of leprosy: official organ of the Japanese Leprosy Association
1342-3681
Continues: Nippon Rai Gakkai zasshi.
1996 9702338

Nihon Hoigaku Zasshi
Nihon hōigaku zasshi = The Japanese journal of legal medicine
0047-1887
Beginning 1999. articles in English are published separately in: Legal medicine (Tokyo. Japan).
1944 0413715

Nihon Hotetsu Shika Gakkai Zasshi
Nihon Hotetsu Shika Gakkai zasshi
0389-5386 1883-177X
Supersedes: Nippon Hotetsu Shika Gakkai kaishi.
1957 7505724

Nihon Kango Kagakkaishi
Nihon Kango Kagakkai shi = Journal of Japan Academy of Nursing Science
0287-5330
1981 9315623

Nihon Kokyuki Gakkai Zasshi
Nihon Kokyūki Gakkai zasshi = the journal of the Japanese Respiratory Society
1343-3490
Continues: Nihon Kyōbu Shikkan Gakkai zasshi.
1998 9808802

Nihon Kyobu Shikkan Gakkai Zasshi
Nihon Kyōbu Shikkan Gakkai zasshi
0301-1542
Continued by: Nihon Kōkyuki Gakkai zasshi.
1963-1997 7505737

Nihon Rinsho Meneki Gakkai Kaishi
Nihon Rinshō Men'eki Gakkai kaishi = Japanese journal of clinical immunology
0911-4300 1349-7413
1978 9505992

Nihon Rinsho Shishubyo Danwakai Kaishi
Nihon Rinshō Shishūbyō Danwakai kaishi
Continues: Rinshō Shishūbyō Danwakai kaishi. Continued by: Nihon Rinshō Shishūbyō Gakkai kaishi.
1985-1996 9114963

Nihon Shinkei Seishin Yakurigaku Zasshi
Nihon shinkei seishin yakurigaku zasshi = Japanese journal of psychopharmacology
1340-2544
Continues: Yakubutsu. seishin. kōdō.
1994 9509023

Nihon Sutoma Rihabiriteshon Gakkaishi J Jpn Soc Stoma Rehabil
Nihon Sutoma Rihabiriteshon Gakkaishi [Journal Of Japanese Society Of Stoma Rehabilitation]
0912-0408
Continues: Nihon Sutoma Rihabiriteshon Kenkyukai Shi.
1989 9884879

Niigata Igakkai Zasshi
Niigata Igakkai zasshi. Niigata medical journal
0029-0440
Continues the Zasshi of the Hokuetsu Igakkai.
1946 0413713

Ninety Nine
Ninety nine
Continues Doctor; health and hygiene in the home.
1948-19uu 19120450R

NIPH Ann
NIPH annals
0332-5652
1978-1993 7805819

Nippon Byori Gakkai Kaishi
Nippon Byori Gakkai kaishi
0300-9181
1911 0420136

Nippon Chokucho Komonbyo
Nippon Chokucho Komonbyo Gakkai zasshi
1940-1966 7505708

Nippon Daicho Komonbyo Gakkai Zasshi
Nippon Daicho Komonbyo Gakkai zasshi
0047-1801 1882-9619
Continues Nippon Chokucho Komonbyo Gakki zasshi.
1967 7501193

Nippon Densenbyo Gakkai Zasshi
Nippon Densenbyo Gakkai zasshi
0021-4817
Continued by Kansenshogaku zasshi.
1926-1969 7505709

Nippon Eiseigaku Zasshi
Nippon eiseigaku zasshi. Japanese journal of hygiene
0021-5082 1882-6482
1946 0417457

Nippon Funin Gakkai Zasshi
Nippon Funin Gakkai zasshi
0029-0629
Continued by: Nihon Seishoku Igakkai zasshi.
1956-2005 7505712

Nippon Gan Chiryo Gakkai Shi
Nippon Gan Chiryo Gakkai shi
0021-4671
1966 7505713

Nippon Ganka Gakkai Zasshi
Nippon Ganka Gakkai zasshi
0029-0203
1897 7505716

Nippon Ganka Kiyo
Nippon ganka kiyo
0015-5667
1950-1986 0413714

Nippon Geka Gakkai Zasshi
Nippon Geka Gakkai zasshi
0301-4894
Continues Nippon Geka Gakkai shi.
1907 0405405

Nippon Geka Hokan
Nippon geka hokan. Archiv für japanische
Chirurgie
0003-9152
1924-2000   0421143

Nippon Heikatsukin Gakkai Zasshi
Nippon Heikatsukin Gakkai zasshi
0374-3527
Continued by: Journal of smooth muscle
research.
1965-1990   7505718

Nippon Hifuka Gakkai Zasshi
Nippon Hifuka Gakkai zasshi. The Japanese
journal of dermatology
0021-499X   1346-8146
Continues Hifuka seibyoka zasshi.
1957   7600571

Nippon Hinyokika Gakkai Zasshi
Nippon Hinyōkika Gakkai zasshi. The
japanese journal of urology
0021-5287
Continues: Zasshi. Nippon Hinyōkibyō
Gakkai.
1928   2984841R

Nippon Hoshasen Gijutsu Gakkai Zasshi
Nippon Hoshasen Gijutsu Gakkai zasshi
0369-4305   1881-4883
Continues Nippon Rentogen Gijutsuin Gakkai
zasshi.
1947   7505722

Nippon Igaku Hoshasen Gakkai Zasshi
Nihon Igaku Hōshasen Gakkai zasshi.
Nippon acta radiologica
0048-0428   1347-7951
Formed by the union of Nihon Hōshasen
Igakkai zasshi and Nihon Rentogen Gakkai
zasshi.
1940   0413544

Nippon Ika Daigaku Zasshi
Nippon Ika Daigaku zasshi
0048-0444
Continues Nippon Igaku Senmon Gakko
zasshi. Absorbed Byori to chiryo and Sanka
fujinka kenkyu in Jan. 1931. Continued by:
Journal of Nippon Medical School.
1927-1999   7505726

Nippon Ishigaku Zasshi
Nihon ishigaku zasshi. [Journal of Japanese
history of medicine]
0549-3323
Continues Chugai iji shinpo.
1941   0165261

Nippon Ishikai Zasshi
Nippon Ishikai zasshi. Journal of the Japan
Medical Association
0021-4493
Continues Isei.
1937   0413545

Nippon Ishinkin Gakkai Zasshi
Nihon Ishinkin Gakkai zasshi = Japanese
journal of medical mycology
0916-4804   1882-0476
Continues: Shinkin to shinkinshō.
1990   9425640

Nippon Jibiinkoka Gakkai Kaiho
Nippon Jibiinkoka Gakkai kaiho
0030-6622   1883-0854
Continues: Dai Nippon Jibiinkoka Kai kaiho.
1947   7505728

Nippon Jinzo Gakkai Shi
Nippon Jinzo Gakkai shi
0385-2385
1959   7505731

Nippon Juigaku Zasshi
Nippon juigaku zasshi. The Japanese
journal of veterinary science
0021-5295
Continued by: Journal of veterinary medical
science.
1939-1990   0057113

Nippon Ketsueki Gakkai Zasshi
Nippon Ketsueki Gakkai zasshi: journal of
Japan Haematological Society
0001-5806
Supersedes Rinsho byorigaku ketsuekigaku
zasshi. Continued by: International journal of
hematology.
1937-1990   2984803R

Nippon Koku Geka Gakkai Zasshi
Nippon Koku Geka Gakkai zasshi
0021-5163
Continues Koku Geka Gakkai zasshi.
1967   7505735

Nippon Koshu Eisei Zasshi
[Nippon kōshū eisei zasshi] Japanese journal
of public health
0546-1766
1954   19130150R

Nippon Kyobu Geka Gakkai Zasshi
[Zasshi] [Journal]. Nihon Kyōbu Geka
Gakkai
0369-4739
Continued by: Japanese journal of thoracic
and cardiovascular surgery.
1953-1997   19130180R

Nippon Kyosei Shika Gakkai Zasshi
Nihon Kyōsei Shika Gakkai zasshi = The
journal of Japan Orthodontic Society
0021-454X
Continues: Nihon Kyōsei Shika Gakkai
kaishi. Continued in part by: Orthodontic
waves (English ed.). Continued in part by:
Orthodontic waves (Japanese ed.).
1932-2003   0055371

Nippon Naibunpi Gakkai Zasshi
Nippon Naibunpi Gakkai zasshi
0029-0661
Continues Naibunpigaku zasshi.
1925   0413717

Nippon Naika Gakkai Zasshi
Nihon Naika Gakkai zasshi. The Journal of
the Japanese Society of Internal Medicine
0021-5384   1883-2083
Supersedes: Nihon Naika Gakkaishi.
1913   19130210R

Nippon Rai Gakkai Zasshi
Nippon Rai Gakkai zasshi
0386-3980
Continues: Repura. Continued by: Nihon
Hansenbyō Gakkai zasshi.
1977-1996   7901165

Nippon Rinsho
Nippon rinsho. Japanese journal of clinical
medicine
0047-1852
Formed by the union of: Chuo igaku, Gendai
no igaku, Jikken chiryo, Osaka iji shinshi,
Rinko, Rinsho to yakubutsu, and Yuseigaku.
1943   0420546

Nippon Rinsho Kekkaku
[Nippon rinshō kekkaku] The Japanese
journal of clinical tuberculosis
Absorbed Kekkaku no rinshō in shigatsu
1940. Continued by: Nippon kyōbu rinshō.
1940-1959   19130310R

Nippon Ronen Igakkai Zasshi
Nippon Ronen Igakkai zasshi. Japanese
journal of geriatrics
0300-9173
1964   7507332

Nippon Saikingaku Zasshi
Nippon saikingaku zasshi. Japanese journal
of bacteriology
0021-4930   1882-4110
Continues: Nihon biseibutsugaku byōrigaku
zasshi.
1944   2984804R

Nippon Sanka Fujinka Gakkai Zasshi
Nippon Sanka Fujinka Gakkai zasshi
0300-9165
Absorbed Acta obstetrica et gynaecologica
Japonica, Jan. 1977. Formed by the union
of Nippon Funjinka Gakkai zasshi and the
Sanka fujinka kiyo.
1949   7505749

Nippon Seikeigeka Gakkai Zasshi
Nippon Seikeigeka Gakkai zasshi
0021-5325
1926   0413716

Nippon Seirigaku Zasshi
Nippon seirigaku zasshi. Journal of the
Physiological Society of Japan
0031-9341
Absorbed Joken hansha, July 1944-47.
1936   0417460

Nippon Shika Hyoron
[Nippon shika hyōron] The Nippon dental
review
0289-0909
Formed by the union of Kuchi, Nippon kōkū
eisei Shika maigetsu tsūshin, and Shin shika
ihō.
1940   19130390R

Nippon Shika Ishikai Zasshi
Nippon Shika Ishikai zasshi
0047-1763
1948   7505756

Nippon Shika Zairyo Kikai Gakkai Zasshi
Nippon Shika Zairyo Kikai Gakkai zasshi.
The Journal of the Japan Research Society
of Dental Materials & Appliances
Merged with: Shika rikōgaku zasshi, to form:
Shika zairyō, kikai.
1952-1981   7505757

Nippon Shishubyo Gakkai Kaishi
Nippon Shishubyo Gakkai kaishi
0385-0110   1880-408X
Continues Nippon Shisonoro Gakkai kaishi.
1968   7505760

Nippon Shokakibyo Gakkai Zasshi
Nippon Shokakibyo Gakkai zasshi The
Japanese journal of gastro-enterology
0446-6586
Supersedes Kaiho of Ichobyo Kenkyukai.
1902   2984683R

Nippon Shonika Gakkai Zasshi
Nippon Shonika Gakkai zasshi. Acta
paediatrica Japonica
0001-6543
Continues Jika zasshi.
1951   0413547

Nippon Yakubutsugaku Zasshi
[Nippon yakubutsugaku zasshi] [Japanese
journal of pharmacology]
Continued by Nippon yakurigaku zasshi.
1925-1943   19130470R

Nippon Yakurigaku Zasshi
Nippon yakurigaku zasshi. Folia
pharmacologica Japonica
0015-5691   1347-8397
Continues: Nippon yakubutsugaku zasshi.
1944   0420550

Nisshin Igaku Jpn J Med Prog
[Nisshin igaku] The Japanese journal of
medical progress
1911-1963   19130520R

NITA
NITA
0160-3930
Continued by: Journal of intravenous nursing.
1978-1987   7909393

Nitric Oxide
Nitric oxide: biology and chemistry / official
journal of the Nitric Oxide Society
1089-8603   1089-8611
1997   9709307

NJPC Bull
NJPC bulletin
0161-5513
1975-1978   7801285

NJSNA Newsl
Njsna Newsletter
Continues: New Jersey Nurse. Continued by:
New Jersey Nurse.
1971-1977   9875616

NLN Conv Pap
NLN convention papers
1967-1982   0172707

NLN Publ
NLN publications
19uu   9870012

NLN Update
NLN update: connecting members of the
National League for Nursing
1080-773X
1995-1997   9516229

NMR Biomed
NMR in biomedicine
0952-3480
1988   8915233

No Shinkei Geka
No shinkei geka. Neurological surgery
0301-2603
1973   0377015

No To Hattatsu
No to hattatsu. Brain and development
0029-0831
1969   0215224

No To Shinkei
Nō to shinkei = Brain and nerve
0006-8969
Merged with: Shinkei Kenkyu No Shimpo. to
form: Brain and nerve.
1948-2006   0413550

Nobel Symp
Nobel Symposium
0346-8313
196u   100960872

Noise Health
Noise & health
1463-1741
1998   9815620

Nonlinear Dynamics Psychol Life Sci
Nonlinear dynamics, psychology, and life
sciences
1090-0578
1997   9704130

Nonprofit Manag Leadersh
Nonprofit management & leadership
1048-6682
1990   9885985

Nor Tannlaegeforen Tid
Den Norske tannlaegeforenings tidende
0029-2303
Continues: Norges tannlaegeforbund.
Tidsskrift.
1945   0414136

Nord Hyg Tidskr
Nordisk hygienisk tidskrift
0029-1374
Merged with Work. environment. health,
to form Scandinavian journal of work,
environment & health.
1920-1974   7511514

Nord Hyg Tidskr Suppl
Nordisk hygienisk tidskrift. Supplementum
0300-9122
1970-1973   0246623

Nord J Psychiatry
Nordic journal of psychiatry
0803-9488   1502-4725
Continues: Nordisk psykiatrisk tidsskrift.
1999   100927567

Nord Med
Nordisk medicin
0029-1420
Merger of: Hospitals-tidende: Finska läkare-
sällskapets handlingar (Helsinki. Finland:
1841): Duodecim (Helsinki. Finland: 1885);
Norsk magazin for lægevidenskaben;
Medicinsk revue; and: Hygiea (Stockholm.
Sweden: 1839).
1939-1998   0401001

Nord Psyk Medl
Nordisk psykiatrisk medlemsblad
Continued by: Nordisk psykiatrisk tidsskrift.
1947-1958   19210200R

Nord Psykiatr Tidsskr
Nordisk psykiatrisk tidsskrift. Nordic
journal of psychiatry
0029-1455
Continues: Nordisk psykiatrisk medlemsblad.
Continued by: Nordic journal of psychiatry.
1959-1998   0401002

Nord Vet Med
Nordisk veterinaermedicin
0029-1579
Formed by the union of Finsk
veterinärtidskrift, Norsk veterinaertidsskrift,
Skandinavisk veterinärtidskrift, and Svensk
veterinärtidskrift.
1949-1986   0203744

Norden News
The Norden news
0890-3727
Continued by: Topics in veterinary medicine.
1927-19uu   19210110R

Norm Pathol Anat (Stuttg)
Normale und pathologische Anatomie
0303-2418
Continues: Zwanglose Abhandlungen aus
dem Gebiet der normalen und pathologischen
Anatomie.
1970-1994   0246434

North Am Vet
The North American veterinarian
Absorbed: Veterinary practice (Evanston. Ill.).
Continued by Modern veterinary practice.
1920-1958   18750060R

North Wing
The north wing; the magazine of the
Sheffield medical and dental schools
193u-19uu   19210800R

Northwest Dent
Northwest dentistry
0029-2915
Continues the Journal of the Minnesota State
Dental Association.
1933   0401073

Northwest Dent Res
Northwestern dental research
1062-0311
1989-1999   9100938

Northwest Med
Northwest medicine
0029-3385
1903-1973   0407175

Noseleutike
Nosēleutikē
1105-6843
Continues: Hellenis adelphe.
1979   8912007

Noshuyo Byori
Nōshuyō byōri = Brain tumor pathology
0914-8108
Continues: Nihon Nōshuyō Byōri Kenkyūkai
kōenshū. Continued by: Brain tumor
pathology.
1988-1996   9315330

Nosokom Chron
Nosokomeiaka chronika
0369-5700
Continued by: Hospital chronicles.
1932-2005   0416621

Not Ammin Sanit (1948)
Notiziario dell'amministrazione sanitaria.
Italy. Alto commissariato per l'igiene e la
sanità pubblica
1722-0203
1948-1969   17720190R

Not Clin
Noticias clínicas
1942-1959   19220430R

Not Farm
Notiziario farmaceutico
1939-19uu   19220520R

Not Med Esp
Noticiero médico español
1941-19uu   19220460R

Notas Salud Publica
Notas de salud pública
1946-1947   19220210R

Note Riv Psichiatr
Note e riviste di psichiatria
0391-0067
Continues: Diario di S. Benedetto in Pesaro.
1908-1980   0413424

Notes Queries
Notes and queries
0029-3970
1849   00110640R

Notes Rec R Soc Lond
Notes and records of the Royal Society of
London
0035-9149
Continues: Occasional notices of the Royal
Society of London.
1938   7505774

Notes Tuberc
Notes on tuberculosis ...
1938-1939   19220380R

Notes Undergr
Notes from the underground (New York, N.Y.)
199u-1999   9300979

Nourrisson
Le Nourrisson
1913-1960   0070765

Nouv Com Int Cathol Infirm Assist Med Soc
Nouvelles - Comité international catholique des infirmières et assistantes médico-sociales. News - International Committee of Catholic Nurses and Medico-Social Workers
0926-3209
Formed by the union of C.I.C.I.A.M.S. nouvelles and C.I.C.I.A.M.S. news.
1975-2002   7701468

Nouv Presse Med
La Nouvelle presse médicale
0301-1518
Supersedes La Presse médicale. Continued by La presse médicale (Paris, France: 1983).
1972-1982   0312552

Nouv Rev Fr Hematol
Nouvelle revue française d'hématologie
Continues: Nouvelle revue française d'hématologie; blood cells. Continued by: Hematology and cell therapy.
1978-1995   7909092

Nouv Rev Fr Hematol
Nouvelle revue française d'hématologie
0029-4810
Formed by the union of Le Sang and Revue d'hématologie. Continued by Nouvelle revue française d'hématologie; blood cells.
1961-1975   0401074

Nouv Rev Fr Hematol Blood Cells
Nouvelle revue française d'hématologie; blood cells
Continues Nouvelle revue française d'hématologie. Continued by Nouvelle revue française d'hématologie.
1976-1977   7701899

Nov Khir
Novaia khirurgiia
Merged with Zhurnal sovremennoĭ khirurgii to form Khirurgiia.
1925-1931   19220730R

Nov Med Priborostr
Novosti meditsinskogo priborostroeniia
0300-9106
Continues Novosti meditsinskoĭ tekhniki. Continued by Novosti meditsinskoĭ tekhniki.
1967-1973   0170720

Nov Med Tekh
Novosti meditsinskoĭ tekhniki
0321-2165
Continues Novosti meditsinskogo priborostroeniia.
1974-1984   7706624

Nov Med Tekh
Novosti meditsinskoĭ tekhniki
0546-8655
Continued by Novosti meditsinskogo priborostroeniia.
1959-1966   0170774

Nova Acta Paracelsica
Nova acta Paracelsica: ... Jahrbuch der Schweizerischen Paracelsus-Gesellschaft
0254-8712
1944   8219749

Nova Acta Stomatol
Nova acta stomatologica
Supersedes Rivista di odontojatria e ortognatodonzia.
1949-19uu   19220700R

Novartis Found Symp
Novartis Foundation symposium
1528-2511
Continues: Ciba Foundation symposium.
1998   9807767

Now Lekarskie Organ Wydz Lekarskiego Tow Przyj Nauk Posnanskiego
Nowiny lekarskie: organ Wydziału Lekarskiego Towarzystwa Przyjaciół Nauk Poznańskiego
0860-7397
1889   0021114

Nowotwory
Nowotwory
0029-540X
1950   0401003

NP News
NP news (Bellevue, Wash.)
1069-6903
1993-1996   9309830

NT Learn Curve
NT learning curve
Absorbed by: Nursing times.
1997-1999   9709306

NTM
NTM
0036-6978
1960   0347631

NTP CERHR MON
NTP CERHR MON
1556-2271
uuuu   101229556

Nucl Med (Stuttg)
Nuclear-Medizin
0029-5566
Supersedes Zeitschrift für medizinische Isotopenforschung und deren Grenzgebiete. Continued by Nuklearmedizin.
1959-1975   7607194

Nucl Med Biol
Nuclear medicine and biology
0969-8051
Continues: International journal of radiation applications and instrumentation. Part B, Nuclear medicine and biology.
1993   9304420

Nucl Med Commun
Nuclear medicine communications
0143-3636
1980   8201017

Nucl Med Rev Cent East Eur
Nuclear medicine review. Central & Eastern Europe: journal of Bulgarian, Czech, Macedonian, Polish, Romanian, Russian, Slovak, Yugoslav societies of nuclear medicine and Ukrainian Society of Radiology
1506-9680
1998   100886103

Nucl Recept Signal
Nuclear receptor signaling
1550-7629
2003   101237902

Nucl Sci Abstr
Nuclear science abstracts
0029-5612
Supersedes U. S. Atomic Energy Commission. Guide to published research on atomic energy and U. S. Atomic Energy Commission. Abstracts of declassified documents. Absorbed Atomic energy in biophysics, biology and medicine, Sept. 30, 1948.
1948-1976   7702350

Nucleic Acids Res
Nucleic acids research
0305-1048   1362-4962
1974   0411011

Nucleic Acids Res Suppl
Nucleic acids research. Supplement (2001)
Continues: Nucleic acids symposium series. Continued by: Nucleic acids symposium series (2004).
2001-2003   101169367

Nucleic Acids Symp Ser
Nucleic acids symposium series
0261-3166
Continues: Nucleic acids research. Special publication. Continued by: Nucleic acids research. Supplement (2001).
1979-2000   8007206

Nucleic Acids Symp Ser (Oxf)
Nucleic acids symposium series (2004)
1746-8272
Continues: Nucleic acids research. Supplement (2001).
2004   101259965

Nucleonics
Nucleonics
0096-6207
Formed by the union of: Atomic power, and; Atomic engineering. Absorbed by: Nucleonics week.
1947-1967   0333520

Nucleosides Nucleotides
Nucleosides & nucleotides
0732-8311
Continues in part: Journal of carbohydrates, nucleosides, nucleotides. Continued by: Nucleosides, nucleotides & nucleic acids.
1982-1999   8215930

Nucleosides Nucleotides Nucleic Acids
Nucleosides, nucleotides & nucleic acids
1525-7770   1532-2335
Continues: Nucleosides & nucleotides.
2000   100892832

Nueva Enferm
Nueva enfermeria
0210-8275
Continues: Boletín cultural e informativo de A.T.S.
1979-1988   8103157

Nuklearmedizin
Nuklearmedizin. Nuclear medicine
0029-5566
Continues: Nuclear-Medizin.
1976   7609387

Nuncius
Nuncius / Istituto e museo di storia della scienza
0394-7394
Continues: Annali dell'Istituto e museo di storia della scienza di Firenze.
1986   8807530

Nunt Radiol
Nuntius radiologicus
0029-6120
1933-1975   0401005

Nuova Riv Neurol
Nuova rivista di neurologia
1122-035X
Continues: Rivista di neurologia.
1991-2003   9211383

Nuovi Ann Ig Microbiol
Nuovi annali d'igiene e microbiologia
0029-6287
Absorbed: Annali d'igiene in 1952. Continued by: Annali di igiene.
1950-1988   0404446

Nurs Adm Q
Nursing administration quarterly
0363-9568 1550-5103
1976 7703976

Nurs BC
Nursing BC / Registered Nurses Association
of British Columbia
1185-3638
 Continues: RNABC news.
1991 9105915

Nurs Care
Nursing care
0091-2379
 Continues: Bedside nurse. Continued by:
 Journal of nursing care.
1973-1977 0366141

Nurs Careers
Nursing careers
0273-7124
 Continues: CE focus.
1980-1982 8214544

Nurs Case Manag
Nursing case management: managing the
process of patient care
1084-3647
 Continued by: Lippincott's case management.
1996-2000 9606068

Nurs Clin North Am
The Nursing clinics of North America
0029-6465
1966 0042033

Nurs Crit Care
Nursing in critical care
1362-1017 1478-5153
1996 9808649

Nurs Diagn
Nursing diagnosis: ND: the official journal
of the North American Nursing Diagnosis
Association
1046-7459
 Continued by: International journal of nursing
 terminologies and classifications.
1990-2002 9101481

Nurs Dyn
Nursing dynamics
1992-1995 9309428

Nurs Econ
Nursing economic$
0746-1739
1983 8404213

Nurs Educ Microworld
Nursing educators microworld
0893-1356
 Continues: Nurse educator's microworld.
 Absorbed by: Interactive Healthcare
 Newsletter.
1987-1994 8812203

Nurs Educ Monogr
Nursing education monographs
0078-2831
1962-1963 19230370R

Nurs Educ Perspect
Nursing education perspectives
1536-5026
 Continues: Nursing and health care
 perspectives.
2002 101140025

Nurs Elder
Nursing the elderly: in hospital, homes and
the community
0956-8115
 Continues: Geriatric nursing and home care.
 Continued by: Elderly care.
1989-1992 9002004

Nurs Ethics
Nursing ethics
0969-7330 1477-0989
1994 9433357

Nurs Focus
Nursing focus
0144-4069
 Continued by Senior nurse.
1979-1984 8000188

Nurs Forum
Nursing forum
0029-6473 1744-6198
1961 0401006

Nurs Forum (Auckl)
Nursing forum
0110-0890
 Continued by New Zealand nursing forum.
1973-1977 7508031

Nurs Health Care
Nursing & health care: official publication
of the National League for Nursing
0276-5284
 Continues: NLN News. Continued by: N &
 HC perspectives on community.
1980-1994 8107256

Nurs Health Care Perspect
Nursing and health care perspectives
1094-2831
 Continues: N & HC perspectives on
 community. Continued by: Nursing education
 perspectives.
1997-2001 9711055

Nurs Health Sci
Nursing & health sciences
1441-0745 1442-2018
1999 100891857

Nurs Hist Rev
Nursing history review: official journal of
the American Association for the History of
Nursing
1062-8061
1993 9303945

Nurs Homes
Nursing homes
0029-649X
 Continued by: Nursing homes and senior
 citizen care.
1952-1986 19230390R

Nurs Homes Sr Citiz Care
Nursing homes and senior citizen care
0896-6915
 Continues: Nursing homes. Continued by:
 Nursing homes (Cleveland, Ohio: 1991).
1986-1991 8710677

Nurs Inq
Nursing inquiry
1320-7881 1440-1800
1994 9505881

Nurs J (Manila)
Nursing journal
 Supersedes Santo Tomas nursing journal.
1978-1983 7906917

Nurs J India
The Nursing journal of India
0029-6503
1912 0376403

Nurs J Singapore
The Nursing journal of Singapore
0067-5814
 Continues: Berita jururawat.
1972-1985 0411330

Nurs Law Ethics
Nursing law & ethics,
0270-6636
 Merged with Medicolegal news, to form Law,
 medicine & health care.
1980-1981 8005047

Nurs Law Regan Rep
Nursing law's Regan report
1528-848X
 Continues: Regan report on nursing law.
2000 100936959

Nurs Leadersh
Nursing leadership
0164-7865
 Continued by: Nursing success today.
1978-1983 7905038

Nurs Leadersh (Tor Ont)
Nursing leadership (Toronto, Ont.)
1910-622X
 Continues: Canadian journal of nursing
 leadership.
2003 101470760

Nurs Leadersh Forum
Nursing leadership forum
1076-1632
1995 9503422

Nurs Life
NursingLife
0279-3091
 Absorbed in part by: Nursing.
1981-1988 8208357

Nurs Manag (Harrow)
Nursing management (Harrow, London,
England: 1994)
1354-5760
 Continues: Senior nurse.
1994 9433248

Nurs Manage
Nursing management
0744-6314 1538-8670
 Absorbed: Recruitment. retention &
 restructuring report. Feb. 1999 Continues:
 Supervisor nurse.
1981 8219243

Nurs Mirror
Nursing mirror
0029-6511
 Formed by the union of: Nursing mirror
 and midwives journal. and: Queen's nursing
 journal. Absorbed by Nursing times. Nov.
 13-19. 1985.
1977-1985 7708429

Nurs Mirror Midwives J
Nursing mirror and midwives journal
0143-2524
 Absorbed: Scottish nurse. Nursing illustrated.
 Merged with: Queen's nursing journal. to
 form: Nursing mirror.
1888-1977 7708428

Nurs Montreal
Nursing Montréal
0710-6157
 Continues: Format XI. Continued by:
 Actualités professionnelles.
1976-1996 7905824

Nurs N Z
Nursing New Zealand
1172-1979
 Formed by the union of: New Zealand
 nursing journal; and: NZNU news. Continued
 by a publication with the same title published
 vol. 1 (Feb. 1995)- .
1993-1995 9313253

Nurs N Z
Nursing New Zealand (Wellington, N.Z.: 1995)
1173-2032
Continues a journal with the same title published vols. 1-2 (Apr. 1993-Dec./Jan 1994/95).
1995   9507374

Nurs News
Nursing news
0029-6538
Continues: Newsletter. New Hampshire State Nurses Association.
1952   0061156

Nurs News (Meriden)
Nursing news
0029-652X
Continues Connecticut nursing news.
Continued by: Connecticut nursing news (Meriden, Conn.: 1980).
1953-1980   16410070R

Nurs Older People
Nursing older people
1472-0795
Continues: Elderly care.
2000   101084156

Nurs Outlook
Nursing outlook
0029-6554   1528-3968
Absorbed: Public health nursing.
1953   0401075

Nurs Pap
Nursing papers. Perspectives en nursing
0318-1006
Continued by: Canadian journal of nursing research.
1969-1987   7609832

Nurs Philos
Nursing philosophy: an international journal for healthcare professionals
1466-7681   1466-769X
2000   100897394

Nurs Pract
Nursing practice (Edinburgh, Scotland)
0266-6146
1985-1992   8508166

Nurs Prax N Z
Nursing praxis in New Zealand inc
0112-7438
1985   9212162

Nurs Qual Connect
Nursing quality connection
1055-6818
1991-1996   9209917

Nurs Que
Nursing Québec
0381-6419
Supersedes: Notes et nouvelles de l'Ordre des infirmières et infirmiers du Québec.
Continued by: Infirmière du Québec.
1976-1993   7908787

Nurs Res
Nursing research
0029-6562   1538-9847
1952   0376404

Nurs Res Conf
Nursing Research Conference
1965-1973   0100153

Nurs Res Rep
Nursing research report
0044-7781
1966-1977   0101770

Nurs Rev
Nursing review (North Sydney, N.S.W.)
1326-0472
1996   9891281

Nurs RSA
Nursing RSA = Verpleging RSA
0258-1647
1986-1994   8703817

Nurs Sci
Nursing science
1963-1965   2984807R

Nurs Sci Q
Nursing science quarterly
0894-3184
1988   8805022

Nurs Spectr (Fla Ed)
Nursing spectrum (Florida ed.)
1077-7946
19uu   9892043

Nurs Spectr (Gt Chic Ne Ill Nw Indiana Ed)
Nursing spectrum (Illinois ed.)
1988   9892046

Nurs Spectr (Gt Phila Tri State Ed)
Nursing spectrum (Greater Philadelphia/ Tri-state ed.)
1074-858X
19uu   9892045

Nurs Spectr (N Engl Ed)
Nursing spectrum (New England ed.)
1557-8038
19uu   9892047

Nurs Spectr (Wash D C)
Nursing spectrum (D.C./Baltimore metro ed.)
1098-9153
Continued by: Nursing spectrum (DC/ Maryland/Virginia ed.).
1991-2004   9421079

Nurs Staff Dev Insid
Nursing staff development insider
1057-8323
1992-1996   9214493

Nurs Stand
Nursing standard (Royal College of Nursing (Great Britain): 1987)
0029-6570
Absorbed: Tradimus. 1990 Continues: Nursing standard.
1987   9012906

Nurs Stand
Nursing standard: official newspaper of the Royal College of Nursing
0029-6570
Continues: RCN nursing standard. Continued by: Nursing standard (Royal College of Nursing (Great Britain): 1987).
1984-1987   8508427

Nurs Stand Spec Suppl
Nursing standard (Royal College of Nursing (Great Britain): 1987). Special supplement
0963-522X
1988-1991   9012905

Nurs Success Today
Nursing success today
0743-6726
Continues: Nursing leadership.
1984-1986   8410115

Nurs Times
Nursing times
0954-7762
Absorbed: NT learning curve. Nursing mirror.
1905   0423236

Nurs Times Nurs Homes
Nursing times. Nursing homes
1999-1999   100890994

Nurs Womens Health
Nursing for women's health
1751-4851   1751-486X
Continues: AWHONN lifelines.
2007   101304602

Nurs World
Nursing world
Continues Trained nurse and hospital review.
1950-1960   19230480R

Nurse Anesth
Nurse anesthesia
0897-7437
1990-1993   9009407

Nurse Author Ed
Nurse author & editor
1054-2353   1750-4910
1991   9312545

Nurse Educ
Nurse educator
0363-3624   1538-9855
1976   7701902

Nurse Educ Oppor Innov
Nurse Educators Opportunities And Innovations
1983-198u   9880100

Nurse Educ Pract
Nurse education in practice
1471-5953   1873-5223
2001   101090848

Nurse Educ Today
Nurse education today
0260-6917
1981   8511379

Nurse Managers Bookshelf
Nurse managers' bookshelf
1989-1990   9009036

Nurse Pract
The Nurse practitioner
0361-1817   1538-8662
1975   7603663

Nurse Pract Forum
Nurse practitioner forum
1045-5485
1990-2001   9100939

Nurse Res
Nurse researcher
1351-5578
1993   9435953

Nurses Lamp
Nurses Lamp
0885-5854
Continued by: Journal Of Christian Nursing.
1950-1984   9875104

Nursing
Nursing
0360-4039   1538-8689
Absorbed: Nursing update, Sept. 1976, and: NursingLife, May 1988.
1971   7600137

Nursing (Brux)
Nursing
0029-6457
1929-1975   19230340R

Nursing (Lond)
Nursing
0142-0372
Continued by: British journal of nursing (Mark Allen Publishing).
1979-1992   8009575

Nursingconnections
NursingConnections
0895-2809
1988-2000   8809326

Nutr Abstr Rev
Nutrition abstracts and reviews
0029-6619
Continued by Nutrition abstracts and reviews.
Series A: Human and experimental, and by
Nutrition abstracts and review. Series B:
Livestock feeds and feeding.
1931-1976   7803155

Nutr Abstr Rev Ser Hum Exp
Nutrition abstracts and reviews. Series A:
Human and experimental
0309-1295
Continues in part Nutrition abstracts and
reviews.
1977   7802919

Nutr Cancer
Nutrition and cancer
0163-5581   1532-7914
1978   7905040

Nutr Clin Care
Nutrition in clinical care: an official
publication of Tufts University
1096-6781   1523-5408
1998   9809674

Nutr Clin Pract
Nutrition in clinical practice: official
publication of the American Society for
Parenteral and Enteral Nutrition
0884-5336   1941-2452
1986   8606733

Nutr Dieta Eur Rev Nutr Diet
Nutritio et dieta; European review of
nutrition and dietetics
0550-4031
Continued by Nutrition and metabolism.
1959-1969   0250415

Nutr Health
Nutrition and health (Berkhamsted,
Hertfordshire)
0260-1060
1982   8306569

Nutr Healthy Living
Nutrition for healthy living
Continues: Nutrition for life.
1998-2001   101122856

Nutr Hosp
Nutrición hospitalaria: organo oficial de la
Sociedad Española de Nutrición Parenteral
y Enteral
0212-1611
1986   9100365

Nutr J
Nutrition journal
1475-2891
2002   101152213

Nutr Life
Nutrition for life
Continued by: Nutrition for healthy living.
1996-1998   9891296

Nutr Metab
Nutrition and metabolism
0029-6678
Continues Nutritio et dieta. Continued by
Annals of nutrition & metabolism.
1970-1980   0330472

Nutr Metab Cardiovasc Dis
Nutrition, metabolism, and cardiovascular
diseases: NMCD
0939-4753   1590-3729
1991   9111474

Nutr Neurosci
Nutritional neuroscience
1028-415X   1476-8305
1998-uuuu   100892202

Nutr News (Rosemt)
Nutrition news
0369-6464
1937-1998   19230640R

Nutr Res
Nutrition research (New York, N.Y.)
0271-5317   1879-0739
1981   8303331

Nutr Res Rev
Nutrition research reviews
0954-4224   1475-2700
1988   9113797

Nutr Rev
Nutrition reviews
0029-6643   1753-4887
1942   0376405

Nutrition
Nutrition (Burbank, Los Angeles County, Calif.)
0899-9007
Continues: Nutrition international.
1987   8802712

NYO Rep
NYO [reports]. U.S. Atomic Energy Commission
0099-278X
194u-1969   21830590R

NYSSNTA J
NYSSNTA journal
0145-3300
Continues Journal - New York State School
Nurse-Teachers Association. Continued by
The Journal of the New York State Nurse
Teachers Association.
1975-1977   7612820

O

Oalma J
The OALMA journal
Continued by the Journal of OALMA.
1946-1950   0130310

Obes Res
Obesity research
1071-7323   1550-8528
Continued by: Obesity (Silver Spring. Md.).
1993-2005   9305691

Obes Rev
Obesity reviews: an official journal of the
International Association for the Study of
Obesity
1467-7881   1467-789X
2000   100897395

Obes Surg
Obesity surgery
0960-8923
1991   9106714

Obesity (Silver Spring)
Obesity (Silver Spring, Md.)
1930-7381
Continues: Obesity research.
2006   101264860

Obstet Ginecol (Bucur)
Obstetrică şi ginecologia
0029-781X
Continued by: Revista de pediatrie. obstetrică
şi ginecologie. Obstetrică şi ginecologie.
1953-1974   7513657

Obstet Ginecol Lat Am
Obstetricia y ginecología latino-americanas
0029-7836
1943   19310500R

Obstet Gynecol
Obstetrics and gynecology
0029-7844
Vols. for 2000- include issues of: ACOG
committee opinion; ACOG eduational
bulletin; and: ACOG practice bulletin.
which were formerly published separately.
Beginning with: <2002-> ACOG practice
bulletin published separately.
1953   0401101

Obstet Gynecol Annu
Obstetrics and gynecology annual
0091-3332
1972-1985   0322340

Obstet Gynecol Clin North Am
Obstetrics and gynecology clinics of North
America
0889-8545
Continues in part: Clinics in obstetrics and
gynaecology.
1987   8709551

Obstet Gynecol Surv
Obstetrical & gynecological survey
0029-7828   1533-9866
1946   0401007

Obstet Prat
Obstetrícia prática
Continued by Arquivos de obstetrícia e
ginecologia.
1959-1960   19310490R

Occas Newsl Lindsay Club
Occasional newsletter (Lindsay Club)
Continued by: Dental historian.
197u-1984   8803871

Occas Pap R Coll Gen Pract
Occasional paper (Royal College of General
Practitioners)
1352-2450
Continues: Journal of the Royal College of
General Practitioners. Occasional paper.
1988   9305692

Occup Environ Med
Occupational and environmental medicine
1351-0711   1470-7926
Continues: British journal of industrial
medicine.
1994   9422759

Occup Health (Auckl)
Occupational Health
1967   9881881

Occup Health (Lond)
Occupational health; a journal for
occupational health nurses
0029-7917
Continues: Journal for industrial nurses.
Absorbed: Occupational health review
(London. England).
1963   0021263

Occup Health Nurs
Occupational health nursing
0029-7933
Continues the Journal of the American
Association of Industrial Nurses. Continued
by: AAOHN journal.
1969-1985   0200443

Occup Health Nurse (Auckl)
The Occupational health nurse
Continued by: Occupational health New
Zealand.
1967-1968   0254561

Occup Health Rev
Occupational health review
0029-7941
Continues Industrial health review.
1953-1971   0401102

Occup Health Saf
Occupational health & safety (Waco, Tex.)
0362-4064
Continues: International journal of
occupational health & safety.
1976   7610574

Occup Med
Occupational medicine (Philadelphia, Pa.)
0885-114X
Absorbed by: Clinics in occupational and
environmental medicine.
1986-2002   8605629

Occup Med (Chic Ill)
Occupational medicine
0096-0659
Merged with: Journal of industrial hygiene
and toxicology to form: Archives of industrial
hygiene and occupational medicine.
1946-1948   19310650R

Occup Med (Lond)
Occupational medicine (Oxford, England)
0962-7480   1471-8405
Continues: Journal of the Society of
Occupational Medicine.
1992   9205857

OCCUP Outlook Q
Occupational outlook quarterly / United
States Department of Labor, Bureau
of Labor Statistics in cooperation with
Veterans Administration
0199-4786
Continues: Occupational outlook.
1958   9875077

Occup Psychol
Occupational psychology
0029-7976
Continues: Human factor. Continued by:
Journal of occupational psychology.
1938-1973   0412774

Occup Ther Int
Occupational therapy international
0966-7903
1994   9433361

Occup Ther Rehabil
Occupational therapy and rehabilitation
Continues Archives of occupational therapy.
Continued by the American journal of
physical medicine.
1925-1951   19310670R

Occupations
Occupations; the vocational guidance
journal
Continues: Vocational guidance magazine.
Continued by: Personnel and guidance
journal.
1933-1952   19310680R

OCDS Bull
Ocds Bulletin
Continues: Orange County Dental Society
bulletin. Continued by: Orange County
Dental Society bulletin.
1959-1964   9882375

Ochanomizu Igaku Zasshi
[Ochanomizu igaku zasshi] The Ochanomizu
medical journal
0472-4674
1952   19310700R

Ochsner Clin Rep
Ochsner Clinic reports
1955-1957   19310720R

Ocul Fr
L'Oculiste français
Continued by L'Ophtalmologiste français.
1907-1958   19410320R

Ocul Immunol Inflamm
Ocular immunology and inflammation
0927-3948   1744-5078
1993   9312169

Ocul Surf
The ocular surface
1542-0124
2003   101156063

Odont
Odont
0105-189X
Continued by: Infodont.
1959-1979   7605677

Odontes
Odontes
0472-5069
1952-1970   19320020R

Odontiatriki
Odontiatrike
0377-1970
1968-1976   0437224

Odontoestomatologia
Odontoestomatología
0797-0374
1988-1995   9003024

Odontoiatr Prat
Odontoiatria pratica
0390-6000
Continued by Rivista di odontoiatria degli
Amici di Brugg.
1966-1981   7610578

Odontoiatr Protesi Dent
Odontoiatria e protesi dentaria
1934-1959   19320100R

Odontoiatr Rev Iberoam Med Boca
Odontoiatría; revista ibero-americana de
medicina de la boca
0029-8395
1944-19uu   19320110R

Odontol Am
Odontologia de América
1958-1963   19320210R

Odontol Atual
Odontologia Atual
0473-7865
1968   9875642

Odontol Bull
Odontological bulletin
0029-8433
Continues: Official bulletin (Odontological
Society of Western Pennsylvania). Continued
by: Bulletin (Dental Society of Western
Pennsylvania).
1937-1989   19320300R

Odontol Capixaba
Odontologia capixaba
1963-1992   19320170R

Odontol Chil
Odontología chilena
1955   0313241

Odontol Clin
Odontologia Clinica
1986-1988   9883953

Odontol Conserv
Odontologie Conservatrice
1974   9870007

Odontol Din
Odontologia dinámica
0078-334X
1966-1968   0155161

Odontol Foren Tidskr
Odontologiska föreningens tidskrift
0029-8468
Continued by: Odontologiska föreningens
tidskrift alias experimentet.
1937-1991   0404450

Odontol Infant
Odontología infantil
1022-7369
1947-1958   19320220R

Odontol Jalisc
Odontologia Jalisciense
1957   9883848

Odontol Peru
Odontologia Peruana
1971   9877854

Odontol Postgrado
Odontología de postgrado
0797-0234
Continued by: Odonto postgrado.
1987-1992   8813591

Odontol Pract
Odontologia practica
0905-2070
1990-2000   9107588

Odontol Revy
Odontologisk revy
0029-8441
Merged with Svensk tandläkare tidskrift.
Swedish dental journal to form Swedish
dental journal.
1950-1976   0404451

Odontol Revy Suppl
Odontologisk revy. Supplement
0472-5131
1952-1976   0401011

Odontol Tidskr
Odontologisk tidskrift
Continued by: Scandinavian journal of dental
research.
1893-1969   0270517

Odontol Urug
Odontologia uruguaya
0029-8425
1947-1999   0401103

Odontol [Mexico]
Odontologia
1983   9816310

Odontologia
Odontologia (Paris, France)
0244-9331
Continued by: Clinic odontologia.
1980-1988   8708715

Odontologia (Lima)
Odontología
0471-0215
1954-1972   2984091R

Odontologica
Odontologica
1952-1957   19320290R

Odontologie
L'Odontologie
Supersedes the Bulletin of the Cercle des
dentistes de Paris. Absorbed La Revue
internationale d'odontologie and issues for
jan. 1894-juin 1896 have title: L'Odontologie
et la revue internationale d'ontologie.
1881-1953   19320310R

Odontologo
El Odontólogo
0472-5158
Supersedes El Odontólogo.
1974-1996   7605087

Odontologo (Belo Horizonte)
Odontologo
0104-1681
1938-1955　　　　　　　　　　19320350R

Odontology
Odontology / the Society of the Nippon
Dental University
1618-1247　　　　　　　　　　1618-1255
　Continues: Shigaku.
2001　　　　　　　　　　　　101134822

Odontoprotesi
Odontoprotesi
0029-8492
1951-1984　　　　　　　　　　19320390R

Odontostomatol Implantoprotesi
Odontostomatologia E Implantoprotesi
　Continues: Rassegna Internazionale Di
　Stomatologia Pratica. Continued by: Rivista
　Di Odontostomatologia E Implantoprotesi.
1974-1982　　　　　　　　　　9883669

Odontostomatol Proodos
Odontostomatologike proodos
0029-8506
1947　　　　　　　　　　　　0401104

Odontostomatol Trop
Odonto-stomatologie tropicale = Tropical
dental journal
0251-172X
　Continues: Revue du SESDA.
1978　　　　　　　　　　　　8103679

Oecologia
Oecologia
0029-8549　　　　　　　　　　1432-1939
　Supersedes in part Zeitschrift für
　Morphologie und Oekologie der Tiere.
1968　　　　　　　　　　　　0150372

Off J Can Assoc Crit Care Nurs
Official journal of the Canadian Association
of Critical Care Nurses / CACCN
1201-2580
　Continued by: Dynamics (Pembroke. Ont.).
1990-1999　　　　　　　　　　9815867

Off Publ Dent Hyg Assoc State N Y
Official publication. Dental Hygienists'
Association of the State of New York
0011-8621
　Continues the association's News-letter.
1951-1979　　　　　　　　　　16520390R

Off Rec World Health Organ
Official records. World Health Organization
1947-1978　　　　　　　　　　0413540

Offentl Gesundheitsdienst
Der Öffentliche Gesundheitsdienst
　Continues: Zeitschrift für Medizinalbeamte.
　Continued by: Das Öffentliche
　Gesundheitswesen.
1935-1967　　　　　　　　　　19320430R

Offentl Gesundheitswes
Das Offentliche Gesundheitswesen
0029-8573
　Continues Der Offentliche Gesundheitsdienst.
　Continued by: Gesundheitswesen
　(Bundesverband der Ärzte des Öffentlichen
　Gesundheitsdienstes (Germany).
　Gesundheitswesen.
1967-1991　　　　　　　　　　0107170

Office
The Office
0030-0128
　Continues: Office economics. Absorbed by:
　Managing office technology.
1936-1993　　　　　　　　　　9876429

Oftalmol Zh
Oftalmologicheskiĭ zhurnal
0030-0675
1946　　　　　　　　　　　　0401105

Oftalmologia
Oftalmologia (Bucharest, Romania: 1990)
1220-0875
　Continues: Revista de chirurgie. oncologie.
　radiologie. o. r. l., oftalmologie. stomatologie.
　Oftalmologie.
1990　　　　　　　　　　　　9111247

OH
OH. Osteopathic hospitals
0161-0007
　Continues The Osteopathic hospital.
　Continued by Osteopathic hospital leadership.
1975-1984　　　　　　　　　　7800066

Ohio Dent J
The Ohio dental journal
0030-087X
　Continues the Journal of the Ohio State
　Dental Association.
1959-1993　　　　　　　　　　0365664

Ohio Med
Ohio medicine: journal of the Ohio State
Medical Association
0892-2454
　Continues: The Ohio State medical journal.
1987-2001　　　　　　　　　　8703563

Ohio Nurses Rev
Ohio nurses review
0030-0993
　Continues Ohio State Nurses' Association.
　Quarterly bulletin.
1930　　　　　　　　　　　　19330290R

Ohio Public Health
Ohio public health
　Continued by the Magazine of the Ohio
　Tuberculosis and Health Association.
1937-1953　　　　　　　　　　19330460R

Ohio State Med J
The Ohio State medical journal
0030-1124
　Continues: Transactions. Ohio State Medical
　Association. Continued by: Ohio medicine.
1905-1986　　　　　　　　　　0401013

OHMS Dig
OHMS digest
1978　　　　　　　　　　　　9875494

Okajimas Folia Anat Jpn
Okajimas folia anatomica Japonica
0030-154X　　　　　　　　　　1881-1736
　Continues: Folia anatomica Japonica.
1936　　　　　　　　　　　　0401014

Okayama Igakkai zasshi
Okayama Igakkai zasshi
0030-1558　　　　　　　　　　1882-4528
　Continues Zasshi of Koyukai. Okayama Igaku
　Senmongakko.
1889　　　　　　　　　　　　0413552

Okla Nurse
The Oklahoma nurse
0030-1787
1926　　　　　　　　　　　　19330740R

Oligonucleotides
Oligonucleotides
1545-4576　　　　　　　　　　1557-8526
　Continues: Antisense & nucleic acid drug
　development.
2003　　　　　　　　　　　　101188415

Omega (Westport)
Omega
0030-2228　　　　　　　　　　1541-3764
1970　　　　　　　　　　　　1272106

OMICS
Omics: a journal of integrative biology
1536-2310　　　　　　　　　　1557-8100
　Continues: Microbial & comparative genomics.
2002　　　　　　　　　　　　101131135

Omnia Med
Omnia medica
1923-1961　　　　　　　　　　0212412

Omnia Med Suppl
Omnia medica. Supplemento
　Merged with Omnia therapeutica.
　Supplemento to form Omnia medica et
　therapeutica. Supplemento.
19uu-1961　　　　　　　　　　0212475

Omnia Med Ther
Omnia medica et therapeutica
0030-2260
　Formed by the union of Omnia medica
　and Omnia therapeutica. and assumed the
　vol. numbering of the former. Continued
　by: Omnia medicamenta, which is classed
　separately at NLM.
1962-1974　　　　　　　　　　0212414

Omnia Ther
Omnia therapeutica
1949-1961　　　　　　　　　　0212476

Omnia Ther Suppl
Omnia therapeutica. Supplemento
1950-1961　　　　　　　　　　0212477

Omvardaren
Omvårdaren
0280-4123
　Continues: Tidskrift för sjukvårdspedagoger.
1982　　　　　　　　　　　　8410691

ONA J
ONA journal
0098-4337
1974-1979　　　　　　　　　　7508036

Oncodev Biol Med
Oncodevelopmental biology and medicine:
the journal of the International Society for
Oncodevelopmental Biology and Medicine
0167-1618
　Continued by: Tumour biology
1980-1983　　　　　　　　　　8100446

Oncogene
Oncogene
0950-9232　　　　　　　　　　1476-5594
1987　　　　　　　　　　　　8711562

Oncogene Res
Oncogene research
0890-6467
1987-1991　　　　　　　　　　8801457

Oncol
Oncologia
　Continues Rassegna italiana di oncologia.
1947-1949　　　　　　　　　　19410020R

Oncol Nurs Forum
Oncology nursing forum
0190-535X　　　　　　　　　　1538-0688
　Continues Oncology Nursing Society
　newsletter.
1977　　　　　　　　　　　　7809033

Oncol Rep
Oncology reports
1021-335X　　　　　　　　　　1791-2431
1994　　　　　　　　　　　　9422756

Oncol Res
Oncology research
0965-0407
　Absorbed: Anti-cancer drug design. 2002
　Continues: Cancer communications.
1992　　　　　　　　　　　　9208097

Oncologia
Oncologia
0369-7606
    Continued by Oncology.
1948-1966   **0134456**

Oncologica
Oncologica / Vereniging van Oncologie
Verpleegkundigen
0929-8703
1984   **9438654**

Oncologist
The oncologist
1083-7159   **1549-490X**
1996   **9607837**

Oncology
Oncology
0030-2414   **1423-0232**
    Continues Oncologia.
1967   **0135054**

Oncology (Williston Park)
Oncology (Williston Park, N.Y.)
0890-9091
1987   **8712059**

Onderstepoort J Vet Res
The Onderstepoort journal of veterinary
research
0030-2465
    Continues the Onderstepoort journal of
    veterinary science and animal industry.
1951   **0401107**

Onderstepoort J Vet Sci Anim Ind
The Onderstepoort journal of veterinary
science and animal industry
0369-7428
    Supersedes the Report of the Director of
    Veterinary Services and Animal Industry of
    South Africa. Continued by the Onderstepoort
    journal of veterinary research.
1933-1950   **19410050R**

Ondontol Bonaer
Odontología bonaerense. / FOPBA,
Federacion Odontologica de la Pcia. de Bs.
As
0326-8454
1978-1997   **9317168**

One One
One on one
0270-6628
    Supersedes UNA communiqué. Continued
    by: Pro re nata.
1979-198u   **8005054**

Onkologie
Onkologie
0378-584X   **1423-0240**
    Supersedes Oesterreichische Zeitschrift für
    Onkologie.
1978   **7808556**

Online J Curr Clin Trials
The Online journal of current clinical trials
        1059-2725
1992-1996   **9300367A**

Online J Issues Nurs
Online journal of issues in nursing
        1091-3734
1996   **9806525**

Online J Knowl Synth Nurs
The online journal of knowledge synthesis
for nursing
1072-7639   **1072-7639**
    Continued by: Worldviews on evidence-based
    nursing.
1993-2003   **9432589**

ONS Connect
ONS connect
1935-1623
    Continues: ONS news.
2007   **101300056**

ONS News
ONS news / Oncology Nursing Society
0890-5215
    Continued by: ONS connect.
1986-2006   **8906187**

Onsen Kagaku
[Onsen kagaku] Journal of the Balneological
Society of Japan
0030-2821
1941   **19410100R**

Ont Dent
Ontario dentist
0300-5275
    Continues: Journal of the Ontario Dental
    Association. Ontario Dental Association.
1972   **0360775**

Ontogenez
Ontogenez
0475-1450
1970   **0341527**

Oper Dent
Operative dentistry
0361-7734
    Supersedes The Journal of the American
    Academy of Gold Foil Operators.
1976   **7605679**

Oper Dent Suppl
Operative dentistry. Supplement
0163-3473
1977   **7805058**

Oper Orthop Traumatol
Operative Orthopädie und Traumatologie
0934-6694
1989   **9604937**

Oper Res
Operations research
0030-364X
    Continues the Journal of the Operations
    Research Society of America.
1955   **19410300R**

Oper Res Q
Operational research quarterly
0030-3623
    Continues O. R.: operational research
    quarterly. Continued by The Journal of the
    Operational Research Society.
1970-1977   **0352506**

Opera Pharm Rariora
Opera pharmaceutica rariora
0303-6502
1973-197u   **0436777**

Ophtalmologie
Ophtalmologie: organe de la Société
française d'ophtalmologie
0989-3105
    Continues: Bulletins et mémoires de la
    Société française d'ophtalmologie. Continued
    by: Journal français d'ophtalmologie.
1987-1998   **8900549**

Ophthal Plast Reconstr Surg
Ophthalmic plastic and reconstructive
surgery
0740-9303   **1537-2677**
1985   **8508431**

Ophthalmic Epidemiol
Ophthalmic epidemiology
0928-6586   **1744-5086**
1994   **9435674**

Ophthalmic Genet
Ophthalmic genetics
1381-6810   **1744-5094**
    Continues: Ophthalmic paediatrics and
    genetics.
1994   **9436057**

Ophthalmic Lit
Ophthalmic literature
0030-3720
1947-1998   **60120260R**

Ophthalmic Paediatr Genet
Ophthalmic paediatrics and genetics
0167-6784
    Continued by: Ophthalmic genetics.
1981-1993   **8206832**

Ophthalmic Physiol Opt
Ophthalmic & physiological optics: the
journal of the British College of Ophthalmic
Opticians (Optometrists)
0275-5408   **1475-1313**
    Continues: The British journal of
    physiological optics.
1981   **8208839**

Ophthalmic Res
Ophthalmic research
0030-3747   **1423-0259**
1970   **0267442**

Ophthalmic Semin
Ophthalmic seminars
0361-249X
1976-1977   **7607784**

Ophthalmic Surg
Ophthalmic surgery
0022-023X
    Supersedes: Journal of cryosurgery.
    Continued by: Ophthalmic surgery and lasers.
1970-1995   **0241035**

Ophthalmic Surg Lasers
Ophthalmic surgery and lasers
1082-3069
    Continued by: Ophthalmic surgery, lasers &
    imaging.
1995-2002   **9517132**

Ophthalmic Surg Lasers Imaging
Ophthalmic surgery, lasers & imaging: the
official journal of the International Society
for Imaging in the Eye
1542-8877
    Continues: Ophthalmic surgery and lasers.
2003   **101155780**

Ophthalmol Clin North Am
Ophthalmology clinics of North America
0896-1549
1988   **8905383**

Ophthalmol Ibero Am
Ophthalmologia ibero americana
1939-1962   **19410400R**

Ophthalmologe
Der Ophthalmologe: Zeitschrift der
Deutschen Ophthalmologischen Gesellschaft
0941-293X
    Continues in part: Fortschritte der
    Ophthalmologie.
1992   **9206148**

Ophthalmologica
Ophthalmologica. Journal international
d'ophtalmologie. International journal
of ophthalmology. Zeitschrift für
Augenheilkunde
0030-3755   **1423-0267**
    Continues Zeitschrift für Augenheilkunde.
1938   **0054655**

Ophthalmology
Ophthalmology
0161-6420 1549-4713
Absorbed: American orthoptic journal.
Continues in part: Transactions - American
Academy of Ophthalmology.
1978 7802443

Opt Acta (Lond)
Optica acta
0030-3909
Continued by: Journal of modern optics.
1954-1986 0401203

Opt Dev
Optical developments
1931-19uu 19410620R

Opt Express
Optics express
1094-4087
1997 101137103

Opt J Rev Optom
Optical journal and review of optometry
0030-3925
Formed by the union of Optical review and
The Optical journal. Continued by Chilton's
review of optometry.
1910-1977 0405557

Opt Lett
Optics letters
0146-9592 1539-4794
1977 7708433

Optician
The Optician
0030-3968
Continues: Optician and scientific instrument
maker.
1932 19410670R

Optom Clin
Optometry clinics: the official publication of
the Prentice Society
1050-6918
1991-1996 9106715

Optom Vis Sci
Optometry and vision science: official
publication of the American Academy of
Optometry
1040-5488 1538-9235
Continues: American journal of optometry
and physiological optics.
1989 8904931

Optom Wkly
The Optometric weekly
0030-4093
Continues The Optometric weekly and the
optometrist and optician. Continued by
Optometric monthly.
1928-1978 0405560

Optometra
Optometra
Continues Revista optómetra.
1947-19uu 19420010R

Optometry
Optometry (St. Louis, Mo.)
1529-1839 1558-1527
Continues: Journal of the American
Optometric Association.
2000 100912421

Opusc Med
Opuscula medica
0030-414X
1956-1992 2985034R

Or Health Bull
Oregon health bulletin
0030-4700
1943-1981 0376407

OR Manager
OR manager
8756-8047
1985 8700332

OR Tech
OR tech
0275-4622
Continues AORT news. Continued by the
Surgical technologist.
1972-1978 7802445

Oral Dis
Oral diseases
1354-523X 1601-0825
1995 9508565

Oral Health
Oral health
0030-4204
1911 7511948

Oral Health Prev Dent
Oral health & preventive dentistry
1602-1622
2003 101167768

Oral Hyg
Oral hygiene
1076-0644
Supersedes Dental headlight. Continued by
Dental economics-oral hygiene.
1911-1967 0135425

Oral Implantol
Oral implantology
0048-2064
Absorbed: Newsletter of the American
Academy of Implant Dentistry. Continued by:
The Journal of oral implantology.
1970-1977 0256003

Oral Maxillofac Surg
Oral and maxillofacial surgery
1865-1550 1865-1569
Continues: Mund Keifer Gesichtschirurgie.
2008 101319632

Oral Maxillofac Surg Clin North Am
Oral and maxillofacial surgery clinics of
North America
1042-3699 1558-1365
1989 9001454

Oral Microbiol Immunol
Oral microbiology and immunology
0902-0055 1399-302X
1986 8707451

Oral Oncol
Oral oncology
1368-8375
Continues: European journal of cancer. Part
B, Oral oncology.
1997 9709118

Oral Sci Rev
Oral sciences reviews
0300-4759
1972-1977 0361042

Oral Surg Oral Diagn
Oral surgery, oral diagnosis: OSD
0788-6020
1990-1998 9435677

Oral Surg Oral Med Oral Pathol
Oral surgery, oral medicine, and oral
pathology
0030-4220
Continues the Oral surgery section of the
American journal of orthodontics and oral
surgery. Continued by: Oral surgery, oral
medicine, oral pathology, oral radiology and
endodontics.
1948-1994 0376406

**Oral Surg Oral Med Oral Pathol Oral Radiol
Endod**
Oral surgery, oral medicine, oral pathology,
oral radiology, and endodontics
1079-2104 1528-395X
Continues: Oral surgery, oral medicine, and
oral pathology.
1995 9508562

Orale Implantol
Orale Implantologie
0172-1496
1974-1988 7901173

Oralprophylaxe
Oral-prophylaxe / Herausgeber, Verein für
Zahnhygiene e.V
0724-4991
Continues: Kariesprophylaxe. Continued by:
Oralprophylaxe & Kinderzahnheilkunde.
1983-2003 8402927

Orange Cty Dent Soc Bull
Orange County Dental Society Bulletin
0471-7406
Continues: Ocds Bulletin. Continued by:
Impressions.
1964-1978 9877927

Orbit
Orbit (Amsterdam, Netherlands)
0167-6830 1744-5108
1982 8301221

Ordre Natl Chir Dent Cons Natl Bull Off
Bulletin officiel du Conseil national de
l'Ordre / Ordre national des chirurgiens-
dentistes
0755-2378
Continued by: Lettre de l'Ordre national des
chirurgiens-dentistes..
1950-199u 19420280R

Oreg Nurse
The Oregon nurse
0030-4751
1935 1276216

Oreg State Dent J
Oregon state dental journal
Continues the Journal of the Oregon State
Dental Association. Continued by the Journal
of the Oregon Dental Association.
1949-1968 0157227

Org Biomol Chem
Organic & biomolecular chemistry
1477-0520 1477-0539
Merger of: Perkin 1, and: Perkin 2.
2003 101154995

Org Lett
Organic letters
1523-7060 1523-7052
1999 100890393

Organ Behav Hum Decis Process
Organizational behavior and human
decision processes
0749-5978
Continues: Organizational behavior and
human performance.
1985 8504453

Organ Behav Hum Perform
Organizational behavior and human
performance
0030-5073
Continued by: Organizational behavior and
human decision processes.
1966-1984 0312747

Organ Dyn
Organizational dynamics
0090-2616
1972 9877787

Organ Ethic
Organizational ethics: healthcare, business, and policy: OE
1541-1036
2004   101261882

Organon
Organon
0078-6500
Supersedes a publication with the same title, issued 1936-39.
1964   0117627

Orig Life
Origins of life
0302-1688
Continued by: Origins of life and evolution of the biosphere. Continues Space life sciences.
1974-1984   0420542

Orig Life Evol Biosph
Origins of life and evolution of the biosphere: the journal of the International Society for the Study of the Origin of Life
0169-6149
Continues: Origins of life.
1984   8610391

ORINS Rep US At Energy Comm
ORINS [reports]. U.S. Atomic Energy Commission
1950-uuuu   21830620R

Orizz Ortop Odie Riabil
Orizzonti della ortopedia odierna e della riabilitazione
0030-5626
1956-1967   0401023

ORL Head Neck Nurs
ORL-head and neck nursing: official journal of the Society of Otorhinolaryngology and Head-Neck Nurses
1064-3842
Continues: Journal (Society of Otorhinolaryngology and Head-Neck Nurses (U.S.)).
1991   9206573

ORL J Otorhinolaryngol Relat Spec
ORL; journal for oto-rhino-laryngology and its related specialties
0301-1569   1423-0275
Continues Practica oto-rhino-laryngologica.
1972   0334721

ORNL
ORNL. U.S. Atomic Energy Commission
0735-9861
1940-1974   7513664

ORNL-NSIC Rep
ORNL-NSIC [reports]. U.S. Atomic Energy Commission
1963-1971   0201746

ORNL-TM Rep
ORNL-TM [reports]. U.S. Atomic Energy Commission
0149-5526
1963-1971   21830630R

ORO Rep
ORO [reports]. U.S. Atomic Energy Commission
0272-4774
194u-197u   21830640R

Orphanet J Rare Dis
Orphanet journal of rare diseases
1750-1172
2006   101266602

Orthod Craniofac Res
Orthodontics & craniofacial research
1601-6335
Merger of: Journal of craniofacial genetics and developmental biology; and: Clinical orthodontics and research, continuing the numbering of the later.
2002   101144387

Orthod Epitheorese
Orthodontikē epitheōrēsē: epiotēmoniko periodiko tēs Orthodontikēs Etaireias tēs Ellados / OEE
1105-204X
Continued by: Hellēnikē orthodontikē epitheōrēse.
1988-199u   9108787

Orthod Fr
L' Orthodontie française
0078-6608
1921   0200547

Orthod Rev
Orthodontic review
0895-5034
1987-1998   8904020

Orthodontist
The Orthodontist
0048-2250
1969-1972   0375457

Orthop Clin North Am
The Orthopedic clinics of North America
0030-5898
1970   0254463

Orthop Nurs
Orthopaedic nursing / National Association of Orthopaedic Nurses
0744-6020   1542-538X
Continues: Orthopedic nursing.
1983   8409486

Orthop Nurs
Orthopedic nursing / National Association of Orthopedic Nurses
0744-6020
Continued by: Orthopaedic nursing.
1981-1982   8205859

Orthop Rev
Orthopaedic review
0094-6591
Continued by: American journal of orthopedics (Belle Mead, N.J.).
1972-1994   0431766

Orthop Surg
Orthopaedic audio-synopsis continuing medical education
0093-7738
1969-1976   7604410A

Orthopade
Der Orthopäde
0085-4530
1972   0331266

Orthopedics
Orthopedics
0147-7447   1938-2367
1978   7806107

Ortodoncia
Ortodoncia
0030-5944
1937   0376410

Ortodontia
Ortodontia
0030-5944
1968   0270147

Ortop Maxilar
Ortopedia maxilar
0473-436X
Continued by: Revista del ateneo argentino de odontologia.
1962-1979   8010181

Ortop Traumatol Appar Mot
Ortopedia e traumatologia dell'apparato motore
0369-7924
1929-1965   0413425

Ortop Traumatol Rehabil
Ortopedia, traumatologia, rehabilitacja
1509-3492
1999   101240146

Ortop Travmatol Protez
Ortopediia travmatologiia i protezirovanie
0030-5987
Supersedes Ortopediia i travmatologiia.
1955   0376411

Orv Hetil
Orvosi hetilap
0030-6002   1788-6120
1857   0376412

Orvosok Lapja Nepeu
Orovosok lapja (Magyar Orvosok Szabad Szakszervezete)
19uu-19uu   9429384

Orvostort Kozl
Orvostörténeti közlemények
0010-3551
Continues: Communicationes ex Bibliotheca Historiae Medicae Hungarica.
1968   0435507

Osaka City Med J
Osaka city medical journal
0030-6096
1954   0376413

Osaka Daigaku Shigaku Zasshi
[Osaka Daigaku shigaku zasshi] The journal of Osaka University Dental Society
0473-4629
1956   19430280R

Osiris
Osiris
0369-7827
1936   0057764

Osp Ital Chir
Ospedali d'Italia - chirurgia
0030-6266
1959   0376414

Osp Maggiore
L' Ospedale maggiore
0369-7843
1913-2001   0022210

Osp Psichiatr
L'Ospedale psichiatrico
0048-2285
Continued by: Archivio di psichiatria generale.
1933-19uu   0312304

Osteoarthritis Cartilage
Osteoarthritis and cartilage / OARS, Osteoarthritis Research Society
1063-4584   1522-9653
1993   9305697

Osteopath Hosp
The Osteopathic hospital
0048-2293
Continued by OH. Osteopathic hospitals.
1957-1975   7708992

Osteopath Hosp Leadersh
Osteopathic hospital leadership
8750-9202
Continues: OH. Osteopathic hospitals.
Continued by: AOHA today.
1985-1989 **8507547**

Osteopath Mag
The Osteopathic magazine
Superseded by: Health (American
Osteopathic Association).
1914-1955 **19440170R**

Osteopath Med Surg
Osteopathic medicine and surgery
Continues the Digest of osteopathic medicine.
1945-1949 **0175010**

Osteopath Prof
The Osteopathic profession
0191-4324
Continued by: OP. The Osteopathic physician.
1933-1967 **0161312**

Osteoporos Int
**Osteoporosis international: a journal
established as result of cooperation between
the European Foundation for Osteoporosis
and the National Osteoporosis Foundation
of the USA**
0937-941X **1433-2965**
1990 **9100105**

Osterr Dent Rev
Österreichische Dental-Revue
Continues Zahnärztliche und dentistische
Presse-Korrespondenz. Continued by Dental
Revue.
1946-1950 **19320530R**

Osterr Dent Z
Oesterreichische Dentisten Zeitschrift
0029-9006
1949-1989 **0404452**

Osterr Hebammenztg
Österreichische Hebammenzeitung
0048-1432
1954-1983 **19320540R**

Osterr Krankenpflegez
Österreichische Krankenpflegezeitschrift
0303-4461
Continues: Österreichische
Schwesternzeitung. Continued by:
Österreichische Pflegezeitschrift.
1974-2000 **0423177**

Osterr Pflegezeitschrift
**Österreichische Pflegezeitschrift: Organ
des Österreichischen Gesundheits- und
Krankenpflegeverbands**
Continues: Österreichische
Krankenpflegezeitschrift.
2001 **101122359**

Osterr Schwesternztg
Österreichische Schwesternzeitung
0029-9480
Continues: Die Krankenschwester. Continued
by: Oesterreichische Krankenpflegezeitschrift.
1967-1973 **0423200**

Osterr Z Erforsch Bekampf Krebskr
**Österreichische Zeitschrift für Erforschung
und Bekämpfung der Krebskrankheit**
0300-8703
Continues Der Krebsarzt.
1970-1973 **7513401**

Osterr Z Onkol
**Österreichische Zeitschrift für Onkologie.
Austrian journal of oncology**
0377-2004
Superseded by: Onkologie.
1974-1977 **7507343**

Osterr Z Stomatol
Österreichische Zeitschrift für Stomatologie
0029-9642
Continued by Zeitschrit für Stomatologie
(Österreichische Gesellschaft für Zahn-,
Mund und Kieferheilkunde).
1903-1983 **1272426**

Osterr Zahnarzteztg
**Österreichische Zahnärzts-Zeitung;
Mitteilungen der Bundesfachgruppe für
Zahnheilkunde der Österreichischen
Ärztekammer**
0029-9596
Continues the Mitteilungen of the
Bundesfachgruppe für Zahnheilkunde of
the Österreichische Ärztekammer. Absorbed
in July 1989: Österreichische Dentisten
Zeitschrift
1958 **19320630R**

Osterr Zahnprothet
Österreichische Zahnprothetik
0250-4839
Continues: Öesterreichische Zahntechniker
Handwerk. Continued by: Österreichische
Zahntechniker Handwerk.
1977-1990 **7901350**

Osterr Zahntech Handw
**Das Österreichische Zahntechniker
Handwerk: offizielles Organ der
Bundesinnung der Zahntechniker**
Continues: Österreichische Zahnprothetik.
Continued by: Österreichische Zahntechniker
(1998).
1991-1998 **9204423**

Osterr Zahntech Handwerk
Das Österreichische Zahntechniker Handwerk
Continued by: Österreichische Zahnprothetik.
1955-1976 **9875447**

Ostomy Wound Manage
Ostomy/wound management
0889-5899
Continues: Ostomy management.
1980 **8912029**

Otol Neurotol
**Otology & neurotology: official publication
of the American Otological Society,
American Neurotology Society [and]
European Academy of Otology and
Neurotology**
1531-7129 **1537-4505**
Continues: American journal of otology.
2001 **100961504**

Otolaryngol Clin North Am
Otolaryngologic clinics of North America
0030-6665
1968 **0144042**

Otolaryngol Head Neck Surg
Otolaryngology and head and neck surgery
0194-5998
Continues Otolaryngology. Continued by
Otolaryngology--head and neck surgery.
1979-1980 **7909794**

Otolaryngol Head Neck Surg
**Otolaryngology--head and neck surgery:
official journal of American Academy of
Otolaryngology-Head and Neck Surgery**
0194-5998
Continues: Otolaryngology and head and
neck surgery.
1981 **8508176**

Otolaryngol Pol
**Otolaryngologia polska. The Polish
otolaryngology**
0030-6657
Supersedes Polski przegląd
otolaryngologiczny.
1947 **0404453**

Otolaryngology
Otolaryngology
0161-6439
Continues in part Transactions -
American Academy of Ophthalmology
and Otolaryngology. Continued by
Otolaryngology and head and neck surgery.
1978-1978 **7906928**

Otorhinolaryngol Danub
Oto-rhino-laryngologia Danubiana
1947-19uu **0022245**

Otorhinolaryngolog Int
L'Oto-rhino-laryngologie internationale
1913-1951 **19440280R**

Otorinolaringol Ital
L'Oto-rino-laringologia italiana
0030-6630
Merged with: Minerva otorinolaringologica;
Nuovo archivio italiano di otologia, rinologia
e laringologia; and Bollettino delle malattie
dellórecchio, della gola, del naso; to form:
Otorinolaringologia.
1930-1970 **0401024**

Otorinolaringol Oftalmol
Oto-rino-laringologia şi oftalmologia
0303-5123
Continued by Revista de chirurgie, oncologie,
radiologie, o. r. l., oftalmologie, stomatologie.
Seria: Oftalmologie and Revista de chirurgie,
oncologie, radiologie, o. r. l., oftalmologie,
stomatologie. Seria: Oto-rino-laringologie.
1974-1974 **7506369**

Otorinolaringologie
Oto-rino-laringologie
0030-6649
1956-1973 **7506370**

Ou Daigaku Shigakushi
ōu Daigaku shigakushi
0916-2313
Continues: Tōhoku Shika Daigaku Gakkai
shi.
1989 **8915132**

Outcomes Manag
Outcomes management
1535-2765 **1538-9820**
Continues: Outcomes management for
nursing practice.
2002-2004 **101150637**

Outcomes Manag Nurs Pract
Outcomes management for nursing practice
1093-1783
Continued by: Outcomes management.
1997-2001 **9716901**

Outlook Blind Teach Forum
**Outlook for the blind and the teachers
forum**
Absorbed the Teachers forum for instructors
of blind children in Feb. 1942. Continued by
the New outlook for the blind.
1907-1951 **19440370R**

Outlook Bull South Dent Soc N J
**Outlook and bulletin. Southern Dental
Society of New Jersey**
0049-1594
1931-1984 **20920510R**

Overseas Postgrad Med J
The overseas post-graduate medical journal
1946-1951 **19440420R**

Oxf Med Sch Gaz
Oxford Medical School gazette
0030-7661
1949 **19440440R**

Oxf Rev Reprod Biol
Oxford reviews of reproductive biology
0260-0854
Merged with: Bibliography of reproduction,
to form: Human reproduction update.
1979-1994   8005460

Oxf Surv Eukaryot Genes
Oxford surveys on eukaryotic genes
0265-0738
1984-1991   8813988

P

P N G Med J
Papua and New Guinea medical journal
0031-1480
1955   0376417

P R Enferm
Puerto Rico y su enfermera
0145-6652
Continued by: Boletin - Colegio de Profesionales
de la Enfermerúa de Puerto Rico.
1927-1974   7700256

P R Health Sci J
Puerto Rico health sciences journal
0738-0658
1982   8303541

P V Expo Discuss Congr Soc Int Chir
Procès-verbaux, exposés et discussions
[du] congrès de la Société internationale de
chirurgie. International Society of Surgery
1905   24410910R

Pa Dent J (Harrisb)
Pennsylvania dental journal
0031-4439
Continues the Pennsylvania state dental journal.
1949   0404456

Pa Health You
Pennsylvania health & you
1539-8684
Continues: Pennsylvania medicine.
2002-2002   101150438

Pa Hosp Bull
The Pennsylvania Hospital bulletin
1943-1966   19530670R

PA J
The P. A. journal
0091-4614
Continues Physician's associate.
1973-1978   0371225

Pa Med
Pennsylvania medicine
0031-4595
Continues: Pennsylvania medical journal.
Absorbed: Current concepts in ophthalmology
(Harrisburg, Pa.). Continued by: Pennsylvania
health & you.
1966-2002   0045606

Pa Med J
Pennsylvania medical journal (1897)
0096-0667
Formed by the union of the Pittsburgh
medical review and the Transactions of the
Medical Society of the State of Pennsylvania.
Merged with: Delaware state medical journal,
to form: Atlantic medical journal, which
continued the volume numbering of the
Pennsylvania medical journal.
1897-1923   0200647

Pa Med J
Pennsylvania medical journal (1928)
0096-0667
Continues in part: Atlantic medical journal.
Continued by: Pennsylvania medicine.
1928-1966   101245788

Pa Nurse
The Pennsylvania nurse
0031-4617
Supersedes Penn points.
1946   19540010R

Pac Health Dialog
Pacific health dialog: a publication of the
Pacific Basin Officers Training Program and
the Fiji School of Medicine
1015-7867
1994   9434923

Pac Med Surg
Pacific medicine and surgery
Continues Western journal of surgery,
obstetrics, and gynecology.
1964-1968   0232664

Pac Symp Biocomput
Pacific Symposium on Biocomputing. Pacific
Symposium on Biocomputing
1793-5091
1996   9711271

Pacing Clin Electrophysiol
Pacing and clinical electrophysiology: PACE
0147-8389   1540-8159
1978   7803944

Padiatr Grenzgeb
Pädiatrie und Grenzgebiete
0030-932X
1962-2002   0401115

Padiatr Padol
Pädiatrie und Pädologie
0030-9338
Supersedes Neue österreichische Zeitschrift
für Kinderheilkunde.
1965   0022370

Padiatr Padol Suppl
Pädiatrie und Pädologie. Supplementum
0300-9556
1972-1984   0334010

Paediatr Anaesth
Paediatric anaesthesia
1155-5645   1460-9592
1991   9206575

Paediatr Danub
Paediatria Danubiana …
1947-1949   19510330R

Paediatr Drugs
Paediatric drugs
1174-5878
1999   100883685

Paediatr Indones
Paediatrica Indonesiana
0030-9311
1961   0376416

Paediatr Jpn
Paediatria Japonica
Continued by Acta paediatrica Japonica;
overseas edition in June 1963.
1958-1961   19510340R

Paediatr Nurs
Paediatric nursing
0962-9513
1989   9013329

Paediatr Perinat Epidemiol
Paediatric and perinatal epidemiology
0269-5022   1365-3016
1987   8709766

Paediatr Respir Rev
Paediatric respiratory reviews
1526-0542   1526-0550
2000   100898941

Paediatr Univ Tokyo
Paediatria Universitatis Tokyo
0030-9303
1957-1970   0243721

Paediatrician
Paediatrician
0300-1245
Continued by: Pediatrician.
1973-1982   0352330

Paedovita
Paedovita
0737-5131
1984-1986   8501477

Pages Doc
Pages documentaires
0500-8786
1963-1971   0344534

Pagine Stor Med
Pagine di storia della medicina
0030-9400
1957-1973   0401116

Pahlavi Med J
Pahlavi medical journal
0030-9427
Continued by Iranian journal of medical
sciences.
1970-1978   1251605

Pain
Pain
0304-3959   1872-6623
1975   7508686

Pain Headache
Pain and headache
0255-3910
Continues: Research and clinical studies in
headache.
1985   8410364

Pain Manag Nurs
Pain management nursing: official
journal of the American Society of Pain
Management Nurses
1524-9042   1532-8635
2000   100890606

Pain Med
Pain medicine (Malden, Mass.)
1526-2375   1526-4637
2000   100894201

Pain Physician
Pain physician
1533-3159
1999   100954394

Pain Pract
Pain practice: the official journal of World
Institute of Pain
1530-7085   1533-2500
2001   101130835

Pain Res Manag
Pain research & management: the journal
of the Canadian Pain Society = journal de
la société canadienne pour le traitement de
la douleur
1203-6765
1996   9612504

Pain Suppl
Pain. Supplement
0167-6482
1981-1990   8109110

Pak Dent Rev
The Pakistan dental review
0030-9710
1951-1979   0401117

Pak J Biol Sci
Pakistan journal of biological sciences: PJBS
1028-8880 1812-5735
1998 101247723

Pak J Health
Pakistan journal of health
0030-9834
1951-1973 0413426

Pak J Pharm Sci
Pakistan journal of pharmaceutical sciences
1011-601X
Continues: Journal of pharmacy, University
of Karachi.
1988 9426356

Pak J Surg Gynaecol Obstet
The Pakistan journal of surgery,
gynaecology, and obstetrics
0030-9907
1959-1975 0401120

Pak Nurs Health Rev
The Pakistan nursing and health review
1956-1976 19510520R

Paleopathol Newsl
Paleopathology newsletter
0148-4737
1973 7704329

Palliat Med
Palliative medicine
0269-2163 1477-030X
1987 8704926

Palliat Support Care
Palliative & supportive care
1478-9515 1478-9523
2003 101232529

Pammatone
Pammatone
0031-0549
1959-1969 0413427

Pan Am Med Womans J
Pan American medical woman's journal
Continues Medical woman's journal.
Absorbed by: International record of
medicine and general practice clinics.
1952-1952 19520100R

Pancreas
Pancreas
0885-3177 1536-4828
1986 8608542

Pancreatology
Pancreatology: official journal of the
International Association of Pancreatology
(IAP) ... [et al.]
1424-3903 1424-3911
2001 100966936

Panminerva Med
Panminerva medica
0031-0808
1959 0421110

Pap Natl Conf Prof Nurses Physicians
Papers / National Conference for
Professional Nurses and Physicians
1964-uuuu 100961135

Pap Ser United Hosp Fund N Y
Paper series (United Hospital Fund of New
York)
0898-3135
1985-19uu 8610109

Paracelsus Arch Prakt Med
Paracelsus; Archiv der praktischen Medizin
0379-363X
1948-1984 0401205

Paradentologie
Paradentologie
Continued by Parodontologie.
1947-1953 0204202

Paramed Int
Paramedics international
0191-6351
Continued by JEMS.
1976-1979 7802924

Paraplegia
Paraplegia
0031-1758
Continued by: Spinal cord.
1963-1996 2985038R

Parasite
Parasite (Paris, France)
1252-607X
Continues: Annales de parasitologie humaine
et comparée.
1994 9437094

Parasite Immunol
Parasite immunology
0141-9838 1365-3024
1979 7910948

Parasitol Int
Parasitology international
1383-5769
Continues: Kiseichūgaku zasshi.
1997 9708549

Parasitol Res
Parasitology research
0932-0113 1432-1955
Continues: Zeitschrift für Parasitenkunde
(Berlin, Germany).
1987 8703571

Parasitol Today
Parasitology today (Personal ed.)
0169-4758
Continued by: Trends in parasitology.
1985-2000 8605563

Parasitology
Parasitology
0031-1820 1469-8161
Absorbed: Symposia of the British Society
for Parasitology. British Society for
Parasitology.
1908 0401121

Parassitologia
Parassitologia
0048-2951
1959 0413724

Parazitologiia
Parazitologiia
0031-1847
1967 0101672

Paris Med
Paris médical
Merged with the Journal des praticiens to
form Revue du praticien.
1910-1951 19520510R

Parking
Parking
0031-2193
19uu 9892142

Parkinsonism Relat Disord
Parkinsonism & related disorders
1353-8020
1995 9513583

Parma Med
Parma medica
1953-1968 19520640R

Parodontol
Parodontologie (Berlin, Germany)
0937-1532
1990 9112403

Parodontol Acad Rev
Parodontologie and academy review
0369-8092
Formed by the merger of: Academy review
of the California Academy of Periodontology,
United Staes Section. ARPA internationale,
and: Parodontologie (Zurich, Switzerland:
1954). Continued by: Parodontologie.
1967-1968 0104661

Parodontol Stomatol (Nuova)
Parodontologia e stomatologia (nuova):
organo ufficiale dell'ARPA italiana, della
Società italiana Jonoforesi stomatologica e
della Accademia ligustica di stomatologia
0301-1429
Continues: Parodontologia e stomatologia.
1980-1993 8703825

Parodontologie
Parodontologie
0031-2339
Continues: Parodentologie and academy
review.
1969-1971 0204370

Parodontologie
Parodontologie (Zurich, Switzerland: 1954)
Continues: Paradentologie. Merged
with: Academy review of the California
Academy of Periodontology, United States
Section. ARPA Internationale, to become:
Parodontologie and academy review.
1954-1966 9716297

Parodontopathies
Parodontopathies
1954-1966 9875617

Paroi Arterielle
Paroi artérielle
0398-7655
1973-1981 7606268

Part A News
Part A news: independent news to legally
maximize Medicare part A dollars
Continues: Prospective payment guide.
Merged with: Health care marketer, to form:
Hospital revenue report.
1987-1990 9005471

Part B News
Part B news
0893-8121
Absorbed: Managed medicare & medicaid
news. 1997
1987 9007503

PAS Rep
PAS reporter
0078-7353
Continues The Record.
1968-1979 0234403

Pathobiol Annu
Pathobiology annual
0362-3025
1971-1982 1305471

Pathobiology
Pathobiology: journal of immunopathology,
molecular and cellular biology
1015-2008 1423-0291
Formed by the union of: Experimental
cell biology, and: Pathology and
immunopathology research.
1990 9007504

Pathol Annu
Pathology annual
0079-0184
Continued by: Anatomic pathology (Chicago, Ill.: annual).
1966-1996   0050610

Pathol Biol
Pathologie et biologie
Continued by Pathologie-biologie.
1953-1968   0266544

Pathol Biol (Paris)
Pathologie-biologie
0369-8114   1768-3114
Continues: Pathologie et biologie.
1969   0265365

Pathol Eur
Pathologia Europaea
0031-2967
Continues: Revue belge de pathologie et de médecine expérimentale.
1966-1976   0062702

Pathol Gen
La Pathologie générale
Continues Revue de pathologie comparée et d'hygiène générale. Continued by Revue de pathologie générale et comparée.
1952-1952   20320400R

Pathol Immunopathol Res
Pathology and immunopathology research
0257-2761
Continues: Survey and synthesis of pathology research. Merged with: Experimental cell biology, to form: Pathobiology.
1986-1989   8708069

Pathol Int
Pathology international
1320-5463   1440-1827
Continues: Acta pathologica japonica.
1994   9431380

Pathol Microbiol (Basel)
Pathologia et microbiologia
0031-2959
Continues Schweizerische Zeitschrift für Pathologie und Bakteriologie. Continued by Experimental cell biology.
1960-1975   0401122

Pathol Oncol Res
Pathology oncology research: POR
1219-4956   1532-2807
1995   9706087

Pathol Res Pract
Pathology, research and practice
0344-0338
Continues Beiträge zur Pathologie.
1978   7806109

Pathol Vet
Pathologia veterinaria
0031-2975
Continued by Veterinary pathology.
1964-1970   0311355

Pathologe
Der Pathologe
0172-8113
1979   8006541

Pathologica
Pathologica
0031-2983
1908   0401123

Pathologist
Pathologist
0031-3017
Continues: Bulletin - College of American Pathologists.
1969-1986   0200552

Pathology
Pathology
0031-3025
1969   0175411

Pathology (Phila)
Pathology (Philadelphia, Pa.)
1041-3480
1992-1996   9208681

Pathophysiol Haemost Thromb
Pathophysiology of haemostasis and thrombosis
1424-8832   1424-8840
Continues: Haemostasis.
2002   101142710

Patient Acc
Patient accounts
0195-7775
Continued by: Revenue-cycle strategist.
1978-2003   8203286

Patient Care
Patient care
0031-305X   1939-1897
1967-2007   0246161

Patient Care Manag
Patient care management
1532-8880
Continues: Aspen's advisor for nurse executives.
2000-2003   101083317

Patient Couns Health Educ
Patient counselling and health education
0190-2040
Continued by Patient education and counseling.
1978-1983   7806110

Patient Educ Couns
Patient education and counseling
0738-3991
Continues: Patient counselling and health education.
1983   8406280

Patient Educ Newsl
Patient education newsletter
0278-8209
Continues: Physician's patient education newsletter.
1981-1985   9879873

Patient Focus Care
Patient-focused care: the health care executive's guide to organizational restructuring
1082-8672
Continued by: Patient-focused care and satisfaction.
1993-1997   9423870

Patient Focus Care Satisf
Patient-focused care and satisfaction / American Health Consultants
1097-9530
Continues: Patient-focused care.
1998-2000   9802916

Patol Clin Ostet Ginecol
Patologia e clinica ostetrica e ginecologica
0304-0313
Supersedes La Clinica ostetrica e ginecologica.
1973-1993   0434617

Patol Fiziol Eksp Ter
Patologicheskaia fiziologiia i èksperimental'naia terapiia
0031-2991
1957   0376421

Patol Pol
Patologia polska
0031-3114
Continued by: Polish journal of pathology.
1950-1993   0404244

Pavlov J Biol Sci
The Pavlovian journal of biological science
0093-2213
Continues: Conditonal reflex. Continued by: Integrative physiological and behavioral science.
1974-1990   0414243

Pavlov J High Nerv Act
Pavlov journal of higher nervous activity
0553-416X
1958-1961   0172416

Pawlow Z Hohere Nerventatigkeit
Pawlow-Zeitschrift für höhere Nerventätigkeit. Deutsche Ausg
0479-7221
1951-1961   0413431

PCR Methods Appl
PCR methods and applications
1054-9803
Continued by: Genome research.
1991-1995   9201445

PCR Rep
The PCR reporter
0830-9604
1985-1989   8602600

PDA J Pharm Sci Technol
PDA journal of pharmaceutical science and technology / PDA
1079-7440
Continues: Journal of pharmaceutical science and technology.
1994   9439538

PDM
PDM: Physicians' drug manual
0031-9058
1969-1978   0217255

Pediatr AIDS HIV Infect
Pediatric AIDS and HIV infection
1045-5418
Absorbed by: AIDS patient care and STDs. June 1997
1990-1997   9107942

Pediatr Akus Ginekol
Pediatriiâ akusherstvo i ginekologiiâ
0031-4048
Continues: Pediatriiâ (Kiev, Ukraine).
1945   2985041R

Pediatr Allergy Immunol
Pediatric allergy and immunology: official publication of the European Society of Pediatric Allergy and Immunology
0905-6157   1399-3038
1990   9106718

Pediatr Am
Pediatria de las Américas
1943-1954   19530270R

Pediatr Ann
Pediatric annals
0090-4481
1972   0356657

Pediatr Blood Cancer
Pediatric blood & cancer
1545-5009   1545-5017
Continues: Medical and pediatric oncology.
2004   101186624

Pediatr Cardiol
Pediatric cardiology
0172-0643
1979   8003849

Pediatr Case Rev
Pediatric case reviews (Print)
1532-9798   1533-0664
2001-2004   101090844

Pediatr Clin North Am
Pediatric clinics of North America
0031-3955
1954   0401126

Pediatr Crit Care Med
Pediatric critical care medicine: a journal
of the Society of Critical Care Medicine and
the World Federation of Pediatric Intensive
and Critical Care Societies
1529-7535
2000   100954653

Pediatr Dent
Pediatric dentistry
0164-1263
1979   7909102

Pediatr Dermatol
Pediatric dermatology
0736-8046   1525-1470
1983   8406799

Pediatr Dev Pathol
Pediatric and developmental pathology: the
official journal of the Society for Pediatric
Pathology and the Paediatric Pathology
Society
1093-5266   1615-5742
    Continues: Perspectives in pediatric
    pathology.
1998   9809673

Pediatr Diabetes
Pediatric diabetes
1399-543X   1399-5448
2000   100939345

Pediatr Emerg Care
Pediatric emergency care
0749-5161   1535-1815
1985   8507560

Pediatr Endocrinol Rev
Pediatric endocrinology reviews: PER
1565-4753
2003   101202124

Pediatr Exerc Sci
Pediatric exercise science
0899-8493   1543-2920
1989   8909729

Pediatr Hematol Oncol
Pediatric hematology and oncology
0888-0018   1521-0669
    Absorbed: International journal of pediatric
    hematology/oncology. Continues: European
    paediatric haematology and oncology.
1986   8700164

Pediatr Infect Dis
Pediatric infectious disease
0277-9730
    Continued by: The Pediatric infectious
    disease journal.
1982-1986   8209468

Pediatr Infect Dis J
The Pediatric infectious disease journal
0891-3668   1532-0987
    Continues: Pediatric infectious disease.
1987   8701858

Pediatr Int
Pediatrics international: official journal of
the Japan Pediatric Society
1328-8067   1442-200X
    Continues: Acta paediatrica Japonica.
1999   100886002

Pediatr Listy
Pediatrické listy
    Continued by Ceskoslovenská pediatrie.
1946-1954   0204303

Pediatr Med Chir
La Pediatria medica e chirurgica: Medical
and surgical pediatrics
0391-5387
1979   8100625

Pediatr Med Prat
La Pediatria del medico pratico
0391-0393
    Merged with Medicina italiana and
    Policlinico infantile to form Minerva
    pediatrica.
1926-1948   19530280R

Pediatr neonatol
Pediatrics and neonatology
1875-9572
    Continues: Acta paediatrica Taiwanica.
2008   101484755

Pediatr Nephrol
Pediatric nephrology (Berlin, Germany)
0931-041X   1432-198X
1987   8708728

Pediatr Neurol
Pediatric neurology
0887-8994
1985   8508183

Pediatr Neurosci
Pediatric neuroscience
0255-7975
    Continues in part: Child's brain. Continued
    by: Pediatric neurosurgery.
1985-1989   8601677

Pediatr Neurosurg
Pediatric neurosurgery
1016-2291   1423-0305
    Continues: Pediatric neuroscience.
1990   9114967

Pediatr Nurs
Pediatric nursing
0097-9805
1975   7505804

Pediatr Panam
Pediatria panamericana
1955-1965   19530330R

Pediatr Panam
Pediatría panamericana
0325-1462
1972-1975   7511521

Pediatr Pathol
Pediatric pathology / affiliated with
the International Paediatric Pathology
Association
0277-0938
    Continued by: Pediatric pathology &
    laboratory medicine.
1983-1994   8303527

Pediatr Pathol Lab Med
Pediatric pathology & laboratory medicine:
journal of the Society for Pediatric
Pathology, affiliated with the International
Paediatric Pathology Association
1077-1042
    Continues: Pediatric pathology. Continued by:
    Pediatric pathology & molecular medicine.
1995-1998   9518033

Pediatr Pathol Mol Med
Pediatric pathology & molecular medicine
1522-7952
    Continues: Pediatric pathology & laboratory
    medicine. Continued by: Fetal and pediatric
    pathology.
1999-2003   100885435

Pediatr Pharmacol (New York)
Pediatric pharmacology (New York, N.Y.)
0270-322X
1980-1986   8400778

Pediatr Phys Ther
Pediatric physical therapy: the official
publication of the Section on Pediatrics of
the American Physical Therapy Association
0898-5669   1538-005X
1989   8912748

Pediatr Pol
Pediatria polska
0031-3939
    Supersedes Przeglad pedyatryczny.
1921   2985039R

Pediatr Prat
Pediatria prática
0031-3947
1928-1979   0401125

Pediatr Pulmonol
Pediatric pulmonology
8755-6863   1099-0496
1985   8510590

Pediatr Pulmonol Suppl
Pediatric pulmonology. Supplement
1054-187X
1987   9014095

Pediatr Radiol
Pediatric radiology
0301-0449
1973   0365332

Pediatr Rehabil
Pediatric rehabilitation
1363-8491
    Continued by: Developmental
    neurorehabilitation.
1997-2006   9709256

Pediatr Res
Pediatric research
0031-3998   1530-0447
    Supersedes Annales paediatrici.
1967   0100714

Pediatr Rev
Pediatrics in review / American Academy of
Pediatrics
0191-9601   1526-3347
    Vol. 1 issued with Pediatrics, v. 64. Issues for
    July-Dec. 1999 include an online-only section
    called NeoReviews, published separately
    beginning in Jan. 2000.
1979   8103046

Pediatr Surg Int
Pediatric surgery international
0179-0358   1437-9813
1986   8609169

Pediatr Transplant
Pediatric transplantation
1397-3142   1399-3046
1997   9802574

Pediatria (Bucur)
Pediatria
0031-3904
    Continued by Revista de pediatrie, obstetrică
    şi ginecologie. Pediatria.
1952-1974   7502431

Pediatria (Napoli)
La Pediatria
0031-3890
1893-1983   0401207

Pediatria (Rio)
A Pediatria; revista mensal de clinica,
patologia e higiene infantil
1934-19uu   19530350R

Pediatria (Santiago)
Pediatria
0375-9563
1958   0420103

Pediatrician
Pediatrician
0300-1245
    Continues: Paediatrician.
1985-1991   8511837

Pediatrics
Pediatrics
0031-4005   1098-4275
1948   0376422

Pediatrie
Pédiatrie
0031-4021
    Merged with: Archives françaises de
    pediatrie, to form: Archives de pédiatrie.
1912-1993   0401127

Pediatrie (Bucur)
Pediatrie (Bucharest, Romania)
    Continues: Revista de pediatrie, obstetrica
    si ginecologie. Pediatria. Continued by:
    Pediatria (Bucharest, Romania: 1993).
1990-1992   9109803

Pediatriia
Pediatriia
0031-403X   1990-2182
    Continues Sovetskaia pediatriia.
1937   0405563

Pedod Fr
Pedodontie Francaise
0996-3278
1967-1970   9875620

Pelican News
Pelican news
0031-4161
1953   19530550R

Penn Dent J (Phila)
The Penn dental journal
0031-4331
1897   0417461

Pensiero Med (Milano)
Pensiero medico
0391-0423
    Formed by the union of Corriere sanitario and
    Italia sanitaria.
1911-1951   19540240R

People
People
0301-5645
1973-1992   0411340

Pept Res
Peptide research
1040-5704
    Merged with: International journal of peptide
    & protein research, to form: The journal of
    peptide research.
1988-1996   8913494

Peptides
Peptides
0196-9781
1980   8008690

Percept Mot Skills
Perceptual and motor skills
0031-5125
    Continues: Perceptual and motor skills
    research exchange.
1955   0401131

Percept Psychophys
Perception & psychophysics
0031-5117   1532-5962
1966   0200445

Perception
Perception
0301-0066   1468-4233
1972   0372307

Perfusion
Perfusion
0267-6591   1477-111X
1986   8700166

Periodontal Abstr
Periodontal abstracts
0048-3389
    Continues The Journal of the Western Society
    of Periodontology. Continued by The Journal
    of the Western Society of Periodontology/
    Periodontal abstracts.
1965-1976   0113632

Periodontal Case Rep
Periodontal case reports: a publication of
the Northeastern Society of Periodontists
0277-4216
    Continued by: Periodontal clinical
    investigations.
1979-1991   8101999

Periodontal Clin Investig
Periodontal clinical investigations: official
publication of the Northeastern Society of
Periodontists
1065-2418
    Continues: Periodontal case reports.
1992-2002   9209040

Periodontics
Periodontics
0553-6685
1963-1968   0173712

Periodontol 2000
Periodontology 2000
0906-6713   1600-0757
1993   9313276

Perioper Nurs Q
Perioperative nursing quarterly
8755-9935
1985-1987   8505284

Perit Dial Int
Peritoneal dialysis international: journal
of the International Society for Peritoneal
Dialysis
0896-8608
    Continues: Peritoneal dialysis bulletin.
1988   8904033

Perm Found Med Bull
Permanente Foundation medical bulletin
0099-8893
1943-1953   19540420R

Pers Adm
The Personnel administrator
0031-5729
    Supersedes: Journal for personnel
    administration. Continued by: HRMagazine.
1956-1989   9877815

Pers J
The Personnel journal
0031-5745
    Continues the Journal of personnel research.
1927-1996   19540510R

Pers Soc Psychol Bull
Personality and social psychology bulletin
0146-1672
1975   7809042

Pers Soc Psychol Rev
Personality and social psychology review: an
official journal of the Society for Personality
and Social Psychology, Inc
1088-8683   1532-7957
1997   9703164

Personnel
Personnel
0031-5702
    Continued by: HR focus.
1919-1991   19540490R

Perspect Accredit
Perspectives on accreditation
0099-2402
    Continues: Bulletin of the Joint Commission
    on Accreditation of Hospitals. Continued by:
    JCAH perspectives.
1972-1981   7511523

Perspect Addict Nurs
Perspectives on addictions nursing: a
publication of the National Nurses Society
on Addictions
1057-1639
    Continues: NNSA news.
1990-1995   9302030

Perspect Biol Med
Perspectives in biology and medicine
0031-5982   1529-8795
1957   0401132

Perspect Dev Neurobiol
Perspectives on developmental neurobiology
1064-0517
    Continues: Comments on modern biology.
    Part D. Comments on developmental
    neurobiology.
1992-1998   9417971

Perspect Health Inf Manag
Perspectives in health information
management / AHIMA, American Health
Information Management Association
    1559-4122
2004   101219871

Perspect Healthc Risk Manage
Perspectives in healthcare risk management
/ American Society for Healthcare Risk
Management of the American Hospital
Association
0899-1073
    Continues: Perspectives in hospital risk
    management. Continued by: Journal of
    healthcare risk management.
1987-1992   8905393

Perspect Infirm
Perspective infirmière: revue officielle de
l'Ordre des infirmières et infirmiers du
Québec
1708-1890
    Continues: Infirmière du Québec.
2003   101196674

Perspect Med Virol
Perspectives in medical virology
0168-7069
1985   8500364

Perspect Medicaid Manage
Perspectives on medicaid management
    Continues: Journal for medicaid management.
    Continued by: Perspectives on medicaid and
    medicare management.
1979-1979   9878669

Perspect Medicaid Medicare Manage
Perspectives on Medicaid and Medicare management
0273-0413
Continues: Perspectives on Medicare management.
1979-1981   8001253

Perspect Nephrol Hypertens
Perspectives in nephrology and hypertension
0092-2900
1973-1976   0402144

Perspect Pediatr Pathol
Perspectives in pediatric pathology
0091-2921
Continued by: Pediatric and developmental pathology.
1973-1997   0366560

Perspect Psychiatr Care
Perspectives in psychiatric care
0031-5990   1744-6163
1963   0401133

Perspect Respir Nurs
Perspectives in respiratory nursing: a publication of the Respiratory Nursing Society
1075-5756
1990-1998   9421080

Perspect Sex Reprod Health
Perspectives on sexual and reproductive health
1538-6341
Continues: Family planning perspectives.
2002   101140654

Perspect Vasc Surg Endovasc Ther
Perspectives in vascular surgery and endovascular therapy
1531-0035
Continues: Perspectives in vascular surgery.
2001   100970607

Perspectivas
Perspectivas
0379-8208
1972-1981   7708436

Perspectives
Perspectives (Gerontological Nursing Association (Canada))
0831-7445
1977   8500942

Perspectives (Montclair)
Perspectives
0191-6556
1976-1977   7901355

Pesqui Odontol Bras
Pesquisa odontológica brasileira = Brazilian oral research
1517-7491
Continues: Revista de odontologia da Universidade de São Paulo. Continued by: Brazilian oral research.
2000-2003   100941949

Pest Control
Pest control
0031-6121
Continues: Pests and their control. Continued by: Pest management professional.
1949-2007   0404457

Pest Control
Pests and their control
0096-2147
Continues Exterminators log. Continued by Pest control.
1938-1949   19540650R

Pest Manag Sci
Pest management science
1526-498X
Continues: Pesticide science.
2000   100898744

Pestic Monit J
Pesticides monitoring journal
0031-6156
1967-1981   0110540

PFCA Rev
PFCA review
1081-5597
Continues: Review (Patient Focused Care Association).
1993-1996   9500520

Pflege
Pflege
1012-5302
1988   8907069

Pflege Aktuell
Pflege aktuell / DBfK, Deutscher Berufsverband für Pflegeberufe
0944-8918
Continues: Krankenpflege (Frankfurt am Main. Germany).
1993   9423842

Pflege Z
Pflege Zeitschrift
0945-1129
Continues: Deutsche Krankenpflegezeitschrift.
1994   9430463

Pflugers Arch
Pflügers Archiv: European journal of physiology
0031-6768   1432-2013
Continues Pflüger's Archiv für die gesamte Physiologie des Menschen und der Tiere.
1968   0154720

Pflugers Arch Gesamte Physiol Menschen Tiere
Pflügers Archiv für die gesamte Physiologie des Menschen und der Tiere
0365-267X
Continues: Archiv für die gesammte Physiologie des Menschen und der Thiere. Absorbed: Archiv für Anatomie und Physiologie. Physiologische Abt. Archiv für Physiologie. 1920 Zentralblatt für Physiologie. 1921 Continued by: Pflügers Archiv.
1910-1968   0154722

Pharm Acta Helv
Pharmaceutica acta Helvetiae
0031-6865
Supplement to Schweizerische Apotheker-Zeitung. Absorbed by: European journal of pharmaceutical sciences in 2000.
1926-2000   0401134

Pharm Beih
Die Pharmazie. Beihefte
Continues: Pharmazie. Ergänzungsband.
1954-1962   19610590R

Pharm Biol
Le Pharmacien biologiste
0553-9323
Continued by: Biologiste.
1956-1986   19610300R

Pharm Biotechnol
Pharmaceutical biotechnology
1078-0467
1992-2002   9310302

Pharm Bull
Pharmaceutical bulletin
Continued by Chemical and pharmaceutical bulletin.
1953-1957   19610100R

Pharm Dev Technol
Pharmaceutical development and technology
1083-7450   1097-9867
1996   9610932

Pharm Fr
Pharmacien de France
0031-6938
1940   19610310R

Pharm Hist
Pharmacy in history
0031-7047
Continues: A. I. H. P. notes.
1959   0135654

Pharm Hist (Lond)
Pharmaceutical historian
0079-1393
1967   0146631

Pharm Hist Aust
Pharmacy history Australia: the newsletter of the Australian Academy of the History of Pharmacy
1997   100958810

Pharm Ind
La Pharmacie industrielle
1946-1980   19610290R

Pharm Ind
Die Pharmazeutische Industrie
0031-711X
1934   19610500R

Pharm J
The Pharmaceutical journal
0031-6873
Continues: Pharmaceutical journal and pharmacist.
1933   0410466

Pharm Manage Comb Am J Pharm
Pharmacy management combined with the American journal of pharmacy: PM
0163-464X
Formed by the union: of Pharmacy management; and: American journal of pharmacy and the sciences supporting public health. Continued by: American journal of pharmacy and the sciences supporting public health (Philadelphia. Pa.: 1981).
1979-1980   7902571

Pharm Pract Manag Q
Pharmacy practice management quarterly
1080-5737
Continues: Topics in hospital pharmacy management. Continued by: Advances in pharmacy.
1995-2001   9508902

Pharm Prax
Pharmazeutische Praxis
0048-3656
1955-1991   0401136

Pharm Res
Pharmaceutical research
0724-8741   1573-904X
1984   8406521

Pharm Rundsch
Pharmazeutische Rundschau
0031-7128
Continued by: Pharma Rundschau.
1959-1998   0401137

Pharm Stat
Pharmaceutical statistics
1539-1604   1539-1612
2002   101201192

Pharm Times
Pharmacy times
0003-0627
Continues American professional pharmacist.
1969   0216507

Pharm Unserer Zeit
Pharmazie in unserer Zeit
0048-3664
1972   0337763

Pharm Weekbl
Pharmaceutisch weekblad
0031-6911
Absorbed the Nederlandsch tijdschrift voor
pharmacie, chemie, en toxicologie in 1902.
1864   0401211

Pharm Weekbl Sci
Pharmaceutisch weekblad. Scientific edition
0167-6555
Continued by: Pharmacy world & science.
1979-1992   7907992

Pharm World Sci
Pharmacy world & science: PWS
0928-1231   1573-739X
Continues: Pharmaceutisch weekblad.
Scientific edition.
1993   9307352

Pharm Zentralhalle Dtschl
Pharmazeutische Zentralhalle für Deutschland
Merged with Arzneimittelstandardisierung
to form Zentralblatt für
Pharmazie, Pharmakotherapie und
Laboratoriumsdiagnostik.
1859-1969   0320011

Pharmacal Adv
Pharmacal advance
1914-1952   19610040R

Pharmacoeconomics
PharmacoEconomics
1170-7690
1992   9212404

Pharmacoepidemiol Drug Saf
Pharmacoepidemiology and drug safety
1053-8569   1099-1557
1992   9208369

Pharmacogenet Genomics
Pharmacogenetics and genomics
1744-6872   1744-6880
Continues: Pharmacogenetics.
2005   101231005

Pharmacogenetics
Pharmacogenetics
0960-314X
Continued by: Pharmacogenetics and
genomics.
1991-2004   9211735

Pharmacogenomics
Pharmacogenomics
1462-2416   1744-8042
2000   100897350

Pharmacogenomics J
The pharmacogenomics journal
1470-269X   1473-1150
2001   101083949

Pharmacol Biochem Behav
Pharmacology, biochemistry, and behavior
0091-3057
1973   0367050

Pharmacol Physicians
Pharmacology for physicians
0097-0115
Supersedes Physiology & pharmacology for
physicians. Continued by Rational drug therapy.
1967-1970   1247035

Pharmacol Rep
Pharmacological reports: PR
1734-1140
Continues: Polish journal of pharmacology.
2005   101234999

Pharmacol Res
Pharmacological research: the official journal
of the Italian Pharmacological Society
1043-6618
Continues: Pharmacological research
communications.
1989   8907422

Pharmacol Res Commun
Pharmacological research communications
0031-6989
Continues: Archivio italiano di farmacologia.
Continued by: Pharmacological research.
1969-1988   0236354

Pharmacol Rev
Pharmacological reviews
0031-6997   1521-0081
1949   0421737

Pharmacol Ther
Pharmacology & therapeutics
0163-7258
Formed by the union of Pharmacology
& therapeutics. Part A: Chemotherapy,
toxicology and metabolic inhibitors, of
Pharmacology & therapeutics. Part B:
General & systematic pharmacology, and
of Pharmacology & therapeutics. Part C:
Clinical pharmacology and therapeutics.
1979   7905840

Pharmacol Ther Dent
Pharmacology and therapeutics in dentistry
0001-4389
1970-1981   1252372

Pharmacol Ther [B]
Pharmacology & therapeutics. Part B:
General & systematic pharmacology
0306-039X
Merged with Pharmacology & therapeutics.
Part A: Chemotherapy, toxicology and
metabolic inhibitors and with Pharmacology
& therapeutics. Part C: Clinical pharmacology
and therapeutics to form Pharmacology &
therapeutics.
1975-1978   7508692

Pharmacol Toxicol
Pharmacology & toxicology
0901-9928
Continues: Acta pharmacologica et
toxicologica. Continued by: Basic & clinical
pharmacology & toxicology.
1987-2003   8702180

Pharmacology
Pharmacology
0031-7012   1423-0313
Supersedes in part Medicina et pharmacologia
experimentalis.
1968   0152016

Pharmacopsychiatria
Pharmacopsychiatria
0720-4280
Continues: Pharmakopsychiatrie Neuro-
Psychopharmakologie. Continued by:
Pharmacopsychiatry.
1981-1983   8103699

Pharmacopsychiatry
Pharmacopsychiatry
0176-3679
Continues: Pharmacopsychiatria.
1984   8402938

Pharmacotherapy
Pharmacotherapy
0277-0008
1981   8111305

Pharmakopsychiatr Neuropsychopharmakol
Pharmakopsychiatrie, Neuro-
Psychopharmakologie
0031-7098
Continued by: Pharmacopsychiatria.
1968-1980   0146540

Pharmakotherapia
Pharmakotherapia
0553-9439
1963-1965   0022452

Pharmatherapeutica
Pharmatherapeutica
0308-051X
1976-1989   7606274

Pharmazie
Die Pharmazie
0031-7144
1946   9800766

Pharmeur Sci Notes
Pharmeuropa scientific notes
1814-2435   1814-2443
2005   101262672

Pharmeuropa Bio
Pharmeuropa bio / the Biological
Standardisation Programme, EDQM
1684-7075
Continues: Pharmeuropa. Special issue
biologicals.
2003   101193650

Pharmeuropa Spec Issue Biol
Pharmeuropa. Special issue biologicals
Continued by: Pharmeuropa bio.
19uu-2002   100910522

Pharmindex
Pharmindex
0031-7152
1958-1993   2985071R

Pharos Alpha Omega Alpha Honor Med Soc
The Pharos of Alpha Omega Alpha-Honor
Medical Society. Alpha Omega Alpha
0031-7179
19uu   19610620R

PHC4 FYI
PHC4 FYI / Pennsylvania Health Care Cost
Containment Council
2001   101141791

Phi Lambda Kappa Q
The Phi Lambda Kappa quarterly
0733-4400
Continued by: Quarterly (Phi Lambda Kappa
Medical Fraternity).
1926-1963   8207226

Phila Health Bull
Philadelphia health bulletin
Continues the Quarterly bulletin of the Dept.
of Public Health.
1940-1951   22830540R

Philipp J Cancer
Philippine journal of cancer
0031-7608
1957-1966   0401215

Philipp J Nurs
The Philippine journal of nursing
0048-3818
Continues The Filipino nurse.
1953-2001   19620310R

Philipp J Ophthalmol Otolaryngol
Philippine journal of ophthalmology and
otolaryngology
1955-1969   **0404460**

Philipp J Surg
Philippine journal of surgery
Continued by: Philippine journal of surgery.
obstetrics. and gynecology.
1946-1954   **19620330R**

Philipp J Surg Surg Spec
Philippine journal of surgery and surgical
specialties
0370-0267
Continues the Philippine journal of surgery.
obstetrics and gynecology. Continued by the
Philippine journal of surgical specialties.
1955-1967   **0200355**

Philipp Med World
The Philippine medical world
1946-1951   **19620380R**

Phillip J
Phillip Journal
0945-1412
Continues: Phillip Journal für restaurative
Zahnmedizin. Absorbed: Zahnarztliche
Praxis. Continued by: Dental Praxis.
1989-2000   **9306483**

Phillip J Restaur Zahnmed
Phillip Journal für restaurative Zahnmedizin
0174-5980
Continued by: Phillip Journal.
1984-1988   **8609626**

Philos Ethics Humanit Med
Philosophy, ethics, and humanities in
medicine: PEHM
    1747-5341
2006   **101258058**

Philos Trans R Soc Lond B Biol Sci
Philosophical transactions of the Royal
Society of London. Series B, Biological
sciences
0962-8436   1471-2970
Continues: Philosophical transactions of
the Royal Society of London. Series B,
Containing papers of a biological character.
1934   **7503623**

Philos Transact A Math Phys Eng Sci
Philosophical transactions. Series A,
Mathematical, physical, and engineering
sciences
1364-503X   1471-2962
Continues: Philosophical transactions.
Physical sciences and engineering.
1996   **101133385**

Phlebologie
Phlébologie
0031-8280
Continues the Bulletin de la Société
française de phlébologie.
1952   **0376212**

Phlebology
Phlebology / Venous Forum of the Royal
Society of Medicine
0268-3555
Absorbed: Australian and New Zealand
journal of phlebology.
1986   **9012921**

Phonetica
Phonetica
0031-8388   1423-0321
1957   **0376424**

Photochem Photobiol
Photochemistry and photobiology
0031-8655
1962   **0376425**

Photochem Photobiol Sci
Photochemical & photobiological
sciences: Official journal of the European
Photochemistry Association and the
European Society for Photobiology
1474-905X   1474-9092
2002   **101124451**

Photodermatol
Photo-dermatology
0108-9684
Continued by: photodermatology.
photoimmunology & photomedicine.
1984-1989   **8407997**

Photodermatol Photoimmunol Photomed
Photodermatology, photoimmunology &
photomedicine
0905-4383   1600-0781
Continues: Photodermatology.
1990   **9013641**

Photomed Laser Surg
Photomedicine and laser surgery
1549-5418   1557-8550
Continues: Journal of clinical laser medicine
and surgery.
2004   **101222340**

Photophysiology
Photophysiology
0090-6999
1964-1973   **0317543**

Photosynth Res
Photosynthesis research
0166-8595   1573-5079
1980   **100954728**

Phys Biol
Physical biology
1478-3967   1478-3975
2004   **101197454**

Phys Chem Chem Phys
Physical chemistry chemical physics: PCCP
1463-9076
Formed by the merger of: Journal of the
Chemical Society. Faraday transactions.
and: Berichte der Bunsen-Gesellschaft für
Physikalische Chemie.
1999   **100888160**

Phys Med
Physica medica: PM: an international
journal devoted to the applications of
physics to medicine and biology: official
journal of the Italian Association of
Biomedical Physics (AIFB)
1120-1797
Continues: Fisica in medicina.
1987   **9302888**

Phys Med Biol
Physics in medicine and biology
0031-9155   1361-6560
1956   **0401220**

Phys Med Rehabil Clin N Am
Physical medicine and rehabilitation clinics
of North America
1047-9651
Absorbed: Physical medicine and rehabilitation.
1990   **9102787**

Phys Occup Ther Pediatr
Physical & occupational therapy in pediatrics
0194-2638   1541-3144
1980   **8109120**

Phys Rev E Stat Nonlin Soft Matter Phys
Physical review. E, Statistical, nonlinear, and
soft matter physics
1539-3755
Continues: Physical review. E. Statistical
physics, plasmas, fluids, and related
interdisciplinary topics.
2001   **101136452**

**Phys Rev E Stat Phys Plasmas Fluids Relat
Interdiscip Topics**
Physical review. E, Statistical physics,
plasmas, fluids, and related interdisciplinary
topics
1063-651X
Continues in part: Physical review. A.
Continued by: Physical review. E. Statistical.
nonlinear. and soft matterphysics.
1993-2000   **9887340**

Phys Rev Lett
Physical review letters
0031-9007   1079-7114
1958   **0401141**

Phys Ther
Physical therapy
0031-9023   1538-6724
Continues: Journal of the American Physical
Therapy Association.
1964   **0022623**

Phys Ther Rev
The Physical therapy review
0735-7435
Continues the Physiotherapy review.
Continued by the Journal of the American
Physical Therapy Association.
1948-1961   **19620720R**

Phys Ther Sport
Physical therapy in sport: official
journal of the Association of Chartered
Physiotherapists in Sports Medicine
1466-853X   1873-1600
2000   **100940513**

Physician Assist
Physician assistant
0147-3999
Merged with Health practitioner to form
Health practitioner. Physician assistant.
1976-1977   **7703992**

Physician Assist
Physician assistant (American Academy of
Physician Assistants)
8750-7544
Continues: Physician assistant. Health
practitioner.
1983-2003   **8403486**

Physician Assist Health Pract
Physician assistant. Health practitioner
0197-713X
Continues Health practitioner. Physician
assistant. Continued by Physician assistant
(American Academy of Physician Assistants).
1979-1982   **8000597**

Physician Exec
Physician executive
0898-2759
Continues: Medical director.
1986   **8610398**

Physician Perform Paym Rep
Physician performance & payment report
1528-7378
Continues: Medical network strategy report.
Absorbed by: Internet healthcare strategies.
1999-2001   **100927887**

Physician Relat Update
Physician relations update / American
Health Consultants
1079-0349
Continues: Physician relations advisor.
Absorbed by: Healthcare risk management.
1994-1998   **9709715**

Physician's Bull
Physician's bulletin
1926-1963   **0022635**

Physicians Manage
Physician's management
0031-9066
1960-1998   19630040R

Physiol Behav
Physiology & behavior
0031-9384
1966   0151504

Physiol Biochem Zool
Physiological and biochemical zoology: PBZ
1522-2152   1537-5293
Continues: Physiological zoology.
1999   100883369

Physiol Bohemoslov
Physiologia Bohemoslovaca
0369-9463
Continued by: Physiological research.
1966-1990   0175317

Physiol Bohemoslov
Physiologia bohemoslovenica
Continues Chekhoslovatskaia fiziologiia.
1956-1965   0175320

Physiol Chem Phys
Physiological chemistry and physics
0031-9325
Continued by Physiological chemistry and
physics and medical NMR.
1969-1982   0202364

Physiol Chem Phys Med NMR
Physiological chemistry and physics and
medical NMR
0748-6642
Continues: Physiological chemistry and
physics.
1983   8502230

Physiol Comp Ocol Int J Comp Physiol Ecol
Physiologia comparata et oecologia; an
international journal of comparative
physiology and ecology
Continued by Monographiae biologicae.
1948-1957   19630180R

Physiol Genomics
Physiological genomics
1094-8341   1531-2267
1999   9815683

Physiol Meas
Physiological measurement
0967-3334
Continues: Clinical physics and physiological
measurement.
1993   9306921

Physiol Pharmacol Physicians
Physiology & pharmacology for physicians
0554-1417
Supersedes Physiology for physicians.
1966-1966   0045406

Physiol Plant
Physiologia plantarum
0031-9317   1399-3054
1948   1256322

Physiol Res
Physiological research / Academia
Scientiarum Bohemoslovaca
0862-8408   1802-9973
Continues: Physiologia bohemoslovaca.
1991   9112413

Physiol Rev
Physiological reviews
0031-9333   1522-1210
1921   0231714

Physiol Rev Suppl
Physiological reviews. Supplement
0554-1395
1952-1962   0401221

Physiol Teach
The Physiology teacher
0048-4075
Absorbed by: The Physiologist.
1971-1978   0361045

Physiol Zool
Physiological zoology
0031-935X
Continued by: Physiological and biochemical
zoology.
1928-1998   0401142

Physiologie
Physiologie
1011-6206
Continued by: Revue roumaine de
physiologie (Bucharest, Romania: 1990).
1975-1989   7510964

Physiologist
The Physiologist
0031-9376
Absorbed The Physiology teacher, Apr. 1978.
1957   0401143

Physiology (Bethesda)
Physiology (Bethesda, Md.)
1548-9213   1548-9221
Continues: News in physiological sciences.
2004   101208185

Physiother Can
Physiotherapy Canada. Physiothérapie
Canada
0300-0508   1708-8313
Continues: Journal of the Canadian
Physiotherapy Association.
1972   0346574

Physiother Res Int
Physiotherapy research international: the
journal for researchers and clinicians in
physical therapy
1358-2267
1996   9612022

Physiother Theory Pract
Physiotherapy theory and practice
0959-3985   1532-5040
Continues: Physiotherapy practice.
1990   9015520

Physiotherap Rev
The Physiotherapy review
Continues the P. T. review. Continued by the
Physical therapy review.
1926-1948   19620710R

Physiotherapy
Physiotherapy
0031-9406
Continues: Journal. Chartered Society of
Physiotherapy (Great Britain).
1948   0401223

Physis Riv Int Stor Sci
Physis; rivista internazionale di storia della
scienza
0031-9414
1959   0076224

Phytochem Anal
Phytochemical analysis: PCA
0958-0344   1099-1565
1990   9200492

Phytochemistry
Phytochemistry
0031-9422
1961   0151434

Phytomedicine
Phytomedicine: international journal of
phytotherapy and phytopharmacology
0944-7113   1618-095X
1994   9438794

Phytopathology
Phytopathology
0031-949X   1943-7684
1911   9427222

Phytother Res
Phytotherapy research: PTR
0951-418X   1099-1573
1987   8904486

PI Perspect
PI perspective
1058-7454
Continued by: Project Inform perspective.
198u-1997   9102818

Pieleg Polozna
Pielęgniarka i położna
0048-4148
Formed by the merger of Pielęgniarka polska
and Położna.
1958-1989   19630310R

Pigment Cell Melanoma Res
Pigment cell & melanoma research
1755-1471   1755-148X
Continues: Pigment cell research.
2008   101318927

Pigment Cell Res
Pigment cell research / sponsored by the
European Society for Pigment Cell Research
and the International Pigment Cell Society
0893-5785   1600-0749
Continued by: Pigment cell and melanoma
research.
1987-2007   8800247

Pinheiros Ter
Pinheiros terapêutico
1949-1967   19630410R

Pisani
Il Pisani: organo del Manicomio di Palermo
0391-0466
Continues: Gazzetta sicula.
1878-19uu   9427221

Pituitary
Pituitary
1386-341X
1998   9814578

Placenta
Placenta
0143-4004
1980   8006349

Placenta Suppl
Placenta. Supplement
0265-7023
1981-1982   8306308

Plant Biol (Stuttg)
Plant biology (Stuttgart, Germany)
1435-8603
Formed by the union of: Acta botanica
Neerlandica, and: Botanica acta.
1999   101148926

Plant Biotechnol J
Plant biotechnology journal
1467-7644   1467-7652
2003   101201889

Plant Cell
The Plant cell
1040-4651   1532-298X
1989   9208688

Plant Cell Environ
Plant, cell & environment
0140-7791   1365-3040
1978   9309004

Plant Cell Physiol
Plant & cell physiology
0032-0781   1471-9053
1959   9430925

Plant Cell Rep
Plant cell reports
0721-7714   1432-203X
1981   9880970

Plant Foods Hum Nutr
Plant foods for human nutrition (Dordrecht, Netherlands)
0921-9668   1573-9104
Continues: Qualitas plantarum - plant foods for human nutrition.
1987   8803554

Plant Health
Plantation health
1936-1964   19630570R

Plant J
The Plant journal: for cell and molecular biology
0960-7412   1365-313X
1991   9207397

Plant Mol Biol
Plant molecular biology
0167-4412
1981   9106343

Plant Physiol
Plant physiology
0032-0889   1532-2548
1926   0401224

Plant Physiol Biochem
Plant physiology and biochemistry: PPB / Société française de physiologie végétale
0981-9428
Continues: Physiologie végétale.
1987   9882449

Planta
Planta
0032-0935   1432-2048
1925   1250576

Planta Med
Planta medica
0032-0943
1953   0066751

Plasmid
Plasmid
0147-619X   1095-9890
1977   7802221

Plast Reconstr Surg
Plastic and reconstructive surgery
0032-1052   1529-4242
Continues: Plastic and reconstructive surgery and the transplantation bulletin.
1963   1306050

Plast Reconstr Surg (1946)
Plastic and reconstructive surgery (1946)
1075-1270
Continued by: Plastic and reconstructive surgery and the transplantation bulletin.
1946-1957   101243648

Plast Reconstr Surg Transplant Bull
Plastic and reconstructive surgery and the transplantation bulletin
0096-8501
Continues: Plastic and reconstructive surgery. Superseded in part by: Transplantation. Continued in part by: Plastic and reconstructive surgery (1963).
1958-1962   101243645

Plast Surg Nurs
Plastic surgical nursing: official journal of the American Society of Plastic and Reconstructive Surgical Nurses
0741-5206
Continues: Journal of plastic and reconstructive surgical nursing.
1983   8403490

Platelets
Platelets
0953-7104   1369-1635
1990   9208117

PLoS Biol
PLoS biology
1544-9173   1545-7885
2003   101183755

PLoS Comput Biol
PLoS computational biology
1553-734X   1553-7358
2005   101238922

PLoS Genet
PLoS genetics
1553-7390   1553-7404
2005   101239074

PLoS Med
PLoS medicine
1549-1277   1549-1676
2004   101231360

PLoS ONE
PLoS ONE
    1932-6203
Continues: PLoS clinical trials.
2006   101285081

PLoS Pathog
PLoS pathogens
1553-7366   1553-7374
2005   101238921

Plucne Bolesti
Plućne bolesti: casopis Udruzenja pneumoftiziologa Jugoslavije = the journal of Yugoslav Association of Phthisiology and Pneumology
0352-5503
Continues: Plućne bolesti i tuberkuloza.
1984-1991   8413310

Plucne Bolesti Tuberk
Plućne bolesti i tuberkuloza
0370-0380
Continues Tuberkuloza. Continued by Plućne bolesti.
1969-1983   0226072

Plugger
Plugger (Waterloo, Ia.)
19uu   9875619

Plzen Lek Sb
PlzenÄÜský lékařský sborník
0551-1038
1945   19630650R

Pneumoftiziologia
Pneumoftiziologia: revista Societătii Române de Pneumoftiziologie / [Societatea Română de Pneumoftiziologie]
0377-5011
Continues: Revista de igienă, medicina muncii, medicină socială, bacteriologie, virusologie, parazitologie, epidemiologie, pneumoftiziologie. Pneumoftiziologie. Continued by: Pneumologia (Bucharest, Romania).
1991-199u   9212780

Pneumologia
Pneumologia (Bucharest, Romania)
Continues: Pneumoftiziologia.
199u   100941067

Pneumologie
Pneumologie (Stuttgart, Germany)
0934-8387   1438-8790
Continues: Praxis und Klinik der Pneumologie.
1989   8906641

Pneumonol Alergol Pol
Pneumonologia i alergologia polska: organ Polskiego Towarzystwa Ftyzjopneumonologicznego, Polskiego Towarzystwa Alergologicznego, i Instytutu Gruźlicy i Chorób Płuc
0867-7077
Continues: Pneumonologia polska.
1991   9302892

Pneumonol Danub
Pneumonologia Danubiana
0324-4229
Continued by: Tuberkulózis kérdései.
1948-1949   21330370R

Pneumonol Phymatiologike Epitheor
Pneumonologike kai phymatiologike epitheoresis
0551-1062
Supersedes Soteria: hellenika phymatiologika chronika. Continued by Hellenike pneumonologike & phymatiologike epitheoresis.
1960-1972   7504330

Pneumonol Pol
Pneumonologia polska
0376-4761
Continues Gruźlica i choroby płuc. Continued by: Pneumonologia i alergologia polska.
1976-1990   7605692

Pneumonologie
Pneumonologie. Pneumonology
0033-4073
Continues Beiträge zur Klinik und Erforschung der Tuberkulose und der Lungenkrankheiten. Continued by Lung.
1970-1976   1250075

Pol Arch Med Wewn
Polskie archiwum medycyny wewnętrznej
0032-3772   1897-9483
1923   0401225

Pol Arch Weter
Polskie archiwum weterynaryjne
0079-3647
Continued by: Archivum veterinarium Polonicum.
1951-1991   0023271

Pol J Microbiol
Polish journal of microbiology / Polskie Towarzystwo Mikrobiologów = The Polish Society of Microbiologists
1733-1331
Continues: Acta microbiologica Polonica.
2004   101229003

Pol J Occup Med
Polish journal of occupational medicine
0860-6536
Continued by: Polish journal of occupational Medicine and environmental health.
1988-1990   9012925

Pol J Occup Med Environ Health
Polish journal of occupational medicine and environmental health
0867-8383
Continues: Polish journal of occupational medicine. Continued by: International journal of occupational medicine and environmental health.
1991-1993   9215008

Pol J Pathol
Polish journal of pathology: official journal of the Polish Society of Pathologists
1233-9687
Continues: Patologia polska.
1994   9437432

Pol J Pharmacol
Polish journal of pharmacology
1230-6002
Continues: Polish journal of pharmacology and pharmacy. Continued by: Pharmacological reports.
1993-2004   9313882

Pol J Pharmacol Pharm
Polish journal of pharmacology and pharmacy
0301-0244
Continues Dissertationes pharmaceuticae et pharmacologicae. Continued by: Polish journal of pharmacology.
1973-1992   0366561

Pol J Vet Sci
Polish journal of veterinary sciences
1505-1773
Continues: Archivum veterinarium Polonicum.
1998   101125473

Pol Med Hist Sci Bull
Polish medical history and science bulletin
0007-5051
Continued by: Polish medical science and history bulletin.
1956-1959   9427068

Pol Med J
Polish medical journal
0032-2938
1962-1972   0376721

Pol Med Sci Hist Bull
Polish medical science and history bulletin
0091-3340
Continues Polish medical history and science bulletin. Superseded by Polish medical sciences and history bulletin.
1960-1971   0367052

Pol Med Sci Hist Bull
Polish medical sciences and history bulletin
0301-0236
Continues Polish medical science and history bulletin.
1973-1976   0414140

Pol Merkur Lekarski
Polski merkuriusz lekarski: organ Polskiego Towarzystwa Lekarskiego
1426-9686
Continues: Polski tygodnik lekarski (Warsaw, Poland: 1960).
1996   9705469

Pol Przegl Chir
Polski przeglad chirurgiczny
0032-373X
1921   0376426

Pol Przegl Radiol
Polski przeglad radiologii / Polskie Lekarskie Towarzystwo Radiologiczne
0860-1089
Continues: Polski przeglad radiologii i medycyny nuklearnej. Continued by: Polish journal of radiology.
1983-2002   8409860

Pol Przegl Radiol Med Nukl
Polski przeglaÄúd radiologii i medycyny nuklearnej
0137-7183
Continues Polski przeglaÄúd radiologiczny. Continued by Polski przeglaÄúd radiologii.
1961-1982   0401226

Pol Tyg Lek
Polski tygodnik lekarski (Warsaw, Poland: 1960)
0032-3756
Continues in part: Polski tygodnik lekarski i wiadomosci lekarskie. Continued by: Polski merkuriusz lekarski.
1960-1996   9705468

Pol Tyg Lek (Wars)
Polski tygodnik lekarski
0860-8857
Merged with: Wiadomości lekarski (Warsaw, Poland: 1948), to form: Polski tygodnik lekarski i wiadomości lekarskie.
1946-1958   9706227

Policlin Infant
Policlinico infantile
0391-0474
Merged with: Medicina italiana, and La Pediatria del medico pratico, to form: Minerva pediatrica.
1933-1948   19710100R

Policlinico [Chir]
Il Policlinico. Sezione chirurgica
0032-2636
1893   0404461

Policlinico [Med]
Il Policlinico. Sezione medica
0048-4717
1893   0401144

Policlinico [Prat]
Il Policlinico. Sezione pratica
0032-2644
Continues Supplemento al Policlinico.
1900   0410122

Policlinico [Prat]
Policlinico; sezione practica
1894   100971284

Policy Anal
Policy analysis
0098-2067
Merged with Public policy, to form Journal of policy analysis and management.
1975-1981   7703761

Policy Anal Brief H Ser
Policy analysis brief. H series / Project Hope, Center for Health Affairs
1999   101130969

Policy Anal Brief W Ser
Policy analysis brief. W series / Project Hope, Walsh Center for Rural Health Analysis
1998   101130970

Policy Brief (Cent Home Care Policy Res)
Policy brief (Center for Home Care Policy and Research (U.S.))
Continues: Fact sheet (Center for Home Care Policy and Research (U.S.)).
2000   101206020

Policy Brief Commonw Fund
Policy brief (Commonwealth Fund)
19uu   101130806

Policy Brief George Wash Univ Cent Health Serv Res Policy
Policy brief (George Washington University. Center for Health Services Research and Policy)
2001   101133097

Policy Brief Health Care Technol Inst
Policy brief (Alexandria, Va.)
1993-1995   9412760

Policy Brief UCLA Cent Health Policy Res
Policy brief (UCLA Center for Health Policy Research)
1994   100972707

Policy Polit Nurs Pract
Policy, politics & nursing practice
1527-1544   1552-7468
2000   100901316

Policy Statement R Coll Gen Pract
Policy statement / Royal College of General Practitioners. Royal College of General Practitioners
0957-0357
1985-1985   8604205

Polim Med
Polimery w medycynie
0370-0747
1971   7509477

Politics Life Sci
Politics and the life sciences: the journal of the Association for Politics and the Life Sciences
0730-9384   1471-5457
1982   8800535

Popul Health Manag
Population health management
1942-7891   1942-7905
Continues: Disease management.
2008   101481266

Popul Rep A
Population reports. Series A: Oral contraceptives
0097-9074
1974   7501604

Popul Rep B
Population reports. Series B: Intrauterine devices
0092-9344
1973   0410014

Popul Rep C
Population reports (Washington, D.C.). Series C,, Female sterilization
0891-0030
Continues: Population reports. Series C: Sterilization [Female].
1980-1990   9213379

Popul Rep C
Population reports. Series C: Sterilization [Female]
Continued by: Population reports (Washington, D.C.). Series C, Female sterilization.
1973-1976   0376213

Popul Rep D
Population reports (Washington, D.C.). Series D, Male sterilization
0891-0049
Continues: Population reports (Washington, D.C.). Series D, Sterilization.
1983-1992   9215009

Popul Rep D
Population reports (Washington, D.C.). Series D, Sterilization
0093-4488
Continued by: Population reports (Washington, D.C.). Series D, Male sterilization.
1973-1976   0415050

Popul Rep E
Population reports. Series E, Law and policy
0097-9082
1974-1984   7501605

Popul Rep F
Population reports. Series F: Pregnancy
termination
0091-9284
1973-1980   0376215

Popul Rep G
Population reports. Series G, Prostaglandins
0091-9276
   Absorbed: Research in prostaglandins.
1973-1980   0376216

Popul Rep H
Population reports. Series H: Barrier
methods
0093-4496
1973-1999   0415051

Popul Rep I
Population reports. Series I: Periodic
abstinence
0097-9090
1974-1981   7501606

Popul Rep J
Population reports. Series J: Family
planning programs
0091-925X
1973   0377050

Popul Rep K
Population reports. Series K: Injectables
and implants
0097-9104
1975-1995   7505819

Popul Rep L
Population reports. Series L, Issues in world
health
0197-5838
1979   7903810

Popul Rep M
Population reports. Series M, Special topic
monographs
0275-8792
   Continues: Population reports. Special topic
   monographs. Continued by: Population
   reports. Series M. Special topics.
1979-1979   8204976

Popul Rep M
Population reports. Series M. Special topics
0733-9135
   Continues: Population reports. Series M.
   Special topic monographs.
1981   8204224

Popul Rep Spec Top Monogr
Population reports. Special topic
monographs
0161-679X
   Continued by Population reports. Series M.
   Special topic monographs.
1977-1978   7708440

Popul Soc (Paris)
Population et sociétés; bulletin mensuel
d'informations démographiques,
économiques, sociales
0184-7783
1968   0154572

Popul Stud (Camb)
Population studies
0032-4728   1477-4747
1947   0376427

Popul Trends
Population trends
0307-4463
   Continues in part: The Registrar general's
   quarterly return for England and Wales.
1975   7608016

Port Med
Portugal médico
1915-1961   19720190R

Portland Clin Bull
Bulletin. Portland, Or. Clinic
1947-1969   19720090R

Posit Aware
Positively aware: the monthly journal of the
Test Positive Aware Network
1523-2883
   Continues: TPA news.
1990   9413754

Posit Dir News
Positive Directions news: a support and
information network of people with HIV/
AIDS, their families, friends and providers
19uu-2002   100891227

Posit Health News
Positive health news
   Continues: HIV treatment news. Merged
   with: Progressive health news, to form:
   Journal of immunity.
1994-2002   9890538

Posit Living
Positive living (Los Angeles, Calif.)
1992-2002   9886875

Postep Chir
Postępy chirurgii
1954-19uu   19720250R

Postep Neurol Neurochir Psychiatr
Postępy neurologii, neurochirurgii, i
psychiatrii
1954-1958   19720290R

Postep Reumatol
Postępy reumatologii
1954-1957   19720320R

Postep Wiedzy Med
Postępy wiedzy medycznej
   Absorbed by: Postępy higieny i medycyny
   doświadczalnej.
1954-1957   19720340R

Postepy Biochem
Postepy biochemii
0032-5422
1955   0023525

Postepy Hig Med Dosw
Postępy higieny i medycyny doświadczalnej
0032-5449
   Absorbed: Postępy wiedzy medycznej.
   Continued by: Postępy higieny i medycyny
   doświadczalnej (Online).
1949-2003   0421052

Postepy Hig Med Dosw (Online)
Postępy higieny i medycyny doświadczalnej
(Online)
    1732-2693
   Continues: Postępy higieny i medycyny
   doświadczalnej.
2004   101206517

Postgrad Med
Postgraduate medicine
0032-5481   1941-9260
   Vols. for <May 15, 2000-> include: e.MD,
   which was formerly published separately, and
   is now a separately paged insert in some issues.
1947   0401147

Postgrad Med J
Postgraduate medical journal
0032-5473   1469-0756
   Supersedes: Bulletin of the Fellowship
   of Medicine and Post-Graduate Medical
   Association.
1925   0234135

Postgrad Semin Am Urol Assoc North Cent
Postgraduate seminar. American Urological
Association. North Central Section
1956-1958   23610900R

Poult Sci
Poultry science
0032-5791
   Continues: Journal. Poultry Science
   Association.
1921   0401150

Poumon
Le Poumon
   Continued by Le Poumon et le coeur.
1945-1954   19720410R

Poumon Coeur
Le Poumon et le coeur
0032-5821
   Continues Le Poumon. Continued by Revue
   de pneumologie clinique.
1954-1983   0404462

Pr Kom Med Dosw
Prace Komisji Medycyny Doświadczalnej /
Poznańskie Towarzystwo Przyjaciół Nauk,
Wydział Lekarski
0301-1658
   Continues: Prace. Poznanskie Towarzystwo
   Przyjaciol Nauk. Komisja Lekarska.
   Continued by: Medycyna doświadczalna.
1948-1961   9442868

Pr Lodz Tow Nauk [IV]
Prace. Łódzkie Towarzystwo Naukowe.
Wydział IV, Nauk Lekarskich
1951-1967   18331170R

Prac Lek
Pracovní lékařstvi
0032-6291
   Continued in part by: Ceské pracovní
   lékařstvi.
1949   0404463

Pract Dent Monogr
Practical dental monographs
1957-1966   0232533

Pract Dig
Practice digest
0161-0287
1978-1984   7808568

Pract Midwife
The practising midwife
1461-3123
   Continues: Modern midwife.
1998   9814758

Pract Neurol
Practical neurology
1474-7758   1474-7766
2001   101130961

Pract Odontol
Práctica odontológica
0185-5905
1979-2001   8700949

Pract Otorhinolaryngol (Basel)
Practica oto-rhino-laryngologica
0032-6305
   Absorbed Mitteilungen über Sprach- und
   Stimmheilkunde. Continued by ORL: journal
   for oto-rhino-laryngology and its borderlands.
1938-1971   0340156

Pract Periodontics Aesthet Dent
Practical periodontics and aesthetic
dentistry: PPAD
   Continued by: Practical procedures &
   aesthetic dentistry.
1989-2000   9002247

Pract Proced Aesthet Dent
Practical procedures & aesthetic dentistry:
PPAD
1534-6846
Continues: Practical periodontics and
aesthetic dentistry.
2001   101089932

Pract Resour
Practice resource / AWHONN, Association
of Women's Health, Obstetric, and Neonatal
Nurses
Continues: OGN nursing practice resource.
1993-1993   9315641

Practitioner
The Practitioner
0032-6518
1868   0404245

Prague Med Rep
Prague medical report
1214-6994
Continues: Sborník lékarský.
2004   101227436

Prairie Rose
The Prairie rose
0032-6666
1932   19730190R

Prakt Anaesth
Praktische Anästhesie, Wiederbelebung und
Intensivtherapie
0302-7600
Continues Zeitschrift für praktische
Anästhesie, Wiederbelebung und
Intensivtherapie. Continued by Anästhesie,
Intensivtherapie, Notfallmedizin.
1974-1979   0417656

Prakt Arzt
Der Praktische Arzt
0048-5128
Continued by: Arzt & Praxis (Göttlesbrunn,
Austria).
1947-1994   0060366

Prakt Kieferorthop
Praktische Kieferorthopädie
0931-6965
Continued by: Kieferorthopädie.
1987-1993   8806628

Prakt Lek
Praktický lékar
0032-6739
1921   2985132R

Prakt Zubn Lek
Praktické zubní lékarství
0032-6720
1953   19730200R

Prax Kinderpsychol Kinderpsychiatr
Praxis der Kinderpsychologie und
Kinderpsychiatrie
0032-7034
1952   0404246

Prax Kinderpsychol Kinderpsychiatr Beih
Praxis der Kinderpsychologie und
Kinderpsychiatrie. Beiheft
0085-5073
1958-1989   0200651

Prax Klin Pneumol
Praxis und Klinik der Pneumologie
0342-7498
Continues Praxis der Pneumologie vereinigt
mit Der Tuberkulosearzt. Continued by:
Pneumologie (Stuttgart, Germany).
1977-1988   7705449

Prax Pneumol
Praxis der Pneumologie vereinigt mit Der
Tuberkulosearzt
0032-7069
Continues Der Tuberkulosearzt. Continued by
Praxis und Klinik der Pneumologie.
1964-1977   7705926

Prax Psychother
Praxis der Psychotherapie
0032-7077
Continues: Psychotherapie. Continued by:
Praxis der Psychotherapie und Psychosomatik.
1959-1978   0413136

Praxis
Praxis
0369-8394
Continues: Schweizerische Rundschau
für Medizin. Revu suisse de Médecine.
Continued by: Schweizerische Rundschau für
Medizin Praxis.
1923-1969   0401230

Praxis (Bern 1994)
Praxis
1661-8157   1661-8165
Continues: Schweizerische Rundschau für
Medizin Praxis.
1994   101468093

Preconf Papers Natl Dent Health Conf (U S)
[Preconference papers]. National Dental
Health Conference
195u-1979   0020066

Prehosp Disaster Med
Prehospital and disaster medicine: the
official journal of the National Association of
EMS Physicians and the World Association
for Emergency and Disaster Medicine in
association with the Acute Care Foundation
1049-023X
Formed by the union of: Journal of the World
Association for Emergency and Disaster
Medicine, and: Journal of prehospital
medicine.
1989   8918173

Prehosp Emerg Care
Prehospital emergency care: official
journal of the National Association of EMS
Physicians and the National Association of
State EMS Directors
1090-3127   1545-0066
1997   9703530

Premed J Columbia Univ
Pre-medical journal of Columbia University
1942-19uu   19730470R

Prenat Diagn
Prenatal diagnosis
0197-3851
1981   8106540

Prensa Med Argent
Prensa médica argentina
0032-745X
1914-2001   0204056

Prensa Med Mex
La Prensa médica mexicana
0032-7468
1936-1979   0413433

Prensa Pediatr Rev Am Puericu Pediatr
Prensa pediátrica; revista americana de
puericultura y pediatría
1949-19uu   19740020R

Prep Biochem
Preparative biochemistry
0032-7484
Continued by: Preparative biochemistry &
biotechnology.
1971-1995   1276634

Prep Biochem Biotechnol
Preparative biochemistry & biotechnology
1082-6068   1532-2297
Continues: Preparative biochemistry.
1996   9607037

Presbyt St Lukes Hosp Med Bull
Presbyterian-St. Luke's Hospital medical
bulletin
Continued by Rush-Presbyterian-St. Luke's
medical bulletin.
1962-1970   1277377

Prescriber
The Prescriber
0370-145X
Continued by the Medical review.
1906-1948   19740080R

Prescrire Int
Prescrire international
1167-7422
1992   9439295

Presse Med
La Presse médicale
0032-7867
Continued by: Nouvelle presse médicale.
1893-1971   0312556

Presse Med
Presse médicale (Paris, France: 1983)
0755-4982
Absorbed: Annales de médecine interne. 2004
Continues: Nouvelle presse médicale.
1983   8302490

Presse Therm Clim
La Presse thermale et climatique
0032-7875
Continues La Gazette des eaux.
1920-1999   0401151

Prev Assist Dent
Prevenzione & assistenza dentale
0393-9960
Continues: Prevenzione stomatologica.
1985   8603623

Prev Cardiol
Preventive cardiology
1520-037X
1998   9813731

Prev Chronic Dis
Preventing chronic disease
                                        1545-1151
2004   101205018

Prev Hum Serv
Prevention in human services
0270-3114
Continues: Community mental health review.
Continued by: Journal of prevention &
intervention in the community.
1981-1995   8209843

Prev Med
Preventive medicine
0091-7435   1096-0260
1972   0322116

Prev Sci
Prevention science: the official journal of the
Society for Prevention Research
1389-4986
2000   100894724

Prev Stomatol
Prevenzione stomatologica
Continued by: Prevenzione & assistenza
dentale.
1975-1985   7603982

Prev Vet Med
Preventive veterinary medicine
0167-5877
1982   8217463

Pride Inst J Long Term Home Health Care
Pride Institute journal of long term home health care
0743-5088
Continued by: Journal of long term home health care.
1982-1993   8310856

Prikl Biokhim Mikrobiol
Prikladnaia biokhimiia i mikrobiologiia
0555-1099
1965   0023416

Prilozi
Prilozi / Makedonska akademija na naukite i umetnostite, Oddelenie za biološki i medicinski nauki = Contributions / Macedonian Academy of Sciences and Arts, Section of Biological and Medical Sciences
0351-3254
1980   101189513

Prim Care
Primary care
0095-4543   1558-299X
1974   0430463

Prim Care Diabetes
Primary care diabetes
1751-9918
20uu   101463825

Prim Care Respir J
Primary care respiratory journal: journal of the General Practice Airways Group
1471-4418   1475-1534
Continues: Asthma in general practice.
2000   101121543

Prim Dent Care
Primary dental care: journal of the Faculty of General Dental Practitioners (UK)
1355-7610
1994   9617339

Primates
Primates; journal of primatology
0032-8332
1957   0401152

Primates Med
Primates in medicine
0079-5119
1968-1978   0127433

Princess Takamatsu Symp
Princess Takamatsu symposia
1971-1995   9301172

Prion
Prion
1933-6896   1933-690X
2007   101472305

Prir Clovek Zdravje
Priroda, človek in zdravje
1945-1980   19740290R

PRN Forum
PRN forum
0743-345X
Continued by: Journal of pain and symptom management.
1982-1985   8508457

Pro Fono
Pró-fono: revista de atualização científica
0104-5687   1809-399X
1989   100930630

Pro Infirm
Pro Infirmis
1942-1993   19740390R

Pro Med Arztl Ref
Pro medico; ärztliches Referatenblatt
0032-907X
1930-1984   0376435

Pro Re Nata
Pro re nata PRN: the official publication of the Utah Nurses' Association
1044-4025
Continues: One on one. Continued by: Pro re nata (1992) published v. 1. no. 1 (June 1992).
1986-1991   8812220

Probe
Probe (Ottawa, Ont.)
0834-1494
Continues: Canadian dental hygienist.
Continued by: Canadian journal of dental hygiene.
1986-2004   8703585

Probe (Adelaide)
Probe
1949-1969   2984823R

Probe (Lond)
The Probe
0032-9185
1954   19740410R

Probl Actuels Endocrinol Nutr
Problèmes actuels d'endocrinologie et de nutrition
0079-5666
1957-1977   0063734

Probl Actuels Otorhinolaryngol
Problèmes actuels d'oto-rhino-laryngologie
0079-5674
Continues L'année oto-rhino-laryngologique.
1961-1975   0404464

Probl Cardiol
Probleme de cardiologie
1955-1959   0401231

Probl Endokrinol (Mosk)
Problemy eÄändokrinologii
0375-9660
Continues Problemy eÄändokrinologii i gormonoterapii.
1967   0140673

Probl Endokrinol Gormonoter
Problemy éndokrinologii i gormonoterapii
0032-9509
Continues: Problemy éndokrinologii (1936-1941). Continued by: Problemy éndokrinologii.
1955-1966   0140721

Probl Gematol Pereliv Krovi
Problemy gematologii i perelivaniia krovi
0552-2080
Continued by Gematologiia i transfuziologiia.
1956-1982   0401232

Probl Hematol Blood Transfus
Problems of hematology and blood transfusion. Problemy gematologii i perelivaniia krovi
1957-1961   19810030R

Probl Khig
Problemi na khigienata
0323-9179
1975   7703299

Probl Kosm Biol
Problemy kosmicheskoĭ biologii
0555-2788
1962-1994   0151523

Probl Med Wieku Rozwoj
Problemy medycyny wieku rozwojowego
0303-2264
Continued by: Medycyna wieku rozwojowego.
1972-1990   0420627

Probl Oncol
Problems of oncology. Voprosy onkologii
1957-1961   19810040R

Probl Onkol
Problemi na onkologiiata
0323-9209
1973-1990   7502161

Probl Reumatol
Probleme de reumatologie
Superseded by: Studii şi cercetări de medicină internă.
1953-1959   19740510R

Probl Sev
Problemy Severa
0555-2982
1958   0401154

Probl Sotsialnoi Gig Istor Med
Problemy sotŝiaĭnoĭ gigieny i istoriiâ meditŝiny / NII sotŝiaĭnoĭ gigieny, ėkonomiki i upravleniiâ zdravookhraneniem im. N.A. Semashko RAMN ; AO "Assotŝiatŝiiâ 'Meditŝinskaiâ literatura'."
Continues: Sovetskoe zdravookhranenie. Continued by: Problemy sotŝiaĭnoĭ gigieny, zdravookhraneniiâ i istorii meditŝiny.
1994-1998   9707929

Probl Sotsialnoi Gig Zdravookhranenniiai Istor Med
Problemy sotŝiaĭnoĭ gigieny, zdravookhraneniiâ i istorii meditŝiny / NII sotŝiaĭnoĭ gigieny, ėkonomiki i upravleniiâ zdravookhraneniem im. N.A. Semashko RAMN ; AO "Assotŝiatŝiiâ 'Meditŝinskaiâ literatura'."
0869-866X
Continues: Problemy sotŝiaĭnoĭ gigieny i istoriiâ meditŝiny.
1999   101270373

Probl Sovrem Neirokhirurgii
Problemy sovremennoĭ neĭrokhirurgii
1957-19uu   19810190R

Probl Symp Aktuell Ther
Probleme. Symposien aktueller therapeutischer
1959-1960   24930260R

Probl Ter
Probleme de terapeutică
1954-1959   19740520R

Probl Tuberculoza
Probleme de tuberculoză
1960-1966   19740530R

Probl Tuberk
Problemy tuberkuleza
0032-9533
Continues: Bor ᴕba s tuberkulezom. Continued by: Problemy tuberkuleza i bolezneĭ legkikh.
1935-2003   0414141

Probl Tuberk Bolezn Legk
Problemy tuberkuleza i bolezneĭ legkikh
1728-2993
Continues: Problemy tuberkuleza.
2003   101211108

Probl Vet Med
Problems in veterinary medicine
1041-0228
1989-1992   8912755

Probl Virol
Problems of virology
0555-2621
1957-1961   19810080R

Proc Am Fed Clin Res
Proceedings. American Federation for Clinical Research
1944-1952   14810560R

Proc Am Philos Soc
Proceedings of the American Philosophical
Society
0003-049X
1838   7507374

Proc Am Thorac Soc
Proceedings of the American Thoracic
Society
1546-3222
2004   101203596

Proc AMIA Annu Fall Symp
Proceedings: a conference of the American
Medical Informatics Association / ...
AMIA Annual Fall Symposium. AMIA Fall
Symposium
1091-8280
   Continues: Proceedings. Symposium
   on Computer Applications in Medical
   Care. Continued by: Proceedings. AMIA
   Symposium.
   1996-1997   9617342

Proc AMIA Symp
Proceedings / AMIA ... Annual Symposium.
AMIA Symposium
1531-605X
   Continues: Proceedings. AMIA Fall
   Symposium. Continued by: AMIA ... Annual
   Symposium proceedings. AMIA Symposium.
   1998-2002   100883449

Proc Anim Care Panel
Proceedings. Animal Care Panel (U.S.)
0097-076X
   Continued by Laboratory animal care.
   1950-1962   0243753

Proc Annu Clin Spinal Cord Inj Conf
Proceedings. Clinical Spinal Cord Injury
Conference
   Continues the Proceedings of the Clinical
   Paraplegia Conference. Continued by the
   Proceedings of the Veterans Administration
   Spinal Cord Injury Conference.
   1959-1967   1265166

Proc Annu Conf Res Med Educ
Proceedings of the ... annual Conference on
Research in Medical Education. Conference
on Research in Medical Education
0892-2543
   Continues: Annual Conference on Research in
   Medical Education. Conference on Research
   in Medical Education. Continued by:
   Research in medical education. Conference
   on Research in Medical Education.
   1983-1983   8402509

Proc Annu Manage Conf Am Dent Assoc
Proceedings, Annual Management
Conference - American Dental Association
0148-4699
1970-1978   7704006

Proc Annu Meet Am Psychopathol Assoc
Proceedings of the annual meeting of the
American Psychopathological Association
0091-7389
1944-1974   7505842

Proc Annu Meet Med Sect Am Counc Life Insur
Proceedings, the annual meeting of the
Medical Section of the American Council of
Life Insurance
0148-4931
   Continues: Proceedings, the annual meeting
   of the Medical Section of the American Life
   Insurance Association. Continued by: Medical
   Section proceedings. American Council of
   Life Insurance. Medical Section. Meeting.
   1976-1982   7704005

Proc Annu Meet Med Sect Am Life Conv
Proceedings, annual meeting of the Medical
Section of the American Life Convention
0065-9126
   Merged with the Proceedings of the annual
   meeting of Life Insurance Association of
   America to form Proceedings, annual meeting
   of the Medical Section of the American Life
   Insurance Association.
   1911-1972   0432130

Proc Annu Meet Med Sect Am Life Insur Assoc
Proceedings, the annual meeting of the
Medical Section of the American Life
Insurance Association
0361-1752
   Formed by the union of the Proceedings of
   the annual meeting of the Life Insurance
   Association of America and the Proceedings,
   annual meeting of the Medical Section of
   the American Life Convention. Superseded
   by Proceedings, the annual meeting of the
   Medical Section of the American Council of
   Life Insurance.
   1973-1975   0432131

Proc Annu Meet U S Anim Health Assoc
Proceedings, annual meeting of the United
States Animal Health Association
0082-8750
   Continues Proceedings, annual meeting of the
   United States Livestock Sanitary Association.
   1969   7505825

Proc Annu Meet U S Livest Sanit Assoc
Proceedings, annual meeting of the United
States Livestock Sanitary Association
   Continues the Proceedings of the Interstate
   Association of Live Stock Sanitary Boards.
   Continued by Proceedings, annual meeting of
   the United States Animal Health Association.
   1910-1968   7505826

Proc Annu Symp Comput Appl Med Care
Proceedings / the ... Annual Symposium on
Computer Application [sic] in Medical Care.
Symposium on Computer Applications in
Medical Care
0195-4210
   Continued by: Proceedings. AMIA Fall
   Symposium.
   1977-1995   8113685

Proc Annu Symp Eugen Soc
Proceedings of the annual symposium of the
Eugenics Society
196u-19uu   100961271

Proc Assoc Am Physicians
Proceedings of the Association of American
Physicians
1081-650X   1525-1381
   Continues: Transactions of the Association of
   American Physicians.
   1995-1999   9514310

Proc Aust Assoc Neurol
Proceedings of the Australian Association of
Neurologists
0084-7224
   Continued by Clinical and experimental
   neurology.
   1963-1976   7505855

Proc Biol Sci
Proceedings. Biological sciences / The Royal
Society
0962-8452   1471-2954
   Continues: Proceedings of the Royal Society
   of London. Series B, Biological sciences.
   Royal Society (Great Britain).
   1990   101245157

Proc Br Paedod Soc
Proceedings of the British Paedodontic
Society
0308-4922
   Continued by Journal of paediatric dentistry.
   1971-1983   7600160

Proc Br Soc Dent Maxillofac Radiol
Proceedings of the British Society of Dental
and Maxillofacial Radiology
0957-7173
   Continues: Newsletter of the British Society
   of Dental and Maxillofacial Radiology.
   1986-1994   9517999

Proc Can Cancer Conf
Proceedings. Canadian Cancer Conference
0068-8436
   1954-1973   23710060R

Proc Cardiff Med Soc
The Proceedings of the Cardiff Medical
Society
   Continued by Scientific proceedings of the
   Cardiff Medical Society.
   1938-1969   7505858

Proc Chem Soc
Proceedings. Chemical Society (Great
Britain)
   Merged with the Journal of the Royal
   Institute of Chemistry to form Chemistry in
   Britain.
   1885-1964   0071570

Proc Chin Acad Med Sci Peking Union Med Coll
Proceedings of the Chinese Academy of
Medical Sciences and the Peking Union
Medical College = Chung-kuo i hsüeh k'o
hsüeh yüan, Chung-kuo hsieh ho i k'o ta
hsüeh hsüeh pao
0258-8757
   Continued by: Chinese medical sciences
   journal.
   1986-1990   8712086

Proc Clin Dial Transplant Forum
Proceedings of the Clinical Dialysis and
Transplant Forum
0094-6044
   1971-1980   0432324

Proc Conf Oral Cancer
Proceedings of the ... Conference on Oral
Cancer. Conference on Oral Cancer
   1960-1963   9875618

Proc Eur Dial Transplant Assoc
Proceedings of the European Dialysis and
Transplant Association. European Dialysis
and Transplant Association
0071-2736
   Continued by European Dialysis and
   Transplant association - European Renal
   Association. Congress. Proceedings of the
   European Dialysis and Transplant Association
   - European Renal Association.
   1964-1982   0355210

Proc Eur Dial Transplant Assoc Eur Ren Assoc
Proceedings of the European Dialysis
and Transplant Association - European
Renal Association. European Dialysis and
Transplant Association - European Renal
Association. Congress
0308-9401
   Continues: European Dialysis and Transplant
   Association. Proceedings of the European
   Dialysis and Transplant Association.
   Continued by: Nephrology, dialysis,
   transplantation.
   1983-1984   8503947

Proc Eur Prosthodontic Assoc
The proceedings of the European
Prosthodontic Association ... Annual
Meeting. European Prosthodontic
Association. Meeting
197u   9879984

Proc Finn Dent Soc
Proceedings of the Finnish Dental Society.
Suomen Hammaslääkäriseuran toimituksia
0355-4651
Continues Suomen Hammaslääkäriseuran
toimituksia.
1972-1993   0366632

Proc Found Orthod Res
Proceedings of the Foundation for
Orthodontic Research
1971   7507378

Proc Health Policy Forum
Proceedings of the Health Policy Forum.
Health Policy Forum
0195-976X
1978-1980   7909110

Proc IEEE Comput Soc Bioinform Conf
Proceedings / IEEE Computer Society
Bioinformatics Conference. IEEE Computer
Society Bioinformatics Conference
1555-3930
Continued by: Proceedings. IEEE
Computational Systems Bioinformatics
Conference.
2002-2003   101223605

Proc IEEE Comput Syst Bioinform Conf
Proceedings / IEEE Computational Systems
Bioinformatics Conference, CSB. IEEE
Computational Systems Bioinformatics
Conference
1551-7497
Continues: Proceedings. IEEE Computer
Society Bioinformatics Conference.
Continued by: Computational systems
bioinformatics. Computational Systems
Bioinformatics Conference
2004-2005   101240586

Proc Inst Mech Eng [H]
Proceedings of the Institution of Mechanical
Engineers. Part H, Journal of engineering in
medicine
0954-4119
Continues: Engineering in medicine.
1989   8908934

Proc Inst Med Chic
The Proceedings of the Institute of Medicine
of Chicago
0091-746X
1916-1992   7505869

Proc Int Acad Oral Pathol
Proceedings Of The International Academy
Of Oral Pathology
19uu   9870009

Proc Int Conf Intell Syst Mol Biol
Proceedings / ... International Conference
on Intelligent Systems for Molecular Biology
; ISMB. International Conference on
Intelligent Systems for Molecular Biology
1553-0833
1993   9509125

Proc Jpn Acad Ser B Phys Biol Sci
Proceedings of the Japan Academy. Series B,
Physical and biological sciences
0386-2208   1349-2896
Continues in part: Proceedings of the Japan
Academy.
1977   9318162

Proc K Ned Akad Wet C
Proceedings of the Koninklijke Nederlandse
Akademie van Wetenschappen. Series C.
Biological and medical sciences
0023-3374
Continues the Proceedings of the Section of
Sciences. Series C: Biological and medical
sciences. of the academy's Afdeeling
Natuurkunde.
1957-1989   7505873

Proc Mine Med Off Assoc
Proceedings of the Mine Medical Officers'
Association
0026-4490
Continues Transvaal Mine Medical Officers'
Association. Proceedings. Continued by
Proceedings of the Mine Medical Officers'
Association of S. A.
1957-1969   7707378

Proc Mine Med Off Assoc SA
Proceedings of the Mine Medical Officers'
Association of S. A
0026-4490
Continues Proceedings of the Mine Medical
Officers' Association. Continued by: Journal
of the Mine Medical Officers' Association of
South Africa.
1969-1983   7707377

Proc Natl Acad Sci U S A
Proceedings of the National Academy of
Sciences of the United States of America
0027-8424   1091-6490
1915   7505876

Proc Natl Cancer Conf
Proceedings. National Cancer Conference
0077-3670
1949-1972   7612873

Proc Natl Conf Methadone Treat
Proceedings. National Conference on
Methadone Treatment
0360-263X
1970-1974   7513674

Proc Natl Sci Counc Repub China B
Proceedings of the National Science Council,
Republic of China. Part B, Life sciences
0255-6596
Continues: Proceedings of the National
Science Council, Republic of China. Part B.
Basic science.
1984-2001   8502426

Proc Nurs Theory Conf
Proceedings. Nursing Theory Conference
(University of Kansas)
1969-1970   1255777

Proc Nutr Soc
The Proceedings of the Nutrition Society
0029-6651
1944   7505881

Proc Pap Annu Conf Calif Mosq Control Assoc
Proceedings and papers of the annual
conference of the California Mosquito
Control Association, inc
0091-6501
Continued by Proceedings and papers of the
annual conference of the California Mosquito
and Vector Control Association, inc.
1941-1976   7505833

Proc R Australas Coll Physicians
Proceedings. Royal Australasian College of
Physicians
1946-1951   20440350R

Proc R Coll Physicians Edinb
Proceedings of the Royal College of
Physicians of Edinburgh
0953-0932
Continues: Chronicle (Royal College of
Physicians of Edinburgh). Continued by:
Journal of the Royal College of Physicians of
Edinburgh.
1987-2001   8800264

Proc R Ir Acad [B]
Proceedings of the Royal Irish Academy.
Section B: Biological, geological, and
chemical science
0035-8983
Continues in part the Proceedings of the
Royal Irish Academy.
1902-1992   7505887

Proc R Soc Edinb [Biol]
Proceedings of the Royal Society of
Edinburgh. Section B: Biology
0080-455X
Continues in part the society's Proceedings.
Continued by Proceedings - Royal Society of
Edinburgh. Section B: Natural environment.
1941-1974   7602713

Proc R Soc Edinb [Nat Environ]
Proceedings - Royal Society of Edinburgh.
Section B: Natural environment
0308-2113
Continues: Proceedings - Royal Society of
Edinburgh. Section B: Biology. Continued by:
Proceedings - Royal Society of Edinburgh.
Section B: Biological Sciences.
1975-1977   7602711

Proc R Soc Lond A Math Phys Sci
Proceedings of the Royal Society of London.
Series A: Mathematical and physical
sciences
0080-4630
Continues in part: Proceedings of the
Royal Society of London. Royal Society
(Great Britain). Continued by: Proceedings.
Mathematical and physical sciences.
1905-1990   7505888

Proc R Soc Lond B Biol Sci
Proceedings of the Royal Society of London.
Series B, Containing papers of a Biological
character. Royal Society (Great Britain)
0080-4649
Continues in part: Proceedings of the
Royal Society of London. Royal Society
(Great Britain). Continued by: Proceedings.
Biological sciences.
1905-1990   7505889

Proc R Soc Med
Proceedings of the Royal Society of
Medicine
0035-9157
Formed by union of: Medico-Chirurgical
Transactions. Continued by Journal of the
Royal Society of Medicine.
1907-1977   7505890

Proc Rudolf Virchow Med Soc City N Y
Proceedings of the Rudolf Virchow Medical
Society in the City of New York
0080-4797
Continued by Proceedings of the Virchow-
Pirquet Medical Society.
1942-1973   7505891

Proc Soc Exp Biol Med
Proceedings of the Society for Experimental
Biology and Medicine. Society for
Experimental Biology and Medicine (New
York, N.Y.)
0037-9727   1525-1373
Continued by: Experimental biology and
medicine (Maywood, N.J.).
1904-2000   7505892

Proc Soc Study Fertil
Proceedings. Society for the Study of
Fertility
1949-1958   20910190R

Proc Staff Meet Honol Clin
Proceedings of the staff meetings. Honolulu.
Clinic
Continued by the Proceedings of the staff
meetings of the Straub Clinic, Honolulu.
1934-1951   17410670R

Proc Staff Meet Mayo Clin
Proceedings of the staff meetings. Mayo
Clinic
0092-699X
Continued by the Mayo Clinic proceedings.
1926-1963   0405544

Proc Staff Meet Pethah Tiqva Isr Beilinson Hosp
Proceedings of the staff meetings. Pethah-
Tiqva, Israel. Beilinson Hospital
1953-19uu   19540700R

Proc Staff Meet Tulsa Okla Hillcrest Meml Hosp
Proceedings of staff meeting. Tulsa, Okla.
Hillcrest Memorial Hospital
1944-19uu   21340210R

Proc State Secr Manage Conf Am Dent Assoc
Proceedings / State Secretaries Management
Conference, American Dental Association
Continued by: Proceedings, Annual
Management Conference - American Dental
Association..
1965-1969   100961141

Proc Transvaal Mine Med Off Assoc
Proceedings. Transvaal Mine Medical
Officers' Association
Continued by the Proceedings of the Mine
Medical Officers' Association.
1921-1957   21310040R

Proc Veterans Adm Spinal Cord Inj Conf
Proceedings. Veterans Administration Spinal
Cord Injury Conference
0083-3568
Continues the Proceedings of the Clinical
Spinal Cord Injury Conference.
1969-1977   1265262

Proc Virchow Pirquet Med Soc
Proceedings of the Virchow-Pirquet Medical
Society
0885-7857
Continues Proceedings of the Rudolf Virchow
Medical Society in the City of New York and
Pirquet bulletin of clinical medicine.
1976-1980   7905619

Proc West Pharmacol Soc
Proceedings of the Western Pharmacology
Society
0083-8969
1958   7505899

Proc Wkly Semin Neurol
Proceedings of the Weekly Seminar in
Neurology
1949-1969   7505898

Prod Pharm
Produits pharmaceutiques
Supersedes Pharmacie; produits
pharmaceutiques. Continued by Produits et
problèmes pharmaceutiques.
1946-1961   0123305

Prod Probl Pharm
Produits & problêmes pharmaceutiques
0032-9959
Continues Produits pharmaceutiques.
1962-1973   0376436

Prof Care Mother Child
Professional care of mother and child
0964-4156
Continues: Midwife, health visitor &
community nurse. Continued by: Journal of
family health care.
1991-2001   9301173

Prof Case Manag
Professional case management
1932-8087   1932-8095
Continues: Lippincott's case management.
2007   101291585

Prof Dev Ser (Chic Ill)
Professional development series (Chicago,
Ill.)
19uu-1998   100891567

Prof Flashes
Professional flashes
0033-0108
1935-1974   19830090R

Prof Inferm
Professioni infermieristiche
0033-0205
Continues the Bollettino d'informazioni
of the Consociazione nazionale infermiere
professionali e assistenti sanitarie visitatrici.
1970   0244135

Prof Nurs Home
Professional nursing home
0555-3393
1959-1968   0243343

Prof Nurse
Professional nurse (London, England)
0266-8130
Absorbed: Community nurse. Sept. 2001
Absorbed by: Nursing times.
198u-2005   8612884

Prof Saf
Professional safety
0099-0027
Continues: American Society of Safety
Engineers. ASSE journal.
1974   9878792

Prof Sanit Manage
Professional sanitation management
0033-0191
Continued by: Environmental management.
19uu-19uu   9877641

Profile Med Pract
Profile of medical practice / Center for
Health Services Research and Development,
American Medical Association
0194-2921
Continues: Reference data on profile of
medical practice.
1978-1981   8204644

Profiles Healthc Commun
Profiles in healthcare communications
1931-9592
Continues: Profiles in healthcare marketing.
2006   101279978

Profiles Healthc Mark
Profiles in healthcare marketing
1040-7480
Continues: Profiles in hospital marketing.
Continued by: Profiles in healthcare
communications.
1988-2006   8804347

Profiles Hosp Mark
Profiles in hospital marketing
0275-9632
Continued by: Profiles in healthcare
marketing.
1981-1987   8509475

Prog AIDS Pathol
Progress in AIDS pathology
1042-363X
1989-1992   8916539

Prog Allergy
Progress in allergy
0079-6034
Continues Fortschritte der Allergielehre.
Continued by: Chemical immunology.
1949-1988   0376440

Prog Arch
Progressive architecture
0033-0752
1920-1995   9877788

Prog At Med
Progress in atomic medicine
0085-5189
Continued by Recent advances in nuclear
medicine.
1965-1974   7514072

Prog Behav Modif
Progress in behavior modification
0099-037X
1975-1996   7511775

Prog Biochem Pharmacol
Progress in biochemical pharmacology
0079-6085
1965-1990   0036761

Prog Biocybern
Progress in biocybernetics
0079-6093
1964-1966   0116424

Prog Biometeorol
Progress in biometeorology. Division A:
Progress in human biometeorology
0301-1011
Continued by: Biometerological survey. Part
A. Human biometeorology.
1970-197u   0374370

Prog Biophys Biophys Chem
Progress in biophysics and biophysical
chemistry
0096-4174
Continued by Progress in biophysics and
molecular biology.
1950-1962   19830340R

Prog Biophys Mol Biol
Progress in biophysics and molecular
biology
0079-6107
Continues Progress in biophysics and
biophysical chemistry.
1963   0401233

Prog Brain Res
Progress in brain research
0079-6123   1875-7855
1963   0376441

Prog Cardiovasc Dis
Progress in cardiovascular diseases
0033-0620   1532-8643
1958   0376442

Prog Cardiovasc Nurs
Progress in cardiovascular nursing
0889-7204
1986   8704064

Prog Cell Cycle Res
Progress in cell cycle research
1087-2957
1995   9609058

Prog Chem Fats Other Lipids
Progress in the chemistry of fats and other
lipids
0079-6832
Continued by Progress in lipid research.
1952-1978   7900833

Prog Chem Toxicol
Progress in chemical toxicology
0079-6158
1963-1974   0376443

Prog Clin Biol Res
Progress in clinical and biological research
0361-7742
1975-1998   7605701

Prog Clin Cancer
Progress in clinical cancer
0079-6166
1965-1982   19830360R

Prog Clin Immunol
Progress in clinical immunology
0090-3310
1972-1980   0344745

Prog Clin Parasitol
Progress in clinical parasitology
1062-0338
1989-1994   9004907

Prog Clin Pathol
Progress in clinical pathology
0079-6174
1966-1984   0047556

Prog Drug Res
Progress in drug research. Fortschritte
der Arzneimittelforschung. Progrès des
recherches pharmaceutiques
0071-786X
Continues: Fortschritte der
Arzneimittelforschung.
1968   1304021

Prog Exp Pers Psychopathol Res
Progress in experimental personality &
psychopathology research
1056-7151
Continues: Progress in experimental
personality research.
1992-1994   9317694

Prog Exp Pers Res
Progress in experimental personality
research
0079-6255
Continued by: Progress in experimental
personality & psychopathology research.
1964-1986   0023623

Prog Exp Tumor Res
Progress in experimental tumor research.
Fortschritte der experimentellen
Tumorforschung. Progrès de la recherche
expérimentale des tumeurs
0079-6263   1662-3916
1960   0376446

Prog Food Nutr Sci
Progress in food & nutrition science
0306-0632
1975-1993   7508713

Prog Growth Factor Res
Progress in growth factor research
0955-2235
Continued by: Cytokine & growth factor
reviews.
1989-1995   8912757

Prog Hematol
Progress in hematology
0079-6301
1956-1987   0204655

Prog Hemost Thromb
Progress in hemostasis and thrombosis
0362-6350
1972-1991   0335011

Prog Histochem Cytochem
Progress in histochemistry and
cytochemistry
0079-6336
1970   0253725

Prog Immunobiol Stand
Progress in immunobiological
standardization
0079-6344
Merged with Symposia series in
immunobiological standardization to form
Developments in biological standardization.
1962-1972   0427362

Prog Ind Microbiol
Progress in industrial microbiology
0079-6352
1959   7513447

Prog Lipid Res
Progress in lipid research
0163-7827   1873-2194
Continues Progress in the chemistry of fats
and other lipids.
1978   7900832

Prog Liver Dis
Progress in liver diseases
1060-913X
1961-1997   0376447

Prog Med
Progress in medicine
1972-1974   8507031

Prog Med
Progressos da medicina
1952-1964   19840200R

Prog Med (Napoli)
Il Progresso medico
0370-1514
1945-1995   2984827R

Prog Med (Paris)
Le Progrés médical
0033-0450
1873-1982   2984825R

Prog Med Chem
Progress in medicinal chemistry
0079-6468
1961   0376452

Prog Med Genet
Progress in medical genetics
0079-6441
1961-1988   0376450

Prog Med Virol
Progress in medical virology. Fortschritte
der medizinischen Virusforschung. Progrès
en virologie médicale
0079-645X
1958-1993   0376451

Prog Mol Subcell Biol
Progress in molecular and subcellular
biology
0079-6484
1969   0233223

Prog Neurobiol
Progress in neurobiology
0555-4047
1956-1962   19830410R

Prog Neurobiol
Progress in neurobiology
0301-0082
1973   0370121

Prog Neurol Psychiatry
Progress in neurology and psychiatry
0079-6506
1945-1973   7513448

Prog Neurol Surg
Progress in neurological surgery
0079-6492   1662-3924
1966   0076033

Prog Neuropsychopharmacol
Progress in neuro-psychopharmacology
0364-7722
Continued by Progress in neuropsychopharmacology & biological psychiatry.
1977-1981   7708294

Prog Neuropsychopharmacol Biol Psychiatry
Progress in neuro-psychopharmacology &
biological psychiatry
0278-5846
Continues: Progress in neuropsychopharmacology.
1982   8211617

Prog Nucl Energy 6 Biol Sci
Biological sciences
0555-4098
Consists of edited papers from the
Proceedings of the 1st International
Conference on the Peaceful Uses of
Atomic Energy. Merged with: Physics and
mathematics. ISSN 0555-4055; Reactors.
ISSN 0555-4063; Process chemistry. ISSN
0079-6514; Technology. engineering.
and safety. ISSN 0079-6522; Metallurgy
and fuels. ISSN 0555-408X; Medical
sciences.ISSN 0555-4101; The economics of
nuclear power. including administration and
law. ISSN 0555-411X; Analytical chemistry.
ISSN 0079-6530; Law and administration,
ISSN 0079-6549; Plasma physics and
thermonuclear research. ISSN 0555-4136;
Health physics. ISSN 0079-6557; to form:
Progress in nuclear energy. ISSN 0149-1970.
1956-19uu   0376454

Prog Nucl Energy 7 Med Sci
Medical sciences (London, England)
0555-4101
Merged with: Physics and mathematics.
ISSN 0555-4055; Reactors. ISSN 0555-
4063; Process chemistry. ISSN 0079-6514;
Technology. engineering, and safety. ISSN
0079-6522; Metallurgy and fuels. ISSN 0555-
408X; Biological sciences. ISSN 0555-4098;
The economics of nuclear power. including
administration and law. ISSN 0555-411X;
Analytical chemistry. ISSN 0079-6530; Law
and administration. ISSN 0079-6549; Plasma
physics and thermonuclear research. ISSN
0555-4136; Health physics. ISSN 0079-6557;
to form: Progress in nuclear energy. ISSN
0149-1970.
1956-1959   0401234

Prog Nucl Med
Progress in nuclear medicine
0091-7559
1972-1984   0322202

Prog Nucleic Acid Res Mol Biol
Progress in nucleic acid research and
molecular biology
0079-6603
Continues: Progress in nucleic acid research.
1964   0102753

Prog Odontoiatr
Progresso odontoiatrico
1988-1991   9204318

Prog Odontostomatol
Le Progrés odonto-stomatologique
0048-5470
1967-1973   1270512

Prog Orthod
Progress in orthodontics
1723-7785
2000   100936353

Prog Pediat Study
Progress pediatric study. American Academy
of Pediatrics. Committee for the Study of
Child Health Services
1946-1948   14740130R

Prog Pediatr Pueric
Progresos de pediatría y puericultura
0033-0515
1958-1975   60030180R

Prog Pediatr Surg
Progress in pediatric surgery
0079-6654
1971-1991   9814248

Prog Phys Ther
Progress in physical therapy
0048-5519
1970-1970   0321450

Prog Psychother
Progress in psychotherapy
1956-1960   19840020R

Prog Radiat Ther
Progress in radiation therapy
1958-1965   19840030R

Prog Retin Eye Res
Progress in retinal and eye research
1350-9462
     Continues: Progress in retinal research.
1994   9431859

Prog Surg
Progress in surgery
0079-6824
1961-1998   7701488

Prog Ter Clin
Progresos de terapéutica clínica
0033-0523
1948-1975   19830250R

Prog Transplant
Progress in transplantation (Aliso Viejo,
Calif.)
1526-9248
     Continues: Journal of transplant coordination.
2000   100909380

Prog Urol
Progrès en urologie: journal de l'Association
française d'urologie et de la Société
française d'urologie
1166-7087
1991   9307844

Prog Vet Microbiol Immunol
Progress in veterinary microbiology and
immunology
0255-3686
1985-1989   8410145

Program Notes Assoc Univ Programs Health Adm
Program notes (Association of University
Programs.)
0098-1559
     Continues Program notes - Association
of University Programs in Hospital
Administration. Continued by The Journal of
health administration education.
1973-1982   7512982

Progress Nurse
The Progressive nurse
1962-1967   0023627

Progress Ter
Progressi di terapia
1912-19uu   19840100R

Proj Inf Perspect
Project Inform perspective
1058-7454
     Continues: PI perspective.
1997   100965794

Proj Rep USAF Sch Aviat Med
Project report. USAF School of Aviation
Medicine
     Continued by: Technical documentary report
SAM-TDR of the School of Aerospace
Medicine, Brooks Air Force Base, Tex.
1942-1961   22410740R

Promot Dent
La Promotion dentaire
1968-1974   0311556

Promot Educ
Promotion & education
1025-3823
     Continues: Hygie.
1993   9431615

Promot Health
Promoting health
0272-9709
1980-1987   8009595

Prophyl Antivenerienne
La Prophylaxie antivénérienne
     Supersedes the Bulletin of the Société
française de prophylaxie sanitaire et morale.
Continued by La Prophylaxie sanitaire et
morale.
1929-1951   19840310R

Prophyl Sanit Morale
La Prophylaxie sanitaire et morale
0337-0208
     Continues La Prophylaxie antivénérienne.
Continued by Informations sur les maladies
vénériennes.
1952-1974   7506701

Prostaglandins
Prostaglandins
0090-6980
     Merged with: Journal of lipid mediators and
cell signalling, to form: Prostaglandins &
other lipid mediators.
1972-1997   0320271

Prostaglandins Leukot Essent Fatty Acids
Prostaglandins, leukotrienes, and essential
fatty acids
0952-3278
     Continues: Prostaglandins, leukotrienes, and
medicine.
1988   8802730

Prostaglandins Leukot Med
Prostaglandins, leukotrienes, and medicine
0262-1746
     Continues: Prostaglandins and medicine.
Continued by: Prostaglandins, leukotrienes
and essential fatty acids.
1982-1987   8206868

Prostaglandins Med
Prostaglandins and medicine
0161-4630
     Continued by Prostaglandins, leukotrienes
and medicine.
1978-1981   7810330

Prostaglandins Other Lipid Mediat
Prostaglandins & other lipid mediators
1098-8823
     Merger of: Prostaglandins, and: Journal of
lipid mediators and cell signalling.
1998   9808648

Prostate
The Prostate
0270-4137   1097-0045
1980   8101368

Prostate Cancer Prostatic Dis
Prostate cancer and prostatic diseases
1365-7852   1476-5608
1997   9815755

Prostate Suppl
The Prostate. Supplement
1050-5881
1981   9003050

Prosthet Orthot Int
Prosthetics and orthotics international
0309-3646   1746-1553
     Supersedes: Prosthetics international.
1977   7707720

Prot Soc
Protección social
     Continued by: Seguridad social.
1938-1955   0140451

Protein Eng
Protein engineering
0269-2139   1460-213X
     Continued by: Protein engineering, design
and selection.
1986-2003   8801484

Protein Eng Des Sel
Protein engineering, design & selection:
PEDS
1741-0126   1741-0134
     Continues: Protein engineering.
2004   101186484

Protein Expr Purif
Protein expression and purification
1046-5928   1096-0279
1990   9101496

Protein J
The protein journal
1572-3887
     Continues: Journal of protein chemistry.
2004   101212092

Protein Pept Lett
Protein and peptide letters
0929-8665
1994   9441434

Protein Profile
Protein profile
1070-3667
1994-1995   9423530

Protein Sci
Protein science: a publication of the Protein
Society
0961-8368   1469-896X
1992   9211750

Protein Seq Data Anal
Protein sequences & data analysis
0931-9506
1987-1993   8800894

Proteins
Proteins
0887-3585   1097-0134
1986   8700181

Proteomics
Proteomics
1615-9853   1615-9861
2001   101092707

Protes Clin
Protesis clínica; periódico técnico
informativo para la profesión dental
1940-19uu   19840450R

Protes Dent
El Protesista dental
0325-8807
     Continues El Mecánico dental. Buenos Aires.
1957-1987   19840460R

Protet Stomatol
Protetyka stomatologiczna
0033-1783
1965   0045533

Protist
Protist
1434-4610
Continues: Archiv für Protistenkunde.
1998   9806488

Protoplasma
Protoplasma
0033-183X
1927   9806853

Prov Med
La Provence médicale
0755-2130
1931-1984   19840520R

Provid Stud Res Note Agency Health Care Policy Res
Provider studies research note
Continues: Research note (Hospital Studies Program (United States. Agency for Health Care Policy and Research)). Continued by: HCUP-3 research note.
1992-1996   9313896

Provider
Provider (Washington, D.C.)
0888-0352
Continues: Journal - American Health Care Association.
1986   8608563

Przegl Dermatol
Przegląd dermatologiczny
0033-2526
1905   19840710R

Przegl Epidemiol
Przegląd epidemiologiczny
0033-2100
1947   0413725

Przegl Lek
Przegląd lekarski
0033-2240
Absorbed Czasopismo lekarskie in 1909 and called Przegląd lekarski oraz czasopismo lekarskie, 1909-39?
1945   19840720R

Psicothema
Psicothema
0214-9915   1886-144X
1989   101189384

Psihoterapija
Psihoterapija
0350-3186
1973-1995   7603405

Psiquis (Mexico)
Psiquis
1946-19uu   19910070R

Psyche (Camb Mass)
Psyche; a journal of entomology
0033-2615
1874-2002   0401155

Psyche (Stuttg)
Psyche
0033-2623
1947   0421055

Psyche Rev Int Sci Homme Psychanal
Psyché; revue internationale des sciences de l'homme et de psychanalyse
1946-196u   19910110R

Psychiatr Clin (Basel)
Psychiatria clinica
0033-264X
Supersedes in part Psychiatria et neurologia. Continued by Psychopathology.
1968-1983   0150761

Psychiatr Clin North Am
The Psychiatric clinics of North America
0193-953X   1558-3147
1978   7708110

Psychiatr Commun
Psychiatric communications
0033-2682
1958-1975   0401235

Psychiatr Danub
Psychiatria Danubina
0353-5053
1989   9424753

Psychiatr Dev
Psychiatric developments
0262-9283
1983-1989   8305469

Psychiatr Enfant
La Psychiatrie de l'enfant
0079-726X
1958   0376466

Psychiatr Genet
Psychiatric genetics
0955-8829   1473-5873
1990   9106748

Psychiatr Hosp
The Psychiatric hospital
0885-7717
Continues: Journal - National Association of Private Psychiatric Hospitals.
1982-1993   8404268

Psychiatr Hung
Psychiatria Hungarica: A Magyar Pszichiátriai Társaság tudományos folyóirata
0237-7896
1986   9426825

Psychiatr J Univ Ott
Psychiatric journal of the University of Ottawa: Revue de psychiatrie de l'Université d'Ottawa
0702-8466
Continued by: Journal of psychiatry and neuroscience.
1976-1990   7703518

Psychiatr Med
Psychiatric medicine
0732-0868
1983-1992   8301688

Psychiatr Neurol (Basel)
Psychiatria et neurologia
0370-1956
Continues Monatsschrift für Psychiatrie und Neurologie. Superseded by Psychiatria clinica and European neurology.
1957-1967   0150763

Psychiatr Neurol Med Psychol (Leipz)
Psychiatrie, Neurologie, und medizinische Psychologie
0033-2739
1949-1990   0376467

Psychiatr Neurol Med Psychol Beih
Psychiatrie, Neurologie und medizinische Psychologie. Beihefte
0555-5469
1963-1990   0125315

Psychiatr Neurol Neurochir
Psychiatria, neurologia, neurochirurgia
0033-2666
Continues Folia psychiatrica, neurologica et neuro-chirurgica Neerlandica. Continued in part by Clinical neurology and neurosurgery.
1960-1973   7502170

Psychiatr News
Psychiatric news
0033-2704
Supersedes: A.P.A. newsletter and mail pouch.
1966   0226533

Psychiatr Pol
Psychiatria polska
0033-2674
Continues in part: Neurologia, neurochirurgia i psychiatria polska.
1967   0103314

Psychiatr Prax
Psychiatrische Praxis
0303-4259
1974   0423204

Psychiatr Q
The Psychiatric quarterly
0033-2720
Continues: State hospital quarterly.
1927   0376465

Psychiatr Q Suppl
The Psychiatric quarterly. Supplement
0887-3984
1927-1968   0311421

Psychiatr Rehabil J
Psychiatric rehabilitation journal
1095-158X
Formed by the union of: Psychosocial rehabilitation journal, and: Innovations and research in clinical services, community support, and rehabilitation.
1995   9601800

Psychiatr Res Rep Am Psychiatr Assoc
Psychiatric research reports
0555-5434
1955-1968   7706096

Psychiatr Serv
Psychiatric services (Washington, D.C.)
1075-2730   1557-9700
Continues: Hospital & community psychiatry.
1995   9502838

Psychiatry
Psychiatry
0033-2747
1938   0376470

Psychiatry Clin Neurosci
Psychiatry and clinical neurosciences
1323-1316   1440-1819
Continues: Japanese journal of psychiatry and neurology.
1995   9513551

Psychiatry Dig
Psychiatry digest
0033-2771
Absorbed Journal of clinical and experimental psychopathology & quarterly review of psychiatry and neurology in Mar. 1963 and assumed its numbering. Continued by The Journal of continuing education in psychiatry.
1962-1977   7805834

Psychiatry Med
Psychiatry in medicine
0033-278X
Continued by International journal of psychiatry in medicine.
1970-1972   0365601

Psychiatry Res
Psychiatry research
0165-1781
1979   7911385

Psychoanal Psychoanal Rev
Psychoanalysis and the psychoanalytic
review
Continued by Psychoanalytic review.
1958-1962   19910300R

Psychoanal Q
The Psychoanalytic quarterly
0033-2828
1932   0226661

Psychoanal Rev
Psychoanalytic review
0033-2836
Continues Psychoanalysis and the
psychoanalytic review.
1963   0401156

Psychoanal Soc Sci
Psychoanalysis and the social sciences
1947-1958   19910310R

Psychoanal Study Child
The Psychoanalytic study of the child
0079-7308
1945   0376472

Psychol Addict Behav
Psychology of addictive behaviors: journal
of the Society of Psychologists in Addictive
Behaviors
0893-164X
Continues: Bulletin of the Society of
Psychologists in Addictive Behaviors.
1987   8802734

Psychol Aging
Psychology and aging
0882-7974
1986   8904079

Psychol Assess
Psychological assessment
1040-3590
Continues in part: Journal of consulting and
clinical psychology.
1989   8915253

Psychol Bull
Psychological bulletin
0033-2909
1904   0376473

Psychol Forsch
Psychologische Forschung
0033-3026
Continued by Psychological research.
1921-1974   0435063

Psychol Health
Psychology & health
0887-0446   1476-8321
1987   8807983

Psychol Health Med
Psychology, health & medicine
1354-8506   1465-3966
1996   9604099

Psychol Issues
Psychological issues
0048-5748
1959   0376474

Psychol Med
Psychological medicine
0033-2917
1970   1254142

Psychol Med Monogr Suppl
Psychological medicine. Monograph
supplement
0264-1801
1982-1993   8301104

Psychol Methods
Psychological methods
1082-989X
1996   9606928

Psychol Monogr
Psychological monographs
0096-9753
Continues the Monograph supplements of the
Psychological review. Absorbed the Applied
psychology monographs and the Archives of
psychology in 1948.
1908-1966   19920010R

Psychol Neuropsychiatr Vieil
Psychologie & neuropsychiatrie du
vieillissement
1760-1703
2003   101203421

Psychol Prax
Psychologische Praxis; Schriftenreihe für
Erziehung und Jugendpflege
0079-7413
1943-1980   19920080R

Psychol Psychother
Psychology and psychotherapy
1476-0835
Continues: British journal of medical
psychology.
2002   101135751

Psychol Rep
Psychological reports
0033-2941
1955   0376475

Psychol Res
Psychological research
0340-0727
Continues Psychologische Forschung.
1974   0435062

Psychol Rev
Psychological review
0033-295X
1894   0376476

Psychol Sci
Psychological science: a journal of the
American Psychological Society / APS
0956-7976   1467-9280
1990   9007542

Psychometrika
Psychometrika
0033-3123
1936   0376503

Psychon Bull Rev
Psychonomic bulletin & review
1069-9384
Continues: Bulletin of the Psychonomic Society.
1994   9502924

Psychoneuroendocrinology
Psychoneuroendocrinology
0306-4530
1975   7612148

Psychooncology
Psycho-oncology
1057-9249   1099-1611
1992   9214524

Psychopathology
Psychopathology
0254-4962   1423-033X
Continues: Psychiatria clinica.
1984   8401537

Psychopharmacol Bull
Psychopharmacology bulletin
0048-5764
Continues Psychopharmacology Service
Center bulletin.
1966   0101123

Psychopharmacol Commun
Psychopharmacology communications
0098-616X
1975-1976   7508718

Psychopharmacol Ser
Psychopharmacology series
0931-6795
Continues: Psychopharmacology.
Supplementum.
1987-1993   8701884

Psychopharmacol Serv Cent Bull
Psychopharmacology Service Center bulletin
Continued by Psychopharmacology bulletin.
1959-1965   7505919

Psychopharmacologia
Psychopharmacologia
0033-3158
Continued by Psychopharmacology.
1959-1976   7609417

Psychopharmacologie
Psychopharmacologie
1966-1973   0235727

Psychopharmacology (Berl)
Psychopharmacology
0033-3158   1432-2072
Continues Psychopharmacologia.
1976   7608025

Psychopharmacology Suppl
Psychopharmacology. Supplementum
0179-8456
Continued by: Psychopharmacology series.
1984-1985   8403197

Psychophysiology
Psychophysiology
0048-5772
Supersedes the Psychophysiology newsletter.
1964   0142657

Psychosom Med
Psychosomatic medicine
0033-3174   1534-7796
1939   0376505

Psychosomatics
Psychosomatics
0033-3182   1545-7206
1960   0376506

Psychother Med Psychol (Stuttg)
Psychotherapie und medizinische
Psychologie
0302-8984
Continues Zeitschrift für Psychotherapie und
medizinische Psychologie. Continued by
Psychotherapie, medizinische Psychologie.
1974-1974   7510345

Psychother Med Psychol (Stuttg)
Psychotherapie, medizinische Psychologie
0302-8984
Continues Psychotherapie und medizinische
Psychologie. Continued by Psychotherapie,
Psychosomatik, medizinische Psychologie.
1975-1979   7509753

Psychother Psychosom
Psychotherapy and psychosomatics
0033-3190   1423-0348
Continues: Acta psychotherapeutica et
psychosomatica.
1965   0024046

Psychother Psychosom Med Psychol
Psychotherapie, Psychosomatik,
medizinische Psychologie
0937-2032
Continues Psychotherapie. medizinische
Psychologie.
1980   8002823

Psychother Res
Psychotherapy research: journal of the
Society for Psychotherapy Research
1050-3307   1468-4381
1991   9110958

Publ Am Inst Hist Pharm
Publication - American Institute of the
History of Pharmacy
0270-0611
1972   8003639

Publ B Aires Cent Investig
Publicaciones. Buenos Aires. Centro de
Investigaciones Tisiológicas
Continues the center's Anales.
1939-1955   15750280R

Publ Child Dev Univ Calif
Publications in child development.
University of California, Berkeley
1949-19uu   16020290R

Publ Cient Oficina Sanit Panam
Publicación científica - Oficina Sanitaria
Panamericana
0254-2668
Supersedes in part Pan American Sanitary
Bureau. Publication. Continued by
Publicación científica - Organización
Panamericana de la Salud.
1953-1959   7810135

Publ Group Adv Psychiatry
Publication - Group for the Advancement of
Psychiatry
0149-2640
Continues Report - Group for the
Advancement of Psychiatry. Continued
by Report (Group for the Advancement of
Psychiatry: 1984).
1976-1983   7705149

Publ Inst Antitubers Francisco Moragas
Publicaciones del Instituto Antituberculoso
"Francisco Moragas" de la Caja de
Pensiones para la Vejez y de Ahorros
0302-7406
1933-1975   7507403

Publ Inst Pasteur Guyane Fr Inini
Publication. Cayenne, French Guiana.
Institut Pasteur de la Guyane française et
de l'Inini
1940-1973   16040640R

Publ Psychol
Publications in psychology. University of
California (1868-1952)
1910-1959   16020300R

Publ Public Health Univ Calif
Publications in public health. University of
California (1868-1952)
1928-1962   16020310R

Public Adm Rev
Public administration review
0033-3352
1940   0045715

Public Aff Rep
Public affairs report: bulletin of the Bureau
of Public Administration
0033-3417
1960   9877789

Public Health
Public health
0033-3506   1476-5616
Supersedes: Transactions. Society of Medical
Officers of Health.
1888   0376507

Public Health Genomics
Public health genomics
1662-4246   1662-8063
Continues: Community genetics.
2008   101474167

Public Health Lab
The Public health laboratory
0033-3522
1943-1984   0376511

Public Health Monogr
Public health monograph
0079-7596
Continues Public health technical monograph
of the U. S. Public Health Service.
1951-1971   7507399

Public Health News
Public health news
0033-3530
1915-1971   0376512

Public Health Nurs
Public health nursing
Continues the Public health nurse. Continued
by the Nursing outlook.
1931-1952   19930080R

Public Health Nurs
Public health nursing (Boston, Mass.)
0737-1209   1525-1446
1984   8501498

Public Health Nutr
Public health nutrition
1368-9800
1998   9808463

Public Health Pap
Public health papers
0555-6015
1959-1987   0376513

Public Health Rep
Public health reports
0094-6214
Continues: Weekly abstract of sanitary
reports. United States. Marine Hospital
Service. Absorbed: CDC bulletin. Jan. 1952
Journal of venereal disease information. Jan.
1952 Continued by: HSMHA health reports.
1896-1970   0433021

Public Health Rep
Public health reports (Washington, D.C.: 1974)
0033-3549   1468-2877
Continues: Health services reports.
1974   9716844

Public Health Rev
Public health reviews
0301-0422
1972   0370123

Public health tech monogr US
Public health technical monograph. United
States. Public Health Service
Continued by U. S. Public Health Service.
Public health monograph.
1950-1950   21420640R

Public Hist
The Public historian
0272-3433
1978   8510642

Public Interest
The Public interest
0033-3557
1965   9877790

Public Opin Q
Public opinion quarterly
0033-362X   1537-5331
1937   19930130R

Public Policy
Public policy
0033-3646
Merged with Policy analysis. to form Journal
of policy analysis and management.
1940-1981   7703771

Public Relat J
The Public relations journal
0033-3670
1945-1995   9877791

Public Sect Contract Rep
Public sector contracting report: the
monthly guide to Medicare and Medicaid
managed care
1084-9483
1995-1999   9891454

Public Sector Health Care Risk Manage
Public sector, health care risk management
0270-8973
1980-1987   8101373

Public Underst Sci
Public understanding of science (Bristol,
England)
0963-6625
1992   9306503

Public Welf
Public welfare
0033-3816
Supersedes: Public welfare news. Continued
by: Policy & practice of public human services.
1943-1998   0024064

Public Welf Indiana
Public welfare in Indiana
Continues The Indiana welfare news.
1938-1953   19930170R

Puericulture
La Puériculture
1910-19uu   19930270R

Pulm Pharmacol
Pulmonary pharmacology
0952-0600
Continued by: Pulmonary pharmacology &
therapeutics.
1988-1996   9007551

Pulm Pharmacol Ther
Pulmonary pharmacology & therapeutics
1094-5539
Continues: Pulmonary pharmacology.
1997   9715279

Pulse
The Pulse of the Montana State Nurses'
Association
0033-4189
Continues the Bulletin of the Montana State
Nurses' Association.
1957   18820110R

Punjab Med J
The Punjab medical journal
0033-4340
1951-1972   0404247

Purch Adm
Purchasing administration
0192-4311
Continued by: Hospital purchasing news. 1981
1977-1981   9877739

Purdue Pharm
The Purdue pharmacist
0033-4529
1924   19930400R

Pure Appl Chem
Pure and applied chemistry. Chimie pure et
appliquée
0033-4545
1960   0376514

Q

Q Bull Chin Bibliogr
Quarterly bulletin of Chinese bibliography
1007-2292
1934-19uu   58520570R

Q Bull Commonw Med Assoc
Quarterly bulletin (Commonwealth Medical
Association)
Continued by: CommonHealth (London,
England).
19uu-1992   9209546

Q Bull Indiana Univ Med Cent
The Quarterly bulletin of the Indiana
University Medical Center
0097-014X
Continued by the Medical quarterly of the
Indiana University School of Medicine.
1939-1965   7502661

Q Bull Northwest Univ Med Sch
Quarterly bulletin. Northwestern University
(Evanston, Ill.). Medical School
1899-1962   19220080R

Q Bull Sea View Hosp
Quarterly bulletin of Sea View Hospital.
New York. Sea View Hospital, Staten Island.
Clinical Society
Continued by the Sea View Hospital bulletin.
1935-1954   20710010R

Q Dent Rev
Quarterly Dental Review
Absorbed by: Journal Of Dentistry.
1967-1975   9877838

Q J Exp Physiol
Quarterly journal of experimental
physiology (Cambridge, England)
0144-8757
Continues: Quarterly journal of experimental
physiology and cognate medical sciences.
Continued by: Experimental physiology.
1981-1989   8206873

Q J Exp Physiol Cogn Med Sci
Quarterly journal of experimental
physiology and cognate medical sciences
0033-5541
Continues Quarterly journal of experimental
physiology (London, England). Continued by
Quarterly journal of experimental physiology
(Cambridge, England).
1938-1980   0404466

Q J Exp Psychol
The Quarterly journal of experimental
psychology
0033-555X
Split into: The Quarterly journal of
experimental psychology. A, Human
experimental psychology; and the Quarterly
journal of experimental psychology. B,
Comparative and physiological psychology.
1948-1980   0401241

Q J Exp Psychol (Colchester)
Quarterly journal of experimental
psychology (2006)
1747-0218   1747-0226
Merger of: Quarterly journal of experimental
psychology. A, Human experimental
psychology and: Quarterly journal of
experimental psychology. B, Comparative and
physiological psychology.
2006   101259775

Q J Exp Psychol A
The Quarterly journal of experimental
psychology. A, Human experimental
psychology
0272-4987   1464-0740
Continues in part: Quarterly journal of
experimental psychology. Merged with:
Quarterly journal of experimental psychology.
B, Comparative and physiological
psychology, to form: Quarterly journal of
experimental psychology (2006).
1981-2005   8107269

Q J Exp Psychol B
The Quarterly journal of experimental
psychology. B, Comparative and
physiological psychology
0272-4995   1464-1321
Continues in part: Quarterly journal of
experimental psychology. Merged with:
Quarterly journal of experimental psychology.
A, Human experimental psychology, to form:
Quarterly journal of experimental psychology
(2006).
1981-2005   8107270

Q J Med
The Quarterly journal of medicine
0033-5622
Continued by: QJM.
1907-1994   0401027

Q J Microsc Sci
The Quarterly journal of microscopical
science
0370-2952
Superseded by: Journal of cell science.
1853-1965   0061353

Q J Nucl Med
The quarterly journal of nuclear
medicine: official publication of the Italian
Association of Nuclear Medicine (AIMN)
[and] the International Association of
Radiopharmacology (IAR)
1125-0135
Continues: Journal of nuclear biology and
medicine (Turin, Italy: 1991). Continued by:
Quarterly journal of nuclear medicine and
molecular imaging.
1995-2003   9512274

Q J Nucl Med Mol Imaging
The quarterly journal of nuclear medicine
and molecular imaging: official publication
of the Italian Association of Nuclear
Medicine (AIMN) [and] the International
Association of Radiopharmacology
(IAR), [and] Section of the Society of
Radiopharmaceutical Chemistry and
Biology
1824-4785   1827-1936
Continues: Quarterly journal of nuclear
medicine.
2004   101213861

Q J Pharm Pharmacol
Quarterly journal of pharmacy and
pharmacology
0370-2979
Supersedes the Year-book of pharmacy.
Superseded by the Journal of pharmacy and
pharmacology. Continued by: Journal of
Pharmacy and Pharmacology.
1928-1948   19940200R

Q J Stud Alcohol
Quarterly journal of studies on alcohol
0033-5649
Continued by: Journal of studies on alcohol.
1940-1974   7503879

Q Med Rev
Quarterly medical review
0481-2158
1950-1986   0401242

Q Natl Dent Assoc
The Quarterly of the National Dental
Association, Inc
0163-5565
Continues Bulletin of the National Dental
Association. Continued by National Dental
Association journal.
1959-1981   7507414

**Q Prog Rep United States Air Force Radiat Lab
Univ Chic**
Quarterly progress report. United States.
Air Force. Radiation Laboratory, University
of Chicago
Supersedes U. S. Atomic Energy
Commission. Quarterly progress report
[from the] University of Chicago Toxicity
Laboratory.
1951-uuuu   22410690R

Q Res Rep
Quarterly research report. USAF School of
Aviation Medicine
1900-1949   22410760R

Q Rev Allergy Appl Immunol
Quarterly review of allergy and applied
immunology
Continued by Review of allergy and applied
immunology.
1947-1956   59310090R

Q Rev Biol
The Quarterly review of biology
0033-5770   1539-7718
1926   0376515

Q Rev Biophys
Quarterly reviews of biophysics
0033-5835
1968   0144032

Q Rev Br Red Cross Soc
Quarterly review. British Red Cross Society
1930-1956   20040130R

Q Rev DC Nurses Assoc
The Quarterly review
0012-4079
1933-1971   19940260R

Q Rev Drug Metab Drug Interact
Quarterly reviews on drug metabolism and
drug interactions
0334-2190
Continues: Reviews on drug interactions.
Continued by: Reviews on drug metabolism
and drug interactions.
1980-1984   8106225

Q Rev Econ Bus
The Quarterly review of economics and
business
0033-5797
Supersedes: Current economic comment.
Continued by: Quarterly review of economics
and finance.
1961-1991   9877921

Q Rev Econ Finance
The Quarterly review of economics and
finance: journal of the Midwest Economics
Association
1062-9769
Continues: Quarterly review of economics
and business.
1992   9886817

Q Rev Med
Quarterly review of medicine
0096-7114
Absorbed by: International record of
medicine and general practice clinics.
1943-1952   19940290R

Q Rev Obstet Gynecol
Quarterly review of obstetrics and gynecology
0096-9230
Supersedes Obstetrics and gynecology guide.
1943-1952   **60020540R**

Q Rev Otorhinolaryngol Bronchoesophagol
Quarterly review of otorhinolaryngology and broncho-esophagology
Absorbed by: International record of medicine and general practice clinics.
1942-1951   **19940310R**

Q Rev Pediatr
Quarterly review of pediatrics
Merged with American practitioner and Archives of pediatrics to form Clinical pediatrics.
1946-1962   **19940320R**

Q Rev Psychiatry Neurol
Quarterly review of psychiatry and neurology
1946-1952   **59930270R**

Q Rev Surg
Quarterly review of surgery
Continued by Review of surgery.
1943-1961   **60020110R**

Q Rev Surg Obstet Gynecol
Quarterly review of surgery, obstetrics and gynecology
0096-543X
Formed by the union of: Quarterly review of surgery and surgical specialties. and: Quarterly review of obstetrics and gynecology. Continued by: Quarterly review of surgery.
1952-1961   **60020130R**

QA Rev
QA review: quality assurance news and views
1047-4773
1989-1992   **8916543**

QJM
QJM: monthly journal of the Association of Physicians
1460-2725   1460-2393
Continues: Quarterly journal of medicine.
1994   **9438285**

Qld Dent J
The Queensland dental journal
1038-703X
Supersedes the Australian dental mirror. Superseded by the Australian dental journal.
1947-1956   **19940420R**

Qld Nurse
The Queensland nurse
0815-936X
1982   **8406538**

Qld Nurses J
Queensland nurses journal
1959-1969   **0245020**

QRB Qual Rev Bull
QRB. Quality review bulletin
0097-5990
Continued by: Joint Commission journal on quality improvement.
1974-1993   **7504127**

QRC Advis
QRC advisor
0747-7384
1984-2001   **8914468**

Quad Antibiot
Quaderni di antibiotica
1975-1975   **7807998**

Quad Clin Ostet Ginecol
Quaderni di clinica ostetrica e ginecologica
0033-491X
1946-1999   **0401026**

Quad Criminol Clin
Quaderni di criminologia clinica
0033-4928
Issued 1959-Jan./Mar. 1960 as a supplement to Rassegna di studi penitenziari. Continued by Rassegna penitenziaria e criminologica.
1959-1978   **0420141**

Quad Nutr
Quaderni della nutrizione
0033-488X
Continued by: SeTA.
1934-1971   **0171203**

Quad Ostet
Il Quaderno dell'ostetrica
1949-19uu   **19940110R**

Quad Radiol
Quaderni di radiologia
0048-6086
1937-1980   **0401237**

Quad Sclavo Diagn
Quaderni Sclavo di diagnostica clinica e di laboratorio
0033-4979
1965-1988   **0040616**

Quad Stor Univ Padova
Quaderni per la storia dell'Università di Padova
0300-175X
1968   **0354247**

Qual Assur
Quality assurance (San Diego, Calif.)
1052-9411   1521-0677
1991-2005   **9214530**

Qual Assur Health Care
Quality assurance in health care: the official journal of the International Society for Quality Assurance in Health Care / ISQA
1040-6166
Continued by: International journal for quality in health care.
1989-1993   **9001007**

Qual Assur Util Rev
Quality assurance and utilization review: official journal of the American College of Utilization Review Physicians
0885-713X
Continued by: American journal of medical quality.
1986-1992   **8703596**

Qual Connect
Quality connection (Brookline, Mass.)
1991   **9709471**

Qual Health Care
Quality in health care: QHC
0963-8172
Continued by: Quality & safety in healthcare.
1992-2001   **9209948**

Qual Health Res
Qualitative health research
1049-7323
1991   **9202144**

Qual Life Res
Quality of life research: an international journal of quality of life aspects of treatment, care and rehabilitation
0962-9343   1573-2649
1992   **9210257**

Qual Manag Health Care
Quality management in health care
1063-8628   1550-5154
1992   **9306156**

Qual Prim Care
Quality in primary care
1479-1072   1479-1064
Absorbed: Journal of clinical excellence. Continues: Journal of clinical governance.
2003   **101182136**

Qual Resume
Quality résumé: Health Care Financing Administration's Medicare quality of care report of surveillance measures
1997   **9805547**

Qual Saf Health Care
Quality & safety in health care
1475-3898   1475-3901
Continues: Quality in health care.
2002   **101136980**

Quarterly Phi Beta Pi Med Fratern
Quarterly. Phi Beta Pi Medical Fraternity
1904-1959   **19610630R**

Queens Med Mag (1972)
Queen's medical magazine
0033-6033
1897   **0362621**

Queens Nurs J
Queen's nursing journal
0301-0821
Continues District nursing. Merged with Nursing mirror and midwives journal to form Nursing mirror.
1973-1977   **0370124**

Quest Alcool
La Question de l'alcool ... The Alcohol problem ... Die Alkoholfrage ...
Supersedes Forschungen zur Alkoholfrage.
1947-19uu   **19940490R**

Quintessence Dent Technol
Quintessence of dental technology
0362-0913
Continued by: QDT yearbook.
1976-1987   **7706832**

Quintessence Int
Quintessence international (Berlin, Germany: 1985)
0033-6572   1936-7163
Absorbed: Anesthesia & pain control in dentistry. 1994 Continues in part: Quintessence international, dental digest.
1985   **0342677**

Quintessence Int (Berl)
Quintessence international
0033-6572
Merged with: Dental digest, to form: Quintessence international, dental digest.
1970-1972   **101281345**

Quintessence Int Dent Dig
Quintessence international, dental digest
0033-6572
Absorbed: FDI news letter. Merger of: Quintessence international, and: Dental digest. Split into: Quintessence international (Berlin, Germany: 1985), and: FDI newsletter (London, England: 1985). Vols. for May 1979?-Dec. 1984? include a separately paged section with its own volume numbering: IADS newsletter.
1972-1984   **101281344**

Quintessence Int [Fr]
Quintessence International. Edition Francaise
0338-2214
19uu   **9878064**

Quintessencia
Quintessência
0101-9465
1974-1983   8301856

Quintessencia Protese Lab
Quintessência de prótese de laboratório
0100-8870
1977-19uu   8301855

Quintessenz
Die Quintessenz
0033-6580
Continues: Quintessenz der zahnärztlichen
Literatur.
1965   0217057

Quintessenz Impulse
Quintessenz-Impulse: magazin für
Kommunikation & Praxismanagement
0931-8259
1986-1987   9427051

Quintessenz J
Quintessenz Journal
0033-6599
Continued by: Quintessenz Team-Journal.
1971-1997   7801840

Quintessenz Zahntech
Die Quintessenz der Zahntechnik
0340-4641
1975   7600588

Quintessenza
La Quintessenza
0390-6841
1970-1989   7701936

R

R Can Dent Corps Q
The Royal Canadian Dental Corps quarterly
0557-3890
Continued by the Canadian Forces Dental
Services quarterly.
1960-1970   0271141

R I Dent J
Rhode Island dental journal
0091-8903
Continues Journal of the Rhode Island State
Dental Society.
1972-2001   0375713

R I Med
Rhode Island medicine
1061-222X
Continues: Rhode Island medical journal.
Continued by: Medicine and health, Rhode
Island.
1992-1995   9203052

R I Med J
R.I. medical journal
0360-067X
Continues Rhode Island medical journal.
Continued by Rhode Island medical journal.
1974-1975   7605977

R I Med J
Rhode Island medical journal
0363-7913
Continues R.I. medical journal. Continued by:
Rhode Island medicine.
1976-1991   7605981

R I Med J
Rhode Island medical journal
0035-4627
Supersedes the Providence medical journal.
Continued by R. I. medical journal.
1917-1973   7512464

R Inst Public Health Hyg J
The Royal Institute of Public Health and
Hygiene journal
0370-5609
Continues Journal of the Royal Institute of
Public Health and Hygiene. Superseded by
Community health.
1964-1968   7506003

R Nav Med Bull
Royal naval medical bulletin
1943-1950   20440770R

R Soc Health J
Royal Society of Health journal
0035-9130
Continues: Journal. Royal Society of Health
(Great Britain). Continued by: Journal of the
Royal Society of Health.
1960-1982   2983212R

Rad Jugosl Akad Znan Umjet Razred Med Znan
Rad Jugoslavenske akademije znanosti i
umjetnosti. Razred za medicinske znanosti
0351-1812
Continues: Knjiga. Jugoslavenska akademija
znanosti i umjetnosti. Odjel za medicinske
nauke.
1976-1991   9426502

Rad Med Fak Zagrebu
Radovi Medicinskog faculteta u Zagrebu
0033-8575
Continued by: Croatian medical journal.
1953-1990   21720420R

Radiat Data Rep
Radiation data and reports
0091-6722
Continues Radiological health data and
reports.
1972-1974   0317250

Radiat Environ Biophys
Radiation and environmental biophysics
0301-634X   1432-2099
Continues Biophysik.
1974   0415677

Radiat Meas
Radiation measurements
1350-4487
Continues: Nuclear tracks and radiation
measurements (Oxford, England: 1993).
1994   9890953

Radiat Med
Radiation medicine
0288-2043   1862-5274
1983   8412264

Radiat Oncol
Radiation oncology (London, England)
                              1748-717X
2006   101265111

Radiat Oncol Investig
Radiation oncology investigations
1065-7541
Absorbed by: International journal of cancer.
1993-1999   9437448

Radiat Prot Dosimetry
Radiation protection dosimetry
0144-8420
1981   8109958

Radiat Res
Radiation research
0033-7587
1954   0401245

Radiat Res Suppl
Radiation research. Supplement
0485-8611
1959-1985   0401246

Radiats Biol Radioecol
Radiatsionnaia biologiia, radioecologiia /
Rossiĭskaia akademiia nauk
0869-8031
Continues: Radiobiologiia.
1993   9317212

Radiobiol Radioter Fis Med
Radiobiologia, radioterapia, e fisica medica
0033-8176
Continues Radioterapia, radiobiologia, e
fisica medica.
1960-1970   0401250

Radiobiol Radiother (Berl)
Radiobiologia, radiotherapia
0033-8184
1960-1990   0401247

Radiobiologiia
Radiobiologiia
0033-8192
Continued by: Radiatsionnaia biologiia,
radioecologiia.
1961-1993   0401251

Radiogr Today
Radiography today
0954-8211
Formed by the union of: Radiography, and its
supplement: Radiography news. Continued
by: Synergy (Faversham, England).
1988-1995   9002036

Radiographics
Radiographics: a review publication of the
Radiological Society of North America, Inc
0271-5333   1527-1323
1981   8302501

Radiography
Radiography
0033-8281
Merged with its supplement: Radiography
news, to form: Radiography today.
1935-1988   0401252

Radioisotopes
Radioisotopes
0033-8303
195u   20010290R

Radiol Austriaca
Radiologia Austriaca
1948-1968   20010320R

Radiol Clin
Radiologia clinica
Continues Radiologische Rundschau.
Continued by Radiologia clinica et biologica.
1939-1964   0024237

Radiol Clin (Basel)
Radiologia clinica
0376-6748
Continues Radiologia clinica et biologica.
Continued by Diagnostic imaging.
1975-1978   7513002

Radiol Clin Biol
Radiologia clinica et biologica
0033-8346
Continues and is continued by Radiologia
clinica.
1965-1974   7513001

Radiol Clin North Am
Radiologic clinics of North America
0033-8389
1963   0123703

Radiol Diagn (Berl)
Radiologia diagnostica
0033-8354
1960-1994   0401253

Radiol Health Data Rep
Radiological health data and reports
0033-8400
Continues: Radiological health data.
Continued by: Radiation data and reports.
1966-1971   0320551

Radiol Interam
Radiología interamericana
1962-1962   0076155

Radiol Manage
Radiology management
0198-7097
1979   8001971

Radiol Med
La Radiologia medica
0033-8362   1826-6983
Absorbed: Minerva radiologica. 1971
1914   0177625

Radiol Prat
Radiologia pratica
0481-6692
1951-1968   0401254

Radiol Technol
Radiologic technology
0033-8397   1943-5657
Continues the X-ray technician.
1963   0401256

Radiologe
Der Radiologe
0033-832X
1961   0401257

Radiologia
Radiología
0033-8338
1960   0120775

Radiologia (Panama)
Radiologia
1950-1968   0404470

Radiologia (Roma)
Radiologia; rassegna internazionale
trimestrale di radiobiologia, radioterapia,
radiodiagnostica, terapia fisica e fisica
applicata alla medicina
0390-7759
Continued by: Rivista di radiol.
1945-1959   0401255

Radiologica
Radiologica
0370-4211
Continued by: Fundamenta radiologica.
1937-1938   9429409

Radiology
Radiology
0033-8419   1527-1315
1923   0401260

Radioter Radiobiol Fis Medica
Radioterapia, radiobiologia e fisica medica
Formed by the union of Radioterapia e fisica
medica, Scritti italiani di radiobiologia and
Bollettino di marconiterapia ed elettrologia
medica. Continued by Radiobiologia.
radioterapia e fisica medica.
1946-1959   20020080R

Radiother Oncol
Radiotherapy and oncology: journal of the
European Society for Therapeutic Radiology
and Oncology
0167-8140
1983   8407192

Rand J Econ
The Rand journal of economics
0741-6261
Continues: Bell journal of economics.
1984   9884570

RANF Rev
RANF review
Supersedes the Queensland nurses journal.
1970-1978   0245021

Rapid Commun Mass Spectrom
Rapid communications in mass
spectrometry: RCM
0951-4198
1987   8802365

Rapp Congr Natl Tuberc
Rapports. Congrès national de la
tuberculose
Continues: Comptes-rendus et mémoires of
the Congrès pour l'étude de la tuberculose
chez l'homme et chez les animaux. Continued
by: Rapports of the Congrès national de la
tuberculose et des maladies respiratoires.
1923-1966   0252744

Rapp Fonct Tec Inst Pasteur Guyane Fr
Rapport sur le fonctionnement technique.
Cayenne, French Guiana. Institut Pasteur de
la Guyane française et de l'Inini
1940-1972   16040650R

Rass Clin Sci
Rassegna clinico-scientifica
0370-4165
1922-1995   0422562

Rass Clin Ter
La Rassegna di clinica, terapia e scienze
affini
0370-4181
Continues Rassegna di terapia.
1909-1966   0152670

Rass Dermatol Sifilogr
Rassegna di dermatologia e di sifilografia
0033-9490
1948-1996   0401261

Rass Fisiopatol Clin Ter
Rassegna di fisiopatologia clinica e
terapeutica
0033-9520
Continues Rassegna di terapia e patologia
clinica.
1937-1970   0401262

Rass Giuliana Med
Rassegna giuliana di medicina
Supersedes Associazione medica triestina.
Bollettino.
1945-19uu   20020430R

Rass Int Clin Ter
Rassegna internazionale di clinica e terapia
0033-9695
1920-1995   0401266

Rass Int Stomatol Prat
Rassegna internazionale di stomatologia
pratica
0033-9717
1950-1973   7908508

Rass Ital Chir Med
Rassegna italiana di chirurgia e medicina
1952-1962   0060441

Rass Ital Gastroenterol
Rassegna italiana di gastro-enterologia
0483-9811
1955-1969   0413727

Rass Med Ind Ig Lav
Rassegna di medicina industriale e di igiene
del lavoro
0370-6249
Continues: Rassegna di medicina industriale.
Absorbed by: Securitas.
1957-1964   20020370R

Rass Med Sarda
Rassegna medica sarda
0033-9776
Continues the Atti of the Società fra i cultori
delle scienze mediche e naturali in Cagliari.
1936-1992   0413553

Rass Medica
Rassegna medica
Merged with Convivium sanitatis to form
Rassegna medica - Convivium sanitatis.
1921-1953   20020460R

Rass Neurol Veg
Rassegna di neurologia vegetativa
0048-6752
1938-1969   0401264

Rass Neuropsichiatr
Rassegna di neuropsichiatria e scienze affini
0048-6760
1947-1971   0401265

Rass Odontotec
Rassegna odontotecnica
0048-6787
1954-1999   20020590R

Rass Penititenziaria Crim
Rassegna penitenziaria e criminologica
0392-7156
Continues: Quaderni di criminologia clinica.
1979   8219818

Rass Studi Psichiatr
Rassegna di studi psichiatrici
0033-9636
1911-1996   2985048R

Rass Trimest Odontoiatr
Rassegna trimestrale di odontoiatria
0033-9911
1919-1979   20020625R

Ration Drug Ther
Rational drug therapy
0031-7020
Continues Pharmacology for physicians.
1971-1988   1247445

Rays
Rays
0390-7740
1976   7707724

RCM Midwives
RCM midwives: the official journal of the
Royal College of Midwives
1479-2915
Continues: RCM midwives journal.
Continued by: Midwives.
2002-2007   101189530

RCM Midwives J
RCM midwives journal: official journal of
the Royal College of Midwives
1462-138X
Continues: Midwives. Continued by: RCM
midwives.
1998-2002   9815872

RCN Nurs Stand
RCN nursing standard
Continued by: Nursing standard.
1968-1984   0163572

RDH
RDH
0279-7720
1981   8201125

Read Dig
The Reader's digest
0034-0375
1922   9877792

Real Clin
Réalités cliniques: revue européenne
d'odontologie
0999-5021
1990   9100122

Reanim Organes Artif
Réanimation et organes artificiels.
Wiederbelebung und künstliche Organe.
Reanimation and artificial organs
0079-9904
1964-1966   0401267

Rec Chem Prog
Record of chemical progress
0034-1584
1939-1971   7514094

Rec Columbia Med Soc Richland Cty SC
The Recorder of the Columbia Medical
Society of Richland County, S. C
1937   20030230R

Rec Med Vet Ec Alfort
Recueil de médecine vétérinaire
0034-1843
1824-1999   0413730

Recent Adv Biol Psychiatry
Recent advances in biological psychiatry
0376-2122
    Continues: Biological psychiatry. Society
    of Biological Psychiatry. Superseded by:
    Biological psychiatry.
1959-1968   0213316

Recent Adv Clin Nucl Med
Recent advances in clinical nuclear medicine
0308-2458
1975-1975   7513008

Recent Adv Nurs
Recent advances in nursing
0144-6592
1981-1990   8011213

Recent Adv Stud Cardiac Struct Metab
Recent advances in studies on cardiac
structure and metabolism
0363-5872
1972-1978   0325677

Recent Dev Alcohol
Recent developments in alcoholism: an
official publication of the American Medical
Society on Alcoholism, the Research Society
on Alcoholism, and the National Council on
Alcoholism
0738-422X
1983   8301996

Recent Pat Anticancer Drug Discov
Recent patents on anti-cancer drug
discovery
1574-8928
2006   101266081

Recent Pat Antiinfect Drug Discov
Recent patents on anti-infective drug
discovery
1574-891X
2006   101266084

Recent Pat Biotechnol
Recent patents on biotechnology
1872-2083
2007   101309942

Recent Pat Cardiovasc Drug Discov
Recent patents on cardiovascular drug
discovery
1574-8901
2006   101263805

Recent Pat CNS Drug Discov
Recent patents on CNS drug discovery
1574-8898
2006   101265656

Recent Pat DNA Gene Seq
Recent patents on DNA & gene sequences
1872-2156
2007   101299745

Recent Pat Drug Deliv Formul
Recent patents on drug delivery &
formulation
1872-2113
2007   101462399

Recent Pat Inflamm Allergy Drug Discov
Recent patents on inflammation & allergy
drug discovery
1872-213X
2007   101309297

Recent Pat Nanotechnol
Recent patents on nanotechnology
1872-2105
2007   101291922

Recent Prog Horm Res
Recent progress in hormone research
0079-9963
    Absorbed by: Endocrine reviews.
1947-2004   0404471

Recent Results Cancer Res
Recent results in cancer research.
Fortschritte der Krebsforschung. Progrès
dans les recherches sur le cancer
0080-0015
1965   0044671

Recenti Prog Med
Recenti progressi in medicina
0034-1193
1946   0401271

Recept Signal Transduct
Receptors & signal transduction
1087-8475
    Continues: Receptor.
1996-1997   9617134

Receptor
Receptor
1052-8040
    Continued by: Receptors & signal
    transduction.
1991-1995   9109671

Rech Soins Infirm
Recherche en soins infirmiers
0297-2964
1985   9715370

Recomb DNA Tech Bull
Recombinant DNA technical bulletin
0196-0229
    Continues Nucleic acid recombinant scientific
    memoranda.
1977-1993   7807151

Reconstr Surg Traumatol
Reconstruction surgery and traumatology
0080-0260
    Continues Wiederherstellungschirurgie und
    Traumatologie. Reconstruction surgery and
    traumatology.
1968-1990   0136516

Record (Washington)
Record
0160-0036
    Supersedes The Social and rehabilitation
    record. Superseded by Forum.
1977-1977   7708448

Recruit Retain
Recruit & retain: a monthly publication
for professionals concerned with nurse
recruitment and retention
0278-2766
198u   9879301

Recruit Retent Rep
Recruitment & retention report
1044-0666
    Continued by: Recruitment, retention &
    restructuring report.
1988-1994   9312216

Recruit Retent Restruct Rep
Recruitment, retention & restructuring
report
    Continues: Recruitment & retention report.
    Continued by: Nursing management. Feb.
    1999
1994-1998   9436564

Red Cross Cour
The Red Cross courier
1922-1950   20030430R

Redox Rep
Redox report: communications in free
radical research
1351-0002   1743-2928
1994   9511366

Ref Guide Health Care Technol Ind
Reference guide for the health care
technology industry
1082-6858
1993-1995   9413191

Reflections
Reflections / Sigma Theta Tau
0885-8144
    Continued by: Reflections on nursing
    leadership.
1975-1999   9302919

Reforma Med
La Reforma médica
1915-1967   0401272

Refract Corneal Surg
Refractive & corneal surgery
1042-962X
    Continues: Journal of refractive surgery.
    Continued by: Journal of refractive and
    corneal surgery.
1989-1993   8908429

Refu Vet
Refu æah yeterinarit: riv øon Histadrut
ha-rof æim ha-yeterinariyim be-Erets-
Yiśra æel
0034-3153
1939   0404473

Refuat Hapeh Vehashinayim
Refu æat ha-peh yeha-shinayim (1993)
0792-9935
    Continues: Refu æat ha-shinayim (Tel Aviv,
    Israel: 1983).
1993   9816240

Refuat Hapeh Vehashinayim
Refu æat ha-peh yeha-shinayim (Tel Aviv,
Israel: 1969)
0034-3161
    Continued by: Refu æat ha-shinayim (Tel
    Aviv, Israel: 1983).
1969-1983   0227721

Refuat Hashinayim
Refu æat ha-shinayim (Tel Aviv, Israel:
1944)
1944-1968   0227735

Refuat Hashinayim
Refu æat ha-shinayim (Tel Aviv, Israel: 1983)
0334-1402
Continues: Refu æat ha-peh yeha-shinayim (Tel Aviv, Israel: 1969). Continued by: Refu æat ha-peh yeha-shinayim (1993).
1983-199u   8500286

Reg Anaesth
Regional-Anaesthesie
0171-1946
1978-1991   8309693

Reg Anesth
Regional anesthesia
0146-521X
Continued by: Regional anesthesia and pain medicine.
1976-1997   7707549

Reg Anesth Pain Med
Regional anesthesia and pain medicine
1098-7339   1532-8651
Continues: Regional anesthesia.
1998   9804508

Reg Immunol
Regional immunology
0896-0623
1988-1994   9001013

Regan Rep Nurs Law
The Regan report on nursing law
0034-3196
Continued by: Nursing law's Regan report.
1960-1999   0352140

Regen Med
Regenerative medicine
1746-0751   1746-076X
2006   101278116

Regensb Jahrb Arztl Fortbild
Regensburger Jahrbuch für ärztliche Fortbildung
Continued by Regensburger ärztliche Fortbildung.
1949-1965   20040740R

Regist Nurse
Registered nurse (Toronto, Ont.)
0840-8831
Continued by: Registered nurse journal.
1989-1995   8907459

Regul Anal Med Waste
Regulatory analyst. Medical waste
1065-1063
Continued by: Medical waste analyst.
1992-1993   9434067

Regul Pept
Regulatory peptides
0167-0115
1980   8100479

Regul Pept Suppl
Regulatory peptides. Supplement
0169-5134
1980-1985   8308791

Regul Toxicol Pharmacol
Regulatory toxicology and pharmacology: RTP
0273-2300   1096-0295
1981   8214983

Regulation
Regulation
0147-0590
1977-1988   7807387

Rehab Manag
Rehab management
0899-6237
1988   9216135

Rehabil Lit
Rehabilitation literature
0034-3579
Continues the society's Bulletin on current literature.
1956-1986   0401274

Rehabil Nurs
Rehabilitation nursing: the official journal of the Association of Rehabilitation Nurses
0278-4807
Continues: ARN journal.
1981   8104825

Rehabil Rec
Rehabilitation record
0034-3587
Merged with Human needs to form the Social and rehabilitation record.
1960-1973   2985050R

Rehabilitation
Rehabilitation
0034-3528
1948-1977   0257746

Rehabilitation (Bonn)
Rehabilitation: Sozialmedizin, physikalische Medizin, Präventivmedizin; internationale Zeitschrift mit Zentralblatt
0048-7147
Continues Rehabilitation: internationale Zeitschrift für physikalische Medizin und Rehabilitation mit Zentralblatt.
1970-1996   1302716

Rehabilitation (Stuttg)
Die Rehabilitation
0034-3536
1962   0401273

Rein Foie
Rein et foie, maladies de la nutrition; actualités
0085-5464
Supersedes Annales médicales de Vittel.
1960-1980   0401276

Rejuvenation Res
Rejuvenation research
1549-1684
Continues: Journal of anti-aging medicine.
2004   101213381

Rem Actual
Remèdes-Actualités
0484-3800
Supersedes Victoires sur le cancer. Superseded by Remèdes des corps et des âmes.
1960-1964   0024571

Ren Fail
Renal failure
0886-022X   1525-6049
Continues: Uremia investigation.
1987   8701128

Ren Physiol
Renal physiology
0378-5858
Continued by: Renal physiology and biochemistry.
1978-1987   7901911

Ren Physiol Biochem
Renal physiology and biochemistry
1011-6524
Continues: Renal physiology. Continued by: Kidney & blood pressure research.
1988-1995   8906670

Rend Ist Sup Sanit
Rendiconti - Istituto superiore di sanità
0370-5811
Continues: Rendiconti. Continued by: Annali dell'Istituto superiore di sanità.
1941-1964   7507425

Rep Can Def Res Chem Lab
Report. Canada. Defence Research Chemical Laboratories
1940-uuuu   22930240R

Rep Can Def Res Kings Lab
Report. Canada. Defence Research Kingston Laboratory
1950-uuuu   22930250R

Rep Carcinog
Report on carcinogens: carcinogen profiles / U.S. Dept. of Health and Human Services, Public Health Service, National Toxicology Program
1551-8272   1551-8280
Merger of: Report on carcinogens. Summary, and: National Toxicology Program (U.S.). Report on carcinogens. Full report.
2000   101157309

Rep Civ Aeromed Res Inst US
[Report]. Civil Aeromedical Research Institute (U.S.)
1962   0075005

Rep Comm Accredit Rehabil Facil
Report - Commission on Accreditation of Rehabilitation Facilities
0045-7590
1968-1989   7704349

Rep Congr (Ser)
Report to Congress (United States. Physician Payment Review Commission: Series)
Merged with: Background paper (United States. Physician Payment Review Commission). to form: Physician Payment Review Commission (Series).
1989-1989   9417781

Rep Congr Eur Orthod Soc
Report of the congress. European Orthodontic Society
Continues: Transactions. European Orthodontic Society. Continued by: Transactions of the European Orthodontic Society.
1935-1969   0261425

Rep Congr Physician Paym Rev Comm
Report to Congress / Physician Payment Review Commission. United States. Physician Payment Review Commission
Continues: Medicare physician payment. United States. Physician Payment Review Commission. Continued by: Annual report to Congress. United States. Physician Payment Review Commission.
1988-1988   9316884

Rep Del Nurses Assoc
Reporter (Wilmington, Del.)
0418-5412
Supersedes: Delaware nurse. Continued by: DNA reporter.
1968-19uu   7507435

Rep Dep Health Scotl
Report. Great Britain. Dept. of Health for Scotland
0302-3400
Continues the department's Summary report. Continued by Health and welfare services in Scotland; report.
1945-1961   0410322

Rep Group Adv Psychiatry
Report (Group for the Advancement of Psychiatry: 1984)
0888-3394
Continues: Publication - Group for the Advancement of Psychiatry.
1984   8500115

Rep Group Adv Psychiatry
Report (Group for the Advancement of
Psychiatry)
0072-775X
Continued by: Publication (Group for the
Advancement of Psychiatry).
1947-1976   **7507434**

Rep Health Soc Subj (Lond)
Reports on health and social subjects
0300-8045
Absorbed: Reports on public health and
medical subjects.
1972-2002   **0351235**

Rep Natl Forum Hosp Health Aff
A report of the ... National Forum on
Hospital and Health Affairs / conducted
by the Graduate Program in Hospital
Administration of Duke University. National
Forum on Hospital and Health Affairs
1965-uuuu   **100961267**

Rep Nav Med Neuropsychiatr Res Unit
Report - Navy Medical Neuropsychiatric
Research Unit
1962-1974   **7706104**

**Rep No NAEC ACEL United States Aerosp Crew
Equip Lab Phila**
[Report no.] NAEC-ACEL-. United States.
Aerospace Crew Equipment Laboratory,
Philadelphia
1963-uuuu   **22420180R**

**Rep No NAMC ACEL United States Air Crew
Equip Lab Phila**
[Report no.] NAMC-ACEL-. United
States. Air Crew Equipment Laboratory,
Philadelphia
Continued by the Laboratory's [Report no.]
NAEC-ACEL-
1950-1963   **22420170R**

Rep Popul Fam Plann
Reports on population/family planning
0079-3892
1969-1977   **0342340**

Rep Public Health Med Subj (Lond)
Reports on public health and medical
subjects
0072-6117
Supersedes Reports on public health and
medical subjects. Absorbed by: Reports on
health and social subjects.
1920-1979   **7507439**

Rep Rheum Dis
Reports on rheumatic diseases
0048-7279
Continued by: Rheumatic diseases (London,
England: 1984)
1959-1983   **0401277**

Rep U S Nav Med Res Lab
Report (U.S. Naval Medical Research
Laboratory)
0099-3018
Continues in part: Report. Medical Research
Laboratory (New London, Conn.). Continued
by: Report (U.S. Naval Submarine Medical
Center).
1942-1964   **0243634**

Rep US Army Med Res Lab
Report. U.S. Army Medical Research
Laboratory
0097-5362
1947-uuuu   **22120420R**

Rep US Army Med Res Nutr Lab Denver
Report. United States. Army Medical
Research and Nutrition Laboratory, Denver
Continues the Report of the Army Medical
Nutrition Laboratory, Denver.
1958-1974   **22211040R**

Rep US Nav Submar Med Cent
Report (U.S. Naval Submarine Medical
Center)
0730-8515
Continues: Report (U.S. Naval Medical
Research Laboratory). Continued by:
Report (Naval Submarine Medical Research
Laboratory).
1964-1972   **0046347**

Rep US Navy Exp Diving Unit
Report. United States. Navy Experimental
Diving Unit, Washington, D. C
1944-1967   **22421120R**

Reprod Abstr Ser
Reproduction (Cambridge, England).
Abstract series
1476-3990
Continues: Journal of reproduction and
fertility. Abstract series.
2001   **100972078**

Reprod Biol
Reproductive biology
1642-431X
2001   **101160559**

Reprod Biol Endocrinol
Reproductive biology and endocrinology:
RB&E
    1477-7827
2003   **101153627**

Reprod Biomed Online
Reproductive biomedicine online
1472-6483   1472-6491
2000   **101122473**

Reprod Domest Anim
Reproduction in domestic animals =
Zuchthygiene
0936-6768   1439-0531
Continues: Zuchthygiene.
1990   **9015668**

Reprod Fertil Dev
Reproduction, fertility, and development
1031-3613
Continues in part: Australia journal of
biological sciences. Continues: Clinical
reproduction and fertility.
1989   **8907465**

Reprod Health Matters
Reproductive health matters
0968-8080   1460-9576
1993   **9420826**

Reprod Nutr Dev
Reproduction, nutrition, development
0926-5287   1297-9708
Continues: Reproduction, nutrition,
développement. Merged with: Animal science
and: Animal research, to form: Animal.
1989-2006   **8913069**

Reprod Nutr Dev
Reproduction, nutrition, development
0181-1916
Continues Annales de biologie animale,
biochimie, biophysique. Continued by:
Reproduction, nutrition, development.
1980-1988   **8005903**

Reprod Sci
Reproductive sciences (Thousand Oaks,
Calif.)
1933-7191   1933-7205
Continues: Journal of the Society for
Gynecologic Investigation.
2007   **101291249**

Reprod Suppl
Reproduction (Cambridge, England)
Supplement
1477-0415
Continues: Journal of reproduction and
fertility. Supplement. Continued by: Society
of Reproduction and Fertility supplement.
2001-2003   **101142074**

Reprod Toxicol
Reproductive toxicology (Elmsford, N.Y.)
0890-6238
Continues: Reproductive toxicology.
1987   **8803591**

Reproduccion
Reproducción
0303-5220
1974-1983   **0427161**

Reproduction
Reproduction (Cambridge, England)
1470-1626   1741-7899
Merger of: Journal of reproduction and
fertility, and: Reviews of reproduction.
2001   **100966036**

Repura
Repura. Leprosy
0024-1008
Continued by Nippon Rai Gakkai zasshi.
1930-1976   **0413731**

Res Agenda Brief
Research agenda brief
1995-2004   **101171323**

Res Aging
Research on aging
0164-0275
1979   **7908221**

Res Briefs
Research briefs: center for studying health
system change
2008   **101471881**

Res Clin Stud Headache
Research and clinical studies in headache
0080-1453
Continued by Pain and headache.
1967-1978   **0114314**

Res Commun Chem Pathol Pharmacol
Research communications in chemical
pathology and pharmacology
0034-5164
Continued by: Research communications in
molecular pathology and pharmacology.
1970-1994   **0244734**

Res Commun Inst Ferment
Research communications - Institute for
Fermentation, Osaka
0073-8751
Continues: Annual report. Hakkō Kenkyūjo
(Osaka, Japan)
1971-2001   **7502667**

Res Commun Mol Pathol Pharmacol
Research communications in molecular
pathology and pharmacology
1078-0297
Continues: Research communications in
chemical pathology and pharmacology.
1994   **9437512**

Res Dev Disabil
Research in developmental disabilities
0891-4222   1873-3379
Formed by the union of: Analysis and
intervention in developmental disabilities,
and: Applied research in mental retardation.
1987   **8709782**

Res Dev Tech Rep
Research and development technical report. United States. Naval Radiological Defense Laboratory, San Francisco
Supersedes the Laboratory's Research and development report.
1954-1969   22421000R

Res Exp Med (Berl)
Research in experimental medicine. Zeitschrift für die gesamte experimentelle Medizin einschliesslich experimenteller Chirurgie
0300-9130
Merged with: International journal of clinical & laboratory research. to form: Clinical and experimental medicine.
1972-2001   0324736

Res Health Econ
Research in health economics
0197-0690
Continued by: Advances in health economics and health services research.
1979-1979   7911404

Res Immunol
Research in immunology
0923-2494
Continues: Annales de l'Institut Pasteur. Immunology. Merged with: Research in virology; and: Bulletin de l'Institut Pasteur. to form: Microbes and infection.
1989-1998   8907467

Res Initiat Treat Action
Research initiative, treatment action: RITA
1520-8745
1995   100891089

Res Med Educ
Research in medical education: proceedings of the ... annual Conference. Conference on Research in Medical Education
Continues: Proceedings of the ... annual Conference on Research in Medical Education. Conference on Research in Medical Education.
1984   101287181

Res Microbiol
Research in microbiology
0923-2508
Continues: Annales de l'Institut Pasteur. Microbiology.
1989   8907468

Res Nurs Health
Research in nursing & health
0160-6891   1098-240X
1978   7806136

Res Prog Org Biol Med Chem
Research progress in organic, biological and medicinal chemistry
0486-5111
1964-1972   0043605

Res Program
Research program. United States. Army Medical Dept
Continues the Department's Monthly status report on Medical Department research and development projects. Continued by the Research program of the U. S. Army Medical Service.
1946-1950   22210810R

Res Publ Assoc Res Nerv Ment Dis
Research publications - Association for Research in Nervous and Mental Disease
0091-7443
Continues the association's A series of research publications.
1939-1994   7505942

Res Q
Research quarterly
0034-5377
Continued by Research quarterly for exercise and sport.
1930-1979   0401301

Res Q Exerc Sport
Research quarterly for exercise and sport
0270-1367
Continues Research quarterly.
1980   8006373

Res Rep Health Eff Inst
Research report (Health Effects Institute)
1041-5505
1985   8812230

Res Rep Nav Med Res Inst (US)
Research report. Naval Medical Research Institute (U.S.)
1943-uuuu   22420790R

Res Rep U S Nav Med Field Res Lab
[Research reports]. Naval Medical Field Research Laboratory (Camp Lejeune, N.C.)
1944-1972   22420690R

Res Rep U S Nav Sch Aviat Med
Research report. Naval School of Aviation Medicine (U.S.)
0099-9237
1943-196u   22421050R

Res Reprod
Research in reproduction
0034-5253
1969-1990   0210606

Res Rev
Research reviews. United States. Office of Naval Research
0193-1334
Continued by Naval research reviews.
1948-1959   21420380R

Res Serv Med
Research in the service of medicine
1944-1967   20120200R

Res Social Adm Pharm
Research in social & administrative pharmacy: RSAP
1551-7411
2005   101231974

Res Sports Med
Research in sports medicine (Print)
1543-8627   1543-8635
Continues: Sports medicine. training, and rehabilitation.
2003   101167637

Res Stat Note
Research and statistics note - Social Security Administration, Office of Research and Statistics
0566-0327
Continues Research and statistics note - Social Security Administration. Division of Research and Statistics. Continued by: ORSIP note.
1965-1984   0174412

Res Stat Note Health Care Financ Adm Off Policy Plan Res
Research and statistics note - Health Care Financing Administration, Office of Policy, Planning, and Research
0196-1241
1978-1978   7903582

Res Theory Nurs Pract
Research and theory for nursing practice
1541-6577
Continues: Scholarly inquiry for nursing practice.
2002   101146940

Res Today
Research today
0096-2910
1944-1960   20130030R

Res Vet Sci
Research in veterinary science
0034-5288
1960   0401300

Res Virol
Research in virology
0923-2516
Continues: Annales de l'Institut Pasteur. Virology. Merged with: Research in immunology; and: Bulletin de l'Institut Pasteur. to form: Microbes and infection.
1989-1998   8907469

Research
Research; a journal of science and its applications
1947-1962   20120060R

Resen Clin Cient
Resenha clínico-científica
0048-735X
1932-1972   0404474

Resid Staff Physician
Resident and staff physician
0034-5555
Continues Resident physician.
1969   0210223

Residue Rev
Residue reviews
0080-181X
Continued by: Review of environmental contamination and toxicology.
1962-1986   1310631

Resour Biomed Res Educ
Resources for biomedical research and education
0090-4686
Continues Resources for medical research. Continued by Resources for biomedical research.
1969-1970   0211320

Respir Care
Respiratory care
0020-1324
Continues Inhalation therapy.
1971   7510357

Respir Care Clin N Am
Respiratory care clinics of North America
1078-5337
1995   9612026

Respir Manage
Respiratory management
0892-9289
Continues: Respiratory therapy. Continued by: Choices in respiratory management.
1987-1988   8703867

Respir Med
Respiratory medicine
0954-6111   1532-3064
Continues: British journal of diseases of the chest.
1989   8908438

Respir Physiol
Respiration physiology
0034-5687
Continued by: Respiratory physiology & neurobiology.
1966-2002   0047142

Respir Physiol Neurobiol
Respiratory physiology & neurobiology
1569-9048
Continues: Respiration physiology.
2002   101140022

Respir Res
Respiratory research
1465-9921 1465-993X
2000 101090633

Respir Ther
Respiratory therapy
0048-7392
Continued by: Respiratory management.
1971-1986 0314172

Respiration
Respiration; international review of thoracic diseases
0025-7931 1423-0356
Continues Medicina thoracalis.
1968 0137356

Respirology
Respirology (Carlton, Vic.)
1323-7799 1440-1843
1996 9616368

Restaurants Inst
Restaurants & institutions
0273-5520
Continues: Institutions.
1981 9879056

Restor Neurol Neurosci
Restorative neurology and neuroscience
0922-6028
1989 9005499

Restorative Dent
Restorative dentistry
0266-9315
Continued by; European journal of prosthodontics and restorative dentistry.
1984-1991 8502980

Results Probl Cell Differ
Results and problems in cell differentiation
0080-1844 1861-0412
1968 0173555

Resume
Résumé
Continues: NAHSE's résumé.
197u-19uu 9877319

Resuscitation
Resuscitation
0300-9572
1972 0332173

Retina
Retina (Philadelphia, Pa.)
0275-004X 1539-2864
1981 8309919

Retrovirology
Retrovirology
1742-4690
2004 101216893

Reumatismo
Reumatismo
0048-7449
1949 0401302

Reumatizam
Reumatizam
0374-1338
1954 0216650

Reumatol Pol
Reumatologia polska
0484-5986
Continues: Postępy reumatologii. Continued by: Reumatologia.
1959-1962 0024675

Reumatologia
Reumatologia
0034-6233
Supersedes Reumatologia polska.
1963 20130190R

Rev Actual Estomatol Esp
Revista de actualidad estomatológica española / Ilustre Consejo General de Colegios de Odontólogos y Estomatólogos de España
0212-9701
Continues: Boletín de información dental. Continued by: Revista de actualidad odontoestomatológica española.
1984-1989 8408031

Rev Actual Odontoestomatol Esp
Revista de actualidad odontoestomatológica española: boletín de información, del Ilustre Consejo General de Colegios de Odontólogos y Estomatólogos de España
0212-9701
Continues: Revista de actualidad estomatológica española. Continued by: Actualidad odontoestomatologica española.
1990-1994 9007565

Rev ADM
Revista ADM (Asociación Dental Mexicana: 1988)
0001-0944
Continues: ADM (Asociación Dental Mexicana: 1986).
1988 9212425

Rev ADM
Revista ADM: organo oficial de la Asociación Dental Mexicana
0001-0944
Continues: ADM. Continued by: ADM (Asociación Dental Mexicana: 1986).
1979-1986 8502715

Rev Agrup Odontol Cap Fed
Revista de la Agrupación Odontológica de la Capital Federal
Continues: Revista de la Agrupación Odontológica de la Zona Central de la Capital Federal.
1951-19uu 8706017

Rev Alerg
Revista alergia: organo oficial de la Sociedad Mexicana de Alergia e Inmunlogía
Continues: Revista alergia México. Continued by: Revista alergia México (Tecamachalco, Puebla, Mexico: 1993).
1991-1993 9317222

Rev Alerg Mex
Revista alergia México
Continues: Alergia. Continued by: Revista alergia.
1987-1991 8906244

Rev Alerg Mex
Revista alergia Mexico (Tecamachalco, Puebla, Mexico: 1993)
Continues: Revista alergia.
1993 9438824

Rev Allergy
Review of allergy
0034-6411
Continues the Review of allergy and applied immunology.
1966-1971 0043154

Rev Am Hist
Reviews in American history
0048-7511 1080-6628
1973 9107988

Rev Annu Soc Odontostomatol Nordest
Revue annuelle - Société odonto-stomatologique du Nord-Est
0081-1203
Continued by Revue odonto stomatologique du Nord-Est.
1969-1970 7502188

Rev Argent Alerg
Revista argentina de alergia
1953-1963 20130410R

Rev Argent Cardiol
Revista argentina de cardiología
0034-7000
1934 2985054R

Rev Argent Cir
Revista argentina de cirugía
0048-7600
1960 0401313

Rev Argent Endocrinol Metab
Revista argentina de endocrinología y metabolismo
0080-2077
1955 0421740

Rev Argent Implantol Estomatol
Revista Argentina De Implantologia Estomatologica
19uu 9875628

Rev Argent Microbiol
Revista Argentina de microbiología
0325-7541
Continues Revista de la Asociación Argentina de Microbiología.
1979 8002834

Rev Argent Neurol Psiquiatr
Revista argentina de neurología y psiquiatría
1964-1964 0023573

Rev Argent Pueric Neonatol
Revista argentina de puericultura e neonatología
0486-6304
Supersedes the Revista of the Sociedad de Puericultura de Buenos Aires. Superseded by Revista argentina de perinatología y puericultura.
1965-1971 0337270

Rev Argent Reumatol
Revista argentina de reumatología
1936-1961 20140020R

Rev Argent Urol
Revista argentina de urología
Continued by Revista argentina de urología y nefrología.
1932-1962 0055564

Rev Argent Urol Nefrol
Revista argentina de urología y nefrología
0048-7627
Continues: Revista argentina de urología. Continued by: Revista argentina de urologiá (Buenos Aires, Argentina: 1990).
1963-1987 0055467

Rev Asoc Argent Microbiol
Revista de la Asociación Argentina de Microbiología
0325-1713
Continued by Revista Argentina de microbiología.
1969-1978 7604007

Rev Asoc Bioquim Argent
Revista de la Asociación Bioquímica Argentina. Asociación Bioquímica Argentina
0004-4768
Continued by: Bioquímica y patología clínica.
1936-1996 7505957

Rev Asoc Med Argent
Revista de la Asociación Médica Argentina
0004-4830
Continues: Revista. Absorbed Revista de especialidades and the Revista de la Sociedad de Medicina Interna y de la Sociedad de Tisiología in 1932.
1915 7505961

Rev Asoc Med Latinoam
Revista. Asociación Médica Latinoamericana
Continues El Progreso médico; revista de la Asociación Médica Latinoamericana.
1946-19uu **15330410R**

Rev Asoc Medica Mex
Revista. Asociación Médica Mexicana
Continues A. M. M.
1925-19uu **0002552**

Rev Asoc Mex Enferm
Revista de la Asociación Mexicana de Enfermeras
Continued by Revista del Colegio Nacional de Enfermeras.
1956-1966 **7505959**

Rev Asoc Odontol Argent
Revista de la Asociación Odontológica Argentina
0004-4881
Continues Revista odontológica.
1955 **7505963**

Rev Asoc Odontol Costa Rica
Revista de la Asociación Odontológica de Costa Rica
0066-8575
Continued by Revista odontológica de Costa Rica.
1957-1970 **7505962**

Rev Asoc Prof Hosp Nac Odontol
Revista De La Asociacion De Profesionales Del Hospital Nacional De Odontologia
1974-19uu **9877840**

Rev Assoc Med Bras
Revista da Associação Médica Brasileira
0004-5241
Continued by: AMB. Associação Médica Brasileira.
1954-1967 **7505951**

Rev Assoc Med Bras
Revista da Associação Médica Brasileira (1992)
0104-4230
Continues: AMB.
1992 **9308586**

Rev Assoc Med Minas Gerais
Revista da Associação Médica de Minas Gerais
0004-525X
1949-1986 **7505949**

Rev Assoc Med Rio Grande Do Sul
Revista da Associação Médica do Rio Grande do Sul
0004-5268
Continued by Revista Amrigs.
1957-1974 **7505950**

Rev Assoc Paul Cir Dent
Revista da Associação Paulista de Cirurgiões Dentistas
0004-5276
1947 **7609858**

Rev Assoc Paul Cir Dent Reg Aracatuba
Revista da Associação Paulista de Cirurgiões Dentistas Regional de Araçatuba
0004-5276
Continued by: Revista Regional de Araçatuba. Associação Paulista de Cirurgiões Dentistas.
1980-1981 **8208428**

Rev Ateneo Argent Odontol
Revista del Ateneo Argentino de Odontología: R.A.A.O
0326-3827
Continues: Ortopedia maxilar.
1980 **9440712**

Rev Ateneo Catedra Tec Oper Dent
Revista Del Ateneo De La Catedra De Tecnica De Operatoria Dental
19uu **9875629**

Rev Atheroscler
Revue de l'athérosclérose
Supplement to Archives des maladies du coeur et des vaisseaux. Continued by Revue de l'athérosclérose et des artériopathies périphériques.
1959-1965 **0320677**

Rev Atheroscler (Paris)
Revue de l'athérosclérose et des artériopathies périphériques
0556-7459
Continues Revue de l'athérosclérose. Supplement to Archives des maladies du coeur et des vaisseaux.
1966-1971 **0323634**

Rev Belg Pathol Med Exp
Revue belge de pathologie et de médecine expérimentale
0370-3770
Formed by the union of: Archives internationales de médecine expérimentale, and: Revue belge des sciences médicales. Continued by: Pathologia Europaea.
1947-1965 **20320140R**

Rev Belge Med Dent
Revue belge de médecine dentaire. Belgisch tijdschrift voor tandheelkunde
0035-080X
Issues for June 1983- published also in Dutch with title: Belgisch tijdschrift voor tandheelkunde. Merger of: Revue belge de science dentaire, and: Journal dentaire belge
1962 **2984374R**

Rev Belge Stomatol
Revue belge de stomatologie. Belgisch tijdschrift voor stomatologie
Continues Revue trimestrielle belge de stomatologie. Absorbed Revue belge de science dentaire. mar. 1947-57. Continued by Acta stomatologica Belgica.
1920-1959 **20320170R**

Rev Biol Oral
Revista de biologia oral
0486-6622
1963-1966 **7803590**

Rev Biol Trop
Revista de biología tropical
0034-7744
1953 **0404267**

Rev Bras Anestesiol
Revista brasileira de anestesiologia
0034-7094 **1806-907X**
1951 **0401316**

Rev Bras Biol
Revista brasileira de biologia
0034-7108
Continued by: Brazilian journal of biology.
1941-2000 **2985055R**

Rev Bras Cir
Revista brasileira de cirurgia
0034-7124
1932-1997 **2985056R**

Rev Bras Cir Cardiovasc
Revista brasileira de cirurgia cardiovascular: órgão oficial da Sociedade Brasileira de Cirurgia Cardiovascular
0102-7638 **1678-9741**
1986 **9104279**

Rev Bras Enferm
Revista brasileira de enfermagem
0034-7167
Continues Anais de enfermagem.
1955 **7910105**

Rev Bras Gastroenterol
Revista brasileira de gastroenterologia
0034-7221
1949-1968 **0421116**

Rev Bras Ginecol Obstet
Revista brasileira de ginecologia e obstetrícia: revista da Federação Brasileira das Sociedades de Ginecologia e Obstetrícia
0100-7203 **1806-9339**
1979 **9214757**

Rev Bras Leprol
Revista brasileira de leprologia
0034-7248
Continues Revista de leprologia de São Paulo. Superseded by Hansenologia internationalis.
1936-1970 **0401323**

Rev Bras Malariol Doencas Trop
Revista brasileira de malariologia e doenças tropicais. Publicações avulsas
0034-7256
1949-1986 **20140150R**

Rev Bras Med
Revista brasileira de medicina
0034-7264
1944 **0401324**

Rev Bras Odontol
Revista brasileira de odontologia
0034-7272
1943 **0404254**

Rev Bras Odontol Mil
Revista brasileira de odontologia militar: órgão oficial da Academia Brasileira de Odontologia Militar
0102-3942
1983-1992 **9103574**

Rev Bras Oftalmol
Revista brasileira de oftalmologia
0034-7280
1942 **0136421**

Rev Bras Otorrinolaringol
Revista brasileira de oto-rino-laringologia
0034-7299 **1806-9312**
Continues: Revista oto-laringologica de São Paulo.
1939 **0420632**

Rev Bras Parasitol Vet
Revista brasileira de parasitologia veterinária = Brazilian journal of veterinary parasitology: Órgão Oficial do Colégio Brasileiro de Parasitologia Veterinária
0103-846X
1992 **9440482**

Rev Bras Pesqui Med Biol
Revista brasileira de pesquisas médicas e biológicas
0034-7310
Continued by Brazilian journal of medical and biological research.
1968-1980 **0140423**

Rev Bras Psiquiatr
Revista brasileira de psiquiatria (São Paulo, Brazil: 1999)
1516-4446
Continues: Revista ABP-APAL.
1999 **100895975**

Rev Bras Tuberc Doencas Torac
Revista brasileira de tuberculose e doenças torácicas
1932-19uu **20140230R**

Rev Can Biol
Revue canadienne de biologie / éditée par l'Université de Montréal
0035-0915
Continued by: Revue canadienne de biologie expérimentale.
1942-1981 **8214595**

Rev Can Biol Exp
Revue canadienne de biologie expérimentale
0714-6140
Continues: Revue canadienne de biologie. Continued by: Experimental biology.
1982-1983 **8213593**

Rev Cardiovasc Med
Reviews in cardiovascular medicine
1530-6550
2000 **100960007**

Rev Catarinense Odontol
Revista catarinense de odontologia
0100-7955
1974-1988 **7806422**

Rev Cent Am Odontol
Revista Centro América odontológica
0377-4694
Continues Centro América odontológica.
1967-1975 **7601970**

Rev Centro Cienc Biomed Univ Fed Uberlandia
Revista do Centro de Ciências Biomédicas da Universidade Federal de Uberlândia
0102-5996
Continued by: Bioscience journal.
1985-1997 **9011328**

Rev Chil Hig Med Prev
Revista chilena de higiene y medicina preventiva
1937-1953 **20140260R**

Rev Chil Neuropsiquiatr
Revista chilena de neuro-psiquiatría
1947-1958 **20140270R**

Rev Chil Obstet Ginecol
Revista chilena de obstetricia y ginecología
0048-766X 0717-7526
Continues: Boletín de la Sociedad Chilena de Obstetricia y Ginecología.
1961 **0404260**

Rev Chil Odontoestomatol
Revista chilena de odontoestomatología
0716-4351
1987-1988 **8912771**

Rev Chil Pediatr
Revista chilena de pediatría
0370-4106
1930 **0404261**

Rev Chilena Infectol
Revista chilena de infectología: órgano oficial de la Sociedad Chilena de Infectología
0716-1018
1984 **9305754**

Rev Chir
Revue de chirurgie
Supersedes in part: Revue mensuelle de médecine et de chirurgie.
1881-1955 **20320240R**

Rev Chir Oncol Radiol O R L Oftalmol Stomatol Chir
Revista de chirurgie, oncologie, radiologie, o.r.l., oftalmologie, stomatologie. Chirurgie
0377-5003
Continues Chirurgia, issued 1951-Iunie 1974. Continued by: Chirurgia (Bucharest, Romania: 1990).
1974-1990 **7508736**

Rev Chir Oncol Radiol O R L Oftalmol Stomatol Otorinolaringol
Revista de chirurgie, oncologie, radiologie, o.r.l., oftalmologie, stomatologie. Oto-rino-laringologia
1220-0867
Continues in part: Oto-rino-laringologia şi oftalmologia. Continued by: Revista Societăţii de O.R.L..
1974-1992 **7508737**

Rev Chir Oncol Radiol O R L Oftalmol Stomatol Ser Oftalmol
Revista de chirurgie, oncologie, radiologie, o. r. l., oftalmologie, stomatologie. Oftalmologie
0377-7863
Continues in part: Oto-rino-laringologia şi oftalmologia. Continued by: Oftalmologia (Bucharest, Romania: 1990).
1974-1989 **7506415**

Rev Chir Oncol Radiol O R L Oftalmol Stomatol Ser Stomatol
Revista de chirurgie, oncologie, radiologie, o. r. l., oftalmologie, stomatologie. Seria: Stomatologie
0377-7871
Continues: Stomatologia. Continued by: Stomatologie (Bucharest, Romania).
1974-1989 **7513023**

Rev Cir (Mex)
Revista de cirugía
Continued by the Revista de cirugía del Hospital Juárez.
1950-1970 **1274040**

Rev Cir Urug
Revista de cirugía del Uruguay
0797-3403
Continues: Boletín. Sociedad de Cirugía del Uruguay. Continued by: Cirugía del Uruguay.
1965-1969 **1252044**

Rev Circ Argent Odontol
Revista. Círculo Argentino de Odontología
0325-7479
Continues: Revista. Círculo Odontológico del Oeste, Buenos Aires.
1962 **16220240R**

Rev Circ Odontol Cordoba
Revista del Círculo Odontológico de Córdoba
0045-6942
1936-1968 **7507478**

Rev Circ Odontol Oeste
Revista del Círculo Odontológico del Oeste. Círculo Odontológico del Oeste, Buenos Aires
0328-7807
Continued by: Revista del Círculo Argentino de Odontología.
1937-1961 **0005415**

Rev Circ Odontol Sur
Revista Del Circulo Odontologico Del Sur
0034-902X
1962 **9875647**

Rev Circul Ondontol Ros
Revista. Círculo Odontológico de Rosario
0009-7357
1929-1988 **16220390R**

Rev Clin Basic Pharm
Reviews in clinical & basic pharmacology
0334-1534
Continues: Reviews in pure & applied pharmacological sciences. Continued by: Journal of basic and clinical physiology and pharmacology.
1985-1988 **8700959**

Rev Clin Esp
Revista clínica española
0014-2565 1578-1860
Absorbed: Boletín de la Fundación Jiménez Díaz, 1985. Absorbed: Nuevos archivos de la Facultad de Medicina, Nov. 1985.
1940 **8608576**

Rev Clin Exp Hematol
Reviews in clinical and experimental hematology
1127-0020 1825-151X
1997-2005 **9815344**

Rev Clin Inst Matern Lisb
Revista clínica. Lisbon. Instituto Maternal
Supersedes Arquivo de obstetrícia y ginecologia.
1946-1967 **18330870R**

Rev Clin Sao Paulo
Revista clínica de São Paulo
1937-1954 **20140390R**

Rev Col Estomatol Guatem
Revista del Colegio Estomatológico de Guatemala
0069-5157
Continues Boletín del Colegio Estomatológico de Guatemala.
1964-1969 **7505978**

Rev Col Med Guatem
Revista del Colegio Médico de Guatemala
0413-3137
Continued by: Revista de Colegio de Médicos y Cirujanos.
1950-1984 **0023766**

Rev Col Nac Enferm
Revista del Colegio Nacional de Enfermeras
0045-7329
Continues Revista del Asociación Mexicana de Enfermeras.
1967-1981 **7505980**

Rev Colomb Obstet Ginecol
Revista colombiana de obstetricia y ginecología
0034-7434
1950 **0404263**

Rev Colomb Pediatr Pueric
Revista colombiana de pediatría y puericultura
0120-0402
1941-1993 **0417463**

Rev Coloniale Med Chir
Revue coloniale de médecine & chirurgie
1244-4014
Continued by: Revue de médecine et d'hygiène d'Outre-Mer.
1929-1955 **20320220R**

Rev Corps Sante Armees Terre Mer Air
Revue des corps de santé des armées: terre, mer, air, et du corps vétérinaire
0035-1954
Supersedes: Revue de corps vétérinaire de l'Armée. Supersedes: Revue de médecine navale (métropole et outre-mer). Supersedes: Médecine aéronautique. Supersedes: Revue du corps de santé militaire. Continued in part by: Revue du Service biologique et vétérinaire des armées. Superseded by: Médecine et armées.
1960-1972 **0360137**

Rev Corps Sante Mil
Revue du corps de santé militaire
1945-1959 **20330280R**

Rev Costarric Cienc Med
Revista costarricense de ciencias médicas
0253-2948
1980 **8300226**

Rev Criminol Polic Cient
Revista de criminología y policía científica
Supersedes Detective.
1940-1955   **20150230R**

Rev Cubana Cardiol
Revista cubana de cardiología
Merged with other Cuban medical journals to
form the Revista cubana de medicina.
1938-1960   **20140440R**

Rev Cubana Enferm
Revista cubana de enfermería
0864-0319
1985   **9301327**

Rev Cubana Estomatol
Revista cubana de estomatología
0034-7507
1964   **0023661**

Rev Cubana Lab Clin
Revista cubana de laboratorio clínico
1947-1961   **20140460R**

Rev Cubana Med
Revista cubana de medicina
0034-7523
1962-1998   **0404265**

Rev Cubana Med Trop
Revista cubana de medicina tropical
0375-0760
Continues: Revista Kuba de medicina tropical
y parasitología.
1966   **0074364**

Rev Cubana Pediatr
Revista cubana de pediatría
0034-7531
Continues Boletín de la Sociedad Cubana de
Pediatría. Absorbed Archivos de medicina
infantil in 1961.
1946   **0417464**

Rev Czech Med
Review of Czechoslovak medicine
0034-6497
1955-1977   **0401304**

Rev Dent (San Salv)
Revista dental
0048-7767
1934-1983   **20230090R**

Rev Dent (St Domingo)
Revista dental
1949-1963   **20230050R**

Rev Dent Chile
Revista dental de Chile
0034-9143
Continues Revista dental.
1930   **0407205**

Rev Dent Liban
Revue dentaire libanaise. Lebanese dental
magazine
0035-1873
Continued by: Journal of the Lebanese Dental
Association.
1950-2000   **0204061**

Rev Drug Metab Drug Interact
Reviews on drug metabolism and drug
interactions
0334-2190
Continues: Quarterly reviews on drug
metabolism and drug interactions. Continued
by: Drug metabolism and interactions.
1985-1987   **8609214**

Rev East Med Sci
Review of eastern medical sciences
1956-1958   **20130230R**

Rev Econ Stat
The review of economics and statistics
0034-6535   1530-9142
Continues: Review of economic statistics.
1948   **9877925**

Rev Ecuat Hig Med Trop
Revista ecuatoriana de higiene y medicina
tropical
0013-0745
1944-1987   **9427215**

Rev Ecuat Pediatr
Revista ecuatoriana de pediatría
1949-1963   **20230180R**

Rev Eesp Cir Traumatol Ortop
Revista española de cirugía, traumatología
y ortopedia
1131-0898
1944-1947   **0404300**

Rev Electroencephalogr Neurophysiol Clin
Revue d'électroencéphalographie et de
neurophysiologie clinique
0370-4475
1971-1987   **0320770**

Rev Elev Med Vet Pays Trop
Revue d'élevage et de médecine vétérinaire
des pays tropicaux
0035-1865   1951-6711
Continues: Recueil de médecine vétérinaire
exotique.
1947   **2984776R**

Rev Endocr Metab Disord
Reviews in endocrine & metabolic disorders
1389-9155
2000   **100940588**

Rev Enferm
Revista de enfermería (Barcelona, Spain)
0210-5020
1978   **8309920**

Rev Enferm (Lisboa)
Revista de enfermagem
0034-8090
1953-1974   **20150280R**

Rev Enferm Nov Dimens
Revista enfermagem em novas dimensões
0100-2724
1975-1978   **7607814**

Rev Environ Contam Toxicol
Reviews of environmental contamination
and toxicology
0179-5953
Continues: Residue reviews.
1987   **8703602**

Rev Environ Health
Reviews on environmental health
0048-7554
1972   **0425754**

Rev Epidemiol Med Soc Sante Publique
Revue d'épidémiologie, médecine sociale et
santé publique
0035-2438
Continues Revue d'hygiène et de médecine
sociale. Continued by Revue d'épidémiologie
et de santé publique.
1971-1975   **7608204**

Rev Epidemiol Sante Publique
Revue d'épidémiologie et de santé publique
0398-7620
Continues Revue d'épidémiologie, médecine
sociale et santé publique.
1976   **7608039**

Rev Esc Enferm USP
Revista da Escola de Enfermagem da U S P
0080-6234
1967   **0242726**

Rev Esc Odontol Tucuman
Revista De La Escuela De Odontologia,
Universidad Nacional De Tucuman, Facultad
De Medicina
Continued by: Revista De La Facultad De
Odontologia. Universidad Nacional De
Tucuman.
1968-1973   **9875630**

Rev Esp Anestesiol
Revista española de anestesiología
0210-3591
Continued by Revista española de
anestesiología y reanimación.
1954-1967   **0135226**

Rev Esp Anestesiol Reanim
Revista española de anestesiología y
reanimación
0034-9356
Continues Revista española de anestesiología.
1967   **0134516**

Rev Esp Cardiol
Revista española de cardiología
0300-8932   1579-2242
1947   **0404277**

Rev Esp Endodoncia
Revista española de endodoncia / AEDE
0212-4688
Continued by: Endoconcia (Madrid. Spain).
1983-1989   **8409527**

Rev Esp Enferm Apar Dig
Revista española de las enfermedades del
aparato digestivo
0034-9437
Continues Revista española de las
enfermedades del aparato digestivo y de la
nutrición. Continued by: Revista española de
enfermedades digestivas.
1968-1989   **0143622**

Rev Esp Enferm Apar Dig Nutr
Revista española de las enfermedades del
aparato digestivo y de la nutrición
Continued by Revista española de las
enfermedades del aparato digestivo.
1935-1967   **0143615**

Rev Esp Enferm Dig
Revista española de enfermedades
digestivas: organo oficial de la Sociedad
Española de Patología Digestiva
1130-0108
Continues: Revista española de las
enfermedades del aparato digestivo.
1990   **9007566**

Rev Esp Estomatol
Revista española de estomatología
0484-7563
Continued by: Revista europea de odontoestomatología.
1953-1988   **0404301**

Rev Esp Fisiol
Revista española de fisiología
0034-9402
Continued by: Journal of physiology and
biochemistry.
1945-1997   **0404475**

Rev Esp Geriatr Gerontol
Revista española de geriatría y gerontología
0211-139X   1578-1747
Continues Revista española de gerontología
y geriatría.
1980   **8009022**

Rev Esp Med Nucl
Revista española de medicina nuclear
0212-6982
1982   9208726

Rev Esp Obstet Ginecol
Revista española de obstetricia y ginecología
0034-9445
1944-1989   0270525

Rev Esp Oncol
Revista española de oncología
0482-640X
1952-1985   20230240R

Rev Esp Otoneurooftalmol Neurocir
Revista española de oto-neuro-oftalmología
y neurocirugía
0034-9453
1944-1979   0404302

Rev Esp Parad
Revista Espanola De Paradoncia
0484-7598
1963-19uu   9875631

Rev Esp Pediatr
Revista española de pediatría
0034-947X
1945   0404303

Rev Esp Quimioter
Revista española de quimioterapia:
publicación oficial de la Sociedad Española
de Quimioterapia
0214-3429
1988   9108821

Rev Esp Reum Enferm Osteoartic
Revista española de reumatismo y
enfermedades osteoarticulares
0048-7791
1945-1980   0404304

Rev Esp Reumatol
Revista española de reumatología:
órgano oficial de la Sociedad Española de
Reumatología
0304-4815
  Merged with: Reumatología clinica. To form:
  Revista mexicana de reumatología.
1973-2005   9209964

Rev Esp Salud Publica
Revista española de salud pública
1135-5727
  Continues: Revista de sanidad e higiene
  pública.
1995   9600212

Rev Esp Tuberc
Revista española de tuberculosis
1930-1976   0416675

Rev Estomatol Cuba
Revista estomatológica de Cuba
1933-1960   0404305

Rev Eur Etud Clin Biol
Revue européenne d'études cliniques et
biologiques. European journal of clinical
and biological research
0035-3019
  Continues Revue française d'études cliniques
  et biologiques. Continued by Biomedicine.
1970-1972   0351323

Rev Eur Odontoestomatol
Revista europea de odonto-estomatología
0214-8668
  Continues: Revista española de
  estomatología.
1989   8909773

Rev Fac Cien Med Univ Nac Cordoba
Revista de la Facultad de Ciencias Médicas
(Córdoba, Argentina)
0014-6722
  Continues: Revista de la Facultad de Ciencias
  Médicas de la Universidad Nac. de Córdoba.
1977   8303003

Rev Fac Cien Med Univ Nac Cordoba
Revista de la Facultad de Ciencias Médicas
de la Universidad Nac. de Córdoba
0301-7281
  Continues: Revista de la Facultad de Ciencias
  Médicas de Córdoba. Continued by: Revista
  de la Facultad de Ciencias Medicas (Córdoba,
  Spain).
1975-1977   8103737

Rev Fac Cienc Med
Revista de la Facultad de Ciencias Médicas
0375-0752
  Continues: Revista de la Facultad de Ciencias
  Médicas, Farmacia y Ramos Menores.
  Continued by: Revista de la Facultad de
  Medicina (Rosario, Santa Fe, Argentina).
1959-1982   7507458

Rev Fac Cienc Med Cordoba
Revista de la Facultad de Ciencias Médicas
de Córdoba
0014-6722
  Continues Revista de la Facultad de Ciencias
  Médicas, Universidad Nacional de Córdoba.
  Continued by: Revista de la Facultad de
  Ciencias Médicas de la Universidad Nac. de
  Córdoba.
1954-1974   7505966

Rev Fac Farm Odontol Araraquara
Revista da Faculdade de Farmácia e
Odontologia de Araraquara
0014-6684
  Continued by: Revista da Faculdade de
  Ciências Farmacêuticas.
1967-1976   7505953

Rev Fac Farm Odontol Ribeiro Preto
Revista da Faculdade de Farmácia e
Odontologia de Ribeirão Prêto
0100-0160
  Continues Boletim da Faculdade de Farmácia
  e Odontologia de Ribeirão Prêto. Continued
  by Revista de Faculdade de Odontologia de
  Ribeirão Prêto.
1971-1983   7512232

Rev Fac Farm Univ Cent Venez
Revista de la Facultad de Farmacia,
Universidad Central de Venezuela
0041-8307
  Supersedes Prociencia.
1959-1998   7507461

Rev Fac Med Univ Nac Colomb
Revista de la Facultad de Medicina,
Universidad Nacional de Colombia
0120-0011
1932   7507464

Rev Fac Med Vet (Lima)
Revista de la Facultad de Medicina
Veterinaria de la Universidad Nacional
Mayor de San Marcos
0301-4959
1946-1968   0405411

Rev Fac Med Vet Univ Sao Paulo
Revista da Faculdade de Medicina
Veterinária
0301-7273
  Continued by: Revista da Faculdade de
  Medicina Veterinária e Zootecnia da
  Universidade de São Paulo.
1938-1970   7505100

Rev Fac Odontol Aracatuba
Revista da Faculdade de Odontologia de
Araçatuba
0300-1350
  Supersedes Revista FOA. Merged with:
  Revista da Faculade de Odontologia de
  Araraquara, and: Revista da Faculdade de
  Odontologia de São José dos Campos, to
  form: Revista de odontologia da UNESP.
1972-1978   7505954

Rev Fac Odontol P Alegre
Revista da Faculdade de Odontologia, Pôrto
Alegre
0477-6763
  Continues Revista da Escola de Odontologia
  de Pôrto Alegre, issued 1956.
1960   1260135

Rev Fac Odontol Pernambuco
Revista da Faculdade de Odontologia de
Pernambuco
0048-3419
  Continued by: Odonto divulga.
1968-1983   7507453

Rev Fac Odontol Ribeiro Preto
Revista da Faculdade de Odontologia de
Ribeirão Prêto
0102-129X
  Continues: Revista da Faculdade de Farmácia
  e Odontologia de Ribeirão Prêto.
1983-1986   8509491

Rev Fac Odontol Sao Jose Dos Campos
Revista da Faculdade de Odontologia de São
José dos Campos
0301-1119
  Merged with: Revista da Faculadade de
  Odontologia de Ara çatuba, and: Revista de
  Faculadad de Odontologia de Araraquara, to
  form: Revista de odontologia da UNESP.
1972-1977   7507454

Rev Fac Odontol Sao Paulo
Revista da Faculdade de Odontologia da
Universidade de São Paulo
0581-6866
  Continued by: Revista de odontologia da
  Universidade de São Paulo.
19uu-1986   7507451

Rev Fac Odontol Tucuman
Revista de la Facultad de Odontología (San
Miguel de Tucumán, Argentina)
0325-125X
  Continues: Revista de la Escuela de
  Odontología, Universidad Nacional de
  Tucumán, Facultad de Medicina.
1974-1982   8505321

Rev Fac Odontol Univ Antioq
Revista De La Facultad De Odontologia
Universidad De Antioquia
1989   9884874

Rev Fac Odontol Univ Chile
Revista de la Facultad de Odontología
(Santiago, Chile)
0716-8500
1983   9302483

Rev Fac Odontol Univ Fed Bahia
Revista da Faculdade de Odontologia da
Universidade Federal da Bahia
0101-8418
  Successor to the "Revista ao Boletim da
  FOUFBA," published 1972-1974 and 1980.
1981-1997   8610424

Rev Fac Odontol Univ Nac (Cordoba)
Revista de la Facultad de Odontología
0325-1071
  Continues Revista odontológica (Córdoba).
1974-1998   7806948

Rev Fac Odontol Univ Nac Colomb
Revista de la Facultad de Odontología de la Universidad Nacional de Colombia
0029-8409
Supersedes Odontología?
1963-1973   7505968

Rev Faculdade Odontol FZL
Revista da Faculdade de Odontologia da FZL
0103-4391
Continued by: Revista de odontologia da UNICID.
1989-1992   9010532

Rev Faculdade Odontol Lins
Revista da Faculdade de Odontologia de Lins
0104-7582
1988-1997   9014560

Rev Farm Bioquim Univ Sao Paulo
Revista de farmácia e bioquímica da Universidade de São Paulo
0370-4726
Continues the Revista da Faculdade de Farmácia e Bioquímica da Universidade de São Paulo. Continued by: Revista brasileira de ciências farmacêuticas.
1970-1998   1272000

Rev Farm Cuba
Revista farmacéutica de Cuba
Continues Boletín de farmacía.
1936-19uu   20230360R

Rev Farm Odontol
Revista de farmacia e odontologia
0034-8201
Continued by: Especialidades odontológicas.
1930-1979   20150320R

Rev Fed Am Health Syst
Review (Federation of American Health Systems)
0891-0200
Continued by: Health systems reviews.
Continues: Review - Federation of American Hospitals.
1986-1990   8612375

Rev Fed Am Hosp
Review - Federation of American Hospitals
0148-9496
Continues The Investor-owned hospital review. Continued by: Review (Federation of American Health Systems).
1976-1986   7613945

Rev Fed Odontol Colomb
Revista de la Federación Odontológica Colombiana
0046-354X
1950-1986   7505969

Rev Fed Odontol Ecuat
Revista de la Federación Odontológica Ecuatoriana
1968-1971   9425071

Rev Flora Med
Revista da flora medicinal
0370-484X
1934-1953   20150030R

Rev FOA
Revista F O A
0300-2837
1965-1966   0353332

Rev Foie
La Revue du foie
Merged with the Bulletin of the Association d'études physio-pathologiques du foie et de la nutrition to form Revue internationale d'hépatologie.
1942-1950   20330300R

Rev Fr Allergol
Revue française d'allergologie
0035-2845
Continues Revue française d'allergie.
Continued by Revue française d'allergologie et d'immunologie clinique.
1970-1973   0426573

Rev Fr Endocrinol Clin
La Revue française d'endocrinologie clinique, nutrition, et métabolisme
0048-8062
1960-1999   0404335

Rev Fr Endod
Revue française d'endodontie: publication officielle de la Société française d'endodontie
0294-1813
Continued by: Endo.
1982-1992   8709006

Rev Fr Etud Clin Biol
Revue française d'études cliniques et biologiques
0370-4793
Continued by Revue européenne d'études cliniques et biologiques.
1956-1969   0235616

Rev Fr Gerontol
Revue française de gérontologie
0035-2896
Continued by Revue de gérontologie d'expression française.
1955-1963   0166060

Rev Fr Gynecol Obstet
Revue française de gynécologie et d'obstétrique
0035-290X
Continues: Revue mensuelle de gynécologie. d'obstétrique. et de pédiatrie.
1919-1999   0411346

Rev Fr Mal Respir
Revue française des maladies respiratoires
0301-0279
Supersedes Revue de tuberculose et de pneumologie. Continued by Revue des maladies respiratoires.
1973-1983   0365342

Rev Fr Odontostomatol
Revue française d'odonto-stomatologie
0035-3043
Formed by the union of La Revue odontologique. L'Odontologie, Le Bulletin des chirurgiens dentistes indépendants. and La Revue dentaire de France. Continued by Revue d'odonto-stomatologie.
1954-1971   0327015

Rev Fr Prothes Dent
Revue française des prothésistes dentaires
0242-1828
Supersedes Revue française de la prothèse dentaire.
1979   8006567

Rev Fr Prothese Dent
La Revue française de la prothèse dentaire
0048-8089
Supersedes La Prothèse dentaire française.
Superseded by Revue française des prothésistes dentaires.
1964-1979   0024731

Rev Fr Psychanal
Revue française de psychanalyse
0035-2942
1927   2984777R

Rev Fr Transfus
Revue française de transfusion
0035-2977
Continues Transfusion. Continued by Revue française de transfusion et immuno-hématologie.
1968-1974   7509498

Rev Fr Transfus Hemobiol
Revue française de transfusion et d'hémobiologie: bulletin de la Société nationale de transfusion sanguine
1140-4639
Continues: Revue française de transfusion et immuno-hématologie. Continued by: Transfusion clinique et biologique.
1989-1993   8908966

Rev Fr Transfus Immunohematol
Revue française de transfusion et immuno-hématologie
0338-4535
Continues Revue française de transfusion.
Continued by: Revue française de transfusion et d'hémobiologie.
1975-1988   7509497

Rev Francaise Serol Chimiother
Revue française de sérologie et de chimiothérapie
1940-19uu   20330359R

Rev Gastroenterol
The Review of gastroenterology
0096-2929
Continued by the American journal of gastroenterology.
1934-1953   20130250R

Rev Gastroenterol Disord
Reviews in gastroenterological disorders
1533-001X
2001   101140143

Rev Gastroenterol Mex
Revista de gastroenterología de México
0375-0906
1935   0404271

Rev Gastroenterol Peru
Revista de gastroenterología del Perú: órgano oficial de la Sociedad de Gastroenterología del Perú
1022-5129
1981   9108294

Rev Gaucha Enferm
Revista gaúcha de enfermagem / EENFUFRGS
0102-6933
1979   8504882

Rev Gaucha Odontol
Revista gaúcha de odontologia
0034-9542
Continued by: RGO
1953-1976   0404306

Rev Gen Sci Pures Appl Bull Assoc Fr Av Sci
Revue générale des sciences pures et appliquées et bulletin de l'Association française pour l'avancement des sciences
Absorbed the Bulletin of the Société philomathique in 1948; Sciences in 1953.
1890-1953   20330380R

Rev Gerontol Expr Fr
Revue de gérontologic d'expression française
0035-2896
Continues Revue française de gérontologie.
Superseded by Revue de gériatrie.
1964-1976   0166506

Rev Ginecol Obstet (Sao Paulo)
Revista de ginecologia e d'obstetrícia
0034-8287
Continues Revista de gynecologia,
d'obstetrícia, e de pediatria.
1922-1978   0412020

Rev Goiana Med
Revista Goiana de medicina
0034-9585
1955-1997   0204311

Rev Guatem Estomatol
Revista guatemalteca de estomatología
1017-8554
1971-1983   0321210

Rev Hematol
Revue d'hématologie
Merged with Le Sang to form Nouvelle revue
française d'hématologie.
1946-1960   20330240R

Rev Hist Art Dent
Revue d'histoire de l'art dentaire
0556-7300
Continued by: Revue de la Société française
d'histoire de l'art dentaire.
1962-1978   0043441

Rev Hist Pharm (Paris)
Revue d'histoire de la pharmacie
0035-2349
Continues: Bulletin de la Société d'histoire de
la pharmacie.
1930   0204315

Rev Hosp Clin Fac Med Sao Paulo
Revista do Hospital das Clínicas
0041-8781
Continued by: Clinics (São Paulo, Brazil).
1946-2004   0415246

Rev Hosp Nino (Lima)
Revista del Hospital del Niño
0301-3790
1939-1970   7505982

Rev Hosp Ninos Alejandro Mann
Revista. Guayaquil. Hospital de Niños
"Alejandro Mann"
1962-1989   17220030R

Rev Hyg Med Soc
Revue d'hygiène et de médecine sociale
0484-8454
Continued by Revue d'épidémiologie,
médecine social et santé publique.
1953-1970   1263667

Rev Hyg Prof
Revue de l'hygiène professionnelle
Continues Revue de l'hygiene industrielle.
1953-1967   20320310R

Rev Iber Endocrinol
Revista ibérica de endocrinología
0034-9615
Supersedes Acta endocrinologica Iberica.
1954-1976   0404307

Rev Iber Parasitol
Revista ibérica de parasitología
0034-9623
Continued by: Research and reviews in
parasitology.
1941-1990   9427296

Rev Iberoam Micol
Revista iberoamericana de micología:
órgano de la Asociación Española de
Especialistas en Micología
1130-1406
Absorbed: Revista argentina de micología.
2000 Continues: Revista ibérica de micología.
1990   9425531

Rev Iberoam Ortod
Revista ibero-americana de ortodoncia:
publicación oficial de la Asociación Ibero-
Americana Ortodoncistas
0212-193X
1981-2003   8410736

Rev Ibys
Revista IBYS
1936-1977   20230480R

**Rev Ig Bacteriol Virusol Parazitol Epidemiol
Pneumoftiziol Bacteriol Virusol Parazitol
Epidemiol**
Revista de igienă, bacteriologie,
virusologie, parazitologie, epidemiologie,
pneumoftiziologie. Bacteriologia, virusologia,
parazitologia, epidemiologia
0376-4494
Continues Bacteriologia, virusologia,
parazitologia, epidemiologia. Continued by:
Bacteriologia, virusologia, parazitologia,
epidemiologia (Bucharest, Romania: 1990).
1974-1990   7508738

**Rev Ig Bacteriol Virusol Parazitol Epidemiol
Pneumoftiziol Pneumoftiziol**
Revista de igienă, bacteriologie,
virusologie, parazitologie, epidemiologie,
pneumoftiziologie. Pneumoftiziologia
0377-5011
Continues Ftiziologia. Continued by: Revista
de igienă, medicina muncii, medicină socială,
bacteriologie, virusologie, parazitologie,
epidemiologie, pneumoftiziologie.
Pneumoftiziologie.
1974-1989   7514105

**Rev Ig Med Muncii Med Soc Bacteriol Virusol
Parazitol Epidemiol Pneumoftiziol Pneumoftiziol**
Revista de igienă, medicina muncii,
medicină socială, bacteriologie,
virusologie, parazitologie, epidemiologie,
pneumoftiziologie. Pneumoftiziologie /
Uniunea Societătilor de Stiinte Medicale din
România
0377-5011
Continues: Revista de igienă, bacteriologie,
virusologie, parazitologie, epidemiologie,
pneumoftiziologie. Pneumoftiziologia.
Continued by: Pneumoftiziologia.
1990-1990   9101878

Rev Immunogenet
Reviews in immunogenetics
1398-1714
1999-2000   100883703

Rev Immunol (Paris)
Revue d'immunologie
0035-2454
Continues Revue d'immunologie et de
therapie antimicrobienne. Merged with
Annales de l'Institut Pasteur, in part, to form
Annales d'immunologie.
1970-1972   7801127

Rev Immunol Ther Antimicrob
Revue d'immunologie et de thérapie
antimicrobienne
0035-2454
Continues Revue d'immunologie. Continued
by Revue d'immunologie.
1946-1969   0253026

Rev Infect Dis
Reviews of infectious diseases
0162-0886
Continued by: Clinical infectious diseases.
1979-1991   7905878

Rev Infirm
Revue de l'infirmière
1293-8505
Absorbed Revue de l'infirmière.
Informations, Jan. 1982.
1971   1267175

Rev Infirm Assist Soc
Revue de l'infirmière et de l'assistante
sociale
0397-7900
Continued by: Revue de l'infirmière.
1951-1970   1267176

Rev Infirm Infirm Aux Que
La Revue des infirmières et infirmiers
auxiliaires du Québec
0316-411X
Continues Les Cahiers du nursing. Continued
by L'Auxiliaire.
1974-1977   0420205

Rev Infirm [Inf]
Revue de l'infirmière. Informations
0397-7897
Absorbed by: Revue de l'infirmière.
1974-1981   8102464

Rev Inform Med Ter
Revista de información médico-terapéutica
Continues Revista de información terapéutica.
1944-1980   20210050R

Rev Inst Adolfo Lutz
Revista do Instituto Adolfo Lutz
0073-9855
1941   7505986

Rev Inst Antibiot (Recife)
Revista do Instituto de Antibióticos,
Universidade Federal de Pernambuco
0080-0228
Continues Revista do Instituto de
Antibióticos, Universidade de Recife.
1966-1988   7507483

Rev Inst Hyg Mines (Hasselt)
Revue de l'Institut d'hygiène des mines
0301-5301
Formed by the merger of the institute's
following publications: Communication,
Bulletin de documentation technique, and
Bulletin de documentation médicale.
1960-1983   7502670

Rev Inst Med Trop Sao Paulo
Revista do Instituto de Medicina Tropical de
São Paulo
0036-4665   1678-9946
1959   7507484

Rev Inst Nac Cancerol (Mex)
Revista del Instituto Nacional de
Cancerología
0076-7131
1954-2000   7505984

Rev Inst Salubr Enferm Trop
Revista del Instituto de Salubridad y
Enfermedades Tropicales
0370-5781
Continued by Revista de investigación en
salud pública.
1939-1965   7514106

Rev Int Croix Rouge
Revue internationale de la Croix-rouge
0035-3361
Merged with: Internationale review of the
Red Cross, to form: Revue internationale de
la Croix-rouge (1999)
1919-19uu   20340080R

Rev Int Hepatol
Revue internationale d'hépatologie
Formed by the union of: Revue du
foie, and:Association d'études physio-
pathologiques du foie et de la nutrition
Bulletin
1951-1969   9427142

Rev Int Serv Sante Armees
Revue international des services de santé des
armées de terre, de mer et de l'air
0035-3469
Continues Bulletin international des services
de santé des armées de terre, de mer et de
l'air. Continued by: Revue internationale
des services de santé des forces armeés.
Continued by: Revue internationale des
services de santé des forces armeés.
1958-1985 **7503658**

Rev Int Trach
Revue internationale du trachome.
International review of trachoma
0301-5017
Continues Revue de trachome. Continued
by Revue internationale du trachome et de
pathologie oculaire tropicale et subtropicale.
1926-1974 **7705456**

Rev Int Trach Pathol Ocul Trop Subtrop
Revue internationale du trachome et de
pathologie oculaire tropicale et subtropicale:
organe de la Ligue contre le trachome
avec la collaboration de l'International
Organization against Trachoma et des
organisations nationales et internationales
de santé publique
0249-7026
Continues: Revue internationale du trachome.
Continued by: Revue internationale du
trachome et de pathologie oculaire tropicale
et subtropicale et de santé publicque.
1975-1980 **7705455**

**Rev Int Trach Pathol Ocul Trop Subtrop Sante
Publique**
Revue internationale du trachome et de
pathologie oculaire tropicale et subtropicale
et de santé publique: organe de la Ligue
contre le trachome avec la collaboration
de l'International Organization against
Trachoma et des organisations nationales et
internationales de santé publique
0246-0831
Continues: Revue internationale du trachome
et de pathologie oculaire tropicale et
subtropicale.
1981-1997 **8209867**

Rev Interam Radiol
Revista interamericana de radiología
0034-9704
Supersedes Revista interamericana de
radiología.
1976-1987 **7708012**

Rev Invest (Guadalajara)
Revista de investigación
0556-6037
1961-1965 **20210070R**

Rev Invest Clin
Revista de investigación clínica; organo del
Hospital de Enfermedades de la Nutrición
0034-8376
1948 **9421552**

Rev Invest Salud Publica
Revista de investigación en salud pública
0034-8384
Continues the Revista of the Instituto de
Salubridad y Enfermedades Tropicales.
1966-1977 **0056517**

Rev Kuba Med Trop Parasitol
Revista Kuba de medicina tropical y
parasitología
Continues Kuba: revista de medicina tropical
y parasitología.
1947-1960 **0204312**

Rev Laryngol Otol Rhinol (Bord)
Revue de laryngologie - otologie - rhinologie
0035-1334
Continues: Revue mensuelle de laryngologie,
d'otologie et de rhinologie.
1889 **0414144**

Rev Lat Am Enfermagem
Revista latino-americana de enfermagem
0104-1169
1993 **9420934**

Rev Latinoam Anat Patol
Revista latinoamericana de anatomía
patológica
0034-9763
Supersedes: Revista sudamericana de
morfología. Continued by: Revista
latinoamericana de patología.
1957-1969 **1265420**

Rev Latinoam Cir Plast
Revista latinoamericana de cirugía plástica
0034-9755
Merged with Revista española de cirugía
plástica to form Cirugía plástica ibero-
latinoamericana.
1953-1974 **7601969**

Rev Latinoam Microbiol
Revista latinoamericana de microbiología
0187-4640
1958 **0242625**

Rev Latinoam Microbiol Parasitol (Mex)
Revista latinoamericana de microbiología y
parasitología
0370-5986
Continues and is continued by Revista
latinoamericana de microbiología.
1966-1969 **0242626**

Rev Latinoam Patol
Revista latinoamericana de patología
0300-9068
Continues Revista latinoamericana de
anatomía patológica.
1970-1973 **1265421**

Rev Law Soc Change
Review of law and social change. New York
University
0048-7481
1971 **100883489**

Rev Lyon Med
La Revue lyonnaise de médecine
0556-798X
Merged with Lyon médical to form Lyon
médical - la revue lyonnaise de médecine.
1952-1970 **0334776**

Rev Mal Respir
Revue des maladies respiratoires
0761-8425
Continues: Revue française des maladies
respiratoires.
1984 **8408032**

Rev Med (Mex)
Revista médica (Instituto Mexicano del
Seguro Social)
Continued by: Revista médica del Instituto
Mexicano del Seguro Social.
1962-1983 **20240030R**

Rev Med (Paris)
La Revue de médecine
0987-7835
Continues: Revue de médecine pratique et
bulletin de la Fédération des associations
d'internes de hôpitaux de France. Continued
by: Revue de médecine et d'internat.
1960-1984 **0404337**

Rev Med Aeron
Revista médica da aeronáutica
Continued by: Revista médica da aeronáutica
do Brasil.
1949-1970 **20240110R**

Rev Med Aeron Braz
Revista médica da aeronáutica do Brasil
0370-6141
Continues: Revista médica da aeronáutica.
1971-1996 **9424941**

Rev Med Aeronaut
Revue de médecine aéronautique
0755-3692
Continued by Revue de médecine
aéronautique et spatiale.
1961-1966 **0124462**

Rev Med Bahia
Revista médica da Bahia
1933 **20240120R**

Rev Med Bras
Revista médica brasileira
1938-19uu **20240090R**

Rev Med Brux
Revue médicale de Bruxelles
0035-3639
Absorbed Bruxelles medical, Jan. 1980.
1944 **8003474**

Rev Med Chil
Revista médica de Chile
0034-9887 0717-6163
1872 **0404312**

Rev Med Chir Mal Foie
Revue médico-chirurgicale des maladies du
foie
Continued by: Médecine & chirurgie
digestives.
1926-1971 **0331166**

Rev Med Chir Soc Med Nat Iasi
Revista medico-chirurgicalăÃÜ
a SocietăÃÜţÃúii de Medici şÃßi
NaturalişÃßti din IaşÃßi
0300-8738
Continues Revue médico-chirurgicale, issued
Mar./June 1932-1948.
1956 **0413735**

Rev Med Cienc Afines
Revista de medicina y ciencias afines
1942-1960 **9811064**

Rev Med Cir
Revista de medicina y cirugía
1934 **20220090R**

Rev Med Cir Sao Paulo
Revista de medicina e cirurgia de São Paulo
Supersedes Boletim da Sociedade de
Medicina e Cirurgia de São Paulo.
1941-19uu **20210270R**

Rev Med Cordoba
Revista médica de Córdoba
0370-6125
Continues the Revista of the Círculo Médico
de Córdoba.
1928 **20240190R**

Rev Med Costa Rica
Revista médica de Costa Rica
0034-9909
Continues: Revista médica (San José, Costa
Rica). Continued by: Revista médica de Costa
Rica y Centroamérica.
1942-1993 **0405415**

Rev Med Cubana
Revista médica cubana
1902-1960 **20240100R**

Rev Med Dominic
Revista médica dominicana
0254-4504
1941-1993   20240460R

Rev Med Fr
Revue médicale de France
Continues the Revue médicale issued by
the Office central de médecine de l'Union
nationale des étudiants de France.
1935-19uu   20340180R

Rev Med Hondur
Revista médica hondureña
0375-1112
1949   0404316

Rev Med Hosp Cent Empl
Revista médica del Hospital Central del
Empleado
Supersedes the Boletín informativo del
Hospital Central del Empleado de Lima.
1961-1966   20240350R

Rev Med Hosp Gen (Mex)
Revista médica del Hospital General
0034-9925
Continued by Revista médica del Hospital
General de México, S. S. A.
1938-1967   0413554

Rev Med Hosp Obrero
Revista médica del Hospital Obrero
Merged with Revista del Cuerpo Médico del
Hospital Obrero to form Revista médica de la
Caja Nacional de Seguro Social.
1952-1968   0235420

Rev Med Hyg Outre Mer
Revue de médecine et d'hygiène d'Outre-
Mer
Continues the Revue coloniale de médecine
& chirurgie.
1956-1965   0137557

Rev Med Inst Mex Seguro Soc
Revista médica del Instituto Mexicano del
Seguro Social
0443-5117
Continues: Revista médica (Instituto
Mexicano del Seguro Social).
1983   101243727

Rev Med Int Photo Cinema Telev
Revue médicale internationale de photo,
cinéma, télévision. International journal of
medical photography, cinematography &
television
Continued by Médecine et audio vision.
1962-1965   0060503

**Rev Med Interna Neurol Psihiatr Neurochir
Dermatovenerol Med Interna**
Revista de medicină internă, neurologe,
psihiatrie, neurochirurgie, dermato-
venerologie. Medicină internă
1220-0905
Continues Medicină internă, issued 1955-
1974. Continued by: Medicină internă
(Bucharest, Romania: 1991).
1974-1990   7501915

**Rev Med Interna Neurol Psihiatr Neurochir
Dermatovenerol Neurol Psihiatr Neurochir**
Revista de medicină internă, neurologie,
psihiatrie, neurochirurgie, dermato-
venerologie. Neurologie, psihiatrie,
neurochirurgie
0377-497X
Continues: Neurologia, psihiatria,
neurochirurgia. Continued by: Neurologie,
psihiatrie, neurochirurgie.
1974-1990   7503901

Rev Med Interne
La Revue de médecine interne / fondée … par
la Société nationale francaise de médecine
interne
0248-8663
Continues: Coeur et médecine interne.
1980   8101383

Rev Med Leg
Revista de medicina legal
1946-1959   2984682R

Rev Med Liege
Revue médicale de Liège
0370-629X
1946   0404317

Rev Med Mil
Revista de medicina militar
1912-2000   20210330R

Rev Med Miniere
Revue médicale minière
1948-1973   20340290R

Rev Med Moyen Orient
Revue médicale du Moyen-Orient
0370-632X
Continues Revue médicale française du
Moyen-Orient.
1945-1967   20340240R

Rev Med Nancy
Revue médicale de Nancy
Continues Revue médicale de l'Est et
bulletin de la Société de médecine de Nancy.
Superseded by Annales médicales de Nancy.
1936-1962   0204063

Rev Med Nav Metrop O-M
Revue de médecine navale (métropole
et outre-mer); travaux scientifiques des
médecins et pharmaciens-chimistes de la
marine
0370-6346
Continues: Archives de médecine et de
pharmacie navales. Merged with Revue
du corps de santé militaire, La Médecine
aéronautique, and Revue du Corps vétérinaire
de l'armée to form Revue des corps de
santé des armées terre, mer, air et du corps
vétérinaire.
1946-1959   20320380R

Rev Med Normandes
Les Revues médicales normandes
0035-4376
Formed by the merger of La Normandie
médicale, Rouen médical, and L'Année
médicale de Caen et de Basse-Normandie.
1959-1971   20340470R

Rev Med Panama
Revista médica de Panamá
0379-1629
Supersedes: Revista médica de Panamá.
1976   7706654

Rev Med Pasteur
Revista médica Pasteur
19uu-19uu   9427743

Rev Med Peru
Revista médica peruana
1929-1963   20240510R

Rev Med Psychosom
Revue de médecine psychosomatique (1985)
0298-3850
Continues: Revue de médecine
psychosomatique et de psychologie médicale.
Continued by: Champ psychosomatique.
1985-1994   8712300

Rev Med Psychosom Psychol Med
Revue de médecine psychosomatique et de
psychologie médicale
0397-930X
Continues Revue de médecine
psychosomatique. Continued by: Revue de
médecine psychosomatique (1985).
1966-1983   0140623

Rev Med Quir Oriente
Revista médico-quirúrgica de Oriente
1940-19uu   20240600R

Rev Med Rio Gd Sul
Revista de medicina do Rio Grande do Sul
0482-5896
1944-1963   20210260R

Rev Med Rosario
Revista médica de Rosario
0327-5019
1911   0416672

Rev Med Suisse
Revue médicale suisse
1660-9379
Merger of: Revue médicale de la Suisse
romande, and: Médecine et hygiène.
2005   101219148

Rev Med Suisse Romande
Revue médicale de la Suisse romande
0035-3655
Continues: Bulletin. Société médicale de la
Suisse romande. Merged with: Médecine et
hygiène, to form: Revue médicale suisse.
1881-2004   0421524

Rev Med Univ Navarra
Revista de medicina de la Universidad de
Navarra
0556-6177
Continues Revista de medicina del Estudio
General de Navarra.
1963   0123071

Rev Med Valparaiso
Revista médica de Valparaíso
0034-9917
1948-1988   0404313

Rev Med Veracruzana
Revista médica veracruzana
1921-19uu   20240530R

Rev Med Vet (B Aires)
Revista de medicina veterinaria
0325-6391
Continues the Revista of the Sociedad de
Medicina Veterinaria, Buenos Aires.
1921-1974   0404273

Rev Med Virol
Reviews in medical virology
1052-9276
1991   9112448

Rev Med Yucatan
La Revista médica de Yucatán
1906-19uu   20240320R

Rev Medica Hosp Esp
Revista médica del Hospital Español
1931-1955   20240360R

Rev Medica Minas
Revista médica do sul de Minas
1955-19uu   20240440R

Rev Mex Cir Ginecol Cancer
Revista mexicana de cirugía, ginecología y
cáncer
0034-9984
1933-1979   9427213

Rev Mex Tuberc Enferm Apar Respir
Revista mexicana de tuberculosis y
enfermedades del aparato respiratorio
0370-6435
    Continued by: Neumología y cirugía de tórax.
1939-1961   **19020040R**

Rev Mex Urol
Revista mexicana de urología
0035-0001
    Continues the Revista de urología. México.
1963   **20310090R**

Rev Museo Fac Odontol B Aires
Revista del Museo de la Facultad de
Odontología de Buenos Aires
0327-2745
    Continued by: Revista del Museo y Centro
de Estudios Históricos de la Facultad de
Odontología de Buenos Aires.
1986-199u   **8712299**

Rev Neurol
Revista de neurologia
0210-0010   **1576-6578**
1972   **7706841**

Rev Neurol (Paris)
Revue neurologique
0035-3787
1893   **2984779R**

Rev Neurol Dis
Reviews in neurological diseases
1545-2913
2004   **101223246**

Rev Neuropsiquiatr
Revista de neuro-psiquiatría
0034-8597
1938   **0413734**

Rev Neuropsychiatr Infant
Revue de neuropsychiatrie infantile et
d'hygiène mentale de l'enfance
0035-1628
    Continued by Neuropsychiatrie de l'enfance
et de l'adolescence.
1953-1978   **7905374**

Rev Neurosci
Reviews in the neurosciences
0334-1763
1986   **8711016**

Rev Obras Sanit Nac B Aires
Revista de Obras Sanitarias de la Nación.
Obras Sanitarias de la Nación (Argentina)
0034-8627
    Continues: Revista de la Administración
Nacional del Agua. Argentina. Administración
Nacional del Agua. Continued by:
Saneamiento.
1947-1961   **15240320R**

Rev Obstet Ginecol Venez
Revista de obstetricia y ginecología de
Venezuela
0048-7732
    Continues Revista de obstetricia y
ginecología.
1960   **0405413**

Rev Oculomot Res
Reviews of oculomotor research
0168-8375
1985   **8506449**

Rev Odontoestomatol
Revista odonto-estomatológica
0048-7856
1960-1971   **20310150R**

Rev Odontoimplantol
Revue odonto-implantologique
0035-3817
1966-1973   **1305626**

Rev Odontol (B Aires)
Revista odontologica
1514-1128
    Continued by the Revista of the Asociación
Odontológica Argentina. Absorbed the
Boletín of the Asociación Odontológica
Argentina in 1950.
1910-1954   **20310190R**

Rev Odontol (Cordoba)
Revista Odontologica; Facultad De
Odontologia, Universidad Nacional De
Cordoba
0035-0257
    Continued by: Revista De La Facultad De
Odontologia.
1966-1973   **9875633**

Rev Odontol (La Paz)
Revista Odontologica
1967   **9883817**

Rev Odontol Circ Odontol Parag
Revista odontológica
0080-2409
1955-1965   **20310170R**

Rev Odontol Concepcion
Revista odontológica de Concepción
0035-0265
1954-1979   **20310220R**

Rev Odontol Costa Rica
Revista odontológica de Costa Rica
    Continues the Revista of the Asociación
Odontológica de Costa Rica.
1971-1973   **0315754**

Rev Odontol Ecuat
Revista odontológica ecuatoriana
0484-8020
1955-1996   **8410737**

Rev Odontol P R
Revista odontológica de Puerto Rico
    Supersedes Revista odontológica de Puerto
Rico.
1969-1989   **7904415**

Rev Odontol P R (Santurce)
Revista odontológica de Puerto Rico
1963-1968   **0102366**

Rev Odontol Parana
Revista odontológica do Paraná
1944-19uu   **20310240R**

Rev Odontol St Catarina
Revista De Odontologia Da Universidade
Federal De Santa Catarina
19uu   **9875632**

Rev Odontol UNESP
Revista de odontologia da UNESP /
Universidade Estadual Paulista (UNESP)
0101-1774
    Formed by the union of: Revista da Faculdade
de Odontologia de Araçatuba, and: Revista
da Faculdade de Odontologia de Araraquara,
and: Revista da Faculdade de Odontologia de
São José dos Campos.
1980   **8411399**

Rev Odontol Univ Sao Paulo
Revista de odontologia da Universidade de
São Paulo / USP
0103-0663
    Continues: Revista da Faculdade de
Odontologia da Universidade de São Paulo.
Continued by: Pesquisa odontológica brasileira.
1987-1999   **8900837**

Rev Odontostomatol
Revue d'odonto-stomatologie
    Continued by Revue d'odonto-stomatologie
du Midi de la France.
1937-1964   **0204062**

Rev Odontostomatol (Paris)
Revue d'odonto-stomatologie
0300-9815
    Supersedes Revue francaise d'odonto-
stomatologie.
1972   **7502189**

Rev Odontostomatol Midi Fr
Revue d'odonto-stomatologie du midi de la
France
0035-2470
    Continues Revue d'odonto-stomatologie.
1965-1985   **0024724**

Rev Odontostomatol Nordest
Revue odonto stomatologique du Nord-Est
0398-7760
    Continues Revue annuelle - Société odonto-
stomatologique du Nord-Est.
1971-1983   **7502190**

Rev Orthop Chir Appar Mot
Revue d'orthopédie et de chirurgie de
l'appareil moteur
    Continued by: Revue de chirurgie
orthopédique et réparatrice de l'appareil
moteur.
1890-1950   **20330270R**

Rev Orthop Dento Faciale
Revue d'orthopédie dento-faciale
0337-9736
1967   **8011218**

Rev Ortop Traumatol Ed Lat Am
Revista de ortopedia y traumatología.
Edición latino americana
    Continues Revista de ortopedia y
traumatología latino-americana.
1957-1975   **0341601**

Rev Oto Neuro Oftalmol Cir Neurol Sud Am
Revista oto-neuro-oftalmológica y cirugía
neurologica sudamericana
0375-1228
    Continued by Revista oto-neuro-
oftalmológica.
1927-1972   **7513027**

Rev Otoneuroophtalmol
Revue d'oto-neuro-ophtalmologie
0035-2497
    Continues Revue d'oto-neuro-oculistique.
1927-1984   **0406674**

Rev Otorrinolaringol
Revista de otorrinolaringología
0034-8643
    Continued by: Revista de otorrinolaringología
y cirugiá de cabeza y cuello.
1941-1981   **0425622**

Rev Ouie
Revue de l'ouïe
0048-7961
1924-1974   **20320330R**

Rev Palud Med Trop
Revue du paludisme et de médecine
tropicale
1939-1953   **20330310R**

Rev Panam Med Cir Torax
Revista panamericana de medicina y cirugía
del tórax
1947-19uu   **20310300R**

Rev Panam Salud Publica
Revista panamericana de salud pública =
Pan American journal of public health
1020-4989
    Merger of: Boletín de la Oficina Sanitaria
Panamericana, and: Bulletin of the Pan
American Health Organization.
1997   **9705400**

Rev Pathol Comp
Revue de pathologie comparée
0035-1636
Continues Revue de pathologie générale et
de physiologie clinique. Continued by Revue
de pathologie comparée et de médecine
expérimentale.
1964-1967   0166253

Rev Pathol Gen Physiol Clin
Revue de pathologie générale et de
physiologie clinique
Continues Revue de pathologie générale et
comparée. Continued by Revue de pathologie
comparée.
1956-1964   0204313

Rev Patient Focus Care Assoc
Review (Patient Focused Care Association)
1063-1356
Continued by: PFCA review.
1992-1993   9601257

Rev Paul Endodontia
Revista Paulista De Endodontia
0100-7106
1980-1983   9878933

Rev Paul Enferm
Revista paulista de enfermagem
0100-8889
1981   8215976

Rev Paul Med
Revista paulista de medicina
0035-0362
Continues: Revista. Associação Paulista de
Medicina. Continued by: São Paulo medical
journal.
1941-1993   0404326

Rev Paul Odontol
Revista paulista de odontologia
0100-705X
1963-1988   9105980

Rev Pediatr Obstet Ginecol Obstet Ginecol
Revista de pediatrie, obstetrică si
ginecologie. Obstetrică si ginecologie
1220-0913
Continues: Obstetrică si ginecologia.
Continued by: Obstetrică si ginecologie.
1974-1989   7513686

Rev Pediatr Obstet Ginecol Pediatr
Revista de pediatrie, obstetrică şi
ginecologie. Pediatria
0303-8416
Continues Pediatria. Continued by: Pediatrie
(Bucharest, Romania).
1974-1990   7508739

Rev Pernambucana Odontol
Revista pernambucana de odontologia
0301-4991
1973-1973   0404755

Rev Peru Pediatr
Revista peruana de pediatría
1942-1963   20310420R

Rev Philos France Let
Revue philosophique de la France et de
l'étranger
0035-3833
1876   20340390R

Rev Physiol Biochem Pharmacol
Reviews of physiology, biochemistry and
pharmacology
0303-4240
Continues Ergebnisse der Physiologie,
biologischen Chemie und experimentellen
Pharmakologie.
1974   0434624

Rev Phytother (Paris)
Revue de phytothérapie
0370-453X
1937-1955   20330050R

Rev Pneumol Clin
Revue de pneumologie clinique
0761-8417
Continues: Le Poumon et le coeur.
1984   8406312

Rev Port Cardiol
Revista portuguesa de cardiologia:
orgão oficial da Sociedade Portuguesa
de Cardiologia = Portuguese journal
of cardiology: an official journal of the
Portuguese Society of Cardiology
0870-2551
Continues: Boletim da Sociedade Portuguesa
de Cardiologia.
1982   8710716

Rev Port Cir Cardiotorac Vasc
Revista portuguesa de cirurgia cardio-
torácica e vascular: órgão oficial da
Sociedade Portuguesa de Cirurgia Cardio-
Torácica e Vascular
0873-7215
1992   101154446

Rev Port Estomatol Cir Maxilofac
Revista portuguesa de estomatologia e
cirurgia maxilo-facial
0035-0397
Supersedes: Revista. Sociedade Portuguesa
de Estomatologia Continued by: Revista
portuguesa de estomatologia, medicina
dentária e cirurgia maxilofacial.
1960-1998   0404330

Rev Port Farm
Revista portuguesa de farmácia
0484-811X
Supersedes the Jornal dos farmacêuticos.
1951   20310480R

Rev Port Med Mil
Revista portuguesa de medicina militar
0482-7171
1953-1996   0404331

Rev Port Pediatr
Revista portuguesa de pediatria
0301-147X
Supersedes: Revista portuguesa de
pediatria e puericultura. Continued by: Acta
pediatÀÁrica portuguesa.
1970-1994   0365603

Rev Port Pediatr Pueric
Revista portuguesa de pediatria e
puericultura
0048-7880
Continued by: Revista portuguesa de
pediatria.
1938-1969   0365604

Rev Port Pneumol
Revista portuguesa de pneumologia
0873-2159
Continues: Arquivos da Sociedade Portuguesa
de Patologia Respiratória.
1995   9813736

Rev Pract
Revista del practicante ...
1131-0243
1945-1957   20230010R

Rev Prat
La Revue du praticien
0035-2640
Merger of: Paris médical; and, Revue
générale de clinique et de thérapeutique.
Continued in part by: Revue du praticien.
Médecine générale, in 1987.
1951   0404334

Rev Psicoanal
Revista de psicoanálisis
0034-8740
1943   0404274

Rev Psicol Gen Apl
Revista de psicología general y aplicada
0373-2002
Supersedes Psicotecnia.
1946-1986   20220360R

Rev Psiquiatr Psicol Med Eur Am Lat
Revista de psiquiatría y psicología médica de
Europa y América latinas
0482-6019
1953-1987   0404275

Rev Psychol Appl
Revue de psychologie appliquée
0035-1709
Continued by: European review of Applied
psychology.
1950-1990   0404476

Rev Publ Nav
Revista de publicaciones navales;
suplemento de Sanidad naval
1948-19uu   20220410R

Rev Public Data Use
Review of public data use
0092-2846
Continued by: Journal of economic and social
measurement.
1972-1984   9878817

Rev Pure Appl Pharmacol Sci
Reviews in pure & applied pharmacological
sciences
0197-2839
Continued by: Reviews in clinical & basic
pharmacology.
1980-1983   8109975

Rev Quim Farm
Revista de química e farmácia
1935-1969   20220430R

Rev Quim Farm
Revista de química y farmacia
1946-19uu   20220440R

Rev Quir Esp
Revista quirúrgica española: RQE
0210-2196
1974-1988   8205912

Rev Recent Clin Trials
Reviews on recent clinical trials
1574-8871
2006   101270873

Rev Reg Araçatuba Assoc Paul Cir Dent
Revista Regional de Araçatuba, Associação
Paulista de Cirurgiões Dentistas
0101-8140
Continues: Revista da Associação Paulista de
Cirurgiões Dentistas Regional de Araçatuba.
1981-1993   8410738

Rev Reprod
Reviews of reproduction
1359-6004
Merged with: Journal of reproduction and
fertility, to form: Reproduction (Cambridge,
England).
1996-2000   9602351

Rev Rhum
Revue du rhumatisme
0301-8474
Continued by Revue du rhumatisme et des
maladies ostéo-articulaire.
1934-1945   0407210

Rev Rhum Ed Fr
Revue du rhumatisme (Ed. française: 1993)
1169-8330   1768-3130
Continues: Revue du rhumatisme et des
maladies ostéo-articulaires.
1993   9315664

Rev Rhum Engl Ed
Revue du rhumatisme (English ed.)
1169-8446
Continued by: Joint, bone, spine.
1993-1999   9313916

Rev Rhum Mal Osteoartic
Revue du rhumatisme et des maladies ostéo-
articulaires
0035-2659
Continues Revue du rhumatisme. Continued
by: Revue du rhumatisme (Ed. francaise:
1993).
1946-1992   0407211

Rev Roche
Revista "Roche."
Continues Notas científicas Roche.
1951-1963   19220180R

Rev Roum Endocrinol
Revue roumaine d'endocrinologie
0035-4015
Merged with Revue roumaine de médecine
interne and Revue roumaine de neurologie
et de psychiatrie to form Revue roumaine de
médecine.
1964-1974   7502193

Rev Roum Inframicrobiol
Revue roumaine d'inframicrobiologie
0035-4082
Continued by Revue roumaine de viologie.
1964-1971   0335303

Rev Roum Med
Revue roumaine de médecine
0303-822X
Continued by Endocrinologie. Neurologie et
psychiatrie, and Médecine interne. Formed
by the union of Revue roumaine de médecine
interne, Revue roumaine d'endocrinologie,
and Revue roumaine de neurologie et
de psychiatrie and continues the volume
numbering of these publications.
1974-1974   7509766

Rev Roum Med Intern
Revue roumaine de médecine interne
0035-3973
1964-1974   7502194

Rev Roum Morphol Embryol
Revue roumaine de morphologie et
d'embryologie
0377-4945
Formed by the union of: Revue roumaine
d'embryologie; Revue roumaine
d'embryologie et de cytologie. Série de
cytologie; and: Morfologia normală şi
patologică and continues numbering of
the last. Merged with: Revue roumaine de
physiologie, to form: Revue roumaine de
morphologie et de physiologie.
1974-1974   7511328

Rev Roum Morphol Physiol
Revue roumaine de morphologie et de
physiologie
0377-4953
Formed by the union of Revue roumaine
de morphologie et d'embryologie and
Revue roumaine de physiologie, and adopts
the vol. numbering of the former. Split
into: Morphologie et embryologie, and:
Physiologie.
1974-1974   7510989

Rev Roum Neurol
Revue roumaine de neurologie
0035-3981
Continued by Revue Roumaine de neurologie
et de psychiatrie.
1964-1973   0416720

Rev Roum Neurol Psychiatr
Revue roumaine de neurologie et de
psychiatrie
0301-7303
Continues Revue roumaine de neurologie.
Merged with Revue roumaine de
médecine interne, and Revue roumaine
d'endocrinologie to form Revue roumaine de
médecine.
1974-1974   7502196

Rev Roum Physiol
Revue roumaine de physiologie
0035-399X
Merged with Revue roumaine de morphologie
et d'embryologie to form Revue roumaine de
morphologie et de physiologie.
1964-1974   7510990

Rev Roum Physiol
Revue roumaine de physiologie (Bucharest,
Romania: 1990)
0035-399X
Continues: Physiologie. Continued by:
Romanian journal of physiology.
1990-1992   9103575

Rev Roum Virol
Revue roumaine de virologie
0300-158X
Continues Revue roumaine
d'inframicrobiologie. Continued by Virologie.
1972-1974   7605718

Rev Roum Virol
Revue roumaine de virologie (Bucharest,
Romania: 1990)
1018-0532
Continued by: Romanian journal of virology.
1990-1994   9100120

Rev Salud Publica (Bogota)
Revista de salud pública (Bogotá, Colombia)
0124-0064
1999   100936348

Rev Sanid
Revista de sanidad
1947-19uu   20220490R

Rev Sanid Aeronaut
Revista de sanidad de aeronáutica
1948-1948   20220500R

Rev Sanid Asist Soc
Revista de sanidad y asistencia social
Continues the Boletín of the Ministerio de
Sanidad y Asistencia Social. Continued by the
Revista venezolana de sanidad y asistencia
social.
1940-1959   20320070R

Rev Sanid Hig Publica (Madr)
Revista de sanidad e higiene pública
0034-8899
Continues Boletín técnico. Continued by:
Revista española de salud pública.
1932-1995   0404276

Rev Sanid Mil Peru
Revista de la sanidad militar del Perú
Continues Revista de sanidad militar.
1950-1974   20210120R

Rev Sanid Milit
Revista de sanidad militar
0301-696X
Continues Boletín de sanidad militar.
1954   0407203

Rev Sanid Milit Argent
Revista de la sanidad militar argentina
0048-7716
Continues: Revista de la sanidad militar.
1947-2001   0411345

Rev Sanid Polic
Revista de la sanidad de policía
Continued by the Revista de la sanidad de las
fuerzas policiales del Perú.
1941-1969   0313135

Rev Sanid Vet
Revista de sanidad veterinaria
1946-19uu   0204776

Rev Saude Publica
Revista de saúde pública
0034-8910   1518-8787
Continues: Arquivos da Faculdade de Higiene
e Saúde Pública da Universidade de São
Paulo.
1967   0135043

Rev Sci Instrum
The Review of scientific instruments
0034-6748   1089-7623
1930   0405571

Rev Sci Med
Revue des sciences médicales
Supersedes another periodical with the same
title, issued 1954.
1956-1963   0204314

Rev Sci Tech
Revue scientifique et technique
(International Office of Epizootics)
0253-1933   1608-0637
1982   8712301

Rev Serv Nac Salud
Revista. Chile. Servicio Nacional de Salud
Formed by the union of Revista chilena
de higiene y medicina preventiva, Boletín
médico social, and Revista médico-
asistencial.
1956-1960   0071543

Rev Serv Nac Tubers
Revista do Serviço Nacional de Tuberculose
0520-8734
Continued by Revista da Divisão Nacional de
Tuberculose.
1957-1970   7505988

Rev SESDA
Revue du SESDA
0379-8232
Continued by: Odonto-stomatologie tropicale.
1972-1977   7802480

Rev Sifilogr Leprolog Dermatol
Revista de sifilografía, leprología y
dermatología
Continues Revista de leprología, dermatología
y sifilografía.
1945-1959   20220560R

Rev Soc Argent Biol
Revista de la Sociedad Argentina de Biología
0037-8380
1925-1980   7507470

Rev Soc Bras Med Trop
Revista da Sociedade Brasileira de Medicina
Tropical
0037-8682   1678-9849
1967   7507456

Rev Soc Colomb Ortod
Revista. Sociedad Colombiana de
Ortodoncia
1963-1966   0027050

Rev Soc Colomb Pediatr Pueric
Revista de la Sociedad Colombiana de
Pediatría y Puericultura
Continued by Pediatría.
1958-1965   7507466

Rev Soc Fr Hist Hop
Revue de la Société française d'histoire des
hôpitaux
1255-250X
Continues: Bulletin - Société française
d'histoire des hôpitaux.
1994   9805018

Rev Soc Odontol La Plata
Revista de la Sociedad Odontológica de La
Plata
1988   9506154

Rev Soc Pediatr Litoral
Revista de la Sociedad de Pediatría del
Litoral
Continues and is continued by Revista de la
Sociedad de Pediatría de Rosario.
1944-1961   7507469

Rev Soc Peru Endocrinol
Revista de la Sociedad Peruana de
Endocrinología
0583-7677
1963-1966   7507476

Rev Soc Peru Protes Dent Maxilofac Lima
Revista. Sociedad Peruana de Prótesis
Dental y Máxilo-Facial, Lima
1946-195u   20820330R

Rev Stiint Med
Revista ştiinţelor medicale: medicina internă
Continued by Medicina internă.
1905-1954   20310610R

Rev Stomatol Chir Maxillofac
Revue de stomatologie et de chirurgie
maxillo-faciale
0035-1768
Absorbed: Implantodontie.
1969   0201010

Rev Stomatoodontol Nord Fr
La Revue stomato-odontologique du nord de
la France
0035-4147
1946-1976   0037125

Rev Sudam Morfol
Revista sudamericana de morfología
0375-1368
Continued by: Revista latinoamericana de
anatomía patológica.
1943-1952   20310630R

Rev Suisse Zool
Revue suisse de zoologie; annales de la
Société zoologique suisse et du Muséum
d'histoire naturelle de Genève
0035-418X
Supersedes Recueil zoologique suisse.
1893   0404500

Rev Surg
Review of surgery
0034-6780
Continues Quarterly review of surgery.
Continued by Current surgery.
1962-1977   0401306

Rev Synth
Revue de synthèse / Centre international de
synthèse
0035-1776
Continues: Revue de synthèse historique.
1931   8711586

Rev Tuberc
Revue de la tuberculose
Supersedes Etudes expérimentales et
cliniques sur la tuberculose. Absorbed the
Revue de phtisiologie in 1935. Continued by
the Revue de tuberculose et de pneumologie.
1893-1958   20330090R

Rev Tuberc Pneumol (Paris)
Revue de tuberculose et de pneumologie
0035-1792
Continues Revue de la tuberculose.
Superseded by Revue française des maladies
respiratoires.
1959-1972   0365341

Rev Tuberc Urug
Revista de tuberculosis del Uruguay
1930-1951   20220650R

Rev Uniao Odontol Bras
Revista. União Odontologica Brasileira
1960-19uu   21410070R

Rev Univ San Marcos Fac Farm Bioquim
Revista. Lima. Universidad de San Marcos.
Facultad de Farmacia y Bioquimica
Continues the faculty's Anales, 1944-45.
1945-1968   18330620R

Rev Urol (Mex)
Revista de urología
Continued by the Revista mexicana de
urología.
1943-1962   20220670R

Rev Urug Psicoanal
Revista uruguaya de psicoanálisis
1956   20320040R

Rev Venez Sanid Asist Soc
Revista venezolana de sanidad y asistencia
social
0035-0583
Continues the Revista de sanidad y asistencia
social.
1960-1977   0421523

Rev Venez Urol
Revista venezolana de urología
0035-0591
Continues Revista de urología,
1961-1981   0404333

Rev Vet Mil
Revista de veterinaria militar
1953-19uu   20220680R

Rev Vet Mil (Paris)
Revue vétérinaire militaire
0996-1372
Continued by: Revue du corps vétérinaire de
l'armée.
1910-1953   20340460R

Rev Viernes Med
Revista de Viernes Médico
0504-2372
1950-1977   7505973

Revenue-cycle Strateg
Revenue-cycle strategist
1549-0858
Continues: Patient accounts.
2004   101286623

Revis Biol Celular
Revisiones sobre biología celular: RBC
0213-7119
Continued by: Cell biology reviews.
1983-1991   8712458

Revmatologiia (Mosk)
Revmatologiia (Moscow, Russia)
0233-7029
Continues: Voprosy revmatizma.
1983-1993   8309921

Revolution
Revolution (Oakland, Calif.)
1059-0927
Continues: Revolution (Staten Island, N.Y.).
2000-2006   100956124

Revolution
Revolution (Staten Island, N.Y.)
1059-0927
Continued by: Revolution (Oakland, Calif.).
1991-1998   9211449

Revue Stomatol
Revue de stomatologie
Continued by Revue de stomatologie et de
chirurgie maxillo-faciale.
1894-1968   0201163

RGO
RGO
0103-6971
Continues: Revista gaúcha de odontologia.
1976   8901001

Rheum Dis Clin North Am
Rheumatic diseases clinics of North America
0889-857X   1558-3163
Continues in part: Clinics in rheumatic
diseases.
1987   8708093

Rheumatism
Rheumatism
0370-5250
1938-1967   0127375

Rheumatol Balneol Allergol
Rheumatologia, balneologia, allergologia
0035-4554
Continued by Magyar reumatológia.
1960-1979   0404344

Rheumatol Int
Rheumatology international
0172-8172
1981   8206885

Rheumatol Phys Med
Rheumatology and physical medicine
0003-4908
Continues Annals of physical medicine.
Continued by Rheumatology and
rehabilitation.
1970-1972   0355003

Rheumatol Rehabil
Rheumatology and rehabilitation
0300-3396
Continues: Rheumatology and physical
medicine. Continued by: British journal of
rheumatology.
1973-1982   0355004

Rheumatology
Rheumatology
0080-2727
1967   0173721

Rheumatology (Oxford)
Rheumatology (Oxford, England)
1462-0324   1462-0332
Continues: British journal of rheumatology.
1999   100883501

Rhinol Suppl
Rhinology. Supplement
1013-0047
1987   9004674

Rhinology
Rhinology
0300-0729
Continues International rhinology.
1970   0347242

Rhod Nurse
The Rhodesia nurse
0250-4898
Supersedes in part: Rhodesian nurse.
Continued by: Zimbabwe Rhodesia nurse.
1978-1978   7905060

Rhod Nurse
The Rhodesian nurse
1967-1977   0233441

Rhumatologie
Rhumatologie
0249-7581
Continues: Archives de rhumatologie.
1949   0421126

Ric Clin Lab
La Ricerca in clinica e in laboratorio
0390-5748
Continued by: International journal of clinical
and laboratory research.
1971-1991   7613947

Ric Sci
La Ricerca scientifica
0035-5011
Continues the Bollettino d'informazioni of
the Consiglio nazionale delle ricerche.
1931-1976   0054204

Ric Sci 2 Ser Pt 1 Riv
La Ricerca scientifica. 2. ser., pt.1: Rivista
0556-9672
Supersedes and is superseded in part by La
Ricerca scientifica.
1961-1965   0054202

Ric Sci 2 Ser Pt 2 Rend [B]
La Ricerca scientifica. 2. ser., pt. 2:
Rendiconti. Sezione B: Biologica
0556-9699
Supersedes and is superseded in part by La
Ricerca scientifica.
1961-1965   0054211

Riforma Med
La Riforma medica
0035-5259
1885-1995   0404345

Rinsho Biseibutshu Jinsoku Shindan Kenkyukai Shi
Rinshō Biseibutsu Jinsoku Shindan
Kenkyūkai shi = JARMAM: Journal of
the Association for Rapid Method and
Automation in Microbiology
0915-1753
1988   9419185

Rinsho Byori
Rinsho byori. The Japanese journal of
clinical pathology
0047-1860
1953   2984781R

Rinsho Eiyo
[Rinshō eiyō] [Clinical nutrition]
0485-1412
1952   20410410R

Rinsho Ganka
Rinsho ganka. Japanese journal of clinical
ophthalmology
0370-5579
1947   0413737

Rinsho Geka
Rinsho geka. Journal of clinical surgery
0386-9857
1946   1266623

Rinsho Hoshasen
Rinsho hoshasen. Clinical radiography
0009-9252
1956   0413556

Rinsho Ketsueki
[Rinshō ketsueki] The Japanese journal of
clinical hematology
0485-1439   1882-0824
1960   2984782R

Rinsho Kyobu Geka
Rinshō kyōbu geka = Japanese annals of
thoracic surgery
0389-7893
1981-1994   8211641

Rinsho Naika Shonika Intern Med
Rinsho naika shonika. Internal medicine
and pediatrics
1946-1964   0143636

Rinsho Shika
[Rinshō shika] [Clinical dentistry]
0035-5488
1929-1992   20420070R

Rinsho Shinkeigaku
Rinshō shinkeigaku = Clinical neurology
0009-918X   1882-0654
1960   0417466

Rinsho Shishubyo Danwakai Kaishi
Rinshō Shishūbyō Danwakai kaishi
Continued by: Nihon Rinshō Shishūbyō
Danwaka: kaishi.
1983-1984   8703870

Rinsho Shokakibyogaku
[Rinshō shōkakibyōgaku] Clinical gastroenterology
1953-1961   20420090R

Riogrande Odontol
Riogrande odontológico
1942-1956   1260355

Risk Anal
Risk analysis: an official publication of the
Society for Risk Analysis
0272-4332   1539-6924
1981   8109978

Risk Manage
Risk management (New York, N.Y.)
0035-5593
Continues: National insurance buyer.
1969   9877953

RISO Rep
Risø report
0418-6443
Continued by: Risø-R, which is cataloged
separately in NLM.
1956-1978   7803386

Riv Anat Patol Oncol
Rivista di anatomia patologica e di oncologia
0048-8364
1948-1991   0404350

Riv Biol
Rivista di biologia
0035-6050
1919   0416643

Riv Biol Coloniale
Rivista di biologia coloniale
0370-3703
Supersedes: Bollettino dell'Istituto zoologico
della R. Università di Roma.
1938-1958   20420480R

Riv Chir Med
Rivista di chirurgia e medicina
1949-19uu   20420500R

Riv Chir Pediatr
Rivista di chirurgia pediatrica
0035-6069
Continued by Rassegna italiana di chirurgia
pediatrica.
1959-1975   0404351

Riv Clin Pediatr
Rivista di clinica pediatrica
0035-6077
Absorbed by: Minerva pediatrica.
1903-1973   0404503

Riv Crit Clin Med
Rivista critica di clinica medica
0048-833X
1899-1970   0436026

Riv Dif Soc
Rivista di difesa sociale
Continued by Revue internationale de défense
sociale.
1947-1951   20420520R

Riv Emoter Immunoematol
Rivista di emoterapia ed immunoematologia
0035-6204
1954-1985   0404352

Riv Eur Sci Med Farmacol
Rivista europea per le scienze mediche
e farmacologiche = European review for
medical and pharmacological sciences =
Revue européenne pour les sciences médicales
et pharmacologiques
0392-291X
Continued by: European review for medical
and pharmacological sciences.
1979-1996   8100897

Riv Gastroenterol
Rivista di gastro-enterologia
0035-6255
1949-1996   20420540R

Riv Inferm
Rivista dell'infermiere
1120-3803
Continued by: Assistenza infermieristica e
ricerca.
1982-1998   8408033

Riv Infort Mal Prof
Rivista degli infortuni e delle malattie
professionali
0035-5836
Continues: Infortuni e malattie professionali.
1944   0404347

Riv Ist Sieroter Ital
Rivista dell'Istituto sieroterapico italiano
0300-9904
Continues Rivista di bioterapia e
immunologia.
1947-1969   7505994

Riv Istochim Norm Patol
Rivista di istochimica, normale e patologica
0485-2400
Continued by Basic and applied
histochemistry.
1954-1978   0404353

Riv Ital Ginecol
Rivista italiana di ginecologia
0035-6840
1922-1980   0404361

Riv Ital Ig
Rivista italiana d'igiene
0035-6921
1941   0404362

Riv Ital Med Leg
Rivista italiana di medicina legale:
dottrina, casistica, ricerca sperimentale,
giurisprudenza e legislazione
1979   9424923

Riv Ital Odontoiatr Infant
Rivista italiana di odontoiatria infantile: organo ufficiale della Società italiana di odontoiatria infantile
1120-8716
Continued by: Italian journal of paediatric dentistry.
1990-1998   9111498

Riv Ital Odontotec
Rivista italiana degli odontotecnici
0391-5611
Continues: Dental press.
1978-2000   7806140

Riv Ital Stomatol
Rivista italiana di stomatologia
0035-6905
1946-1997   0404364

Riv Ital Trac Patol Ocul Esotica
Rivista italiana del tracoma e di patologia oculare esotica
1949-1967   20430040R

Riv Malariol
Rivista di malariologia
0370-565X
Continues Bollettino malariologica.
1926-1967   20420570R

Riv Med Aeronaut
Rivista di medicina aeronautica
0301-6757
Continued by Rivista di medicina aeronautica e spaziale.
1938-1958   0407206

Riv Med Aeronaut Spaz
Rivista di medicina aeronautica e spaziale
0035-631X
Continues Rivista di medicina aeronautica.
1959-1992   0407207

Riv Neurobiol
Rivista di neurobiologia: organo ufficiale della Società dei neurologi, neuroradiologi e neurochirurghi ospedalieri
0035-6336
Continued by: Rivista italiana di neurobiologia.
1955-1987   7501004

Riv Neurol
Rivista di neurologia
0035-6344
Absorbed Annali di neurologia in Feb. 1933. Continued by: Nuova rivista di neurologia.
1928-1990   0413740

Riv Odontoiatr Amici Brugg
Rivista di odontoiatria degli Amici di Brugg
0393-4780
Continues: Odontoiatria pratica.
1982   8502436

Riv Odontojatria Ortognatod
Rivista di odontojatria e ortognatodonzia
1947-1948   20420620R

Riv Odontostomatol Implantoprotesi
Rivista di odontostomatologia e implantoprotesi
Continues: Odontostomatologia e implantoprotesi. Continued by: Odontostomatologia e implantoprotesi (Milan, Italy: 1989).
1982-1984   8411976

Riv Ostet Ginecol
Rivista di ostetricia e ginecologia
0394-977X
1946-2001   0404354

Riv Ostet Ginecol Prat
Rivista d'ostetricia e ginecologia pratica
0370-6591
Continued by Rivista d'ostetricia e ginecologia pratica e di medicina perinatale.
1919-1971   0333535

Riv Ostet Ginecol Prat Med Perinat
Rivista di ostetricia ginecologia pratica e medicina perinatale
0391-0970
Continues Rivista d'ostetricia e ginecologia pratica e di medicina perinatale.
1973-1982   8012151

Riv Otoneurooftalmol
Rivista oto-neuro-oftalmologica
0048-8410
1923-1969   0417467

Riv Parassitol
Rivista di parassitologia
0035-6387
1937-2005   0404355

Riv Patol Clin
Rivista di patologia e clinica
0035-6417
1946-1999   0404504

Riv Patol Clin Sper
Rivista di patologia clinica e sperimentale
0035-6409
Continued by: Rivista di patologia e sperimentazione clinica.
1960-1986   0404356

Riv Patol Clin Tuberc
Rivista di patologia e clinica della tubercolosi
0035-6425
Continued by: Rivista di patologia e clinica della tubercolosi e di pneumologia.
1927-1971   9705950

Riv Patol Nerv Ment
Rivista di patologia nervosa e mentale
0035-6433
1896-1984   0431335

Riv Pediatr Sicil
Rivista pediatrica siciliana
0035-7014
1946-1993   20430230R

Riv Psicoanal
Rivista di psicoanalisi
0035-6492
1955   20420640R

Riv Psicol
Rivista di psicologia
0035-6506
Continues Rivista di psicologia applicata.
1912-1978   0417311

Riv Psicol Scr
Rivista di psicologia della scrittura
0485-2419
1955-1966   0374070

Riv Radiol
Rivista di radiologia
1947-1949   20420660R

Riv Radiol
Rivista di radiologia
1961-1990   0404357

Riv Sicil Tuberc
Rivista siciliana della tubercolosi
0035-7049
Continued by Rivista siciliana della tubercolosi e delle malattie dell'apparato respiratorio.
1947-1959   0402342

Riv Sper Freniatr Med Leg Alien Ment
Rivista sperimentale di freniatria e medicina legale delle alienazioni mentali
0370-7261
Absorbed: Archivio italiano per le malattie nervose e più particolarmente per le alienazioni mentali. 1892 Continued by: Rivista sperimentale di freniatria.
1875-1997   9811063

Riv Stor Med
Rivista di storia della medicina
0035-6565
Supersedes Rivista di storia delle scienze mediche e naturali.
1957-1977   2984784R

Riv Stor Sci Mediche Nat
Rivista di storia delle scienze mediche e naturali
1912-1956   20420680R

Riv Tuberc Mal Appar Respir
Rivista della tubercolosi e delle malattie dell'apparato respiratorio
0483-1454
1953-1971   0420106

RN
RN
0033-7021
1937   20010080R

RN (For Managers)
RN (For managers)
0885-8667
1982-1983   8309700

RN Ida
RN Idaho
0192-298X
Continues: Gem State RN news letter.
1977   7902968

RNA
RNA (New York, N.Y.)
1355-8382   1469-9001
1995   9509184

RNA Biol
RNA biology
1547-6286   1555-8584
2004   101235328

RNABC News
RNABC news
0048-7104
Continued by: Nursing BC.
1969-1990   0371232

RNAO News
RNAO news
0048-7112
Continues: News bulletin (Registered Nurses' Association of Ontario).
1965-1991   0251242

Roche Rev
Roche review
1936-1947   20430350R

Rocky Mt Med J
Rocky Mountain medical journal
0035-760X
Formed by the Union of Colorado medicine and Utah state medical journal. Continued by: Colorado medicine.
1938-1979   0404505

Rocz Akad Med Bialymst
Roczniki Akademii Medycznej w Białymstoku (1995)
Continues: Annals of the Medical University, Białystok, Poland. Continued by: Advances in medical sciences.
1994-2005   9515551

Rocz Akad Med Bialymst
Roczniki Akademii Medycznej w
Białymstoku = Annales Academiae Medicae
Bialostocensis
0067-6489
Continues: Roczniki Akademii Medycznej
im. Juliana Marchlewskiego w Białymstoku.
Continued by: Annals of the Medical
Universitiy, Białystok, Poland.
1989-1991   9108825

Rocz Akad Med Bialymst Supl
Roczniki Akademii Medycznej w
Białymstoku. Suplement = Annales
Academiae Medicae Bialostocensis.
Supplementum
0523-1507
Continues: Roczniki Akademii Medycznej
im. Juliana Marchlewskiego w Białymstoku.
Suplement.
1990-1991   9439577

**Rocz Akad Med Im Juliana Marchlewskiego
Bialymst**
Roczniki Akademii Medycznej im. Juliana
Marchlewskiego w Białymstoku
1427-941X
Continued by: Roczniki Akademii Medycznej
w Białymstoku.
1955-1987   7501229

**Rocz Akad Med Im Juliana Marchlewskiego
Bialymst Suppl**
Roczniki Akademii Medycznej im. Juliana
Marchlewskiego w Białymstoku. Suplement
1427-9401
Continued by: Roczniki Akademii Medycznej
w Białymstoku. Suplement.
1958-1988   7501228

Rocz Panstw Zakl Hig
Roczniki Państwowego Zakładu Higieny
0035-7715
1950   0414756

Rocz Pomor Akad Med
Rocznik Pomorskiej Akademii Medycznej
im. Gen. Karola świerczewskiego w
Szczecinie
0066-1945
Continued by: Annales Academiae Medicae
Stetinensis.
1951-1962   7503659

Rodo Kagaku
Rodo kagaku. The Journal of science of
labour
0022-443X
Continues Rodo kagaku kenkyu.
1940   0140205

Rodo Kagaku Kenkyu
[Rōdō kagaku kenkyū] The Journal of
science of labour
Continued by Rodo kagaku (called Sangyō
igaku, ichigatsu-kugatsu 1940)
1924-1939   20430650R

Rofo
RöFo: Fortschritte auf dem Gebiete der
Röntgenstrahlen und der Nuklearmedizin
1438-9029   1438-9010
Absorbed: Aktuelle Radiologie. 1999
Continues: Fortschritte auf dem Gebiete der
Röntgenstrahlen und der Nuklearmedizin.
1975   7507497

Rogerian Nurs Sci News
Rogerian nursing science news: newsletter of
the Society of Rogerian Scholars
1050-9089
1988-2001   9005735

Rom J Endocrinol
Romanian journal of endocrinology /
sponsore [sic] by the Academy of Medical
Sciences
1221-356X
Continues: Endocrinologie. Continued by:
Acta endocrinologica.
1992-2004   9309485

Rom J Gastroenterol
Romanian journal of gastroenterology
1221-4167
Continued by: Journal of gastrointestinal and
liver diseases.
1992-2005   9315667

Rom J Intern Med
Romanian journal of internal medicine =
Revue roumaine de médecine interne
1220-4749
Continues: Médecine interne.
1991   9304507

Rom J Morphol Embryol
Romanian journal of morphology and
embryology = Revue roumaine de
morphologie et embryologie
1220-0522
Continues: Morphologie et embryologie.
1990   9112454

Rom J Neurol Psychiatry
Romanian journal of neurology and
psychiatry = Revue roumaine de neurologie
et psychiatrie
1017-5644
Continues: Neurologie et psychiatrie.
Continued by: Romanian journal of
neurology.
1990-1995   9014562

Rom J Physiol
Romanian journal of physiology:
physiological sciences / [Academia de Stiinte
Medicale]
1223-4974
Continues: Revue roumaine de physiologie
(Bucharest, Romania: 1990).
1993   9437433

Rom J Virol
Romanian journal of virology
Continues: Revue roumaine de virologie
(Bucharest, Romania: 1990).
1995-1999   9702340

Rom Med Rev
Romanian medical review
0048-8585
Continues the Rumanian medical review.
1966-1974   0132263

Ronenbyo
Ronenbyo. [Geriatrics]
0216-0951
1957-1964   0145070

Rontgen Laborator
Röntgen- und Laboratoriumspraxis
Continues Röntgenphotographie;
medizinische Photographie und medizinische
Laboratoriumspraxis. Continued by
Röntgenpraxis: Zeitschrift für radiologische
Technik.
1950-1962   20430730R

Rontgenblatter
Röntgen-Blätter; Zeitschrift für Röntgen-
Technik und medizinisch-wissenschaftliche
Photographie
0300-8592
Continued by: Aktuelle Radiologie.
1948-1990   0413560

Rontgendiagnostik Ergeb
Röntgendiagnostik; Ergebnisse
1952-1956   20430700R

Rontgeneur Radiodiagn Clin Eur
Roentgen-Europ; radiodiagnostic clinique
européen
1961-1964   20430710R

Rontgenphotogr Med Photogr Med Lab Prax
Röntgenphotographie; medizinsche
Photographie und medizinische
Laboratoriumspraxis
0176-6287
Continued by Röntgen- und
Laboratoriumspraxis.
1947-1950   20430720R

Rontgenprax Diagn Rontgen Radium Lichtther
Röntgenpraxis; Diagnostik, Röntgen-,
Radium-, Lichttherapie
1929-1948   20430740R

Rontgenpraxis
Röntgenpraxis; Zeitschrift für radiologische
Technik
0035-7820
Continues in part Röntgen- und
Laboratoriumspraxis.
1963   0404365

Rorschach Res Exch J Proj Tech
Rorschach research exchange and journal of
projective techniques
1068-3402
Continued by the Journal of projective
techniques.
1936-1949   20440090R

Ross Fiziol Zh Im I M Sechenova
Rossiĭskiĭ fiziologicheskiĭ zhurnal imeni I.M.
Sechenova / Rossiĭskaia akademiia nauk
0869-8139
Continues: Fiziologicheskiĭ zhurnal imeni
I.M. Sechenova.
1997   9715665

Ross Gastroenterol Zh
Rossiĭskiĭ gastroénterologicheskiĭ zhurnal:
ezhekvartalnyĭ nauchno-prakticheskiĭ
zhurnal
1560-408X
Continued by: Éksperimental'naiâ i
klinicheskaiâ gastroénterologiiâ.
1993-2001   100964455

Ross Med Zh
Rossiĭskiĭ meditŝinskiĭ zhurnal: organ
Ministerstva zdravookhraneniiâ RSFSR
0869-2106
Continues: Sovetskaiâ meditŝina.
1992   9209559

Roum Arch Microbiol Immunol
Roumanian archives of microbiology and
immunology
1222-3891
Continues: Archives roumaines de pathologie
expérimentales et de microbiologie.
1991   9204717

Rozhl Chir
Rozhledy v chirurgii: měsíčník
československé chirurgické společnosti
0035-9351
Continues in part: Rozhledy v chirurgii a
gynaekologii.
1938   9815441

Rozhl Tuberk
Rozhledy v tuberkulose
Continued by Rozhledy v tuberkulose a v
nemocech plicních.
1940-1951   20441050R

Rozpr Wydz Nauk Med
Rozprawy Wydziału Nauk Medycznych
0079-3558
Continues Rozprawy Komitetu Nauk
Medycznych, Polska Akademia Nauk.
1957-1967   7506005

Rum Med Rev
Rumanian medical review
Continued by: Romanian medical review.
1957-1966   9421500

Rural Policy Brief
Rural policy brief / RUPRI Rural Health
Panel
1997   101130373

Rural Remote Health
Rural and remote health
                             1445-6354
2001   101174860

Russ Coiles Health Trends
Russ Coile's health trends
1079-7726
Continues: Hospital strategy report.
1995-2003   9514805

Russ J Immunol
Russian journal of immunology: RJI: official
journal of Russian Society of Immunology
1028-7221
1996   9713940

Ryan Advis Health Serv Gov Boards
The Ryan advisory for health services
governing boards
0161-7680
Continues The Ryan advisory for hospital
governing boards.
1977-1983   7802253

Ryoikibetsu Shokogun Shirizu
Ryōikibetsu shōkōgun shirīzu
1993   9501926

Ryumachi
Ryūmachi. [Rheumatism]
0300-9157
1958-2003   0153217

S

S Afr Dent J
South African dental journal. Suid
Afrikaanse tandarts tydskrif
1927-1953   20920110R

S Afr J Clin Sci
South African journal of clinical science.
Suid-Afrikaanse tydskrif vir kliniese
wetenskap
Supersedes Clinical proceedings. Superseded
by South African journal of laboratory and
clinical medicine.
1950-1954   20920140R

S Afr J Commun Disord
The South African journal of communication
disorders. Die Suid-Afrikaanse tydskrif vir
Kommunikasieafwykings
0379-8046
Continues Journal of the South African
Speech and Hearing Association. Tydskrif van
die Suid-Afrikaanse Vereniging vir Spraak-
en Gehoorheelkunde.
1977h   7805099

S Afr J Lab Clin Med
South African journal of laboratory and
clinical medicine. Suid-Afrikaanse tydskrif
vir laboratorium- en kliniekwerk
0038-2299
Supersedes the South African journal of
clinical science.
1955-1964   0263741

S Afr J Med Sci
The South African journal of medical
sciences
0038-2310
1935-1976   2984853R

S Afr J Surg
South African journal of surgery. Suid-
Afrikaanse tydskrif vir chirurgie
0038-2361
1963   2984854R

S Afr Med J
South African medical journal = Suid-
Afrikaanse tydskrif vir geneeskunde
0256-9574
Has supplement: South African journal
of obstetrics and gynaecology which was
issued separately, 1963-1973. In 1999, this
supplement again became an independent
publication. Absorbed: Southern African
journal of critical care, which was issued as
a section, Nov. 1994-<Sept. 1998> and later
issued separately, Apr. 2000- .
1932   0404520

S Afr Pharm J
South African pharmaceutical journal. Suid-
Afrikaanse tydskrif vir apteekwese
0257-8719
Absorbed African chemist and druggist.
Continued by S-A tydskrif vir apteekwese.
SA pharmaceutical journal.
1934-1975   7609868

S C Dent J
South Carolina dental journal
0049-1489
Continues: Journal of the South Carolina
Dental Association. Absorbed by: Palmetto
state dental journal.
194u-1983   0421132

S C Nurs
South Carolina nursing
0038-3155
Supersedes Palmetto leaves.
1949-1974   20920370R

S C Nurse
South Carolina nurse (Columbia, S.C.: 1994)
1046-7394
Continues: The South Carolina nurse,
published v. 1-8, 1986-1993.
1994   9423819

S C Nurse
The South Carolina nurse / South Carolina
Nurses' Association
1046-7394
Continues: SCNA newsletter. Continued by:
The South Carolina nurse, published v. 1- ,
1994- .
1986-1993   8913099

S D J Med
South Dakota journal of medicine
0038-3317
Continues in part: South Dakota journal of
medicine and pharmacy. Continued by: South
Dakota medicine.
1965-2005   0040162

S D Med
South Dakota medicine: the journal of the
South Dakota State Medical Association
0038-3317
Continues: South Dakota journal of medicine.
2006   101265265

S D Nurse
The South Dakota nurse
0038-335X
1957   0044560

S TA NU
S & TA & NU. Rivista di scienza e tecnologia
degli alimenti e di nutrizione umana
Continues S & TA; scienza e tecnologia degli
alimenti.
1975-1976   7702717

SA Nurs J
SA nursing journal. SA verplegingstydskrif
Continues the South African nursing journal.
Superseded by Curationis.
1963-1978   0046024

SAAD Dig
SAAD digest
0049-1160
1970   0403245

SAAS Bull Biochem Biotechnol
SAAS bulletin, biochemistry and
biotechnology
1052-6781
1988   8917120

Sabouraudia
Sabouraudia
0036-2174
Continued by: Journal of medical and
veterinary mycology.
1961-1985   0417341

Sac Explor
Sac Explorer
Continued by: Explorer.
1958-1968   9884823

SADJ
SADJ: journal of the South African Dental
Association = tydskrif van die Suid-
Afrikaanse Tandheelkundige Vereniging
1029-4864
Continues: Journal of the Dental Association
of South Africa.
1998   9812497

Saguenay Med
Le Saguenay médical
0036-2581
1952-1978   0404370

SAHARA J
SAHARA J: journal of Social Aspects of
HIV/AIDS Research Alliance / SAHARA ,
Human Sciences Research Council
1729-0376   1813-4424
2004   101226212

Sairaanh Vuosik
Sairaanhoidon vuosikirja
0301-0651
Continued by: Hoitotiede.
1958-1988   0366565

Sairaanhoitaja
Sairaanhoitaja (Helsinki, Finland: 1991)
0785-7527
Separated from: Tehy.
1991   9114981

Sairaanhoitaja
Sairaanhoitaja. Sjuksköterskan
0036-3278
Continues Sairaanhoitajalehti.
Absorbed Epione in 1966. Merged with
Laboratoriohoitaja and Lastenhoitajalehti to
form Tehy.
1966-1980   0105422

Sairaanhoitajalehti
Sairaanhoitajalehti
Continued by Sairaanhoitaja.
1925-1965   0102640

Saishin Igaku
Saishin igaku. Modern medicine
0370-8241
1946   0413561

Salud Bucal
Salud bucal / Confederación Odontológica
de la República Argentina
0325-0741
1974-1984   8411401

Salud Publica Mex
Salud pública de México
0036-3634   1606-7916
1959   0404371

Salzburger Beitr Paracelsusforsch
Salzburger Beiträge zur
Paracelsusforschung
0558-3489
1960   20530510R

Same Day Surg
Same-day surgery
0190-5066
1977   7810150

Samiska
Samiksa
1947   0416650

Samml Zwangl Abh Geb Psychiatr Neurol
Sammlung zwangloser Abhandlungen aus
dem Gebiete der Psychiatrie und Neurologie
0558-373X
Continued by: Beiträge zur klinischen
Neurologie und Psychiatrie.
1950-1980   0404372

San Fernando Val Dent Soc Bull
San Fernando Valley Dental Society bulletin
0581-4944
Continued by Dental dimensions.
1967-1972   7900363

San Gabriel Val Dent Soc Bull
San Gabriel Valley Dental Society bulletin
0048-9093
1937   7503663

Sanfujinka Chiryo
[Sanfujinka chiryō] Obstetrical and
gynecological therapy
0558-471X
1960   20540340R

Sanfujinka No Jissai
Sanfujinka no jissai. Practice of gynecology
and obstetrics
0558-4728
1952   0413562

Sanfujinka No Shinpo
[Sanfujinka no shinpo] Advances in
obstetrics and gynecology
0370-8446   1347-6742
1949   20540360R

Sang
Le Sang
Merged with Revue d'hématologie to form
Nouvelle revue française d'hématologie.
1927-1960   20540380R

Sangre (Barc)
Sangre
0036-4355
Continues: Trabajos de hematología y
hemoterapia.
1956-1999   0404373

Sangue
Il Sangue
1937-1967   20540400R

Sangyo Eiseigaku Zasshi
Sangyō eiseigaku zasshi = Journal of
occupational health
1341-0725   1349-533X
Continues: Sangyō igaku, published 1959-
1994?. Continued in part by: Journal of
occupational health.
1995   9507473

Sangyo Igaku
Sangyō igaku. Japanese journal of industrial
health
0047-1879
Continued by: Sangyō eiseigaku zasshi.
1959-1994   0150531

Sanid Benefic Munic
Sanidad y beneficencia municipal; revista
médico social
1941-1957   20540440R

Sanita Pubblica
Sanità pubblica
0393-4101
Continued by: Sanità pubblica e privata.
1981-2002   8710721

Sanitarian
The Sanitarian
0096-560X
Continued by Journal of environmental
health.
1938-1962   20540480R

Sanitatswarte
Sanitätswarte
1900-1955   20540470R

Sante
Santé (Montrouge, France)
1157-5999
1990   9212437

Sante Ment Que
Santé mentale au Québec
0383-6320
1976   9424773

Sante Publique
Santé publique (Vandoeuvre-lès-Nancy,
France)
0995-3914
Formed by the union of: Cahiers de l'Ecole
nationale de la santé publique. and: Revue
française de la santé publique.
1988   9216153

Sante Publique (Bucur)
La Santé publique
0048-9107
1958-1990   0404374

Sante Publique (Paris)
Santé publique
1946-19uu   20610100R

Sante Que
Santé Québec: revue de la Corporation
professionnelle des infirmières et infirmiers
auxiliaires du Québec
1180-3983
Continues in part: Infirmière auxiliaire.
1990   9014566

Sao Paulo Med
São Paulo médico
1928-1948   0204544

Sao Paulo Med J
São Paulo medical journal = Revista paulista
de medicina
1516-3180   1806-9460
Continues: Revista paulista de medicina.
1994   100897261

Sapporo Igaku Zasshi
Sapporo igaku zasshi. The Sapporo medical
journal
0036-472X
Continues the Kiyo of Sapporo Ika Daigaku.
1949   0420551

SAR QSAR Environ Res
SAR and QSAR in environmental research
1062-936X   1029-046X
1993   9440156

Sarcoidosis
Sarcoidosis
0393-1447
Continued by: Sarcoidosis, vasculitis, and
diffuse lung diseases.
1984-1995 ·   8500778

Sarcoidosis Vasc Diffuse Lung Dis
Sarcoidosis, vasculitis, and diffuse lung
diseases: official journal of WASOG /
World Association of Sarcoidosis and Other
Granulomatous Disorders
1124-0490
Continues: Sarcoidosis.
1996   9610928

Saturday Rev
Saturday review
0361-1655
Continues: Saturday review. World.
1975-1986   9877080

Saudi J Kidney Dis Transpl
Saudi journal of kidney diseases and
transplantation: an official publication of
the Saudi Center for Organ Transplantation,
Saudi Arabia
1319-2442
Continues: Saudi kidney diseases and
transplantation bulletin.
1994   9436968

Saudi Med J
Saudi medical journal
0379-5284
1979   7909441

Sb Lek
Sborník lékařský
0036-5327
Continued by: Prague medical report.
1887-2003   0025770

Sb Pathofysiol Traveni Vyz Gastroenterol Bohema
Sborník pro pathofysiologii trávení a výživy;
gastroenterologia bohema
Continues Gastroenterologia bohema.
Continued by Ceskoslovenská
gastroenterologia a výživa.
1951-1954   17040190R

Sb Tr Azerbaidzhanskii Gos Meditsinskii Inst N Narimanova
Sbornik trudov. Azerbaǐdzhanskiǐ
gosudarstvennyǐ meditsinskiǐ institut im. N.
Narimanova
1955-19uu   15430350R

Sb Ved Pr Lek Fak Karlovy Univerzity Hradci Kralove
Sborník vědeckých prací Lékařské fakulty
Karlovy university v Hradci Králové
0049-5514
Continued by: Acta medica (Hradec Králové).
1958-1995   0414147

Sb Ved Pr Lek Fak Karlovy Univerzity Hradci Kralove Suppl
Sborník vědeckých prací Lékařské fakulty
Karlovy univerzity v Hradci Králové.
Supplementum
0049-5522
Continued by: Acta medica (Hradec Králové).
Supplementum.
1958-1995   0414150

SC Rep
SC [reports]. U.S. Atomic Energy
Commission
195u-1970   21830700R

SC Trodent
SC Trodent
Continued by: Trodent.
1952-1969   9880768

SCADA J
Scada Journal
0885-9558
1981-1981 9880031

Scalpel (Brux)
Le Scalpel
0036-5440
1847-1971 0412023

Scalpel Alpha Epsil Delta
The Scalpel of Alpha Epsilon Delta
1931-1995 20620090R

Scan Electron Microsc
Scanning electron microscopy
0586-5581
 Continued by: Scanning microscopy.
1968-1986 0371617

Scand Audiol
Scandinavian audiology
0105-0397
 Merged with: Audiology, and: British journal
 of audiology, to form: International journal of
 audiology. Supersedes Nordisk audiologi.
1972-2001 0342230

Scand Audiol Suppl
Scandinavian audiology. Supplementum
0107-8593
1972-2001 0325221

Scand Cardiovasc J
Scandinavian cardiovascular journal: SCJ
1401-7431 1651-2006
 Continues: Scandinavian journal of thoracic
 and cardiovascular surgery.
1997 9708377

Scand Cardiovasc J Suppl
Scandinavian cardiovascular journal.
Supplement
1401-7458 1651-2510
 Continues: Scandinavian journal of thoracic
 and cardiovascular surgery. Supplementum.
1997 9711058

Scand J Caring Sci
Scandinavian journal of caring sciences
0283-9318 1471-6712
1987 8804206

Scand J Clin Lab Invest
Scandinavian journal of clinical and
laboratory investigation
0036-5513 1502-7686
1949 0404375

Scand J Clin Lab Invest Suppl
Scandinavian journal of clinical and
laboratory investigation. Supplementum
0085-591X
1951 2984789R

Scand J Dent Res
Scandinavian journal of dental research
0029-845X
 Continues Odontologisk tidskrift. Continued
 by: European journal of oral sciences.
1970-1994 0270023

Scand J Gastroenterol
Scandinavian journal of gastroenterology
0036-5521 1502-7708
1966 0060105

Scand J Gastroenterol Suppl
Scandinavian journal of gastroenterology.
Supplement
0085-5928
1968 0437034

Scand J Haematol
Scandinavian journal of haematology
0036-553X
 Continued by: European journal of
 haematology.
1964-1986 0404507

Scand J Haematol Suppl
Scandinavian journal of haematology.
Supplementum
0080-6722
 Continued by: European journal of
 haematology. Supplementum.
1967-1986 0104315

Scand J Immunol
Scandinavian journal of immunology
0300-9475 1365-3083
1972 0323767

Scand J Immunol Suppl
Scandinavian journal of immunology.
Supplement
0301-6323
1973-1992 7501626

Scand J Infect Dis
Scandinavian journal of infectious diseases
0036-5548
1969 0215333

Scand J Infect Dis Suppl
Scandinavian journal of infectious diseases.
Supplementum
0300-8878
1970 0251025

Scand J Med Sci Sports
Scandinavian journal of medicine & science
in sports
0905-7188 1600-0838
1991 9111504

Scand J Occup Ther
Scandinavian journal of occupational
therapy
1103-8128
1994 9502210

Scand J Plast Reconstr Surg
Scandinavian journal of plastic and
reconstructive surgery
0036-5556
 Continued by: Scandinavian journal of plastic
 and reconstructive surgery and hand surgery.
1967-1986 0121375

Scand J Plast Reconstr Surg Hand Surg
Scandinavian journal of plastic and
reconstructive surgery and hand surgery
/ Nordisk plastikkirurgisk forening [and]
Nordisk klubb for handkirurgi
0284-4311
 Continues: Scandinavian journal of plastic
 and reconstructive surgery.
1987 8707869

Scand J Plast Reconstr Surg Hand Surg Suppl
Scandinavian journal of plastic and
reconstructive surgery and hand surgery.
Supplementum
0346-6612
 Supplement to: Scandinavian journal of
 plastic and reconstructive surgery and hand
 surgery. Continues: Scandinavian journal
 of plastic and reconstructive surgery.
 Supplementum.
1990 9204339

Scand J Plast Reconstr Surg Suppl
Scandinavian journal of plastic and
reconstructive surgery. Supplementum
0581-9474
 Continued by: Scandinavian journal of plastic
 and reconstructive surgery and hand surgery.
 Supplementum.
1967-1984 0112055

Scand J Prim Health Care
Scandinavian journal of primary health care
0281-3432 1502-7724
1983 8510679

Scand J Prim Health Care Suppl
Scandinavian journal of primary health
care. Supplement
0284-6020
1988 8812233

Scand J Psychol
Scandinavian journal of psychology
0036-5564
1960 0404510

Scand J Public Health
Scandinavian journal of public health
1403-4948 1651-1905
 Continues: Scandinavian journal of social
 medicine.
1999 100883503

Scand J Public Health Suppl
Scandinavian journal of public health.
Supplement
1403-4956
 Continues: Scandinavian journal of social
 medicine. Supplementum.
2001 100883504

Scand J Rehabil Med
Scandinavian journal of rehabilitation
medicine
0036-5505
 Continued by: Journal of rehabilitation
 medicine.
1969-2000 0212503

Scand J Rehabil Med Suppl
Scandinavian journal of rehabilitation
medicine. Supplement
0346-8720
1970 0254404

Scand J Respir Dis
Scandinavian journal of respiratory diseases
0036-5572
 Continues Acta tuberculosea et pneumologica
 Scandinavica. Merged with Acta tuberculosea
 et pneumologica Belgica to form European
 journal of respiratory diseases.
1966-1979 0055427

Scand J Respir Dis Suppl
Scandinavian journal of respiratory
diseases. Supplementum
0080-6730
 Continues Acta tuberculosea et pneumologica
 Scandinavica. Supplementum. Continued
 by European journal of respiratory diseases.
 Supplement.
1966-1979 0057161

Scand J Rheumatol
Scandinavian journal of rheumatology
0300-9742 1502-7732
 Supersedes: Acta rheumatologica
 Scandinavica.
1972 0321213

Scand J Rheumatol Suppl
Scandinavian journal of rheumatology.
Supplement
0301-3847
 Supersedes the Supplementum to Acta
 rheumatologica Scandinavica.
1973 0400360

Scand J Soc Med
Scandinavian journal of social medicine
0300-8037
 Supersedes Acta socio-medica Scandinavica.
 Continued by: Scandinavian journal of public
 health.
1973-1998 0365610

Scand J Soc Med Suppl
Scandinavian journal of social medicine.
Supplementum
0301-7311
Continues: Acta socio-medica Scandinavica.
Supplement. Continued by: Scandinavian
journal of public health. Supplement.
1973-1998   0412776

Scand J Surg
Scandinavian journal of surgery: SJS:
official organ for the Finnish Surgical Society
and the Scandinavian Surgical Society
1457-4969
Continues: Annales chirurgiae et
gynaecologiae.
2002   101144297

Scand J Thorac Cardiovasc Surg
Scandinavian journal of thoracic and
cardiovascular surgery
0036-5580
Continued by: Scandinavian cardiovascular
journal.
1967-1996   0121343

Scand J Thorac Cardiovasc Surg Suppl
Scandinavian journal of thoracic and
cardiovascular surgery. Supplementum
0586-9587
Continued by: Scandinavian cardiovascular
journal. Supplement.
1969-1996   0265737

Scand J Urol Nephrol
Scandinavian journal of urology and
nephrology
0036-5599
1967   0114501

Scand J Urol Nephrol Suppl
Scandinavian journal of urology and
nephrology. Supplementum
0300-8886
1968   0153034

Scand J Work Environ Health
Scandinavian journal of work, environment
& health
0355-3140   1795-990X
Formed by merger of Nordisk hygienisk
tidskrift. and Work. environment. health.
1975   7511540

Scanning
Scanning
0161-0457
1978   7903371

Scanning Microsc
Scanning microscopy
0891-7035
1987-1996   8704616

Scanning Microsc Suppl
Scanning microscopy. Supplement
0892-953X
1987-1996   8710881

Scanodont
Scan'odont
0105-1881
1973-1976   7601982

Sch Dent Serv Gaz N Z
School Dental Service gazette, New Zealand
0048-0126
Continues New Zealand School Dental
Service gazette. Continued by New Zealand
School Dental Service gazette.
1952-1970   7704025

Sch Health Rev
School health review
0036-6579
Continued by Health education.
1969-1974   7514117

Sch Inq Nurs Pract
Scholarly inquiry for nursing practice
0889-7182
Continued by: Research and theory for
nursing practice.
1987-2001   8709011

SCHA J
Scha Journal
1975   9875076

Schizofrenie
Schizofrenie
1931-1952   20620140R

Schizophr Bull
Schizophrenia bulletin
0586-7614   1745-1701
1969   0236760

Schizophr Res
Schizophrenia research
0920-9964
1988   8804207

Schmerz
Schmerz (Berlin, Germany)
0932-433X   1432-2129
1987   8906258

School Nurse News
School nurse news
1080-7543
Continues: Community nurse forum.
19uu   100956395

Schriftenr Geb Off Gesundheitswes
Schriftenreihe aus dem Gebiete des
öffentlichen Gesundheitswesens
0487-708X
Supersedes Veröffentlichungen aus dem
Gebiete des Volksgesundheitsdienstes.
1954-1974   0423430

Schriftenr Neurol
Schriftenreihe Neurologie
0080-715X
Supersedes in part Monographien aus dem
Gesamtgebiete der Neurologie und Psychiatrie.
1969-1993   0222673

Schriftenr Ver Wasser Boden Lufthyg
Schriftenreihe des Vereins für Wasser-,
Boden- und Lufthygiene
0300-8665
1949   7507514

Schriftenr Zentralbl Arbeitsmed Arbeitsschutz Prophyl
Schriftenreihe Zentralblatt für
Arbeitsmedizin, Arbeitsschutz und
Prophylaxe
0344-7219
Continued by: Schriftenreihe Zentralblatt für
Arbeitsmedizin Arbeitsschutz. Prophylaxe
und Ergonomie.
1977-1979   7704350

Schriftenr Zentralbl Arbeitsmed Arbeitsschutz Prophyl Ergonomie
Schriftenreihe Zentralblatt für
Arbeitsmedizin, Arbeitsschutz, Prophylaxe,
und Ergonomie
0721-7056
Continues: Schriftenreihe Zentralblatt
für Arbeitsmedizin, Arbeitsschutz und
Prophylaxe. Continued by: Schriftenreihe
Zentralblatt für Arbeitsmedizin.
1980-1986   8103175

Schweiz Apoth Ztg
Schweizerische Apotheker Zeitung
0036-7508
Continues: Schweizerische Wochenschrift
für Chemie und Pharmacie. Continued by:
Schweiz. Apotheker-Zeitung.
1914-1972   7613213

Schweiz Arch Neurol Neurochir Psychiatr
Schweizer Archiv für Neurologie,
Neurochirurgie und Psychiatrie = Archives
suisses de neurologie, neurochirurgie et de
psychiatrie
0036-7273
Continues: Schweizer Archiv für Neurologie
und Psychiatrie. Continued by: Schweizer
Archiv für Neurologie und Psychiatrie
(Zurich, Switzerland: 1985).
1959-1984   8709012

Schweiz Arch Neurol Psychiatr
Schweizer Archiv für Neurologie und
Psychiatrie (Zurich, Switzerland: 1985)
0258-7661
Continues: Schweizer Archiv für Neurologie,
Neurochirurgie und Psychiatrie.
1985   8503709

Schweiz Arch Neurol Psychiatr
Schweizer Archiv für Neurologie und
Psychiatrie. Archives suisses de neurologie
et de psychiatrie. Archivio svizzero di
neurologia e psichiatria
Continued by Schweizer Archiv für
Neurologie, Neurochirurgie und Psychiatrie.
1917-1959   20630130R

Schweiz Arch Tierheilkd
Schweizer Archiv für Tierheilkunde
0036-7281
Absorbed: Schweizerisches Archiv für
Thierheilkunde und Thierheilkunde.
1859   0424247

Schweiz Arzteztg Standesfr
Schweizerische Ärztezeitung für
Standesfragen. Bulletin professionnel des
médecins suisses. Bollettino dei medici
svizzeri per interessi professionali
1423-0623
Continued by: Schweizerische Ärztezeitung.
1920-1951   20630190R

Schweiz Bl Krankenpfl
Schweizerische Blätter für Krankenpflege.
Revue suisse des infirmières
Continues: Blätter für Krankenpflege.
Continued by: Zeitschrift für Krankenpflege.
1945-1961   0026222

Schweiz Drog Ztg (1901)
Schweizerische Drogisten Zeitung
0376-5113
Continued by Journal suisse des droguistes.
1901-1950   7513041

Schweiz Hebamme
Die Schweizer Hebamme
1422-4526
Continued by: Hebamme.
1903-2004   20630160R

Schweiz Krankenkassen Ztg
Schweizerische Krankenkassen-Zeitung
0253-0422
Continues Krankenkassen-Zeitung. Continued
by SKZ. Scweizerische Krankenkassen-
Zeitung.
1925-1951   8007256

Schweiz Med Jahrb
Schweizerisches medizinisches jahrbuch
0080-7400
1929   27410490R

Schweiz Med Wochenschr
Schweizerische medizinische Wochenschrift
0036-7672
Continues: Correspondenz-Blatt für schweizer
Aertze. Continued by: Swiss medical weekly.
1920-2000   0404401

Schweiz Med Wochenschr Suppl
Schweizerische medizinische Wochenschrift.
Supplementum
0250-5525
   Absorbed by: Swiss medical weekly.
1976-2000   7708316

Schweiz Monatsschr Zahnmed
Schweizer Monatsschrift für Zahnmedizin
= Revue mensuelle suisse d'odonto-
stomatologie = Rivista mensile svizzera di
odontologia e stomatologia / SSO
1011-4203
   Continues: Schweizerische Monatsschrift für
   Zahnmedizin.
1987   8709597

Schweiz Monatsschr Zahnmed
Schweizerische Monatsschrift für
Zahnmedizin = Revue mensuelle suisse
d'odonto-stomatologie = Rivista mensile
svizzera di odontologia e stomatologia / SSO
0256-2855
   Continues: Schweizerische Monatsschrift für
   Zahnheilkunde. Continued by: Schweizer
   Monatsschrift für Zahnmedizin.
1984-1986   8402985

Schweiz Opt Opt Suisse
Der Schweizer Optiker. L'Opticien suisse
1420-0821
1925   20630170R

Schweiz Rundsch Med Prax
Schweizerische Rundschau für Medizin
Praxis = Revue suisse de médecine Praxis
1013-2058
   Continues: Praxis. Continued by: Praxis.
1970-1994   8403202

Schweiz Z Homoopath
Schweizerische Zeitschrift für Homöopathie.
Journal suisse d'homoeopathie
1955-1962   20630410R

Schweiz Z Med Traumatol
Schweizerische Zeitschrift für Medizin
und Traumatologie = Revue suisse pour
médecine et traumatologie
1022-6699
   Continues: Schweizerische Zeitschrift für
   Sportmedizin. Continued by: Schweizerische
   Zeitschrift für Sportmedizin und
   Sporttraumatologie.
1994-1995   9431737

Schweiz Z Pathol Bakteriol
Schweizerische Zeitschrift für Pathologie
und Bakteriologie. Revue suisse de
pathologie et de bactériologie
   Continued by Pathologia et microbiologia.
1938-1959   20630440R

Schweiz Z Psychol Anwend
Schweizerische Zeitschrift für Psychologie
und ihre Andwendungen. Revue suisse de
psychologie, pure et appliquée
0036-7869
   Continues: Zeitschrift für diagnostische
   Psychologie und Persönlichkeitsforschung.
   Continued by: Psychologie (Bern,
   Switzerland).
1942-1967   0316747

Schweiz Z Sportmed
Schweizerische Zeitschrift für Sportmedizin
0036-7885
   Continued by: Schweizerische Zeitschrift für
   Medizin und Traumatologie.
1953-1993   2984794R

Schweiz Z Tuberc Pneumonol
Schweizerische Zeitschrift für Tuberkulose
und Pneumonologie. Revue suisse de
la tuberculose et de pneumonologie.
Rivista svizzera della tubercolosi e della
pneumonologia
   Continues Schweizerische Zeitschrift für
   Tuberkulose. Continued by Medicina
   thoracalis.
1956-1961   20630470R

Schweiz Z Tuberk
Schweizerische Zeitschrift für Tuberkulose.
Revue suisse de la tuberculose. Rivista
svizzera della tubercolosi
   Continued by Schweizerische Zeitschrift für
   Tuberkulose und Pneumonologie.
1944-1955   20630460R

Schwest Rev
Schwestern Revue
0048-9549
   Continued by Krankenpflege Journal.
1963-1979   0045677

Sci Aging Knowledge Environ
Science of aging knowledge environment:
SAGE KE
           1539-6150
2001-2006   101146039

Sci Am
Scientific American
0036-8733
1845   0404400

Sci Basis Med Annu Rev
The Scientific basis of medicine annual
reviews
0080-7729
   Continues Lectures on the scientific basis of
   medicine.
1961-1973   0243617

Sci Can
Scientia canadensis
0829-2507
   Continues: HSTC bulletin.
1984   8709014

Sci China B
Science in China. Series B, Chemistry, life
sciences & earth sciences
1001-652X
   Continues: Scientia Sinica. Series B,
   Chemical, biological, agricultural, medical &
   earth sciences. Split into: Science in China.
   Series B, Chemistry; Science in China. Series
   C, Life sciences; and: Science in China.
   Series D, Earth sciences.
1989-1995   8913082

Sci China C Life Sci
Science in China. Series C, Life sciences /
Chinese Academy of Sciences
1006-9305
   Continues in part: Science in China. Series B,
   Chemistry, life sciences & earth sciences.
1996   9611809

Sci Context
Science in context
0269-8897
1987   8904113

Sci Dig
Science digest
0036-8296
   Continued by: Science digest (New York,
   N.Y.).
1937-1986   9877793

Sci Educ Bull
Scientific And Educational Bulletin
   Continued by: Scientific and educational
   journal.
1965-1973   9877187

Sci Educ J
Scientific and educational journal
   Continues: Scientific And Educational
   Bulletin. Continued by: Icd Scientific And
   Educational Journal.
1973-1973   9883482

Sci Eng Ethics
Science and engineering ethics
1353-3452   1471-5546
1995   9516228

Sci Genet
Scientia genetica; periodico di genetica per i
paesi latini
1939-1954   20640150R

Sci Illus
Science illustrated
1946-1949   20640100R

Sci Justice
Science & justice: journal of the Forensic
Science Society
1355-0306
   Continues: Journal - Forensic Science
   Society.
1995   9508563

Sci Med Ital
Scientia medica italica. English ed
1950-1960   20640160R

Sci Med Man
Science, medicine and man
0300-9955
   Continued by Ethics in science & medicine.
1973-1974   7510997

Sci Med Prat
La Science médicale pratique
1926-1954   20640110R

Sci Mon
The Scientific monthly
0096-3771
   Absorbed by: Science.
1915-1957   20640290R

Sci News
Science news
0036-8423
   Continues: Science news letter.
1966   0176400

Sci News Lett
Science news letter
0096-4018
   Continues: Science news bulletin. Continued
   by: Science news (Washington, D.C.).
1921-1966   0177067

SCI Nurs
SCI nursing: a publication of the American
Association of Spinal Cord Injury Nurses
0888-8299
1984   8503185

Sci Pharm
Scientia pharmaceutica
0036-8709
1930   0026251

Sci Pract Perspect
Science & practice perspectives / a
publication of the National Institute on Drug
Abuse, National Institutes of Health
1930-4307   1930-4315
   Continued by: Addiction science & clinical
   practice.
2002-2007   101275423

Sci Proc Cardiff Med Soc
Scientific proceedings of the Cardiff Medical
Society
0307-3394
Continues Proceedings of the Cardiff Medical
Society.
1969-1976   7501234

Sci Proc R Dublin Soc
The scientific proceedings of the Royal
Dublin Society. Royal Dublin Society
0371-2303
Supersedes in part: The Journal of the Royal
Dublin Society.. Royal Dublin Society.
Continued by: The scientific proceedings of
the Royal Dublin Society. Series A.. Royal
Dublin Society.
1878-1957   9427128

Sci Prog
Science progress
0036-8504
Continues Science progress in the twentieth
century. and scattered title pages of individual
issues bear that title until Apr. 1933.
1916   0411361

Sci Prog (New Haven)
Science in progress
0097-0611
1937-1966   0232536

Sci Prog Twent Century
Science progress in the twentieth century
0302-1785
Continued by Science progress.
1906-1916   0411362

Sci Rech Odontostomatol
Science & recherche odontostomatologiques
0371-2729
1971-1972   1300065

Sci Rep Ist Super Sanita
Scientific reports of the Istituto superiore di
sanità
0579-0972
1961-1962   17720270R

Sci Rep Res Inst Tohoku Univ [Med]
The science reports of the research
institutes, Tohoku University. Ser. C,
Medicine. Tōhoku Daigaku
0371-2761
1949-1993   0234153

Sci Signal
Science signaling
                                        1937-9145
Continues: Science's STKE.
2008   101465400

Sci Sin
Scientia Sinica
0250-7870
Continues: Acta scientia Sinica. Split into:
Scientia Sinica. Series A. Mathematical.
physical. astronomical. & technical sciences;
and Scientia Sinica. Series B. Chemical.
biological. agricultural. medical. & earth
sciences.
1954-1981   8209876

Sci Sin [B]
Scientia Sinica. Series B, Chemical,
biological, agricultural, medical & earth
sciences / Chung-kuo k'o hsüeh yüan, chu
pan
0253-5823
Continues in part: Scientia Sinica. Continued
by: Science in China. Series B. Chemistry.
life sciences & earth sciences.
1982-1988   8209875

Sci STKE
Science's STKE: signal transduction
knowledge environment
                                        1525-8882
Continued by: Science signaling.
1999-2007   100964423

Sci Stud (St Bonaventure)
Science studies
0036-8539
1932-1976   20640115R

Sci Technol China
Science & technology in China
0371-3342
Continues: Acta brevia sinensia.
1948-1949   20640070R

Sci Total Environ
The Science of the total environment
0048-9697
1972   0330500

Science
Science (New York, N.Y.)
0036-8075   1095-9203
Absorbed: Scientific monthly. Jan. 1958
1880   0404511

Sciences (New York)
The Sciences
0036-861X
1961-2001   0404513

ScientificWorldJournal
TheScientificWorldJournal
                                        1537-744X
2001   101131163

SCNA Newsl
Scna Newsletter
0199-3399
Continues: South Carolina Nurses Association
Newsletter. Continued by: South Carolina
Nurse.
1979-1985   9878961

Scott Med J
Scottish medical journal
0036-9330
Formed by the union of Edinburgh medical
journal and Glasgow medical journal.
1956   2983335R

Scr Med (Brno)
Scripta medica
1211-3395
Continues the Spisy of Brünn Universita.
Lékařska fakulta.
1949   2984844R

SDA Dent
Sda Dentist
0024-5968
Merger of: Loma Linda University dentistry
magazine and: Journal of the National
Association of Seventh-day Adventist Dentist.
1967-1972   9875637

Se Pu
Se pu = Chinese journal of chromatography
/ Zhongguo hua xue hui
1000-8713
1984   9424804

Sea View Hosp Bull
Sea View Hospital bulletin
0096-6843
Continues the Quarterly bulletin of Sea View
Hospital.
1955-1960   20710020R

Seara Med
Seara médica
Continued by: Seara médica neurocirúrgica.
1941-1962   20710060R

SEB Exp Biol Ser
SEB experimental biology series
Continues: Symposia of the Society for
Experimental Biology.
2005   101308820

Second Messengers Phosphoproteins
Second messengers and phosphoproteins
0895-7479
Continues: Journal of cyclic nucleotide and
protein phosphorylation research. Merged
with: Journal of receptor research, to form:
Journal of receptor and signal transduction
research.
1988-1993   9002049

Second Opin
Second opinion (Park Ridge, Ill.)
0890-1570
Continued by: Making the rounds in health.
faith. & ethics.
1986-1995   8704074

Second Opin Health Care Issues
Second opinions on health care issues
0738-8802
198u   9878738

Seikagaku
Seikagaku. The Journal of Japanese
Biochemical Society
0037-1017
Continues: Nihon Seikagakkai shi..
1948   0413564

Seikei Geka
Seikeigeka. Orthopedic surgery
0030-5901
1950   0413745

Seiroka Kango Daigaku Kiyo
Sei Roka Kango Daigaku kiyō
0289-2863
1975   9213446

Seishin Igaku
Seishin igaku. Clinical psychiatry
0488-1281
1959   0413565

Seishin Igaku Kenkyusho Gyosekishu
Seishin Igaku Kenkyūjo gyōsekishū =
Bulletin of the Seishin-Igaku Institute
0080-8547
1954   0413746

Seishin Shinkeigaku Zasshi
Seishin shinkeigaku zasshi = Psychiatria et
neurologia Japonica
0033-2658
Continues: Shinkeigaku zasshi.
1935   9801787

Seitai Kagaku
[Seitai no kagaku] [Science of the living
body]
0370-9531
1946   20710390R

Seizure
Seizure: the journal of the British Epilepsy
Association
1059-1311
1992   9306979

Sel Cancer Ther
Selective cancer therapeutics
1043-0733
Continues: Cancer drug delivery. Continued
by: Cancer biotherapy.
1989-1991   8912502

Sel Odontol (Sao Paulo)
Seleções odontológicas
0049-0075
1946-1974   20710490R

Sem Hop
La semaine des hôpitaux: organe fondé par
l'Association d'enseignement médical des
hôpitaux de Paris
Absorbed: Semaine des hôpitaux.
Informations. Continues: Semaine des
hôpitaux de Paris.
1945-2000 9410059

Sem Hop Inf
Semaine des hôpitaux: informations
0582-5326
1945-1977 2984845R

Sem Hop Ther
Semaine des hôpitaux. Therapeutique
0040-5922
Continues Therapeutique (La Semaine des
hôpitaux).
1973-1977 0415603

Sem Hop Ther Paris
La Semaine des hôpitaux: thérapeutique
Continued by Semaine thérapeutique.
1955-1961 20710590R

Sem Med Prof Med Soc
Semaine médicale professionelle et médico-
sociale
1954-1971 1272005

Sem Medicale Med Soc
La Semaine médicale [médecine sociale.
Edition: couverture jaune]
Continues in part La Semaine médicale,
issued in 1951. Continued by Semaine
professionnelle et médico-sociale.
1952-1953 20710630R

Sem Ther
Semaine thérapeutique
0040-5922
Continues La Semaine des hôpitaux;
thérapeutique. Continued by Thérapeutique
(La Semaine des hôpitaux)
1962-1968 0205463

Semin Adolesc Med
Seminars in adolescent medicine
0748-6480
1985-1987 8508464

Semin Arthritis Rheum
Seminars in arthritis and rheumatism
0049-0172 1532-866X
1971 1306053

Semin Arthroplasty
Seminars in arthroplasty
1045-4527
1990 9100390

Semin Cancer Biol
Seminars in cancer biology
1044-579X 1096-3650
1990 9010218

Semin Cardiothorac Vasc Anesth
Seminars in cardiothoracic and vascular
anesthesia
1089-2532
1997 9807630

Semin Cell Biol
Seminars in cell biology
1043-4682
Merged with: Seminars in developmental
biology, to form: Seminars in cell &
developmental biology.
1990-1995 9007587

Semin Cell Dev Biol
Seminars in cell & developmental biology
1084-9521
Merger of: Seminars in developmental
biology; and: Seminars in cell biology.
1996 9607332

Semin Clin Neuropsychiatry
Seminars in clinical neuropsychiatry
1084-3612 1532-8678
1996-2003 9604647

Semin Cutan Med Surg
Seminars in cutaneous medicine and surgery
1085-5629 1558-0768
Continues: Seminars in dermatology.
1996 9617260

Semin Dent Hyg
Seminars in dental hygiene
1042-718X
1989-1995 9012406

Semin Dermatol
Seminars in dermatology
0278-145X
Continued by: Seminars in cutaneous
medicine and surgery.
1982-1996 8211646

Semin Diagn Pathol
Seminars in diagnostic pathology
0740-2570
1984 8502262

Semin Dial
Seminars in dialysis
0894-0959 1525-139X
1988 8911629

Semin Drug Treat
Seminars in drug treatment
0091-6714
1971-1974 0437157

Semin Ensen Odontopediatr
Seminario De Ensenanza De La
Odontopediatria
0001-1703
19uu 9875634

Semin Fetal Neonatal Med
Seminars in fetal & neonatal medicine
1744-165X
Continues: Seminars in neonatology.
2004 101240003

Semin Gastrointest Dis
Seminars in gastrointestinal disease
1049-5118
1990-2003 9100391

Semin Hematol
Seminars in hematology
0037-1963
1964 0404514

Semin Immunol
Seminars in immunology
1044-5323
1989 9009458

Semin Immunopathol
Seminars in immunopathology
1863-2297 1863-2300
Continues: Springer seminars in
immunopathology.
2007 101308769

Semin Int
Seminar international
1952-19uu 20720040R

Semin Interv Cardiol
Seminars in interventional cardiology: SIIC
1084-2764
1996-2000 9606070

Semin Laparosc Surg
Seminars in laparoscopic surgery
1071-5517
Continued by: Surgical innovation.
1994-2004 9432584

Semin Liver Dis
Seminars in liver disease
0272-8087
1981 8110297

Semin Musculoskelet Radiol
Seminars in musculoskeletal radiology
1089-7860
1997 9717520

Semin Neonatol
Seminars in neonatology: SN
1084-2756 1532-2815
Continued by: Seminars in fetal & neonatal
medicine.
1996-2004 9606001

Semin Nephrol
Seminars in nephrology
0270-9295
1981 8110298

Semin Neurol
Seminars in neurology
0271-8235
1981 8111343

Semin Nucl Med
Seminars in nuclear medicine
0001-2998 1558-4623
1971 1264464

Semin Nurse Manag
Seminars for nurse managers
1066-3851
Continued by: Nurse leader.
1993-2002 9431621

Semin Oncol
Seminars in oncology
0093-7754 1532-8708
1974 0420432

Semin Oncol Nurs
Seminars in oncology nursing
0749-2081
1985 8504688

Semin Ophthalmol
Seminars in ophthalmology
0882-0538 1744-5205
1986 8610759

Semin Orthod
Seminars in orthodontics
1073-8746
1995 9511978

Semin Pediatr Infect Dis
Seminars in pediatric infectious diseases
1045-1870
1990-2006 9008093

Semin Pediatr Neurol
Seminars in pediatric neurology
1071-9091 1558-0776
1994 9441351

Semin Pediatr Surg
Seminars in pediatric surgery
1055-8586
1992 9216162

Semin Perinatol
Seminars in perinatology
0146-0005 1558-075X
1977 7801132

Semin Perioper Nurs
Seminars in perioperative nursing
1056-8670
1992-2001 9206988

Semin Psychiatry
Seminars in psychiatry
0037-1971
1969-197u 0235734

Semin Radiat Oncol
Seminars in radiation oncology
1053-4296   1532-9461
1991   9202882

Semin Rep Merck Sharp Dohme
Seminar report. Merck Sharp & Dohme
Formed by the union of the Merck report and
the Sharp and Dohme seminar.
1956-1961   18650060R

Semin Reprod Endocrinol
Seminars in reproductive endocrinology
0734-8630
Continued by: Seminars in reproductive
medicine.
1983-1999   8308354

Semin Reprod Med
Seminars in reproductive medicine
1526-8004   1526-4564
Continues: Seminars in reproductive
endocrinology.
2000   100909394

Semin Respir Crit Care Med
Seminars in respiratory and critical care
medicine
1069-3424   1098-9048
Continues: Seminars in respiratory medicine.
1994   9431858

Semin Respir Infect
Seminars in respiratory infections
0882-0546
1986-2003   8700961

Semin Roentgenol
Seminars in roentgenology
0037-198X   1558-4658
1966   0053252

Semin Speech Lang
Seminars in speech and language
0734-0478
Continues in part: Seminars--speech.
language, hearing.
1983   8405117

Semin Surg Oncol
Seminars in surgical oncology
8756-0437   1098-2388
Continues: International advances in surgical
oncology. Absorbed by: Journal of surgical
oncology.
1985-2003   8503713

Semin Thorac Cardiovasc Surg
Seminars in thoracic and cardiovascular
surgery
1043-0679   1532-9488
1989   8917640

Semin Thorac Cardiovasc Surg Pediatr Card Surg Annu
Seminars in thoracic and cardiovascular
surgery. Pediatric cardiac surgery annual
1092-9126
1998   9815944

Semin Thromb Hemost
Seminars in thrombosis and hemostasis
0094-6176   1098-9064
Absorbed: Seminars in vascular medicine. 2006
1974   0431155

Semin Ultrasound CT MR
Seminars in ultrasound, CT, and MR
0887-2171   1558-5034
Continues: Seminars in ultrasound.
1984   8504689

Semin Urol
Seminars in urology
0730-9147
Continued by: Seminars in urologic oncology.
1983-1995   8306110

Semin Urol Oncol
Seminars in urologic oncology
1081-0943
Continues: Seminars in urology. Absorbed by:
Urologic oncology.
1995-2002   9514993

Semin Vasc Med
Seminars in vascular medicine
1528-9648   1529-3505
Absorbed by: Seminars in thrombosis and
hematosis.
2001-2005   100940307

Semin Vasc Surg
Seminars in vascular surgery
0895-7967
1988   8809602

Semin Vet Med Surg (Small Anim)
Seminars in veterinary medicine and
surgery (small animal)
0882-0511
Continued by: Clinical techniques in small
animal practice.
1986-1997   8610760

Semina
Semina
0101-3742
1978   9884653

Seminar
Seminar
1939-1956   20720030R

Sens Processes
Sensory processes
0363-3799
1976-1979   7610632

Sentinel Event Alert
Sentinel event alert / Joint Commission on
Accreditation of Healthcare Organizations
1998   101140092

Ser Haematol
Series haematologica
0037-2463
Supersedes Series haematologica.
1968-1975   0135574

Ser Nurs Adm
Series on nursing administration
0895-4364
1988-1998   8805715

Ser Paedopsychiatr
Series paedopsychiatrica
0080-9012
1965-1985   0036662

Ser Rev Med Soc
Ser (revista médico-social)
1942-1956   20720160R

Servir
Servir (Lisbon, Portugal)
0871-2379
1953   8601748

Seton Hall Law Rev
Seton Hall law review
0586-5964
Continues: Seton Hall law journal.
1970   100892382

Settim Med
Settimana medica
0037-2927
Continues Rivista sanitaria siciliana.
1939-1981   0404406

Sewage Ind Waste
Sewage and industrial wastes
0096-364X
Continues Sewage and industrial waste
engineering. Continued by the Journal of the
Water Pollution Control Federation.
1950-1959   20720310R

Sewage Work J
Sewage works journal
0096-9362
Continued by Sewage and industrial wastes.
1928-1949   20720340R

Sex Abuse
Sexual abuse: a journal of research and
treatment
1079-0632   1573-286X
Continues: Annals of sex research.
1995   9506704

Sex Dev
Sexual development: genetics, molecular
biology, evolution, endocrinology,
embryology, and pathology of sex
determination and differentiation
1661-5425   1661-5433
2007   101316472

Sex Health
Sexual health
1448-5028   1449-8987
2004   101242667

Sex Transm Dis
Sexually transmitted diseases
0148-5717   1537-4521
Continues Journal of the American Venereal
Disease Association.
1977   7705941

Sex Transm Infect
Sexually transmitted infections
1368-4973   1472-3263
Continues: Genitourinary medicine.
1998   9805554

Shandong Yi Kan
[Shandong yi kan] [Shantung medical
publication]
1957-19uu   20720470R

Shanghai Kou Qiang Yi Xue
Shanghai kou qiang yi xue = Shanghai
journal of stomatology
1006-7248
1992   101090220

Shendet Pop
Shëndetësia popullore
0559-7714
1964-1982   20730110R

Sheng Li Ke Xue Jin Zhan
Sheng li ke xue jin zhan [Progress in
physiology]
0559-7765
1957   20730140R

Sheng Li Xue Bao
Sheng li xue bao: [Acta physiologica Sinica]
0371-0874
Continues the Chinese journal of physiology,
issued 1927-44?
1953   20730130R

Sheng Wu Gong Cheng Xue Bao
Sheng wu gong cheng xue bao = Chinese
journal of biotechnology
1000-3061
1985   9426463

Sheng Wu Hua Xue Yu Sheng Wu Wu Li Xue Bao (Shanghai)
Sheng wu hua xue yu sheng wu wu li xue bao Acta biochimica et biophysica Sinica
0582-9879
Continued by: Acta biochimica et biophysica Sinica.
1959-2003 20730160R

Sheng Wu Yi Xue Gong Cheng Xue Za Zhi
Sheng wu yi xue gong cheng xue za zhi = Journal of biomedical engineering = Shengwu yixue gongchengxue zazhi
1001-5515
1984 9426398

Shi Yan Sheng Wu Xue Bao
Shi yan sheng wu xue bao
0001-5334
Continues: Zhongguo shi yan sheng wu xue za zhi. Continued by: Fen zi xi bao sheng wu xue bao.
1954-2005 0413570

Shigaku
Shigaku. Odontology; journal of Nippon Dental College
0029-8484
Continues Zasshi of Nippon Koka Gakkai. Continued by: Odontology.
1907-2000 1275704

Shika Igaku
[Shika igaku] [Dental medicine]
0371-0246
1930 20730300R

Shika Kiso Igakkai Zasshi
Shika Kiso Igakkai zasshi = Japanese journal of oral biology
0385-0137
Continued by: Journal of oral biosciences.
1959-2003 7506047

Shika Rikogaku Zasshi
Shika rikōgaku zasshi. Journal of the Japan Society for Dental Apparatus and Materials
0583-0273
Merged with: Nihon Shika Zairyō Kikai Gakkai zasshi, to form: Shika zairyō, kikai.
1960-1982 0136676

Shika Zairyo Kikai
Shika zairyō, kikai = Journal of the Japanese Society for Dental Materials and Devices
0286-5858
Formed by the union of: Shika rikōgaku zasshi; and, Nihon Shika Zairyō Kikai Gakkai zasshi.
1982 8502723

Shikai Tenbo
Shikai tenbo = Dental outlook
0011-8702
Continues Nippon shika kōhō.
1946 20730400R

Shikwa Gakuho
Shika gakuho. Dental science reports
0037-3710
Continues Shika igaku sodan.
1900 0413747

Shimane J Med Sci
Shimane journal of medical science
0386-5959
1977 7910970

Shinkei Kenkyu No Shimpo
Shinkei kenkyū no shimpo. Advances in neurological sciences
0001-8724
Merged with: Nō to shinkei, to form: Brain and nerve.
1956-2006 0067457

Shinrigaku Kenkyu
Shinrigaku kenkyu: The Japanese journal of psychology
0021-5236
1926 0413571

Shinryo
[Shinryō] [Diagnosis and treatment]
Continues Rinshō.
1953-1971 20730560R

Shiyo
Shiyo. The journal of the Tokyo Dental Association
0912-4462
Continues Tokyo-to Shika Ishikai geppo.
1955 7604322

Shock
Shock (Augusta, Ga.)
1073-2322 1540-0514
1994 9421564

Shokuhin Eiseigaku Zasshi
Shokuhin eiseigaku zasshi. Journal of the Food Hygienic Society of Japan
0015-6426 1882-1006
1960 0142214

Shoni Shikagaku Zasshi
Shōni shikagaku zasshi. The Japanese journal of pedodontics
0583-1199
1963 0136612

Shonika
Shonika. Pediatrics of Japan
0037-4121
1960 7511977

Shonika Kiyo
Shonika kiyo. Annales paediatrici Japonici
0003-4495
Supersedes Nyujigaku zasshi.
1955-1990 0413572

Showa Igakkai Zasshi
Shōwa Igakkai zasshi = The Journal of the Showa Medical Association
0037-4342
Continues: Showa igakushi zasshi.
1939 0413750

Showa Shigakkai Zasshi
Shōwa Shigakkai zasshi = The Journal of Showa University Dental Society
0285-922X
1981 8302367

SHSTF
Shstf
1981 9879321

Shujutsu
Shujutsu. Operation
0037-4423
1947 0413751

Sichuan Da Xue Xue Bao Yi Xue Ban
Sichuan da xue xue bao. Yi xue ban = Journal of Sichuan University. Medical science edition
1672-173X
Continues: Hua xi yi ke da xue xue bao.
2003 101162609

Sichuan Yi Xue Yuan Xue Bao
Sichuan yi xue yuan xue bao = Acta Academiae Medicinae Sichuan
0253-4290
Continued by: Hua xi yi ke da xue xue bao.
1971-1985 8212608

Sicil Sanit
Sicilia sanitaria
0371-0394
Absorbed Sicilia medica, 15 luglio 1950.
1948-1967 20740130R

Sicilia Med
Sicilia medica
Absorbed by: Sicilia sanitaria.
1944-1950 20740120R

Sidahora
SIDAhora: un proyecto del Departamento de Publicaciónes del PWA Coalition, NY
1551-9074
1989-2005 9001504

Sight Sav Rev
The Sight-saving review
0037-4822
Continued by The Sightsaving review.
1931-1978 0404407

Sightsav Rev
The Sightsaving review: official publication of the National Society for the Prevention of Blindness
0037-4822
Continues: The Sight-saving review. Continued by: Sightsaving.
1978-1980 8300993

Sightsaving
Sightsaving
0735-5688
Continues: The Sightsaving review.
1982-1986 8300481

Signature
Signature (Ramsey, N.J.)
1091-5222
199u 9609817

Simul Healthc
Simulation in healthcare: journal of the Society for Simulation in Healthcare
1559-2332 1559-713X
2006 101264408

Sinai Hosp J (Balt)
Sinai Hospital journal
0583-337X
1952-1969 0061432

Singapore Dent J
Singapore dental journal
0377-5291
Continues in part Dental journal of Malaysia & Singapore.
1974 7513690

Singapore Med J
Singapore medical journal
0037-5675
Continues: Proceedings of the Alumni Association, Malaya. Malaya (Federation) University, Singapore. Faculty of Medicine. Alumni Association of the King Edward VII College of Medicine, Singapore and the Faculty of Medicine, University of Malaya.
1960 0404516

Sint Trab Cient
Síntesis de trabajos científicos
19uu-19uu 20740470R

Sintesi Medica
Sintesi medica
1950-19uu 20740450R

Sist Nerv
Sistema nervoso
0049-0636
1949-1971 2984851R

Sistole
Sistole
0560-1711
1950-1981 20740560R

Sjuksköterskan
Sjuksköterskan / Svensk sjuksköterskeförening
0280-3526
1983-1990   9423167

Skandinavisk Vet Tidsskr Bakteriol Patol Samt Kjottoch Mjokhygienen
Skandinavisk veterinär-tidsskrift för bakteriologi, patologi, samt kjöttoch mjölkhygienen
Merged with Finsk veterinärtidsskrift. Norsk veterinaertidsskrift and Svensk veterinärtidsskrift to form Nordisk veterinaermedicin.
1911-1948   0026740

Skeletal Radiol
Skeletal radiology
0364-2348   1432-2161
1976   7701953

Skin (Los Angeles)
Skin
0560-2076
1962-1964   20740650R

Skin Pharmacol
Skin pharmacology: the official journal of the Skin Pharmacology Society
1011-0283
Absorbed: Bioengineering and the skin. Continued by: Skin pharmacology and applied skin physiology.
1988-1997   8810069

Skin Pharmacol Appl Skin Physiol
Skin pharmacology and applied skin physiology
1422-2868   1422-2906
Continues: Skin pharmacology. Continued by: Skin pharmacology and physiology.
1998-2003   9807277

Skin Pharmacol Physiol
Skin pharmacology and physiology
1660-5527   1660-5535
Continues: Skin pharmacology and applied skin physiology.
2004   101188418

Skin Res Technol
Skin research and technology: official journal of International Society for Bioengineering and the Skin (ISBS) [and] International Society for Digital Imaging of Skin (ISDIS) [and] International Society for Skin Imaging (ISSI)
0909-752X   1600-0846
1995   9504453

Skin Therapy Lett
Skin therapy letter
1201-5989
1995   9891441

Skinmed
Skinmed
1540-9740
2002   101168327

Sleep
Sleep
0161-8105   1550-9109
1978   7809084

Sleep Breath
Sleep & breathing = Schlaf & Atmung
1520-9512   1522-1709
Continued in part by Atmung & Schlaf with v. 3. 1998.
1996   9804161

Sleep Med
Sleep medicine
1389-9457
2000   100898759

Sleep Med Rev
Sleep medicine reviews
1087-0792
1997   9804678

Sleep Res Online
Sleep research online: SRO
    1096-214X
1998   100901064

Sloan Manage Rev
Sloan management review
0019-848X
Continues IMR. Industrial management review. Continued by: MIT Sloan management review.
1970-2000   7705943

Slov Lek
Slovensky lekár
1939-1951   20740780R

Slown Biogr Pol Med XX Wieku
Słownik biograficzny polskich nauk medycznych XX wieku / Instytut Historii Nauki, Oświaty i Techniki PAN, Pracownia Historii Nauk Medycznych
1991   9440320

Small
Small (Weinheim an der Bergstrasse, Germany)
1613-6810   1613-6829
2005   101235338

SMU Law Rev
SMU law review: a publication of Southern Methodist University School of Law
1066-1271
Continues: Southwestern law journal.
1992   100883492

Soap Sanit Chem
Soap and sanitary chemicals
0376-2610
Continues: Soap. Continued by: Soap & chemical specialties.
1938-1954   20810020R

Soc Appl Bacteriol Symp Ser
Society for Applied Bacteriology symposium series
0300-9610
Continued by: Symposium series (Society for Applied Microbiology).
1971-1997   0330732

Soc Biol
Social biology
0037-766X
Continues the Eugenics quarterly.
1969   0205621

Soc Casework
Social casework
0037-7678
Continues Journal of social casework. Continued by: Families in society.
1950-1989   20810060R

Soc Cogn Affect Neurosci
Social cognitive and affective neuroscience
1749-5016   1749-5024
2006   101288795

Soc Forces
Social forces; a scientific medium of social study and interpretation
0037-7732
Continues: Journal of social forces.
1922   20810070R

Soc Gen Physiol Ser
Society of General Physiologists series
0094-7733
1974-1997   0433431

Soc Hist Med
Social history of medicine: the journal of the Society for the Social History of Medicine / SSHM
0951-631X   1477-4666
Continues: Society for the Social History of Medicine bulletin.
1988   8810360

Soc Ital Dermatol Sifilogr Sezioni Interprov Soc Ital Dermatol Sifilogr
Atti della Società italiana di dermatologia e sifilografia e delle sezioni interprovinciali. Società italiana di dermatologia e sifilografia
1938-1966   20820760R

Soc Med Tidskr
Social-Medicinsk tidskrift
0037-833X
1924   0423432

Soc Neurosci
Social neuroscience
1747-0919   1747-0927
2006   101279009

Soc Nurs Hist Gaz
The Society for Nursing History gazette
0886-9278
1981-1989   8505332

Soc Policy
Social policy
0037-7783
1970   0367361

Soc Probl
Social problems
0037-7791
1953   20810170R

Soc Psychiatry
Social psychiatry. Sozialpsychiatrie. Psychiatrie sociale
0037-7813
Continued by: Social psychiatry and psychiatric epidemiology.
1966-1987   0072265

Soc Psychiatry Psychiatr Epidemiol
Social psychiatry and psychiatric epidemiology
0933-7954   1433-9285
Continues: Social psychiatry.
1988   8804358

Soc Psychol
Social psychology
0147-829X
Continues Sociometry. Continued by Social psychology quarterly.
1978-1978   7806155

Soc Psychol Q
Social psychology quarterly
0190-2725
Continues Social psychology.
1979   7910380

Soc Rehabil Rec
The Social and rehabilitation record
0092-7759
Formed by the union of Human needs and Rehabilitation record. Superseded by Record.
1974-1977   0415065

Soc Reprod Fertil Suppl
Society of Reproduction and Fertility supplement
Continues: Reproduction (Cambridge, England). Supplement.
2006   101295315

Soc Sci Med
Social science & medicine
0037-7856
Split into: Social science & medicine.
Medical psychology & medical sociology,
Social science & medicine. Medical
anthropology, Social science & medicine.
Medical geography, and Social science &
medicine. Medical economics.
1967-1977 **0121744**

Soc Sci Med
Social science & medicine (1982)
0277-9536
Formed by the union of: Social science
& medicine. Part A, Medical sociology;
Social science & medicine. Part B, Medical
anthropology; Social science & medicine.
Part C, Medical economics; Social science
& medicine. Part D, Medical geography;
Social science & medicine. Part E, Medical
psychology; Social science & medicine. Part
F, Medical & social ethics.
1982 **8303205**

Soc Sci Med [A]
Social science & medicine. Part A, Medical
sociology
0271-7123
Continues in part: Social science & medicine.
Medical psychology & medical sociology.
1981-1981 **8106599**

Soc Sci Med [B]
Social science & medicine. Part B, Medical
anthropology
0160-7987
Continues: Social science & medicine.
Medical anthropology.
1979-1981 **8109995**

Soc Sci Med [C]
Social science & medicine. Part C, Medical
economics
0160-7995
1979-1981 **8109996**

Soc Sci Med [D]
Social science & medicine. Part D, Medical
geography
0160-8002
Continues: Social science & medicine.
Medical geography. Merged with: Social
science & medicine. Part A. Medical
sociology, Social science & medicine. Part
B. Medical anthropology, Social science
& medicine. Part C. Medical economics,
Social science & medicine. Part E. Medical
psychology, Social science & medicine. Part
F. Medical & social ethics, to form: Social
science & medicine.
1979-1981 **8109997**

Soc Sci Med [E]
Social science & medicine. Part E, Medical
psychology
0271-5384
Continues in part: Social science & medicine.
Medical Psychology & medical sociology.
1981-1981 **8106600**

Soc Sci Med [F]
Social science & medicine. Part F, Medical
& social ethics
0271-5392
Continues: Ethics in science & medicine.
1981-1981 **8108895**

Soc Sci Med [Med Anthropol]
Social science & medicine. Medical
anthropology
0160-7987
Continues in part: Social science & medicine.
Continued by: Social science & medicine.
Part B, Medical anthropology.
1978-1979 **7905391**

Soc Sci Med [Med Econ]
Social science & medicine. Medical
economics
0160-7995
Continues in part: Social science & medicine.
Continued by: Social science & medicine.
Part C, Medical economics.
1978-1979 **7905392**

Soc Sci Med [Med Geogr]
Social science & medicine. Medical
geography
0160-8002
Continues in part: Social science & medicine.
Continued by: Social science & medicine.
Part D, Medical geography.
1978-1979 **7905393**

Soc Sci Med [Med Psychol Med Sociol]
Social science & medicine. Medical
psychology & medical sociology
0160-7979
Continues in part Social science & medicine.
Split into Social science & medicine. Part
A, medical sociology; and Social science &
medicine. Part E, Medical psychology.
1978-1980 **7905394**

Soc Sci Res
Social science research
0049-089X
1972 **0330501**

Soc Secur Bull
Social security bulletin
0037-7910
Absorbed: Monthly benefit statistics. United
States. Social Security Administration.
Office of Research and Statistics. Continues
a publication with the same title. Calendar
year data for 1939-1948 published in: Social
security yearbook. Annual statistics for 1949-
1954 published in the Sept. issues, 1950-
1955. Issues for 1955-1991 accomapnied
by: Annual statistical supplement; 1992- by:
Annual statistical supplement, … to the
Social security bulletin.
1938 **22030305R**

Soc Secur Bull Annu Stat Suppl
Social security bulletin. Annual statistical
supplement / U.S. Dept. of Health,
Education, and Welfare, Social Security
Administration
0098-6259
Continues: Social security yearbook.
Continued by: Annual statistical supplement,
… to the Social security bulletin.
1955-1991 **8302370**

Soc Serv Rev
The Social service review
0037-7961
1927 **0413573**

Soc Stud Sci
Social studies of science
0306-3127
Continues: Science studies.
1975 **7506743**

Soc Work
Social work
0037-8046
Continues: Social work journal.
1956 **2984852R**

Soc Work Health Care
Social work in health care
0098-1389 1541-034X
1975 **7603729**

Soc Work Public Health
Social work in public health
1937-1918 1937-190X
Continues: Journal of health & social policy.
2007 **101308228**

Soc Work Res
Social work research
1070-5309
Continues in part: Social work research and
abstracts.
1994 **9434315**

Soc Work Res Abstr
Social work research & abstracts
0148-0847
Continues: Abstracts for social workers. Split
into: Social work abstracts; and: Social work
research.
1977-1993 **7802723**

Socialmed Tidskr Skriftser
Socialmedicinsk tidskrift. Skriftserie
1945-1998 **20810160R**

Society
Society
0147-2011
Continues: Trans-action.
1972 **0317062**

Socioecon Issues Health
Socioeconomic issues of health
0198-7399
Continues: Reference data on socioeconomic
issues of health.
1979-1981 **8211649**

Socioecon Plann Sci
Socio-economic planning sciences
0038-0121
1967 **9877811**

Sociol Health Illn
Sociology of health & illness
0141-9889 1467-9566
1979 **8205036**

Sociol Rev
The Sociological review
0038-0261
Supersedes Sociological papers.
1908 **0357344**

Sociol Rev [Monogr]
Sociological review monograph
0081-1769
1958-1992 **0246313**

Sociometry
Sociometry
0038-0431
Continued by Social psychology.
1937-1977 **7806156**

Softw Healthc
Software in healthcare
0742-1621
1983-1987 **8511884**

Sogo Igaku
Sogo igaku. Medicine
Continues Senji igaku.
1944-1964 **0142217**

Sogo Kango
Sogo kango. Comprehensive nursing,
quarterly
0038-0660
1966 **0313161**

Sogo Rinsho
[Sōgō rinshō] Clinic all-round
0371-1900
1952 **20910550R**

Soins
Soins; la revue de référence infirmière
0038-0814
1956 **20910580R**

Soins Cardiol
Soins. Cardiologie
0755-1916
1983-1986   8406863

Soins Chir
Soins. Chirurgie
0038-0814
Continued by: Soins. Chirurgie generale et
specialisée.
1981-1981   8203333

Soins Chir
Soins. Chirurgie (Paris, France: 1982)
0249-6429
Continues: Soins. Chirurgie generale et
specialisée. Absorbed by: Interbloc.
1982-1997   8406864

Soins Chir Gen Spec
Soins. Chirurgie generale et specialisée
0249-6429
Continues: Soins. Chirurgie. Continued by:
Soins. Chirurgie (Paris. France: 1982).
1981-1982   8215995

Soins Form Pedagog Encadr
Soins. Formation, pédagogie, encadrement:
avec la participation du CEEIEC
1163-4723
Continues: Infirmière enseignante. Continued
by: Soins. Cadres.
1992-1999   9310889

Soins Gerontol
Soins. Gérontologie
1268-6034
1996   9616322

Soins Gynecol Obstet Pueric
Soins. Gynécologie, obstétrique, puériculture
0151-6655
Continued by: Soins. Gynécologie.
obstétrique. puériculture. pédiatrie.
1980-1981   8209882

Soins Gynecol Obstet Pueric Pediatr
Soins. Gynécologie, obstétrique,
puériculture, pédiatrie
0766-1193
Continues: Soins. Gynécologie. obstétrique.
puériculture. Continued by: Soins. Pédiatrie.
puériculture.
1981-1994   8213615

Soins Pathol Trop
Soins. Pathologie tropicale
0222-9307
Continues: Soins. Édition africaine.
1978-1986   8215994

Soins Pediatr Pueric
Soins. Pédiatrie, puériculture
1259-4792
Continues: Soins. Gynécologie. obstétrique.
puériculture. pédiatrie.
1995   9604503

Soins Psychiatr
Soins. Psychiatrie
0241-6972
1980   8203334

SOLAIAT
Solaiat; Sociedad Odontologica Latino-
Americana De Implantes Aloplasticos Y
Transplantes
0036-1771
19uu   9875638

Solid State Nucl Magn Reson
Solid state nuclear magnetic resonance
0926-2040
1992   9306181

Somat Cell Mol Genet
Somatic cell and molecular genetics
0740-7750
Continues: Somatic cell genetics.
1984-2002   8403568

Somatic Cell Genet
Somatic cell genetics
0098-0366
Continued by Somatic cell and molecular
genetics.
1975-1983   7506054

Somatosens Mot Res
Somatosensory & motor research
0899-0220   1536-8793
Continues: Somatosensory research.
1988   8904127

Somatosens Res
Somatosensory research
0736-7244
Continued by: Somatosensory & motor
research.
1983-1988   8404780

Sonde
Die Sonde
0584-1143
1959-1970   20910650R

Sonderb Strahlenther Onkol
Sonderbände zur Strahlentherapie und
Onkologie
0931-2447
Continues: Strahlentherapie. Sonderbände.
Supplement to: Strahlentherapie und
Onkologie.
1987-1988   8702243

Sonderb Z Strahlenther Onkol
Sonderband ... der Zeitschrift
Strahlentherapie und Onkologie
Supplement to: Strahlentherapie und
Onkologie. Continues: Sonderbände zur
Strahlentherapie und Onkologie.
1992-1998   9312251

Soproden
Soproden
0213-831X
1985-2000   9108831

Sotilaslaak Aikak
Sotilaslääketieteellinen aikakauslehti
0300-8797
1926-2003   2984855R

Soud Lek
Soudní lékarství / casopis Sekce soudního
lékarstvi Cs. lékarské spolecnosti J. Ev.
Purkyne
0371-1854
1956   9601665

Soundings
Soundings
0038-1861
Continues: Christian scholar.
1968   9878462

South Hosp
Southern hospitals
0038-4178
Continues the Bulletin of the North Carolina
Hospital Association.
1935-1992   0417504

South J Optom
Southern journal of optometry
0038-4275
Absorbed the Journal of the Florida
Optometric Association in Mar. 1959.
Continued by: Southern journal of optometry.
1959-1999   0404521

South Med
Southern medicine
0097-5419
Continues: Southern medical bulletin.
Continued by: New southern medicine.
1972-1998   0316751

South Med J
The Southern medical journal
1959-1964   20920580R

South Med J
Southern medical journal
0038-4348   1541-8243
Absorbed: Mobile medical and surgical
journal. Gulf States journal of medicine and
surgery.
1908   0404522

South Med Surg
Southern medicine and surgery
0099-5754
Continues: Charlotte medical journal.
Absorbed by: Clinical medicine.
·1921-1953   20920620R

South Surg
The Southern surgeon
Continued by the American surgeon.
1932-1950   20930060R

Southeast Asian J Trop Med Public Health
The Southeast Asian journal of tropical
medicine and public health
0125-1562
1970   0266303

Southwest Med
Southwestern medicine
0038-4860
Formed by the union of New Mexico medical
journal. Arizona medical journal. and Bulletin
- El Paso County Medical Society. Continued
by: Arizona medicine.
1917-1972   7511346

Sov Genet
Soviet genetics
0038-5409
Continued by: Genetika. English. Russian
journal of genetics.
1965-1993   0063413

Sov J Dev Biol
The Soviet journal of developmental biology
0049-173X
Translation of Ontogenez. a publication
of the Academy of Sciences of the USSR.
Continued by: Ontogenez. English. Russian
journal of developmental biology.
1970-1991   0315573

Sov J Ecol
The Soviet journal of ecology
0096-7807
Translation of Ekologiia. a publication of
the Academy of Sciences of the USSR.
Continues Ecology. Continued by: Ekologiia.
English. Russian journal of ecology.
1971-1992   0321347

Sov Med
Sovetskaia meditsina
0038-5077
Continued by: Rossiĭskiĭ meditsinskiĭ
zhurnal.
1937-1991   0404525

Sov Varchebnyii Sb
Sovetskiĭ vrachebnyĭ sbornik
1946-19uu   20930170R

Sov Zdravookhr
Sovetskoe zdravookhranenie / Ministerstvo zdravookhraneniiâ SSSR
0038-5239
Continues: Bol'nichnoe delo. Continued by: Problemy sotŝiaĭnoĭ gigieny i istoriiâ meditŝiny.
1942-199u   0404526

Sov Zdravookhr Kirg
Sovetskoe zdravookhranenie Kirgizii
Continued by Zdravookhranenie Kirgizii.
1938-1974   0404527

Sovrem Probl Onkol
Sovremennye problemy onkologii
1uuu-1uuu   59320360R

Sovrem Probl Tuberk
Sovremennye problemy tuberkuleza
1950-19uu   59830570R

Sowjetwiss Naturwiss Beitr
Sowjetwissenschaft; Naturwissenschaftliche Beiträge
1950-1961   20930290R

Soz Praventivmed
Sozial- und Präventivmedizin
0303-8408   1420-911X
Continues: Präventivmedizin. Continued by: International journal of public health.
1974-2006   7502479

Sozialmed Padagog Jugendkd
Sozialmedizinische und pädagogische Jugendkunde
0303-643X
Continues Medizinische und padagogische Jugendkunde.
1971-1982   0436033

Space Life Sci
Space life sciences
0038-6286
Continued by Origins of life.
1968-1973   0422620

Space Med Med Eng (Beijing)
Hang tian yi xue yu yi xue gong cheng = Space medicine & medical engineering
1002-0837
1988   9425305

Span J Psychol
The Spanish journal of psychology
1138-7416
1998   101095192

Spat Vis
Spatial vision
0169-1015
1985   8602662

Spec Care Dentist
Special care in dentistry: official publication of the American Association of Hospital Dentists, the Academy of Dentistry for the Handicapped, and the American Society for Geriatric Dentistry
0275-1879
Formed by the union of: Journal of hospital dental practice; Journal of dentistry for the handicapped; and The Journal of the American Society for Geriatric Dentistry.
1981   8103755

Spec Educ
Special education
0038-6707
Continues Special schools quarterly. Merged with Forward trends to form Special education: forward trends.
1958-1973   0423211

Spec Educ Forward Trends
Special education: forward trends
0305-7526
Formed by the union of Special education and Forward trends. Continued by: British journal of special education.
1974-1984   0423517

Spec Law Dig Health Care (Mon)
Specialty law digest. Health care (Monthly)
0198-8778
Continued by: Specialty law digest. Health care law.
1979-1991   8302514

Spec Law Dig Health Care Law
Specialty law digest. Health care law
1082-5657
Continues: Specialty law digest. Health care (Monthly).
1991   9423043

Spec Libr
Special libraries
0038-6723
Merged with: Specialist (New York, N.Y.), to form: Information outlook.
1910-1996   57630800R

Spec Rep Ser Indian Counc Med Res
Special report series - Indian Council of Medical Research
0073-6325
Continues the Special report of the Indian Research Fund Association.
1951-1970   7506056

Spec Rep Ser Med Res Counc (G B)
Special report series (Medical Research Council (Great Britain))
0072-6575
Continues: Special report series (Great Britain. Medical Research Committee).
1920-1971   18530300R

Spec Top Endocrinol Metab
Special topics in endocrinology and metabolism
0193-0982
1979-1985   8001537

Specif Eng
Specifying engineer
0164-5242
Continues: Actual specifying engineer. Merged with: Consulting-specifying engineer. To form: Consulting engineer.
1975-1986   9877750

Spectrochim Acta A Mol Biomol Spectrosc
Spectrochimica acta. Part A, Molecular and biomolecular spectroscopy
1386-1425
Continues: Spectrochimica acta. Part A, Molecular spectroscopy.
1995   9602533

Spectrum
Spectrum (Lexington, Ky.)
1067-8530
Continues: Journal of state government.
1992   9886962

Speech Pathol Ther
Speech pathology and therapy
0584-8687
Continued by: British journal of disorders of communication.
1958-1965   0123303

Sperimentale
Lo sperimentale
0038-7355
Continues: Gazzetta medica italiana, Toscana. Absorbed: Giornale veneto di scienze mediche. Segno. Imparziale. Medicina contemporanea (Milan, Italy).
1858-1971   0413755

Sphincter
Sphincter
1937-19uu   20940070R

Spinal Cord
Spinal cord: the official journal of the International Medical Society of Paraplegia
1362-4393
Continues: Paraplegia.
1996   9609749

Spine
Spine
0362-2436   1528-1159
1976   7610646

Spine J
The spine journal: official journal of the North American Spine Society
1529-9430   1878-1632
2001   101130732

Spitalul
Spitalul
0038-7673
1881-1973   0072026

Sportarzt Ver Sportmed
Der Sportarzt vereinigt mit Sportmedizin
Continued by Sportarzt und Sportmedizin.
1959-1963   20940110R

Sports Biomech
Sports biomechanics / International Society of Biomechanics in Sports
1476-3141
2002   101151352

Sports Med
Sports medicine (Auckland, N.Z.)
0112-1642
1984   8412297

Sports Med Arthrosc
Sports medicine and arthroscopy review
1062-8592   1538-1951
1993   9315689

Sportverletz Sportschaden
Sportverletzung Sportschaden: Organ der Gesellschaft für Orthopädisch-Traumatologische Sportmedizin
0932-0555
1987   8904133

Spraw Czynnosci Posiedz Lodz Tow Nauk
Sprawozdania z czynności i posiedzeń - Lódzkie Towarzystwo Naukowe
0208-628X
1957-197u   0432606

Springer Semin Immunopathol
Springer seminars in immunopathology
0344-4325   1432-2196
Continued by: Seminars in immunopathology.
1978-2006   7910384

Springer Ser Health Care Soc
Springer series on health care and society
0748-0334
1977-1982   7906144

SPVN
SPVN: journal of the Society for Peripheral Vascular Nursing
Continued by: Journal of vascular nursing.
1983-1990   9004141

Sr Nurse
Senior nurse
0265-9999
Continues: Nursing focus. Continued by: Nursing management (Harrow, London, England: 1994).
1984-1994   8500287

Srp Arh Celok Lek
Srpski arhiv za celokupno lekarstvo
0370-8179
19uu   0027440

SSO Schweiz Monatsschr Zahnheilkd
Schweizerische Monatsschrift für
Zahnheilkunde = Revue mensuelle suisse
d'odonto-stomatologie / SSO
0036-7702
Absorbed: Helvetica odontologica acta.
Continues: Schweizerische Vierteljahrsschrift
für Zahnheilkunde. Continued by:
Schweizerische Monatsschrift für
Zahnmedizin.
1922-1983   20520010R

St Barnabas Hosp Med Bull
St. Barnabas Hospital medical bulletin
0558-1761
1960-1966   0105723

St Bartholomews Hosp J
St. Bartholomew's Hospital journal
0036-2778
1893-1975   20520300R

St Luc Med
Saint-Luc médical. Sint-Lucas tijdschrift
0036-3057
Continued by: Acta medica Catholica.
1932-1987   0200142

St Lukes Hosp Gaz (Guardamangia)
The St. Luke's Hospital gazette
0036-3081
1966-1976   0103531

St Thomas Hosp Gaz
St. Thomas's Hospital gazette
0036-3200
Continued by: S.T.H. gazette.
1891-1969   7500333

St Tomas Nurs J
Santo Tomas nursing journal
0048-9123
Continued by: Nursing journal.
1962-1978   0121503

ST Vincents Hosp Med Bull
St. Vincent's Hospital medical bulletin
0558-2385
Continued by St. Vincent's/Park City
Hospitals medical bulletin.
1958-1970   8007707

St. Lukes Hosp Staff Clin Bull
St. Luke's Hospital staff clinics bulletin
1937-19uu   9429356

Stadtehygiene
Städtehygiene
0038-9005
Continued by Umwelthygiene.
1950-1973   7504521

Staff Bull Easton Hosp (Easton, Pa.)
Staff bulletin. Easton, Pa. Hospital
1948-19uu   16650050R

Stain Technol
Stain technology
0038-9153
Continued by: Biotechnic & histochemistry.
1926-1990   0404535

Stand News
Standardization news: SN
1094-4656
Continues: ASTM standardization news.
American Society for Testing and Materials.
1985   101221787

Stanford Law Rev
Stanford law review
0038-9765
Continues: Stanford intramural law review.
1948   7703790

Stanford Med Bull
Stanford medical bulletin
0376-2602
Supersedes Stanford medical alumni bulletin.
1942-1962   21010060R

Stapp Car Crash J
Stapp car crash journal
1532-8546
Continues: Proceedings. Stapp Car Crash
Conference.
2000   101133951

Star
The Star
0049-2116
1941   52430320R

Stat
Stat
0038-9986
Continues: Bulletin. Wisconsin State Nurses'
Association.
19uu   9875635

Stat Appl Genet Mol Biol
Statistical applications in genetics and
molecular biology
1544-6115
2002   101176023

Stat Bull Czechoslov
Statistical bulletin of Czechoslovakia.
Czechoslovak Republic. Státni Urad
Statistický
Absorbed by: Statistický zpravodaj.
Czechoslovak Republic. Státni Urad
Statistický.
1946-1948   23120130R

Stat Bull Metrop Insur Co
Statistical bulletin (Metropolitan Life
Insurance Company: 1984)
0741-9767
Continues: Statistical bulletin (Metropolitan
Life Foundation).
1984-2000   8410965

Stat Bull Metrop Life Found
Statistical bulletin (Metropolitan Life
Foundation)
0736-4822
Continues: Statistical bulletin (Metropolitan
Life Insurance Company). Continued by:
Statistical bulletin (Metropolitan Life
Insurance Company: 1984).
1982-1983   8301711

Stat Bull Metropol Life Insur Co
Statistical bulletin (Metropolitan Life
Insurance Company)
0026-1513
Continued by: Statistical bulletin
(metropolitan Life Foundation)
1920-1981   7503677

Stat Med
Statistics in medicine
0277-6715
1982   8215016

Stat Methods Med Res
Statistical methods in medical research
0962-2802   1477-0334
1992   9212457

Stat Nachr Osterr Stat Zent Amt
Statistische Nachrichten. Österreichisches
Statistisches Zentralamt
0029-9960
Continues Austria. Bundesamt für Statistik.
Statistische Nachrichten.
1946   01550150R

Stat Navy Med
Statistics of Navy medicine
0146-3020
1945-1985   22420370R

Stat Notes Health Plann
Statistical notes for health planners
0147-278X
1976-1981   8007965

State Coverage Initiat Issue Brief
State Coverage Initiatives issue brief: a
national initiative of the Robert Wood
Johnson Foundation
2000   101140003

State Gov
State government (Denver, Colo.)
0039-0097
Continues: Legislator (Denver. Colo.).
Continued in 1986 by: Journal of state
government.
1930-1986   9877795

State Health Care Am
The state of health care in America
1551-8299
199u-2002   9713417

State Legis
State legislatures
0147-6041
Continues: State legislatures today.
1975   100890177

State Nurs Legis Q
State nursing legislation quarterly
0891-8341
Continues: State legislative report (Kansas
City. Mo.).
1985-1993   8609408

States Health
States of health
1524-4830
199u   100966540

Stem Cell Rev
Stem cell reviews
1550-8943   1558-6804
2005   101255952

Stem Cells
Stem cells
0250-6793
Continued by: Natural immunity and cell
growth regulation.
1981-1982   8110002

Stem Cells
Stem cells (Dayton, Ohio)
1066-5099   1549-4918
Continues: International journal of cell
cloning.
1993   9304532

Stem Cells Dev
Stem cells and development
1547-3287   1557-8534
Continues: Journal of hematotherapy & stem
cell research.
2004   101197107

STEP Perspect
STEP perspective
19uu   9888939

Stereotact Funct Neurosurg
Stereotactic and functional neurosurgery
1011-6125   1423-0372
Continues: Applied neurophysiology.
1989   8902881

Sterile World
Sterile world
Continued by: Journal of sterile services
management.
19uu-1983   9879304

Steroidologia
Steroidologia
0049-2221
Supersedes the European journal of steroids.
Continued by Steroids and lipids research.
1970-1971   0350154

Steroids
Steroids
0039-128X
1963   0404536

Steroids Lipids Res
Steroids and lipids research
0300-0621
Continues Steroidologia.
1972-1974   0350520

Stethosc
De Stethoscoop
1944-19uu   21010420R

STNS J Trauma Nurs
STN's journal of trauma nursing: the official
journal of the Society of Trauma Nurses
1076-4747
Continued by: Journal of trauma nursing.
1994-1994   9439500

Stoma (Heidelb)
Stoma
0039-1697
Absorbed by: ZWR. Jan. 1972
1948-1971   8006577

Stoma (Lisb)
Stoma (Lisbon, Portugal)
0870-4287
1986   8907513

Stoma (Thessaloniki)
Stoma (Thessalonikē, Greece)
1105-5928
1969   9211536

Stomatol Chron (Athenai)
Stomatologika chronika. Acta stomatologica
Hellenica
Continued by Hellenika stomatologika
chronika.
1957-1969   0322351

Stomatol DDR
Stomatologie der DDR
0302-4725
Continues Deutsche Stomatologie. Continued
by: Deutsche Stomatologie (Berlin, Germany:
1990).
1974-1990   0421506

Stomatol Glas Srb
Stomatološki glasnik Srbije
0039-1743
1953   21010730R

Stomatol Mediterr
Stomatologia mediterranea: SM
1120-9402
1981-19uu   8508471

Stomatol Vestn
Stomatologický věstník
1930-1951   21010710R

Stomatol Vjesn
Stomatološki vjesnik. Stomatological review
0350-5499
1967-1986   7904438

Stomatol Zpr
Stomatologické zprávy / SPOFA
0324-5004
1954   9875636

Stomatologia
Stomatologia
1946-19uu   21010680R

Stomatologia (Athenai)
Stomatologia
0039-1700
1938   0404540

Stomatologia (Bucur)
Stomatologia
0039-1719
Continued by Revista de chirurgie,
oncologie, radiologie, o. r. l., oftalmologie,
stomatologie. Seria: Stomatologie.
1954-1974   7513067

Stomatologica (Genova)
Stomatologica
0039-1727
Continued by: Parodontologia e stomatologia.
1957-1968   21010700R

Stomatologie
Stomatologie (Bucharest, Romania)
1220-1898
Continues: Revista de chirurgie, oncologie,
radiologie, o. r. l., oftalmologie, stomatologie.
Seria: Stomatologie. Continued by: Revista
română de stomatologie (Bucharest,
Romania: 2004).
1990-2003   9111525

Stomatologiia (Mosk)
Stomatologiia
0039-1735
Continues Sovetskaia stomatologiia.
1937   0412072

Stomatologiia (Sofiia)
Stomatologiia. Stomatology
0491-0982
Supersedes: Zúbolekarski pregled.
1952-1997   0404542

Stomatologija
Stomatologija / issued by public institution
"Odontologijos studija" ... [et al.]
1392-8589
Continues: Stomatologijos praktika.
1999   101248498

Strabismus
Strabismus
0927-3972   1744-5132
1993   9310896

Strada Maestra
Strada maestra; quaderni della Biblioteca
comunale "G. C. Croce" di San Giovanni in
Persiceto
1968   1272726

Strahlenschutz Forsch Prax
Strahlenschutz in Forschung und Praxis
0081-5888
1961   0404543

Strahlenther Onkol
Strahlentherapie und Onkologie: Organ der
Deutschen Röntgengesellschaft ... [et al]
0179-7158   1439-099X
Continues: Strahlentherapie.
1986   8603469

Strahlentherapie
Strahlentherapie
0039-2073
Continued by: Strahlentherapie und
Onkologie.
1912-1985   1260024

Strahlentherapie [Sonderb]
Strahlentherapie. Sonderbände
0371-3822
Continued by: Sonderbände zur
Strahlentherapie und Onkologie.
1912-1986   0404544

Strasb Med
Strasbourg médical
0491-1377
Continues Gazette médicale de Strasbourg.
1923-1969   21020030R

Strateg Healthc Excell
Strategies for healthcare excellence:
organizational productivity, quality and
effectiveness
1058-7829
Continues: Healthcare productivity report.
1991-2000   9216695

Stress
Stress (Amsterdam, Netherlands)
1025-3890   1607-8888
1996   9617529

Stroke
Stroke; a journal of cerebral circulation
0039-2499   1524-4628
1970   0235266

Structure
Structure (London, England: 1993)
0969-2126
Absorbed: Folding & design. 1999
1993   101087697

Stud Anc Med
Studies in ancient medicine
0925-1421
1991   9112135

Stud Cercet Endocrinol
Studii şi cercetari de endocrinologie
0039-3924
1950-1973   7908548

Stud Cercet Fiziol
Studii şi cercetări de fiziologie
0039-3959
Supersedes in part Studii şi cercetări de
fiziologie şi neurologie.
1956   0417345

Stud Cercet Inframicrobiol
Studii şi cercetări de inframicrobiologie
0039-3975
Continued by Studii şi cercetări de
virusologie.
1950-1971   0341024

Stud Cercet Med Interna
Studii şi cercetări de medicină internă
0039-4025
Supersedes Probleme de terapeutică.
1960-1973   0417346

Stud Cercet Neurol
Studii si cercetări de neurologie
0515-1724
Supersedes in part Studii si cercetări de
fiziologie si neurologie. Absorbed by: Revue
roumaine de neurologie.
1956-1970   2984860R

Stud Cercet Virusol
Studii și cercetări de virusologie
0303-531X
Continues Studii și cercetări de
inframicrobiologie. Absorbed by: Revue
roumaine de virologie.
1972-1973 0425614

Stud Fam Plann
Studies in family planning
0039-3665
1963 7810364

Stud Gen (Berl)
Studium generale; Zeitschrift für die Einheit
der Wissenschaften im Zusammenhang ihrer
Begriffsbildungen und Forschungsmethoden
0039-4149
1947-1971 0424250

Stud Gesch Krankenhauswesens
Studien zur Geschichte des
Krankenhauswesens
0342-4952
1976 7805512

Stud Gesch Univ Wien
Studien zur Geschichte der Universität Wien
0506-9300
1965-19uu 0102652

Stud Hastings Cent
Studies - Hastings Center
0093-3252
Absorbed by: Hastings Center report.
1973-1974 0425113

Stud Health Technol Inform
Studies in health technology and informatics
0926-9630
1991 9214582

Stud Hist Philos Biol Biomed Sci
Studies in history and philosophy of
biological and biomedical sciences
1369-8486
1998 9810965

Stud Hist Philos Sci
Studies in history and philosophy of science
0039-3681
Issues for Dec. 1993, June 1994, and Dec.
1994 also have section title: Studies in history
and philosophy of modern physics, which
does not have its own volume numbering.
Beginning with Apr. 1995 this became a
separate journal. Issued in conjunction with
companion journal: Studies in history and
philosophy of biological and biomedical
sciences. Mar. 1998-
1970 1250602

Stud Hum Ecol
Studies in human ecology
0324-8666
1973-1994 7514136

Stud Med
Student medicine
Continued by the Journal of the American
College Health Association.
1952-1962 21020150R

Stud Medizingesch Neunzehnten Jahrhunderts
Studien zur Medizingeschichte des
neunzehnten Jahrhunderts
0081-7333
1967-1978 0102562

Stud Neuroanat
Studies in neuro-anatomy
0081-8305
1964-1971 2984859R

Stud Tokugawa Inst
Studies from the Tokugawa Institute.
Tokugawa Seibutsugaku Kenkyūsho, Tokyo
1924 21220180R

Studenterraad Med
Stud. med
Supersedes Medicineren.
1943-1972 21020120R

Studi Med Chir Sport
Studi di medicina e chirurgia dello sport
0371-3687
Continued by: Medicina sportiva.
1947-1954 21020190R

Studi Sassar
Studi sassaresi
0371-3172
Supersedes Studi sassaresi, sez. II, issued
1901-10.
1922-1983 1246300

Subacute Care
Subacute care
199u-1996 9890192

Subcell Biochem
Sub-cellular biochemistry
0306-0225
Continued in part by: Blood cell
biochemistry.
1971 0316571

Subsid Med
Subsidia medica
0039-4378
1949-1976 2984812R

Subst Abus
Substance abuse: official publication of
the Association for Medical Education and
Research in Substance Abuse
0889-7077 1547-0164
1980 8808537

Subst Abuse Treat Prev Policy
Substance abuse treatment, prevention, and
policy
1747-597X
2006 101258060

Subst Alcohol Actions Misuse
Substance and alcohol actions/misuse
0191-8877
Continued by: Alcohol and drug research.
1980-1985 8010224

Subst Use Misuse
Substance use & misuse
1082-6084 1532-2491
Continues: International journal of the
addictions.
1996 9602153

Sud Med Chir
Le Sud médical et chirurgical
0301-7923
Absorbed by: Corse méditerranée médicale in
Nov. 1970?.
1868-1970 0410476

Sud Med Ekspert
Sudebno-meditsinskaia ekspertiza
0039-4521
1958 0404546

Suddeutsch Apoth Ztg
Süddeutsche Apotheker-Zeitung
Merged with Apotheker Zeitung to form
Deutsche Apotheker-Zeitung. vereinigt mit
Süddeutsche Apotheker-Zeitung.
1861-1950 21030070R

Sudest Med
Sud-est médical
1949-19uu 21030060R

Sudhoffs Arch
Sudhoffs Archiv
0039-4564
Continues: Sudhoffs Archiv für Geschichte
der Medizin und der Naturwissenschaften.
1966 0240376

Sudhoffs Arch Gesch Med Naturwiss
Sudhoffs Archiv für Geschichte der Medizin
und der Naturwissenschaften
0365-2610
Continues: Archiv für Geschichte der
Medizin. Continued by: Sudhoffs Archiv.
1934-1965 0066175

Sudhoffs Arch Z Wissenschaftsgesch Beih
Sudhoffs Archiv; Zeitschrift für
Wissenschaftsgeschichte. Beihefte
0341-0773
Continues the Beihefte of Sudhoffs Archiv;
Vierteljahrsschrift für Geschichte der Medizin
und der Naturwissenschaften. der Pharmazie
und der Mathematik.
1970 1256455

Sudwestdtsch Arztebl
Südwestdeutsches Ärzteblatt
0371-4675
Continues: Württembergisches Ärzteblatt.
Continued by: Ärzteblatt für Baden-
Württemberg.
1947-1956 21030110R

Suffield Tech Note Can Suffield Exp Stn Ralston Alta
Suffield technical note. Canada. Suffield
Experimental Station, Ralston, Alta
1900-uuuu 22940020R

Suffield Tech Pap Can Suffield Exp Stn Ralston Alta
Suffield technical paper. Canada. Suffield
Experimental Station, Ralston, Alta
1950-uuuu 22940010R

Sugestiones
Sugestiones
1935-1962 21030140R

Suicide
Suicide
0360-1390
Continues Life-threatening behavior.
Continued by Suicide & life-threatening
behavior.
1975-1975 7605741

Suicide Life Threat Behav
Suicide & life-threatening behavior
0363-0234
Continues Suicide.
1976 7608054

Summ Shute Inst
The Summary
1949-1977 21030210R

Suom Apteenkkaril
Suomen apteekkarilehti. Finlands
apotekartidning
0355-533X
Continues: Suomen apteekkariyhdistyksen
aikakauslehti. Continued by: Apteekkari.
1956-1990 21030330R

Suom Hammaslaak Toim
Suomen Hammaslaakariseuran Toimituksia
0039-551X
Continued by: Proceedings Of The Finnish
Dental Society.
1904-1971 9427301

Suom Hammaslaakarilehti
Suomen hammaslääkärilehti = Finlands
tandläkartidning / [HT]
0355-4090
1954 8704977

Suom Laakaril
Suomen lääkärilehti. Finlands läkartidning
0039-5560
Supersedes Aikakauslehti of Suomen lääkäriliitto.
1946   0404547

Superv Manage
Supervisory management
0039-5919
Continued by: Management solutions.
1955-1986   9877490

Superv Nurse
Supervisor nurse
0039-5870
Continued by Nursing management.
1970-1981   0270745

Supl Pract Med
Practica médica
1943-1945   0023124

Suppl Clin Neurophysiol
Supplements to Clinical neurophysiology
1567-424X
Continues: Electroencephalography and clinical neurophysiology. Supplement.
2000   100967410

Suppl Eur J Neurosci
Supplement ... to the European journal of neuroscience
1359-5962
1988-2000   9214590

Suppl Int J Gynecol Obstet
Supplement to International journal of gynecology and obstetrics
0924-8447
1989-1989   8917888

Suppl J Med Oncol Tumor Pharmacother
Supplement ... to the journal Medical oncology and tumor pharmacotherapy
1988-1988   8906287

Suppl Public Health Rep
Supplement ... to the Public health reports
1050-0952
1913-1950   21420630R

Suppl Thromb Haemost
Supplementum ... ad Thrombosis and haemostasis
0344-7618
Continues: Supplementum ... ad Thrombosis et diathesis haemorrhagica.
1978-1978   8106612

Suppl Tumori
I supplementi di Tumori: official journal of Società italiana di cancerologia ... [et al.]
2002   101153052

Support Cancer Ther
Supportive cancer therapy
1543-2912   1943-3395
2003   101223683

Support Care Cancer
Supportive care in cancer: official journal of the Multinational Association of Supportive Care in Cancer
0941-4355   1433-7339
1993   9302957

Surg Annu
Surgery annual
0081-9638
1969-1995   0221302

Surg Bus
Surgical business
0039-6095
Continued by Health industry today.
1938-1982   0404550

Surg Circ Lett U S Army Far East Command Med Sect
The Surgeon's circular letter. United States. Army. Far East Command. Medical Section
1945-1952   22210360R

Surg Clin North Am
The Surgical clinics of North America
0039-6109
Continues: Surgical clinics of Chicago.
1921   0074243

Surg Endosc
Surgical endoscopy
0930-2794   1432-2218
1987   8806653

Surg Equip
Surgical equipment
1934-19uu   21030430R

Surg Forum
Surgical forum
0071-8041
Absorbed by: Journal of the American College of Surgeons. 2002
1950-2001   0337723

Surg Gastroenterol
Surgical gastroenterology
0730-2681
1982-1984   8301001

Surg Gynecol Obstet
Surgery, gynecology & obstetrics
0039-6087
Continued by: Journal of the American College of Surgeons.
1905-1993   0101370

Surg Infect (Larchmt)
Surgical infections
1096-2964
2000   9815642

Surg Innov
Surgical innovation
1553-3506   1553-3514
Continues: Seminars in laparoscopic surgery.
2004   101233809

Surg Laparosc Endosc
Surgical laparoscopy & endoscopy
1051-7200
Continued by: Surgical laparoscopy, endoscopy & percutaneous techniques.
1991-1999   9107230

Surg Laparosc Endosc Percutan Tech
Surgical laparoscopy, endoscopy & percutaneous techniques
1530-4515   1534-4908
Continues: Surgical laparoscopy & endoscopy.
1999   100888751

Surg Neurol
Surgical neurology
0090-3019
1973   0367070

Surg Obes Relat Dis
Surgery for obesity and related diseases: official journal of the American Society for Bariatric Surgery
1550-7289
2005   101233161

Surg Oncol
Surgical oncology
0960-7404
1992   9208188

Surg Oncol Clin N Am
Surgical oncology clinics of North America
1055-3207
1992   9211789

Surg Radiol Anat
Surgical and radiologic anatomy: SRA
0930-1038   1279-8517
Continues: Anatomia clinica.
1986   8608029

Surg Staff Semin U S Veterans Adm Hosp Minneap
Surgical staff seminars. United States. Veterans Administration. Hospital, Minneapolis
1946-1953   21420750R

Surg Technol
The Surgical technologist
0164-4238
Continues OR tech.
1979   7907517

Surg Technol Int
Surgical technology international
1090-3941
1991   9604509

Surg Today
Surgery today
0941-1291
Continues: Japanese journal of surgery.
1992   9204360

Surgeon
The surgeon: journal of the Royal Colleges of Surgeons of Edinburgh and Ireland
1479-666X
Continues: Journal of the Royal College of Surgeons of Edinburgh.
2003   101168329

Surgery
Surgery
0039-6060   1532-7361
1937   0417347

Surgo Glasg Univ Med J
Surgo; Glasgow University medical journal
0039-6125
1934   21030460R

Surv Biol Prog
Survey of biological progress
1949-1962   21030480R

Surv Immunol Res
Survey of immunologic research
0252-9564
Continued by: Immunologic research.
1982-1986   8215669

Surv Ophthalmol
Survey of ophthalmology
0039-6257
1956   0404551

Surv Synth Pathol Res
Survey and synthesis of pathology research
0253-438X
Continued by: Pathology and immunopathology research.
1983-1985   8303576

Surv World Obstet Gynecol (Jpn)
[Sekai sanfujinka sōran] [Survey of world obstetrics and gynecology]
Supersedes Sanka fujinka chūō zasshi.
1953-1968   60020400R

Surveil Effic
Surveillance efficace
0834-4760
Continued by: Bulletin du gestionnaire avisé.
19uu-1989   101092586

Surviv News (Atlanta Ga)
Survival news (Atlanta, Ga.)
1551-8876   1551-8914
19uu   100893938

Suvr Med (Sofiia)
Süvremenna meditŝina
0562-7192
1950   2984813R

Sveikatos Apsauga
Sveikatos apsauga
0491-6514
Continued by: Sveikata.
1956-1990   21040010R

Sven Farm Tidskr
Svensk farmaceutisk tidskrift
0039-6524
1897-1996   0413575

Sven Lakartidn
Svenska läkartidningen
Continues Allmänna svenska läkartidningen.
Continued by Läkartidningen.
1920-1964   0030130

Sven Med Tidskr
Svensk medicinhistorisk tidskrift
1402-9871
Merger of: Nordisk medicinhistorisk
årsbok, and: Sydsvenska medicinhistoriska
sällskapets årsskrift.
1997   9812689

Sven Tandlak Tidskr
Svensk tandläkare tidskrift. Swedish dental
journal
0039-6745
Supersedes Nordisk tandläkare-tidskrift.
Merged with Odontologisk revy to form
Swedish dental journal.
1908-1976   7708466

Svensk Sjukkasse Tidn
Svensk sjukkasse-tidning
Continued by Tidskrift för allmän försäkring.
1907-1962   21040040R

Sver Tandlakarforb Tidn
Tidning. Sveriges Tandläkarförbund
1909-1976   21040330R

Swed Dent J
Swedish dental journal
0347-9994
Formed by the union of Svensk tandläkare
tidskrift. Swedish dental journal and
Odontologisk revy.
1977   7706129

Swed Dent J Suppl
Swedish dental journal. Supplement
0348-6672
Formed by the union of: Svensk tandläkare-
tidskrift. Supplementum, and: Odontologisk
revy. Supplementum.
1977   7905899

Swiss Dent
Swiss dent
0251-1657
1980   9875536

Swiss Med Wkly
Swiss medical weekly: official journal of
the Swiss Society of Infectious Diseases, the
Swiss Society of Internal Medicine, the Swiss
Society of Pneumology
1424-7860   1424-3997
Absorbed: Schweizerische medizinische
Wochenschrift. Supplementum. Continues:
Schweizerische medizinische Wochenschrift.
2001   100970884

Swiss Surg
Swiss surgery = Schweizer Chirurgie =
Chirurgie suisse = Chirurgia svizzera
1023-9332
Merger of: Zeitschrift für Unfallchirurgie und
Versicherungsmedizin; Helvetica chirurgica
acta; and: Helvetica chirurgica acta.
Supplementum. Absorbed by: British journal
of surgery.
1995-2003   9514313

Swiss Surg Suppl
Swiss surgery. Supplement
1995   9514311

Sydn Univ Med J
Sydney University medical journal
0085-7041
Continues the University of Sydney medical
journal.
1947-1974   21040400R

Sygeplejersken
Sygeplejersken
0106-8350
Continues Tidsskrift for sygeplejersker.
1972   0421366

Sykepl Fag
Sykepleien. Fag
0804-1342
Continues: Fag tidskriftet sykepleien.
Merged with: Journalen sykepleien, to
become: Tidsskriftet sykepleien.
1992-1995   9313367

Sykepleien
Sykepleien
0039-7628
Split into: Fag tidskriftet sykepleien, and:
Journalen sykepleien.
1912-1989   21040500R

Symp Fundam Cancer Res
Symposium on Fundamental Cancer
Research
0190-1214
1947-1986   100961284

Symp Oral Sens Percept
Symposium on Oral Sensation and
Perception
1964-1972   100961341

Symp Pharmacol Ther Toxicol Group
Symposium Of The Pharmacology,
Therapeutics And Toxicology Group,
International Association For Dental
Research
0163-1551
19uu   9870010

Symp Ser Soc Appl Microbiol
Symposium series (Society for Applied
Microbiology)
1467-4734
Continues: Society for Applied Bacteriology
symposium series.
1998-2002   100892834

Symp Soc Dev Biol
The symposium / The Society for
Developmental Biology. Society for
Developmental Biology. Symposium
0583-9009
Continues: Symposium. Society for the Study
of Development and Growth. Symposium.
Continued by: Symposium of the Society
for Developmental Biology. Society for
Developmental Biology. Symposium.
1965-1972   100963225

Symp Soc Exp Biol
Symposia of the Society for Experimental
Biology
0081-1386
Continued by: SEB experimental biology
series.
1947-2004   0404517

Symp Swed Nutr Found
Symposia of the Swedish Nutrition
Foundation
0082-0415
1963-1986   7801135

Synapse
Synapse (New York, N.Y.)
0887-4476   1098-2396
1987   8806914

Syst Appl Microbiol
Systematic and applied microbiology
0723-2020
Continues: Zentralblatt für Bakteriologie.
Mikrobiologie und Hygiene. 1. Abt.
Originale. C. Allgemeine, angewandte, und
ökologische Mikrobiologie.
1983   8306133

Syst Biol
Systematic biology
1063-5157   1076-836X
Continues: Systematic zoology.
1992   9302532

Syst Biol (Stevenage)
Systems biology
1741-2471   1741-248X
Continued by: IET systems biology.
2004-2006   101232067

Syst Biol Reprod Med
Systems biology in reproductive medicine
1939-6368   1939-6376
Continues: Archives of andrology.
2008   101464963

Syst Parasitol
Systematic parasitology
0165-5752
1979   8111384

Syst Zool
Systematic zoology
0039-7989
Continued by: Systematic biology.
1952-1991   2984815R

Szczecin Tow Nauk Wydz Nauk Lek
Szczecińskie Towarzystwo Naukowe,
Wydział Nauk Lekarskich
0082-125X
1958-1976   7809101

Szemeszet
Szemészet
0039-8101
1867   0404552

T

Tabulae Biol
Tabulae biologicae
1925-1963   05110020R

Taehan Chikkwa Uisa Hyophoe Chi
Taehan Ch'ikkwa Uisa Hyŏphoe chi
0376-4672
1959-1991   7604341

Taehan Kan Hakhoe Chi
Taehan Kan Hakhoe chi = The Korean
journal of hepatology
1226-0479
Continued by: Korean journal of hepatology.
1995-2003   9607534

Taehan Kanho
Taehan kanho. The Korean nurse
0047-3618
1961   1264143

Taehan Kanho Hakhoe Chi
Taehan Kanho Hakhoe chi
1598-2874
    Continues: Kanho Hakhoe chi. Continued by:
    Journal of Korean Academy of Nursing.
2003-2008   101191388

Taehan Naekwa Hakhoe Chapchi
Taehan Naekwa Hakhoe chapchi = The
Korean journal of internal medicine
0494-4712
    Continued by: Taehan Naekwa Hakhoe chi.
1960-1993   21110130R

Taehan Oekwa Hakhoe Chapchi
[Chapchi] Journal. Taehan Oekwa Hakhoe
1226-0053
1959   21110140R

Taehan Sanbuinkwa Hakhoe Chapchi
Taehan Sanbuinkwa Hakhoe chapchi =
Korean journal of obstetrics and gynecology
0494-4755
1958   21110170R

Tag Ber Osterr Arztetag
Tagungsbericht. Österreichische
Ärztetagung
1947-19uu   19320490R

Tairyoku Eiyo Menekigaku Zasshi
Tairyoku, eiyō men'ekigaku zasshi =
Journal of physical fitness, nutrition and
immunology
1341-0865
    Continues: Tairyoku. Eiyō Men'ekigaku
    Kenkyūkai zasshi.
199u   9715196

Taiwan J Obstet Gynecol
Taiwanese journal of obstetrics &
gynecology
1028-4559   1875-6263
1985   101213819

Taiwan Yi Xue Hui Za Zhi
Taiwan yi xue hui za zhi. Journal of the
Formosan Medical Association
0371-7682
    Continues the Zasshi of Taiwan Igakkai.
    Continued by: Journal of the Formosan
    Medical Association.
1946-1990   0413761

Takamine Kenkyusho Nenpo
[Nenpō] The Annual report of Takamine
Laboratory. Takamine Kenkyūsho
    Continued by Sankyo Kenkyusho nenpo.
1949-1962   20540700R

Talanta
Talanta
0039-9140   1873-3573
1958   2984816R

Tandlaegebladet
Tandlaegebladet
0039-9353
1897   0404553

Tandlaegernes Tidsskr
Tandlaegernes nye tidsskrift
0901-9898
    Continues: DB-DBat.
1986   9005525

Tandlakartidningen
Tandläkartidningen
0039-6982
    Continues Sveriges Tandläkarförbunds
    tidning.
196u   0432622

Tandteknikern
Tandteknikern
0039-9361
1932   1276570

Tani Girisim Radyol
Tanısal ve girişimsel radyoloji: Tıbbi
Görüntüleme ve Girişimsel Radyoloji
Derneği yayın organı
1300-4360
    Continued by: Diagnostic and interventional
    radiology.
1994-2004   9710449

Tannlaeknabladid
Tannlaeknabladid: blad tannlaeknafélags
Íslands = Icelandic dental journal
1018-7138
19uu   9100592

Tanpakushitsu Kakusan Koso
Tanpakushitsu kakusan koso. Protein,
nucleic acid, enzyme
0039-9450
1956   0413762

Tanzan Health Res Bull
Tanzania health research bulletin
0856-6496
    Continued by: Tanzania journal of health
    research.
199u-2007   101262014

Tanzan J Health Res
Tanzania journal of health research
1821-6404
    Continues: Tanzania health research bulletin.
2008   101479163

Tar Heel Nurse
Tar heel nurse
0039-9620
    Continues North Carolina State Nurses'
    Association. New letter.
1941   21110560R

Targeted Diagn Ther
Targeted diagnosis and therapy
1046-1906
1988-1992   8913519

Teach Learn Med
Teaching and learning in medicine
1040-1334   1532-8015
1989   8910884

TEC Bull (Online)
TEC bulletin (Online)
                                       1543-1622
    Continues: TEC bulletin.
uuuu   101145436

Tech Belge Prothese Dent
Le Technicien belge en prothèse dentaire
0040-1021
1954-1968   21120440R

Tech Bull Dep Army
Department of the Army technical bulletin.
TB MED
    Continues: War Department technical
    bulletin. TB MED.
1947-uuuu   9427179

Tech Bull Regist Med Technol
Technical bulletin of the Registry of Medical
Technologists
0097-0654
    Merged with the Bulletin of pathology to
    form Laboratory medicine.
1949-1969   7501250

Tech Bull United States Veterans Admin
Technical bulletin. United States. Veterans
Administration
1946-uuuu   22110080R

Tech Coloproctol
Techniques in coloproctology
1123-6337   1128-045X
199u   9613614

Tech Doc Rep Arct Aeromed Lab US
Technical documentary report; AAL-TDR.
Arctic Aeromedical Laboratory (U.S.)
    Continues the Technical report of the Arctic
    Aeromedical Laboratory.
1965   0106600

Tech Doc Rep ARL TDR
Technical documentary report, ARL-TDR.
United States. Aeromedical Research
Laboratory, Holloman Air Force Base, N. M
1962-1970   22330910R

Tech Doc Rep SAMTDR USAF Sch Aerosp Med
Technical documentary report. SAM-TDR.
USAF School of Aerospace Medicine
    Continues: Project report. USAF School of
    Aviation Medicine. Continued by: [Technical
    Report] SAM-TR. USAF School of
    Aerospace Medicine.
1961-1964   22410750R

Tech Doc Rep U S Air Force Syst Command Electron Syst Div
Technical documentary report. United
States. Air Force. Systems Command.
Electronic Systems Division
1961-1967   22410870R

Tech Hand Up Extrem Surg
Techniques in hand & upper extremity
surgery
1089-3393   1531-6572
1997   9704676

Tech Hosp Med Soc Sanit
Techniques hospitalières, médico-sociales et
sanitaires
0040-1374
    Continues: Techniques hospitalières,
    sanitaires et sociales. Continued by:
    Techniques hospitalières (Paris, France:
    1987).
1950-1987   21120470R

Tech Man US Army Biol Lab
Technical manual. U.S. Army Biological
Laboratories
1963-uuuu   22120470R

Tech Manuscr US Army Biol Lab
Technical manuscript. U.S. Army Biological
Laboratories
1960-uuuu   22120480R

Tech Note Arct Aeromed Lab (US)
Technical note; TN. Arctic Aeromedical
Laboratory (U.S.)
1964   0106602

Tech Note U S Natl Aeronaut Space Adm
Technical note. United States. National
Aeronautics and Space Administration
1959-1973   21930180R

Tech Rep Arct Aeromed Lab US
Technical report.; TR. Arctic Aeromedical
Laboratory (U.S.)
    Continued by the Technical documentary
    report of the Arctic Aeromedical Laboratory.
1962-1uuu   0106601

Tech Rep Brookhaven Natl Lab
T[echnical report]. Brookhaven National
Laboratory
1948-1971   21840060R

Tech Rep CRDLR US Army Chem Res Dev Lab
Technical report. CRDLR. U.S. Army
Chemical Research and Development
Laboratories
1960-uuuu   22130290R

Tech Rep CWLR US Army Chem Warf Lab
Technical report. CWLR. U.S. Army
Chemical Warfare Laboratories
1956-1960   22130280R

Tech Rep NAVTRADEVCEN
Technical report: NAVTRADEVCEN. Naval
Training Device Center
1965-1967   22421090R

Tech Rep NY Nav Shipyard Mater Lab
Technical report. New York Naval Shipyard.
Material Laboratory
1958   0103775

Tech Rep SAM-TR
[Technical report] SAM-TR. USAF School
of Aerospace Medicine
    Continues: Technical documentary report.
    USAF School of Aerospace Medicine.
1964-1980   0032306

Tech Urol
Techniques in urology
1079-3259
1995-2001   9508161

Tech Vasc Interv Radiol
Techniques in vascular and interventional
radiology
1089-2516   1557-9808
1998   9806675

Technol Cancer Res Treat
Technology in cancer research & treatment
1533-0346   1533-0338
2002   101140941

Technol Cult
Technology and culture
0040-165X   1097-3729
1959   21120500R

Technol Eval Cent Asses Program Exec Summ
Technology Evaluation Center Assessment
Program. Executive summary
2001   101213260

Technol Health Care
Technology and health care: official journal
of the European Society for Engineering and
Medicine
0928-7329
1993   9314590

Technol Rev
Technology review
0040-1692
    Continued by: MIT's technology review.
1899-1997   7703797

Tecnologica
Tecnologica (Chicago, Ill.)
    Absorbed: Clearinghouse update (Chicago,
    Ill.).
19uu-2001   9712382

Tecnologica MAP Suppl
Tecnologica. MAP supplement. Blue Cross
and Blue Shield Association. Medical
Advisory Panel
1998-2001   100883490

Tegen Tuberc
Tegen de tuberculose
0040-2125
    Continues Tuberculose.
1921   0404555

Telemed J
Telemedicine journal: the official journal of
the American Telemedicine Association
1078-3024
    Continued by: Telemedicine journal and
    e-health.
1995-2000   9507612

Telemed J E Health
Telemedicine journal and e-health: the
official journal of the American Telemedicine
Association
1530-5627   1556-3669
    Continues: Telemedicine journal.
2000   100959949

Telemed Telehealth Netw
Telemedicine and telehealth networks:
newsmagazine of distance healthcare
1091-7853
    Continued by: Telehealth magazine.
1995-1998   9601797

Telemed Today
Telemedicine today
1078-0351
    Continues: Telemedicine newsletter.
1994-2002   9505215

Telemed Virtual Real
Telemedicine and virtual reality
1089-5841
1996-1998   9617314

Temas Odontol
Temas odontológicos
0040-2907
1946-1977   0417351

Temple Dent Rev
Temple dental review
1930-1976   21130130R

Tenn Med
Tennessee medicine: journal of the
Tennessee Medical Association
1088-6222
    Continues: Journal of the Tennessee Medical
    Association.
1996   9609310

Tenn Nurse
Tennessee nurse / Tennessee Nurses
Association
1055-3134
    Continues: Bulletin - Tennessee Nurses
    Association.
1990   9102869

Teor Prak Fiz Kult
Teoriia i praktika fizicheskoĭ kul'tury
0040-3601
1937   21130280R

Teor Prax Teles Vychovy
Teorie a praxe tělesné výchovy a sportu
0040-358X
1953-1990   21130270R

Ter Arkh
Terapevticheskiĭ arkhiv
0040-3660
1923   2984818R

Terapia
Terapia
1910-1977   21130350R

Teratog Carcinog Mutagen
Teratogenesis, carcinogenesis, and
mutagenesis
0270-3211   1520-6866
    Continued by: Birth defects research. Part B
    Developmental and reproductive toxicology.
1980-2003   8100917

Teratology
Teratology
0040-3709
    Continued by: Birth defects research. Part A.
    Clinical and molecular teratology.
1968-2002   0153257

Terramycine Inf
Terramycine informations
1959-1965   21130460R

Tetrahedron
Tetrahedron
0040-4020
1957   2984170R

Tetrahedron Lett
Tetrahedron letters
0040-4039
1959   2984819R

Tex Cancer Bull
Texas cancer bulletin
0892-8290
1948-1949   21130520R

Tex Dent Assist Assoc Bull
Texas Dental Assistants Association bulletin
0049-3503
1965-19uu   7503683

Tex Dent J
Texas dental journal
0040-4284
1883   2984821R

Tex Heart Inst J
Texas Heart Institute journal / from the
Texas Heart Institute of St. Luke's Episcopal
Hospital, Texas Children's Hospital
0730-2347   1526-6702
    Continues: Cardiovascular diseases.
1982   8214622

Tex Hosp
Texas hospitals
0040-4357
    Continued by: HealthTexas.
1945-1988   0415175

Tex J Pharm
Texas journal of pharmacy
    Supersedes the Bulletin of the College of
    Pharmacy, the Bulletin of the Pharmacy
    Extension Service, and the Longhorn
    pharmacist.
1960-1964   21130570R

Tex Med
Texas medicine
0040-4470   1938-3223
    Continues Texas state journal of medicine.
1966   0051012

Tex Nurs
Texas nursing
0095-036X
    Continues Bulletin - Texas Nurses
    Association.
1973   0436240

Tex Rep Biol Med
Texas reports on biology and medicine
0040-4675
    Continues: Bulletin of the John Sealy
    Hospital and the School of Medicine.
1943-1982   2984820R

Text Rent
Textile rental
0195-0118
    Continues: Linen supply news.
197u   9878386

Thai J Nurs
Thai journal of nursing
0125-0078
    Continues: Chot mai hēt kān phayābān.
1972   7605750

Theor Appl Genet
TAG. Theoretical and applied genetics.
Theoretische und angewandte Genetik
0040-5752   1432-2242
Continues Der Züchter.
1968   0145600

Theor Biol Med Model
Theoretical biology & medical modelling
                                   1742-4682
2004   101224383

Theor Med
Theoretical medicine
0167-9902
Continues: Metamedicine. Continued by:
Theoretical medicine and bioethics.
1983-1997   8405140

Theor Med Bioeth
Theoretical medicine and bioethics
1386-7415
Continues: Theoretical medicine.
1998   9805378

Theor Popul Biol
Theoretical population biology
0040-5809   1096-0325
1970   0256422

Theor Prax Korperkult
Theorie und Praxis der Körperkultur
0563-4458
1952-1990   21140120R

Theory Biosci
Theory in biosciences = Theorie in den
Biowissenschaften
1431-7613   1611-7530
Continues: Biologisches Zentralblatt.
1997   9708216

Ther Adv Cardiovasc Dis
Therapeutic advances in cardiovascular
disease
1753-9447   1753-9455
2007   101316343

Ther Adv Respir Dis
Therapeutic advances in respiratory disease
1753-4658   1753-4666
2007   101316317

Ther Apher
Therapeutic apheresis: official journal of the
International Society for Apheresis and the
Japanese Society for Apheresis
1091-6660   1526-0968
Continued by: Therapeutic apheresis and
dialysis.
1997-2002   9706703

Ther Apher Dial
Therapeutic apheresis and dialysis: official
peer-reviewed journal of the International
Society for Apheresis, the Japanese Society
for Dialysis Therapy, the Japanese Society for
Dialysis Therapy
1744-9979   1744-9987
Continues: Therapeutic apheresis.
2003   101181252

Ther Ber
Therapeutische Berichte
1924-1970   0223727

Ther Drug Monit
Therapeutic drug monitoring
0163-4356   1536-3694
1979   7909660

Ther Ggw
Therapie der Gegenwart
0040-5965
Continues Medicinisch-chirurgische
Rundschau.
1895-1993   0413576

Ther Hung
Therapia Hungarica (English edition)
0133-3909
1953-1994   8706535

Ther Immunol
Therapeutic immunology
0967-0149
1994-1995   9421528

Ther Notes
Therapeutic notes
0888-6423
1894-1968   21140170R

Ther Nova
Therapeutica nova
1947-1967   21140190R

Ther Recreation J
Therapeutic recreation journal
0040-5914
Continues TR; therapeutic recreation.
1968   0230530

Ther Umsch
Therapeutische Umschau. Revue
thérapeutique
0040-5930
Continues: Therapeutische Umschau und
medizinische Bibliographie.
1961   0407224

Ther Umsch Med Bibliogr
Therapeutische Umschau und medizinische
Bibliographie. Revue thérapeutique et
bibliographie médicale
0302-8291
Continued by Therapeutische Umschau.
1944-1960   0407225

Therapeutique
Therapeutique (La Semaine des hôpitaux)
0040-5922
Continues Semaine therapeutique. Continued
by Semaine des hôpitaux, Therapeutique.
1969-1972   0415606

Therapie
Thérapie
0040-5957
Continues: Bulletin de la Société de
thérapeutique. Société de thérapeutique
(Paris, France).
1946   0420544

Therapiewoche
Die Therapiewoche
0040-5973
Continued by: Therapie & Erfolg.
1973-1996   0417352

Theriaca
Theriaca
0082-4003
1956   21140380R

Theriogenology
Theriogenology
0093-691X
1974   0421510

Thorac Cardiovasc Surg
The Thoracic and cardiovascular surgeon
0171-6425
Continues Thoraxchirurgie, vaskuläre
Chirurgie.
1979   7903387

Thorac Surg Clin
Thoracic surgery clinics
1547-4127
Continues: Chest surgery clinics of North
America.
2004   101198195

Thorax
Thorax
0040-6376   1468-3296
1946   0417353

Thoraxchir Vask Chir
Thoraxchirurgie und vaskuläre Chirurgie
0040-6384
Continues Thoraxchirurgie. Continued by
Thoraxchirurgie; vaskuläre Chirurgie.
1962-1966   0404412

Thoraxchir Vask Chir
Thoraxchirurgie, vaskuläre Chirurgie
0040-6384
Continues Thoraxchirurgie und vaskuläre
Chirurgie. Continued by The Thoracic and
cardiovascular surgeon.
1967-1978   7706134

Thoraxchirurgie
Thoraxchirurgie
Continued by Thoraxchirurgie und vaskuläre
Chirurgie.
1953-1962   21140500R

Thromb Diath Haemorrh
Thrombosis et diathesis haemorrhagica
0340-5338
Continued by Thrombosis and haemostasis.
1957-1975   7608420

Thromb Diath Haemorrh Suppl
Thrombosis et diathesis haemorrhagica.
Supplementum
0040-6597
Continued by Supplementum ... ad
Thrombosis and haemostasis.
1960-1976   8106633

Thromb Haemost
Thrombosis and haemostasis
0340-6245
Continues: Thrombosis et diathesis
haemorrhagica.
1976   7608063

Thromb Res
Thrombosis research
0049-3848
1972   0326377

Thromb Res Suppl
Thrombosis research. Supplement
0049-3848
1974-1991   8309239

Thymus
Thymus
0165-6090
1979-1997   8009032

Thyroid
Thyroid: official journal of the American
Thyroid Association
1050-7256   1557-9077
1990   9104317

Thyroidology
Thyroidology / A.P.R.I.M
1989   9100266

TIC
Tic
0040-6716
1942-1987   21210020R

TID Rep
TID [reports]. U.S. Atomic Energy
Commission
194u-1971   21830730R

Tid Tann
Tidens tann
1940   9875640

Tidskr Mil Halsov
Tidskrift i militär hälsovård
Supersedes Tidskrift i hälsovård.
1876-1964   0034745

Tidskr Sjukvardspedagog
Tidskrift för sjukvårdspedagoger
0346-2722
Continues Pedagogiska sektionens
medlemsblad - Svensk sjuksköterskeförening.
Continued by Omvårdaren.
1974-1981   7610665

Tidskr Sver Sjukskot
Tidskrift för Sveriges sjuksköterskor
0037-6027
1934-1976   7708470

Tidsskr Nor Laegeforen
Tidsskrift for den Norske lægeforening:
tidsskrift for praktisk medicin, ny række
0029-2001   0807-7096
Continues: Tidsskrift for praktisk medicin.
1890   0413423

Tidsskr Prakt Tandlaeg
Tidsskrift for praktiserende tandlaeger
0105-0273
Continued by Tidsskrift for tandlaeger.
(Copenhagen, Denmark: 1981).
1971-1981   7503930

Tidsskr Sygepl
Tidsskrift for sygeplejersker
0049-3856
Continued by Sygeplejersken.
1901-1971   0421367

Tidsskr Sykepl
Tidsskriftet sykepleien
0806-7511
Merger of: Journalen sykepleien, and:
Sykepleien. Fag.
1995   9603908

Tidsskr Tandlaeger
Tidsskrift for tandlaeger (Copenhagen,
Denmark: 1981)
0108-1284
Continues: Tidsskrift for praktiserende
tandlaeger.
1981-1990   8412321

Tierarztl Prax
Tierärztliche Praxis
0303-6286
Split into: Tierärztliche praxis. Ausgabe
G. Grosstiere/Nutztiere. and: Tierärztliche
praxis. Ausgabe K. Kleintiere/Heimtiere.
1973-1997   7501042

Tierarztl Prax Ausg G Grosstiere Nutztiere
Tierärztliche Praxis. Ausgabe G, Grosstiere/
Nutztiere
1434-1220
Continues in part: Tierärztliche Praxis.
1997   9715779

Tierarztl Prax Ausg K Klientiere Heimtiere
Tierärztliche Praxis. Ausgabe K, Kleintiere/
Heimtiere
1434-1239
Continues in part: Tierärztliche Praxis.
1997   9717383

Tierarztl Prax Suppl
Tierärztliche Praxis. Supplement
0930-6447
1985-19uu   9012743

Tierarztl Umsch
Tierärztliche Umschau
0049-3864
1946   0404413

Tijdschr Bejaarden Kraam Ziekenverzorging
Tijdschrift voor bejaarden-, kraam- en
ziekenversorging: bkz
0049-3880
Continued by: Tijdschrift voor verzorgenden.
1968-1987   8411420

Tijdschr Diergeneeskd
Tijdschrift voor diergeneeskunde
0040-7453
Continues the Tijdschrift voor
veeartsenijkunde. Absorbed The Netherlands
journal of veterinary science. 1973.
1916   0031550

Tijdschr Gastroenterol
Tijdschrift voor gastro-enterologie
0049-3899
1958   0404414

Tijdschr Gerontol Geriatr
Tijdschrift voor gerontologie en geriatrie
0167-9228
Continues: Gerontologie.
1982   8210346

Tijdschr Kindergeneeskd
Tijdschrift voor kindergeneeskunde
0376-7442
Continues Maandschrift voor
kindergeneeskunde.
1976   7704039

Tijdschr Psychiatr
Tijdschrift voor psychiatrie
0303-7339
Continues: Nederlands tijdschrift voor
psychiatrie.
1974   0423731

Tijdschr Soc Geneeskd
Tijdschrift voor sociale geneeskunde
0040-7607
Supersedes Sociaal-medisch maandschrift.
Continued by: Tijdschrift voor sociale
gezondheidzorg.
1923-1982   0413002

Tijdschr Voor Tandheelkd
Tijdschrift Voor Tandheelkunde
Continued by the Nederlands tijdschrift voor
Tandkeelkunde.
1894-1961   0032075

Tijdschr Voor Ziekenverpl
Tijdschrift voor ziekenverpleging
Continues the Maandsblad voor
ziekenverpleging. Continued by TVZ:
tijdschrift voor ziekenverpleging.
1914-1963   0032101

Tijdschr Ziekenverpl
Tijdschrift voor ziekenverpleging
0303-6456
Continues: TVZ, Tijdschrift voor
ziekenverpleging. Continued by: TVZ.
1969-1987   7505126

Tile Till
Tile and till
0040-7674
1915-1980   21210470R

Timarit Hjukrunarfel Isl
Tímarit Hjúkrunarfélags Islands
0046-7634
Continues Hjúkrunarkvennabladid. Continued
by Hjúkrun.
1960-1977   7809746

Time
Time
0040-781X
Absorbed: Literary digest (New York, N.Y.:
1937).
1923   9877130

Timely Top Med Cardiovasc Dis
Timely topics in medicine. Cardiovascular
diseases
                             1579-0789
1997   101166310

Times
Times / Tennessee Hospital Association
Continued by: Tennessee hospital times.
19uu-1982   9877740

Timisoara Med
Timişoara medicală
0493-3079
Continued by: Timisoara medical journal.
1956-uuuu   21210500R

Tip Fak Mecm
Tip Fakültesi mecmuasi
0047-1623
Continued by Istanbul Tip Fakültesi
mecmuasi.
1938-1970   0414152

Tissue Antigens
Tissue antigens
0001-2815   1399-0039
1971   0331072

Tissue Cell
Tissue & cell
0040-8166
1969   0214745

Tissue Eng
Tissue engineering
1076-3279   1557-8690
Continued in part by: Tissue engineering. Part
A. Tissue engineering. Part B, Reviews, and:
Tissue engineering. Part C, Methods.
1995-2007   9505538

Tissue Eng Part A
Tissue engineering. Part A
1937-3341
Continues in part: Tissue engineering.
2008   101466659

Tissue Eng Part B Rev
Tissue engineering. Part B, Reviews
1937-3368
Continues in part: Tissue engineering.
2008   101466660

Tissue Eng Part C Methods
Tissue engineering. Part C, Methods
1937-3384
Continues in part: Tissue engineering.
2008   101466663

TIT J Life Sci
T.-I.-T. journal of life sciences
0039-8160
1971-1979   1305601

TMJ Update
TMJ update
0885-9191
1983   8907535

Tob Control
Tobacco control
0964-4563   1468-3318
1992   9209612

Todays FDA
Today's FDA: official monthly journal of the
Florida Dental Association
1048-5317
Merger of: Dental times dispatch, and:
Florida dental journal.
1989   9012957

Todays Nurs Home
Today's nursing home
0274-5089
Continued by: Today's nursing home &
Retirement housing today quarterly.
1980-1988   8101403

Todays OR Nurse
Today's OR nurse
0194-5181
Continued by: Today's surgical nurse.
1979-1996   7911719

Todays Surg Nurse
Today's surgical nurse
1087-1667
Continues: Today's OR nurse.
1996-1999   9606921

Tohoku Igaku Zasshi
Tohoku igaku zasshi
0040-8700
Supersedes Kaiho of Tohoku Igakkai.
1916   0413765

Tohoku J Exp Med
The Tohoku journal of experimental
medicine
0040-8727   1349-3329
1920   0417355

Tohoku Shika Daigaku Gakkai Shi
Tōhoku Shika Daigaku Gakkai shi
0385-0161
Continued by: ōu Daigaku shigakushi.
1974-1988   8709317

Tokai J Exp Clin Med
The Tokai journal of experimental and
clinical medicine
0385-0005
1976   7704186

Tokoginecol Pract
Toko-ginecología práctica
0040-8867
1936   0404557

Tokushima J Exp Med
The Tokushima journal of experimental
medicine
0040-8875
Continued by: Journal of medical
investigation.
1954-1996   0417356

Tokyo Igaku
Tokyo igaku. The Tokyo journal of medical
sciences
0285-6131
Continues Tokyo igaku zasshi.
1968   0165106

Tokyo Iji Shinshi
[Tokyo iji shinshi] The Tokyo medical journal
Merged with Kenkō hoken ihō in hachigatsu
1940.
1877-19uu   21220270R

Tokyo Ika Shika Daigaku Iyo Kizai Kenkyusho Hokoku
Iyō Kizai Kenkyūjo hōkoku. Reports
of the Institute for Medical and Dental
Engineering, Tokyo Medical and Dental
University
0082-4739
Continues in part: Tōkyō Ika Shika Daigaku
Shika Zairyō Kenkyūjo hōkoku.. Continued
by: Seitai Zairyō Kōgaku Kenkyūjo hōkoku,.
1967-1998   0165447

Tokyo Jikeikai Ika Daigaku Zasshi
[Zasshi] Tokyo Jikeikai medical journal.
Tōkyō Jikeikai Ika Daigaku
0375-9172
Continues Zasshi of Sei-I-Kai.
1951   21220300R

Top Clin Nurs
Topics in clinical nursing
0164-0534
Continued by: Holistic nursing practice.
1979-1986   7906353

Top Companion Anim Med
Topics in companion animal medicine
1938-9736
Continues: Clinical techniques in small
animal practice.
2008   101465592

Top Curr Chem
Topics in current chemistry
0340-1022
Continues Fortschritte der chemischem
Forschung.
1973   0432204

Top Emerg Med
Topics in emergency medicine
0164-2340
Continued by: Advanced emergency nursing
journal.
1979-2006   7906354

Top Health Care Financ
Topics in health care financing
0095-3814
Continued by: Journal of health care finance.
1974-1994   7509107

Top Health Inf Manage
Topics in health information management
1065-0989
Continues: Topics in health record
management.
1992-2003   9212861

Top Health Rec Manage
Topics in health record management
0270-5230
Continued by: Topics in health information
management.
1980-1992   8100921

Top HIV Med
Topics in HIV medicine: a publication of the
International AIDS Society, USA
1542-8826
Continues: Improving the management of
HIV disease.
uuuu   100954650

Top Hosp Pharm Manage
Topics in hospital pharmacy management /
Aspen Systems Corporation
0271-1206
Continued by: Pharmacy practice
management quarterly.
1981-1995   8110018

Top Magn Reson Imaging
Topics in magnetic resonance imaging:
TMRI
0899-3459   1536-1004
1988   8913523

Top Probl Psychother
Topical problems of psychotherapy
0082-4925
1960-1965   7511370

Top Stroke Rehabil
Topics in stroke rehabilitation
1074-9357
1994   9439750

Torace
Il Torace
0390-5357
Continues Giornale di pneumologia.
1973-1979   7511829

Torax
El Torax
0049-4143
Supersedes Revista de tuberculosis del
Uruguay.
1952-1983   0417357

Torreon Med
Torreon médico
1946-19uu   21230250R

Tort Insur Law J
Tort & insurance law journal
0885-856X
Continues: Forum (Chicago, Ill.). Continued
by: Tort trial & insurance practice law
journal.
1985-2002   9892369

Tort Trial Insur Pract Law J
Tort trial & insurance practice law journal
1543-3234
Continues: Tort & insurance law journal.
2002   101180799

Torture
Torture: quarterly journal on rehabilitation
of torture victims and prevention of torture
1018-8185   1997-3322
Continues: International newsletter on
treatment and rehabilitation of torture victims.
1991   9309086

Toulouse Med
Toulouse médical
0372-042X
Absorbed Echo médical in 1903 and issues
for 1903-09 have title: Toulouse-médical et
echo médical réunis. Superseded by Revue de
médecine de Toulouse. Continued by: Revue
de médecine de Toulouse.
1899-1964   0035523

Toxic Rep Ser
Toxicity report series
1521-4621
Continues: NTP TOX.
199u   101122696

Toxicol Appl Pharmacol
Toxicology and applied pharmacology
0041-008X   1096-0333
1959   0416575

Toxicol Eur Res
Toxicological European research. Recherche
européenne en toxicologie
0249-6402
Supersedes European journal of toxicology
and environmental hygiene. Journal européen
de toxicologie.
1978-1983   7901212

Toxicol In Vitro
Toxicology in vitro: an international journal
published in association with BIBRA
0887-2333
1987   8712158

Toxicol Ind Health
Toxicology and industrial health
0748-2337   1477-0393
1985   8602702

Toxicol Lett
Toxicology letters
0378-4274
1977   7709027

Toxicol Pathol
Toxicologic pathology
0192-6233   1533-1601
Continues: Bulletin of the Society of
Pharmacological and Environmental
Pathologists.
1978   7905907

Toxicol Rev
Toxicological reviews
1176-2551
Continues: Adverse drug reactions and toxicological reviews.
2003   101162874

Toxicol Sci
Toxicological sciences: an official journal of the Society of Toxicology
1096-6080   1096-0929
Continues: Fundamental and applied toxicology.
1998   9805461

Toxicology
Toxicology
0300-483X
1973   0361055

Toxicon
Toxicon: official journal of the International Society on Toxinology
0041-0101
1962   1307333

Tr Akad Med Nauk Sssr Mosc Inst Grudn Khir
Trudy. Institut grudnoĭ khirurgii (Akademiiâ meditŝinskikh nauk SSSR)
0515-930X
1959-19uu   14710140R

Tr Akad Nauk SSSR Inst Genet
Trudy. Akademiia nauk SSSR. Institut genetiki
1935-uuuu   14710380R

Tr Fiziol Lab Akad I P Pavlova
Trudy fiziologicheskikh laboratoriĭ akademika I.P. Pavlova
1924-1949   21320050R

Tr Inst Biol
Trudy Instituta biologii
0301-2387
Continued by Trudy Instituta èkologii rasteniĭ i zhivotnykh.
1946-1966   7507612

Tr Inst Fiz Akad Nauk Gruz Ssr
Trudy Instituta fiziologii, Akademiia nauk Gruzinskoĭ SSR
Continues Trudy of Institut fiziologii of Universitet, Tiflis.
194u-1965   7507618

Tr Inst Fiziol Im I P Pavlova
Trudy - Institut fiziologii imeni I. P. Pavlova
0568-5745
Supersedes the Trudy of the institute under its earlier name: Akademiia nauk SSSR. Fiziologicheskii institut imeni I. P. Pavlova.
1952-1968   7507568

Tr Inst Im Pastera
Trudy Instituta imeni Pastera
0202-1447
Continues: Trudy Leningradskogo nauchno-issledovateĭskogo instituta èpidemiologii i mikrobiologii imeni Pastera.
1975-1992   7709028

Tr Inst Morfol Zhivotn An Severtsova
Trudy Instituta morfologii zhivotnykh im. A. N. Severtsova
Supersedes Trudy of Institut evoliutssionnoĭ morfologii and of Institut tsitologii, gistologii i embriologii of the Akademiia nauk SSSR.
1949-1961   7507624

Tr Inst Norm Patol Fiziol
Trudy - Institut normal'noĭ i patologicheskoĭ fiziologii
0515-9369
1958-1971   7507570

Tr Latv Padomju Soc Repub Zinat Akad Mikrobiol Inst
Trudy. Mikrobiologijas institūts (Latvijas PSR Zinātnu akadēmija)
1952-19uu   18240340R

Tr Leningr Inst Epidemiol Mikrobiol
Trudy Leningradskogo instituta èpidemiologii i mikrobiologii im. Pastera
Continues: Trudy Leningradskogo instituta èpidemiologii. mikrobiologii. i gigieny im. Pastera. Continued by: Trudy Leningradskogo nauchno-issledovateĭskogo instituta èpidemiologii i mikrobiologii imeni Pastera.
1961-1961   9427271

Tr Leningr Nauchnoissled Inst Epidemiol Mikrobiol
Trudy Leningradskogo nauchno-issledovateĭskogo instituta èpidemiologii i mikrobiologii imeni Pastera
0131-4955
Continues: Trudy Leningradskogo instituta èpidemiologii i mikrobiologii im. Pastera. Continued by: Trudy Instituta imeni Pastera.
1963-1974   7507641

Tr Leningr Sanitarnogig Med Inst
Trudy Leningradskogo sanitarno-gigienicheskogo meditsinskogo instituta
0371-9367
1949-1982   7507643

Tr Mosk Nauchnoissled Inst Epidmiol Mikrobiol
Trudy Moskovskogo nauchno-issledovatel'skogo instituta epidemiologii i mikrobiologii
0301-2409
Continues Trudy of the Moskovskiĭ institut epidemiologii. mikrobiologii i gigieny.
1960   7507644

Trab Inst Cajal
Trabajos del Instituto Cajal / Consejo Superior de Investigaciones Cientificas
0211-8343
Continues: Trabajos del Instituto Cajal de investigaciones biológicas.
1980-1984   8509522

Trab Inst Cajal Invest Biol
Trabajos del Instituto Cajal de investigaciones biológicas
0020-3696
Continues Travaux du Laboratoire de recherches biologiques de l'Université de Madrid. Continued by Trabajos del Instituto Cajal.
1940-1979   7503687

Track Rep
Tracking report / Center for Studying Health System Change
                                        1553-0787
2002   101161177

Tradimus
Tradimus: the magazine for RCN nursing students
0269-0977
Absorbed by: Nursing standard.
1985-1989   8612916

Traffic
Traffic (Copenhagen, Denmark)
1398-9219   1600-0854
2000   100939340

Traffic Inj Prev
Traffic injury prevention
1538-9588   1538-957X
Continues: Crash prevention and injury control.
2002   101144385

Train Dev J
Training and development journal
0041-0861
Continues: Training directors journal. Continued by: Training & development (Alexandria, Va.).
1966-1991   9877738

Train Sch Bull (Vinel)
The Training school bulletin
0041-0918
Continues The Training School.
1913-1974   0414174

Trained Nurse Hosp Rev
The Trained nurse and hospital review
0893-3251
Continued by Nursing world. Absorbed the Journal of practical nursing in Jan. 1889; the Nightingale in Aug.? 1891; the Nurse (Boston) in 1895?; the Nursing record in 1899?; the Nursing world in 1900?; the Nurse (Jamestown) in Jan. 1918: the Southern registered nurse in Sept. 1929; Industrial nursing in May 1949.
1888-1950   21240120R

Training
Training (New York, N.Y.)
0095-5892
Continues: Training in business and industry.
1974   9877757

Trans Am Acad Insur Med
Transactions of the American Academy of Insurance Medicine: Annual Meeting. American Academy of Insurance Medicine. Meeting
1064-4709
Continues: Transactions of the Association of Life Insurance Medical Directors of America. annual meeting.
1992-1993   9316679

Trans Am Acad Ophthalmol Otolaryngol
Transactions - American Academy of Ophthalmology and Otolaryngology. American Academy of Ophthalmology and Otolaryngology
0002-7154
Continues: Transactions of the annual meeting of the American Academy of Ophthalmology and Otolaryngology. Absorbed: American Academy of Ophthalmology and Otolaryngology. Bulletin. Split into: American Academy of Ophthalmology and Otolaryngology. Transactions. Section on Ophthalmology. and: American Academy of Ophthalmology and Otolaryngology. Transactions. Section on Otolaryngology.
1940-1974   7506085

Trans Am Assoc Genitourin Surg
Transactions of the American Association of Genito-Urinary Surgeons
0065-7204
1906-1979   7506098

Trans Am Clin Climatol Assoc
Transactions of the American Clinical and Climatological Association
0065-7778
Continues: Transactions of the American Climatological and Clinical Association. American Climatological and Clinical Association.
1933   7507559

Trans Am Coll Cardiol
Transactions. American College of Cardiology
1951-1957   14810120R

Trans Am Gynecol Soc
Transactions of the American Gynecological Society
0065-8480
Merged with: Transactions of the American Association of Obstetricians and Gynecologists, to form: Transactions of the American Association of Obstericians and Gynecologists, American Gynecological Society.
1876-1979   7506102

Trans Am Laryngol Assoc
Transactions of the ... annual meeting of the American Laryngological Association. American Laryngological Association. Meeting
0891-1940
1879   14830200R

Trans Am Laryngol Rhinol Otol Soc
Transactions of the American Laryngological, Rhinological and Otological Society, Inc
0065-9037
1896-1989   7506103

Trans Am Microsc Soc
Transactions of the American Microscopical Society
0003-0023
Continues: Proceedings. American Microscopical Society. Continued by: Invertebrate biology.
1895-1994   7506104

Trans Am Neurol Assoc
Transactions of the American Neurological Association
0065-9479
1875-1981   7506105

Trans Am Ophthalmol Soc
Transactions of the American Ophthalmological Society
0065-9533   1545-6110
1864   7506106

Trans Am Otol Soc
Transactions of the American Otological Society
0096-6851
1868   7506107

Trans Am Soc Artif Intern Organs
Transactions - American Society for Artificial Internal Organs
0066-0078
Merged with: ASAIO journal, to form: ASAIO transactions.
1955-1985   7506088

Trans Am Soc Ophthalmol Otolaryngol Allergy
Transactions - American Society of Ophthalmologic and Otolaryngologic Allergy
0066-0655
Continued by: American Academy of Otolaryngic Allergy. Meeting. Transactions.
1960-1980   7506089

Trans Annu Meet Am Bronchoesophagol Assoc
Transactions of the ... Annual Meeting of the American Broncho-Esophagological Association. American Broncho-Esophagological Association. Meeting
0065-7603
Continues Transactions of the annual meeting of the American Bronchoscopic Society.
1940-2002   14740770R

Trans Annu Meet Natl Tuberc Assoc
Transactions of the annual meeting. National Tuberculosis Association
0096-6290
Continues the Transactions of the annual meeting of the National Association for the Study and Prevention of Tuberculosis.
1918-1954   18930740R

Trans Assoc Am Physicians
Transactions of the Association of American Physicians
0066-9458
Continued by: Proceedings of the Association of American Physicians.
1886-1993   7506109

Trans Assoc Ind Med Off
The Transactions of the Association of Industrial Medical Officers
Continued by the Transactions of the Society of Occupational Medicine.
1951-1965   7506110

Trans Assoc Life Insur Med Dir Am
Transactions of the Association of Life Insurance Medical Directors of America
0066-9598
Continues the association's Abstract of the proceedings of the annual meeting. Continued by: American Academy of Insurance Medicine. Meeting. Transactions of the American Academy of Insurance Medicine.
1941-1991   7506111

Trans Aust Coll Ophthalmol
Transactions of the Australian College of Ophthalmologists
0067-1789
Supersedes Transactions of the Ophthalmological Society of Australia. Superseded by Australian journal of ophthalmology.
1969-1971   7506112

Trans Br Soc Study Orthod
Transactions of the British Society for the Study of Orthodontics
0068-2527
Merged with: Orthodontist, to form: British journal of orthodontics.
1908-1971   7513095

Trans Can Opthalmolog Soc
Transactions of the Canadian Ophthalmological Society
0068-9408
1948-1963   7506115

Trans Conf Liver Inj
Transactions. Conference on Liver Injury
1943-1953   23810060R

Trans Conf Metab Asp Conval
Transactions. Conference on Metabolic Aspects of Convalescence
Continues the Proceedings of the Conference on Metabolic Aspects of Convalescence Including Bone and Wound Healing. Superseded by Transaction of the 1st Conference on Metabolic Interrelations.
1945-1948   23810190R

Trans Eur Orthod Soc
Transactions. European Orthodontic Society
Continues the society's Report of the congress.
1969-1977   0261426

Trans Indiana Acad Ophthalmol Otolaryngol
Transactions - Indiana Academy of Ophthalmology and Otolaryngology
0073-6740
Continued by Annual meeting - Indiana Academy of Ophthalmology and Otolaryngology.
1918-1971   7506092

Trans Int Conf Endod
Transaction of the International Conference on Endodontics. International Conference on Endodontics
0074-3054
Continues International Congress on Endodontics. Transactions of the International Congress on Endodontics.
1958-1973   7704718

Trans Int Conf Oral Surg
Transactions of the International Conference on Oral Surgery
196u-uuuu   100961348

Trans Kans Acad Sci
Transactions of the Kansas Academy of Science. Kansas Academy of Science
0022-8443
Continues: Transactions of the ... annual meetings of the Kansas Academy of Science. Kansas Academy of Science. Meeting.
1903   7506117

Trans Med Soc Lond
Transactions of the Medical Society of London
0076-6011
Supersedes the society's Memoirs.
1810   7506118

Trans Meet Am Surg Assoc Am Surg Assoc
Transactions of the ... Meeting of the American Surgical Association. American Surgical Association. Meeting
0066-0833
Continues: Transactions of the American Surgical Association. American Surgical Association. Absorbed: Scientific papers of the meeting of the American Surgical Association. Continued in part by: Scientific papers of the meeting of the American Surgical Association. 1969-1985
1935   101153387

Trans N Engl Obstet Gynecol Soc
Transactions of the New England Obstetrical and Gynecological Society
0091-6587
1941-1969   7506119

Trans N Y Acad Sci
Transactions of the New York Academy of Sciences
0028-7113
1881-1983   7506121

Trans Natl Saf Congr
Transactions. National Safety Council. National Safety Congress
0197-050X
Continues the Transactions of the council's Annual Safety Congress.
1936-1977   24710250R

Trans New Orleans Acad Ophthalmol
Transactions of the New Orleans Academy of Ophthalmology
0077-8605
1981-1988   8113204

Trans Ophthalmol Soc Aust
Transactions of the Ophthalmological Society of Australia
1939-1968   7506123

Trans Ophthalmol Soc N Z
Transactions of the Ophthalmological Society of New Zealand
0300-8983
Issued as Supplement to the New Zealand medical journal. Merged with Australian journal of ophthalmology, to form Australian and New Zealand journal of ophthalmology.
1947-1984   7506124

Trans Ophthalmol Soc U K
Transactions of the ophthalmological
societies of the United Kingdom
0078-5334
    Continues Transactions of the
    Ophthalmological Society of the United
    Kingdom. London. Continued by: Eye
    (London. England). Eye.
    1962-1986   0200570

Trans Pa Acad Ophthalmol Otolaryngol
Transactions - Pennsylvania Academy of
Ophthalmology and Otolaryngology
0048-3206
    1948-1990   7506093

Trans Pac Coast Obstet Gynecol Soc
Transactions of the Pacific Coast Obstetrical
and Gynecological Society
0078-7442
    Continues the Transactions of the Pacific
    Coast Society of Obstetrics and Gynecology.
    1944-1996   7506125

Trans Pac Coast Otoophthalmol Soc Annu Meet
Transactions of the Pacific Coast Oto-
Ophthalmological Society annual meeting
0097-0093
    1913-1991   7506126

Trans R Sch Dent Stockh Umea
Transactions of the Royal Schools of
Dentistry, Stockholm and Umeå. Stockholm.
Tandläkarhögskolan
0082-7401
    1958-1968   21010640R

Trans R Soc Can 5 Biol Sci
Transactions of the Royal Society of Canada.
Section 5, Biological sciences Royal Society
of Canada
    Continues in part: Transactions of the Royal
    Society of Canada. Section 4. Geological and
    biological sciences.
    1918-1961   20440910R

Trans R Soc Trop Med Hyg
Transactions of the Royal Society of Tropical
Medicine and Hygiene
0035-9203
    Continues the Transactions of the Society of
    Tropical Medicine and Hygiene. London.
    1920   7506129

Trans Sect Ophthalmol Am Acad Ophthalmol Otolaryngol
Transactions. Section on Ophthalmology.
American Academy of Ophthalmology and
Otolaryngology
0161-6978
    Continues in part: Transactions -
    American Academy of Ophthalmology
    and Otolaryngology. Continued by:
    Ophthalmology.
    1975-1977   101227536

Trans Sect Otolaryngol Am Acad Ophthalmol Otolaryngol
Transactions. Section on Otolaryngology.
American Academy of Ophthalmology and
Otolaryngology
0161-696X
    Continues in part: Transactions -
    American Academy of Ophthalmology
    and Otolaryngology. Continued by:
    Otolaryngology.
    1975-1977   101227538

Trans Soc Occup Med
The Transactions of the Society of
Occupational Medicine
0037-9972
    Continues Transactions of the Association
    of Industrial Medical Officers. Continued
    by Journal of the Society of Occupational
    Medicine.
    1966-1972   7506130

Trans South Cent Sect Am Urol Assoc
Transactions. American Urological
Association. South Central Section
    Continues the Transactions of the
    Southwestern Branch of the American
    Urological Association.
    1939-1957   14910230R

Trans South Surg Assoc
Transactions of the Southern Surgical
Association. Southern Surgical Association
(U.S.)
0891-3633
    Continues: Transactions of the Southern
    Surgical and Gynecological Association.
    Southern Surgical and Gynecological
    Association (U.S.).
    1916   20930080R

Trans Southeast Sect Am Urol Assoc
Transactions. American Urological
Association. Southeastern Section
    Continues the Transactions of the
    Southeastern Branch of the American
    Urological Association.
    194u-1960   14910270R

Trans St Johns Hosp Dermatol Soc
Transactions of the St. John's Hospital
Dermatological Society
0036-2891
    Continues London Dermatological Society.
    Transactions and annual report. Superseded
    by Clinical and experimental dermatology.
    1927-1975   7610672

Trans Stud Coll Physicians Phila
Transactions & studies of the College of
Physicians of Philadelphia
0010-1087
    Continues: Transactions of the College of
    Physicians of Philadelphia.
    1938-2002   7506084

Trans West Sect Am Urol Assoc
Transactions. American Urological
Association. Western Section
    1932-1960   0001640

Trans West Surg Assoc
Transactions. Western Surgical Association
    1891-uuuu   21620510R

Transbound Emerg Dis
Transboundary and emerging diseases
1865-1674   1865-1682
    Continues: Journal of veterinary medicine. A.
    Physiology. pathology. clinical medicine.
    2008   101319538

Transcult Psychiatry
Transcultural psychiatry
1363-4615
    Continues: Transcultural psychiatric research
    review.
    1997   9708119

Transfus Apher Sci
Transfusion and apheresis science: official
journal of the World Apheresis Association:
official journal of the European Society for
Haemapheresis
1473-0502
    Continues: Transfusion science.
    2001   101095653

Transfus Clin Biol
Transfusion clinique et biologique: journal
de la Société française de transfusion
sanguine
1246-7820
    Continues: Revue française de transfusion et
    d'hémobiologie.
    1994   9423846

Transfus Med
Transfusion medicine (Oxford, England)
0958-7578   1365-3148
1991   9301182

Transfus Med Rev
Transfusion medicine reviews
0887-7963   1532-9496
1987   8709027

Transfus Sci
Transfusion science
0955-3886
    Continues: Plasma therapy & transfusion
    technology. Continued by: Transfusion and
    apheresis science.
    1989-2000   9001514

Transfusion
Transfusion
0041-1132   1537-2995
1961   0417360

Transfusion (Paris)
Transfusion
    Continued by Revue française de transfusion.
    1958-1967   0155412

Transgenic Res
Transgenic research
0962-8819   1573-9368
1991   9209120

Transl Res
Translational research: the journal of
laboratory and clinical medicine
1931-5244
    Continues: Journal of laboratory and clinical
    medicine.
    2006   101280339

Transpl Immunol
Transplant immunology
0966-3274
1993   9309923

Transpl Infect Dis
Transplant infectious disease: an official
journal of the Transplantation Society
1398-2273   1399-3062
1999   100883688

Transpl Int
Transplant international: official journal
of the European Society for Organ
Transplantation
0934-0874
1988   8908516

Transplant Proc
Transplantation proceedings
0041-1345
1969   0243532

Transplant Rev
Transplantation reviews
0082-5948
    Continued by Immunological reviews.
    1969-1976   0215244

Transplant Rev (Orlando)
Transplantation reviews (Orlando, Fla.)
0955-470X   1557-9816
    Continues: Progress in transplantation.
    1987   8804364

Transplant Sci
Transplantation science
1063-2964
1991-1994   9210307

Transplantation
Transplantation
0041-1337   1534-6080
    Supersedes Transplantation bulletin.
    1963   0132144

Trauma Violence Abuse
Trauma, violence & abuse
1524-8380
2000   100890578

Trav Lab Matiere Med Pharm Galenique Fac Pharm Paris
Travaux des Laboratoires de matière médicale et de pharmacie galénique de la Faculté de pharmacie de Paris
    Continues the Travaux of the Laboratoire de matière médicale.
1920-1976   7506134

Trav Soc Pharm Montp
Travaux de la Société de pharmacie de Montpellier
0037-9115
1942-1982   7507562

Travel Med Infect Dis
Travel medicine and infectious disease
1477-8939
2003   101230758

Trazos (Bilbao)
Trazos; entretenimientos de clínica y terapéutica
1131-1703
1944-19uu   21310110R

Treat Endocrinol
Treatments in endocrinology
1175-6349
2002   101132977

Treat Guidel Med Lett
Treatment guidelines from the Medical Letter
1541-2784   1541-2792
2002   101154157

Treat Respir Med
Treatments in respiratory medicine
1176-3450
    Continues: American journal of respiratory medicine.
2004   101196148

Treat Rev
Treatment review
199u-2000   9507417

Treat Serv Bull
Treatment services bulletin. Canada. Dept. of Veterans' Affairs
    Continued by Canadian services medical journal.
1946-1954   16020690R

TreatmentUpdate
TreatmentUpdate
1181-7186
    Continues: AIDS update (Toronto, Ont.).
1989   100891076

Tree Physiol
Tree physiology
0829-318X   1758-4469
1986   100955338

Trends Amplif
Trends in amplification
1084-7138
1996   9709254

Trends Biochem Sci
Trends in biochemical sciences
0968-0004
1976   7610674

Trends Biotechnol
Trends in biotechnology
0167-7799
1983   8310903

Trends Cardiovasc Med
Trends in cardiovascular medicine
1050-1738   1873-2615
1991   9108337

Trends Cell Biol
Trends in cell biology
0962-8924   1879-3088
1991   9200566

Trends Cogn Sci
Trends in cognitive sciences
1364-6613
1997   9708669

Trends Ecol Evol
Trends in ecology & evolution (Personal edition)
0169-5347
1986   8805125

Trends Endocrinol Metab
Trends in endocrinology and metabolism: TEM
1043-2760
1989   9001516

Trends Genet
Trends in genetics: TIG
0168-9525
1985   8507085

Trends Health Care Law Ethics
Trends in health care, law & ethics
1062-5364
    Continues: Info trends.
1992-1995   9206683

Trends Immunol
Trends in immunology
1471-4906
    Continues: Immunology today.
2001   100966032

Trends Microbiol
Trends in microbiology
0966-842X
1993   9310916

Trends Mol Med
Trends in molecular medicine
1471-4914
    Continues: Molecular medicine today.
2001   100966035

Trends Neurosci
Trends in neurosciences
0166-2236
1978   7808616

Trends Parasitol
Trends in parasitology
1471-4922
    Continues: Parasitology today (Personal ed.).
2001   100966034

Trends Pharmacol Sci
Trends in pharmacological sciences
0165-6147
1979   7906158

Trends Plant Sci
Trends in plant science
1360-1385
1996   9890299

Trends Tech Contemp Dent Lab
Trends & techniques in the contemporary dental laboratory
0746-8962
    Continues: NADL journal. Continued by: Journal of dental technoloogy.
1984-1996   8409547

Trial
Trial (Boston, Mass.)
0041-2538
    Continues: PI & E bulletin.
1964   9876723

Triangle
Triangle; the Sandoz journal of medical science
0041-2597
1952-1993   0417362

Triangulo Rev Sandoz Cienc Med
Triangulo
0493-8798
1952-1986   21310170R

Trib Farm
Tribuna farmacêutica
0371-6619
1932   21310180R

Trib Odontol (B Aires)
La Tribuna odontológica
0041-2775
1916-1978   0404556

Trib Odontol (Guanabara)
Tribuna Odontologica Do Sindicato Dos Odontologistas Do Estado Da Guanabara
19uu   9875641

Trodent
Trodent
    Supersedes: Trodent.
1965   9880767

Trop Anim Health Prod
Tropical animal health and production
0049-4747
1969   1277355

Trop Biomed
Tropical biomedicine
0127-5720
1984   8507086

Trop Dis Bull
Tropical diseases bulletin
0041-3240
    Supersedes the Bulletin of the Sleeping Sickness Bureau and the Kala azar bulletin.
1912   0410477

Trop Doct
Tropical doctor
0049-4755
1971   1301706

Trop Gastroenterol
Tropical gastroenterology: official journal of the Digestive Diseases Foundation
0250-636X
1980   8107122

Trop Geogr Med
Tropical and geographical medicine
0041-3232
    Continues Documenta de medicina geographica et tropica. Merged with: Tropical medicine and parasitology; Annales de la Société belge de médecine tropicale; and: Journal of tropical medicine and hygiene; to form: Tropical medicine & international health.
1958-1995   0376231

Trop Med Int Health
Tropical medicine & international health: TM & IH
1360-2276   1365-3156
    Formed by the merger of: Annales de la Société belge de médecine tropicale; Journal of tropical medicine and hygiene; Tropical and geographical medicine; and: Tropical medicine and parasitology.
1996   9610576

Trop Med Parasitol
Tropical medicine and parasitology: official organ of Deutsche Tropenmedizinische Gesellschaft and of Deutsche Gesellschaft für Technische Zusammenarbeit (GTZ)
0177-2392
  Continues: Tropenmedizin und Parasitologie. Merged with: Annales de la Société belge de médecine tropicale; Journal of tropical medicine and hygiene; and: Tropical and geographical medicine; to form: Tropical medicine & international health.
  1985-1995   8503728

Tropenmed Parasitol
Tropenmedizin und Parasitologie
0303-4208
  Continues Zeitschrift für Tropenmedizin und Parasitologie. Continued by Tropical medicine and parasitology.
  1974-1984   0423216

Trudy Inst Mikrobiol
Trudy Instituta mikrobiologii
0568-5915
  1951-1961   14710400R

Trudy Leningr Inst Epidemiol Mikrobiol Gig Im Pastera
Trudy Leningradskogo instituta épidemiologii, mikrobiologii, i gigieny im. Pastera
  Continued by: Trudy Leningradskogo instituta épidemiologii i mikrobiologii im. Pastera.
  1952-1960   18320240R

Trudy Mosc Russ Vsesoiuznyi Nauchno Issled Vitam Inst
Trudy. Moscow (Russia). Vsesoiuznyĭ nauchno-issledovatel'skiĭ vitaminnyĭ institut
  1936-19uu   18830450R

Trudy Vsesoiuznoe Fiziol Obshchestvo Im I P Pavlov Orenb Otd
Trudy. Vsesoiuznoe fiziologicheskoe obshchestvo imeni I. P. Pavlova. Orenburgskoe otdelenie
  19uu-19uu   21540670R

Trustee
Trustee: the journal for hospital governing boards
0041-3674
  1947   21330020R

Tsa Chih Gaoxiong Yi Xue Yuan Tong Xue Hui
[Tsa chih] [Journal of the] Alumni of the University of Takau. Gaoxiong yi xue yuan. Tong xue hui
  1955-19uu   18120140R

Tsitol Genet
TÕ°Sitologiiâ i genetika
0564-3783
  Continues a periodical with the same title which was published 1965-1966: TÕ°Sitologiiâ i genetika.
  1967   0101671

Tsitologiia
Tsitologiia
0041-3771
  1959   0417363

Tsurumi Shigaku
Tsurumi shigaku. Tsurumi University dental journal
0385-020X
  1975   7700683

Tuber Lung Dis
Tubercle and lung disease: the official journal of the International Union against Tuberculosis and Lung Disease
0962-8479
  Formed by the union of: Tubercle. and: Bulletin of the International Union against Tuberculosis and Lung Disease. Continued by: Tuberculosis (Edinburgh, Scotland).
  1992-2000   9212467

Tubercle
Tubercle
0041-3879
  Merged with: Bulletin of the International Union against Tuberculosis and Lung Disease. to form: Tubercle and lung disease.
  1919-1991   1273730

Tuberculol Thorac Dis
Tuberculology and thoracic diseases
  Continues: Bulletin. American Academy of Tuberculosis Physicians.
  1943-1967   0243626

Tuberculosis (Edinb)
Tuberculosis (Edinburgh, Scotland)
1472-9792   1873-281X
  Continues: Tubercle and lung disease.
  2001   100971555

Tuberk Grenzgeb Einzeldarst
Die Tuberkulose und ihre Grenzgebiete in Einzeldarstellungen
  1927-1967   1302217

Tuberk Kerdesei
Tuberkulózis kérdései
  Continues Pneumonologia Danubiana. Continued by Tuberkulózis.
  1949-1956   21330390R

Tuberk Toraks
Tüberküloz ve toraks
0494-1373
  1953   0417364

Tuberk Tudobetegsegek
Tuberkulózis és tüdöbetegségek
0041-3887
  Continues Tuberkulozis. Continued by Pneumonologia Hungarica.
  1961-1975   7613535

Tuberkulosearzt
Der Tuberkulosearzt
  Continued by Praxis der Pneumologie vereinigt mit "Der Tuberkulosearzt."
  1947-1963   21330340R

Tuberkuloza
Tuberkuloza
  Continued by Plućne bolesti i tuberkuloza.
  1949-1968   0226300

Tuberkulozis
Tuberkulózis
  Continues Tuberkulózis kérdései. Continued by Tuberkulózis és tüdöbetegségek.
  1957-1960   21330380R

Tufts Dent Outlook
Tufts dental outlook
0041-3941
  Continues: Tufts dental students outlook.
  1928-1971   21340140R

Tufts Folia Med
Tufts folia medica
  Continues the Bulletin of Tufts-New England Medical Center.
  1961-1963   0135024

Tufts Health Sci Rev
Tufts health science review
0041-395X
  Supersedes Tufts University Schools of Medicine and Dental Medicine scientific news.
  1970-1977   1252155

Tufts Med J
Tufts medical journal
  Continues Tufts College medical journal. Merged with the Bulletin of the New England Medical Center to form the Bulletin of the Tufts-New England Medical Center.
  1939-1954   21340170R

Tumori
Tumori
0300-8916
  1911   0111356

Tumour Biol
Tumour biology: the journal of the International Society for Oncodevelopmental Biology and Medicine
1010-4283   1423-0380
  Continues: Oncodevelopmental biology and medicine.
  1984   8409922

Tunis Med
La Tunisie médicale
0041-4131
  Continues Revue tunisienne des sciences médicales. Absorbed the Bulletin of the Hôpital Sadiki in Jan. 1947.
  1929   0413766

Turk Hemsire Derg
Türk hemşireler dergisi
0254-234X
  Continued by: Hemşire.
  1950-1995   7802736

Turk Hij Deney Biyol Derg
Türk hijiyen ve deneysel biyoloji dergisi. Turkish bulletin of hygiene and experimental biology
0377-9777
  Continues Türk hijiyen ve tecrübi biyoloji dergisi. Continued by Türk hijiyen ve tecrübî biyoloji dergisi. Turkish bulletin of hygiene and experimental biology.
  1975-1977   7605188

Turk Hij Tecr Biyol Derg
Türk hijiyen ve tecrübi biyoloji dergisi
0049-4844
  Continues Türk ijiyen ve tecrübi biyoloji dergisi. Continued by Türk hijiyen ve deneysel biyoloji dergisi. Turkish bulletin of hygiene and experimental biology.
  1961-1974   7605189

Turk Hij Tecr Biyol Derg
Türk hijiyen ve tecrübî biyoloji dergisi. Turkish bulletin of hygiene and experimental biology
0049-4844
  Continues: Türk hijiyen ve deneysel biyoloji dergisi. Turkish bulletin of hygiene and experimental biology. Continued by: Türk hijiyen ve deneysel biyoloji dergisi (1982).
  1977-1978   7802267

Turk J Gastroenterol
The Turkish journal of gastroenterology: the official journal of Turkish Society of Gastroenterology
1300-4948
  Continues: Gastroenteroloji.
  1995   9515841

Turk J Pediatr
The Turkish journal of pediatrics
0041-4301
  1958   0417505

Turk Kardiyol Dern Ars
Türk Kardiyoloji Derneği arşivi: Türk Kardiyoloji Derneğinin yayın organıdır
1016-5169   1308-4488
  1972   9426239

Turk Neurosurg
Turkish neurosurgery
1019-5149
  1989   9423821

Turk Ortodonti Derg
Türk ortodonti dergisi: Ortodonti
Derneğ'nin resmi yayin organidir = Turkish
journal of orthodontics
1300-3550
1988　　　　　　　　　　　9114702

Turk Psikiyatri Derg
Türk psikiyatri dergisi = Turkish journal of
psychiatry
1300-2163
1990　　　　　　　　　　　9425936

Turk Tip Cemiy Mecm
Türk Tip Cemīyetī mecmuasi
0494-2736
　　　Continued by Türk Tip Derneğī dergīsī.
1935-1973　　　　　　　　7600196

Turk Tip Dernegi Derg
Türk Tip Derneğī dergīsī
0377-2497
　　　Continues Türk Tip Cemīyetī mecmuasi.
1973-1989　　　　　　　　7600197

Turkiye Parazitol Derg
Türkiye parazitolojii dergisi / Türkiye
Parazitoloji Derneği = Acta parasitologica
Turcica / Turkish Society for Parasitology
1300-6320
1978-uuuu　　　　　　　　9425544

Turtox News
Turtox news
0096-3895
1923-1975　　　　　　　21340280R

TVZ
TVZ: het vakblad voor de verpleging
0303-6456
　　　Continues: Tijdschrift voor ziekenverpleging.
1988　　　　　　　　　　　8915593

Twin Res
Twin research: the official journal of the
International Society for Twin Studies
1369-0523
　　　Continued by: Twin research and human
　　　genetics.
1998-2004　　　　　　　　9815819

Twin Res Hum Genet
Twin research and human genetics: the
official journal of the International Society
for Twin Studies
1832-4274
　　　Continues: Twin research.
2005　　　　　　　　　101244624

U

U S Armed Forces Med J
United States Armed Forces medical journal
0566-0777
　　　Supersedes Bulletin of the U. S. Army
　　　Medical Dept. and U. S. Naval medical
　　　bulletin.
1950-1960　　　　　　　21410750R

U S Nav Med Bull
United States naval medical bulletin
1907-1949　　　　　　　21420350R

Uch Zap Inst Farmakol Khimioter AMN SSSR
Uchenye zapiski Instituta farmakologii i
khimioterapii AMN SSSR
0515-9296
1958-1963　　　　　　　　7514166

Uchenye Zap Mosk Meditsinskii Inst
Uchenye zapiski. Vtoroĭ Moskovskiĭ ordena
Lenina gosudarstvennyĭ meditŝinskiĭ institut
im N.I. Pirogova
1951-19uu　　　　　　　18830110R

Uchenye Zap Seriia Biolog Leningr Univ
Uchenye zapiski. Seriia biologicheskaia.
Leningrad. Universitet
1935-19uu　　　　　　　18320230R

UCLA Forum Med Sci
UCLA forum in medical sciences
0082-7134
1961-1990　　　　　　　　0067303

UCLA Rep
UCLA [reports]. U.S. Atomic Energy
Commission
1949-1971　　　　　　　21830740R

UCRL US At Energy Comm
UCRL [reports]. U.S. Atomic Energy
Commission
0096-8188
1969-19uu　　　　　　　　0231433

Ugeskr Laeger
Ugeskrift for laeger
0041-5782　　　　　　　　1603-6824
　　　Continued in part by: Klaringsrapport.
1839　　　　　　　　　　　0141730

Uirusu
Uirusu. Journal of virology
0042-6857
　　　Continues Virus.
1951　　　　　　　　　　　0417475

Uisahak
ŭi sahak
1225-505X
1992　　　　　　　　　　　9605018

UJCD Union Jeunes Chir Dent
Ujcd. Union Des Jeunes Chirurgiens-Dentistes
　　　Continued by: Fluxio.
1973　　　　　　　　　　　9881979

Ukr Biokhim Zh
Ukraïns'kyĭ biokhimichnyĭ zhurnal
0041-610X
　　　Continues Biokhimichnyĭ zhurnal. Continued
　　　by Ukrainskiĭ biokhimicheskiĭ zhurnal.
1946-1977　　　　　　　　0414153

Ukr Biokhim Zh
Ukrainskiĭ biokhimicheskiĭ zhurnal
0201-8470
　　　Continues Ukraïns'kyĭ biokhimichnyĭ zhurnal.
1978　　　　　　　　　　　7804246

Ulster Med J
The Ulster medical journal
0041-6193
　　　Supersedes: Transactions of the Ulster
　　　Medical Society.
1932　　　　　　　　　　　0417367

Ultramicroscopy
Ultramicroscopy
0304-3991
1975　　　　　　　　　　　7513702

Ultraschall Med
Ultraschall in der Medizin (Stuttgart,
Germany: 1980)
0172-4614　　　　　　　　1438-8782
1980　　　　　　　　　　　8303585

Ultrason Imaging
Ultrasonic imaging
0161-7346　　　　　　　　1096-0910
1979　　　　　　　　　　　7909167

Ultrason Sonochem
Ultrasonics sonochemistry
1350-4177
1994　　　　　　　　　　　9433356

Ultrasonics
Ultrasonics
0041-624X　　　　　　　　1874-9968
1963　　　　　　　　　　　0050452

Ultrasound Med Biol
Ultrasound in medicine & biology
0301-5629　　　　　　　　1879-291X
1973　　　　　　　　　　　0410553

Ultrasound Obstet Gynecol
Ultrasound in obstetrics & gynecology: the
official journal of the International Society
of Ultrasound in Obstetrics and Gynecology
0960-7692　　　　　　　　1469-0705
1991　　　　　　　　　　　9108340

Ultrasound Q
Ultrasound quarterly
0894-8771　　　　　　　　1536-0253
　　　Continues: Ultrasound annual.
1988　　　　　　　　　　　8809459

Ultrastruct Pathol
Ultrastructural pathology
0191-3123　　　　　　　　1521-0758
1980　　　　　　　　　　　8002867

Ulus Travma Acil Cerrahi Derg
Ulusal travma ve acil cerrahi dergisi =
Turkish journal of trauma & emergency
surgery: TJTES
1306-696X
　　　Continues: Ulusal travma dergisi.
2003　　　　　　　　　101274231

Ulus Travma Derg
Ulusal travma dergisi = Turkish journal of
trauma & emergency surgery: TJTES
1300-6738
　　　Continued by: Ulusal travma ve acil cerrahi
　　　dergisi.
1995-2002　　　　　　　　9700063

UNA Commun
UNA communiqué
0162-7287
　　　Continued by: One on one.
1975-1979　　　　　　　　7802522

UNA Nurs J
UNA nursing journal
1904-1976　　　　　　　21410020R

Undersea Biomed Res
Undersea biomedical research
0093-5387
　　　Merged with: Journal of hyperbaric medicine,
　　　to form: Undersea & hyperbaric medicine.
1974-1992　　　　　　　　0421514

Undersea Hyperb Med
Undersea & hyperbaric medicine: journal
of the Undersea and Hyperbaric Medical
Society, Inc
1066-2936
　　　Merger of: Undersea biomedical research,
　　　and: Journal of hyperbaric medicine, and
　　　continues the numbering of the former.
1993　　　　　　　　　　　9312954

Unfallchirurg
Der Unfallchirurg
0177-5537
　　　Continues: Unfallheilkunde.
1985　　　　　　　　　　　8502736

Unfallchirurgie
Unfallchirurgie
0340-2649
　　　Continued by: European journal of trauma.
1975-1999　　　　　　　　7909168

Unfallheilkunde
Unfallheilkunde
0341-5694
　　　Continues Monatsschrift für Unfallheilkunde.
　　　Continued by Der Unfallchirurg.
1976-1984　　　　　　　　7612225

Union Med Can
L'union médicale du Canada
0041-6959
Absorbed the Bulletin of the Association des médecins de langue française de l' Amérique du Nord in jan. 1938-
1872-1995 **0030444**

Union Med Prat Francais
L'Union médicale des praticiens français
Continues L'Union médicale; journal des médecins praticiens français. - cf. Academie des sciences. Paris. Inventaire des periodiques scientifiques des bibliothèques de Paris.
1912-19uu **21410190R**

Univ Coll Hosp Mag
The University College Hospital magazine
1910-1970 **21430010R**

Univ Durh Med Gaz
University of Durham medical gazette
Continues: University of Durham School of Medicine gazette. Continued by: University of Newcastle upon Tyne medical gazette.
1943-19uu **21430120R**

Univ Hosp Bull
University Hospital bulletin
0199-9680
Continued by: Medical bulletin (Ann Arbor. Mich.).
1935-1949 **21430030R**

Univ Manit Med J
The University of Manitoba medical journal
0076-4108
Continued by: Manitoba medicine.
1929-1986 **0413770**

Univ Mich Med Cent J
University of Michigan Medical Center journal
0041-9826
Continues: Medical bulletin (Ann Arbor. Mich.).
1964-1981 **0417371**

Univ Minn Med Bull
University of Minnesota medical bulletin
Continues the Bulletin of the University of Minnesota Hospitals and Minnesota Medical Foundation.
1955 **0417454**

Univ Newcastle Tyne Med Gaz
University of Newcastle upon Tyne medical gazette
Continues the University of Durham medical gazette.
1963-1975 **0045472**

Univ South Calif Bull Sch Med
School of Medicine. University of Southern California. School of Medicine
Continues: Announcements.. University of Southern California. School of Medicine. Continued by: Medicine. University of Southern California. School of Medicine.
1932-199u **101144289**

Univ Tor Dent J
University of Toronto dental journal
0843-5812
Continues: University of Toronto undergraduate dental journal.
1987-1998 **8808558**

Univ Toronto Med J
University of Toronto medical journal
0042-0239
Continued by Medical journal. University of Toronto.
1923-1976 **0413577**

Univ Toronto Undergrad Dent J
University of Toronto undergraduate dental journal
0042-0255
Continued by: University of Toronto dental journal.
1964-1978 **7905911**

Univ West Ont Med J
University of Western Ontario medical journal
Continued by: UWO medical journal.
1930-1956 **21350030R**

Update Ethics
Update On Ethics
Continued by: Journal Of Nursing Ethics.
1977-1977 **9878819**

Update Natl Minor AIDS Counc
Update (National Minority AIDS Council)
Continued by: LifeLine online.
199u-uuuu **9888940**

Update Pediatr Dent
Update in pediatric dentistry
0897-876X
1987-1991 **8915897**

Ups J Med Sci
Upsala journal of medical sciences
0300-9734
Continues Acta Societatis Medicorum Upsaliensis.
1972 **0332203**

Ups J Med Sci Suppl
Upsala journal of medical sciences. Supplement
0300-9726
Continues Acta Societatis Medicorum Upsaliensis. Supplement.
1972 **0331622**

Upsala Lakareforen Forh
Upsala läkareförenings förhandlingar
Continued by Acta Societatis Medicorum Upsaliensis.
1865-1949 **0072564**

UR Rep
UR [reports]. U.S. Atomic Energy Commission
1948-1971 **21830790R**

Urban Health
Urban health
0191-8257
1972-1985 **0332570**

Uremia Invest
Uremia investigation
0740-1353
Continues: Clinical and experimental dialysis and apheresis. Continued by: Renal failure.
1984-1986 **8411625**

Urol Clin North Am
The Urologic clinics of North America
0094-0143
1974 **0423221**

Urol Int
Urologia internationalis
0042-1138 **1423-0399**
Absorbed: Acta urologica italica. 2000
1955 **0417373**

Urol J
Urology journal
1735-1308 **1735-546X**
2003 **101286676**

Urol Mosc
Urologiiâ (Moscow, Russia: 1923)
Continued by Urologiia i nefrologiia.
1923-1964 **0032351**

Urol Nefrol (Mosk)
Urologiiâ i nefrologiiâ
0042-1154
Continues: Urologiia. Continued by: Urologiiâ (Moscow, Russia: 1999).
1965-1999 **0032352**

Urol Nurs
Urologic nursing: official journal of the American Urological Association Allied
1053-816X
Continues: AUAA journal.
1988 **8812256**

Urol Oncol
Urologic oncology
1078-1439
1995 **9805460**

Urol Pol
Urologia polska
0500-7208
1951 **21430310R**

Urol Radiol
Urologic radiology
0171-1091
Merged with: Gastrointestinal radiology; to form: Abdominal imaging.
1979-1992 **7909483**

Urol Res
Urological research
0300-5623
1973 **0364311**

Urol Surv
Urological survey
0042-1146
1951-1981 **0417375**

Urologe
Der Urologe
Continued by Der Urologe. Ausg. A.
1962-1969 **1304107**

Urologe A
Der Urologe. Ausg. A
0340-2592
Absorbed: Urologe. Ausg. B. 2003 Continues Der Urologe.
1970 **1304110**

Urologia
Urologia
0391-5603
1934 **0417372**

Urologiia
Urologiiâ (Moscow, Russia: 1999)
1728-2985
Continues: Urologiiâ i nefrologiiâ.
1999 **100900900**

Urology
Urology
0090-4295 **1527-9995**
1973 **0366151**

US Healthc
U.S. healthcare
1040-3973
Continues: Healthcare computing & communications. Continued by: Healthcare informatics.
1988-1990 **8812252**

US Med
U. S. medicine
0191-6246
1965 **0243631**

US Navy Med
U. S. Navy medicine
0364-6807
Continues: Navy medical newsletter. Continued by: Navy medicine.
1970-1987 **1253474**

US News World Rep
U.S. news & world report
0041-5537
Formed by the union of: United States news, and: World report.
1948   9877797

Usp Biol Khim
Uspekhi biologicheskoĭ khimii
0130-7371
1950   0417376

Usp Fiziol Nauk
Uspekhi fiziologicheskikh nauk
0301-1798
1970   0310750

Usp Khim
Uspekhi khimii
0042-1308
1932   2984864R

Usp Sovrem Biol
Uspekhi sovremennoĭ biologii
0042-1324
1932   0413771

Utah Nurse
Utah nurse
0049-5727
Continued by: UNA communiqué.
1950-1975   21430480R

Uttar Pradesh State Dent J
The Uttar Pradesh State dental journal: an official publication of the State U.P. Dental Branch of the Indian Dental Association
0253-8016
1970-1980   8109330

UWFL Rep
UWFL [reports]. U.S. Atomic Energy Commission
1955-1965   21830800R

V

Va Dent J
Virginia dental journal
0049-6472
Continues the Bulletin of the Virginia State Dental Association.
1964   0055616

Va Health Bull
Virginia health bulletin
0042-6547
Continues: Health bulletin (Virginia. Dept. of Health). Continued by: Virginia's health.
1948-1979   0251150

Va J Sci
Virginia journal of science
0042-658X
1940   21520650R

Va Med
Virginia medical
0146-3616
Continues Virginia medical monthly. Continued by: Virginia medical quarterly.
1976-1990   7701976

Va Med Mon (1918)
Virginia medical monthly
0042-6644
Supersedes: Virginia medical semimonthly. Continued by: Virginia medical.
1918-1976   0407231

Va Med Q
Virginia medical quarterly: VMQ
1052-4231
Continues: Virginia medical.
1990-1998   9104333

Va Nurse
Virginia nurse
0270-7780
Continues Virginia nurse quarterly. Continued by: Virginia nurses today.
1976-1992   8005511

Va Nurse Q
Virginia nurse quarterly
0042-6695
Continued by Virginia nurse.
1934-1975   0042334

Vaccine
Vaccine
0264-410X
1983   8406899

Vakbl Biol
Vakblad voor biologen
0042-2215
Continued by: Biovisie.
1919-1988   21440140R

Valsalva
Il Valsalva
0042-2371
1925   0417400

Value Health
Value in health: the journal of the International Society for Pharmacoeconomics and Outcomes Research
1098-3015   1524-4733
1998   100883818

Vard Nord Utveckl Forsk
Vård i Norden
0107-4083
1981   8700224

Vardfacket
Vårdfacket
0347-0911
Supersedes Tidskrift för Sveriges sjuksköterskor.
1977   7708473

Vasa
VASA. Zeitschrift für Gefässkrankheiten. Journal for vascular diseases
0301-1526
Supersedes Zentralblatt für Phlebologie.
1972   0317051

Vasa Suppl
VASA. Supplementum
0251-1029
1973   8704474

Vasc Dis
Vascular diseases
0506-4287
Absorbed by: Angiology, Jan. 1969.
1964-1968   0202051

Vasc Endovascular Surg
Vascular and endovascular surgery
1538-5744
Continues: Vascular surgery.
2002   101136421

Vasc Health Risk Manag
Vascular health and risk management
1176-6344   1178-2048
2005   101273479

Vasc Med
Vascular medicine (London, England)
1358-863X
Merger of: Journal of vascular medicine and biology, and: Vascular medicine review.
1996   9610930

Vasc Surg
Vascular surgery
0042-2835
Continued by: Vascular and endovascular surgery.
1967-2001   0103277

Vascul Pharmacol
Vascular pharmacology
1537-1891
Continues: General pharmacology.
2002   101130615

Vascular
Vascular
1708-5381   1708-539X
Continues: Cardiovascular surgery (London, England).
2004   101196722

Vector Borne Zoonotic Dis
Vector borne and zoonotic diseases (Larchmont, N.Y.)
1530-3667   1557-7759
2001   100965525

Veg Bode
Vegetarische bode
1897-1969   21440390R

Venez Odontol
Venezuela odontológica
1934-1985   21440530R

Verh Anat Ges
Verhandlungen der Anatomischen Gesellschaft
0066-1562
1887   7501276

Verh Dtsch Ges Herz Kreislaufforsch
Verhandlungen der Deutschen Gesellschaft für Herz- und Kreislaufforschung
0174-2817
Continues Verhandlungen der Deutschen Gesellschaft für Kreislaufforschung.
1979-1983   8005742

Verh Dtsch Ges Inn Med
Verhandlungen der Deutschen Gesellschaft für Innere Medizin
0070-4067
Continues the Verhandlungen of the Deutscher Kongress für Innere Medizin.
1921-1991   7503702

Verh Dtsch Ges Kreislaufforsch
Verhandlungen der Deutschen Gesellschaft für Kreislaufforschung
0070-4075
Continued by Verhandlungen der Deutschen Gesellschaft für Herz- und Kreislaufforschung.
1928-1978   7503703

Verh Dtsch Ges Pathol
Verhandlungen der Deutschen Gesellschaft für Pathologie
0070-4113
Continues the Verhandlungen of the Deutsche Pathologische Gesellschaft.
1948   7503704

Verh Dtsch Ges Rheumatol
Verhandlungen der Deutschen Gesellschaft für Rheumatologie
0070-4121
1969-1981   7507680

Verh K Acad Geneeskd Belg
Verhandelingen - Koninklijke Academie voor Geneeskunde van België
0302-6469
Continues Verhandelingen - Koninklijke Vlaamse Academie voor Geneeskunde van België.
1973   0413210

Verh K Vlaam Acad Geneeskd Belg
Verhandelingen - Koninklijke Vlaamse
Academie voor Geneeskunde van België
0300-9017
Continued by Verhandelingen - Koninklijke
Academie voor Geneeskunde van België.
1939-1972   0413004

Veroff Morphol Pathol
Veröffentlichungen aus der morphologischen
Pathologie
0372-6312
Continues Veröffentlichungen aus der
Konstitutions- und Wehrpathologie.
Continued by Veröffentlichungen aus der
Pathologie.
1950-1974   7503946

Veroff Pathol
Veröffentlichungen aus der Pathologie
0340-241X
Continues Veröffentlichungen aus der
morphologischen Pathologie.
1974-1997   7504167

Veroff Schweiz Ges Gesch Med Naturwiss
Veröffentlichungen der Schweizerischen
Gesellschaft für Geschichte der Medizin und
der Naturwissenschaften
Continued by: Gesnerus. Supplement.
1922-1987   7507682

Veroff Schweiz Ges Gesch Pharm
Veröffentlichungen der Schweizerischen
Gesellschaft für Geschichte der Pharmazie
/ herausgegeben vom Vorstand der
Schweizerischen Gesellschaft für Geschichte
der Pharmazie (SGGP)
0258-6940
1982   8307714

Verpleegkd Gem
Verpleegkundigen en gemeenschapszorg:
tijdschrift van de het Nationaal Verbond der
Katholieke Vlaamse Verplegenden
Continues: Verplegenden en
gemeenschapszorg.
1975-1996   9425471

Verpleegkunde
Verpleegkunde
0920-3273
1986   9419243

Versicherungsmedizin
Versicherungsmedizin / herausgegeben
von Verband der Lebensversicherungs-
Unternehmen e.V. und Verband der Privaten
Krankenversicherung e.V
0933-4548
Continues: Lebensversicherungs Medizin.
1988   8803623

Verslag Meded Betreff Volksgezond
Verslagen en mededelingen betreffende de
volksgezondheid
0300-1024
Continued by Volksgezonheid.
1921-1969   0351060

Vertex
Vertex (Buenos Aires, Argentina)
0327-6139
1990   9440528

Vesalius
Vesalius: acta internationales historiae
medicinae
1995   9517855

Veska
Veska
1937-1979   0031153

Vestn Akad Med Nauk SSSR
Vestnik Akademii meditsinskikh nauk SSSR
0002-3027
Continued by: Vestnik Rossiĭskoĭ akademii
meditsinskikh nauk.
1946-1992   7506153

Vestn Akad Nauk SSSR
Vestnik Akademii nauk SSSR
0002-3442
Continued by: Vestnik Rossiiskoi akademii
nauk.
1931-1992   7501279

Vestn Ceskoslov Lekaru
Věstník československých lékařů
0231-5157
Continues Věstník českých lékařů.
1945-1950   7901950

Vestn Dermatol Venerol
Vestnik dermatologii i venerologii
0042-4609
Continues Vestnik venerologii i dermatologii.
1957   0414246

Vestn Khir Im I I Grek
Vestnik khirurgii imeni I. I. Grekova
0042-4625
Continues Vestnik khirurgii i pogranichnykh
oblasteĭ.
1935   0411377

Vestn Leningr Univ [Biol]
Vestnik Leningradskogo universiteta.
Biologiia
0321-186X
Continues Vestnik Leningradskogo
universiteta. Seriia biologii.
1956-1997   0414647

Vestn Oftalmol
Vestnik oftalmologii
0042-465X
Continues Sovetskii vestnik oftalmologii.
1937   0415216

Vestn Otorinolaringol
Vestnik otorinolaringologii
0042-4668
Continues: Vestnik sovetskoĭ oto-rino-
laringologii.
1936   0416577

Vestn Rentgenol Radiol
Vestnik rentgenologii i radiologii
0042-4676
1920   0424741

Vestn Ross Akad Med Nauk
Vestnik Rossiĭskoĭ akademii meditsinskikh
nauk / Rossiĭskaia akademiia meditsinskikh
nauk
0869-6047
Continues: Vestnik Akademii meditsinskikh
nauk SSSR.
1992   9215641

Vestn Venerol Dermatol
Vestnik venerologii i dermatologii
0302-6051
Continues Sovetskiĭ vestnik venerologii i
dermatologii.
1937-1956   0412033

Vet Anaesth Analg
Veterinary anaesthesia and analgesia
1467-2987   1467-2995
Continues: Journal of veterinary anaesthesia.
2000   100956422

Vet Bull
The Veterinary bulletin
0042-4854
Supersedes the Tropical veterinary bulletin.
1931   0111277

Vet Clin North Am
The Veterinary clinics of North America
0091-0279
Continued by Veterinary clinics of North
America. Small animal practice.
1971-1978   1247712

Vet Clin North Am Equine Pract
The Veterinary clinics of North America.
Equine practice
0749-0739   1558-4224
Continues in part: Veterinary clinics of North
America. Large animal practice.
1985   8511904

Vet Clin North Am Exot Anim Pract
The veterinary clinics of North America.
Exotic animal practice
1094-9194
1998   9815628

Vet Clin North Am Food Anim Pract
The Veterinary clinics of North America.
Food animal practice
0749-0720
Continues in part: The Veterinary clinics of
North America. Large animal practice.
1985   8511905

Vet Clin North Am Large Anim Pract
The Veterinary clinics of North America.
Large animal practice
0196-9846
Split into: Veterinary clinics of North
America. Equine practice; and: Veterinary
clinics of North America. Food animal
practice.
1979-1984   7810187

Vet Clin North Am Small Anim Pract
The Veterinary clinics of North America.
Small animal practice
0195-5616
Continues Veterinary clinics of North
America.
1979   7809942

Vet Clin Pathol
Veterinary clinical pathology / American
Society for Veterinary Clinical Pathology
0275-6382
Continues: Bulletin of the American Society
of Veterinary Clinical Pathologists. American
Society of Veterinary Clinical Pathologists.
1977   9880575

Vet Comp Oncol
Veterinary and comparative oncology
1476-5810   1476-5829
2003   101185242

Vet Comp Orthop Traumatol
Veterinary and comparative orthopaedics
and traumatology: V.C.O.T
0932-0814
1988   8906319

Vet Dermatol
Veterinary dermatology
0959-4493   1365-3164
1989   9426187

Vet Ext Q
Veterinary extension quarterly
0097-6989
1921-1959   21520010R

Vet Herit
Veterinary heritage: bulletin of the
American Veterinary History Society
Continues: Newsletter (American Veterinary
Historical Society).
1982   8508267

Vet Hum Toxicol
Veterinary and human toxicology
0145-6296
Continues: Veterinary toxicology.
1977-2004   7704194

Vet Immunol Immunopathol
Veterinary immunology and
immunopathology
0165-2427
1979   8002006

Vet J
Veterinary journal (London, England: 1997)
1090-0233
Continues: British veterinary journal.
1997   9706281

Vet Med
Veterinary medicine
0372-5588
Continues the American journal of veterinary
medicine. Merged with Small animal
clinician, to form: Veterinary medicine and
small animal clinician.
1920-1963   21520030R

Vet Med (Praha)
Veterinární medicína
0375-8427
1956   0063417

Vet Med Nauki
Veterinarno-meditsinski nauki
0324-1068
1964-1987   0414760

Vet Med Rev
Veterinary medical review
0506-8274
1966-1991   0060752

Vet Med Small Anim Clin
Veterinary medicine, small animal clinician:
VM, SAC
0042-4889
Formed by the union of: Veterinary medicine;
and: Small animal clinician. Continued by:
Veterinary medicine (Edwardsville, Kan.).
1964-1984   8707901

Vet Microbiol
Veterinary microbiology
0378-1135
1976   7705469

Vet Ophthalmol
Veterinary ophthalmology
1463-5216   1463-5224
Continues: Veterinary & comparative
ophthalmology.
1998   100887377

Vet Parasitol
Veterinary parasitology
0304-4017
1975   7602745

Vet Pathol
Veterinary pathology
0300-9858
Continues Pathologia veterinaria.
1971   0312020

Vet Pathol Suppl
Veterinary pathology. Supplement
0191-3808
1978-1982   7901021

Vet Q
The Veterinary quarterly
0165-2176   1875-5941
Supersedes the quarterly English issues of
Tijdschrift voor diergeneeskunde.
1979   7909485

Vet Radiol Ultrasound
Veterinary radiology & ultrasound: the
official journal of the American College of
Veterinary Radiology and the International
Veterinary Radiology Association
1058-8183   1740-8261
Continues: Veterinary radiology.
1992   9209635

Vet Rec
The Veterinary record
0042-4900
Supersedes: Veterinary record, and
Transactions of the Veterinary Medical
Association.
1888   0031164

Vet Res
Veterinary research
0928-4249
Continues: Annales de recherches
vétérinaires.
1993   9309551

Vet Res Commun
Veterinary research communications
0165-7380
Continues: Veterinary science
communications.
1980   8100520

Vet Surg
Veterinary surgery: VS: the official journal
of the American College of Veterinary
Surgeons
0161-3499   1532-950X
Continues: Journal of veterinary surgery.
1978   8113214

Vet Ther
Veterinary therapeutics: research in applied
veterinary medicine
1528-3593
2000   100936368

Veterinaria
Veterinaria
1937   0115340

Veterinaria
Veterinária
1964-19uu   0064270

Veterinarian
The Veterinarian
1963-1969   21510270R

Veterinariia
Veterinariia
0042-4846
Continues Sovetskaia veterinariia.
1941   0412751

Veterinarstvi
Veterinářství
0506-8231
1950-19uu   0102017

Viata Med
Viaţa medicală
0042-5036
Continued by Viaţa medicală; revista
de informare profesională şi ştiinţifică a
medicilor.
1954-1974   7609485

Viata Med Rev Inf Prof Stiint Cadrelor Medii Sanit
Viaţa medicală; revistă de informare
profesională şi ştiinţifică a cadrelor medii
sanitare
Continues Munca sanitară.
1974-1990   7609486

Vic Stud
Victorian studies
0042-5222
1957   9426344

Vida Med
Vida médica
1931-19uu   21520170R

Vida Nueva
Vida nueva
1909-19uu   21520190R

Vida Odontol
Vida Odontologica
1978-uuuu   9880753

Vie Med Can Fr
La Vie médicale au Canada français
0301-1534
Continues: Laval médical.
1972-1982   0316264

Vie Med Evolut Med Ther
La Vie médicale. Evolution médicale et
thérapeutique
0505-4966
1961-1967   21520270R

Vierteljahrsschr Schweiz Sanitatsoff
Vierteljahrsschrift für schweizerische
Sanitätsoffiziere. Journal trimestriel des
officiers suisses du service de santé. Rivista
trimestrale degli ufficiali sanitari svizzeri
Continued by Schweizerische Zeitschrift für
Militärmedizin.
1924-1966   0126374

Vigilando
Vigilando
Continues: Johns Hopkins Nurses' alumni
magazine.
1991-1992   9307041

Villaclara Med
Villaclara médica
1933-19uu   21520560R

VINA Q
Vina quarterly
0049-6464
Superseded by: Vina news.
1964-1967   0031221

Violence Against Women
Violence against women
1077-8012
1995   9506308

Violence Vict
Violence and victims
0886-6708
1986   8916436

Viral Immunol
Viral immunology
0882-8245   1557-8976
1987   8801552

Virchows Arch
Virchows Archiv: an international journal of
pathology
0945-6317
Merger of: Virchows Archiv. A, Pathological
anatomy and histopathology, and: Virchows
Archiv. B, Cell pathology including
molecular pathology, and continues the
numbering of the former.
1994   9423843

Virchows Arch A Pathol Anat Histol
Virchows Archiv. A, Pathological anatomy
and histology
0340-1227
Continues: Virchows Archiv. A, Pathology.
Pathologische Anatomie. Continued by:
Virchows Archiv. A, Pathological anatomy
and histopathology.
1974-1982   7505137

Virchows Arch A Pathol Anat Histopathol
Virchows Archiv. A, Pathological anatomy
and histopathology
0174-7398
Continues: Virchows Archiv. A. Pathological
anatomy and histology. Merged with:
Virchows Archiv. B, Cell pathology including
molecular pathology, to form: Virchows
Archiv.
1982-1993   8302198

Virchows Arch A Pathol Pathol Anat
Virchows Archiv. A: Pathology.
Pathologische Anatomie
0042-6423
Continued by Virchows Archiv. A.
Pathological anatomy and histology.
1968-1973   0141343

Virchows Arch B Cell Pathol
Virchows Archiv. B: Cell pathology
0340-6075
Continues: Frankfurter Zeitschrift für
Pathologie. Continues in part: Virchows
Archiv für pathologische Anatomie und
Physiologie und für klinische Medizin.
Formed in part by the union of Virchows
Archiv für pathologische Anatomie und
Physiologie und für klinische Medizin;
and Frankfurter Zeitschrift für Pathologie.
Continued by: Virchows Archiv. B. Cell
pathology including molecular pathology.
1968-1979   0437105

Virchows Arch B Cell Pathol Incl Mol Pathol
Virchows Archiv. B, Cell pathology including
molecular pathology
0340-6075
Continues: Virchows Archiv. B. Cell
pathology. Merged with: Virchows Archiv. A,
Pathological anatomy and histopathology, to
form: Virchows Archiv.
1979-1993   9316922

Virchows Arch Pathol Anat Physiol Klin Med
Virchows Archiv für pathologische Anatomie
und Physiologie und für klinische Medizin
0376-0081
Continues Archiv für pathologische Anatomie
und Physiologie und für klinische Medizin.
Merged with Frankfurter Zeitschrift füe
Pathologie to form Virchows Archiv. A:
Pathology. Pathologische Anatomie: and
Virchows Archiv. B: cell pathology.
1903-1968   0217007

Virol J
Virology journal
      1743-422X
2004   101231645

Virol Monogr
Virology monographs. Die Virusforschung in
Einzeldarstellungen
0083-6591
Supersedes Handbook of virus research.
1968-1981   0170663

Virologie
Virologie
0377-8177
Continues Revue roumaine de virologie.
Continued by: Revue roumaine de virologie
(Bucharest. Romania: 1990).
1975-1989   7605765

Virology
Virology
0042-6822   1096-0341
1955   0110674

Virus
Virus
Continued by Uirusu.
1951-1957   21530010R

Virus Genes
Virus genes
0920-8569
1987   8803967

Virus Res
Virus research
0168-1702
1984   8410979

Virus Res Suppl
Virus research. Supplement
0921-2590
1985-1988   8611941

Vis Neurosci
Visual neuroscience
0952-5238   1469-8714
1988   8809466

Vision Res
Vision research
0042-6989   1878-5646
Absorbed: Clinical vision sciences.
1961   0417402

Vita Hum Int Z Lebensalterforsch
Vita humana. Internationale Zeitschrift
für Lebensaltersforschung. International
journal of human development. Journal
international de développement humain
Continued by Human development.
1958-1964   0166302

Vital Health Stat 1
Vital and health statistics. Ser. 1, Programs
and collection procedures
0083-2014
Supersedes Health statistics, ser. A. of the U.
S. National Health Survey.
1963   0414006

Vital Health Stat 10
Vital and health statistics. Series 10, Data
from the National Health Survey
0083-1972
1963   7604043

Vital Health Stat 11
Vital and health statistics. Series 11, Data
from the national health survey
0083-1980
1964   0414007

Vital Health Stat 13
Vital and health statistics. Series 13, Data
from the National Health Survey
0083-2006
Absorbed: Vital and health statistics. Series
12. Data from the national health survey.
1966   0403032

Vital Health Stat 14
Vital & health statistics. Series 14, Data
from the national health survey
Continues: Vital & health statistics. Series 14.
Data from the national inventory of family
planning services.
1982-1989   8900574

Vital Health Stat 14
Vital & health statistics. Series 14, Data
from the national inventory of family
planning services
Continues: Vital and health statistics. Series
14, Data on national health resources.
Continued by: Vital & health statistics. Series
14. Data from the national health survey.
1982-1982   8900451

Vital Health Stat 14
Vital and health statistics. Series 14, Data on
national health resources
0083-1999
Continued by: Vital & health statistics. Series
14. Data from the national inventory of
family planning services.
1968-1981   0165703

Vital Health Stat 2
Vital and health statistics. Series 2, Data
evaluation and methods research
0083-2057
Supersedes National Health Survey's Health
statistics, ser. D.
1963   0330122

Vital Health Stat 20
Vital and health statistics. Series 20, Data
from the National Vital Statistics System
0083-2022
1965   0044071

Vital Health Stat 21
Vital and health statistics. Series 21, Data
from the National Vital Statistics System
0083-2030
Continued by: Vital and health statistics.
Series 21, Data on natality. marriage, and
divorce.
1964-1989   0032510

Vital Health Stat 21
Vital and health statistics. Series 21, Data on
natality, marriage, and divorce
1057-7629
Continues: Vital and health statistics. Series
21. Data from the National Vital Statistics
System.
1989   9105104

Vital Health Stat 23
Vital and health statistics. Series 23, Data
from the National Survey of Family Growth
0278-5234
1977   7901947

Vital Health Stat 3
Vital & health statistics. Series 3, Analytical
and epidemiological studies / [U.S. Dept.
of Health and Human Services, Public
Health Service, National Center for Health
Statistics]
0886-4691
Continues: Vital and health statistics. Series
3. Analytical studies.
1983   8405154

Vital Health Stat 3
Vital and health statistics. Series 3,
Analytical studies
0083-2065
Continued by Vital & health statistics. Series
3, Analytical and epidemiological studies.
1964-1981   0403031

Vital Health Stat 4
Vital and health statistics. Ser. 4: Documents
and committee reports
0083-2073
1965   0036665

Vital Health Stat 5
Vital and health statistics. Series 5,
Comparative international vital and health
statistics reports
0892-8959
1984   8406579

Vital Signs
Vital Signs
1976   9877427

Vital Speeches Day
Vital speeches of the day
0042-742X
1934   9877798

Vital Stat Spec Rep
Vital statistics. Special reports. United
States. National Office of Vital Statistics
Continues U. S. Bureau of the Census. Vital
statistics. Special reports.
1946-1960   22010130R

Vitalst Zivilisationskr
Vitalstoffe-Zivilisationskrankheiten
Continued by the Protectio vitae.
1956-1970   1305557

Vitam D Dig
Vitamin D digest
0099-9652
Supersedes Vitamin D milk.
1939-1947   21530260R

Vitam Horm
Vitamins and hormones
0083-6729
1943   0413601

Vitam Horm Leipzig
Vitamine und Hormone
1941-1961   21530330R

Vnitr Lek
Vnitřní lékařství
0042-773X
Supersedes Lékařské listy.
1955   0413602

Voeding
Voeding
0042-7926
Continued by: Voeding nu.
1939-1998   0413603

Voen Med Delo
Voenno meditsinsko delo
0324-1211
Continues Voenno-sanitarno delo. Continued by: Voenna meditsina.
1949-1990   21530550R

Voen Med Zh
Voenno-meditsinskiĭ zhurnal
0026-9050
1944   2984871R

Voix Dent
La Voix dentaire
0042-8353
1934-1968   21530650R

Vojen Zdrav Listy
Vojenské zdravotnické listy
0372-7025
1925   0230326

Vojenskozdrav Knih
Vojenskozdravotnická knihovna
1947-1966   21530680R

Vojnosanit Pregl
Vojnosanitetski pregled. Military-medical and pharmaceutical review
0042-8450
1944   21530700R

Volksgesundheit Bad Hombg
Volksgesundheit (Bern, Switzerland)
0042-8493
Continued by: VGS Gesundheitsmagazin.
1908-1988   0413605

Volunt Action Leadersh
Voluntary action leadership
0149-6492
Absorbed: Voluntary action news. Continued by: Leadership (Washington, D.C.: 1993).
19uu-1992   9878119

Volunt Adm
Volunteer administration
0362-773X
Continued by: Journal of volunteer administration.
1967-1982   9877807

Volunt Leader
The Volunteer leader
0005-1861
Continues: Auxiliary leader.
1969-1999   0253612

Vopr Biokhim Mozga
Voprosy biokhimii mozga
0507-2972
1964-1980   0036162

Vopr Eksper Klinicheskoi Urol
Voprosy Eksperimentalnoi I Klinicheskoi Urologii
1973   9884762

Vopr Elektropatol Elektrotravmatizma Elektrobezop
Voprosy eÃälektropatologii, eÃälektrotravmatizma i eÃälektrobezopasnosti
Continues Voprosy eÃälektropatologii i eÃälektrotravmatizma.
1962   0156503

Vopr Fiziol
Voprosy fiziologii
1951-19uu   21540050R

Vopr Klin Eksp Oftalmol
Voprosy klinicheskoĭ i eksperimental'noĭ oftalmologii
1952-19uu   21540120R

Vopr Klin Lecheniia Zlokachestvennykh Novoobraz
Voprosy kliniki i lecheniia zlokachestvennykh novoobrazovaniĭ
Continued by Klinika i lechenie zlokachestvennykh novoobrazovaniĭ.
1953-1962   0152445

Vopr Kurortol Fizioter Lech Fiz Kult
Voprosy kurortologii, fizioterapii, i lechebnoĭ fizicheskoĭ kultury
0042-8787
Supersedes Voprosy kurortologii, which ceased publication with 1941, no. 4.
1955   2984868R

Vopr Med Khim
Voprosy meditŝinskoĭ khimii
0042-8809
Continued by: Biomeditŝinskaiâ khimiiâ.
1955-2002   0416601

Vopr Med Khimii
Voprosy meditsinskoĭ khimii
1949-1953   21540180R

Vopr Med Virusol
Voprosy meditsinskof virusologii
0506-0206
1948-1971   2984869R

Vopr Neirokhir
Voprosy neĭrokhirurgii
0042-8817
Continued by: Zhurnal voprosy neĭrokhirurgii imeni N. N. Burdenko.
1937-1976   0424743

Vopr Okhr Materin Det
Voprosy okhrany materinstva i detstva
0042-8825
Continued by: Materinstvo i detstvo.
1956-1991   0416600

Vopr Onkol
Voprosy onkologii
0507-3758
Supersedes earlier publication with the same title, issued 1928-38.
1955   0413775

Vopr Onkologii
Voprosy onkologii
1949-1955   0023001R

Vopr Patol Serdechno Sosud Sist
Voprosy patologii serdechno-sosudistoĭ sistemy
1952-1959   21540250R

Vopr Pediatrii
Voprosy pediatrii
1962-19uu   0165563

Vopr Pitan
Voprosy pitaniia
1950-1951   0023012R

Vopr Pitan
Voprosy pitaniia
0042-8833
1932   2984870R

Vopr Psikhiatr Nevropatol
Voprosy psikhiatrii i nevropatologii; sbornik trudov
1957-1976   21540350R

Vopr Psikhiatrii Nevrol
Voprosy psikhīatrīi i nevrologīi
1912-1914   21540340R

Vopr Psikhol
Voprosy psikhologii
0042-8841
1955   0417403

Vopr Revm
Voprosy revmatizma
0042-885X
Supersedes an earlier publication with the same title issued 1929-40. Continued by Revmatlogiia (Moscow, Russia).
1961-1982   0064753

Vopr Virusol
Voprosy virusologii
0507-4088
1956   0417337

Vox Sang
Vox sanguinis
0042-9007   1423-0410
Continues the Bulletin of the Centraal Laboratorium van de Bloedtransfusiedienst of the Nederlandse Rode Kruis.
1953   0413606

Vrach Delo
Vrachebnoe delo
0049-6804
Continued by: Likars'ka sprava.
1918-1991   0413607

Vt Regist Nurse
Vermont registered nurse
0191-1880
Absorbed by: Vermont nurse connection.
19uu-1999   7900230

Vutr Boles
Vŭtreshni bolesti
0506-2772
1962   0032666

Vyziva Lidu
Výživa lidu
0042-9414
Continued by: Výživa.
1945-1990   21540730R

W

W V Dent J
West Virginia dental journal
0043-3225
Continues: Bulletin of the West Virginia State Dental Society.
1935-1997   0413776

W V Med J
The West Virginia medical journal
0043-3284
Supersedes: Transactions. West Virginia State
Medical Association.
1906 **0413777**

**WADC Tech Note United States Air Force Wright
Air Dev Cen Day Ohio**
WADC technical note. United States. Air
Force. Wright Air Development Center,
Dayton, Ohio
1950-uuuu **22420100R**

**WADC Tech Rep United States Air Force Wright
Air Dev Cent Day Ohio**
WADC technical report. United States. Air
Force. Wright Air Development Center,
Dayton, Ohio
Supersedes in part U. S. Air Force. Air
Matériel Command. AF technical report.
1952-uuuu **22420090R**

Wakayama Med Rep
Wakayama medical reports
0511-084X
1953 **0413610**

Waking Sleeping
Waking and sleeping
0340-0905
1976-1980 **7801884**

Wall St J [Midwest Ed]
Wall Street journal (Midwest ed.)
0163-089X
Continues: Chicago journal of commerce
edition of the Wall Street journal. Eastern
eds.: Wall Street journal (New York. N.Y.:
1889), 1951-1959, and: Wall Street journal
(Eastern ed.), 1959-1996. Western ed.: Wall
Street journal (Western ed.). <1986>-1996.
European ed.: Wall Street journal (Europe).
1983-1996. Asian ed.: Asian Wall Street
journal, 1976-1996. Merged with: Wall Street
journal (Southwest ed.): to form: Wall Street
journal (Central ed.).
1951-1996 **9877745**

Wash Nurse
The Washington nurse
0734-5666
Continues: WSNA mini journal.
1977 **8005132**

WASH Rep
WASH [reports]. U.S. Atomic Energy
Commission
195u-1974 **21830810R**

Wash Rep Med Health
Washington report on medicine & health
0043-0730
Continues Washington report on the medical
sciences. Continued by: McGraw-Hill's
Washington report on medicine & health.
1968-1986 **0174072**

Wash State Dent J
Washington State dental journal
0083-7431
Continues: Journal of the Washington State
Dental Association. Absorbed: Washington
State Dental Association. Roster of member
in 1955. Continued by: Washington State
Dental Association. WSDA roster.
193u-1987 **21610440R**

Wash State J Nurs
Washington State journal of nursing
0043-0781
Continues: Bulletin (Washington State
Graduate Nurses Association).
1928-1983 **21610460R**

Wash Univ Dent J
Washington University dental journal
0049-6936
Supersedes another publication with the same
title issued June 1922- June 1924.
1934-1967 **21610550R**

Wash Univ Med Alumni Q
The Washington University medical alumni
quarterly
1937-1951 **21610560R**

Waste Manag
Waste management (New York, N.Y.)
0956-053X
Continues: Nuclear and chemical waste
management.
1989 **9884362**

Waste Manag Res
Waste management & research: the journal
of the International Solid Wastes and Public
Cleansing Association, ISWA
0734-242X **1399-3070**
1983 **9881064**

Water Air Soil Pollut
Water, air, and soil pollution
0049-6979
1971 **0312676**

Water Bodem Lucht
Water, bodem, lucht
0043-1176
1910-1971 **21610610R**

Water Environ Res
Water environment research: a research
publication of the Water Environment
Federation
1061-4303
Continues: Research journal of the Water
Pollution Control Federation.
1992 **9886167**

Water Res
Water research
0043-1354
Supersedes in part Air and water pollution.
1967 **0105072**

Water Sci Technol
Water science and technology: a journal
of the International Association on Water
Pollution Research
0273-1223
Continues: Progress in water technology.
1981 **9879497**

Water Sew Works
Water & sewage works
0043-1125
Continues Water works and sewerage.
Merged with Water & wastes engineering to
form Water - engineering and management.
1946-1980 **21610590R**

Watermark
Watermark (Association of Librarians in the
History of the Health Sciences)
Continued by: Watermark (Archivists and
Librarians in the History of the Health
Sciences).
1976-1992 **9883814**

Way
Way
0386-1449
1975-1981 **7910152**

WDA J
WDA journal
1046-9338
Continues: Wisconsin Dental Association
journal. Continued by: Wisconsin Dental
Association journal (Milwaukee. Wis.: 1992).
1988-1992 **9003417**

We Blind
We the blind
1936-19uu **21610690R**

Weather Vane
The Weather vane
0043-1664
Continued by: West Virginia nurse. West
Virginia Nurses Association.
1932-1992 **21610700R**

Wehrmed Mitt
Wehrmedizinische Mitteilungen
Continued by Wehrmedizinische
Monatsschrift. Supplement to Truppenpraxis.
1957-1964 **0114367**

Wei Sheng Wu Xue Bao
Wei sheng wu xue bao = Acta microbiologica
Sinica
0001-6209
1953 **21610860R**

Wei Sheng Yan Jiu
Wei sheng yan jiu = Journal of hygiene
research
1000-8020
1972 **9426367**

Wendepunkt Leben Leiden
Der Wendepunkt im Leben und im Leiden
0043-2687
1923-1978 **0417404**

West Afr J Med
West African journal of medicine
0189-160X
1981 **8301891**

West Afr J Pharmacol Drug Res
West African journal of pharmacology and
drug research
0303-691X
1974-1991 **0427176**

West Afr Med J
The West African medical journal
0043-3004
Continued by The West African medical
journal and Nigerian practitioner.
1927-1966 **0417406**

West Afr Med J Niger Med Dent Pract
The West African medical journal and
Nigerian medical & dental practitioner
0189-0565
Continues: West African medical journal and
Nigerian practitioner.
1972-1978 **7905921**

West Afr Med J Niger Pract
The West African medical journal and
Nigerian practitioner
0266-6502
Continues The West African medical journal.
Continued by The West African medical
journal and Nigerian medical & dental
practitioner.
1967-1972 **7905922**

West Afr Pharm
West African pharmacist
0043-3012
Absorbed the West African druggist and
chemist.
1959-1971 **0347251**

West Dent Soc Bull
Bulletin (Western Dental Society)
1971-1973 **9875605**

West Engl Med J
West of England medical journal
0960-6440
Continues: Bristol medico-chirurgical journal.
1990-1992 **9010984**

West Indian Med J
The West Indian medical journal
0043-3144
Supersedes the Jamaica medical review.
1951   0417410

West J Med
The Western journal of medicine
0093-0415
Continues: California medicine. Vols. for
-Oct. 1987 include monthly insert: Bulletin
(Utah State Medical Association); Nov.
1987- Bulletin (Utah Medical Association).
Absorbed: Arizona medicine in 1985;
continued in part by: Arizona medicine
(Phoenix, Ariz.: 1990).
1974-2002   0410504

West J Nurs Res
Western journal of nursing research
0193-9459
1979   7905435

West Lond Med J
West London medical journal
Supersedes and later is superseded by the
Proceedings of the West London Medico-
Chirurgical Society.
1896-1956   21620110R

West Med Med J West
Western medicine; the medical journal of
the west
0511-7712
1960-1967   0232025

Westchest Med Bull
Westchester medical bulletin
0098-4787
1933-1986   0422305

Whats New
What's new
0191-3328
Absorbed: Journal of chemotherapy and
advanced therapeutics. Issued also in Italian,
Portugese, and Spanish under the title
Abbotterapia and in French under the title
Abbotherapie. Merged with Abbotterapia and
Abbotherapie to form Abbottempo.
1935-1962   0114364

WHO Chron
WHO chronicle
0042-9694
Continues Chronicle of the World Health
Organization.
1959-1986   0414010

WHO Offset Publ
WHO offset publication
0303-7878
1973-1988   0434640

WHO Reg Publ Eur Ser
WHO regional publications. European series
0378-2255
1976   7612236

Wiad Lek
Wiadomości lekarskie (Warsaw, Poland:
1960)
0043-5147
Continues in part: Polski tygodnik lekarski i
wiadomości lekarskie.
1960   9705467

Wiad Lek Wars Pol 1948
Wiadomości lekarskie (Warsaw, Poland:
1948)
0860-8865
Merged with: Polski tygodnik lekarski,
published 1946-58, to form: Polski tygodnik
lekarski i wiadomości lekarskie.
1948-1958   0414000

Wiad Parazytol
Wiadomości parazytologiczne
0043-5163
1955   0420554

Wiederherstellungschir Traumatol
Wiederherstellungschirurgie und
Traumatologie. Reconstruction surgery and
traumatology
Continued by Reconstruction surgery and
traumatology.
1953-1967   0136743

Wien Arch Psychol Psychiatr Neurologie
Wiener Archiv für Psychologie, Psychiatrie
und Neurologie
1951-19uu   21620710R

Wien Beitr Chir
Wiener Beiträge zur Chirurgie
1948-1956   21620720R

Wien Beitr Dermatol
Wiener Beiträge zur Dermatologie
1947-1956   21620730R

Wien Beitr Geburtshilfe Gynakol
Wiener Beiträge zur Geburtshilfe und
Gynäkologie
1952-1955   21620740R

Wien Beitr Hals Nasen Ohrenheilkd
Wiener Beiträge zur Hals-, Nasen- und
Ohrenheilkunde
1948-1955   21620760R

Wien Beitr Hyg
Wiener Beiträge zur Hygiene
1949-1957   21620770R

Wien Beitr Kinderheilkd
Wiener Beiträge zur Kinderheilkunde
1947-1956   21620790R

Wien Beitr Zahnheilkd
Wiener Beiträge zur Zahnheilkunde
1950-1956   21620850R

Wien Klin Wochenschr
Wiener klinische Wochenschrift
0043-5325
Absorbed: Acta medica Austriaca. 2005
Absorbed in 1996: Wiener klinische
Wochenschrift. Supplementum, which was
formerly published separately.
1888   21620870R

Wien Klin Wochenschr Suppl
Wiener klinische Wochenschrift.
Supplementum
0300-5178
Absorbed: Mitteilungen der Österreichischen
Gesellschaft für Tropenmedizin und
Parasitologie. 2003 Absorbed by: Wiener
klinische Wochenschrift.
1972-1995   0357046

Wien Med Wochenschr
Wiener medizinische Wochenschrift (1946)
0043-5341   1563-258X
Continues in part: Medizinische Zeitschrift.
1946   8708475

Wien Med Wochenschr Beih
Wiener medizinische Wochenschrift. Beihefte
1970-1976   7801339

Wien Med Wochenschr Suppl
Wiener medizinische Wochenschrift.
Supplement
0301-7826
1971   0413007

Wien Tierarztl Monatsschr
Wiener tierärztliche Monatsschrift
0043-535X
1914   0413611

Wien Z Inn Med
Wiener Zeitschrift für innere Medizin und
ihre Grenzgebiete
0043-5376
Continues Wiener Archiv für innere Medizin
und deren Grenzgebiete. Superseded by Acta
medica Austriaca.
1946-1973   7502231

Wien Z Nervenheilkd Grenzgeb
Wiener Zeitschrift für Nervenheilkunde und
deren Grenzgebiete
0043-5384
1947-1973   0414001

Wien Z Prakt Psychol
Wiener Zeitschrift für praktische
Psychologie
1949-19uu   21620920R

Wilderness Environ Med
Wilderness & environmental medicine
1080-6032
Continues: Journal of wilderness medicine.
1995   9505185

Wildl Dis
Wildlife disease
0043-5465
1959-1977   0035301

Wilhelm Roux Arch Entwickl Mech Org
Wilhelm Roux' Archiv für
Entwicklungsmechanik der Organismen
0043-5546
Continues: Archiv für mikroskopische
Anatomie und Entwicklungsmechanik.
Continued by: Wilhelm Roux's archives of
developmental biology.
1925-1975   7508795

Windows Time
Windows in time
1993   9607541

Wis Dent Assoc J
Wisconsin Dental Association journal
(Milwaukee, Wis.: 1992)
1073-029X
Continues: WDA journal. Continued by:
WDA journal (Milwaukee, Wis.: 1995).
1992-1994   101120055

Wis Dent Assoc J
Wisconsin Dental Association journal / WDA
0887-9699
Continues: Journal of the Wisconsin Dental
Association. Continued by: WDA journal.
1985-1988   8601371

Wis Med J
Wisconsin medical journal
0043-6542
Continued by: WMJ.
1903-1997   0110663

Wis Welf
Wisconsin welfare
1942-1959   0157555

Wiss Mitt
Wissenschaftliche Mitteilungen.
Österreichischer Apothekerverein, Vienna.
Pharmazeutisches Forschungsinstitut
1948-19uu   19320690R

Wiss Veroff Dtsch Ges Ernahr
Wissenschaftliche Veröffentlichungen.
Deutsche Gesellschaft für Ernährung
1958-1973   16540210R

Wiss Z Ernst Moritz Arndt Univ [Math]
Wissenschaftliche Zeitschrift.
Mathematisch-naturwissenschaftliche Reihe.
Ernst-Moritz-Arndt-Universität Greifswald
0138-2853
1951-1990   17210390R

Wiss Z Humboldt Univ Berl [Math Naturwiss]
Wissenschaftliche Zeitschrift der Humboldt-
Universität zu Berlin. Mathematisch-
Naturwissenschaftliche Reihe
0522-9863
Split into: Wissenschaftliche Zeitschrift
der Humboldt-Universität zu Berlin.
Reihe Mathematik/Naturwissenschaften,
and: Wissenschaftliche Zeitschrift
der Humboldt-Universität zu Berlin. Reihe
Medizin. and: Wissenschaftliche Zeitschrift
der Humboldt-Universität zu Berlin. Reihe
Agrarwissenschaften.
1952-1987   1263363

Wistar Inst Symp Monogr
The Wistar Institute symposium monograph
0084-1013
1964-1969   0035247

Wkly Epidemiol Rec
Relevé épidémiologique hebdomadaire
/ Section d'hygiène du Secrétariat
de la Société des Nations = Weekly
epidemiological record / Health Section of
the Secretariat of the League of Nations
0049-8114
Continues: Relevé hebdomadaire.
1928   0240017

**Wkly Rec Conv Dis Ports Other Localities Home
Abroad**
Weekly record of convention diseases at
ports and other localities at home and
abroad. Great Britain. Ministry of Health
Continued by the Ministry's Weekly record of
certain infectious diseases.
1934-1950   23030400R

Wkly Rep Ill
Weekly report. Illinois. Dept. of Public
Health. Division of Communicable Diseases
1900-1950   22540170R

WMJ
WMJ: official publication of the State
Medical Society of Wisconsin
1098-1861
Continues: Wisconsin medical journal.
1997   9716054

Woman Physician
The Woman physician
0002-7103
Continues: Journal of the American Medical
Women's Association. Continued by:
Journal of the American Medical Women's
Association (1972).
1970-1972   0324401

Women Alive
Women alive (Los Angeles, Calif.)
1096-1372
19uu   9892185

Women Birth
Women and birth: journal of the Australian
College of Midwives
1871-5192
Continues: Australian journal of midwifery.
2006   101266131

Women Health
Women & health
0363-0342   1541-0331
1976   7608076

Womens Health
Women's health (Hillsdale, N.J.)
1077-2928
1995-1998   9507419

Womens Health (Lond Engl)
Women's health (London, England)
1745-5057   1745-5065
2005   101271249

Womens Health Data Book
The women's health data book: a profile
of women's health in the United States /
[Jacob's Institute of Women's Health]
1551-8841
1992   9510047

Womens Health Issues
Women's health issues: official publication
of the Jacobs Institute of Women's Health
1049-3867
1990   9101000

Worcester Med News
Worcester medical news
0043-7905
Continued by: Worcester medicine.
1937-1989   21630460R

Work
Work (Reading, Mass.)
1051-9815
1990   9204382

Work Environ Health
Work, environment, health
0300-3221
Merged with Nordisk hygienisk tidskrift,
to form Scandinavian journal of work,
environment & health.
1962-1974   7511561

Worklife
Worklife
0361-7718
Supersedes: Manpower (Washington, D.C.).
1976-1979   9877742

WORLD
WORLD (Oakland, Calif.: 1993)
1538-0726
19uu   9309937

World Health Forum
World health forum
0251-2432
Starting in 1999, incorporated with: Bulletin
of the World Health Organization.
1980-1998   8010746

World Health Organ Tech Rep Ser
World Health Organization technical report
series
0512-3054
1950   7903212

World Health Popul
World health & population
                                   1718-3340
Continues: Journal of health & population in
developing countries.
2006-uuuu   101307691

World Health Stat Q
World health statistics quarterly. Rapport
trimestriel de statistiques sanitaires
mondiales
0379-8070
Continues World health statistics report.
Rapport de statistiques sanitaires mondiales.
Absorbed by: Bulletin of the World Health
Organization. 1999
1978-1998   7900237

World Health Stat Rep
World health statistics report. Rapport de
statistiques sanitaires mondiales
0043-8510
Continues Epidemiological and vital
statistics report. Rapport epidémiologique et
démographique. Continued by World health
statistics quarterly. Rapport trimestriel de
statistiques sanitaires mondiales.
1968-1977   0161006

World Hosp
World hospitals
0512-3135
Absorbed The Hospital services of Europe,
with Jan. 1973. Continued by: World
hospitals and health services.
1964-1993   0033046

World Hosp Health Serv
World hospitals and health services: the
official journal of the International Hospital
Federation
1029-0540
Absorbed: Hospitals international. Continues:
World hospitals.
1994   9441450

World Ir Nurs
World of Irish nursing
0332-3056
Absorbed: Irish nurses' journal. Irish nurse,
and Irish nurses' magazine. Continued by:
New world of Irish nursing.
1972-1992   0323527

World Ir Nurs
World of Irish nursing (Dublin, Ireland:
1995)
1393-8088
Continues: New world of Irish nursing.
Continued by: World of Irish nursing &
midwifery.
1995-2004   9609641

World J Biol Psychiatry
The world journal of biological psychiatry:
the official journal of the World Federation
of Societies of Biological Psychiatry
1562-2975
2000   101120023

World J Gastroenterol
World journal of gastroenterology: WJG
1007-9327
Continues: China national journal of new
gastroenterology.
1997   100883448

World J Orthod
World journal of orthodontics
1530-5678
2000   100959981

World J Pediatr
World journal of pediatrics: WJP
1708-8569
2005   101278599

World J Surg
World journal of surgery
0364-2313   1432-2323
Supersedes Bulletin de la Société
internationale de chirurgie.
1977   7704052

World J Surg Oncol
World journal of surgical oncology
                                   1477-7819
2003   101170544

World J Urol
World journal of urology
0724-4983   1433-8726
1983   8307716

World Med J
World medical journal
0049-8122
Supersedes: Bulletin of the World Medical
Association.
1954   0417413

World Neurol
World neurology
1960-1962   21630720R

World News Maxillofac Radiol
World news on maxillofacial radiology
0084-2079
1969-19uu   1273122

World Rev Nutr Diet
World review of nutrition and dietetics
0084-2230   1662-3975
1959   0117263

World Wide Abstr Gen Med
World-wide abstracts of general medicine
1958-1966   0202411

Worlds Poult Sci J
World's poultry science journal
0043-9339
    Continues: International review of poultry
    science.
1945   0033040

Worldviews Evid Based Nurs
Worldviews on evidence-based nursing
/ Sigma Theta Tau International, Honor
Society of Nursing
1545-102X   1741-6787
    Continues: Online journal of knowledge
    synthesis for nursing.
2004   101185267

WormBook
WormBook: the online review of C. elegans
biology
    1551-8507
2005   101303985

Wound Repair Regen
Wound repair and regeneration: official
publication of the Wound Healing Society
[and] the European Tissue Repair Society
1067-1927   1524-475X
1993   9310939

Wurzbg Medizinhist Forsch
Würzburger medizinhistorische Forschungen
0344-6948
1975   7704729

Wurzbg Medizinhist Mitt
Würzburger medizinhistorische
Mitteilungen / im Auftrage der Würzburger
medizinhistorischen Gesellschaft und in
Verbindung mit dem Institut für Geschichte
der Medizin der Universität Würzburg
0177-5227
1983   8704998

Wyo Nurses Newsl
Wyoming nurses' newsletter
    Continued by: Wyoming nurse.
19uu-1972   9875645

X

Xenobiotica
Xenobiotica; the fate of foreign compounds
in biological systems
0049-8254   1366-5928
1971   1306665

Xenotransplantation
Xenotransplantation
0908-665X   1399-3089
1994   9438793

Xi Bao Yu Fen Zi Mian Yi Xue Za Zhi
Xi bao yu fen zi mian yi xue za zhi = Chinese
journal of cellular and molecular immunology
1007-8738
    Continues: Dan ke long kang ti tong xun.
1996   101139110

Xi Psi Phi Q
The Xi Psi Phi quarterly
0049-8262
    Continued by: Xi Psi Phi Fraternity quarterly.
1902-1988   21630920R

Xianggang Hu Li Za Zhi
Xianggang hu li za zhi. The Hong Kong
nursing journal
0073-3253
1965   0061242

Xray Tech
The X-ray technician
    Continued by: Radiologic technology.
1929-1963   21630910R

Y

Y Rep
Y [report]. U.S. Atomic Energy Commission
194u-1970   21830830R

Yakubutsu Seishin Kodo
Yakubutsu, seishin, kōdō = Japanese journal
of psychopharmacology
0285-5313
    Continued by: Nihon Shinkei Seishin
    Yakurigaku zasshi.
1981-1993   8211681

Yakugaku Kenkyu
[Yakugaku kenkyū] Japanese journal of
pharmacy and chemistry
    Continues Yakuji kagaku.
1947-1968   21710130R

Yakugaku Zasshi
Yakugaku zasshi: Journal of the
Pharmaceutical Society of Japan
0031-6903   1347-5231
1881   0413613

Yakushigaku Zasshi
Yakushigaku zasshi. The Journal of
Japanese history of pharmacy
0285-2314
1966   1267223

Yale J Biol Med
The Yale journal of biology and medicine
0044-0086   1551-4056
1928   0417414

Yale J Health Policy Law Ethics
Yale journal of health policy, law, and ethics
1535-3532
2001   101134827

Yale Sci Mag
Yale scientific magazine
0044-0140
    Continued by Yale scientific.
1929-1958   0417677

Yan Ke Xue Bao
Yan ke xue bao = Eye science / "Yan ke xue
bao" bian ji bu
1000-4432
1985   8605666

Yan ke xue shu hui kan
[Yan ke xue shu hui kan] =
Ophthalmological series
1949-19uu   21720150R

Yao Xue Xue Bao
Yao xue xue bao = Acta pharmaceutica Sinica
0513-4870
    Supersedes Zhongguo yao xue za zhi.
1953   21710340R

Yatros
Yatros
1947-1974   21710410R

Year B R Soc Edinb
Year book - Royal Society of Edinburgh
0080-4576
    Split into: Royal Society of Edinburgh.
    Directory; and: Royal Society of Edinburgh.
    Review of the session.
1941-2001   7506168

Year Immunol
The Year in immunology
0256-2308
1982-1993   8403229

Yearb Med Inform
Yearbook of medical informatics
0943-4747
1992   9312666

Yeast
Yeast (Chichester, England)
0749-503X   1097-0061
1985   8607637

Yeni Tip Tarihi Arastirmalari
Yeni tıp tarihi araştırmaları = The new
history of medicine studies
1300-669X
1995   9703828

Yi Chuan
Yi chuan = Hereditas / Zhongguo yi chuan
xue hui bian ji
0253-9772
1979   9436478

Yi Chuan Xue Bao
Yi chuan xue bao = Acta genetica Sinica
0379-4172
    Continued by: Journal of genetics and
    genomics.
1974-2006   7900784

Ying Yong Sheng Tai Xue Bao
Ying yong sheng tai xue bao = The journal
of applied ecology / Zhongguo sheng tai xue
xue hui, Zhongguo ke xue yuan Shenyang
ying yong sheng tai yan jiu suo zhu ban
1001-9332
1990   9425159

Yngre Laeger
Yngre laeger
1946-1967   1307001

Yokohama Med Bull
Yokohama medical bulletin
0044-0531
1950   0417415

Yokufuen Chosa Kenkyu Kiyo
Yokufuen chosa kenkyu kiyo. Acta
gerontologica Japonica
0001-5768
    Continued by Yokufukai chosa kenkyu kiyo.
1930-1972   0376025

Yonago Acta Med
Yonago acta medica
0513-5710
1954   0414002

Yonago Igaku Zasshi
Yonago igaku zasshi. The Journal of the
Yonago Medical Association
0044-0558
1948   0417502

Yonsei Med J
Yonsei medical journal
0513-5796   1976-2437
1960   0414003

Your Child Patient
Your Child Patient
1949   9883822

Your Okla Dent Assoc J
Your Oklahoma Dental Association journal
0149-2594
    Continues Journal - Oklahoma State
    Dental Association. Continued by Journal -
    Oklahoma Dental Association.
1974-1978   7706679

Z

Z Allg Mikrobiol
Zeitschrift für allgemeine Mikrobiologie
0044-2208
Continued by Journal of basic microbiology.
1960-1984   0413631

Z Allgemeinmed
Zeitschrift für Allgemeinmedizin
0300-8673
Formed by the union of: Der Landarzt. and:
Ärztliche Sammelblätter. Continued by: ZFA.
Zeitschrift für Allgemeinmedizin.
1969-1975   7700691

Z Alternsforsch
Zeitschrift für Alternsforschung
0044-2224
Continued by ZfA. Zeitschrift für
Alternsforschung.
1938-1974   0414005

Z Anat Entwicklungsgesch
Zeitschrift für Anatomie und
Entwicklungsgeschichte
0044-2232
Continues Anatomische Hefte. 1. Abt.:
Arbeiten aus anatomischen Instituten.
Continued by Anatomy and embryology.
1921-1974   7513131

Z Angew Bader Klimaheilkd
Zeitschrift für angewandte Bäder- und
Klimaheilkunde
0084-5280
Continued by Zeitschrift für Bäder- und
Klimaheilkunde.
1954-1979   8007741

Z Arztl Fortbild (Berl)
Zeitschrift für ärztliche Fortbildung (Berlin)
0172-8385
Absorbed by: Berliner Aerzteblatt (Rotes
Blatt).
1958-1972   0177654

Z Arztl Fortbild (Jena)
Zeitschrift für ärztliche Fortbildung
0044-2178
Continued by: Zeitschrift für ärztliche
Fortbildung und Qualitätssicherung.
1904-1996   0414004

Z Arztl Fortbild Beih (Jena)
Zeitschrift für ärztliche Fortbildung. Beiheft
0323-8970
Continued by: Medizin und Gesellschaft.
1970-1975   7905437

Z Arztl Fortbild Qualitatssich
Zeitschrift für ärztliche Fortbildung und
Qualitätssicherung
1431-7621   1618-0992
Continues: Zeitschrift für ärztliche
Fortbildung. Continued by: Zeitschrift
für Evidenz. Fortbildung und Qualität im
Gesundheitswesen.
1997-2007   9707934

Z Biol
Zeitschrift für Biologie
1865-1971   1302046

Z Erkr Atmungsorgane
Zeitschrift für Erkrankungen der
Atmungsorgane
0303-657X
Continues in part: Monatsschrift
für Lungenkrankheiten und
Tuberkulosebekämpfung. Continues:
Zeitschrift für Erkrankungen der
Atmungsorgane mit Folia bronchologica.
1974-1991   7503239

Z Erkr Atmungsorgane Folia Bronchol
Zeitschrift für Erkrankungen der
Atmungsorgane mit Folia bronchologica
0044-2631
Continues: Zeitschrift für Tuberkulose und
Erkrankungen der Thoraxorgane. Continued
by: Zeitschrift für Erkrankungen der
Atmungsorgane.
1969-1974   7501670

Z Ernahrungswiss
Zeitschrift für Ernährungswissenschaft
0044-264X
Continued by: European journal of nutrition.
1960-1998   0413632

Z Ernahrungswiss Suppl
Zeitschrift für Ernährungswissenschaft.
Journal of nutritional sciences. Supplementa
0084-5337
1961-1979   0413633

Z Evid Fortbild Qual Gesundhwes
Zeitschrift für Evidenz, Fortbildung und
Qualität im Gesundheitswesen
1865-9217
Continues: Zeitschrift für ärztliche
Fortbildung und Qualitätssicherung.
2008   101477604

Z Exp Angew Psychol
Zeitschrift für experimentelle und
angewandte Psychologie
0044-2712
Continued by: Zeitschrift für experimentelle
Psychologie.
1953-1994   0433000

Z Exp Chir
Zeitschrift für experimentelle Chirurgie
0323-5580
1968-1982   0154510

Z Exp Chir Transplant Kunstliche Organe
Zeitschrift für experimentelle Chirurgie,
Transplantation, und künstliche Organe:
Organ der Sektion Experimentelle Chirurgie
der Gesellschaft für Chirurgie der DDR
0232-7295
Continues: Zeitschrift für experimentelle
Chirurgie.
1983-1990   8302880

Z Exp Psychol
Zeitschrift für experimentelle Psychologie:
Organ der Deutschen Gesellschaft für
Psychologie
0949-3964
Continues: Zeitschrift für experimentelle
und angewandte Psychologie. Continued by:
Experimental psychology.
1995-2001   9514804

Z Gastroenterol
Zeitschrift für Gastroenterologie
0044-2771
1963   0033370

Z Gastroenterol Verh
Zeitschrift für Gastroenterologie.
Verhandlungsband
0172-8504
1969-1991   1256344

Z Geburtshilfe Neonatol
Zeitschrift für Geburtshilfe und
Neonatologie
0948-2393
Continues: Zeitschrift für Geburtshilfe und
Perinatologie.
1995   9508901

Z Geburtshilfe Perinatol
Zeitschrift für Geburtshilfe und
Perinatologie
0300-967X
Continues: Zeitschrift für Geburtshilfe und
Gynäkologie. Continued by: Zeitschrift für
Geburtshilfe und Neonatologie.
1972-1994   0326205

Z Gerontol
Zeitschrift für Gerontologie
0044-281X
Absorbed: Aktuelle Gerontologie. Continued
by: Zeitschrift für Gerontologie und Geriatrie.
1968-1994   0140107

Z Gerontol Geriatr
Zeitschrift für Gerontologie und Geriatrie:
Organ der Deutschen Gesellschaft für
Gerontologie und Geriatrie
0948-6704
Continues: Zeitschrift für Gerontologie.
1995   9506215

Z Gesamte Exp Med
Zeitschrift für die gesamte experimentelle
Medizin
Absorbed the Zeitschrift für experimentelle
Pathologie und Therapie in 1921 and issued
from that date until June 1963 with title:
Zeitschrift für die gesamte experimentelle
Medizin. zugleich Fortsetzung der Zeitschrift
für experimentelle Pathologie und Therapie.
Continued by Zeitschrift für die gesamte
experimentelle Medizin einschliesslich
experimentelle Chirurgie.
1913-1965   0142427

Z Gesamte Exp Med
Zeitschrift für die gesamte experimentelle
Medizin einschliesslich experimentelle
Chirurgie
0044-2534
Continues Zeitschrift für die gesamte
experimentelle Medizin. Continued by
Research in experimental medicine.
1966-1971   0325332

Z Gesamte Hyg
Zeitschrift für die gesamte Hygiene und ihre
Grenzgebiete
0049-8610
1955-1991   0420111

Z Gesamte Inn Med
Zeitschrift für die gesamte innere Medizin
und ihre Grenzgebiete
0044-2542
1946-1993   21730470R

Z Haut Geschlechtskr
Zeitschrift für Haut- und
Geschlechtskrankheiten
0044-2844
Continued by Zeitschrift für Hautkrankheiten.
1946-1973   0367575

Z Hautkr
Zeitschrift für Hautkrankheiten
0301-0481
Continues Zeitschrift für Haut- und
Geschlechtskrankheiten. Continued by:
Journal der Deutschen Dermatologischen
Gesellschaft.
1973-2002   0367576

Z Hyg Infektionskr
Zeitschrift für Hygiene und
Infektionskrankheiten; medizinische
Mikrobiologie, Immunologie und Virologie
0340-1782
Continued by Zeitschrift für medizinische
Mikrobiologie und Immunologie
1886-1965   21740090R

Z Immun exp ther
Zeitschrift für Immunitätsforschung und
experimentelle Therapie
Continued by Zeitschrift für Immunitäts- und
Allergieforschung.
1908-1962   0033360

Z Immunitats Allergieforsch
Zeitschrift für Immunitats- und
Allergieforschung
Continues Zeitschrift für
Immunitätsforschung und experimentelle
Therapie. Continued by Zeitschrift für
Immunitätsforschung, Allergie und klinische
Immunologie.
1963-1965   0053225

Z Immunitatsforsch Allerg Klin Immunol
Zeitschrift für Immunitätsforschung,
Allergie und klinische Immunologie
0044-2879
Continued by: Zeitschrift für
Immunitätsforschung, experimentelle und
klinische Immunologie.
1966-1970   1270213

Z Immunitatsforsch Exp Klin Immunol
Zeitschrift für Immunitätsforschung,
experimentelle und klinische Immunologie
0300-872X
Continues Zeitschrift für
Immunitätsforschung, Allergie und klinische
Immunologie. Continued by Zeitschrift für
Immunitätsforschung.
1970-1975   7608241

Z Immunitatsforsch Immunobiol
Zeitschrift für Immunitätsforschung.
Immunobiology
0340-904X
Continues Zeitschrift für
Immunitätsforschung, experimentelle und
klinische Immunologie. Continued by
Immunobiology.
1976-1979   7608602

Z Immunitatsforsch Immunobiol Suppl
Zeitschrift für Immunitätsforschung.
Immunobiology. Supplemente
0343-3803
Continues Zeitschrift für
Immunitätsforschung, experimentelle und
klinische Immunologie. Supplemente.
Continued by: Immunobiology.
Supplement. Supplement to: Zeitschrift für
Immunitätsforschung. Immunobiology.
1977-1977   7708140

Z Indukt Abstamm Vererbungsl
Zeitschrift für induktive Abstammungs- und
Vererbungslehre
0372-901X
Continued by Zeitschrift für Vererbungslehre.
1908-1957   21740110R

Z Kardiol
Zeitschrift für Kardiologie
0300-5860   1435-1285
Continues Zeitschrift für Kreislaufforschung.
Continued by: Clinical research in cardiology.
1973-2005   0360430

Z Kardiol Suppl
Zeitschrift für Kardiologie. Supplementum
0303-6308
Absorbed by: Zeitschrift für Kardiologie.
1974-1978   7505145

Z Kinder Jugendpsychiatr
Zeitschrift für Kinder- und
Jugendpsychiatrie
0301-6811
Supersedes: Jahrbuch für Jugendpsychiatrie
und ihre Grenzgebiete. Continued by:
Zeitschrift für Kinder- und Jugendpsychiatrie
und Psychotherapie.
1973-1995   0410336

Z Kinder Jugendpsychiatr Psychother
Zeitschrift für Kinder- und
Jugendpsychiatrie und Psychotherapie
1422-4917
Continues: Zeitschrift für Kinder- und
Jugendpsychiatrie.
1996   9801717

Z Kinderchir
Zeitschrift für Kinderchirurgie: organ
der Deutschen, der Schweizerischen und
der Osterreichischen Gesellschaft für
Kinderchirurgie = Surgery in infancy and
childhood
0174-3082
Continues: Zeitschrift für Kinderchirurgie
und Grenzgebiete. Merged with: Chirurgie
pédiatrique, to form: European journal of
pediatric surgery.
1980-1990   8103794

Z Kinderchir Grenzgeb
Zeitschrift für Kinderchirurgie und
Grenzgebiete
0044-2909
Continued by: Zeitschrift für kinderchirurgie.
1964-1980   0413634

Z Kinderheilkd
Zeitschrift für Kinderheilkunde
0044-2917
Continued by European journal of pediatrics.
1910-1975   7604363

Z Kinderpsychiatr
Zeitschrift für Kinderpsychiatrie. Revue de
psychiatrie infantile
0372-8447
Continued by: Acta paedopsychiatrica.
1934-1952   14610020R

Z Klin Chem Klin Biochem
Zeitschrift für klinische Chemie und
klinische Biochemie
0044-2933
Continues Zeitschrift für klinische Chemie.
Continued by Journal of clinical chemistry
and clinical biochemistry.
1967-1975   7607250

Z Klin Med
Zeitschrift für klinische Medizin
0372-9192
Merged with Deutsches Archiv für klinische
Medizin to form Archiv für klinische
Medizin.
1879-1965   0060757

Z Klin Psychol Psychiatr Psychother
Zeitschrift für klinische Psychologie,
Psychiatrie und Psychotherapie / im Auftrag
der Görres-Gesellschaft
1431-8172
Continues: Zeitschrift für klinische
Psychologie, Psychopathologie und
Psychotherapie. Continued by: Zeitschrift
furÄä Psychiatrie, Psychologie und
Psychoterapie.
1996-2005   9709507

Z Klin Psychol Psychopathol Psychother
Zeitschrift für klinische Psychologie,
Psychopathologie und Psychotherapie / im
Auftrag der Görres-Gesellschaft
0723-6557
Continues: Zeitschrift für klinische
Psychologie und Psychotherapie. Continued
by: Zeitschrift für klinische Psychologie,
Psychiatrie und Psychotherapie.
1983-1995   8400562

Z Klin Psychol Psychother
Zeitschrift für klinische Psychologie und
Psychotherapie
0300-869X
Continues Jahrbuch für Psychologie,
Psychotherapie und medizinische
Anthropologie. Continued by Zeitschrift für
klinische Psychologie, Psychopathologie, und
Psychotherapie.
1971-1982   1302504

Z Krankenpfl
Zeitschrift für Krankenpflege. Revue suisse
des infirmières
0044-2941
Continues Schweizerische Blätter für
Krankenpflege. Continued by Krankenpflege.
Soins infirmiers.
1962-1979   8000272

Z Krebsforsch
Zeitschrift für Krebsforschung
0301-1585
Continued by Zeitschrift für Krebsforschung
und klinische Onkologie.
1903-1971   1302230

Z Krebsforsch Klin Onkol Cancer Res Clin Oncol
Zeitschrift für Krebsforschung und klinische
Onkologie. Cancer research and clinical
oncology
0084-5353
Continues Zeitschrift für Krebsforschung.
Continued by Journal of cancer research and
clinical oncology.
1971-1978   1276653

Z Kreislaufforsch
Zeitschrift für Kreislaufforschung
0044-295X
Continues Zentralblatt für Herz- und
Gefässkrankheiten. Continued by Zeitschrift
für Kardiologie.
1927-1972   0361356

Z Laryngol Rhinol Otol
Zeitschrift für Laryngologie, Rhinologie,
Otologie und ihre Grenzgebiete
0044-3018
Continued by: Laryngologie, Rhinologie,
Otologie und ihre Grenzgebiete.
1948-1973   0413010

Z Lebensm Unters Forsch
Zeitschrift für Lebensmittel-Untersuchung
und -Forschung
0044-3026
Continues zeitschrift für Untersuchung der
Lebensmittel.
1943-1996   7509812

Z Lymphol
Zeitschrift für Lymphologie. Journal of
lymphology
0343-8554
1977-1996   7805527

Z Med Isotopenforsch Deren Grenzgeb
Zeitschrift für medizinische
Isotopenforschung und deren Grenzgebiete
1956-1957   21740150R

Z Med Lab Diagn
Zeitschrift für medizinische
Laboratoriumsdiagnostik
0323-5637
Continues Zeitschrift für medizinische
Labortechnik.
1977-1991   7706146

Z Med Labortech
Zeitschrift für medizinische Labortechnik
0044-3069
Continued by Zeitschrift für medizinische
Laboratoriumsdiagnostik.
1960-1976   0413636

Z Med Mikrobiol Immunol
Zeitschrift für medizinische Mikrobiologie und Immunologie
0044-3077
Continues Zeitschrift für Hygiene und Infektionskrankheiten; medizinische Mikrobiologie, Immunologie und Virologie. Continued by Medical microbiology and immunobiology.
1966-1971   0314554

Z Med Phys
Zeitschrift für medizinische Physik
0939-3889
19uu   100886455

Z Mensch Vererb Konstitutionsl
Zeitschrift für menschliche Vererbungs- und Konstitutionslehre
Continues Zeitschrift für Konstitutionslehre. Superseded by Humangenetik.
1935-1964   0033356

Z Mikrosk Anat Forsch
Zeitschrift für mikroskopisch-anatomische Forschung
0044-3107
1924-1990   0413637

Z Morphol Anthropol
Zeitschrift für Morphologie und Anthropologie
0044-314X
Supersedes Morphologische Arbeiten. Absorbed by: Anthropologischer Anzeiger. 2002
1899-2002   0413640

Z Naturforsch B
Zeitschrift für Naturforschung. Teil B: Chemie, Biochemie, Biophysik, Biologie
0044-3174
Continues in part: Zeitschrift für Naturforschung. Continued by: Zeitschrift für Naturforschung. Teil B: Anorganische Chemie, organische Chemie, Biochemie, Biophysik, Biologie.
1947-1971   0364315

Z Naturforsch [B]
Zeitschrift für Naturforschung. Teil B. Anorganische Chemie, organische Chemie, Biochemie, Biophysik, Biologie
0044-3174
Continues: Zeitschrift für Naturforschung. Teil B: Chemie, Biochemie, Biophysik, Biologie.. Split into: Zeitschrift für Naturforschung. Teil B: Anorganische Chemie, organische Chemie. and: Zeitschrift für Naturforschung. Teil C: Biochemie, Biophysik, Biologie. Virologie.
1972-1972   7801144

Z Naturforsch [C]
Zeitschrift für Naturforschung. C, Journal of biosciences
0341-0382   1865-7125
Continues: Zeitschrift für Naturforschung. Section C. Biosciences.
1986   8912155

Z Naturforsch [C]
Zeitschrift für Naturforschung. Section C: Biosciences
0341-0382
Continues Zeitschrift für Naturforschung. Teil C: Biochemie, Biophysik, Biologie. Virologie. Continued by: Zeitschrift für Naturforschung. C. Journal of biosciences.
1974-1985   7801143

Z Naturforsch [C]
Zeitschrift für Naturforschung. Teil C: Biochemie, Biophysik, Biologie, Virologie
0341-0471
Continues in part: Zeitschrift für Naturforschung. Teil B: Anorganische Chemie. organische Chemie. Biochemie, Biophysik, Biologie. Continued by: Zeitschrift für Naturforschung. Section C: Biosciences.
1973-1973   7801145

Z Naturwiss Med Grundlagenforsch
Zeitschrift für naturwissenschaftlichmedizinische Grundlagenforschung
0514-6461
Continues: Medizinische Grundlagenforschung.
1962-1967   21810020R

Z Neurol
Zeitschrift für Neurologie
0012-1037
Continues Deutsche Zeitschrift für Nervenheilkunde. Continued by Journal of neurology.
1970-1974   0424070

Z Orthop Ihre Grenzgeb
Zeitschrift für Orthopädie und ihre Grenzgebiete
0044-3220
Continues: Zeitschrift für orthopädische Chirurgie einschliesslich der Heilgymnastik und Massage. Continued by: Zeitschrift für orthopädie und unfallchirurgie.
1935-2007   1256465

Z Orthop Unfall
Zeitschrift für Orthopädie und Unfallchirurgie
1864-6697   1864-6743
Continues: Zeitschrift für Orthopädie und ihre Grenzgebiete. Absorbed: Aktuelle Traumatologie.
2007   101308227

Z Parasitenkd
Zeitschrift für Parasitenkunde (Berlin, Germany)
0044-3255
Continues: Zeitschrift für wissenschaftliche Biologie. Abteilung F. Zeitschrift für Parasitenkunde. Continued by: Parasitology research.
1934-1986   8710749

Z Phys Ther Bader Klimanheikd
Zeitschrift für physikalische Therapie, Bäder- und Klimaheilkunde
1948-19uu   21810050R

Z Physiother
Zeitschrift für Physiotherapie
0003-9357
Continues: Archiv für physikalische Therapie. Merged with: Zeitschrift für physikalische Medizin. Balneologie, med. Klimatologie. to form: Physikalische Medizin, Rehabilitationsmedizin. Kurortmedizin.
1971-1991   1277604

Z Plast Chir
Zeitschrift für plastische Chirurgie
0342-7978
Merged with Handchirurgie to form Handchirurgie. Mikrochirurgie, plastische Chirurgie.
1977-1981   7801887

Z Prakt Anasth
Zeitschrift für praktische Anästhesie und Wiederbelebung
0044-3387
Continued by Zeitschrift für praktische Anästhesie. Wiederbelebung und Intensivtherapie.
1966-1971   0332052

Z Prakt Anasth Wiederbeleb Intensivther
Zeitschrift für praktische Anästhesie, Wiederbelebung und Intensivtherapie
0300-8789
Continues Zeitschrift für praktische Anästhesie und Wiederbelebung. Continued by Praktische Anästhesie. Wiederbelebung und Intensivtherapie.
1972-1973   0417700

Z Praventivmed
Zeitschrift für Präventivmedizin. Revue de médecine préventive
0044-3379
Supersedes Gesundheit und Wohlfahrt. Continued by Präventivmedizin.
1956-1968   0362555

Z Psychol Z Angew Psychol
Zeitschrift für Psychologie mit Zeitschrift für angewandte Psychologie
0044-3409
Continues: Zeitschrift für Psychologie mit Zeitschrift für angewandte Psychologie und Charakterkunde. Absorbed: Sprache und Kognition. 2003 Continued by: Zeitschrift für Psychologie.
1963-200u   0153706

Z Psychosom Med
Zeitschrift für Psycho-somatische Medizin
Continued by Zeitschrift fur psychosoma
1954-1966   21810110R

Z Psychosom Med Psychoanal
Zeitschrift für Psychosomatische Medizin und Psychoanalyse
0340-5613
Continues: Zeitschrift für Psycho-somatische Medizin. Continued by: Zeitschrift für Psychosomatische Medizin und Psychotherapie.
1967-1998   0107166

Z Psychosom Med Psychother
Zeitschrift für Psychosomatische Medizin und Psychotherapie
1438-3608
Continues: Zeitschrift für Psychosomatische Medizin und Psychoanalyse.
1999   100886617

Z Psychother Med Psychol
Zeitschrift für Psychotherapie und medizinische Psychologie
0044-3417
Supersedes Zentralblatt für Psychotherapie. Continued by Psychotherapie und medizinische Psychologie.
1951-1973   0423230

Z Rechtsmed
Zeitschrift für Rechtsmedizin. Journal of legal medicine
0044-3433
Continues Deutsche Zeitschrift für die gesamte gerichtliche Medizin. Continued by: International journal of legal medicine.
1970-1990   0247437

Z Rheumaforsch
Zeitschrift für Rheumaforschung
0044-345X
Continued by: Zeitschrift für Rheumatologie.
1938-1973   0415612

Z Rheumatol
Zeitschrift für Rheumatologie
0340-1855
Continues Zeitschrift für Rheumaforschung.
1974   0414162

Z Stomatol
Zeitschrift für Stomatologie (1984)
0175-7784
Continues: Österreichische Zeitschrift für
Stomatologie. Continued by: Stomatologie
(Vienna, Austria).
1984-1994   8408177

Z Stomatol (1921)
Zeitschrift für Stomatologie
1012-4748
Continues: Oesterreichische Zeitschrift für
Stomatologie. Continued by: Oesterreichische
Zeitschrift für Stomatologie.
1921-1949   1271625

Z Tierphysiol Tierernahr Futtermittelkd
Zeitschrift für Tierphysiologie,
Tierernährung und Futtermittelkunde
0044-3565
Continues: Zeitschrift für Tierernährung und
Futtermittelkunde. Continued by: Journal of
animal physiology and animal nutrition.
1958-2000   0033335

Z Tierpsychol
Zeitschrift für Tierpsychologie
0044-3573
Continued by: Ethology.
1937-1985   0033336

Z Tierzuecht Zuechtungsbiol
Zeitschrift für Tierzüchtung und
Züchtungsbiologie: Organ der
Reichsarbeitsgemeinschaft Tierzucht im
Forschungsdienst
0044-3581
Continues: Zeitschrift für Züchtung. Reihe
B, Tierzüchtung und Züchtungsbiologie.
Continued by: Journal of animal breeding and
genetics.
1938-1985   0107652

Z Tropenmed Parasitol
Zeitschrift für Tropenmedizin und
Parasitologie
0044-359X
Continued by Tropenmedizin und
Parasitologie.
1949-1973   0423231

Z Tuberk
Zeitschrift für Tuberkulose
1900-1958   0216146

Z Tuberk Erkr Thoraxorg
Zeitschrift für Tuberkulose und
Erkrankungen der Thoraxorgane
0373-0050
Continues Zeitschrift für Tuberkulose.
1958-1969   0216147

Z Unfallchir Versicherungsmed
Zeitschrift für Unfallchirurgie und
Versicherungsmedizin: offizielles Organ
der Schweizerischen Gesellschaft für
Unfallmedizin und Berufskrankheiten =
Revue de traumatologie et d'assicurologie:
organe officiel de la Société suisse de
médecine des accidents et des maladies
professionnelles
1017-1584
Continues: Zeitschrift für Unfallchirurgie,
Versicherungsmedizin und Berufskrankheiten.
Merged with: Helvetica chirurgica acta, to
form: Swiss surgery.
1990-1994   9009507

Z Unfallchir Versicherungsmed Berufskr
Zeitschrift für Unfallchirurgie,
Versicherungsmedizin und
Berufskrankheiten: offizielles Organ
der Schweizerischen Gesellschaft für
Unfallmedizin und Berufskrankheiten =
Revue de traumatologie, d'assicurologie
et des maladies professionnelles: organe
officiel de la Société suisse de médecine des
accidents et des maladies professionnelles
0254-6310
Continues: Zeitschrift für Unfallmedizin
und Berufskrankheiten. Continued
by: Zeitschrift für Unfallchirurgie und
Versicherungsmedizin.
1983-1989   8304632

Z Unfallmed Berufskr
Zeitschrift für Unfallmedizin und
Berufskrankheiten. Revue de médecine des
accidents et des maladies professionelles
0044-3603
Continues Schweizerische Zeitschrift für
Unfallmedizin und Berufskrankheiten.
Continued by Zeitschrift für
Unfallchirurgie, Versicherungsmedizin, und
Berufskrankheiten.
1935-1982   0033334

Z Urol
Zeitschrift für Urologie
Continued by Zeitschrift für Urologie und
Nephrologie.
1907-1963   21810140R

Z Urol Nephrol
Zeitschrift für Urologie und Nephrologie
0044-3611
Continues Zeitschrift für Urologie.
1964-1990   0413643

Z Vererbungsl
Zeitschrift für Vererbungslehre
0372-8609
Continues Zeitschrift für induktive
Abstammungs- und Vererbungslehre.
Continued by Molecular & general genetics.
1958-1966   0125052

Z Versuchstierkd
Zeitschrift für Versuchstierkunde
0044-3697
Continued by: Journal of experimental animal
science.
1961-1990   0413644

Z Vgl Physiol
Zeitschrift für vergleichende Physiologie
0044-362X
Continued by Journal of comparative
physiology.
1924-1972   0326351

Z Vitam Horm Fermentforsch
Zeitschrift für Vitamin-, Hormon- und
Fermentforschung
0373-0220
1947-1967   21810150R

Z Wiss Mikrosk
Zeitschrift für wissenschaftliche
Mikroskopie und mikroskopische Technik
0373-031X
Continued by Microscopica acta.
1884-1971   1306536

Z Zellforch Microsk Anat Histochem
Zeitschrift für Zellforschung und
Mikroskopische Anatomie. Abteilung
Histochemie
Continued by Histochemie.
1958-1964   21810220R

Z Zellforsch Mikrosk Anat
Zeitschrift für Zellforschung und
mikroskopische Anatomie (Vienna, Austria:
1948)
0340-0336
Continues: Zeitschrift für Zellforschung
und mikroskopische Anatomie. Abteilung
A, Allgemeine Zellforschung und
mikroskopische Anatomie. Continued
by: Cell and tissue research. Continued
in part by: Zeitschrift für Zellforschung
und mikroskopische Anatomie. Abteilung
Histochemie. 1958
1948-1974   7503955

Zacchia
Zacchia
0044-1570
1921   0312464

Zahn Mund Kieferheilkd Zentralbl
Zahn-, Mund-, und Kieferheilkunde mit
Zentralblatt
0303-6464
Continues Deutsche Zahn-, Mund-, und
Kieferheilkunde mit Zentralblatt für die
gesamte Zahn-, Mund-, und Kieferheilkunde.
Continued by: Deutsche Zahn, Mund-, und
Kieferheilkunde mit Zentralblatt.
1974-1990   0434643

Zahnarzt
Der Zahnarzt; Colloquium med. dent
0044-1678
Continues Der Kassenzahnarzt: Colloquium
med. dent
1968-1986   0213554

Zahnarztebl Baden Wurttemb
Zahnärzteblatt Baden-Württemberg
0340-3017
1973   7905926

Zahnarztl Gesundheitsdienst
Zahnärztlicher Gesundheitsdienst: offizielles
Organ des Bundesverbandes der Zahnärzte
des Öffentlichen Gesundheitsdienstes E.V
0340-5478
1972   8219375

Zahnarztl Mitt
Zahnärztliche Mitteilungen
0044-1643
1909   0422566

Zahnarztl Nachr Sudwurttemb
Zahnärztliche Nachrichten
Sudwurttemburg-Hohenzollern
1964   9875609

Zahnarztl Prax
Zahnärztliche Praxis
0044-1651
Supersedes Dentistische Rundschau.
Absorbed Dental Post and Zahntechnik:
Prothetik, Pharmazie, technische Ausrüstung
in Nov. 1952. Absorbed by: Phillip Journal.
1950-1996   0413626

Zahnarztl Praxisfuhr
Zahnärztliche Praxisfuhrung
1958-1975   9875606

Zahnarztl Rundsch
Zahnärztliche Rundschau
0372-7963
Absorbed Die Auslese der zahnärztlichen
Fachliteratur in 1957. Merged with
Zahnärztliche Welt, zahnärztliche Reform,
ZWR to form Zahnärztliche Welt,
zahnärztliche Rundschau, ZWR, vereinigt mit
Zahnärztliche Reform.
1892-1968   0171530

Zahnarztl Welt
Zahnärztliche Welt
Merged with: Zahnärztliche Reform, to form:
Zahnärztliche Welt und zahnärztliche Reform.
1946-1956   **21720480R**

Zahnarztl Welt Zahnarztl Reform Zwr
Zahnärztliche Welt, zahnärztliche Reform, ZWR
Merged with Zahnärztliche Rundschau to
form Zahnärztliche Welt. zahnärztliche
Rundschau, ZWR, vereinigt mit Zahnärztliche
Reform.
1956-1968   **0171527**

Zahnarztl Welt Zahnarztl Rundsch ZWR
Zahnarztl Reform
**Zahnärztliche Welt, zahnärztliche
Rundschau, ZWR, vereinigt mit
Zahnärztliche Reform**
0301-1607
Formed by the merger of: Zahnärztliche
Welt. zahnärztliche Reform. ZWR. and:
Zahnärztliche Rundschau. and adopts its
volume numbering from a combination of
the two.
1968-1969   **0171440**

Zahnheilkd Mundheilkd Kieferheilkd Vortr
**Zahn-, Mund- und Kieferheilkunde in
Vorträgen**
1950-1955   **21720550R**

Zahntech (Basel)
Der Zahntechniker. Le Mécanicien-dentiste
1935-1959   **21720580R**

Zahntechnik (Berl)
**Zahntechnik; Zeitschrift für Theorie und
Praxis der wissenschaftlichen Zahntechnik**
0513-7926
1960-1990   **0413630**

Zahntechnik (Zur)
Zahntechnik (Zurich, Switzerland)
0044-1686
Continues: Schweizerische Zahntechniker-
Vereinigung. Fachzeitschrift.
1946-1995   **9200094**

Zambia Nurse
The Zambia nurse
Continued by the Zambia nurse journal.
1965-1968   **0235146**

Zambia Nurse
Zambia nurse (Kitwe, Zambia: 1978)
0044-1740
Continues: Zambia nurse journal.
1978-1990   **8303035**

Zambia Nurse J
The Zambia nurse journal
Continues The Zambia nurse. Continued by
the Zambia nurse (Kitwe. Zambia: 1978).
1968-1978   **0235147**

Zasshi Fukuoka Ika Daigaku
[Zasshi] [Journal]. Fukuoka Ika Daigaku
Continued by Fukuoka igaku zasshi.
1907-1939   **17030100R**

**Zasshi Kanazawa Daigaku Igakubu Juzen
Igakkai**
**[Zasshi] Journal. Kanazawa Daigaku.
Igakubu. Jūzen Igakkai**
0022-7226
Continues the Zasshi of Kanazawa Ika
Daigaku. Jūzen Igakkai.
1954   **18110390R**

Zasshi Tokyo Ika Daigaku
Zasshi. Tokyo Ika Daigaku
0040-8905
Continues Zasshi of Tokyo Igaku
Senmongakko.
1942   **0243625**

Zb Lek Fak Kosice
**Zborník prác. Univerzita Pavla Jozefa
Safárika v Kosiciach. Lekárska fakulta**
Continues: Sborník prác. Univerzita
Komenského v Bratislave. Lékárska fakulta,
Kosice. Continued by: Zborník Lekárskej
fakulty Kosice.
1960-1967   **0236257**

Zb Vojnomed Akad
**Zbornik. Vojnomedicinska akademija
(Yugoslavia)**
0513-3696
Continued by: Godisnjak Vojnomedicinske
akademije.
1900-1983   **0003044**

Zdr Delo
Zdravno delo
1947-19uu   **21730130R**

Zdrav Aktual
Zdravotnické aktuality,
1946-1995   **21730190R**

Zdrav Prac
Zdravotnická pracovnice
0049-8572
Continued by: Sestra.
1951-1990   **8102057**

Zdrav Radn
Zdravstveni radnik
0351-0980
1946-1989   **21730240R**

Zdrav Rev Vestn Minist Zdrav
**Zdravotnická revue; věstník Ministerstva
Zdravotnictví**
1919-1946   **21730180R**

Zdrav Vestn
Zdravstveni vestnik
0350-0063
Continued by: Zdravniski vestnik (Ljubljana,
Slovenia: 1992).
1929-1992   **21730250R**

Zdravookhr Kirg
Zdravookhranenie Kirgizii
0132-8867
Continues: Sovetskoe zdravookhranenie
kirgizii. Continued by: Zdravookhranenie
Kyrgyzstana.
1974-1991   **0437115**

Zdravookhr Ross Fed
**Zdravookhranenie Rossiĭskoĭ Federatsii /
Ministerstvo zdravookhraneniia RSFSR**
0044-197X
1957   **8707911**

Zdravookhr Turkmenistana
Zdravookhranenie Turkmenistana
0513-8736
Continued by: Türkmenistanyň lukmançylygy.
1957-200u   **21730170R**

Zdravookhranenie
Zdravookhranenie
0513-8728
Continued by: MeditĂĂsĂÄinskĭĭ kurér.
1958-1990   **21730140R**

Zdravookhranenie Belarusi
**Zdravookhranenie Belarusi (Belorusskĭ
tsentr nauchnoĭ meditsinskoĭ informatsii)**
1996-2002   **9709060**

Zdravookhranenie Kazakhstana
Zdravookhranenie Kazakhstana
0372-8277
Continued by: Meditŝina (Alma-Ata.
Kazakhstan).
1941-1999   **21730150R**

Zdrow Publiczne
**Zdrowie publiczne / Polskie Towarzystwo
Higjeniczne**
0044-2011
Continues: Zdrowie (Warsaw. Poland: 1885).
1934   **8707912**

Zebrafish
Zebrafish
1545-8547   **1557-8542**
2004   **101225070**

Zent Arb Arb Beih
**Zentralblatt für Arbeitsmedizin und
Arbeitsschutz. Beihefte**
1955-1967   **21810280R**

Zent Arbeitswissenschaft
Zentralblatt für Arbeitswissenschaft
Continued by Zentralblatt für
Arbeitswissenschaft und soziale
Betriebspraxis.
1947-1949   **21810290R**

Zent Bibliothekswesen
Zentralblatt für Bibliothekswesen
0044-4081
1884   **57630870R**

Zentralbl Allg Pathol
**Zentralblatt für allgemeine Pathologie und
pathologische Anatomie**
0044-4030
Continues Centralblatt für allgemeine
Pathologie und pathologische Anatomie.
Continued by Zentralblatt für Pathologie.
1937-1990   **9105593**

Zentralbl Arbeitsmed
**Zentralblatt für Arbeitsmedizin und
Arbeitsschutz**
0044-4049
Supersedes Zentralblatt für Gewerbehygiene
und Unfallverhütung. Merged with
Prophylaxe to form Zentralblatt für
Arbeitsmedizin. Arbeitsschutz und
Prophylaxe.
1951-1975   **7610692**

Zentralbl Arbeitsmed Arbeitsschutz Prophyl
**Zentralblatt für Arbeitsmedizin,
Arbeitsschutz und Prophylaxe**
0340-7047
Formed by the union of Zentralblatt für
Arbeitsmedizin und Arbeitsschutz. and
Prophylaxe. Continued by Zentralblatt für
Arbeitsmedizin. arbeitsschutz, Prophylaxe
und Ergonomie.
1976-1980   **7610693**

**Zentralbl Arbeitsmed Arbeitsschutz Prophyl
Ergonomie**
**Zentralblatt für Arbeitsmedizin,
Arbeitsschutz, Prophylaxe und Ergonomie**
Continues Zentralblatt für Arbeitsmedizin,
Arbeitsschutz, und Prophylaxe. Continued by:
Zentralblatt für Arbeitsmedizin, Arbeitsschutz
und Ergonomie.
1980-1992   **8006595**

Zentralbl Bakteriol
**Zentralblatt für Bakteriologie: international
journal of medical microbiology**
0934-8840
Continues: Zentralblatt für Bakteriologie.
Mikrobiologie. und Hygiene. Series A.
Medical microbiology. infectious diseases.
virology. parasitology. Continued by:
International journal of medical microbiology.
1989-2000   **9203851**

Zentralbl Bakteriol A
Zentralblatt für Bakteriologie. 1. Abt.
Originale. A: Medizinische Mikrobiologie,
Infektionskrankheiten und Parasitologie
0172-5599
Continues Zentralblatt für Bakteriologie,
Parasitenkunde, Infektionskrankheiten
und Hygiene. Erste Abteilung Originale.
Reihe A: Medizinische Mikrobiologie und
Parasitologie. Continued by Zentralblatt
für Bakteriologie, Mikrobiologie und
Hygiene. 1. Abt. Originale A, Medizinische
Mikrobiologie, Infektionskrankheiten und
Parasitologie.
1980-1980   8005748

Zentralbl Bakteriol Mikrobiol Hyg [A]
Zentralblatt für Bakteriologie,
Mikrobiologie und Hygiene. 1. Abt.
Originale A, Medizinische Mikrobiologie,
Infektionskrankheiten und Parasitologie
= International journal of microbiology
and hygiene. A, Medical microbiology,
infectiousdiseases, parasitology
0174-3031
Continues: Zentralblatt für Bakteriologie.
1. Abt. Originale A, Medizinische
Mikrobiologie, Infektionskrankheiten und
Parasitologie. Continued by: Zentralblatt für
Bakteriologie, Mikrobiologie, und Hygiene.
Series A, Medical microbiology, infectious
diseases, virology, parasitology.
1980-1983   8110566

Zentralbl Bakteriol Mikrobiol Hyg [A]
Zentralblatt für Bakteriologie,
Mikrobiologie, und Hygiene. Series A,
Medical microbiology, infectious diseases,
virology, parasitology
0176-6724
Continues: Zentralblatt für Bakteriologie,
Mikrobiologie und Hygiene. 1. Abt.
Originale A, Medizinische Mikrobiologie,
Infektionskrankheiten und Parasitologie.
Continued by: International journal of
medical microbiology.
1983-1989   8403032

Zentralbl Bakteriol Mikrobiol Hyg [B]
Zentralblatt für Bakteriologie,
Mikrobiologie und Hygiene. 1. Abt.
Originale B, Hygiene
0174-3015
Continues: Zentralblatt für Bakteriologie.
1. Abt. Originale B, Hygiene,
Krankenhaushygiene, Betriebshygiene,
präventive Medizin. Continued by:
Zentralbaltt für Bakteriologie, Mikrobiologie
und Hygiene. Serie B, Umwelthygiene,
Krankenhaushygiene, Arbeitshygiene,
Präventive Medizin.
1980-1985   8110036

Zentralbl Bakteriol Mikrobiol Hyg [B]
Zentralblatt für Bakteriologie,
Mikrobiologie und Hygiene. Serie B,
Umwelthygiene, Krankenhaushygiene,
Arbeitshygiene, präventive Medizin
0932-6073
Continues: Zentralblatt für Bakteriologie,
Mikrobiologie und Hygiene. 1. Abt. Originale
B, Hygiene. Continued by: Zentralblatt für
Hygiene und Umweltmedizin.
1985-1989   8606774

Zentralbl Bakteriol Naturwiss
Zentralblatt für Bakteriologie,
Parasitenkunde, Infektionskrankheiten und
Hygiene. Zweite naturwissenschaftliche
Abteilung: Mikrobiologie der
Landwirtschaft der Technologie und des
Umweltschutzes
0323-6056
Continues: Zentralblatt für Bakteriologie,
Parasitenkunde, Infektionskrankheiten und
Hygiene. Zweite naturwissenschaftliche
Abteilung: Allgemeine, landwirtschaftliche
und technische Mikrobiologie. Continued by:
Zentralblatt für Mikrobiologie.
1978-1981   8000422

Zentralbl Bakteriol Parasitenkd Infektionskr Hyg
Zentralblatt für Bakteriologie,
Parasitenkunde, Infektionskrankheiten und
Hygiene. Zweite naturwissenschaftliche
Abt.: Allgemeine, landwirtschaftliche und
technische Mikrobiologie
0044-4057
Continues Zentralblatt für Bakteriologie,
Parasitenkunde und Infektionskrankheiten.
Zweite Abteilung: Allgemeine
jandwirtschaftliche technische Nahrungsmittel
- Bakteriologie und Mykologie,
Protozoologie, Pflanzenkrankheiten … und
Pflanzenschutz, sowie Tierkrankheiten …
Continued by Zentralblatt für Bakteriologie,
Parasitenkunde, Infektionskrankheiten und
Hygiene. Zweite naturwissenschaftliche
Abteilung: Mikrobiologie der Landwirtschaft
der Technologie und des Umweltschutzes.
1959-1977   0414371

Zentralbl Bakteriol [B]
Zentralblatt für Bakteriologie,
Parasitenkunde, Infektionskrankheiten und
Hygiene. Erste Abteilung Originale. Reihe
B: Hygiene, Betriebshygiene, präventive
Medizin
0300-9661
Continues Zentralblatt für Bakteriologie,
Parasitenkunde, Infektionskrankheiten
und Hygiene. Erste Abteilung Originale.
Reihe B: Hygiene, präventive Medizin.
Continued by Zentralblatt für Bakteriologie,
Parasitenkunde, Infektionskrankheiten
und Hygiene. Erste Abteilung Originale.
Reihe B: Hygiene, Krankenhaushygiene,
Betriebshygiene, präventive Medizin.
1976-1978   7809115

Zentralbl Bakteriol [B]
Zentralblatt für Bakteriologie. 1. Abt.
Originale B, Hygiene, Krankenhaushygiene,
Betriebshygiene, präventive Medizin
0172-5602
Continues Zentralblatt für Bakteriologie,
Parasitenkunde, Infektionskrankheiten
und Hygiene. Erste Abteilung Originale.
Reihe B: Hygiene, Krankenhaushygiene,
Betriebshygiene, präventive Medizin.
Continued by: Zentralblatt für Bakteriologie
Mikrobiologie und Hygiene. Abt. B, Hygiene.
1980-1980   8005749

Zentralbl Bakteriol [Orig A]
Zentralblatt für Bakteriologie,
Parasitenkunde, Infektionskrankheiten
und Hygiene. Erste Abteilung Originale.
Reihe A: Medizinische Mikrobiologie und
Parasitologie
0300-9688
Continues Zentralblatt für Bakteriologie,
Parasitenkunde, Infektionskrankheiten
und Hygiene. 1. Abt. Medizinisch-
hygienische Bakteriologie, Virusforschung
und Parasitologie. Originale. Continued
by Zentralblatt für Bakteriologie. 1. Abt.
Originale. A: Medizinische Mikrobiologie,
Infektionskrankheiten und Parasitologie.
1971-1979   0331570

Zentralbl Bakteriol [Orig B]
Zentralblatt für Bakteriologie,
Parasitenkunde, Infektionskrankheiten und
Hygiene. Erste Abteilung Originale. Reihe
B: Hygiene, präventive Medizin
0300-9661
Continues in part Archiv für Hygiene und
Bakteriologie. Continued by Zentralblatt
für Bakteriologie, Parasitenkunde,
Infektionskrankheiten und Hygiene. Erste
Abteilung Originale. Reihe B: Hygiene,
Betriebshygiene, präventive Medizin.
1971-1976   1306477

Zentralbl Bakteriol [Orig]
Zentralblatt für Bakteriologie,
Parasitenkunde, Infektionskrankheiten und
Hygiene. 1. Abt. Medizinisch-hygienische
Bakteriologie, Virusforschung und
Parasitologie. Originale
0372-8110
Continues in part Centralblatt für
Bakteriologie, Parasitenkunde und
Infektionskrankheiten. 1. Abt. Medizinisch-
hygienische Bakteriologie und tierische
Parasitenkunde. Continued by Zentralblatt
für Bakteriologie, Parasitenkunde,
Infektionskrankheiten und Hygiene. 1.
Abt. Originale. Reihe A: Medizinische
Mikrobiologie und Parasitologie.
1902-1971   0337744

Zentralbl Biol Aerosolforsch
Zentralblatt für biologische
Aerosolforschung
0514-7107
Continues Zeitschrift für Aerosol-Forschung
und -Therapie.
1960-1967   0121500

Zentralbl Chir
Zentralblatt für Chirurgie
0044-409X
Absorbed: Viszeralchirurgie.
1903   0413645

Zentralbl Gesamte Rechtsmed Grenzgeb
Zentralblatt für die gesamte Rechtsmedizin
und ihre Grenzgebiete
0044-4154
Continued by Zentralblatt Rechtsmedizin.
1970-1982   1250012

Zentralbl Gynakol
Zentralblatt für Gynäkologie
0044-4197
Continues: Central blatt für Gynäkologie.
Absorbed by: Geburtshile und
frauenheilkunde.
1903-2006   21820100R

Zentralbl Haut Geschlechtskr Grenzgeb
Zentralblatt für Haut- und
Geschlechtskrankheiten, sowie deren
Grenzgebiete
Supersedes Dermatologisches Centralblatt.
Continued by Zentralblatt Haut- und
Geschlechtskrankheiten.
1921-1977   0423435

Zentralbl Hyg Umweltmed
Zentralblatt für Hygiene und
Umweltmedizin = International journal of
hygiene and environmental medicine
0934-8859
Continues: Zentralblatt für Bakteriologie,
Mikrobiologie und Hygiene. Serie B,
Umwelthygiene, Krankenhaushygiene,
Arbeitshygiene, präventive Medizin.
Continued by: International journal of
hygiene and environmental health.
1989-1999   8912563

Zentralbl Mikrobiol
Zentralblatt für Mikrobiologie
0232-4393
  Continues: Zentralblatt für Bakteriologie.
  Parasitenkunde. Infektionskrankheiten und
  Hygiene. Zweite naturwissenschaftliche
  Abteilung. Mikrobiologie der Landwirtschaft
  der Technologie und des Umweltschutzes.
  Continued by: Microbiological research.
  1982-1993   8209932

Zentralbl Neurochir
Zentralblatt für Neurochirurgie
1936   0413646

Zentralbl Pathol
Zentralblatt für Pathologie
0863-4106
  Continues: Zentralblatt für allgemeine
  Pathologie und pathologische Anatomie.
  Continued by: General & diagnostic pathology.
  1991-1995   9105594

Zentralbl Phlebol
Zentralblatt für Phlebologie
0044-426X
  Continued by VASA.
  1962-1971   0317055

Zentralbl Verkehrsmed Verkehrspsychol Luft Raumfahrtmed
Zentralblatt für Verkehrs-Medizin,
Verkehrs-Psychologie, Luft- und Raumfahrt-
Medizin
0044-4286
  Continues Zentralblatt für Verkehrs-Medizin,
  Verkehrs-Psychologie und angrenzende Gebiete.
  1955-1973   0420116

Zentralbl Veterinarmed A
Zentralblatt für Veterinärmedizin. Reihe A
0514-7158
  Continues in part Zentralblatt für
  Veterinärmedizin. Continued by: Journal
  of veterinary medicine. A. Physiology.
  pathology. clinical medicine.
  1963-1999   0331323

Zentralbl Veterinarmed B
Zentralblatt für Veterinärmedizin. Reihe B.
Journal of veterinary medicine. Series B
0514-7166
  Supersedes in part and continues the
  vol. numbering of Zentralblatt für
  Veterinärmedizin. Continued by: Journal of
  veterinary medicine. B. Infectious diseases
  and veterinary public health.
  1963-1999   0331325

Zentralbl Veterinarmed [C]
Zentralblatt für Veterinärmedizin. Reihe C:
Anatomie, Histologie, Embryologie
0300-8649
  Continued by Anatomia. histologia.
  embryologia.
  1972-1972   0331326

Zentralblatt Arbeitsmedizin Arbeitsschutz Erogon
Zentralblatt für Arbeitsmedizin,
Arbeitsschutz und Ergonomie
0944-2502
  Continues: Zentralblatt für Arbeitsmedizin,
  Arbeitsschutz. Prophylaxe und Ergonomie.
  1992   9440408

Zentralblatt Bakteriol Parasitenkd Infekt Hyg
Zentralblatt für Bakteriologie,
Parasitenkunde, Infektionskrankheiten und
Hygiene. 1. Abt. Medizinisch-hygienische
Bakteriologie, Virusforschung und
Parasitologie. Referate
  Continues in part Centralblatt für Bakteriologie.
  Parasitenkunde und Infektionskrankheiten: 1.
  Abt. Medizinisch-hygienische Bakteriologie
  und tierische Parasitenkunde.
  1902-1972   59230420R

ZFA
ZfA. Zeitschrift für Alternsforschung
0044-2224
  Continues Zeitschrift für Alternsforschung.
  1974-1991   7704731

ZFA (Stuttgart)
ZFA. Zeitschrift für Allgemeinmedizin
0341-9835
  Continues: Zeitschrift für Allgemeinmedizin.
  1976   7613263

Zh Eksp Klin Med
Zhurnal eksperimental'noĭ i klinicheskoĭ
meditsiny
0514-7484
  Continued by: Eksperimental'naia i
  klinicheskaia meditsina.
  1961-1989   0420120

Zh Evol Biokhim Fiziol
Zhurnal evoliutsionnoĭ biokhimii i fiziologii
0044-4529
  1965   21820250R

Zh Mikrobiol Epidemiol Immunobiol
Zhurnal mikrobiologii, epidemiologii, i
immunobiologii
0372-9311
  Continues Zhurnal mikrobiologii i
  immunobiologii.
  1935   0415217

Zh Nevrol Psikhiatr Im S S Korsakova
Zhurnal nevrologii i psikhiatrii imeni S.S.
Korsakova / Ministerstvo zdravookhraneniia
i meditsinskoĭ promyshlennosti Rossiĭskoĭ
Federatsii, Vserossiĭskoe obshchestvo
nevrologov [i] Vserossiĭskoe obshchestvo
psikhiatrov
1997-7298
  Continues: Zhurnal nevropatologii i
  psikhiatrii imeni S.S. Korsakova (Moscow.
  R.S.F.S.R.: 1952).
  1993   9712194

Zh Nevropatol Psikhiatr Im S S Korsakova
Zhurnal nevropatologii i psikhiatrii imeni
S.S. Korsakova (Moscow, Russia: 1952)
0044-4588
  Continues: Nevropatologiia i psikhiatriia.
  Continued by: Zhurnal nevrologii i psikhiatrii
  imeni S.S. Korsakova.
  1952-1992   8710066

Zh Obshch Biol
Zhurnal obshcheĭ biologii
0044-4596
  Continues: Biologicheskii zhurnal.
  1940   0424252

Zh Ushn Nos Gorl Bolezn
Zhurnal ushnykh, nosovykh i gorlovykh
bolezneĭ = The journal of otology, rhinology,
and laryngologie [sic]
0044-4650
  Continued by: Zhurnal vushnykh. nosovykh i
  horlovykh khvorob.
  1924-19uu   9427210

Zh Vopr Neirokhir Im N N Burdenko
Zhurnal voprosy neĭrokhirurgii imeni N. N.
Burdenko
0042-8817
  Supersedes Voprosy neĭrokhirurgii.
  1977   7809757

Zh Vyssh Nerv Deiat Im I P Pavlova
Zhurnal vyssheĭ nervnoĭ deiatelnosti imeni
I P Pavlova
0044-4677
  1951   9421551

Zhejiang Da Xue Xue Bao Yi Xue Ban
Zhejiang da xue xue bao. Yi xue ban = Journal
of Zhejiang University. Medical sciences
1008-9292
  Continues: Zhejiang yi ke da xue xue bao.
  1999   100927946

Zhen Ci Yan Jiu
Zhen ci yan jiu = Acupuncture research /
[Zhongguo yi xue ke xue yuan Yi xue qing
bao yan jiu suo bian ji]
1000-0607
  Continues: Zhen ci ma zui.
  1980   8507710

Zhi Wu Sheng Li Yu Fen Zi Sheng Wu Xue Xue Bao
Zhi wu sheng li yu fen zi sheng wu xue
xue bao = Journal of plant physiology and
molecular biology
1671-3877
  Continues: Zhi wu sheng li xue bao.
  2002   101156321

Zhong Nan Da Xue Xue Bao Yi Xue Ban
Zhong nan da xue xue bao. Yi xue ban
= Journal of Central South University.
Medical sciences
1672-7347
  Continues: Hunan yi ke da xue xue bao.
  2004   101230586

Zhong Xi Yi Jie He Xue Bao
Zhong xi yi jie he xue bao = Journal of
Chinese integrative medicine
1672-1977
  2003   101199657

Zhong Xi Yi Jie He Za Zhi
Zhong xi yi jie he za zhi = Chinese journal
of modern developments in traditional
medicine / Zhongguo Zhong xi yi jie he yan
jiu hui (chou), Zhong yi yan jiu yuan, zhu
ban
0254-9034
  Continued by: Zhongguo Zhong xi yi jie he
  za zhi.
  1981-1991   8207427

Zhong Yao Cai
Zhong yao cai = Zhongyaocai = Journal of
Chinese medicinal materials
1001-4454
  1978   9426370

Zhong Yao Tong Bao
Zhong yao tong bao (Beijing, China: 1981)
0254-0029
  Continued by: Zhongguo zhong yao za zhi.
  1981-1988   8303080

Zhongguo Dang Dai Er Ke Za Zhi
Zhongguo dang dai er ke za zhi = Chinese
journal of contemporary pediatrics
1008-8830
  1999   100909956

Zhongguo Gu Shang
Zhongguo gu shang = China journal of
orthopaedics and traumatology
1003-0034
  1987   9815790

Zhongguo Ji Sheng Chong Xue Yu Ji Sheng Chong Bing Za Zhi
Zhongguo ji sheng chong xue yu ji sheng
chong bing za zhi = Chinese journal of
parasitology & parasitic diseases
1000-7423
  Continues: Ji sheng chong xue yu ji sheng
  chong bing za zhi.
  1987   8709992

Zhongguo Shi Yan Xue Ye Xue Za Zhi
Zhongguo shi yan xue ye xue za zhi /
Zhongguo bing li sheng li xue hui = Journal
of experimental hematology / Chinese
Association of Pathophysiology
1009-2137
1993   101084424

Zhongguo Wei Zhong Bing Ji Jiu Yi Xue
Zhongguo wei zhong bing ji jiu yi xue =
Chinese critical care medicine = Zhongguo
weizhongbing jijiuyixue
1003-0603
1989   9887521

Zhongguo Xiu Fu Chong Jian Wai Ke Za Zhi
Zhongguo xiu fu chong jian wai ke za
zhi = Zhongguo xiufu chongjian waike
zazhi = Chinese journal of reparative and
reconstructive surgery
1002-1892
Continues: Xiu fu chong jian wai ke za zhi.
199u   9425194

Zhongguo Yao Li Xue Bao
Zhongguo yao li xue bao = Acta
pharmacologica Sinica
0253-9756
Continued by: Acta pharmacologica Sinica..
1980-1999   8100330

Zhongguo Yi Liao Qi Xie Za Zhi
Zhongguo yi liao qi xie za zhi = Chinese
journal of medical instrumentation
1671-7104
Continues: Yiliao qixie.
1988   9426153

Zhongguo Yi Xue Ke Xue Yuan Xue Bao
Zhongguo yi xue ke xue yuan xue bao. Acta
Academiae Medicinae Sinicae
1000-503X
1979   8006230

Zhongguo Ying Yong Sheng Li Xue Za Zhi
Zhongguo ying yong sheng li xue za zhi =
Zhongguo yingyong shenglixue zazhi =
Chinese journal of applied physiology
1000-6834
1985   9426407

Zhongguo Zhen Jiu
Zhongguo zhen jiu = Chinese acupuncture
& moxibustion
0255-2930
1981   8600658

Zhongguo Zhong Xi Yi Jie He Za Zhi
Zhongguo zhong xi yi jie he za zhi
Zhongguo zhongxiyi jiehe zazhi = Chinese
journal of integrated traditional and
Western medicine / Zhongguo Zhong xi yi
jie he xue hui, Zhongguo Zhong yi yan jiu
yuan zhu ban
1003-5370
Continues: Zhong xi yi jie he za zhi.
1992   9211576

Zhongguo Zhong Yao Za Zhi
Zhongguo zhong yao za zhi = Zhongguo
zhongyao zazhi = China journal of Chinese
materia medica
1001-5302
Continues: Zhong yao tong bao (Beijing,
China: 1981).
1989   8913656

Zhonghua Bing Li Xue Za Zhi
Zhonghua bing li xue za zhi Chinese journal
of pathology
0529-5807
1955   0005331

Zhonghua Er Bi Yan Hou Ke Za Zhi
Zhonghua er bi yan hou ke za zhi
0412-3948
Continued by: Zhonghua er bi yan hou tou
jing wai ke za zhi.
1953-2004   16210350R

Zhonghua Er Bi Yan Hou Tou Jing Wai Ke Za Zhi
Zhonghua er bi yan hou tou jing wai ke za
zhi = Chinese journal of otorhinolaryngology
head and neck surgery
1673-0860
Continues: Zhonghua er bi yan hou ke za zhi.
2005   101247574

Zhonghua Er Ke Za Zhi
Zhonghua er ke za zhi. Chinese journal of
pediatrics
0578-1310
1950   0417427

Zhonghua Fang She Xian Yi Xue Za Zhi
Zhonghua fang she xian yi xue za zhi =
Chinese journal of radiology
1018-8940
1976   9425273

Zhonghua Fang She Xue Za Zhi
Zhonghua fang she xue za zhi Chinese
journal of radiology
1005-1201
1953   16210360R

Zhonghua Fu Chan Ke Za Zhi
Zhonghua fu chan ke za zhi
0529-567X
1953   16210370R

Zhonghua Gan Zang Bing Za Zhi
Zhonghua gan zang bing za zhi = Zhonghua
ganzangbing zazhi = Chinese journal of
hepatology
1007-3418
199u   9710009

Zhonghua Hu Li Za Zhi
Zhonghua hu li za zhi = Chinese journal of
nursing
0254-1769
Continues: Hu li za zhi.
1981   8201928

Zhonghua Jie He He Hu Xi Xi Ji Bing Za Zhi
Zhonghua jie he he hu xi xi ji bing za zhi
= Chinese journal of tuberculosis and
respiratory diseases
0253-2689
Continued by: Zhonghua jie he he hu xi za
zhi.
1978-1986   7904961

Zhonghua Jie He He Hu Xi Za Zhi
Zhonghua jie he he hu xi za zhi = Zhonghua
jiehe he huxi zazhi = Chinese journal of
tuberculosis and respiratory diseases
1001-0939
Continues: Zhonghua jie he he hu xi xi ji
bing za zhi.
1987   8712226

Zhonghua Kou Qiang Ke Za Zhi
Zhonghua kou qiang ke za zhi [Chinese
journal of stomatology]
0412-4014
Continued by: Zhonghua kou qiang yi xue
za zhi.
1953-1986   16210440R

Zhonghua Kou Qiang Yi Xue Za Zhi
Zhonghua kou qiang yi xue za zhi =
Zhonghua kouqiang yixue zazhi = Chinese
journal of stomatology
1002-0098
Continues: Zhonghua kou qiang ke za zhi.
1987   8711066

Zhonghua Lao Dong Wei Sheng Zhi Ye Bing Za Zhi
Zhonghua lao dong wei sheng zhi ye bing za
zhi = Zhonghua laodong weisheng zhiyebing
zazhi = Chinese journal of industrial hygiene
and occupational diseases
1001-9391
1983   8410840

Zhonghua Liu Xing Bing Xue Za Zhi
Zhonghua liu xing bing xue za zhi =
Zhonghua liuxingbingxue zazhi
0254-6450
Continues: Liu xing bing xue za zhi.
1981   8208604

Zhonghua Min Guo Wei Sheng Wu Ji Mian Yi Xue Za Zhi
Zhonghua Minguo wei sheng wu ji mian yi
xue za zhi = Chinese journal of microbiology
and immunology
0253-2662
Continues Zhonghua min guo wei sheng wu
xue za zhi. Chinese journal of microbiology.
Continued by: Journal of microbiology,
immunology, and infection.
1980-1997   8008067

Zhonghua Min Guo Wei Sheng Wu Xue Za Zhi
Zhonghua Minguo wei sheng wu xue za zhi
= Chinese journal of microbiology
0009-4587
Continued by Zhonghua min guo wei sheng
wu ji mian yi xue za zhi. Chinese journal of
microbiology and immunology.
1968-1979   0204022

Zhonghua Min Guo Xiao Er Ke Yi Xue Hui Zhi
Zhonghua Minguo xiao er ke yi xue hui za
zhi [Journal]. Zhonghua Minguo xiao er ke
yi xue hui
0001-6578
Continues: Er ke lin chuang. Continued by:
Acta paediatrica Taiwanica.
1960-1999   16210470R

Zhonghua Nan Ke Xue
Zhonghua nan ke xue = National journal of
andrology
1009-3591
1995   101093592

Zhonghua Nei Ke Za Zhi
Zhonghua nei ke za zhi [Chinese journal of
internal medicine]
0578-1426
Supersedes Nei ke xue bao.
1953   16210490R

Zhonghua Shao Shang Za Zhi
Zhonghua shao shang za zhi = Zhonghua
shaoshang zazhi = Chinese journal of burns
1009-2587
Continues in part: Zhonghua zheng xing shao
shang wai ke za zhi.
2000   100959418

Zhonghua Shen Jing Ge Za Zhi
Zhonghua shen jing ke za zhi = Chinese
journal of neurology
1006-7876
Continues in part: Zhonghua shen jing jing
shen ke za zhi.
1996   9616315

Zhonghua Shen Jing Jing Shen Ke Za Zhi
Zhonghua shen jing jing shen ke za zhi =
Chinese journal of neurology and psychiatry
0412-4057
Continued in part by: Zhonghua jing shen ke
za zhi. Continued in part by: Zhonghua shen
jing ke za zhi.
1955-1995   16210510R

Zhonghua Shi Yan He Lin Chuang Bing Du Xue Za Zhi
Zhonghua shi yan he lin chuang bing du xue za zhi = Zhonghua shiyan he linchuang bingduxue zazhi = Chinese journal of experimental and clinical virology
1003-9279
1987 9602873

Zhonghua Wai Ke Za Zhi
Zhonghua wai ke za zhi [Chinese journal of surgery]
0529-5815
1953 0153611

Zhonghua Wei Chang Wai Ke Za Zhi
Zhonghua wei chang wai ke za zhi = Chinese journal of gastrointestinal surgery
1671-0274
Continues: Zhongguo wei chang wai ke za zhi.
1998 101177990

Zhonghua Xin Xue Guan Bing Za Zhi
Zhonghua xin xue guan bing za zhi [Chinese journal of cardiovascular diseases]
0253-3758
1973 7910682

Zhonghua Xue Ye Xue Za Zhi
Zhonghua xue ye xue za zhi = Zhonghua xueyexue zazhi
0253-2727
1980 8212398

Zhonghua Ya Yi Xue Hui Za Zhi
Zhonghua ya yi xue hui za zhi / Zhonghua ya yi xue hui = Chinese dental journal / Dental Association, Republic of China
1010-3287
Continued by: Zhonghua ya yi xue za zhi (1994-2004).
1982-1993 8804030

Zhonghua Yan Ke Za Zhi
[Zhonghua yan ke za zhi] Chinese journal of ophthalmology
0412-4081
1950 16210540R

Zhonghua Yi Shi Za Zhi
Zhonghua yi shi za zhi (Beijing, China: 1980)
0255-7053
Continues in part: Yi xue shi yu bao jian za zhi.
1980 8303081

Zhonghua Yi Xue Yi Chuan Xue Za Zhi
Zhonghua yi xue yi chuan xue za zhi = Zhonghua yixue yichuanxue zazhi = Chinese journal of medical genetics
1003-9406
Continues: Yi chuan yu ji bing. 1984-1991
1992 9425197

Zhonghua Yi Xue Za Zhi
Zhonghua yi xue za zhi
0376-2491
Separated from: Ren min bao jian.
1960 7511141

Zhonghua Yi Xue Za Zhi (Taipei)
Zhonghua yi xue za zhi = Chinese medical journal; Free China ed
0578-1337
Continued by: Journal of the Chinese Medical Association.
1954-2002 0005327

Zhonghua Yu Fang Yi Xue Za Zhi
Zhonghua yu fang yi xue za zhi [Chinese journal of preventive medicine]
0253-9624
1967 7904962

Zhonghua Zheng Xing Shao Shang Wai Ke Za Zhi
Zhonghua zheng xing shao shang wai ke za zhi = Zhonghua zheng xing shao shang waikf [i.e. waike] zazhi = Chinese journal of plastic surgery and burns / [Chung-hua cheng hsing shao shang wai k'o tsa chih pien chi wei yüan hui pien chi]
1000-7806
Split into: Zhonghua zheng xing wai ke za zhi, and: Zhonghua shao shang za zhi.
1985-1999 8510296

Zhonghua Zheng Xing Wai Ke Za Zhi
Zhonghua zheng xing wai ke za zhi = Zhonghua zhengxing waike zazhi = Chinese journal of plastic surgery
1009-4598
Continues in part: Zhonghua zheng xing shao shang wai ke za zhi.
2000 100957850

Zhonghua Zhong Liu Za Zhi
Zhonghua zhong liu za zhi [Chinese journal of oncology]
0253-3766
1979 7910681

Zhurnal Prikl Him
Zhurnal prikladnoĭ khimii (Leningrad, R.S.F.S.R.)
0044-4618
1928 9876794

Ziekenfondsgids
De Ziekenfondsgids
1947-19uu 21820320R

Ziekenhuiswezen
Het Ziekenhuiswezen
1928-1970 0035477

Zimbabwe Nurse
The Zimbabwe nurse
1012-9103
Continues: Zimbabwe Rhodesia nurse.
1980 8411431

Zimbabwe Rhod Nurse
Zimbabwe Rhodesia Nurse
Continues: Rhodesia Nurse. Continued by: Zimbabwe Nurse.
1979-1979 9878612

Zobozdrav Vestn
Zobozdravstveni vestnik
0044-4928
1945 0417422

Zool Anz
Zoologischer Anzeiger
0044-5231
1878 0031351

Zool Sci Contrib N Y Zool Soc
Zoologica; scientific contributions of the New York Zoological Society
0044-507X
1907-1973 0436560

Zool Zhurnal
Zoologicheskiĭ zhurnal
0044-5134
Continues: Russkiĭ zoologicheskiĭ zhurnal.
1932 8905520

Zoolog Sci
Zoological science
0289-0003
Formed by the union of: Dōbutsugaku zasshi, and: Annotationes zoologicae Japonenses.
1984 8702287

Zoology (Jena)
Zoology (Jena, Germany)
0944-2006
Formed by the union of: Zoologische Jahrbücher. Abteilung für allgemeine Zoologie und Physiologie der Tiere, and: Zoologische Jahrbücher. Abteilung für Anatomie und Ontogenie der Tiere, and continues the volume numbering of the former. Absorbed in 1998 the Hauptvorträge section of Verhandlungen der Deutschen Zoologischen Gesellschaft which will be issued as reviews in a number of each volume beginning with v. 100, 4.
1994 9435608

Zoonoses Public Health
Zoonoses and public health
1863-1959 1863-2378
Continues: Journal of veterinary medicine. B. Infectious diseases and veterinary public health.
2007 101300786

Zoonoses Res
Zoonoses research
0514-4019
1960-1965 21820410R

Zooprofilassi
Zooprofilassi
0044-5290
1946-1972 0417424

Zuchthygiene
Zuchthygiene
0044-5371
Continued by: Reproduction in domestic animals.
1966-1989 0056272

Zur Medizingesch Abh
Zürcher medizingeschichtliche Abhandlungen
0514-4264
1924 21830020R

Zvesti Cerv Kriza
Zvestí červeného kríža
1940-19uu 21830080R

ZWR
ZWR
0044-166X
Formed by the union of: ZWR. ZahnarÄàztliche Welt, Zahnärztliche Rundschau, and: DDZ. Das Deutsche Zahnärzteblatt, assuming the numbering of the first journal.
1970 0233767

Zygote
Zygote (Cambridge, England)
0967-1994 1469-8730
1993 9309124